MyMathLab

Welcome Students!

MyMathLab is an interactive website where you can:
- Self-test & work through practice exercises with step-by-step help to improve your math skills.
- Study more efficiently with a personalized study plan and exercises that match your book.
- Get help when YOU need it. MyMathLab includes multimedia learning aids, videos, animations, and live tutorial help.

Before You Begin:

To register for MyMathLab, you need:

☑ **A MyMathLab student access code** (packaged with your new text, standalone at your bookstore, or available for purchase with a major credit card at www.pearsonmylab.com)

☑ **Your instructors' Course ID:**_____

☑ **A valid email address**

Student Registration:

- Enter www.pearsonmylab.com in your web browser.
- Under Register, click **Student**.
- Enter your **Course ID** exactly as provided by your instructor and click **Continue.** *Your course information appears on the next page. If it does not look correct, contact your instructor to verify the Course ID.*
- Sign in or follow the instructions to create an account. Use an email address that you check and, if possible, use that same email address for your username. Read and accept the License Agreement and Privacy Policy.
- Click **Access Code**. Enter your **Access Code** in the boxes and click **Next**. *If you do not have an access code and want to pay by credit card or PayPal, select the access level you want and follow the instructions. You can also get temporary access without payment for 17 days..*

Once your registration is complete, a **Confirmation** page appears. You will also receive this information by email. Make sure you print the Confirmation page as your receipt. Remember to **write down your username and password**. You are now ready to access your resources!

Signing In:

- Go to www.pearsonmylab.com and click **Sign in**.
- Enter your **username** and **password** and click **Sign In**.
- On the left, click the name of your course.

The first time you enter your course from your own computer and anytime you use a new computer, click the **Installation Wizard** or **Browser Check** on the Announcements page. After completing the installation process and closing the wizard, you will be on your course home page and ready to explore your MyMathLab resources!

Need help?

Contact Product Support at http://www.mymathlab.com/student-support **for live CHAT, email, or phone support.**

Go to www.PearsonMyLab.com

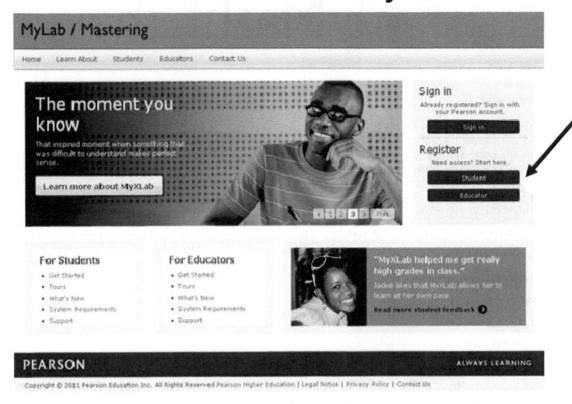

Enter your Course ID

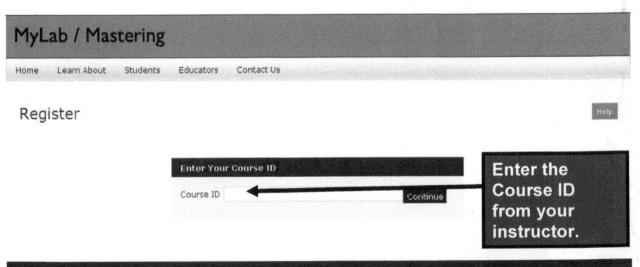

Elayn Martin-Gay

Beginning & Intermediate Algebra, Volume 2

2nd Custom Edition for Mission College

Taken from:
Beginning & Intermediate Algebra, Fifth Edition
by Elayn Martin-Gay

Cover Art: Courtesy of Photodisc/Getty Images.

Taken from:

Beginning & Intermediate Algebra, Fifth Edition
by Elayn Martin-Gay
Copyright © 2013, 2009, 2005, 2001, 1996 by Pearson Education, Inc.
Published by Pearson
Boston, MA 02116

This special edition published in cooperation with Pearson Learning Solutions.

All trademarks, service marks, registered trademarks, and registered service marks are the property of their respective owners and are used herein for identification purposes only.

Pearson Learning Solutions, 501 Boylston Street, Suite 900, Boston, MA 02116
A Pearson Education Company
www.pearsoned.com

Printed in the United States of America

1 2 3 4 5 6 7 8 9 10 V0ZN 17 16 15 14 13 12

000200010271303770

ML

ISBN 10: 1-256-85152-3
ISBN 13: 978-1-256-85152-3

Sign In or Create Account

MyLab / Mastering

Home   Learn About   Students   Educators   Contact Us

Register   Help

Sign In

Sign in with your Pearson account. Create an account if you don't already have one.

Username [   ]

Password [   ]

[Sign In]

Forgot your username or password?

Your Course

Access Code and OLP and Grace Period Course
Course ID: viking89524
Taught by Instructor Viking at AMERICAN INST OF BANKING
Course ends Apr 6, 2012

Not your course? Enter a different course ID.

PEARSON   ALWAYS LEARNING

Copyright © 2011 Pearson Education Inc. All Rights Reserved Pearson Higher Education | Legal Notice | Privacy Policy | Contact Us | Help

---

Create Account

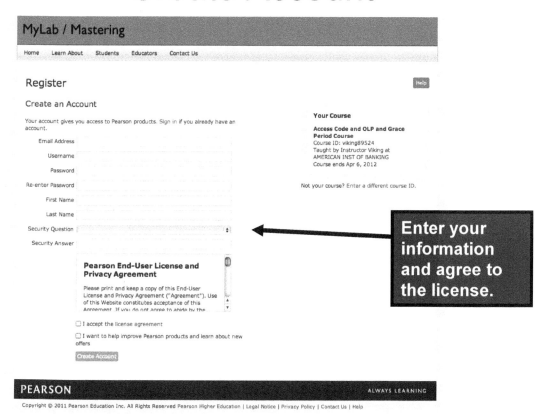

MyLab / Mastering

Home   Learn About   Students   Educators   Contact Us

Register   Help

Create an Account

Your account gives you access to Pearson products. Sign in if you already have an account.

Email Address [   ]
Username [   ]
Password [   ]
Re-enter Password [   ]
First Name [   ]
Last Name [   ]
Security Question [   ]
Security Answer

Pearson End-User License and Privacy Agreement

Please print and keep a copy of this End-User License and Privacy Agreement ("Agreement"). Use of this Website constitutes acceptance of this Agreement. If you do not agree to abide by the

☐ I accept the license agreement

☐ I want to help improve Pearson products and learn about new offers

[Create Account]

Your Course

Access Code and OLP and Grace Period Course
Course ID: viking89524
Taught by Instructor Viking at AMERICAN INST OF BANKING
Course ends Apr 6, 2012

Not your course? Enter a different course ID.

Enter your information and agree to the license.

PEARSON   ALWAYS LEARNING

Copyright © 2011 Pearson Education Inc. All Rights Reserved Pearson Higher Education | Legal Notice | Privacy Policy | Contact Us | Help

Create Account: Reminders

Create an Account

Your account gives you access to Pearson products. Sign in if you already have an account.

Email Address: judyhome@comcast.net

Username: judyhome@comcast.net

Password:

Re-enter Password:

> Use your email address as your username to make your username easier to remember. You can also enter a different username.

Your Cours

Access Cod
Period Cour
Course ID:
by I
AN I
end

Not your course

Password: ●●●●●●

Re-enter Password:

First Name:

Last Name:

Pearson End-User License and

> Enter a password that:
> ✗ Is at least eight characters long
> ✓ Contains at least one letter
> ✗ Contains at least one number
> ✓ Does not include your name or username
> ✓ Does not include unsupported characters

Payment Options

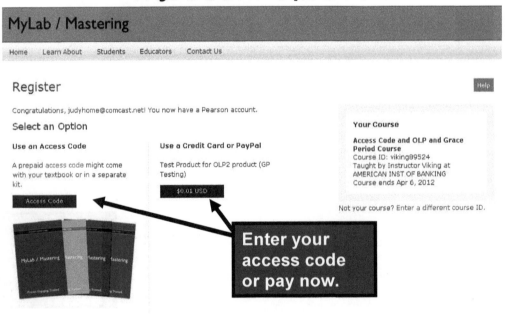

MyLab / Mastering

Home   Learn About   Students   Educators   Contact Us

Register

Help

Congratulations, judyhome@comcast.net! You now have a Pearson account.

Select an Option

Use an Access Code

A prepaid access code might come with your textbook or in a separate kit.

Access Code

Use a Credit Card or PayPal

Test Product for OLP2 product (GP Testing)

$0.01 USD

Enter your access code or pay now.

Your Course

Access Code and OLP and Grace Period Course
Course ID: viking89524
Taught by Instructor Viking at
AMERICAN INST OF BANKING
Course ends Apr 6, 2012

Not your course? Enter a different course ID.

Waiting for financial aid? Get temporary access without payment for 17 days. Pay by August 11, 2011 to stay in your instructor's online course.

Confirmation

Register

You're Done!

You have temporary access to your online course for 17 days. Pay anytime before August 11, 2011 to stay in your course. Check your email for a registration confirmation and payment instructions.

Print this page as your receipt.

Your Course

Access Code and OLP and Grace Period Course
Course ID: viking89524
Taught by Instructor Viking at AMERICAN INST OF BANKING
Course ends Apr 6, 2012

[Go to Your Course]

Account Information

Username: judyhome
Email: judyhome@comcast.net
Account ID: 5093300

Order Details

Order Date: Jul 25 2011
Order ID: 5815822

Support

Go to Pearson 24/7 Technical Support.

Sign In

The moment you know

That inspired moment when something that was difficult to understand makes perfect sense.

[Learn more about MyXLab]

Sign in

Already registered? Sign in with your Pearson account.

[Sign in]

Register

Need access? Start here.

[Student]
[Educator]

For Students

- Get Started
- Tours
- What's New
- System Requirements
- Support

For Educators

- Get Started
- Tours
- What's New
- System Requirements
- Support

"MyXLab helped me get really high grades in class."

Jackie likes that MyXLab allows her to learn at her own pace.

Read more student feedback ▶

MyLab / Mastering Student Temporary Access

Temporary access allows you to fully participate in your instructor's online course for up to 17 days without payment while waiting on financial aid. The temporary access option will appear on the payment page if it is available for your course.

Anytime before the 17th day you should pay or use an access code to maintain access to the course and your work. You can pay after the 17th day and regain access to your course, but you may miss deadlines, or important notices from your instructor.

What You Need to Register

☐ An instructor-provided **Course ID:** _____

☐ **A valid email address**
Your instructor will use this email address to communicate with you. In addition, registration confirmation and payment instructions will also be sent to this address.

Temporary Access Registration and First Time Sign In Instructions

> Go to www.pearsonmylab.com or www.pearsonmastering.com
> and click **Student** under *Register*.

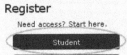

> Enter the Course ID, click **Continue** and verify your course information.

>

Sign In with your existing Pearson account. Username ☐ Password ☐	**OR**	**Create an account** if you don't already have one. Remember to write down the username/password you create.

On the payment page, scroll down and click the temporary access link.

Waiting for financial aid? Get temporary access without payment for 17 days.

> From the confirmation page, click **Go To Your Course**, and then in the left panel, click the *course name* to start your work.

....

To Sign In to Your Course Later
> Return to www.pearsonmylab.com or www.pearsonmastering.com
> Click **Sign In** and enter your Pearson account username/password.

Changing Temporary Access to Full Access Instructions

Your instructor chose MyLab / Mastering to help you succeed in your course. With rich media, eText and much more, your course provides you with the resources to master even the most difficult concepts.

To get full access to your MyLab / Mastering course after registering with temporary access, you must use an access code, a credit card, or a PayPal account.

> Return to www.pearsonmylab.com or www.pearsonmastering.com
> Click **Sign In** and enter your previously created Pearson account username/password.

NOTE: Make sure you upgrade from your existing Pearson account. Creating a new username/password will cause your grades from the first 17 days to be unavailable to you.

> Click the **Pay or use an access code now** link under the course you want to pay for.

NOTE: If your temporary access has expired, you may see an expired subscription notice. After clicking the **Pay or use an access code now** link from the expired notice, you will be asked for the Course ID for which you are paying, so be sure to have that available.

> Select a payment option:

- If you already purchased an *access code*, click **Access Code**, enter the *access code* in the boxes, and click **Finish**.

- If you plan to pay using a *credit card* or *PayPal*, select the access option you want. Enter the billing and payment information, and then click **Review** and **Make Payment**.

> You are now set for the rest of the semester. From the confirmation page, click **Go To Your Course**, and then in the left panel, click the *course name* to continue your work.

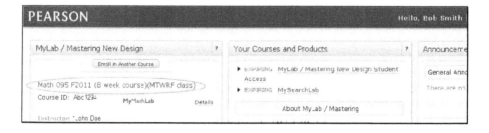

Customer Technical Support

MyMathLab Technical Support

Student Support

In addition to the online Help resources on your course website, our Technical Support website offers student assistance, 24/7.

Go to **http://247pearsoned.custhelp.com**

▶ **Chat online with a representative:** Live Chat Support representatives are available to answer, 24/7

▶ **Email your questions:** Support representatives are available to answer, 24/7

▶ **Self-help:** Access our extensive self-help knowledgebase, 24/7

Call our Student Technical Support phone line

▶ 1 (800) 677-6337
▶ Available Monday-Friday 9am-5pm PT

This book is dedicated to students everywhere—and we should all be students. After all, is there anyone among us who really knows too much? Take that hint and continue to learn something new every day of your life.

Best of wishes from a fellow student: Elayn Martin-Gay

Contents

Preface   xii
Applications Index   xx

CHAPTER 8   MORE ON FUNCTIONS AND GRAPHS   510

8.1   Graphing and Writing Linear Functions   511
8.2   Reviewing Function Notation and Graphing Nonlinear Functions   519
      Integrated Review—Summary on Functions and Equations of Lines   527
8.3   Graphing Piecewise-Defined Functions and Shifting and Reflecting Graphs of Functions   528
8.4   Variation and Problem Solving   536
      Chapter 8 Vocabulary Check   544
      Chapter 8 Highlights   545
      Chapter 8 Review   547
      Chapter 8 Test   548
      Chapter 8 Cumulative Review   550

CHAPTER 9   INEQUALITIES AND ABSOLUTE VALUE   551

9.1   Compound Inequalities   552
9.2   Absolute Value Equations   559
9.3   Absolute Value Inequalities   564
      Integrated Review—Solving Compound Inequalities and Absolute Value Equations and Inequalities   570
9.4   Graphing Linear Inequalities in Two Variables and Systems of Linear Inequalities   570
      Chapter 9 Vocabulary Check   579
      Chapter 9 Highlights   580
      Chapter 9 Review   582
      Chapter 9 Test   583
      Chapter 9 Cumulative Review   583

CHAPTER 10   RATIONAL EXPONENTS, RADICALS, AND COMPLEX NUMBERS   586

10.1   Radicals and Radical Functions   587
10.2   Rational Exponents   596
10.3   Simplifying Radical Expressions   603
10.4   Adding, Subtracting, and Multiplying Radical Expressions   611
10.5   Rationalizing Denominators and Numerators of Radical Expressions   617
       Integrated Review—Radicals and Rational Exponents   623
10.6   Radical Equations and Problem Solving   624
10.7   Complex Numbers   634
       Chapter 10 Vocabulary Check   641
       Chapter 10 Highlights   641
       Chapter 10 Review   645
       Chapter 10 Test   647
       Chapter 10 Cumulative Review   648

CHAPTER 11   QUADRATIC EQUATIONS AND FUNCTIONS   651

11.1   Solving Quadratic Equations by Completing the Square   652
11.2   Solving Quadratic Equations by the Quadratic Formula   662
11.3   Solving Equations by Using Quadratic Methods   672

Integrated Review—Summary on Solving Quadratic Equations   681
11.4   Nonlinear Inequalities in One Variable   682
11.5   Quadratic Functions and Their Graphs   689
11.6   Further Graphing of Quadratic Functions   697
       Chapter 11 Vocabulary Check   705
       Chapter 11 Highlights   705
       Chapter 11 Review   708
       Chapter 11 Test   709
       Chapter 11 Cumulative Review   710

CHAPTER

12

EXPONENTIAL AND LOGARITHMIC FUNCTIONS   712

12.1   The Algebra of Functions; Composite Functions   713
12.2   Inverse Functions   718
12.3   Exponential Functions   729
12.4   Exponential Growth and Decay Functions   738
12.5   Logarithmic Functions   742
12.6   Properties of Logarithms   750
       Integrated Review—Functions and Properties of Logarithms   756
12.7   Common Logarithms, Natural Logarithms, and Change of Base   757
12.8   Exponential and Logarithmic Equations and Problem Solving   763
       Chapter 12 Vocabulary Check   769
       Chapter 12 Highlights   770
       Chapter 12 Review   773
       Chapter 12 Test   775
       Chapter 12 Cumulative Review   777

CHAPTER

13

CONIC SECTIONS   779

13.1   The Parabola and the Circle   780
13.2   The Ellipse and the Hyperbola   789
       Integrated Review—Graphing Conic Sections   796
13.3   Solving Nonlinear Systems of Equations   797
13.4   Nonlinear Inequalities and Systems of Inequalities   802
       Chapter 13 Vocabulary Check   806
       Chapter 13 Highlights   806
       Chapter 13 Review   809
       Chapter 13 Test   810
       Chapter 13 Cumulative Review   810

CHAPTER

14

SEQUENCES, SERIES, AND THE BINOMIAL THEOREM   812

14.1   Sequences   813
14.2   Arithmetic and Geometric Sequences   817
14.3   Series   825
       Integrated Review—Sequences and Series   830
14.4   Partial Sums of Arithmetic and Geometric Sequences   830
14.5   The Binomial Theorem   837
       Chapter 14 Vocabulary Check   842
       Chapter 14 Highlights   842
       Chapter 14 Review   844
       Chapter 14 Test   846
       Chapter 14 Cumulative Review   846

APPENDICES

A   OPERATIONS ON DECIMALS/TABLE OF PERCENT, DECIMAL, AND FRACTION EQUIVALENTS   848
B   REVIEW OF ALGEBRA TOPICS   851
C   AN INTRODUCTION TO USING A GRAPHING UTILITY   876
D   SOLVING SYSTEMS OF EQUATIONS BY MATRICES   881
E   SOLVING SYSTEMS OF EQUATIONS BY DETERMINANTS   886
F   MEAN, MEDIAN, AND MODE   893
G   REVIEW OF ANGLES, LINES, AND SPECIAL TRIANGLES   895
H   CONTENTS OF STUDENT RESOURCES   902

4.4   Solving Systems of Linear Equations in Three Variables   273
4.5   Systems of Linear Equations and Problem Solving   280

Answers to Selected Exercises   A1
Index   I1
Photo Credits   P1

Student Resources

These resources, located in the back of the text, give you a variety of tools conveniently located in one place to help you succeed in math.

Study Skills Builders

Attitude and Study Tips:

1. Have You Decided to Complete This Course Successfully?
2. Tips for Studying for an Exam
3. What to Do the Day of an Exam
4. Are You Satisfied with Your Performance on a Particular Quiz or Exam?
5. How Are You Doing?
6. Are You Preparing for Your Final Exam?

Organizing Your Work:

7. Learning New Terms
8. Are You Organized?
9. Organizing a Notebook
10. How Are Your Homework Assignments Going?

MyMathLab and MathXL:

11. Tips for Turning in Your Homework on Time
12. Tips for Doing Your Homework Online
13. Organizing Your Work
14. Getting Help with Your Homework Assignments
15. Tips for Preparing for an Exam
16. How Well Do You Know the Resources Available to You in MyMathLab?

Additional Help Inside and Outside Your Textbook:

17. How Well Do You Know Your Textbook?
18. Are You Familiar with Your Textbook Supplements?
19. Are You Getting All the Mathematics Help That You Need?

The Bigger Picture–Study Guide Outline

Practice Final Exam

Answers to Selected Exercises

A New Tool to Help You Succeed

Introducing Martin-Gay's New Student Organizer

The new **Student Organizer** guides you through three important parts of studying effectively—note-taking, practice, and homework.

It is designed to help you organize your learning materials and develop the study habits you need to be successful. The Student Organizer includes:

- How to prepare for class
- Space to take class notes
- Step-by-step worked examples
- Your Turn exercises (modeled after the examples)
- Answers to the Your Turn exercises as well as worked-out solutions via references to the Martin-Gay text and videos
- Helpful hints and directions for completing homework assignments

A flexible design allows instructors to assign any or all parts of the Student Organizer.

The Student Organizer is available in a loose-leaf, notebook-ready format. It is also available for download in MyMathLab.

For more information, please go to

www.pearsonhighered.com/martingay

www.mypearsonstore.com
  (search Martin-Gay, Beginning & Intermediate Algebra, Fifth Edition)
your Martin-Gay MyMathLab® course

Martin-Gay Video Resources to Help You Succeed

Interactive DVD Lecture Series

Active Learning at Your Pace

Designed for use on your computer or DVD player, these interactive videos include a 15–20 minute lecture for every section in the text as well as Concept Checks, Study Skills Builders, and a Practice Final Exam.

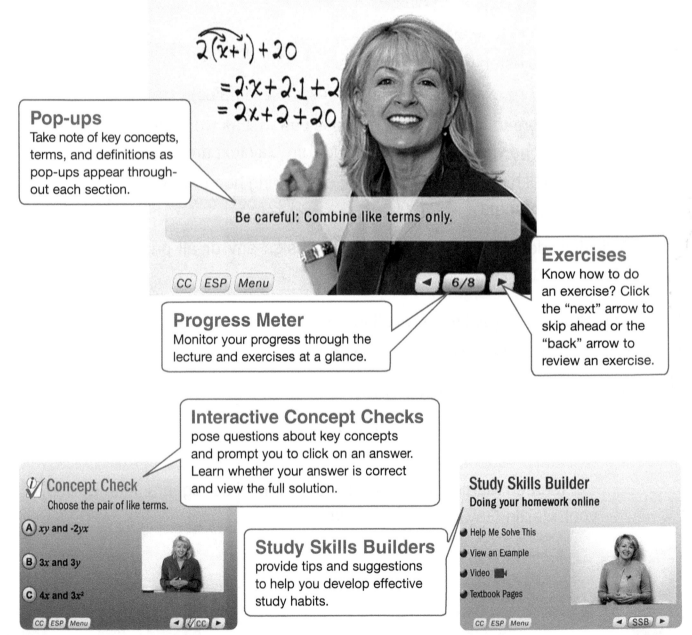

Pop-ups
Take note of key concepts, terms, and definitions as pop-ups appear throughout each section.

$$2(x+1)+20$$
$$=2\cdot x+2\cdot 1+2$$
$$=2x+2+20$$

Be careful: Combine like terms only.

CC   ESP   Menu

◀ 6/8 ▶

Exercises
Know how to do an exercise? Click the "next" arrow to skip ahead or the "back" arrow to review an exercise.

Progress Meter
Monitor your progress through the lecture and exercises at a glance.

Interactive Concept Checks
pose questions about key concepts and prompt you to click on an answer. Learn whether your answer is correct and view the full solution.

Concept Check
Choose the pair of like terms.
(A) xy and $-2yx$
(B) $3x$ and $3y$
(C) $4x$ and $3x^2$

CC ESP Menu   ◀ ✓CC ▶

Study Skills Builders
provide tips and suggestions to help you develop effective study habits.

Study Skills Builder
Doing your homework online

● Help Me Solve This
● View an Example
● Video
● Textbook Pages

CC ESP Menu   ◀ SSB ▶

Chapter Test Prep Videos

Step-by-step solutions on video for all chapter test exercises from the text. Available via:

- Interactive DVD Lecture Series
- MyMathLab®
- You Tube™

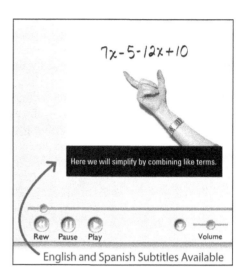

Here we will simplify by combining like terms.

Rew Pause Play Volume

English and Spanish Subtitles Available

AlgebraPrep Apps for the iPhone™ and iPod Touch®

Your 24/7 Algebra Tutor–Anytime, Anywhere!

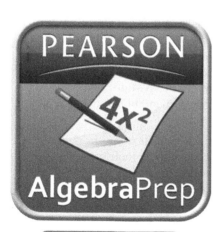

Choose to take a Practice Test or a MiniTest (designed to take 10 minutes or less).

Practice Test exercises provide answer feedback to help you study and self-correct.

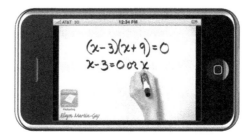

Step-by-step video solutions give you the guidance of an expert tutor whenever you need help.

Preface

Beginning & Intermediate Algebra, **Fifth Edition,** was written to provide a solid foundation in algebra for students who might not have previous experience in algebra. Specific care was taken to make sure students have the most up-to-date, relevant text preparation for their next mathematics course or for nonmathematical courses that require an understanding of algebraic fundamentals. I have tried to achieve this by writing a user-friendly text that is keyed to objectives and contains many worked-out examples. As suggested by AMATYC and the NCTM Standards (plus Addenda), real-life and real-data applications, data interpretation, conceptual understanding, problem solving, writing, cooperative learning, appropriate use of technology, mental mathematics, number sense, estimation, critical thinking, and geometric concepts are emphasized and integrated throughout the book.

The many factors that contributed to the success of the previous editions have been retained. In preparing the Fifth Edition, I considered comments and suggestions of colleagues, students, and many users of the prior edition throughout the country.

What's New in the Fifth Edition?

- **The Martin-Gay Program** has been revised and enhanced with a new design in the text and MyMathLab to actively encourage students to use the text, video program, and Student Organizer as an integrated learning system.

- **The Student Organizer** is designed by me to help students develop the study habits they need to be successful. This Organizer guides students through the three main components of studying effectively—note-taking, practice, and homework—and helps them develop the habits that will enable them to succeed in future courses. The Student Organizer can be packaged with the text in loose-leaf, notebook-ready format and is also available for download in MyMathLab.

- **New Vocabulary, Readiness & Video Check** questions have been added prior to every section exercise set. These exercises quickly check a student's understanding of new vocabulary words. The **readiness** exercises center on a student's understanding of a concept that is necessary in order to continue to the exercise set. **New video check questions for the Martin-Gay Interactive Lecture videos** are now included in every section for each learning objective. **These exercises are all available for assignment in MyMathLab** and are a great way to assess whether students have viewed and understood the key concepts presented in the videos.

- **The Interactive DVD Lecture Series,** featuring your text author (Elayn Martin-Gay), provides students with active learning at their own pace. The videos offer the following resources and more:

  A complete lecture for each section of the text highlights key examples and exercises from the text. New "pop-ups" reinforce key terms, definitions, and concepts.

  An interface with menu navigation features allows students to quickly find and focus on the examples and exercises they need to review.

  Interactive Concept Check exercises measure students' understanding of key concepts and common trouble spots.

  The Interactive DVD Lecture Series also includes the following resources for test prep:

  The Practice Final Exam helps students prepare for an end-of-course final. Students can watch full video solutions to each exercise.

The Chapter Test Prep Videos help students during their most teachable moment–when they are preparing for a test. This innovation provides step-by-step solutions for the Chapter Test exercises found at the end of each chapter in the text. The videos are captioned in English and Spanish. For the Fifth Edition, the chapter test prep videos are also available on YouTube™.

- **The Martin-Gay MyMathLab course** has been updated and revised to provide more exercise coverage, including assignable video check questions, and an expanded video program. There are section lecture videos for every section, students can also access at the specific objective level, and there are an increased number of watch clips at the exercise level to help students while doing homework in MathXL. Suggested homework assignments have been premade for assignment at the instructor's discretion.

- **New MyMathLab Ready to Go courses** (access code required) provide students with all the same great MyMathLab features that you're used to, but make it easier for instructors to get started. Each course includes preassigned homework and quizzes to make creating your course even simpler. Ask your Pearson representative about the details for this particular course or to see a copy of this course.

- **A new section** (12.4) devoted specifically to exponential growth and decay and applications has been added. This section includes the definition and examples of half-life.

- **The new Student Resources** section, located in the back of the text, gives students a variety of tools that are conveniently located in one place to help them achieve success in mathematics.

  — **Study Skills Builders** give students tips and suggestions on successful study habits and help them take responsibility for their learning. Assignable exercises check students' progress in improving their skills.

  — The **Bigger Picture—Study Guide Outline** covers key concepts of the course—simplifying expressions and solving equations and inequalities—to help students transition from thinking section-by-section to thinking about how the material they are learning fits into mathematics as a whole. This outline provides a model for students on how to organize and develop their own study guide.

  — The **Practice Final Exam** helps students prepare for the end-of-the-course exam. Students can also watch the step-by-step solutions to all the Practice Final Exam exercises on the new Interactive DVD Lecture Series and in MyMathLab.

  — The **Answers to Selected Exercises** section allows students to check their answers for all Practice exercises; odd-numbered Vocabulary, Readiness & Video Check exercises; odd-numbered section exercises; odd-numbered Chapter Review and Cumulative Review exercises; and all Integrated Review and Chapter Test exercises.

- **New guided application exercises** appear in many sections throughout the text, beginning with Section 2.4. These applications prompt students on how to set up the application and get started with the solution process. These guided exercises will help students prepare to solve application exercises on their own.

- **Enhanced emphasis on Study Skills** helps students develop good study habits and makes it more convenient for instructors to incorporate or assign study skills in their courses. The following changes have been made in the Fifth Edition:

Section 1.1, Tips for Success in Mathematics, has been updated to include helpful hints for doing homework online in MyMathLab. Exercises pertaining to doing homework online in MyMathLab are now included in the exercise set for 1.1.

The Study Skills Builders, formerly located at the end of select exercise sets, are now included in the new **Student Resources** section at the back of the book and are organized by topic for ease of assignment. This section now also includes new Study Skills Builders on doing homework online in MyMathLab.

- All exercise sets have been reviewed and updated to ensure that even- and odd-numbered exercises are paired.

Key Pedagogical Features

The following key features have been retained and/or updated for the Fifth Edition of the text:

Problem-Solving Process   This is formally introduced in Chapter 2 with a four-step process that is integrated throughout the text. The four steps are **Understand, Translate, Solve,** and **Interpret.** The repeated use of these steps in a variety of examples shows their wide applicability. Reinforcing the steps can increase students' comfort level and confidence in tackling problems.

Exercise Sets Revised and Updated   The exercise sets have been carefully examined and extensively revised. Special focus was placed on making sure that even- and odd-numbered exercises are paired.

Examples   Detailed, step-by-step examples were added, deleted, replaced, or updated as needed. Many of these reflect real life. Additional instructional support is provided in the annotated examples.

Practice Exercises   Throughout the text, each worked-out example has a parallel Practice Exercise. These invite students to be actively involved in the learning process. Students should try each Practice Exercise after finishing the corresponding example. Learning by doing will help students grasp ideas before moving on to other concepts. Answers to the Practice Exercises are provided in the back of the text.

Helpful Hints   Helpful Hints contain practical advice on applying mathematical concepts. Strategically placed where students are most likely to need immediate reinforcement, Helpful Hints help students avoid common trouble areas and mistakes.

Concept Checks   This feature allows students to gauge their grasp of an idea as it is being presented in the text. Concept Checks stress conceptual understanding at the point-of-use and help suppress misconceived notions before they start. Answers appear at the bottom of the page. Exercises related to Concept Checks are included in the exercise sets.

Mixed Practice Exercises   Found in the section exercise sets, each requires students to determine the problem type and strategy needed to solve it just as they would need to do on a test.

Integrated Reviews   A unique, mid-chapter exercise set that helps students assimilate new skills and concepts that they have learned separately over several sections. These reviews provide yet another opportunity for students to work with "mixed" exercises as they master the topics.

Vocabulary Check   Provides an opportunity for students to become more familiar with the use of mathematical terms as they strengthen their verbal skills. These appear at the end of each chapter before the Chapter Highlights. Vocabulary, Readiness & Video Check exercises also provide vocabulary practice at the section level.

Chapter Highlights   Found at the end of every chapter, these contain key definitions and concepts with examples to help students understand and retain what they have learned and help them organize their notes and study for tests.

Chapter Review   The end of every chapter contains a comprehensive review of topics introduced in the chapter. The Chapter Review offers exercises keyed to every section in the chapter, as well as Mixed Review exercises that are not keyed to sections.

Chapter Test and Chapter Test Prep Video   The Chapter Test is structured to include those problems that involve common student errors. The **Chapter Test Prep Videos** give students instant access to a step-by-step video solution of each exercise in the Chapter Test.

Cumulative Review   Follows every chapter in the text (except Chapter 1). Each odd-numbered exercise contained in the Cumulative Review is an earlier worked example in the text that is referenced in the back of the book along with the answer.

Writing Exercises   ＼These exercises occur in almost every exercise set and require students to provide a written response to explain concepts or justify their thinking.

Applications   Real-world and real-data applications have been thoroughly updated and many new applications are included. These exercises occur in almost every exercise set and show the relevance of mathematics and help students gradually, and continuously, develop their problem-solving skills.

Review and Preview Exercises   These exercises occur in each exercise set (except in Chapter 1) and are keyed to earlier sections. They review concepts learned earlier in the text that will be needed in the next section or chapter.

Exercise Set Resource Icons   Located at the opening of each exercise set, these icons remind students of the resources available for extra practice and support:

See Student Resources descriptions on page xviii for details on the individual resources available.

Exercise Icons   These icons facilitate the assignment of specialized exercises and let students know what resources can support them.

- ◯ Video icon: exercise worked on the Interactive DVD Lecture Series and in MyMathLab.
- △ Triangle icon: identifies exercises involving geometric concepts.
- ＼ Pencil icon: indicates a written response is needed.
- ▦ Calculator icon: optional exercises intended to be solved using a scientific or graphing calculator.

Optional: Graphing Calculator Exploration Boxes and Calculator Exercises   The optional Graphing Calculator Explorations provide keystrokes and exercises at appropriate points to give an opportunity for students to become familiar with these tools. Section exercises that are best completed by using a calculator are identified by ▦ for ease of assignment.

Student and Instructor Resources

STUDENT RESOURCES

Student Organizer Guides students through the 3 main components of studying effectively–note-taking, practice, and homework. The organizer includes before-class preparation exercises, note-taking pages in a 2-column format for use in class, and examples paired with exercises for practice for each section. It is 3-hole-punched. Also available in MyMathLab.	**Student Solutions Manual** Provides complete worked-out solutions to • the odd-numbered section exercises; all Practice Exercises; all exercises in the Integrated Reviews, Chapter Reviews, Chapter Tests, and Cumulative Reviews
Interactive DVD Lecture Series Provides students with active learning at their pace. The videos offer: • A complete lecture for each text section. The interface allows easy navigation to examples and exercises students need to review. • Interactive Concept Check exercises • Study Skills Builders • Practice Final Exam • Chapter Test Prep Videos	**Chapter Test Prep Videos** • Step-by-step solutions to every exercise in each Chapter Practice Test. • Available in MyMathLab® and on YouTube, and in the Interactive DVD Lecture Series.

INSTRUCTOR RESOURCES

Annotated Instructor's Edition Contains all the content found in the student edition, plus the following: • Answers to exercises on the same text page • Answers to graphing exercises and all video exercises • Teaching Tips throughout the text placed at key points. • Classroom Examples in the margin paired to each example in the text.	**Instructor's Resource Manual with Tests and Mini-Lectures** • Mini-lectures for each text section • Additional Practice worksheets for each section • Several forms of test per chapter–free response and multiple choice • Group activities • Video key to the example number in the video questions and section exercises worked in the videos • Answers to all items **Instructor's Solutions Manual** **TestGen®** (Available for download from the IRC)
	Online Resources **MyMathLab®** (access code required) **MathXL®** (access code required)

Acknowledgments

There are many people who helped me develop this text, and I will attempt to thank some of them here. Cindy Trimble and Carrie Green were *invaluable* for contributing to the overall accuracy of the text. Dawn Nuttall, Courtney Slade, and JoAnne Thomasson were *invaluable* for their many suggestions and contributions during the development and writing of this Fifth Edition. Debbie Meyer and Amanda Zagnoli of Integra-Chicago provided guidance throughout the production process.

A very special thank you goes to my editor, Mary Beckwith, for being there 24/7/365, as my students say. Last, my thanks to the staff at Pearson for all their support: Patty Bergin, Heather Scott, Michelle Renda, Chris Hoag, and Greg Tobin.

I would like to thank the following reviewers for their input and suggestions:

Sandi Athanassiou, *University of Missouri–Columbia*
Michelle Beerman, *Pasco-Hernandez Community College*
Monika Bender, *Central Texas College*
Bob Hervey, *Hillsborough Community College*
Michael Maltenfort, *Truman College*
Jorge Romero, *Hillsborough Community College*
Joseph Wakim, *Brevard Community College*
Flo Wilson, *Central Texas College*
Marie Caruso and students, *Middlesex Community College*

I would also like to thank the following dedicated group of instructors who participated in our focus groups, Martin-Gay Summits, and our design review for the series. Their feedback and insights have helped to strengthen this edition of the text. These instructors include:

Billie Anderson, *Tyler Junior College*
Joey Anderson, *Central Piedmont Community College*
Cedric Atkins, *Mott Community College*
Teri Barnes, *McLennan Community College*
Andrea Barnett, *Tri-County Technical College*
Lois Beardon, *Schoolcraft College*
Michelle Beerman, *Pasco-Hernandez Community College*
Laurel Berry, *Bryant & Stratton College*
John Beyers, *University of Maryland*
Jennifer Brahier, *Pensacola Junior College*
Bob Brown, *Community College of Baltimore County–Essex*
Lisa Brown, *Community College of Baltimore County–Essex*
NeKeith Brown, *Richland College*
Sue Brown, *Guilford Technical Community College*
Gail Burkett, *Palm Beach State College*
Cheryl Cantwell, *Seminole Community College*
Janie Chapman, *Spartanburg Community College*
Jackie Cohen, *Augusta State College*
Julie Dewan, *Mohawk Valley Community College*
Janice Ervin, *Central Piedmont Community College*
Karen Estes, *St. Petersburg College*
Richard Fielding, *Southwestern College*
Sonia Ford, *Midland College*
Julie Francavilla, *State College of Florida*
Cindy Gaddis, *Tyler Junior College*
Nita Graham, *St. Louis Community College*
Pauline Hall, *Iowa State College*
Elizabeth Hamman, *Cypress College*
Kathy Hoffmaster, *Thomas Nelson Community College*
Pat Hussey, *Triton College*
Dorothy Johnson, *Lorain County Community College*
Sonya Johnson, *Central Piedmont Community College*

Irene Jones, *Fullerton College*
Paul Jones, *University of Cincinnati*
Mike Kirby, *Tidewater Community College*
Kathy Kopelousos, *Lewis and Clark Community College*
Nancy Lange, *Inver Hills Community College*
Judy Langer, *Westchester Community College*
Lisa Lindloff, *McLennan Community College*
Sandy Lofstock, *St. Petersburg College*
Kathy Lovelle, *Westchester Community College*
Jamie Malek, *Florida State College*
Jean McArthur, *Joliet Junior College*
Kevin McCandless, *Evergreen Valley College*
Daniel Miller, *Niagara County Community College*
Marcia Molle, *Metropolitan Community College*
Carol Murphy, *San Diego Miramar College*
Charlotte Newsom, *Tidewater Community College*
Greg Nguyen, *Fullerton College*
Eric Ollila, *Jackson Community College*
Linda Padilla, *Joliet Junior College*
Rena Petrello, *Moorpark College*
Davidson Pierre, *State College of Florida*
Marilyn Platt, *Gaston College*
Susan Poss, *Spartanburg Community College*
Natalie Rivera, *Estrella Mountain Community College*
Judy Roane, *Pearl River Community College*
Claudinna Rowley, *Montgomery Community College, Rockville*
Ena Salter, *State College of Florida*
Carole Shapero, *Oakton Community College*
Janet Sibol, *Hillsborough Community College*
Anne Smallen, *Mohawk Valley Community College*
Mike Stack, *South Suburban College*
Barbara Stoner, *Reading Area Community College*
Jennifer Strehler, *Oakton Community College*
Ellen Stutes, *Louisiana State University Eunice*
Tanomo Taguchi, *Fullerton College*
Sam Tinsley, *Richland College*
Linda Tucker, *Rose State College*
MaryAnn Tuerk, *Elgin Community College*
Gwen Turbeville, *J. Sargeant Reynolds Community College*
Walter Wang, *Baruch College*
Leigh Ann Wheeler, *Greenville Technical Community College*
Jenny Wilson, *Tyler Junior College*
Valerie Wright, *Central Piedmont Community College*

A special thank you to those students who participated in our design review:
Katherine Browne, Mike Bulfin, Nancy Canipe, Ashley Carpenter, Jeff Chojnachi,
Roxanne Davis, Mike Dieter, Amy Dombrowski, Kay Herring, Todd Jaycox, Kaleena
Levan, Matt Montgomery, Tony Plese, Abigail Polkinghorn, Harley Price, Eli Robinson,
Avery Rosen, Robyn Schott, Cynthia Thomas, and Sherry Ward.

Elayn Martin-Gay

About the Author

Elayn Martin-Gay has taught mathematics at the University of New Orleans for more than 25 years. Her numerous teaching awards include the local University Alumni Association's Award for Excellence in Teaching, and Outstanding Developmental Educator at University of New Orleans, presented by the Louisiana Association of Developmental Educators.

Prior to writing textbooks, Elayn Martin-Gay developed an acclaimed series of lecture videos to support developmental mathematics students in their quest for success. These highly successful videos originally served as the foundation material for her texts. Today, the videos are specific to each book in the Martin-Gay series. The author has also created Chapter Test Prep Videos to help students during their most "teachable moment"—as they prepare for a test—along with Instructor-to-Instructor videos that provide teaching tips, hints, and suggestions for each developmental mathematics course, including basic mathematics, prealgebra, beginning algebra, and intermediate algebra. Her most recent innovations are the AlgebraPrep Apps for the iPhone and iPod Touch. These Apps embrace the different learning styles, schedules, and paces of students and provide them with quality math tutoring.

Elayn is the author of 12 published textbooks as well as interactive multimedia mathematics, all specializing in developmental mathematics courses. She has participated as an author across the broadest range of educational materials: textbooks, videos, tutorial software, and courseware. This provides the opportunity of various combinations for an integrated teaching and learning package that offers great consistency for the student.

Applications Index

A

Animals
animal pen side lengths, 125
bear population decrease, 774
beetle and grasshopper species, 112
beetle infestations in lodgepole pines, 844
bison population in national park, 741
California condor population growth rate, 775
cattle holding pen dimensions, 670, 802
cheetah running speed, 457
cricket chirping rates, 114, 124, 125
diet of rabbits in lab, 296
dog pen/run dimensions, 117, 670
drug dosage for dogs, 237, 526
fighting fish tank measurements, 629
fishery products from domestic catch and imports, 257
fish numbers in tank, 124
flying fish travel time, 126
growth time for increasing wood duck population, 776
insects killed by insecticide spraying, 836, 845
learning curve for chimpanzee learning sign language, 768
lemming/rabbit population size estimates, 765
mosquito population, 737, 757
number of baby gorillas born at zoo, 827
number of cranes born each year in aviary, 845
number of opossums killed on highway, 829
number of otters born each year in aquarium, 829
number of species born each year in aquarium, 829
owl population decreasing rate, 829
pet-related expenditures, 180
pets owned in U.S., 128
prairie dog population growth, 776
puppy's weight gain each month, 815
rat population at wharf, 741
sparrow species extinction rate, 816
time for one dog alone to eat dog food, 680
time for running animal to overtake another, 495
wolf population size, 768
Astronomy
alignments of planets, 467
amount of gamma rays produced by Sun, 352
atmospheric pressures, 737, 768
circumference of Earth, 124
diameter of Milky Way, 369
distance light travels in one year, 352
eccentricity of planetary orbits, 795–796
elevation of optical telescope, 351
escape velocities for Earth and moon, 595
magnitudes of stars, 15–16
rocket plane traveling speed, 459
Sarsen Circle, 787–788
surface area of moon, 631
surface temperature of planets, 60, 125
temperature of interior of Earth, 351
time for light to reach Earth from the sun, 126, 353
time for reflected light from moon to reach Earth, 353
transmitting distance of Mars rovers, 351

volume of planet, 369
weight of object above Earth, 542
weight of object on a planet, 491
Automotive/motor vehicles
car rental charges, 293
cell phone use effects on driving, 164
cost of owning compact car, 215
fuel economy for autos, 215
hybrid vehicle sales, 225
median automobile age, 215
motor gasoline daily supply, 671
number of driver's licenses in U.S., 192
oil can stacked display, 844
predicted number of cars sold in one year, 836
registered vehicle percent increase, 136
safe velocity around curved road, 648
skidding distance of car, 631
value of automobile over time, 178, 547
Aviation
arrival and departures at airport, 857
atmospheric pressure, 737, 768
hang glider flight rate, 126
passenger traffic at airport, 709
runway length, 125
speed of airplane in still air, 293–294
speeds of two airplanes traveling apart, 810
time for unmanned aircraft to circumnavigate earth, 126
vertical change in flight elevations, 49
wind speed, 294, 492

B

Business
annual net sales, 173–174
annual salary potentials, 820, 824, 829, 836, 844, 845
apparel and accessory stores in U.S., 225
assembly times for each of several items, 836, 845
average price of new home, 518
book store closings, 225
break-even calculations, 145, 289–290, 296
building value depreciation, 226
charity fund-raiser dinner prices, 294
cheese production in U.S., 564, 736
cost after tax is added, 134
cost of certain quantity of products, 484–485
cost to operate delivery service, 633
cost to produce a single item, 443, 508, 542, 777
cost to produce certain number of items, 182, 296, 704
cost to remove pollutants from environment, 448
cranberry production, 15, 135
defective items sampling, 508
demand calculations, 661, 802
depreciation, 815
discount, 129, 134, 136, 137
display cans in grocery store, 824
eating establishments in U.S., 225
employee numbers before downsizing, 136
employment rate of decrease, 741
farmland prices, 216
fax charges, 836
flexible hours as job benefit priority, 136
gross profit margin, 449

growth and decline of various technologies, 862
hourly wage, 182
hybrid vehicle sales, 225
income during first year of business and total earnings for four years, 836, 845
Internet retail revenue, 736
interval for diameters in manufacture of circular items, 156
investment amounts, 509
items sold at original and at reduced prices, 294
Kraft Foods manufacturing sites, 135
manufacturing plants of each type, 163
market equilibrium, 802
markup, 129, 137, 164
maximum profit, 704
minimum cost, 704
minimum wage, 235–236, 527
net income, 42, 75
new price after markup, 164
number of each item purchased at sale price, 649
number of non-business bankruptcies, 509
number of Walmart stores per year, 183
original price before sale pricing, 164
percent increase/decrease in employee hiring, 165, 166
percent increase in pricing, 164
predicting sales of items, 221–222, 225
price after discount/sale, 134, 135–136
price before taxes, 846
price of each item, 292, 293
price–sales relationship, 518
product lifetime estimate, 776
profit, 688
profit changes over time, 518
purchase price before profit from selling, 136
quantity pricing, 181, 242
rental fees, 836, 845
revenue, 192, 296, 368, 448, 718
revenue predictions, 368
salary after pay raise, 134
sale pricing, 135, 742
sales amount needed to earn certain income, 164
time for one person to work alone, 494, 675–676, 680, 682, 708, 710
time for two people working together, 488, 490, 492, 495, 711
units manufactured at a total cost, 429
units manufactured in certain time, 201, 543
units produced to earn hourly wage, 182
value of a building over time, 547
work rates, 487–488, 492, 495, 527, 543, 679

C

Chemistry and physics
angstrom value, 369
Avogadro's number, 352
carbon dioxide in atmosphere, 736
DDT half-life, 740
depth of lead shield and intensity of radiation passing through, 774
distance olive falls from rest in vacuum, 844
electric current and resistance, 542
force exerted by tractor pulling tree stump, 632
force of wind on a surface, 543

gas pressure and volume, 538–539, 542, 548
half-life, 736, 740, 742, 750, 824
horsepower, 543–544
insects killed by insecticide spraying, 836, 845
intensity of light and distance from source, 542
iodine half-life, 750
isotope decay rate, 741, 829
methane emissions in U.S., 704–705
nickel half-life, 742
nuclear waste rate of decay, 736
percentage of light passing through several sheets of glass, 734
period of pendulum, 632, 824, 829, 834, 844
pH of a liquid, 750
radioactive debris in stream, 741
radioactive decay of uranium, 736, 742
radioactive element half-life, 824
radioactive waste decay rate, 845
radioactivity in milk after nuclear accident, 734–735
solutions/mixtures, 131–137, 160, 164, 248, 287–288, 292, 294–297, 302, 304, 493, 648
spring stretching, 537
weight supported by circular column, 540–541, 543
weight supported by rectangular beam, 543

D

Demographics and populations
age groups predicted to increase, 271
Americans using Internet, 164
annual number of wildfires in U.S., 174
annual visitors to U.S. National Park System, 15
average farm size in U.S., 181
child care centers, 75
college students studying abroad, 736
computer software engineers in U.S., 190
diamonds in carats produced, 112
farm numbers percent decrease, 136
growth and decline in various professions, 862
home-based child care providers, 75
households with at least one computer, 192–193
households with television, 214
IBM employees worldwide, 518
McDonald's restaurants worldwide, 518
national debt of selected countries, 352
number of children born to each woman, 136
number of college students in U.S., 671
number of counties in selected states, 113
number of driver's licenses in U.S., 192
numbers of joggers, 192
occupations predicted to increase/decrease, 272, 295–296
octuplets' birthweights, 73
pets owned in U.S., 128
population and pollutant amounts, 542
population decrease, 768, 769, 771
population growth, 738–739, 741, 769, 771, 774, 775, 846
population per square mile of land in U.S., 225
population prediction, 776, 846

registered nurses in U.S., 189, 518
single-family housing starts and completions, 558
states with most farms, 304
students graduating from public high schools in U.S., 382
sum of populations of metropolitan regions, 856
vehicle fatalities, 295
water use per day per person, 246
world population, 352

E

Education
ACT assessment exam percent score increase, 164
budgeting, 153, 155
college enrollment increase over time, 816
college room and board charges, 836
college students earning associate's degrees, 243
college students earning bachelor's degrees, 264–265
college students studying abroad, 736
enrollment in degree-granting postsecondary institutions, 521
enrollment in postsecondary institutions, 520–521
final exam scores, 156, 559
flexible hours as job benefit priority, 136
floor space for each student in class, 492
grant amounts donated to university, 832
Internet access in classrooms, 136
IQ relationship to nonsense syllables repeated, 632
learning curve for chimpanzee learning sign language, 768
learning curve for memorizing nonsense syllables, 768
learning curve for typing and dictation, 768
number of college students in U.S., 671
number of graduate and undergraduate students, 94
number of students room can accommodate, 492
percent increase of college costs, 130
students attending summer school, 741
students graduating from public high schools in U.S., 382
students per teacher in U.S., 180
students taking ACT assessment exam, 298
time spent studying and quiz scores, 181
Electronics and computers
adult blogging, 295
Americans using Internet, 164
basic cable subscribers, 246–247
car-phone range, 144
cell phone use effects on driving, 164
cell telephone subscriptions in U.S., 602, 736
depreciation in value of office copier, 815
Google.com searches daily, 369
households with at least one computer, 192–193
households with television, 214
Internet access in classrooms, 136
Internet-crime complaint decrease, 134
keypad dimensions, 802
popular online purchases, 135
predicted increase in Wi-Fi-enabled cell phones, 569, 671, 704
price of each item, 292, 293
single digital downloads annually, 382
text message users in age groups, 397
value of computer over time, 177–178
walkie-talkie range, 144

F

Energy
electric current and resistance, 542
electricity generated by wind, 494
gamma rays produced by Sun, 352

F

Finance
account balance, 46, 292, 640–641, 762–763, 772–774, 776
allowance given to child over time, 816
amount needed to pay off loan, 317
amount owed in a loan, 760, 763, 847
budgeting, 153, 155
building value depreciation, 226
charge account balance, 49
charity donation to youth center, 833
coin/bill calculations, 84, 140–141, 143, 144, 161, 164, 292, 293, 302, 303
compound interest, 317, 657, 733, 737, 760, 762, 768, 776
grant amounts donated to university, 832
interest rate, 35, 429, 657–658, 708, 847
investment amounts, 141–144, 164, 166, 292, 509, 737
investment doubling/tripling, 766–768, 847
investment growth over time, 775–776
new customers attracted to bank each day, 836
non-business bankruptcies, 509
real estate investment growth rate, 824
saving money each month, 825
savings account deposits, 836, 844
simple interest, 141–144, 657
stock market losses/gains, 60, 72, 74, 75
stock prices, 293
value of a building over time, 547
Food and nutrition
basal metabolic rate, 602
calories per gram/ounce, 491, 493
cheddar cheese consumption, 295
cheese production in U.S., 564, 736
chili pepper hotness, 137
cost of each food item, 302
cranberry production, 15, 135
food and drink sales annually, 210
food items for barbecue, 467
food mixtures, 135, 137, 294, 297, 302, 493
Kraft Foods manufacturing sites, 135
lettuce consumption percent decrease, 136
nutrition labeling, 137
pH of lemonade, 750
pizza size areas, 124
radioactivity in milk after nuclear accident, 734
red meat and poultry consumption, 280–281
vitamin A and body weight, 672
walking/cycling distance to use calories, 155
yogurt production in selected years, 245

G

Geography and geology
annual snowfall and distances from equator, 181
area of desert, 94, 112
atmospheric pressures, 737
distance across pond/lake, 647, 789
distance seen at a height, 542, 632
earthquake intensity, 762
earthquake magnitude, 759
elevation/depth calculations, 41, 46, 49, 60, 351
glacier flow rate, 115–116, 126
lava flow rate, 116, 125
length of river, 94
sunrise time for Indianapolis, 230
sunset time for Seward, Alaska, 235
volcano eruption height, 611
volcano heights, 159

volume of stalactite, 126
weak tornadoes, 166
weight of meteorite, 94, 112
Geometry
angle measurements, 47, 49, 73, 94, 107–108, 111–114, 290–291, 296, 297, 304, 640
arched bridge height and width, 789, 810
area and perimeter of geometric figure, 122–123, 473, 616–617
area of circle, 526
area of geometric figure, 23, 35, 124, 316, 328, 335–336, 342–343, 352, 369–371, 397, 460, 632
body surface area of human, 595
circumference of earth, 124
complementary angles, 47, 49, 93, 113, 167, 294, 474, 481
connecting pipe length, 647
diagonal lengths in rectangle/square, 629, 661, 682
diameter of circle, 156
Ferris wheel dimensions, 788
golden ratio, 670
golden rectangle dimensions, 114
height of geometric figure from its area, 359, 364, 423–424, 427
lateral surface area of cone, 611
length of figure's sides from its perimeter, 359, 372, 427
length of sides of original/later figure before/after expanding area, 428
length of swimming pool given its volume, 359
original dimensions of cardboard before folded into box, 680
parallelogram base and height lengths, 509
percent increase/decrease in area of geometric figure, 134, 136
perimeter of geometric figure, 24, 34–35, 84, 94, 102, 103, 124, 329, 368, 388, 467, 616, 670, 801
Pythagorean theorem, 627–628, 630–631, 647, 666–667, 669–670
radius of ball and its weight, 542
radius of circle given its area, 427
radius of sphere given surface area, 611
radius of sprinkler to water square garden, 680
rectangle dimensions, 117, 118, 122, 125, 155, 163, 165, 292, 295, 429, 430, 433–436, 670, 704, 802, 809
Sarsen Circle radius and circumference, 787–788
side lengths of quadrilateral, 296, 435
square side lengths, 125, 427, 430, 435
supplementary angles, 47, 49, 93, 113, 167, 294, 474, 481
surface area of a geometric shape, 330, 368, 539–540, 548, 631
surface area of cube, 317
triangle base and height, 124, 423–424, 429, 435, 437, 492, 509, 628–629, 631, 670
triangle side lengths, 125, 155, 292, 303, 370, 425–426, 428, 429, 436, 437, 486, 493, 494, 509, 631, 661, 670
units of measurement conversion, 456–457, 459, 491
volume of a building, 456–457
volume of box, 120
volume of cone, 543
volume of cube, 35, 316, 317, 335, 352, 526
volume of cylinder, 126, 316, 544
volume of Hoberman Sphere, 125
width of box from its volume, 364
Government and military
decisions made by Supreme Court, 136
mayoral election votes received, 93
national debt of selected countries, 352
number of Democrats and Republicans, 107, 248
Pentagon office and storage area, 459

H

Home improvement
area and perimeter of room, 122, 809
board lengths, 84, 93, 102, 106, 111, 113, 163, 473
connecting pipe length, 647
distance across pond/lake, 647, 789
dog pen/run dimensions, 117, 670
fencing needed, 123, 248, 297
fertilizer needed, 124
garden dimensions, 114, 117, 123, 433–434
ladder length, 428
molding lengths, 74, 329
new strawberry plants each year in a garden, 827
number of trees/shrubs in each row of triangular planting, 828, 846
paint needed, 123
radius of sprinkler to water square garden, 680
roof slope/pitch, 215
sewer pipe rise, 214
siding length, 113
weight supported by rectangular beam, 543
width of walk around garden, 430
wire placement from building, 628–629
wooden beam lengths, 329

M

Medicine and health
bacterial culture growth over time, 816, 822, 829
body-mass index, 449
drug dosage for dogs, 237, 526
drug/medicine dosage, 95, 449, 473
flu epidemic size, 768
fungus culture growth rate, 829
heart transplants in U.S., 216
height of woman given length of femur, 237, 526
height-weight calculations, 768
infectious disease cases doubling rate, 816
kidney transplants in U.S., 243
virus culture tripling rate, 824
wheelchair ramp grade, 214
yeast colony doubling amounts, 844, 845
Miscellaneous
adult blogging, 295
allowance given to child over time, 816
area codes, 109, 112, 165
area of canvas, 342
area of square rug, 342
area of table top, 371
average farm size in U.S., 181
block of ice stacked in pyramid, 831
blueprint measurements, 491
board/stick lengths, 84, 93, 102, 106, 111, 113, 163, 437, 473, 648
body surface area of human, 595
book store closings, 225
cell phones recycled each year, 329
cephalic index, 449
charity fund-raiser dinner prices, 294
coin/bill calculations, 84, 140–141, 144, 161, 164, 292, 293, 302, 303
diamonds in carats produced, 112
display cans in grocery store, 824
exponential decay, 741, 742
exponential growth, 741
eye blinking rates, 114
fabric needed to cover ottoman, 317
federally owned acres of land, 861
flagpole cable dimensions, 631
folded paper thickness, 844
guy wire dimensions, 428, 631
height of Washington Monument, 163
height of woman given length of femur, 237, 526
home telephone use, 134
households with television, 214

Miscellaneous (*continued*)

IQ relationship with nonsense syllables repeated, 632
ladder length, 428, 631
laundry costs, 210
money spent on recorded music, 182, 183
newspaper circulation decreasing, 225
number of each item purchased at sale price, 649
number of pencils manufactured in U.S., 351
oil can stacked display, 844
page numbers, 112, 428
pet-related expenditures, 180
picture frame dimensions, 123
popular online purchases, 135
postage for large envelopes, 236
retirement party budgeting, 155
rolls of carpet stacked in pyramid, 831
room dimensions, 809
room/door numbers, 94, 112, 428
rope length, 110
saving money each month, 825
sign dimensions, 122, 123
stamps of each type purchased, 303
steel piece length, 110
string lengths, 93, 112, 165
surfers in each row of human pyramid, 829
swimming pool width, 163
tanning lotion mixture, 137
telephones handled by switchboard, 225
text message users in selected age groups, 397
time for two inlet pipes to fill container, 490, 508
unknown number calculations, 90–91, 110, 112, 113, 127–128, 155, 163, 165, 167, 282–284, 292–293, 296, 302, 303, 305, 372, 422–423, 430, 486–487, 492–494, 508, 680, 704, 711, 802
volume of water in swimming pool, 317
water use per day per person, 246
wedding reception budgeting, 153, 155
wheelchair ramp grade, 214
wire length, 112, 113

Recreation and entertainment

admission price to movie theaters, 201
Adult Contemporary Music radio stations, 265
annual visitors to U.S. national parks, 15, 327–328, 429
average cinema admission price, 182
best-selling albums, 114
bicycling speed, 679
bicycling travel time, 139
box office revenue for movie industry, 180
card game scores, 49, 57
declining admissions at movie theaters, 201
digital movie screen percent increase, 131
exercise program lifecycle riding times, 824
gambling amounts lost on bets, 836
height of sail, 124, 493
hiking distance, 24, 139
hiking rate, 144, 294–295, 304, 493
jogging and biking speeds during workout, 679
jogging speeds, 492, 679
money spent on recorded music, 182, 183

money spent on world tourism, 214
movie screens by theater type, 25, 111
movie ticket sales, 247
number of each ticket type sold, 143–144
numbers of joggers, 192
overnight stays in national parks, 242
players remaining each round of tournament, 739–740, 774
pool scores, 836
popular tourist destinations, 179
rental demand for DVD movies, 611
rowing rate in still water, 293
running speeds during each part of workout, 682
speeds during bicycle race stages, 681
theater seating, 302, 816, 824, 844, 845
ticket prices, 284–285
time for hikers to meet, 144

S

Sports

baseball game attendance, 257
baseball runs batted in, 293
baseball slugging average, 449
baseball team payroll related to number of games won, 549
basketball field goals and free throws, 296–297
basketball player heights, 155
basketball scores, 293
bowling average, 155
disc throwing records, 137
football quarterback ratings, 449
football yards lost/gained, 60, 75
golf scores, 42, 57, 165
hockey penalty killing percentage, 473
men's track event speed, 457
Olympic medals won by selected countries, 112
stock car racing speed, 459
Super Bowl attendance over time, 179
ticket prices, 285

T

Temperature and weather

air temperature and cricket chirping rates, 124
average temperatures, 42, 50
cricket chirping rates and temperature, 125
high/low temperatures, 39, 41, 42, 123, 125, 671
monthly high temperature in Portland, Oregon, 246
monthly rainfall, 298
monthly temperature for Chicago, 231
number of earthquakes in U.S., 861
number of tornadoes in U.S., 861
surface temperature of planets, 60
temperature conversion, 117–118, 125, 164, 559
temperature of interior of Earth, 351
temperatures over time, 39, 41, 49, 50, 60, 75

Time and distance

average speed, 35, 648
bicycling travel time, 138–139
bouncing ball height sequences and total distance covered, 824, 834, 844, 845
car-phone range, 144
catamaran speed, 123
cheetah running speed, 457
cliff-diving time to reach ocean, 422
connecting pipe length, 647
cricket chirping rates, 114, 125
distance above ground of thrown object, 708

distance across pond, 647
distance object falls over time, 34, 670–671, 816, 836, 846
distance of two vehicles from same starting point, 143, 493, 708
distance olive falls from rest in vacuum, 844
distance saved calculations, 666–667, 669–670, 710
distance seen from a height, 542, 632
distance spring stretches, 537
distance traveled within total time, 164
driving distance, 143
driving time, 123, 125
escape velocities for Earth and moon, 595
eye blinking rates, 114
flying fish travel time, 126
hang glider flight rate, 126
height of dropped object, 321, 327, 368, 371, 408–409, 437
height of structure given speed and distance of dropped object, 549
height of Washington Monument, 163
hiking distance, 139
hiking rate, 144, 294–295, 304, 493
intensity of light and distance from source, 542, 543
jogging and biking speeds during workout, 679
length of interstate highway, 94
length of river, 94
lengths of pendulum swings, 632, 824, 829, 834, 844, 845
markings on highways to detect driving speeds, 542
maximum height of object thrown/launched upward, 388, 422, 435, 688, 701–704, 710, 847
men's track event speed, 457
revolutions of rotating flywheel before stopping, 836
rowing distance, 144
rowing rate in still water, 293
rowing time, 492
running speeds during each part of workout, 682
skidding distance of car, 631
speeding time before receiving ticket, 144, 493
speed measurement conversion, 457, 459
speed of airplane in still air, 293–294, 493, 494
speed of boat in still water, 302, 493, 508
speed of car and plane traveling same distance, 504
speed of current, 293, 302
speed of dropped object over time, 225, 518
speed of two vehicles traveling in same time, 489–490, 494, 810
speed on each part of trip, 143, 492, 494, 676–677, 679
speeds during bicycle race stages, 681
speeds of vehicles traveling in opposite directions, 139–140, 144, 286–287, 294, 430, 493, 810
time for dropped/thrown object to hit ground, 408–409, 421, 428–429, 435–437, 660–661, 667–668, 670, 708, 710
time for hikers to meet, 144
time for light to reach Earth from the sun, 126, 353
time for object thrown upward to reach maximum height, 701–702, 709, 847

time for one person to work alone, 494, 675–676
time for pipe and hose together to fill pond, 679
time for pipe or hose alone to fill pond, 679, 680
time for pipes to fill container, 508
time for reflected light from moon to reach Earth, 353
time for running animal to overtake another, 495
time for test run of bullet train, 126
time for two inlet pipes/pumps to fill container, 490, 494, 495, 680
time for two people working together, 488, 490, 495
time for two vehicles to be certain distance apart, 144
time for unmanned aircraft to circumnavigate Earth, 126
time for vehicle to overtake another vehicle, 142, 164, 493
time spent on bicycle, 294
time spent walking and jogging, 302
times traveled by two different vehicles, 493
time to walk a race, 164
velocity of falling object accelerated by gravity, 632
walking/cycling distance to use calories, 155
wind speed, 294, 492–494

Transportation

arrival and departures at airport, 857
bridge length, 93
cell phone use effects on driving, 164
grade of road/railway, 210, 214, 372
height of bridge, 789, 810
markings on highways to detect driving speeds, 542
parking lot dimensions, 123
passenger traffic at airport, 709
registered vehicle percent increase, 136
road sign dimensions, 118–119, 123, 295, 372
safe velocity around curved road, 648
skidding distance of car, 631
speed for each part of trip, 492
speed of trains traveling in opposite directions, 139–140
time for bus to overtake car, 142, 143
train fares for adults and children, 293
vehicle fatalities, 295

W

World records

elevation extremes, 49
fastest trains, 113
heaviest door, 670
largest casino, 457
largest Coca-Cola sign, 122
largest-diameter Ferris wheel, 788
largest meteorite, 94
largest observation wheel, 788
largest office building, 113
largest pink ribbon, 125
longest cross-sea bridge, 677
longest interstate highway, 94
longest river in U.S., 94
second tallest building, 409
steepest street, 214
tallest building in Malaysia, 660
tallest building in the world, 459, 661
tallest dam in the world, 661
tallest self-supporting structure, 327
tallest structure in U.S., 631
temperature extremes, 49

More on Functions and Graphs

8.1 Graphing and Writing Linear Functions

8.2 Reviewing Function Notation and Graphing Nonlinear Functions

Integrated Review— Summary on Functions and Equations of Lines

8.3 Graphing Piecewise-Defined Functions and Shifting and Reflecting Graphs of Functions

8.4 Variation and Problem Solving

In Section 3.6, we introduced the notion of relation and the notion of function, perhaps the single most important and useful concepts in all of mathematics. In this chapter, we explore the concept of functions further.

We define online courses as courses in which at least 80% of the content is delivered online. Although there are many types of course delivery used by instructors, the bar graph below shows the increase in percent of students taking at least one online course. Notice that the two functions, $f(x)$ and $g(x)$, both approximate the percent of students taking at least one online course. Also, for both functions, x is the number of years since 2000. In Section 8.1, Exercises 69–74, we use these functions to predict the growth of online courses.

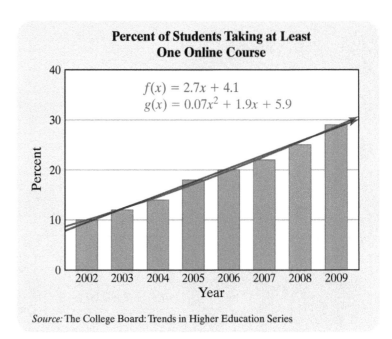

Percent of Students Taking at Least One Online Course

$$f(x) = 2.7x + 4.1$$
$$g(x) = 0.07x^2 + 1.9x + 5.9$$

Source: The College Board: Trends in Higher Education Series

8.1 Graphing and Writing Linear Functions

OBJECTIVES

1 Graph Linear Functions.

2 Write an Equation of a Line Using Function Notation.

3 Find Equations of Parallel and Perpendicular Lines.

OBJECTIVE

1   Graphing Linear Functions

In this section, we identify and graph linear functions. By the vertical line test, Section 3.6, we know that all linear equations except those whose graphs are vertical lines are functions. Thus, all linear equations except those of the form $x = c$ (vertical lines) are linear functions. For example, we know from Section 3.2 that $y = 2x$ is a linear equation in two variables. Its graph is shown.

x	$y = 2x$
1	2
0	0
−1	−2

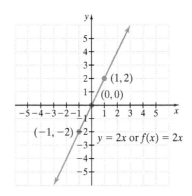

Because this graph passes the vertical line test, we know that $y = 2x$ is a function. If we want to emphasize that this equation describes a function, we may write $y = 2x$ as $f(x) = 2x$.

EXAMPLE 1   Graph $g(x) = 2x + 1$. Compare this graph with the graph of $f(x) = 2x$.

Solution   To graph $g(x) = 2x + 1$, find three ordered pair solutions.

x	$f(x) = 2x$	$g(x) = 2x + 1$
0	0	1
−1	−2	−1
1	2	3

add 1

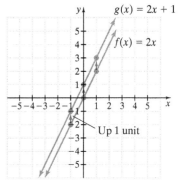

Notice that y-values for the graph of $g(x) = 2x + 1$ are obtained by adding 1 to each y-value of each corresponding point of the graph of $f(x) = 2x$. The graph of $g(x) = 2x + 1$ is the same as the graph of $f(x) = 2x$ shifted upward 1 unit.   ☐

PRACTICE

1   Graph $g(x) = 4x - 3$ and $f(x) = 4x$ on the same axes.   See graphing answer section.

If a linear function is solved for y, we can easily use function notation to describe it by replacing y with $f(x)$. Recall the slope-intercept form of a linear equation, $y = mx + b$, where m is the slope of the line and $(0, b)$ is the y-intercept. Since this form is solved for y, we use it to define a linear function.

In general, a **linear function** is a function that can be written in the form $f(x) = mx + b$. For example, $g(x) = 2x + 1$ is in this form, with $m = 2$ and $b = 1$. Thus, the slope of the linear function $g(x)$ is 2 and the y-intercept is $(0, 1)$.

EXAMPLE 2   Graph the linear functions $f(x) = -3x$ and $g(x) = -3x - 6$ on the same set of axes.

Solution   To graph $f(x)$ and $g(x)$, find ordered pair solutions.

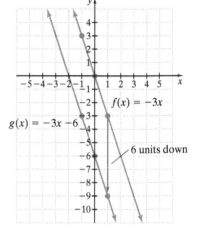

x	$f(x) = -3x$	$g(x) = -3x - 6$
0	0	−6
1	−3	−9
−1	3	−3
−2	6	0

—subtract 6—

Each y-value for the graph of $g(x) = -3x - 6$ is obtained by subtracting 6 from the y-value of the corresponding point of the graph of $f(x) = -3x$. The graph of $g(x) = -3x - 6$ is the same as the graph of $f(x) = -3x$ shifted down 6 units.   □

PRACTICE
2   Graph the linear functions $f(x) = -2x$ and $g(x) = -2x + 5$ on the same set of axes.

OBJECTIVE
2   Writing Equations of Lines Using Function Notation

We now practice writing linear functions.

This means the graph is a line that passes the vertical line test.

Below is a review of some tools we can use.

$y = mx + b$	**Slope-intercept form** of a linear equation. The slope is m, and the y-intercept is $(0, b)$.
$y - y_1 = m(x - x_1)$	**Point-slope form** of a linear equation. The slope is m, and (x_1, y_1) is a point on the line.
$y = c$	**Horizontal line** The slope is 0, and the y-intercept is $(0, c)$.

Note: $x = c$, whose graph is a vertical line, is not included above, as these equations do **not** define functions.

EXAMPLE 3   Find an equation of the line with slope -3 and y-intercept $(0, -5)$. Write the equation using function notation.

Solution   Because we know the slope and the y-intercept, we use the slope-intercept form with $m = -3$ and $b = -5$.

$$y = mx + b \qquad \text{Slope-intercept form}$$
$$y = -3 \cdot x + (-5) \quad \text{Let } m = -3 \text{ and } b = -5.$$
$$y = -3x - 5 \qquad \text{Simplify.}$$

This equation is solved for y. To write using function notation, we replace y with $f(x)$.

$$f(x) = -3x - 5$$ □

PRACTICE
3   Find an equation of the line with slope -4 and y-intercept $(0, -3)$. Write the equation using function notation.

EXAMPLE 4   Find an equation of the line through points $(4, 0)$ and $(-4, -5)$. Write the equation using function notation.

Solution   First, find the slope of the line.

$$m = \frac{-5 - 0}{-4 - 4} = \frac{-5}{-8} = \frac{5}{8}$$

Next, make use of the point-slope form. Replace (x_1, y_1) by either $(4, 0)$ or $(-4, -5)$ in the point-slope equation. We will choose the point $(4, 0)$. The line through $(4, 0)$ with slope $\frac{5}{8}$ is

$$y - y_1 = m(x - x_1) \quad \text{Point-slope form.}$$

$$y - 0 = \frac{5}{8}(x - 4) \quad \text{Let } m = \frac{5}{8} \text{ and } (x_1, y_1) = (4, 0).$$

$$8y = 5(x - 4) \quad \text{Multiply both sides by 8.}$$

$$8y = 5x - 20 \quad \text{Apply the distributive property.}$$

To write the equation using function notation, we solve for y, then replace y with $f(x)$.

$$8y = 5x - 20$$

$$y = \frac{5}{8}x - \frac{20}{8} \quad \text{Divide both sides by 8.}$$

$$f(x) = \frac{5}{8}x - \frac{5}{2} \quad \text{Write using function notation.} \qquad \square$$

PRACTICE
4   Find an equation of the line through points $(-1, 2)$ and $(2, 0)$. Write the equation using function notation.

▶ **Helpful Hint**

If two points of a line are given, either one may be used with the point-slope form to write an equation of the line.

EXAMPLE 5   Find an equation of the horizontal line containing the point $(2, 3)$. Write the equation using function notation.

Solution   A horizontal line has an equation of the form $y = c$. Since the line contains the point $(2, 3)$, the equation is $y = 3$, as shown to the right.
   Using function notation, the equation is

$$f(x) = 3.$$

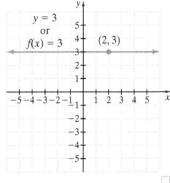

PRACTICE
5   Find the equation of the horizontal line containing the point $(6, -2)$. Use function notation.

3 Finding Equations of Parallel and Perpendicular Lines

Next, we find equations of parallel and perpendicular lines.

⚠ **EXAMPLE 6** Find an equation of the line containing the point (4, 4) and parallel to the line $2x + 3y = -6$. Write the equation in standard form.

Solution Because the line we want to find is *parallel* to the line $2x + 3y = -6$, the two lines must have equal slopes. Find the slope of $2x + 3y = -6$ by writing it in the form $y = mx + b$. In other words, solve the equation for y.

$$2x + 3y = -6$$

$$3y = -2x - 6 \quad \text{Subtract } 2x \text{ from both sides.}$$

$$y = \frac{-2x}{3} - \frac{6}{3} \quad \text{Divide by 3.}$$

$$y = -\frac{2}{3}x - 2 \quad \text{Write in slope-intercept form.}$$

The slope of this line is $-\frac{2}{3}$. Thus, a line parallel to this line will also have a slope of $-\frac{2}{3}$. The equation we are asked to find describes a line containing the point (4, 4) with a slope of $-\frac{2}{3}$. We use the point-slope form.

$$y - y_1 = m(x - x_1)$$

$$y - 4 = -\frac{2}{3}(x - 4) \quad \text{Let } m = -\frac{2}{3}, x_1 = 4, \text{ and } y_1 = 4.$$

$$3(y - 4) = -2(x - 4) \quad \text{Multiply both sides by 3.}$$

$$3y - 12 = -2x + 8 \quad \text{Apply the distributive property.}$$

$$2x + 3y = 20 \quad \text{Write in standard form.} \qquad \square$$

▶ **Helpful Hint**

Multiply both sides of the equation $2x + 3y = 20$ by -1 and it becomes $-2x - 3y = -20$. Both equations are in standard form, and their graphs are the same line.

PRACTICE

6 Find an equation of the line containing the point (8, −3) and parallel to the line $3x + 4y = 1$. Write the equation in standard form.

EXAMPLE 7 Write a function that describes the line containing the point (4, 4) and perpendicular to the line $2x + 3y = -6$.

Solution In the previous example, we found that the slope of the line $2x + 3y = -6$ is $-\frac{2}{3}$. A line perpendicular to this line will have a slope that is the negative reciprocal of $-\frac{2}{3}$, or $\frac{3}{2}$. From the point-slope equation, we have

$$y - y_1 = m(x - x_1)$$

$$y - 4 = \frac{3}{2}(x - 4) \quad \text{Let } x_1 = 4, y_1 = 4 \text{ and } m = \frac{3}{2}.$$

$$2(y - 4) = 3(x - 4) \quad \text{Multiply both sides by 2.}$$

$$2y - 8 = 3x - 12 \quad \text{Apply the distributive property.}$$

$$2y = 3x - 4 \quad \text{Add 8 to both sides.}$$

$$y = \frac{3}{2}x - 2 \quad \text{Divide both sides by 2.}$$

$$f(x) = \frac{3}{2}x - 2 \quad \text{Write using function notation.} \qquad \square$$

PRACTICE
7   Write a function that describes the line containing the point $(8, -3)$ and perpendicular to the line $3x + 4y = 1$.

Graphing Calculator Explorations

You may have noticed by now that to use the $\boxed{Y =}$ key on a graphing calculator to graph an equation, the equation must be solved for y.

Graph each function by first solving the function for y.

1. $x = 3.5y$

2. $-2.7y = x$

3. $5.78x + 2.31y = 10.98$

4. $-7.22x + 3.89y = 12.57$

5. $y - |x| = 3.78$

6. $3y - 5x^2 = 6x - 4$

7. $y - 5.6x^2 = 7.7x + 1.5$

8. $y + 2.6|x| = -3.2$

Vocabulary, Readiness & Video Check

Use the choices given to fill in each blank. Some choices may not be used.

linear	$(0, b)$	m
quadratic	$(b, 0)$	mx

1. A _____ function can be written in the form $f(x) = mx + b$.

2. In the form $f(x) = mx + b$, the y-intercept is _____ and the slope is _____.

State the slope and the y-intercept of the graph of each function.

3. $f(x) = -4x + 12$

4. $g(x) = \dfrac{2}{3}x - \dfrac{7}{2}$

5. $g(x) = 5x$

6. $f(x) = -x$

Decide whether the lines are parallel, perpendicular, or neither.

7. $y = 12x + 6$
$y = 12x - 2$

8. $y = -5x + 8$
$y = -5x - 8$

9. $y = -9x + 3$
$y = \dfrac{3}{2}x - 7$

10. $y = 2x - 12$
$y = \dfrac{1}{2}x - 6$

Martin-Gay Interactive Videos

See Video 8.1

Watch the section lecture video and answer the following questions.

OBJECTIVE
1
11. Based on the lecture before Example 1, in what form can a linear function be written?

OBJECTIVE
2
12. From Example 2, given a *y*-intercept, how do you know which value to use for *b* in the slope-intercept form?

OBJECTIVE
2
13. Example 4 discusses how to find an equation of a line given two points. Under what circumstances might the slope-intercept form be chosen over the point-slope form to find an equation?

OBJECTIVE
3
14. Solve Example 6 again, this time writing the equation of the line in function notation *parallel* to the given line through the given point.

8.1 Exercise Set   MyMathLab®

Graph each linear function. See Examples 1 and 2.

1. $f(x) = -2x$

2. $f(x) = 2x$

3. $f(x) = -2x + 3$

4. $f(x) = 2x + 6$

5. $f(x) = \dfrac{1}{2}x$

6. $f(x) = \dfrac{1}{3}x$

7. $f(x) = \dfrac{1}{2}x - 4$

8. $f(x) = \dfrac{1}{3}x - 2$

The graph of $f(x) = 5x$ follows. Use this graph to match each linear function with its graph. See Examples 1 and 2.

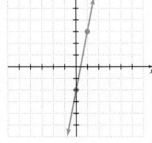

A

B

C

D

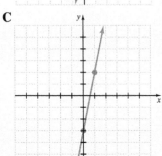

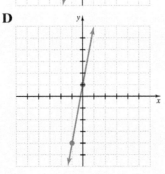

9. $f(x) = 5x - 3$

10. $f(x) = 5x - 2$

11. $f(x) = 5x + 1$

12. $f(x) = 5x + 3$

Use function notation to write the equation of each line with the given slope and y-intercept. See Example 3.

13. Slope -1; *y*-intercept $(0, 1)$

14. Slope $\dfrac{1}{2}$; *y*-intercept $(0, -6)$

15. Slope 2; *y*-intercept $\left(0, \dfrac{3}{4}\right)$

16. Slope -3; *y*-intercept $\left(0, -\dfrac{1}{5}\right)$

17. Slope $\dfrac{2}{7}$; *y*-intercept $(0, 0)$

18. Slope $-\dfrac{4}{5}$; *y*-intercept $(0, 0)$

Find an equation of the line with the given slope and containing the given point. Write the equation using function notation. See Example 3.

19. Slope 3; through $(1, 2)$

20. Slope 4; through $(5, 1)$

21. Slope -2; through $(1, -3)$

22. Slope -4; through $(2, -4)$

23. Slope $\dfrac{1}{2}$; through $(-6, 2)$

24. Slope $\dfrac{2}{3}$; through $(-9, 4)$

25. Slope $-\dfrac{9}{10}$; through $(-3, 0)$

26. Slope $-\dfrac{1}{5}$; through $(4, -6)$

Find an equation of the line passing through the given points. Use function notation to write the equation. See Example 4.

27. $(2, 0), (4, 6)$

28. $(3, 0), (7, 8)$

29. $(-2, 5), (-6, 13)$

30. $(7, -4), (2, 6)$

31. $(-2, -4), (-4, -3)$

32. $(-9, -2), (-3, 10)$

▶ 33. $(-3, -8), (-6, -9)$

34. $(8, -3), (4, -8)$

35. $\left(\dfrac{3}{5}, \dfrac{2}{5}\right)$ and $\left(-\dfrac{1}{5}, \dfrac{7}{10}\right)$

36. $\left(\dfrac{1}{2}, -\dfrac{1}{4}\right)$ and $\left(\dfrac{3}{2}, \dfrac{3}{4}\right)$

Write an equation of each line using function notation. See Example 5.

▶ 37. Slope 0; through $(-2, -4)$

38. Horizontal; through $(-3, 1)$

39. Horizontal; through $(0, 5)$

40. Slope 0; through $(-10, 23)$

Find an equation of each line. Write the equation using function notation. See Examples 6 and 7.

△ 41. Through $(3, 8)$; parallel to $f(x) = 4x - 2$

△ 42. Through $(1, 5)$; parallel to $f(x) = 3x - 4$

▶ 43. Through $(2, -5)$; perpendicular to $3y = x - 6$

△ 44. Through $(-4, 8)$; perpendicular to $2x - 3y = 1$

△ 45. Through $(-2, -3)$; parallel to $3x + 2y = 5$

△ 46. Through $(-2, -3)$; perpendicular to $3x + 2y = 5$

MIXED PRACTICE

Find the equation of each line. Write the equation using standard notation unless indicated otherwise. See Examples 3 through 7.

47. Slope 2; through $(-2, 3)$

48. Slope 3; through $(-4, 2)$

49. Through $(1, 6)$ and $(5, 2)$; use function notation

50. Through $(2, 9)$ and $(8, 6)$; use function notation

51. With slope $-\dfrac{1}{2}$; y-intercept 11; use function notation

52. With slope -4; y-intercept $\dfrac{2}{9}$; use function notation

53. Through $(-7, -4)$ and $(0, -6)$

54. Through $(2, -8)$ and $(-4, -3)$

55. Slope $-\dfrac{4}{3}$; through $(-5, 0)$

56. Slope $-\dfrac{3}{5}$; through $(4, -1)$

57. Horizontal line; through $(-2, -10)$; use function notation

58. Horizontal line; through $(1, 0)$; use function notation

△ 59. Through $(6, -2)$; parallel to the line $2x + 4y = 9$

△ 60. Through $(8, -3)$; parallel to the line $6x + 2y = 5$

61. Slope 0; through $(-9, 12)$; use function notation

62. Slope 0; through $(10, -8)$; use function notation

△ 63. Through $(6, 1)$; parallel to the line $8x - y = 9$

△ 64. Through $(3, 5)$; perpendicular to the line $2x - y = 8$

△ 65. Through $(5, -6)$; perpendicular to $y = 9$

△ 66. Through $(-3, -5)$; parallel to $y = 9$

67. Through $(2, -8)$ and $(-6, -5)$; use function notation

68. Through $(-4, -2)$ and $(-6, 5)$; use function notation

REVIEW AND PREVIEW

From the Chapter 8 opener, we have two functions to describe the percent of college students taking at least one online course. For both functions, x is the number of years since 2000 and y (or f(x) or g(x)) is the percent of students taking at least one online course.

$$f(x) = 2.7x + 4.1 \quad \text{or} \quad g(x) = 0.07x^2 + 1.9x + 5.9$$

Use this for Exercises 69–74. See Section 3.6.

69. Find $f(9)$ and describe in words what this means.

70. Find $g(9)$ and describe in words what this means.

71. Assume the trend of $g(x)$ continues. Find $g(16)$ and describe in words what this means.

72. Assume the trend of $f(x)$ continues. Find $f(16)$ and describe in words what this means.

73. Use Exercises 69–72 and compare $f(9)$ and $g(9)$, then $f(16)$ and $g(16)$. As x increases, are the function values staying about the same or not? Explain your answer.

74. Use the Chapter 8 opener graph and study the graphs of $f(x)$ and $g(x)$. Use these graphs to answer Exercise 73. Explain your answer.

CONCEPT EXTENSIONS

Find an equation of each line graphed. Write the equation using function notation. (Hint: Use each graph to write 2 ordered pair solutions. Find the slope of each line, then refer to Examples 3 or 4 to complete.)

75.

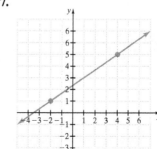

76.

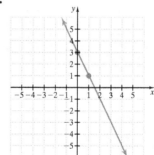

77.

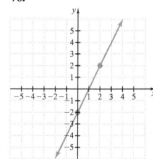

78.

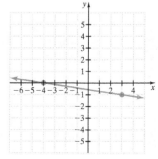

Solve.

79. A rock is dropped from the top of a 400-foot building. After 1 second, the rock is traveling 32 feet per second. After 3 seconds, the rock is traveling 96 feet per second. Let y be the rate of descent and x be the number of seconds since the rock was dropped.

   a. Write a linear equation that relates time x to rate y. [*Hint:* Use the ordered pairs $(1, 32)$ and $(3, 96)$.]

   b. Use this equation to determine the rate of travel of the rock 4 seconds after it was dropped.

80. A fruit company recently released a new applesauce. By the end of its first year, profits on this product amounted to $30,000. The anticipated profit for the end of the fourth year is $66,000. The ratio of change in time to change in profit is constant. Let x be years and y be profit.

   a. Write a linear equation that relates profit and time. [*Hint:* Use the ordered pairs $(1, 30,000)$ and $(4, 66,000)$.]

   b. Use this equation to predict the company's profit at the end of the seventh year.

   c. Predict when the profit should reach $126,000.

81. The Whammo Company has learned that by pricing a newly released Frisbee at $6, sales will reach 2000 per day. Raising the price to $8 will cause the sales to fall to 1500 per day. Assume that the ratio of change in price to change in daily sales is constant and let x be the price of the Frisbee and y be number of sales.

   a. Find the linear equation that models the price–sales relationship for this Frisbee. [*Hint:* The line must pass through $(6, 2000)$ and $(8, 1500)$.]

   b. Use this equation to predict the daily sales of Frisbees if the price is set at $7.50.

82. The Pool Fun Company has learned that, by pricing a newly released Fun Noodle at $3, sales will reach 10,000 Fun Noodles per day during the summer. Raising the price to $5 will cause the sales to fall to 8000 Fun Noodles per day. Let x be price and y be the number sold.

   a. Assume that the relationship between sales price and number of Fun Noodles sold is linear and write an equation describing this relationship. [*Hint:* The line must pass through $(3, 10,000)$ and $(5, 8000)$.]

   b. Use this equation to predict the daily sales of Fun Noodles if the price is $3.50.

83. The number of people employed in the United States as registered nurses was 2619 thousand in 2008. By 2018, this number is expected to rise to 3200 thousand. Let y be the number of registered nurses (in thousands) employed in the United States in the year x, where $x = 0$ represents 2008. (*Source:* U.S. Bureau of Labor Statistics)

   a. Write a linear equation that models the number of people (in thousands) employed as registered nurses in year x.

   b. Use this equation to estimate the number of people employed as registered nurses in 2012.

84. In 2008, IBM had 398,500 employees worldwide. By 2010, this number had increased to 426,751. Let y be the number of IBM employees worldwide in the year x, where $x = 0$ represents 2008. (*Source:* IBM Corporation)

   a. Write a linear equation that models the growth in the number of IBM employees worldwide, in terms of the year x.

   b. Use this equation to predict the number of IBM employees worldwide in 2013.

85. In 2010, the average price of a new home sold in the United States was $272,900. In 2005, the average price of a new home in the United States was $297,000. Let y be the average price of a new home in the year x, where $x = 0$ represents the year 2005. (*Source:* Based on data from U.S. census)

   a. Write a linear equation that models the average price of a new home in terms of the year x. [*Hint:* The line must pass through the points $(0, 297,000)$ and $(5, 272,900)$.]

   b. Use this equation to predict the average price of a new home in 2013.

86. The number of McDonald's restaurants worldwide in 2010 was 32,737. In 2005, there were 31,046 McDonald's restaurants worldwide. Let y be the number of McDonald's restaurants in the year x, where $x = 0$ represents the year 2005. (*Source:* McDonald's Corporation)

   a. Write a linear equation that models the growth in the number of McDonald's restaurants worldwide in terms of the year x. [*Hint:* The line must pass through the points $(0, 31,046)$ and $(5, 32,737)$.]

   b. Use this equation to predict the number of McDonald's restaurants worldwide in 2013.

Example:

Find an equation of the perpendicular bisector of the line segment whose endpoints are $(2, 6)$ and $(0, -2)$.

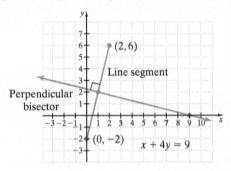

Solution:

A perpendicular bisector is a line that contains the midpoint of the given segment and is perpendicular to the segment.

Step 1: The midpoint of the segment with endpoints $(2, 6)$ and $(0, -2)$ is $(1, 2)$.

Step 2: The slope of the segment containing points $(2, 6)$ and $(0, -2)$ is 4.

Step 3: A line perpendicular to this line segment will have slope of $-\dfrac{1}{4}$.

Step 4: The equation of the line through the midpoint $(1, 2)$ with a slope of $-\dfrac{1}{4}$ will be the equation of the perpendicular bisector. This equation in standard form is $x + 4y = 9$.

Find an equation of the perpendicular bisector of the line segment whose endpoints are given. See the previous example.

△ **87.** $(3, -1); (-5, 1)$

△ **88.** $(-6, -3); (-8, -1)$

△ **89.** $(-2, 6); (-22, -4)$

△ **90.** $(5, 8); (7, 2)$

△ **91.** $(2, 3); (-4, 7)$

△ **92.** $(-6, 8); (-4, -2)$

93. Describe how to check to see if the graph of $2x - 4y = 7$ passes through the points $(1.4, -1.05)$ and $(0, -1.75)$. Then follow your directions and check these points.

8.2   Reviewing Function Notation and Graphing Nonlinear Functions

OBJECTIVES

1   Review Function Notation. ▶

2   Find Square Roots of Numbers. ▶

3   Graph Nonlinear Functions. ▶

In the previous section, we studied linear equations that described functions. Not all equations in two variables are linear equations, and not all graphs of equations in two variables are lines. In Chapter 3, we saw graphs of nonlinear equations, some of which were functions since they passed the vertical line test. In this section, we study the functions whose graphs may not be lines. First, let's review function notation.

OBJECTIVE

1   Reviewing Function Notation ▶

Suppose we have a function f such that $f(2) = -1$. Recall this means that when $x = 2, f(x)$, or $y, = -1$. Thus, the graph of f passes through $(2, -1)$.

> ▶ Helpful Hint
>
> Remember that $f(x)$ is a special symbol in mathematics used to denote a function. The symbol $f(x)$ is read "f of x." It does *not* mean $f \cdot x$ (f times x).

✓CONCEPT CHECK

Suppose $y = f(x)$ and we are told that $f(3) = 9$. Which is not true?

a. When $x = 3, y = 9$.

b. A possible function is $f(x) = x^2$.

c. A point on the graph of the function is $(3, 9)$.

d. A possible function is $f(x) = 2x + 4$.

If it helps, think of a function, f, as a machine that has been programmed with a certain correspondence or rule. An input value (a member of the domain) is then fed into the machine, the machine does the correspondence or rule, and the result is the output (a member of the range).

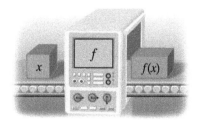 

EXAMPLE 1   Given the graphs of the functions f and g, find each function value by inspecting the graphs.

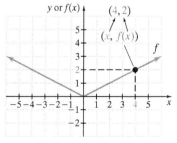

a. $f(4)$ **b.** $f(-2)$ **c.** $g(5)$ **d.** $g(0)$

e. Find all x-values such that $f(x) = 1$.   **f.** Find all x-values such that $g(x) = 0$.

Answer to Concept Check: d

(Continued on next page)

Solution

a. To find $f(4)$, find the y-value when $x = 4$. We see from the graph that when $x = 4$, y or $f(x) = 2$. Thus, $f(4) = 2$.

b. $f(-2) = 1$ from the ordered pair $(-2, 1)$.

c. $g(5) = 3$ from the ordered pair $(5, 3)$.

d. $g(0) = 0$ from the ordered pair $(0, 0)$.

e. To find x-values such that $f(x) = 1$, we are looking for any ordered pairs on the graph of f whose $f(x)$ or y-value is 1. They are $(2, 1)$ and $(-2, 1)$. Thus $f(2) = 1$ and $f(-2) = 1$. The x-values are 2 and -2.

f. Find ordered pairs on the graph of g whose $g(x)$ or y-value is 0. They are $(3, 0)$, $(0, 0)$, and $(-4, 0)$. Thus $g(3) = 0, g(0) = 0$, and $g(-4) = 0$. The x-values are 3, 0, and -4. ☐

PRACTICE

1 Given the graphs of the functions f and g, find each function value by inspecting the graphs.

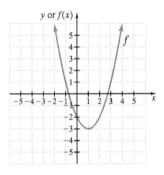
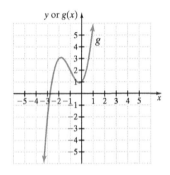

a. $f(1)$ **b.** $f(0)$ **c.** $g(-2)$ **d.** $g(0)$

e. Find all x-values such that $f(x) = 1$.

f. Find all x-values such that $g(x) = -2$.

Many types of real-world paired data form functions. The broken-line graphs below and on the next page show the total and online enrollment in postsecondary institutions.

EXAMPLE 2 The following graph shows the total and online enrollments in postsecondary institutions as functions of time.

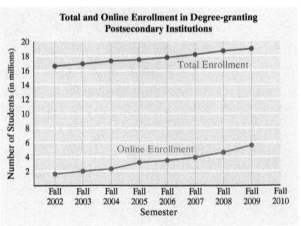

Source: Projections of Education Statistics to 2018, National Center for Education Statistics

a. Approximate the total enrollment in fall 2009.

b. In fall 2002, the total enrollment was 16.6 million students. Find the increase in total enrollment from fall 2002 to fall 2009.

Solution

a. Find the semester fall 2009 and move upward until you reach the top broken-line graph. From the point on the graph, move horizontally to the left until the vertical axis is reached. In fall 2009, approximately 19 million students, or 19,000,000 students, were enrolled in degree-granting postsecondary institutions.

b. The increase from fall 2002 to fall 2009 is 19 million − 16.6 million = 2.4 million or 2,400,000 students.

PRACTICE

  2   Use the graph in Example 2 and approximate the total enrollment in fall 2003.

Notice that each graph separately in Example 2 is the graph of a function since for each semester there is only one total enrollment and only one online enrollment. Also notice that each graph resembles the graph of a line. Often, businesses depend on equations that closely fit data-defined functions like this one to model the data and predict future trends. For example, by a method called **least squares,** the function $f(x) = 0.34x + 16$ approximates the data for the red graph, and the function $f(x) = 0.55x + 0.3$ approximates the data for the blue graph. For each function, x is the number of years since 2000, and $f(x)$ is the number of students (in millions). The graphs and the data functions are shown next.

> **▶ Helpful Hint**
>
> Each function graphed is the graph of a function and passes the vertical line test.

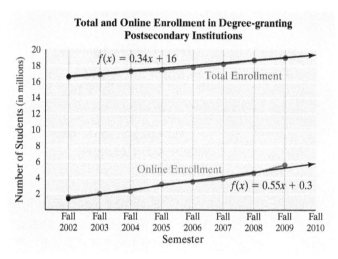

Total and Online Enrollment in Degree-granting Postsecondary Institutions

Source: Projections of Education Statistics to 2018, National Center for Education Statistics

EXAMPLE 3   Use the function $f(x) = 0.34x + 16$ and the discussion following Example 2 to estimate the total enrollment in degree-granting postsecondary institutions for fall 2010.

Solution   To estimate the total enrollment in fall 2010, remember that x represents the number of years since 2000, so $x = 2010 - 2000 = 10$. Use $f(x) = 0.34x + 16$ and find $f(10)$.

$$f(x) = 0.34x + 16$$
$$f(10) = 0.34(10) + 16$$
$$= 19.4$$

We estimate that in the fall 2010 semester, the total enrollment was 19.4 million, or 19,400,000 students.

PRACTICE

  3   Use $f(x) = 0.55x + 0.3$ to approximate the online enrollment in fall 2010.

OBJECTIVE

2 Finding Square Roots of Numbers

Later in this section, we graph the square root function, $f(x) = \sqrt{x}$. To prepare for this graph, let's review finding square roots of numbers.

The opposite of squaring a number is taking the **square root** of a number. For example, since the square of 4, or 4^2, is 16, we say that a square root of 16 is 4. The notation $\sqrt{a}$ is used to denote the **positive, or principal, square root** of a nonnegative number a. We then have in symbols that $\sqrt{16} = 4$. The negative square root of 16 is written $-\sqrt{16} = -4$. The square root of a negative number, such as $\sqrt{-16}$, is not a real number. Why? There is no real number that, when squared, gives a negative number.

EXAMPLE 4   Find the square roots.

a. $\sqrt{9}$ **b.** $\sqrt{25}$ **c.** $\sqrt{\dfrac{1}{4}}$ **d.** $-\sqrt{36}$ **e.** $\sqrt{-36}$ **f.** $\sqrt{0}$

Solution

a. $\sqrt{9} = 3$ since 3 is positive and $3^2 = 9$.   **b.** $\sqrt{25} = 5$ since $5^2 = 25$.

c. $\sqrt{\dfrac{1}{4}} = \dfrac{1}{2}$ since $\left(\dfrac{1}{2}\right)^2 = \dfrac{1}{4}$.   **d.** $-\sqrt{36} = -6$

e. $\sqrt{-36}$ is not a real number.   **f.** $\sqrt{0} = 0$ since $0^2 = 0$.   □

PRACTICE

4   Find the square roots.

a. $\sqrt{121}$ **b.** $\sqrt{\dfrac{1}{16}}$ **c.** $-\sqrt{64}$ **d.** $\sqrt{-64}$ **e.** $\sqrt{100}$

We can find roots other than square roots. Also, not all roots simplify to rational numbers. For example, $\sqrt{3} \approx 1.7$ using a calculator. We study radicals further in Chapter 10.

OBJECTIVE

3 Graphing Nonlinear Functions

Let's practice graphing nonlinear functions. In this section, we graph by plotting enough ordered pair solutions until we see a pattern. In the next section, we learn about shifting and reflecting of graphs.

EXAMPLE 5   Graph $f(x) = x^2$.

Solution   This equation is not linear because the x^2 term does not allow us to write it in the form $Ax + By = C$. Its graph is not a line. We begin by finding ordered pair solutions. Because $f(x) = y$, feel free to think of this equation as $f(x) = x^2$ or $y = x^2$. This graph is solved for y, so we choose x-values and find corresponding y-values.

If $x = -3$, then $f(-3) = (-3)^2$, or 9.

If $x = -2$, then $f(-2) = (-2)^2$, or 4.

If $x = -1$, then $f(-1) = (-1)^2$, or 1.

If $x = 0$, then $f(0) = 0^2$, or 0.

If $x = 1$, then $f(1) = 1^2$, or 1.

If $x = 2$, then $f(2) = 2^2$, or 4.

If $x = 3$, then $f(3) = 3^2$, or 9.

x	y or $f(x)$
-3	9
-2	4
-1	1
0	0
1	1
2	4
3	9

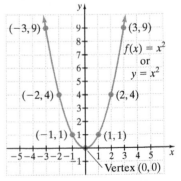

Study the table a moment and look for patterns. Notice that the ordered pair solution $(0, 0)$ contains the smallest y-value because any other x-value squared will give a positive result. This means that the point $(0, 0)$ will be the lowest point on the graph.

Also notice that all other *y*-values correspond to two different *x*-values. For example, $3^2 = 9$ and also $(-3)^2 = 9$. This means that the graph will be a mirror image of itself across the *y*-axis. Connect the plotted points with a smooth curve to sketch the graph.

This curve is given a special name, a **parabola.** We will study more about parabolas in later chapters. ☐

PRACTICE
5   Graph $f(x) = 2x^2$.

· ·

EXAMPLE 6   Graph the nonlinear function $f(x) = |x|$.

Solution   This is not a linear equation since it cannot be written in the form $Ax + By = C$. Its graph is not a line. Because we do not know the shape of this graph, we find many ordered pair solutions. We will choose *x*-values and substitute to find corresponding *y*-values.

If $x = -3$, then $f(-3) = |-3|$, or 3.

If $x = -2$, then $f(-2) = |-2|$, or 2.

If $x = -1$, then $f(-1) = |-1|$, or 1.

If $x = 0$, then $f(0) = |0|$, or 0.

If $x = 1$, then $f(1) = |1|$, or 1.

If $x = 2$, then $f(2) = |2|$, or 2.

If $x = 3$, then $f(3) = |3|$, or 3.

x	*y* or *f(x)*
-3	3
-2	2
-1	1
0	0
1	1
2	2
3	3

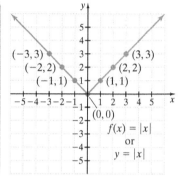

Again, study the table of values for a moment and notice any patterns.

From the plotted ordered pairs, we see that the graph of this absolute value equation is V-shaped. ☐

PRACTICE
6   Graph $f(x) = -|x|$.

· ·

EXAMPLE 7   Graph the nonlinear function $f(x) = \sqrt{x}$.

Solution   To graph this square root function, we identify the domain, evaluate the function for several values of *x*, plot the resulting points, and connect the points with a smooth curve. Since $\sqrt{x}$ represents the nonnegative square root of *x*, the domain of this function is the set of all nonnegative numbers, $\{x | x \geq 0\}$, or $[0, \infty)$. We have approximated $\sqrt{3}$ below to help us locate the point corresponding to $(3, \sqrt{3})$.

If $x = 0$, then $f(0) = \sqrt{0}$, or 0.

If $x = 1$, then $f(1) = \sqrt{1}$, or 1.

If $x = 3$, then $f(3) = \sqrt{3}$, or 1.7.

If $x = 4$, then $f(4) = \sqrt{4}$, or 2.

If $x = 9$, then $f(9) = \sqrt{9}$, or 3.

x	*y* or *f(x)*
0	0
1	1
3	$\sqrt{3} \approx 1.7$
4	2
9	3

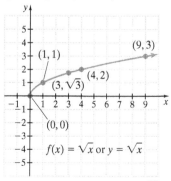

PRACTICE
7   Graph $f(x) = \sqrt{x} + 1$.

· ·

Graphing Calculator Explorations

It is possible to use a graphing calculator to sketch the graph of more than one equation on the same set of axes. For example, graph the functions $f(x) = x^2$ and $g(x) = x^2 + 4$ on the same set of axes.

To graph on the same set of axes, press the $\boxed{Y =}$ key and enter the equations on the first two lines.

$$Y_1 = x^2$$
$$Y_2 = x^2 + 4$$

Then press the $\boxed{\text{GRAPH}}$ key as usual. The screen should look like this.

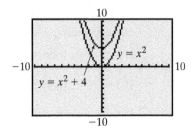

Notice that the graph of y or $g(x) = x^2 + 4$ is the graph of $y = x^2$ moved 4 units upward.

Graph each pair of functions on the same set of axes.

1. $f(x) = |x|$

   $g(x) = |x| + 1$

2. $f(x) = x^2$

   $h(x) = x^2 - 5$

3. $f(x) = x$

   $H(x) = x - 6$

4. $f(x) = |x|$

   $G(x) = |x| + 3$

5. $f(x) = -x^2$

   $F(x) = -x^2 + 7$

6. $f(x) = x$

   $F(x) = x + 2$

Vocabulary, Readiness & Video Check

Use the choices below to fill in each blank. Some choices may not be used.

$(1.7, -2)$	line	parabola	-6	-9
$(-2, 1.7)$	V-shaped	6	9	

1. The graph of $y = |x|$ looks _____.

2. The graph of $y = x^2$ is a _____.

3. If $f(-2) = 1.7$, the corresponding ordered pair is _____.

4. If $f(x) = x^2$, then $f(-3) =$ _____.

Martin-Gay Interactive Videos

See Video 8.2

Watch the section lecture video and answer the following questions.

OBJECTIVE
1
5. From Examples 1 and 2, what is the connection between function notation to evaluate a function at certain values and ordered pair solutions of the function?

OBJECTIVE
2
6. Explain why Example 6 does not simplify to a real number.

OBJECTIVE
3
7. Based on Examples 7, 8, and 9, complete the following statements. When graphing a nonlinear equation, first recognize it as a nonlinear equation and know that the graph is _____ a line. If you don't know the _____ of the graph, plot enough points until you see a pattern.

8.2   Exercise Set   MyMathLab®

Use the graph of the following function f(x) to find each value. See Examples 1 and 2.

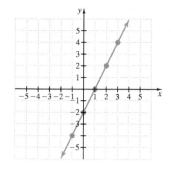

1. $f(1)$

2. $f(0)$

3. $f(-1)$

4. $f(2)$

5. Find x such that $f(x) = 4$.

6. Find x such that $f(x) = -6$.

Use the graph of the functions below to answer Exercises 7 through 18. See Examples 1 and 2.

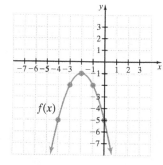
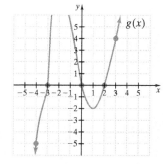

7. If $f(1) = -10$, write the corresponding ordered pair.

8. If $f(-5) = -10$, write the corresponding ordered pair.

9. If $g(4) = 56$, write the corresponding ordered pair.

10. If $g(-2) = 8$, write the corresponding ordered pair.

11. Find $f(-1)$.

12. Find $f(-2)$.

13. Find $g(2)$.

14. Find $g(-4)$.

15. Find all values of x such that $f(x) = -5$.

16. Find all values of x such that $f(x) = -2$.

17. Find all positive values of x such that $g(x) = 4$.

18. Find all values of x such that $g(x) = 0$.

Find the following roots. See Example 4.

19. $\sqrt{49}$ 20. $\sqrt{144}$

21. $-\sqrt{\dfrac{4}{9}}$ 22. $-\sqrt{\dfrac{4}{25}}$

23. $\sqrt{64}$ 24. $\sqrt{4}$

25. $\sqrt{81}$ 26. $\sqrt{1}$

27. $\sqrt{-100}$ 28. $\sqrt{-25}$

MIXED PRACTICE

Graph each function by finding and plotting ordered pair solutions. See Examples 5 through 7.

29. $f(x) = x^2 + 3$ 30. $g(x) = (x + 2)^2$

31. $h(x) = |x| - 2$ 32. $f(x) = |x - 2|$

33. $g(x) = 2x^2$ 34. $h(x) = 5x^2$

35. $f(x) = 5x - 1$ 36. $g(x) = -3x + 2$

37. $f(x) = \sqrt{x + 1}$ 38. $f(x) = \sqrt{x} - 1$

39. $g(x) = -2|x|$ 40. $g(x) = -3|x|$

41. $h(x) = \sqrt{x} + 2$ 42. $h(x) = \sqrt{x + 2}$

Use the graph on page 520 to answer the following. Also see Example 3.

43. a. Use the graph to approximate the online enrollment in fall 2009.

   b. The function $f(x) = 0.55x + 0.3$ approximates the online enrollment (in millions). Use this function to approximate the online enrollment in fall 2009.

44. a. Use the graph to approximate the total enrollment in fall 2008.

   b. The function $f(x) = 0.34x + 16$ approximates the total enrollment (in millions). Use this function to approximate the total enrollment in fall 2008.

The function $f(x) = 0.42x + 10.5$ can be used to predict diamond production. For this function, x is the number of years after 2000, and f(x) is the value (in billions of dollars) of diamond production.

45. Use the function in the directions above to estimate diamond production in 2012.

46. Use the function in the directions above to predict diamond production in 2015.

The function $A(r) = \pi r^2$ may be used to find the area of a circle if we are given its radius.

△ **47.** Find the area of a circle whose radius is 5 centimeters. (Do not approximate π.)

△ **48.** Find the area of a circular garden whose radius is 8 feet. (Do not approximate π.)

The function $V(x) = x^3$ may be used to find the volume of a cube if we are given the length x of a side.

49. Find the volume of a cube whose side is 14 inches.

50. Find the volume of a die whose side is 1.7 centimeters.

Forensic scientists use the following functions to find the height of a woman if they are given the height of her femur bone f or her tibia bone t in centimeters.

$$H(f) = 2.59f + 47.24$$

$$H(t) = 2.72t + 61.28$$

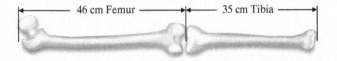

51. Find the height of a woman whose femur measures 46 centimeters.

52. Find the height of a woman whose tibia measures 35 centimeters.

The dosage in milligrams D of Ivermectin, a heartworm preventive, for a dog who weighs x pounds is given by

$$D(x) = \frac{136}{25}x$$

53. Find the proper dosage for a dog that weighs 30 pounds.

54. Find the proper dosage for a dog that weighs 50 pounds.

55. What is the greatest number of x-intercepts that a function may have? Explain your answer.

56. What is the greatest number of y-intercepts that a function may have? Explain your answer.

REVIEW AND PREVIEW

Solve the following equations. See Section 2.3.

57. $3(x - 2) + 5x = 6x - 16$

58. $5 + 7(x + 1) = 12 + 10x$

59. $3x + \frac{2}{5} = \frac{1}{10}$

60. $\frac{1}{6} + 2x = \frac{2}{3}$

CONCEPT EXTENSIONS

For Exercises 61 through 64, match each description with the graph that best illustrates it.

61. Moe worked 40 hours per week until the fall semester started. He quit and didn't work again until he worked 60 hours a week during the holiday season starting mid-December.

62. Kawana worked 40 hours a week for her father during the summer. She slowly cut back her hours to not working at all during the fall semester. During the holiday season in December, she started working again and increased her hours to 60 hours per week.

63. Wendy worked from July through February, never quitting. She worked between 10 and 30 hours per week.

64. Bartholomew worked from July through February. During the holiday season between mid-November and the beginning of January, he worked 40 hours per week. The rest of the time, he worked between 10 and 40 hours per week.

a.

b.

c.

d.

This broken-line graph shows the hourly minimum wage and the years it increased. Use this graph for Exercises 65 through 68.

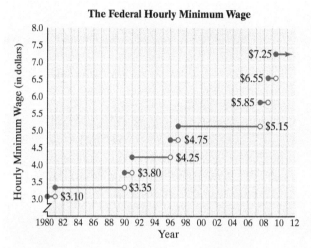

The Federal Hourly Minimum Wage

Source: U.S. Department of Labor

65. What was the first year that the minimum hourly wage rose above $5.00?

66. What was the first year that the minimum hourly wage rose above $6.00?

67. Why do you think that this graph is shaped the way it is?

68. The federal hourly minimum wage started in 1938 at $0.25. How much has it increased by 2011?

69. Graph $y = x^2 - 4x + 7$. Let $x = 0, 1, 2, 3, 4$ to generate ordered pair solutions.

70. Graph $y = x^2 + 2x + 3$. Let $x = -3, -2, -1, 0, 1$ to generate ordered pair solutions.

71. The function $f(x) = [x]$ is called the greatest integer function and its graph is similar to the graph above. The value of $[x]$ is the greatest integer less than or equal to x. For example, $f(1.5) = [1.5] = 1$ since the greatest integer ≤ 1.5 is 1. Sketch the graph of $f(x) = [x]$.

Integrated Review   SUMMARY ON FUNCTIONS AND EQUATIONS OF LINES

Sections 8.1–8.2

Find the slope and y-intercept of the graph of each function.

1. $f(x) = 3x - 5$

2. $f(x) = \dfrac{5}{2}x - \dfrac{7}{2}$

Determine whether each pair of lines is parallel, perpendicular, or neither.

3. $f(x) = 8x - 6$
$g(x) = 8x + 6$

4. $f(x) = \dfrac{2}{3}x + 1$
$2y + 3x = 1$

Find the equation of each line. Write the equation using function notation.

5. Through $(1, 6)$ and $(5, 2)$

6. Through $(2, -8)$ and $(-6, -5)$

7. Through $(-1, -5)$; parallel to $3x - y = 5$

8. Through $(0, 4)$; perpendicular to $4x - 5y = 10$

9. Through $(2, -3)$; perpendicular to $4x + y = \dfrac{2}{3}$

10. Through $(-1, 0)$; parallel to $5x + 2y = 2$

Determine whether each function is linear or not. Then graph the function.

11. $f(x) = 4x - 2$ 12. $f(x) = 6x - 5$
13. $g(x) = |x| + 3$ 14. $h(x) = |x| + 2$
15. $f(x) = 2x^2$ 16. $F(x) = 3x^2$
17. $h(x) = x^2 - 3$ 18. $G(x) = x^2 + 3$
19. $F(x) = -2x$ 20. $H(x) = -3x$
21. $G(x) = |x + 2|$ 22. $g(x) = |x - 1|$

23. $f(x) = \dfrac{1}{3}x - 1$ 24. $f(x) = \dfrac{1}{2}x - 3$

25. $g(x) = -\dfrac{3}{2}x + 1$ 26. $G(x) = -\dfrac{2}{3}x + 1$

8.3 | Graphing Piecewise-Defined Functions and Shifting and Reflecting Graphs of Functions

OBJECTIVES

1 Graph Piecewise-Defined Functions.

2 Vertical and Horizontal Shifts.

3 Reflect Graphs.

OBJECTIVE

1 Graphing Piecewise-Defined Functions

Thus far in Chapter 8, we have graphed functions. There are many special functions. In this objective, we study functions defined by two or more expressions. The expression used to complete the function varies with and depends upon the value of x. Before we actually graph these piecewise-defined functions, let's practice finding function values.

EXAMPLE 1   Evaluate $f(2), f(-6),$ and $f(0)$ for the function

$$f(x) = \begin{cases} 2x + 3 & \text{if } x \le 0 \\ -x - 1 & \text{if } x > 0 \end{cases}$$

Then write your results in ordered pair form.

Solution   Take a moment and study this function. It is a single function defined by two expressions depending on the value of x. From above, if $x \le 0$, use $f(x) = 2x + 3$. If $x > 0$, use $f(x) = -x - 1$. Thus

$f(2) = -(2) - 1$	$f(-6) = 2(-6) + 3$	$f(0) = 2(0) + 3$
$\quad = -3$ since $2 > 0$	$\quad = -9$ since $-6 \le 0$	$\quad = 3$ since $0 \le 0$
$f(2) = -3$	$f(-6) = -9$	$f(0) = 3$
Ordered pairs: $(2, -3)$	$(-6, -9)$	$(0, 3)$

PRACTICE

1   Evaluate $f(4), f(-2),$ and $f(0)$ for the function

$$f(x) = \begin{cases} -4x - 2 & \text{if } x \le 0 \\ x + 1 & \text{if } x > 0 \end{cases}$$

Then write your results in ordered pair form.

Now, let's graph a piecewise-defined function.

EXAMPLE 2   Graph $f(x) = \begin{cases} 2x + 3 & \text{if } x \leq 0 \\ -x - 1 & \text{if } x > 0 \end{cases}$

Solution   Let's graph each piece.

If $x \leq 0$,   If $x > 0$,

$f(x) = 2x + 3$ $f(x) = -x - 1$

Values ≤ 0

x	$f(x) = 2x + 3$
0	3 Closed circle
−1	1
−2	−1

Values > 0

x	$f(x) = -x - 1$
1	−2
2	−3
3	−4

The graph of the first part of $f(x)$ listed will look like a ray with a closed-circle end point at $(0, 3)$. The graph of the second part of $f(x)$ listed will look like a ray with an open-circle end point. To find the exact location of the open-circle end point, use $f(x) = -x - 1$ and find $f(0)$. Since $f(0) = -0 - 1 = -1$, we graph the values from the second table and place an open circle at $(0, -1)$.

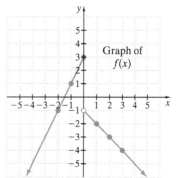

Notice that this graph is the graph of a function because it passes the vertical line test. The domain of this function is $(-\infty, \infty)$ and the range is $(-\infty, 3]$.   □

PRACTICE
2   Graph

$$f(x) = \begin{cases} -4x - 2 & \text{if } x \leq 0 \\ x + 1 & \text{if } x > 0 \end{cases}$$

OBJECTIVE
2   Vertical and Horizontal Shifting

Review of Common Graphs

We now take common graphs and learn how more complicated graphs are actually formed by shifting and reflecting these common graphs. These shifts and reflections are called transformations, and it is possible to combine transformations. A knowledge of these transformations will help make graphing simpler.

Let's begin with a review of the graphs of four common functions. Many of these functions we graphed in earlier sections. (Much of this review can be found in the previous section.)

First, **let's graph the linear function $f(x) = x$, or $y = x$**. Ordered pair solutions of this graph consist of ordered pairs whose x- and y-values are the same.

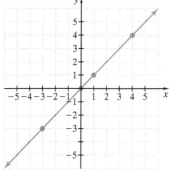

x	y or $f(x) = x$
−3	−3
0	0
1	1
4	4

Next, **let's graph the nonlinear function** $f(x) = x^2$ **or** $y = x^2$.

This equation is not linear because the x^2 term does not allow us to write it in the form $Ax + By = C$. Its graph is not a line. We begin by finding ordered pair solutions. Because this graph is solved for $f(x)$, or y, we choose x-values and find corresponding $f(x)$, or y-values.

If $x = -3$, then $y = (-3)^2$, or 9.

If $x = -2$, then $y = (-2)^2$, or 4.

If $x = -1$, then $y = (-1)^2$, or 1.

If $x = 0$, then $y = 0^2$, or 0.

If $x = 1$, then $y = 1^2$, or 1.

If $x = 2$, then $y = 2^2$, or 4.

If $x = 3$, then $y = 3^2$, or 9.

x	$f(x)$ or y
-3	9
-2	4
-1	1
0	0
1	1
2	4
3	9

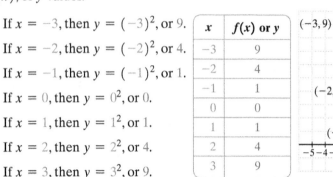

Study the table for a moment and look for patterns. Notice that the ordered pair solution $(0, 0)$ contains the smallest y-value because any other x-value squared will give a positive result. This means that the point $(0, 0)$ will be the lowest point on the graph. Also notice that all other y-values correspond to two different x-values, for example, $3^2 = 9$ and $(-3)^2 = 9$. This means that the graph will be a mirror image of itself across the y-axis. Connect the plotted points with a smooth curve to sketch its graph.

This curve is given a special name, a **parabola.** We will study more about parabolas in later chapters.

Next, **let's graph another nonlinear function,** $f(x) = |x|$ **or** $y = |x|$.

This is not a linear equation since it cannot be written in the form $Ax + By = C$. Its graph is not a line. Because we do not know the shape of this graph, we find many ordered pair solutions. We will choose x-values and substitute to find corresponding y-values.

If $x = -3$, then $y = |-3|$, or 3.

If $x = -2$, then $y = |-2|$, or 2.

If $x = -1$, then $y = |-1|$, or 1.

If $x = 0$, then $y = |0|$, or 0.

If $x = 1$, then $y = |1|$, or 1.

If $x = 2$, then $y = |2|$, or 2.

If $x = 3$, then $y = |3|$, or 3.

x	y
-3	3
-2	2
-1	1
0	0
1	1
2	2
3	3

Again, study the table of values for a moment and notice any patterns.

From the plotted ordered pairs, we see that the graph of this absolute value equation is V-shaped.

Finally, a fourth common function is $f(x) = \sqrt{x}$ or $y = \sqrt{x}$. For this graph, you need to recall basic facts about square roots and use your calculator to approximate some square roots to help locate points. Recall also that the square root of a negative number is not a real number, so be careful when finding your domain.

Now **let's graph the square root function** $f(x) = \sqrt{x}$, **or** $y = \sqrt{x}$.

To graph, we identify the domain, evaluate the function for several values of x, plot the resulting points, and connect the points with a smooth curve. Since $\sqrt{x}$ represents the nonnegative square root of x, the domain of this function is the set of all nonnegative numbers, $\{x | x \geq 0\}$, or $[0, \infty)$. We have approximated $\sqrt{3}$ on the next page to help us locate the point corresponding to $(3, \sqrt{3})$.

If $x = 0$, then $y = \sqrt{0}$, or 0.

If $x = 1$, then $y = \sqrt{1}$, or 1.

If $x = 3$, then $y = \sqrt{3}$, or 1.7.

If $x = 4$, then $y = \sqrt{4}$, or 2.

If $x = 9$, then $y = \sqrt{9}$, or 3.

x	$f(x) = \sqrt{x}$
0	0
1	1
3	$\sqrt{3} \approx 1.7$
4	2
9	3

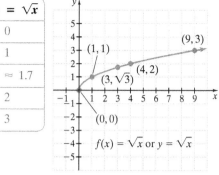

Notice that the graph of this function passes the vertical line test, as expected.

Below is a summary of our four common graphs. Take a moment and study these graphs. Your success in the rest of this section depends on your knowledge of these graphs.

Common Graphs

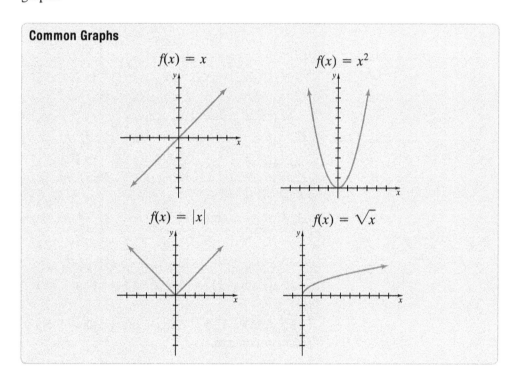

$f(x) = x$

$f(x) = x^2$

$f(x) = |x|$

$f(x) = \sqrt{x}$

Your knowledge of the slope-intercept form, $f(x) = mx + b$, will help you understand simple shifting of transformations such as vertical shifts. For example, what is the difference between the graphs of $f(x) = x$ and $g(x) = x + 3$?

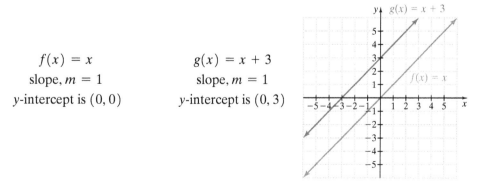

$f(x) = x$

slope, $m = 1$

y-intercept is $(0, 0)$

$g(x) = x + 3$

slope, $m = 1$

y-intercept is $(0, 3)$

Notice that the graph of $g(x) = x + 3$ is the same as the graph of $f(x) = x$, but moved upward 3 units. This is an example of a **vertical shift** and is true for graphs in general.

Vertical Shifts (Upward and Downward)
Let *k* be a Positive Number

Graph of	Same As	Moved
$g(x) = f(x) + k$	$f(x)$	k units upward
$g(x) = f(x) - k$	$f(x)$	k units downward

EXAMPLES Without plotting points, sketch the graph of each pair of functions on the same set of axes.

3. $f(x) = x^2$ and $g(x) = x^2 + 2$ **4.** $f(x) = \sqrt{x}$ and $g(x) = \sqrt{x} - 3$

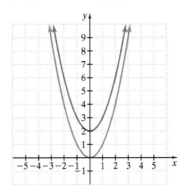   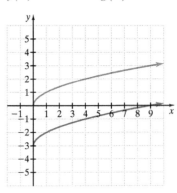

PRACTICES

3–4 Without plotting points, sketch the graphs of each pair of functions on the same set of axes.

3. $f(x) = x^2$ and $g(x) = x^2 - 3$ **4.** $f(x) = \sqrt{x}$ and $g(x) = \sqrt{x} + 1$

A horizontal shift to the left or right may be slightly more difficult to understand. Let's graph $g(x) = |x - 2|$ and compare it with $f(x) = |x|$.

EXAMPLE 5 Sketch the graphs of $f(x) = |x|$ and $g(x) = |x - 2|$ on the same set of axes.

Solution Study the table to the left to understand the placement of both graphs.

x	$f(x) = \lvert x \rvert$	$g(x) = \lvert x - 2 \rvert$
-3	3	5
-2	2	4
-1	1	3
0	0	2
1	1	1
2	2	0
3	3	1

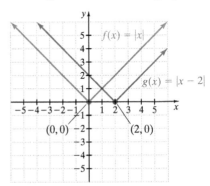

PRACTICE

5 Sketch the graphs of $f(x) = |x|$ and $g(x) = |x - 3|$ on the same set of axes.

The graph of $g(x) = |x - 2|$ is the same as the graph of $f(x) = |x|$, but moved 2 units to the right. This is an example of a **horizontal shift** and is true for graphs in general.

Horizontal Shift (To the Left or Right)
Let h be a Positive Number

Graph of	Same as	Moved
$g(x) = f(x - h)$	$f(x)$	h units to the right
$g(x) = f(x + h)$	$f(x)$	h units to the left

▶ **Helpful Hint**

Notice that $f(x - h)$ corresponds to a shift to the right and $f(x + h)$ corresponds to a shift to the left.

Vertical and horizontal shifts can be combined.

EXAMPLE 6   Sketch the graphs of $f(x) = x^2$ and $g(x) = (x - 2)^2 + 1$ on the same set of axes.

Solution   The graph of $g(x)$ is the same as the graph of $f(x)$ shifted 2 units to the right and 1 unit up.

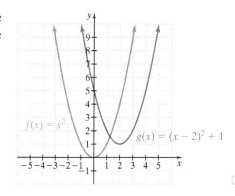

PRACTICE

6   Sketch the graphs of $f(x) = |x|$ and $g(x) = |x - 2| + 3$ on the same set of axes.

OBJECTIVE

3   Reflecting Graphs ▶

Another type of transformation is called a **reflection.** In this section, we will study reflections (mirror images) about the x-axis only. For example, take a moment and study these two graphs. The graph of $g(x) = -x^2$ can be verified, as usual, by plotting points.

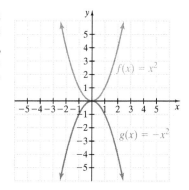

Reflection about the x-axis

The graph of $g(x) = -f(x)$ is the graph of $f(x)$ reflected about the x-axis.

EXAMPLE 7 Sketch the graph of $h(x) = -|x - 3| + 2$.

Solution The graph of $h(x) = -|x - 3| + 2$ is the same as the graph of $f(x) = |x|$ reflected about the x-axis, then moved three units to the right and two units upward.

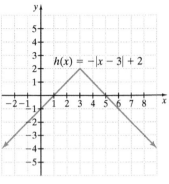

$h(x) = -|x - 3| + 2$

PRACTICE
7 Sketch the graph of $h(x) = -(x + 2)^2 - 1$.

There are other transformations, such as stretching, that won't be covered in this section. For a review of this transformation, see the Appendix.

Vocabulary, Readiness & Video Check

Match each equation with its graph.

1. $y = \sqrt{x}$ **2.** $y = x^2$ **3.** $y = x$ **4.** $y = |x|$

A
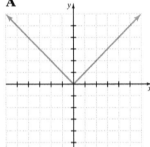

B
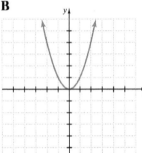

C
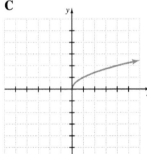

D
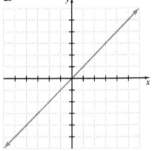

Martin-Gay Interactive Videos

See Video 8.3

Watch the section lecture video and answer the following questions.

OBJECTIVE **1**   **5.** In ⊞ Example 1, only one piece of the function is defined for the value $x = -1$. Why do we find $f(-1)$ for $f(x) = x + 3$?

OBJECTIVE **2**   **6.** For ⊞ Examples 2–8, why is it helpful to be familiar with common graphs and their basic shapes?

OBJECTIVE **3**   **7.** Based on the lecture before ⊞ Example 9, complete the following statement. The graph of $f(x) = -\sqrt{x + 6}$ has the same shape as the graph of $f(x) = \sqrt{x + 6}$ but it is reflected about the _____.

8.3 Exercise Set   MyMathLab®

Graph each piecewise-defined function. See Examples 1 and 2.

1. $f(x) = \begin{cases} 2x & \text{if } x < 0 \\ x + 1 & \text{if } x \geq 0 \end{cases}$

2. $f(x) = \begin{cases} 3x & \text{if } x < 0 \\ x + 2 & \text{if } x \geq 0 \end{cases}$

3. $f(x) = \begin{cases} 4x + 5 & \text{if } x \leq 0 \\ \dfrac{1}{4}x + 2 & \text{if } x > 0 \end{cases}$

4. $f(x) = \begin{cases} 5x + 4 & \text{if } x \leq 0 \\ \dfrac{1}{3}x - 1 & \text{if } x > 0 \end{cases}$

5. $g(x) = \begin{cases} -x & \text{if } x \le 1 \\ 2x + 1 & \text{if } x > 1 \end{cases}$

6. $g(x) = \begin{cases} 3x - 1 & \text{if } x \le 2 \\ -x & \text{if } x > 2 \end{cases}$

7. $f(x) = \begin{cases} 5 & \text{if } x < -2 \\ 3 & \text{if } x \ge -2 \end{cases}$ 8. $f(x) = \begin{cases} 4 & \text{if } x < -3 \\ -2 & \text{if } x \ge -3 \end{cases}$

MIXED PRACTICE

Graph each piecewise-defined function. Use the graph to determine the domain and range of the function. See Examples 1 and 2.

9. $f(x) = \begin{cases} -2x & \text{if } x \le 0 \\ 2x + 1 & \text{if } x > 0 \end{cases}$

10. $g(x) = \begin{cases} -3x & \text{if } x \le 0 \\ 3x + 2 & \text{if } x > 0 \end{cases}$

11. $h(x) = \begin{cases} 5x - 5 & \text{if } x < 2 \\ -x + 3 & \text{if } x \ge 2 \end{cases}$

12. $f(x) = \begin{cases} 4x - 4 & \text{if } x < 2 \\ -x + 1 & \text{if } x \ge 2 \end{cases}$

13. $f(x) = \begin{cases} x + 3 & \text{if } x < -1 \\ -2x + 4 & \text{if } x \ge -1 \end{cases}$

14. $h(x) = \begin{cases} x + 2 & \text{if } x < 1 \\ 2x + 1 & \text{if } x \ge 1 \end{cases}$

15. $g(x) = \begin{cases} -2 & \text{if } x \le 0 \\ -4 & \text{if } x \ge 1 \end{cases}$

16. $f(x) = \begin{cases} -1 & \text{if } x \le 0 \\ -3 & \text{if } x \ge 2 \end{cases}$

MIXED PRACTICE

Sketch the graph of each function. See Examples 3 through 6.

17. $f(x) = |x| + 3$ 18. $f(x) = |x| - 2$
19. $f(x) = \sqrt{x} - 2$ 20. $f(x) = \sqrt{x} + 3$
21. $f(x) = |x - 4|$ 22. $f(x) = |x + 3|$
23. $f(x) = \sqrt{x + 2}$ 24. $f(x) = \sqrt{x - 2}$
25. $y = (x - 4)^2$ 26. $y = (x + 4)^2$
27. $f(x) = x^2 + 4$ 28. $f(x) = x^2 - 4$
29. $f(x) = \sqrt{x - 2} + 3$ 30. $f(x) = \sqrt{x - 1} + 3$
31. $f(x) = |x - 1| + 5$ 32. $f(x) = |x - 3| + 2$
33. $f(x) = \sqrt{x + 1} + 1$ 34. $f(x) = \sqrt{x + 3} + 2$
35. $f(x) = |x + 3| - 1$ 36. $f(x) = |x + 1| - 4$
37. $g(x) = (x - 1)^2 - 1$ 38. $h(x) = (x + 2)^2 + 2$
39. $f(x) = (x + 3)^2 - 2$ 40. $f(x) = (x + 2)^2 + 4$

Sketch the graph of each function. See Examples 3 through 7.

41. $f(x) = -(x - 1)^2$ 42. $g(x) = -(x + 2)^2$
43. $h(x) = -\sqrt{x} + 3$ 44. $f(x) = -\sqrt{x + 3}$
45. $h(x) = -|x + 2| + 3$ 46. $g(x) = -|x + 1| + 1$
47. $f(x) = (x - 3) + 2$ 48. $f(x) = (x - 1) + 4$

REVIEW AND PREVIEW

Match each equation with its graph.

49. $y = -1$ 50. $x = -1$
51. $x = 3$ 52. $y = 3$

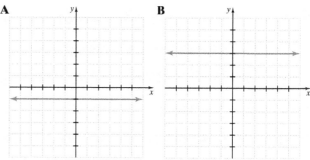

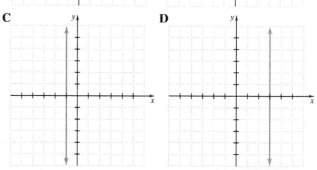

CONCEPT EXTENSIONS

53. Draw a graph whose domain is $(-\infty, 5]$ and whose range is $[2, \infty)$.

54. In your own words, describe how to graph a piecewise-defined function.

55. Graph: $f(x) = \begin{cases} -\dfrac{1}{2}x & \text{if } x \le 0 \\ x + 1 & \text{if } 0 < x \le 2 \\ 2x - 1 & \text{if } x > 2 \end{cases}$

56. Graph: $f(x) = \begin{cases} -\dfrac{1}{3}x & \text{if } x \le 0 \\ x + 2 & \text{if } 0 < x \le 4 \\ 3x - 4 & \text{if } x > 4 \end{cases}$

Write the domain and range of the following exercises.

57. Exercise 29   58. Exercise 30
59. Exercise 45   60. Exercise 46

Without graphing, find the domain of each function.

61. $f(x) = 5\sqrt{x - 20} + 1$
62. $g(x) = -3\sqrt{x + 5}$
63. $h(x) = 5|x - 20| + 1$
64. $f(x) = -3|x + 5.7|$
65. $g(x) = 9 - \sqrt{x + 103}$
66. $h(x) = \sqrt{x - 17} - 3$

Sketch the graph of each piecewise-defined function. Write the domain and range of each function.

67. $f(x) = \begin{cases} |x| & \text{if } x \le 0 \\ x^2 & \text{if } x > 0 \end{cases}$ 68. $f(x) = \begin{cases} x^2 & \text{if } x < 0 \\ \sqrt{x} & \text{if } x \ge 0 \end{cases}$

69. $g(x) = \begin{cases} |x - 2| & \text{if } x < 0 \\ -x^2 & \text{if } x \ge 0 \end{cases}$

70. $g(x) = \begin{cases} -|x + 1| - 1 & \text{if } x < -2 \\ \sqrt{x + 2} - 4 & \text{if } x \ge -2 \end{cases}$

8.4 Variation and Problem Solving

OBJECTIVES

1 Solve Problems Involving Direct Variation.

2 Solve Problems Involving Inverse Variation.

3 Solve Problems Involving Joint Variation.

4 Solve Problems Involving Combined Variation.

OBJECTIVE

1 Solving Problems Involving Direct Variation

A very familiar example of direct variation is the relationship of the circumference C of a circle to its radius r. The formula $C = 2\pi r$ expresses that the circumference is always 2π times the radius. In other words, C is always a constant multiple (2π) of r. Because it is, we say that **C varies directly as r,** that **C varies directly with r,** or that **C is directly proportional to r.**

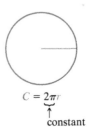

$C = 2\pi r$
constant

Direct Variation

y varies directly as x, or y is directly proportional to x, if there is a nonzero constant k such that

$$y = kx$$

The number k is called the **constant of variation** or the **constant of proportionality.**

In the above definition, the relationship described between x and y is a linear one. In other words, the graph of $y = kx$ is a line. The slope of the line is k, and the line passes through the origin.

For example, the graph of the direct variation equation $C = 2\pi r$ is shown. The horizontal axis represents the radius r, and the vertical axis is the circumference C. From the graph, we can read that when the radius is 6 units, the circumference is approximately 38 units. Also, when the circumference is 45 units, the radius is between 7 and 8 units. Notice that as the radius increases, the circumference increases.

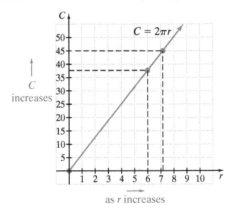

EXAMPLE 1 Suppose that y varies directly as x. If y is 5 when x is 30, find the constant of variation and the direct variation equation.

Solution Since y varies directly as x, we write $y = kx$. If $y = 5$ when $x = 30$, we have that

$$y = kx$$
$$5 = k(30) \quad \text{Replace } y \text{ with 5 and } x \text{ with 30.}$$
$$\frac{1}{6} = k \quad \text{Solve for } k.$$

The constant of variation is $\frac{1}{6}$.

After finding the constant of variation k, the direct variation equation can be written as $y = \frac{1}{6}x$.

PRACTICE

1   Suppose that y varies directly as x. If y is 20 when x is 15, find the constant of variation and the direct variation equation.

EXAMPLE 2   **Using Direct Variation and Hooke's Law**

Hooke's law states that the distance a spring stretches is directly proportional to the weight attached to the spring. If a 40-pound weight attached to the spring stretches the spring 5 inches, find the distance that a 65-pound weight attached to the spring stretches the spring.

Solution

1. UNDERSTAND. Read and reread the problem. Notice that we are given that the distance a spring stretches is **directly proportional** to the weight attached. We let

    d = the distance stretched

    w = the weight attached

    The constant of variation is represented by k.

2. TRANSLATE. Because d is directly proportional to w, we write

    $$d = kw$$

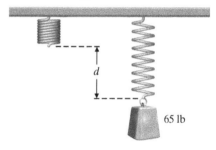

3. SOLVE. When a weight of 40 pounds is attached, the spring stretches 5 inches. That is, when $w = 40$, $d = 5$.

    $$d = kw$$
    $$5 = k(40) \quad \text{Replace } d \text{ with 5 and } w \text{ with 40.}$$
    $$\frac{1}{8} = k \quad \text{Solve for } k.$$

    Now when we replace k with $\frac{1}{8}$ in the equation $d = kw$, we have

    $$d = \frac{1}{8}w$$

    To find the stretch when a weight of 65 pounds is attached, we replace w with 65 to find d.

    $$d = \frac{1}{8}(65)$$
    $$= \frac{65}{8} = 8\frac{1}{8} \quad \text{or} \quad 8.125$$

4. INTERPRET.

Check: Check the proposed solution of 8.125 inches in the original problem.

State: The spring stetches 8.125 inches when a 65-pound weight is attached.

PRACTICE

2   Use Hooke's law as stated in Example 2. If a 36-pound weight attached to a spring stretches the spring 9 inches, find the distance that a 75-pound weight attached to the spring stretches the spring.

2 Solving Problems Involving Inverse Variation

When y is proportional to the **reciprocal** of another variable x, we say that **y varies inversely as x,** or that **y is inversely proportional to x.** An example of the inverse variation relationship is the relationship between the pressure that a gas exerts and the volume of its container. As the volume of a container decreases, the pressure of the gas it contains increases.

Inverse Variation

y varies inversely as x, or y is inversely proportional to x, if there is a nonzero constant k such that

$$y = \frac{k}{x}$$

The number k is called the **constant of variation** or the **constant of proportionality.**

Notice that $y = \dfrac{k}{x}$ is a rational equation. Its graph for $k > 0$ and $x > 0$ is shown. From the graph, we can see that as x increases, y decreases.

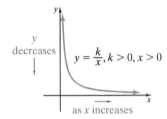

EXAMPLE 3 Suppose that u varies inversely as w. If u is 3 when w is 5, find the constant of variation and the inverse variation equation.

Solution Since u varies inversely as w, we have $u = \dfrac{k}{w}$. We let $u = 3$ and $w = 5$, and we solve for k.

$$u = \frac{k}{w}$$

$$3 = \frac{k}{5} \quad \text{Let } u = 3 \text{ and } w = 5.$$

$$15 = k \quad \text{Multiply both sides by 5.}$$

The constant of variation k is 15. This gives the inverse variation equation

$$u = \frac{15}{w}$$

3 Suppose that b varies inversely as a. If b is 5 when a is 9, find the constant of variation and the inverse variation equation.

EXAMPLE 4 Using Inverse Variation and Boyle's Law

Boyle's law says that if the temperature stays the same, the pressure P of a gas is inversely proportional to the volume V. If a cylinder in a steam engine has a pressure of 960 kilopascals when the volume is 1.4 cubic meters, find the pressure when the volume increases to 2.5 cubic meters.

Solution

1. UNDERSTAND. Read and reread the problem. Notice that we are given that the pressure of a gas is *inversely proportional* to the volume. We will let $P = $ the pressure and $V = $ the volume. The constant of variation is represented by k.

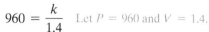

2. TRANSLATE. Because P is inversely proportional to V, we write

$$P = \frac{k}{V}$$

When $P = 960$ kilopascals, the volume $V = 1.4$ cubic meters. We use this information to find k.

$$960 = \frac{k}{1.4} \quad \text{Let } P = 960 \text{ and } V = 1.4.$$

$$1344 = k \quad \text{Multiply both sides by 1.4.}$$

Thus, the value of k is 1344. Replacing k with 1344 in the variation equation, we have

$$P = \frac{1344}{V}$$

Next we find P when V is 2.5 cubic meters.

3. SOLVE.

$$P = \frac{1344}{2.5} \quad \text{Let } V = 2.5.$$

$$= 537.6$$

4. INTERPRET.

Check: Check the proposed solution in the original problem.

State: When the volume is 2.5 cubic meters, the pressure is 537.6 kilopascals.   □

PRACTICE

4   Use Boyle's law as stated in Example 4. If $P = 350$ kilopascals when $V = 2.8$ cubic meters, find the pressure when the volume decreases to 1.5 cubic meters.

OBJECTIVE

3   Solving Problems Involving Joint Variation

Sometimes the ratio of a variable to the product of many other variables is constant. For example, the ratio of distance traveled to the product of speed and time traveled is always 1.

$$\frac{d}{rt} = 1 \quad \text{or} \quad d = rt$$

Such a relationship is called **joint variation.**

> **Joint Variation**
>
> If the ratio of a variable y to the product of two or more variables is constant, then **y varies jointly as,** or **is jointly proportional to,** the other variables. If
> $$y = kxz$$
> then the number k is the **constant of variation** or the **constant of proportionality.**

> ✓**CONCEPT CHECK**
>
> Which type of variation is represented by the equation $xy = 8$? Explain.
>
> **a.** Direct variation   **b.** Inverse variation   **c.** Joint variation

△ **EXAMPLE 5**   **Expressing Surface Area**

The lateral surface area of a cylinder varies jointly as its radius and height. Express this surface area S in terms of radius r and height h.

Answer to Concept Check:
b; answers may vary

(Continued on next page)

Solution Because the surface area varies jointly as the radius r and the height h, we equate S to a constant multiple of r and h.

$$S = krh$$

In the equation $S = krh$, it can be determined that the constant k is 2π, and we then have the formula $S = 2\pi rh$. (The lateral surface area formula does not include the areas of the two circular bases.) □

PRACTICE
5 The area of a regular polygon varies jointly as its apothem and its perimeter. Express the area in terms of the apothem a and the perimeter p.

OBJECTIVE
4 Solving Problems Involving Combined Variation

There are many examples of variation in which y may vary directly or inversely as a *power* of x. Also there are combinations of direct, inverse, and joint variation. We will call these variations **combined variation.**

EXAMPLE 6 Suppose that y varies directly as the square of x. If y is 24 when x is 2, find the constant of variation and the variation equation.

Solution Since y varies directly as the square of x, we have

$$y = kx^2$$

Now let $y = 24$ and $x = 2$ and solve for k.

$$y = kx^2$$
$$24 = k \cdot 2^2$$
$$24 = 4k$$
$$6 = k$$

The constant of variation is 6, so the variation equation is

$$y = 6x^2$$ □

PRACTICE
6 Suppose that y varies inversely as the cube of x. If y is $\dfrac{1}{2}$ when x is 2, find the constant of variation and the variation equation.

△ **EXAMPLE 7** **Finding Column Weight**

The maximum weight that a circular column can support is directly proportional to the fourth power of its diameter and is inversely proportional to the square of its height. A 2-meter-diameter column that is 8 meters in height can support 1 ton. Find the weight that a 1-meter-diameter column that is 4 meters in height can support.

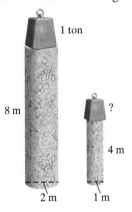

1 ton

8 m

?

4 m

2 m   1 m

Solution

1. UNDERSTAND. Read and reread the problem. Let w = weight, d = diameter, h = height, and k = the constant of variation.

2. TRANSLATE. Since w is directly proportional to d^4 and inversely proportional to h^2, we have

$$w = \frac{kd^4}{h^2}$$

3. SOLVE. To find k, we are given that a 2-meter-diameter column that is 8 meters in height can support 1 ton. That is, $w = 1$ when $d = 2$ and $h = 8$, or

$$1 = \frac{k \cdot 2^4}{8^2} \qquad \text{Let } w = 1, d = 2, \text{ and } h = 8.$$

$$1 = \frac{k \cdot 16}{64}$$

$$4 = k \qquad \text{Solve for } k.$$

Now replace k with 4 in the equation $w = \dfrac{kd^4}{h^2}$ and we have

$$w = \frac{4d^4}{h^2}$$

To find weight w for a 1-meter-diameter column that is 4 meters in height, let $d = 1$ and $h = 4$.

$$w = \frac{4 \cdot 1^4}{4^2}$$

$$w = \frac{4}{16} = \frac{1}{4}$$

4. INTERPRET.

Check: Check the proposed solution in the original problem.

State: The 1-meter-diameter column that is 4 meters in height can support $\dfrac{1}{4}$ ton of weight.

PRACTICE

7 Suppose that y varies directly as z and inversely as the cube of x. If y is 15 when $z = 5$ and $x = 3$, find the constant of variation and the variation equation.

Vocabulary, Readiness & Video Check

State whether each equation represents direct, inverse, or joint variation.

1. $y = 5x$

2. $y = \dfrac{700}{x}$

3. $y = 5xz$

4. $y = \dfrac{1}{2}abc$

5. $y = \dfrac{9.1}{x}$

6. $y = 2.3x$

7. $y = \dfrac{2}{3}x$

8. $y = 3.1st$

Martin-Gay Interactive Videos

See Video 8.4

Watch the section lecture video and answer the following questions.

OBJECTIVE
1

9. Based on the lecture before ▣ Example 1, what kind of equation is a direct variation equation? What does k, the constant of variation, represent in this equation?

OBJECTIVE
2

10. In ▣ Example 3, why is it not necessary to replace the given values of x and y in the inverse variation equation in order to find k?

OBJECTIVE
3

11. Based on ▣ Example 5 and the lecture before, what is the variation equation for "y varies jointly as the square of a and the fifth power of b"?

OBJECTIVE
4

12. From ▣ Example 6, what kind of variation does a combined variation application involve?

8.4 Exercise Set

MyMathLab®

If y varies directly as x, find the constant of variation and the direct variation equation for each situation. See Example 1.

1. $y = 4$ when $x = 20$
2. $y = 9$ when $x = 54$
3. $y = 6$ when $x = 4$
4. $y = 12$ when $x = 8$
5. $y = 7$ when $x = \dfrac{1}{2}$
6. $y = 11$ when $x = \dfrac{1}{3}$
7. $y = 0.2$ when $x = 0.8$
8. $y = 0.4$ when $x = 2.5$

Solve. See Example 2.

9. The weight of a synthetic ball varies directly with the cube of its radius. A ball with a radius of 2 inches weighs 1.20 pounds. Find the weight of a ball of the same material with a 3-inch radius.

10. At sea, the distance to the horizon is directly proportional to the square root of the elevation of the observer. If a person who is 36 feet above the water can see 7.4 miles, find how far a person 64 feet above the water can see. Round to the nearest tenth of a mile.

11. The amount P of pollution varies directly with the population N of people. Kansas City has a population of 460,000 and produces about 270,000 tons of pollutants. Find how many tons of pollution we should expect St. Louis to produce if we know that its population is 319,000. Round to the nearest whole ton. (*Source:* Wikipedia)

12. Charles's law states that if the pressure P stays the same, the volume V of a gas is directly proportional to its temperature T. If a balloon is filled with 20 cubic meters of a gas at a temperature of 300 K, find the new volume if the temperature rises to 360 K while the pressure stays the same.

If y varies inversely as x, find the constant of variation and the inverse variation equation for each situation. See Example 3.

13. $y = 6$ when $x = 5$
14. $y = 20$ when $x = 9$
15. $y = 100$ when $x = 7$
16. $y = 63$ when $x = 3$
17. $y = \dfrac{1}{8}$ when $x = 16$
18. $y = \dfrac{1}{10}$ when $x = 40$
19. $y = 0.2$ when $x = 0.7$
20. $y = 0.6$ when $x = 0.3$

Solve. See Example 4.

21. Pairs of markings a set distance apart are made on highways so that police can detect drivers exceeding the speed limit. Over a fixed distance, the speed R varies inversely with the time T. In one particular pair of markings, R is 45 mph when T is 6 seconds. Find the speed of a car that travels the given distance in 5 seconds.

22. The weight of an object on or above the surface of Earth varies inversely as the square of the distance between the object and Earth's center. If a person weighs 160 pounds on Earth's surface, find the individual's weight if he moves 200 miles above Earth. Round to the nearest whole pound. (Assume that Earth's radius is 4000 miles.)

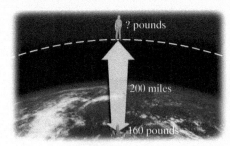

23. If the voltage V in an electric circuit is held constant, the current I is inversely proportional to the resistance R. If the current is 40 amperes when the resistance is 270 ohms, find the current when the resistance is 150 ohms.

24. Because it is more efficient to produce larger numbers of items, the cost of producing a certain computer DVD is inversely proportional to the number produced. If 4000 can be produced at a cost of $1.20 each, find the cost per DVD when 6000 are produced.

25. The intensity I of light varies inversely as the square of the distance d from the light source. If the distance from the light source is doubled (see the figure), determine what happens to the intensity of light at the new location.

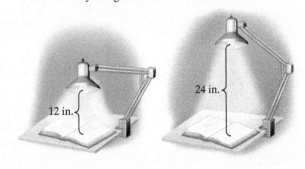

△ **26.** The maximum weight that a circular column can hold is inversely proportional to the square of its height. If an 8-foot column can hold 2 tons, find how much weight a 10-foot column can hold.

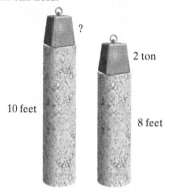

10 feet

?

2 ton

8 feet

MIXED PRACTICE

Write each statement as an equation. Use k as the constant of variation. See Example 5.

27. x varies jointly as y and z.

28. P varies jointly as R and the square of S.

29. r varies jointly as s and the cube of t.

30. a varies jointly as b and c.

For each statement, find the constant of variation and the variation equation. See Examples 5 and 6.

31. y varies directly as the cube of x; $y = 9$ when $x = 3$

32. y varies directly as the cube of x; $y = 32$ when $x = 4$

33. y varies directly as the square root of x; $y = 0.4$ when $x = 4$

34. y varies directly as the square root of x; $y = 2.1$ when $x = 9$

35. y varies inversely as the square of x; $y = 0.052$ when $x = 5$

36. y varies inversely as the square of x; $y = 0.011$ when $x = 10$

⊙ **37.** y varies jointly as x and the cube of z; $y = 120$ when $x = 5$ and $z = 2$

38. y varies jointly as x and the square of z; $y = 360$ when $x = 4$ and $z = 3$

Solve. See Example 7.

△⊙ **39.** The maximum weight that a rectangular beam can support varies jointly as its width and the square of its height and inversely as its length. If a beam $\frac{1}{2}$ foot wide, $\frac{1}{3}$ foot high, and 10 feet long can support 12 tons, find how much a similar beam can support if the beam is $\frac{2}{3}$ foot wide, $\frac{1}{2}$ foot high, and 16 feet long.

40. The number of cars manufactured on an assembly line at a General Motors plant varies jointly as the number of workers and the time they work. If 200 workers can produce 60 cars in 2 hours, find how many cars 240 workers should be able to make in 3 hours.

△ **41.** The volume of a cone varies jointly as its height and the square of its radius. If the volume of a cone is 32π cubic inches when the radius is 4 inches and the height is 6 inches, find the volume of a cone when the radius is 3 inches and the height is 5 inches.

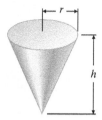

r

h

△ **42.** When a wind blows perpendicularly against a flat surface, its force is jointly proportional to the surface area and the speed of the wind. A sail whose surface area is 12 square feet experiences a 20-pound force when the wind speed is 10 miles per hour. Find the force on an 8-square-foot sail if the wind speed is 12 miles per hour.

43. The intensity of light (in foot-candles) varies inversely as the square of x, the distance in feet from the light source. The intensity of light 2 feet from the source is 80 foot-candles. How far away is the source if the intensity of light is 5 foot-candles?

44. The horsepower that can be safely transmitted to a shaft varies jointly as the shaft's angular speed of rotation (in revolutions per minute) and the cube of its diameter. A 2-inch shaft making 120 revolutions per minute safely transmits 40 horsepower. Find how much horsepower can be safely transmitted by a 3-inch shaft making 80 revolutions per minute.

MIXED PRACTICE

Write an equation to describe each variation. Use k for the constant of proportionality. See Examples 1 through 7.

45. y varies directly as x

46. p varies directly as q

47. a varies inversely as b

48. y varies inversely as x

49. y varies jointly as x and z

50. y varies jointly as q, r, and t

51. y varies inversely as x^3

52. y varies inversely as a^4

53. y varies directly as x and inversely as p^2

54. y varies directly as a^5 and inversely as b

REVIEW AND PREVIEW

Find the exact circumference and area of each circle. See the inside cover for a list of geometric formulas.

△ **55.**

△ **56.**

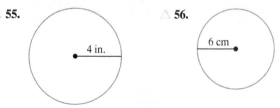

4 in.

6 cm

△ 57.

9 cm

△ 58.

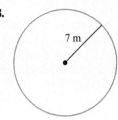

7 m

Simplify. See Sections 1.2, 1.4, and 1.5.

59. $|-1.2|$

60. $|-3|$

61. $-|7|$

62. $|0|$

63. $-\left|-\dfrac{1}{2}\right|$

64. $-\left|\dfrac{1}{5}\right|$

65. $\left(\dfrac{2}{3}\right)^3$

66. $\left(\dfrac{5}{11}\right)^2$

CONCEPT EXTENSIONS

Solve. See the Concept Check in this section. Choose the type of variation that each equation represents. **a.** *Direct variation* **b.** *Inverse variation* **c.** *Joint variation*

67. $y = \dfrac{2}{3}x$

68. $y = \dfrac{0.6}{x}$

69. $y = 9ab$

70. $xy = \dfrac{2}{11}$

71. The horsepower to drive a boat varies directly as the cube of the speed of the boat. If the speed of the boat is to double, determine the corresponding increase in horsepower required.

72. The volume of a cylinder varies jointly as the height and the square of the radius. If the height is halved and the radius is doubled, determine what happens to the volume.

73. Suppose that y varies directly as x. If x is doubled, what is the effect on y?

74. Suppose that y varies directly as x^2. If x is doubled, what is the effect on y?

Complete the following table for the inverse variation $y = \dfrac{k}{x}$ *over each given value of k. Plot the points on a rectangular coordinate system.*

x	$\dfrac{1}{4}$	$\dfrac{1}{2}$	1	2	4
$y = \dfrac{k}{x}$					

75. $k = 3$ **76.** $k = 1$ **77.** $k = \dfrac{1}{2}$ **78.** $k = 5$

Chapter 8 Vocabulary Check

Fill in each blank with one of the words or phrases listed below.

slope-intercept	directly	slope
jointly	parallel	perpendicular
function	inversely	linear function

1. _____ lines have the same slope and different y-intercepts.

2. _____ form of a linear equation in two variables is $y = mx + b$.

3. A(n) _____ is a relation in which each first component in the ordered pairs corresponds to exactly one second component.

4. In the equation $y = 4x - 2$, the coefficient of x is the _____ of its corresponding graph.

5. Two lines are _____ if the product of their slopes is -1.

6. A(n) _____ is a function that can be written in the form $f(x) = mx + b$.

7. In the equation $y = kx$, y varies _____ as x.

8. In the equation $y = \dfrac{k}{x}$, y varies _____ as x.

9. In the equation $y = kxz$, y varies _____ as x and z.

Chapter 8 Highlights

DEFINITIONS AND CONCEPTS	EXAMPLES

Section 8.1   Graphing and Writing Linear Functions

A **linear function** is a function that can be written in the form $f(x) = mx + b$.

To graph a linear function, find three ordered pair solutions. Graph the solutions and draw a line through the plotted points.

Linear functions

$$f(x) = -3, g(x) = 5x, h(x) = -\frac{1}{3}x - 7$$

Graph $f(x) = -2x$.

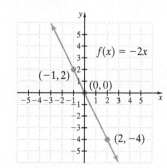

x	y or $f(x)$
-1	2
0	0
2	-4

The point-slope form of the equation of a line is $y - y_1 = m(x - x_1)$, where m is the slope of the line and (x_1, y_1) is a point on the line.

Find an equation of the line parallel to $g(x) = 2x - 1$ and containing the point $(1, -4)$. Write the equation using function notation.

Since we want a parallel line, use the same slope of $g(x)$, which is 2.

$$y - y_1 = m(x - x_1)$$
$$y - (-4) = 2(x - 1)$$
$$y + 4 = 2x - 2$$
$$y = 2x - 6 \qquad \text{Solve for } y.$$
$$f(x) = 2x - 6 \qquad \text{Let } y = f(x)$$

Section 8.2   Reviewing Function Notation and Graphing Nonlinear Functions

The graph of $y = mx + b$ is the same as the graph of $y = mx$, but shifted $|b|$ units up if b is positive and $|b|$ units down if b is negative.

Graph $g(x) = -2x + 3$.

This is the same as the graph of $f(x) = -2x$ shifted 3 units up.

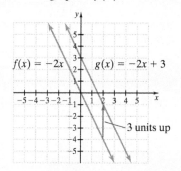

(continued)

DEFINITIONS AND CONCEPTS	EXAMPLES

Section 8.2 Reviewing Function Notation and Graphing Nonlinear Functions (continued)

To graph a function that is not linear, find a sufficient number of ordered pair solutions so that a pattern may be discovered.

Graph $f(x) = x^2 + 2$.

x	y or $f(x)$
-2	6
-1	3
0	2
1	3
2	6

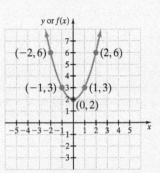

Section 8.3 Graphing Piecewise-Defined Functions and Shifting and Reflecting Graphs of Functions

Vertical shifts (upward and downward):
Let k be a positive number.

Graph of	Same as	Moved	
$g(x) = f(x) + k$	$f(x)$	k units upward
$g(x) = f(x) - k$	$f(x)$	k units downward

Horizontal shift (to the left or right):
Let h be a positive number.

Graph of	Same as	Moved	
$g(x) = f(x - h)$	$f(x)$	h units to the right
$g(x) = f(x + h)$	$f(x)$	h units to the left

Reflection about the x-axis

The graph of $g(x) = -f(x)$ is the graph of $f(x)$ reflected about the x-axis.

The graph of $h(x) = -|x - 3| + 1$ is the same as the graph of $f(x) = |x|$, reflected about the x-axis, shifted 3 units right, then 1 unit up.

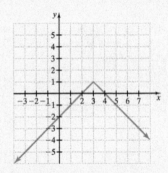

Section 8.4 Variation and Problem Solving

y **varies directly as** x, or y is **directly proportional to** x, if there is a nonzero constant k such that

$$y = kx$$

y **varies inversely as** x, or y is **inversely proportional to** x, if there is a nonzero constant k such that

$$y = \frac{k}{x}$$

y **varies jointly as** x and z or y is **jointly proportional to** x and z if there is a nonzero constant k such that

$$y = kxz$$

The circumference of a circle C varies directly as its radius r.

$$C = \underset{k}{\underbrace{2\pi}} r$$

Pressure P varies inversely with volume V.

$$P = \frac{k}{V}$$

The lateral surface area S of a cylinder varies jointly as its radius r and height h.

$$S = \underset{k}{\underbrace{2\pi}} rh$$

Chapter 8 **Review**

(8.1) *Graph each linear function.*

1. $f(x) = x$

2. $f(x) = -\frac{1}{3}x$

3. $g(x) = 4x - 1$

4. $F(x) = -\frac{2}{3}x + 2$

The graph of $f(x) = 3x$ is sketched below. Use this graph to match each linear function with its graph.

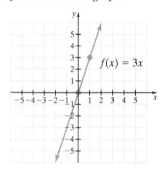

A

B

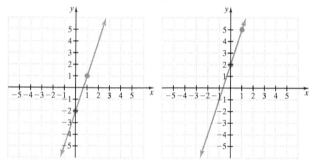

C

D

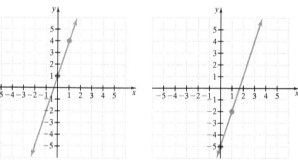

5. $f(x) = 3x + 1$

6. $f(x) = 3x - 2$

7. $f(x) = 3x + 2$

8. $f(x) = 3x - 5$

Find the slope and y-intercept of each function.

9. $f(x) = \frac{2}{5}x - \frac{4}{3}$

10. $f(x) = -\frac{2}{7}x + \frac{3}{2}$

Find the standard form equation of each line satisfying the given conditions.

11. Slope 2; through $(5, -2)$

12. Through $(-3, 5)$; slope 3

13. Through $(-5, 3)$ and $(-4, -8)$

14. Through $(-6, -1)$ and $(-4, -2)$

15. Through $(-2, -5)$; parallel to $y = 8$

16. Through $(-2, 3)$; perpendicular to $x = 4$

Find the equation of each line satisfying the given conditions. Write each equation using function notation.

17. Horizontal; through $(3, -1)$

18. Slope $-\frac{2}{3}$; y-intercept $(0, 4)$

19. Slope -1; y-intercept $(0, -2)$

20. Through $(2, -6)$; parallel to $6x + 3y = 5$

21. Through $(-4, -2)$; parallel to $3x + 2y = 8$

22. Through $(-6, -1)$; perpendicular to $4x + 3y = 5$

23. Through $(-4, 5)$; perpendicular to $2x - 3y = 6$

24. The value of an automobile bought in 2006 continues to decrease as time passes. Two years after the car was bought, it was worth $17,500; four years after it was bought, it was worth $14,300.

   a. Assuming that this relationship between the number of years past 2006 and the value of the car is linear, write an equation describing this relationship. [*Hint*: Use ordered pairs of the form (years past 2006, value of the automobile).]

   b. Use this equation to estimate the value of the automobile in 2012.

25. The value of a building bought in 2000 continues to increase as time passes. Seven years after the building was bought, it was worth $210,000; 12 years after it was bought, it was worth $270,000.

   a. Assuming that this relationship between the number of years past 2000 and the value of the building is linear, write an equation describing this relationship. [*Hint:* Use ordered pairs of the form (years past 2000, value of the building).]

   b. Use this equation to estimate the value of the building in 2018.

26. Decide whether the lines are parallel, perpendicular, or neither.
$$-x + 3y = 2$$
$$6x - 18y = 3$$

(8.2) Use the graph of the function on the next page to answer Exercises 27 through 30.

27. Find $f(-1)$.

28. Find $f(1)$.

29. Find all values of x such that $f(x) = 1$.

30. Find all values of x such that $f(x) = -1$.

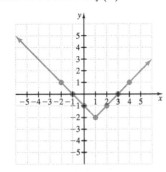

Determine whether each function is linear or not. Then graph the function.

31. $f(x) = 3x$

32. $f(x) = 5x$

33. $g(x) = |x| + 4$

34. $h(x) = x^2 + 4$

35. $F(x) = -\dfrac{1}{2}x + 2$

36. $G(x) = -x + 5$

37. $y = -1.36x$

38. $y = 2.1x + 5.9$

39. $H(x) = (x - 2)^2$

40. $f(x) = -|x - 3|$

(8.3) Graph each function.

41. $g(x) = \begin{cases} -\dfrac{1}{5}x & \text{if } x \le -1 \\ -4x + 2 & \text{if } x > -1 \end{cases}$

42. $f(x) = \begin{cases} -3x & \text{if } x < 0 \\ x - 3 & \text{if } x \ge 0 \end{cases}$

Graph each function.

43. $f(x) = \sqrt{x - 4}$

44. $y = \sqrt{x} - 4$

45. $h(x) = -(x + 3)^2 - 1$

46. $g(x) = |x - 2| - 2$

(8.4) Solve each variation problem.

47. A is directly proportional to B. If $A = 6$ when $B = 14$, find A when $B = 21$.

48. C is inversely proportional to D. If $C = 12$ when $D = 8$, find C when $D = 24$.

49. According to Boyle's law, the pressure exerted by a gas is inversely proportional to the volume, as long as the temperature stays the same. If a gas exerts a pressure of 1250 pounds per square inch when the volume is 2 cubic feet, find the volume when the pressure is 800 pounds per square inch.

△ **50.** The surface area of a sphere varies directly as the square of its radius. If the surface area is 36π square inches when the radius is 3 inches, find the surface area when the radius is 4 inches.

MIXED REVIEW

Write an equation of the line satisfying each set of conditions. Write the equation in the form $f(x) = mx + b$.

51. Slope 0; through $\left(-4, \dfrac{9}{2}\right)$

52. Slope $\dfrac{3}{4}$; through $(-8, -4)$

53. Through $(-3, 8)$ and $(-2, 3)$

54. Through $(-6, 1)$; parallel to $y = -\dfrac{3}{2}x + 11$

55. Through $(-5, 7)$; perpendicular to $5x - 4y = 10$

Graph each piecewise-defined function.

56. $g(x) = \begin{cases} 4x - 3 & \text{if } x \le 1 \\ 2x & \text{if } x > 1 \end{cases}$

57. $f(x) = \begin{cases} x - 2 & \text{if } x \le 0 \\ -\dfrac{x}{3} & \text{if } x \ge 3 \end{cases}$

Graph each function.

58. $f(x) = |x + 1| - 3$

59. $f(x) = \sqrt{x - 2}$

60. y is inversely proportional to x. If $y = 14$ when $x = 6$, find y when $x = 21$.

Chapter 8 Test MyMathLab®  Test Prep VIDEOS ▶ YouTube™

Use the graph of the function f to find each value.

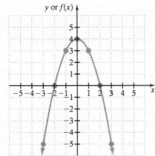

1. Find $f(1)$.

2. Find $f(-3)$.

3. Find all values of x such that $f(x) = 0$.

4. Find all values of x such that $f(x) = 4$.

Graph each line.

5. $2x - 3y = -6$

6. $f(x) = \dfrac{2}{3}x$

Find an equation of each line satisfying the given conditions. Write Exercises 7–9 in standard form. Write Exercises 10–12 using function notation.

7. Horizontal; through $(2, -8)$

8. Through $(4, -1)$; slope -3

9. Through $(0, -2)$; slope 5

10. Through $(4, -2)$ and $(6, -3)$

△ **11.** Through $(-1, 2)$; perpendicular to $3x - y = 4$

△ **12.** Parallel to $2y + x = 3$; through $(3, -2)$

13. Line L_1 has the equation $2x - 5y = 8$. Line L_2 passes through the points $(1, 4)$ and $(-1, -1)$. Determine whether these lines are parallel lines, perpendicular lines, or neither.

Find the domain and range of each relation. Also determine whether the relation is a function.

14.

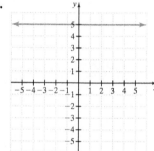

15.

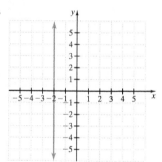

△ **16.**

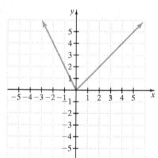

△ **17.**

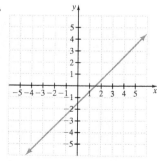

18. For the 2009 Major League Baseball season, the following linear function describes the relationship between a team's payroll x (in millions of dollars) and the number of games y that team won during the regular season.

$$f(x) = 0.096x + 72.81$$

Round to the nearest whole. (*Sources:* Based on data from Major League Baseball and *USA Today*)

a. According to this equation, how many games would have been won during the 2009 season by a team with a payroll of $90 million?

b. The Baltimore Orioles had a payroll of $67 million in 2009. According to this equation, how many games would they have won during the season?

c. According to this equation, what payroll would have been necessary in 2009 to have won 95 games during the season?

d. Find and interpret the slope of the equation.

Graph each function. For Exercises 19 and 21, state the domain and the range of the function.

19. $f(x) = \begin{cases} -\dfrac{1}{2}x & \text{if } x \le 0 \\ 2x - 3 & \text{if } x > 0 \end{cases}$

20. $f(x) = (x - 4)^2$

21. $g(x) = -|x + 2| - 1$

22. $h(x) = \sqrt{x} - 1$

23. Suppose that W is inversely proportional to V. If $W = 20$ when $V = 12$, find W when $V = 15$.

24. Suppose that Q is jointly proportional to R and the square of S. If $Q = 24$ when $R = 3$ and $S = 4$, find Q when $R = 2$ and $S = 3$.

25. When an anvil is dropped into a gorge, the speed with which it strikes the ground is directly proportional to the square root of the distance it falls. An anvil that falls 400 feet hits the ground at a speed of 160 feet per second. Find the height of a cliff over the gorge if a dropped anvil hits the ground at a speed of 128 feet per second.

Chapter 8 Cumulative Review

1. Simplify $3[4 + 2(10 - 1)]$.

2. Simplify $5[3 + 6(8 - 5)]$.

Find the value of each expression when $x = 2$ and $y = -5$.

3. **a.** $\dfrac{x - y}{12 + x}$ **b.** $x^2 - 3y$

4. **a.** $\dfrac{x + y}{3y}$ **b.** $y^2 - x$

Solve.

5. $-3x = 33$

6. $\dfrac{2}{3}y = 7$

7. $8(2 - t) = -5t$

8. $5x - 9 = 5x - 29$

9. Solve $y = mx + b$ for x.

10. Solve $y = 7x - 2$ for x.

11. $-4x + 7 \geq -9$ Write the solution using interval notation.

12. $-5x - 6 < 3x + 1$ Write the solution using interval notation.

13. Find the slope of the line $y = -1$.

14. Find the slope of a line parallel to the line passing through the points $(0, 7)$ and $(-1, 0)$.

15. Given $g(x) = x^2 - 3$, find the following. Then write the corresponding ordered pairs generated.
   a. $g(2)$ **b.** $g(-2)$
   c. $g(0)$.

16. Given $f(x) = 3 - x^2$, find the following. Then write the corresponding ordered pairs generated.
   a. $f(2)$ **b.** $f(-2)$
   c. $f(0)$

17. Solve the system: $\begin{cases} 2x + y = 10 \\ x = y + 2 \end{cases}$

18. Solve the system: $\begin{cases} 3y = x + 10 \\ 2x + 5y = 24 \end{cases}$

19. Solve the system: $\begin{cases} -x - \dfrac{y}{2} = \dfrac{5}{2} \\ \dfrac{x}{6} - \dfrac{y}{2} = 0 \end{cases}$

20. Solve the system: $\begin{cases} \dfrac{x}{2} + y = \dfrac{5}{6} \\ 2x - y = \dfrac{5}{6} \end{cases}$

21. Divide $x^2 + 7x + 12$ by $x + 3$ using long division.

22. Divide: $\dfrac{5x^2y - 6xy + 2}{6xy}$

Factor out the GCF (greatest common factor).

23. **a.** $6t + 18$
   b. $y^5 - y^7$

24. **a.** $5y - 20$
   b. $z^{10} - z^3$

Factor completely.

25. $x^2 + 4x - 12$

26. $x^2 - 10x + 21$

27. $10x^2 - 13xy - 3y^2$

28. $12a^2 + 5ab - 2b^2$

29. $x^3 + 8$

30. $y^3 - 27$

Solve.

31. $x^2 - 9x - 22 = 0$

32. $y^2 - 5y = -6$

Simplify.

33. **a.** $\dfrac{2x^2}{10x^3 - 2x^2}$

   b. $\dfrac{9x^2 + 13x + 4}{8x^2 + x - 7}$

34. **a.** $\dfrac{33x^4y^2}{3xy}$

   b. $\dfrac{9y}{90y^2 + 9y}$

Perform indicated operations.

35. $\dfrac{3x + 3}{5x - 5x^2} \cdot \dfrac{2x^2 + x - 3}{4x^2 - 9}$

36. $\dfrac{2x}{x - 6} - \dfrac{x + 6}{x - 6}$

37. $\dfrac{3x^2 + 2x}{x - 1} - \dfrac{10x - 5}{x - 1}$

38. $\dfrac{9}{y^2} - 4y$

Solve.

39. $3 - \dfrac{6}{x} = x + 8$

40. $\dfrac{x}{2} + \dfrac{x}{5} = \dfrac{x - 7}{20}$

Find an equation of the line through the given points. Write the equation using function notation.

41. $(4, 0)$ and $(-4, -5)$

42. $(-1, 3)$ and $(-2, 7)$

9.1 Compound Inequalities

9.2 Absolute Value Equations

9.3 Absolute Value Inequalities

Integrated Review—Solving Compound Inequalities and Absolute Value Equations and Inequalities

9.4 Graphing Linear Inequalities in Two Variables and Systems of Linear Inequalities

Today, it seems that most people in the world want to stay connected most of the time. In fact, 86% of U.S. citizens own cell phones. Also, computers with Internet access are just as important in our lives. Thus, the merging of these two into Wi-Fi-enabled cell phones might be the next big technological explosion. In Section 9.3, Exercises 83 and 84, you will find the projected increase in the number of Wi-Fi-enabled cell phones in the United States as well as the percent increase. (*Source:* Techcrunchies.com)

Mathematics is a tool for solving problems in such diverse fields as transportation, engineering, economics, medicine, business, and biology. We solve problems using mathematics by modeling real-world phenomena with mathematical equations or inequalities. Our ability to solve problems using mathematics, then, depends in part on our ability to solve different types of equations and inequalities. This chapter includes solving absolute value equations and inequalities and other types of inequalities.

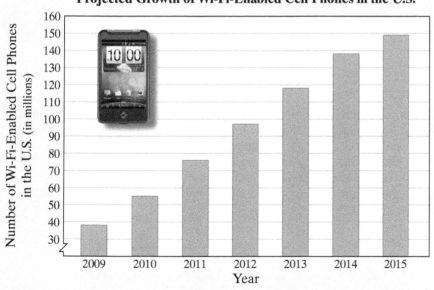

Projected Growth of Wi-Fi-Enabled Cell Phones in the U.S.

9.1 Compound Inequalities

OBJECTIVES

1 Find the Intersection of Two Sets.

2 Solve Compound Inequalities Containing **and**.

3 Find the Union of Two Sets.

4 Solve Compound Inequalities Containing **or**.

Two inequalities joined by the words **and** or **or** are called **compound inequalities.**

Compound Inequalities

$$x + 3 < 8 \quad and \quad x > 2$$

$$\frac{2x}{3} \geq 5 \quad or \quad -x + 10 < 7$$

OBJECTIVE
1 **Finding the Intersection of Two Sets**

The solution set of a compound inequality formed by the word **and** is the **intersection** of the solution sets of the two inequalities. We use the symbol ∩ to represent "intersection."

> **Intersection of Two Sets**
>
> The intersection of two sets, A and B, is the set of all elements common to both sets. A intersect B is denoted by $A \cap B$.
>
> $A \cap B$
>
> $A \quad B$

EXAMPLE 1 If $A = \{x \mid x$ is an even number greater than 0 and less than 10$\}$ and $B = \{3, 4, 5, 6\}$, find $A \cap B$.

Solution Let's list the elements in set A.

$$A = \{2, 4, 6, 8\}$$

The numbers 4 and 6 are in sets A and B. The intersection is $\{4, 6\}$. ☐

PRACTICE
1 If $A = \{x \mid x$ is an odd number greater than 0 and less than 10$\}$ and $B = \{1, 2, 3, 4\}$, find $A \cap B$.

OBJECTIVE
2 **Solving Compound Inequalities Containing "and"**

A value is a solution of a compound inequality formed by the word **and** if it is a solution of *both* inequalities. For example, the solution set of the compound inequality $x \leq 5$ and $x \geq 3$ contains all values of x that make the inequality $x \leq 5$ a true statement **and** the inequality $x \geq 3$ a true statement. The first graph shown below is the graph of $x \leq 5$, the second graph is the graph of $x \geq 3$, and the third graph shows the intersection of the two graphs. The third graph is the graph of $x \leq 5$ **and** $x \geq 3$.

$\{x \mid x \leq 5\}$ −1 0 1 2 3 4 5 6 $(-\infty, 5]$

$\{x \mid x \geq 3\}$ −1 0 1 2 3 4 5 6 $[3, \infty)$

$\{x \mid x \leq 5 \text{ and } x \geq 3\}$ also $\{x \mid 3 \leq x \leq 5\}$ (see below)   −1 0 1 2 3 4 5 6 $[3, 5]$

Since $x \geq 3$ is the same as $3 \leq x$, the compound inequality $3 \leq x$ and $x \leq 5$ can be written in a more compact form as $3 \leq x \leq 5$. The solution set $\{x \mid 3 \leq x \leq 5\}$ includes all numbers that are greater than or equal to 3 and at the same time less than or equal to 5.

In interval notation, the set $\{x \mid x \leq 5 \text{ and } x \geq 3\}$ or the set $\{x \mid 3 \leq x \leq 5\}$ is written as $[3, 5]$.

> ▶ Helpful Hint
>
> Don't forget that some compound inequalities containing "and" can be written in a more compact form.
>
> | Compound Inequality | Compact Form | Interval Notation |
> |:---:|:---:|:---:|
> | $2 \leq x$ and $x \leq 6$ | $2 \leq x \leq 6$ | $[2, 6]$ |
>
> Graph:

EXAMPLE 2   Solve: $x - 7 < 2$ and $2x + 1 < 9$

Solution   First we solve each inequality separately.

$$x - 7 < 2 \quad and \quad 2x + 1 < 9$$
$$x < 9 \quad and \quad 2x < 8$$
$$x < 9 \quad and \quad x < 4$$

Now we can graph the two intervals on two number lines and find their intersection. Their intersection is shown on the third number line.

$\{x \mid x < 9\}$ $\qquad\qquad\qquad\qquad\qquad\qquad\qquad$ $(-\infty, 9)$

$\{x \mid x < 4\}$ $\qquad\qquad\qquad\qquad\qquad\qquad\qquad$ $(-\infty, 4)$

$\{x \mid x < 9 \text{ and } x < 4\} = \{x \mid x < 4\}$ $\qquad\qquad$ $(-\infty, 4)$

The solution set is $(-\infty, 4)$.

PRACTICE
2   Solve: $x + 3 < 8$ and $2x - 1 < 3$. Write the solution set in interval notation.

EXAMPLE 3   Solve: $2x \geq 0$ and $4x - 1 \leq -9$.

Solution   First we solve each inequality separately.

$$2x \geq 0 \quad and \quad 4x - 1 \leq -9$$
$$x \geq 0 \quad and \quad 4x \leq -8$$
$$x \geq 0 \quad and \quad x \leq -2$$

Now we can graph the two intervals and find their intersection.

$\{x \mid x \geq 0\}$ $\qquad\qquad\qquad\qquad\qquad\qquad\qquad$ $[0, \infty)$

$\{x \mid x \leq -2\}$ $\qquad\qquad\qquad\qquad\qquad\qquad\qquad$ $(-\infty, -2]$

$\{x \mid x \geq 0 \text{ and } x \leq -2\} = \varnothing$ $\qquad\qquad\qquad$ $\varnothing$

There is no number that is greater than or equal to 0 *and* less than or equal to -2. The solution set is $\varnothing$.

PRACTICE
3   Solve: $4x \leq 0$ and $3x + 2 > 8$. Write the solution set in interval notation.

> ▶ Helpful Hint
>
> Example 3 shows that some compound inequalities have no solution. Also, some have all real numbers as solutions.

To solve a compound inequality written in a compact form, such as $2 < 4 - x < 7$, we get x alone in the "middle part." Since a compound inequality is really two inequalities in one statement, we must perform the same operations on all three parts of the inequality. For example:

$$2 < 4 - x < 7 \quad \text{means} \quad 2 < 4 - x \quad and \quad 4 - x < 7.$$

EXAMPLE 4 Solve: $2 < 4 - x < 7$

Solution To get x alone, we first subtract 4 from all three parts.

$$2 < 4 - x < 7$$

$$2 - 4 < 4 - x - 4 < 7 - 4 \quad \text{Subtract 4 from all three parts.}$$

$$-2 < -x < 3 \quad \text{Simplify.}$$

$$\frac{-2}{-1} > \frac{-x}{-1} > \frac{3}{-1} \quad \text{Divide all three parts by } -1 \text{ and reverse the inequality symbols.}$$

$$2 > x > -3$$

> **Helpful Hint**
> Don't forget to reverse both inequality symbols.

This is equivalent to $-3 < x < 2$.

The solution set in interval notation is $(-3, 2)$, and its graph is shown.

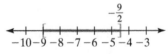

PRACTICE
4 Solve: $3 < 5 - x < 9$. Write the solution set in interval notation.

EXAMPLE 5 Solve: $-1 \le \dfrac{2x}{3} + 5 \le 2$.

Solution First, clear the inequality of fractions by multiplying all three parts by the LCD 3.

$$-1 \le \frac{2x}{3} + 5 \le 2$$

$$3(-1) \le 3\left(\frac{2x}{3} + 5\right) \le 3(2) \quad \text{Multiply all three parts by the LCD 3.}$$

$$-3 \le 2x + 15 \le 6 \quad \text{Use the distributive property and multiply.}$$

$$-3 - 15 \le 2x + 15 - 15 \le 6 - 15 \quad \text{Subtract 15 from all three parts.}$$

$$-18 \le 2x \le -9 \quad \text{Simplify.}$$

$$\frac{-18}{2} \le \frac{2x}{2} \le \frac{-9}{2} \quad \text{Divide all three parts by 2.}$$

$$-9 \le x \le -\frac{9}{2} \quad \text{Simplify.}$$

The graph of the solution is shown.

The solution set in interval notation is $\left[-9, -\dfrac{9}{2}\right]$.

PRACTICE
5 Solve: $-4 \le \dfrac{x}{2} - 1 \le 3$. Write the solution set in interval notation.

OBJECTIVE

3 Finding the Union of Two Sets

The solution set of a compound inequality formed by the word **or** is the **union** of the solution sets of the two inequalities. We use the symbol ∪ to denote "union."

> **Helpful Hint**
> The word *either* in this definition means "one or the other or both."

Union of Two Sets

The **union** of two sets, A and B, is the set of elements that belong to *either* of the sets. A union B is denoted by $A \cup B$.

EXAMPLE 6 If $A = \{x \mid x \text{ is an even number greater than 0 and less than 10}\}$ and $B = \{3, 4, 5, 6\}$, find $A \cup B$.

Solution Recall from Example 1 that $A = \{2, 4, 6, 8\}$. The numbers that are in either set or both sets are $\{2, 3, 4, 5, 6, 8\}$. This set is the union. □

PRACTICE

6 If $A = \{x \mid x \text{ is an odd number greater than 0 and less than 10}\}$ and $B = \{2, 3, 4, 5, 6\}$, find $A \cup B$.

OBJECTIVE

4 Solving Compound Inequalities Containing "or"

A value is a solution of a compound inequality formed by the word **or** if it is a solution of **either** inequality. For example, the solution set of the compound inequality $x \leq 1$ **or** $x \geq 3$ contains all numbers that make the inequality $x \leq 1$ a true statement **or** the inequality $x \geq 3$ a true statement.

$\{x \mid x \leq 1\}$ $(-\infty, 1]$

$\{x \mid x \geq 3\}$ $[3, \infty)$

$\{x \mid x \leq 1 \text{ or } x \geq 3\}$ $(-\infty, 1] \cup [3, \infty)$

In interval notation, the set $\{x \mid x \leq 1 \text{ or } x \geq 3\}$ is written as $(-\infty, 1] \cup [3, \infty)$.

EXAMPLE 7 Solve: $5x - 3 \leq 10 \text{ or } x + 1 \geq 5$.

Solution First we solve each inequality separately.

$$5x - 3 \leq 10 \quad or \quad x + 1 \geq 5$$
$$5x \leq 13 \quad or \quad x \geq 4$$
$$x \leq \frac{13}{5} \quad or \quad x \geq 4$$

Now we can graph each interval and find their union.

$\left\{x \mid x \leq \dfrac{13}{5}\right\}$ $\left(-\infty, \dfrac{13}{5}\right]$

$\{x \mid x \geq 4\}$ $[4, \infty)$

$\left\{x \mid x \leq \dfrac{13}{5} \text{ or } x \geq 4\right\}$ $\left(-\infty, \dfrac{13}{5}\right] \cup [4, \infty)$

(Continued on next page)

The solution set is $\left(-\infty, \dfrac{13}{5}\right] \cup [4, \infty)$.

PRACTICE
7   Solve: $8x + 5 \leq 8$ *or* $x - 1 \geq 2$. Write the solution set in interval notation.

EXAMPLE 8   Solve: $-2x - 5 < -3$ *or* $6x < 0$.

Solution   First we solve each inequality separately.

$$-2x - 5 < -3 \quad or \quad 6x < 0$$
$$-2x < 2 \quad or \quad x < 0$$
$$x > -1 \quad or \quad x < 0$$

Now we can graph each interval and find their union.

$\{x | x > -1\}$ $(-1, \infty)$

$\{x | x < 0\}$ $(-\infty, 0)$

$\{x | x > -1$ *or* $x < 0\}$ $(-\infty, \infty)$
$=$ all real numbers

The solution set is $(-\infty, \infty)$.

PRACTICE
8   Solve: $-3x - 2 > -8$ *or* $5x > 0$. Write the solution set in interval notation.

✓CONCEPT CHECK

Which of the following is *not* a correct way to represent the set of all numbers between -3 and 5?

a. $\{x \mid -3 < x < 5\}$ **b.** $-3 < x$ *or* $x < 5$
c. $(-3, 5)$ **d.** $x > -3$ *and* $x < 5$

Answer to Concept Check:
b is not correct

Vocabulary, Readiness & Video Check

Use the choices below to fill in each blank.

or   ∪   ∅
and   ∩   compound

1. Two inequalities joined by the words "and" or "or" are called _____ inequalities.
2. The word _____ means intersection.
3. The word _____ means union.
4. The symbol _____ represents intersection.
5. The symbol _____ represents union.
6. The symbol _____ is the empty set.

Martin-Gay Interactive Videos

See Video 9.1

Watch the section lecture video and answer the following questions.

**OBJECTIVE
1**
7. Based on ⊞ Example 1 and the lecture before, complete the following statement. For an element to be in the intersection of sets A and B, the element must be in set A _____ in set B.

**OBJECTIVE
2**
8. In ⊞ Example 2, how can using three number lines help us find the solution to this "and" compound inequality?

**OBJECTIVE
3**
9. Based on ⊞ Example 4 and the lecture before, complete the following statement. For an element to be in the union of sets A and B, the element must be in set A _____ in set B.

**OBJECTIVE
4**
10. In ⊞ Example 5, how can using three number lines help us find the solution to this "or" compound inequality?

9.1 Exercise Set   MyMathLab®

MIXED PRACTICE

If $A = \{x \mid x$ is an even integer$\}$, $B = \{x \mid x$ is an odd integer$\}$, $C = \{2, 3, 4, 5\}$, and $D = \{4, 5, 6, 7\}$, list the elements of each set. See Examples 1 and 6.

1. $C \cup D$ **2.** $C \cap D$
3. $A \cap D$ **4.** $A \cup D$
5. $A \cup B$ **6.** $A \cap B$
7. $B \cap D$ **8.** $B \cup D$
9. $B \cup C$ **10.** $B \cap C$
11. $A \cap C$ **12.** $A \cup C$

Solve each compound inequality. Graph the solution set and write it in interval notation. See Examples 2 and 3.

13. $x < 1$ and $x > -3$ **14.** $x \leq 0$ and $x \geq -2$
15. $x \leq -3$ and $x \geq -2$ **16.** $x < 2$ and $x > 4$
17. $x < -1$ and $x < 1$
18. $x \geq -4$ and $x > 1$

Solve each compound inequality. Write solutions in interval notation. See Examples 2 and 3.

19. $x + 1 \geq 7$ and $3x - 1 \geq 5$
20. $x + 2 \geq 3$ and $5x - 1 \geq 9$
21. $4x + 2 \leq -10$ and $2x \leq 0$
22. $2x + 4 > 0$ and $4x > 0$
23. $-2x < -8$ and $x - 5 < 5$
24. $-7x \leq -21$ and $x - 20 \leq -15$

Solve each compound inequality. See Examples 4 and 5.

25. $5 < x - 6 < 11$ **26.** $-2 \leq x + 3 \leq 0$
27. $-2 \leq 3x - 5 \leq 7$ **28.** $1 < 4 + 2x < 7$
29. $1 \leq \frac{2}{3}x + 3 \leq 4$ **30.** $-2 < \frac{1}{2}x - 5 < 1$
31. $-5 \leq \frac{-3x + 1}{4} \leq 2$ **32.** $-4 \leq \frac{-2x + 5}{3} \leq 1$

Solve each compound inequality. Graph the solution set and write it in interval notation. See Examples 7 and 8.

33. $x < 4$ or $x < 5$
34. $x \geq -2$ or $x \leq 2$
35. $x \leq -4$ or $x \geq 1$
36. $x < 0$ or $x < 1$
37. $x > 0$ or $x < 3$
38. $x \geq -3$ or $x \leq -4$

Solve each compound inequality. Write solutions in interval notation. See Examples 7 and 8.

39. $-2x \leq -4$ or $5x - 20 \geq 5$
40. $-5x \leq 10$ or $3x - 5 \geq 1$
41. $x + 4 < 0$ or $6x > -12$
42. $x + 9 < 0$ or $4x > -12$
43. $3(x - 1) < 12$ or $x + 7 > 10$
44. $5(x - 1) \geq -5$ or $5 + x \leq 11$

MIXED PRACTICE

Solve each compound inequality. Write solutions in interval notation. See Examples 1 through 8.

45. $x < \frac{2}{3}$ and $x > -\frac{1}{2}$
46. $x < \frac{5}{7}$ and $x < 1$
47. $x < \frac{2}{3}$ or $x > -\frac{1}{2}$
48. $x < \frac{5}{7}$ or $x < 1$
49. $0 \leq 2x - 3 \leq 9$
50. $3 < 5x + 1 < 11$

51. $\frac{1}{2} < x - \frac{3}{4} < 2$

52. $\frac{2}{3} < x + \frac{1}{2} < 4$

53. $x + 3 \geq 3 \ and \ x + 3 \leq 2$

54. $2x - 1 \geq 3 \ and \ -x > 2$

55. $3x \geq 5 \ or \ -\frac{5}{8}x - 6 > 1$

56. $\frac{3}{8}x + 1 \leq 0 \ or \ -2x < -4$

57. $0 < \frac{5 - 2x}{3} < 5$

58. $-2 < \frac{-2x - 1}{3} < 2$

59. $-6 < 3(x - 2) \leq 8$

60. $-5 < 2(x + 4) < 8$

61. $-x + 5 > 6 \ and \ 1 + 2x \leq -5$

62. $5x \leq 0 \ and \ -x + 5 < 8$

▶ **63.** $3x + 2 \leq 5 \ or \ 7x > 29$

64. $-x < 7 \ or \ 3x + 1 < -20$

65. $5 - x > 7 \ and \ 2x + 3 \geq 13$

66. $-2x < -6 \ or \ 1 - x > -2$

67. $-\frac{1}{2} \leq \frac{4x - 1}{6} < \frac{5}{6}$

68. $-\frac{1}{2} \leq \frac{3x - 1}{10} < \frac{1}{2}$

69. $\frac{1}{15} < \frac{8 - 3x}{15} < \frac{4}{5}$

70. $-\frac{1}{4} < \frac{6 - x}{12} < -\frac{1}{6}$

71. $0.3 < 0.2x - 0.9 < 1.5$

72. $-0.7 \leq 0.4x + 0.8 < 0.5$

REVIEW AND PREVIEW

Evaluate the following. See Sections 1.5 and 1.6.

73. $|-7| - |19|$

74. $|-7 - 19|$

75. $-(-6) - |-10|$

76. $|-4| - (-4) + |-20|$

Find by inspection all values for x that make each equation true.

77. $|x| = 7$

78. $|x| = 5$

79. $|x| = 0$

80. $|x| = -2$

CONCEPT EXTENSIONS

Use the graph to answer Exercises 81 and 82.

Source: U.S. Census Bureau

81. For which years were the number of single-family housing starts greater than 1500 and the number of single-family home completions greater than 1500?

82. For which years were the number of single-family housing starts less than 1000 or the number of single-family housing completions greater than 1500?

83. In your own words, describe how to find the union of two sets.

84. In your own words, describe how to find the intersection of two sets.

Solve each compound inequality for x. See the example below. To solve $x - 6 < 3x < 2x + 5$, notice that this inequality contains a variable not only in the middle but also on the left and the right. When this occurs, we solve by rewriting the inequality using the word **and**.

$$x - 6 < 3x \quad and \quad 3x < 2x + 5$$
$$-6 < 2x \quad and \quad x < 5$$
$$-3 < x$$
$$x > -3 \quad and \quad x < 5$$

$x > -3$

$x < 5$

$$-3 < x < 5 \ or \ (-3, 5)$$

85. $2x - 3 < 3x + 1 < 4x - 5$

86. $x + 3 < 2x + 1 < 4x + 6$

87. $-3(x - 2) \leq 3 - 2x \leq 10 - 3x$

88. $7x - 1 \leq 7 + 5x \leq 3(1 + 2x)$

89. $5x - 8 < 2(2 + x) < -2(1 + 2x)$

90. $1 + 2x < 3(2 + x) < 1 + 4x$

The formula for converting Fahrenheit temperatures to Celsius temperatures is $C = \dfrac{5}{9}(F - 32)$. Use this formula for Exercises 91 and 92.

91. During a recent year, the temperatures in Chicago ranged from $-29°C$ to $35°C$. Use a compound inequality to convert these temperatures to Fahrenheit temperatures.

92. In Oslo, the average temperature ranges from $-10°$ to $18°$ Celsius. Use a compound inequality to convert these temperatures to the Fahrenheit scale.

Solve.

93. Christian D'Angelo has scores of 68, 65, 75, and 78 on his algebra tests. Use a compound inequality to find the scores he can make on his final exam to receive a C in the course. The final exam counts as two tests, and a C is received if the final course average is from 70 to 79.

94. Wendy Wood has scores of 80, 90, 82, and 75 on her chemistry tests. Use a compound inequality to find the range of scores she can make on her final exam to receive a B in the course. The final exam counts as two tests, and a B is received if the final course average is from 80 to 89.

9.2   Absolute Value Equations

OBJECTIVE

1 Solve Absolute Value Equations.

OBJECTIVE

1   Solving Absolute Value Equations

In Chapter 1, we defined the absolute value of a number as its distance from 0 on a number line.

$|-2| = 2$ and $|3| = 3$

In this section, we concentrate on solving equations containing the absolute value of a variable or a variable expression. Examples of absolute value equations are

$$|x| = 3 \qquad -5 = |2y + 7| \qquad |z - 6.7| = |3z + 1.2|$$

Since distance and absolute value are so closely related, absolute value equations and inequalities (see Section 9.3) are extremely useful in solving distance-type problems such as calculating the possible error in a measurement.

For the absolute value equation $|x| = 3$, its solution set will contain all numbers whose distance from 0 is 3 units. Two numbers are 3 units away from 0 on the number line: 3 and -3.

Thus, the solution set of the equation $|x| = 3$ is $\{3, -3\}$. This suggests the following:

> **Solving Equations of the Form $|X| = a$**
>
> If a is a positive number, then $|X| = a$ is equivalent to $X = a$ or $X = -a$.

EXAMPLE 1   Solve: $|p| = 2$.

Solution   Since 2 is positive, $|p| = 2$ is equivalent to $p = 2$ or $p = -2$.

To check, let $p = 2$ and then $p = -2$ in the original equation.

$$\begin{array}{ll} |p| = 2 & \text{Original equation} \\ |2| = 2 & \text{Let } p = 2. \\ \;\;2 = 2 & \text{True} \end{array} \qquad \begin{array}{ll} |p| = 2 & \text{Original equation} \\ |-2| = 2 & \text{Let } p = -2. \\ \;\;2 = 2 & \text{True} \end{array}$$

The solutions are 2 and -2 or the solution set is $\{2, -2\}$.

PRACTICE

1   Solve: $|q| = 3$.

If the expression inside the absolute value bars is more complicated than a single variable, we can still apply the absolute value property.

> ▶ Helpful Hint
> For the equation $|X| = a$ in the box on the previous page, X can be a single variable or a variable expression.

EXAMPLE 2 Solve: $|5w + 3| = 7$.

Solution Here the expression inside the absolute value bars is $5w + 3$. If we think of the expression $5w + 3$ as X in the absolute value property, we see that $|X| = 7$ is equivalent to

$$X = 7 \quad \text{or} \quad X = -7$$

Then substitute $5w + 3$ for X, and we have

$$5w + 3 = 7 \quad \text{or} \quad 5w + 3 = -7$$

Solve these two equations for w.

$$
\begin{aligned}
5w + 3 &= 7 && \text{or} & 5w + 3 &= -7 \\
5w &= 4 && \text{or} & 5w &= -10 \\
w &= \frac{4}{5} && \text{or} & w &= -2
\end{aligned}
$$

Check: To check, let $w = -2$ and then $w = \frac{4}{5}$ in the original equation.

Let $w = -2$

$$
\begin{aligned}
|5(-2) + 3| &= 7 \\
|-10 + 3| &= 7 \\
|-7| &= 7 \\
7 &= 7 \quad \text{True}
\end{aligned}
$$

Let $w = \frac{4}{5}$

$$
\begin{aligned}
\left|5\left(\frac{4}{5}\right) + 3\right| &= 7 \\
|4 + 3| &= 7 \\
|7| &= 7 \\
7 &= 7 \quad \text{True}
\end{aligned}
$$

Both solutions check, and the solutions are -2 and $\frac{4}{5}$ or the solution set is $\left\{-2, \frac{4}{5}\right\}$. ☐

PRACTICE
2 Solve: $|2x - 3| = 5$.

EXAMPLE 3 Solve: $\left|\dfrac{x}{2} - 1\right| = 11$.

Solution $\left|\dfrac{x}{2} - 1\right| = 11$ is equivalent to

$$\frac{x}{2} - 1 = 11 \quad \text{or} \quad \frac{x}{2} - 1 = -11$$

$$2\left(\frac{x}{2} - 1\right) = 2(11) \quad \text{or} \quad 2\left(\frac{x}{2} - 1\right) = 2(-11) \quad \text{Clear fractions.}$$

$$x - 2 = 22 \quad \text{or} \quad x - 2 = -22 \quad \text{Apply the distributive property.}$$

$$x = 24 \quad \text{or} \quad x = -20$$

The solutions are 24 and -20. ☐

PRACTICE
3 Solve: $\left|\dfrac{x}{5} + 1\right| = 15$.

To apply the absolute value property, first make sure that the absolute value expression is isolated.

> ▶ Helpful Hint
>
> If the equation has a single absolute value expression containing variables, isolate the absolute value expression first.

EXAMPLE 4   Solve: $|2x| + 5 = 7$.

Solution   We want the absolute value expression alone on one side of the equation, so begin by subtracting 5 from both sides. Then apply the absolute value property.

$$|2x| + 5 = 7$$
$$|2x| = 2 \qquad \text{Subtract 5 from both sides.}$$
$$2x = 2 \quad \text{or} \quad 2x = -2$$
$$x = 1 \quad \text{or} \quad x = -1$$

The solutions are -1 and 1.

PRACTICE
4   Solve: $|3x| + 8 = 14$.

EXAMPLE 5   Solve: $|y| = 0$.

Solution   We are looking for all numbers whose distance from 0 is zero units. The only number is 0. The solution is 0.

PRACTICE
5   Solve: $|z| = 0$.

The next two examples illustrate a special case for absolute value equations. This special case occurs when an isolated absolute value is equal to a negative number.

EXAMPLE 6   Solve: $2|x| + 25 = 23$.

Solution   First, isolate the absolute value.

$$2|x| + 25 = 23$$
$$2|x| = -2 \quad \text{Subtract 25 from both sides.}$$
$$|x| = -1 \quad \text{Divide both sides by 2.}$$

The absolute value of a number is never negative, so this equation has no solution. The solution set is $\{\ \}$ or $\varnothing$.

PRACTICE
6   Solve: $3|z| + 9 = 7$.

EXAMPLE 7   Solve: $\left| \dfrac{3x + 1}{2} \right| = -2$.

Solution   Again, the absolute value of any expression is never negative, so no solution exists. The solution set is $\{\ \}$ or $\varnothing$.

PRACTICE
7   Solve: $\left| \dfrac{5x + 3}{4} \right| = -8$.

Given two absolute value expressions, we might ask, when are the absolute values of two expressions equal? To see the answer, notice that

$$|2| = |2|, \quad |-2| = |-2|, \quad |-2| = |2|, \quad \text{and} \quad |2| = |-2|$$

same   same   opposites   opposites

Two absolute value expressions are equal when the expressions inside the absolute value bars are equal to or are opposites of each other.

EXAMPLE 8   Solve: $|3x + 2| = |5x - 8|$.

Solution   This equation is true if the expressions inside the absolute value bars are equal to or are opposites of each other.

$$3x + 2 = 5x - 8 \quad \text{or} \quad 3x + 2 = -(5x - 8)$$

Next, solve each equation.

$$
\begin{array}{rcl}
3x + 2 = 5x - 8 & \text{or} & 3x + 2 = -5x + 8 \\
-2x + 2 = -8 & \text{or} & 8x + 2 = 8 \\
-2x = -10 & \text{or} & 8x = 6 \\
x = 5 & \text{or} & x = \dfrac{3}{4}
\end{array}
$$

The solutions are $\dfrac{3}{4}$ and 5.

PRACTICE
8   Solve: $|2x + 4| = |3x - 1|$.

EXAMPLE 9   Solve: $|x - 3| = |5 - x|$.

Solution
$$
\begin{array}{rcl}
x - 3 = 5 - x & \text{or} & x - 3 = -(5 - x) \\
2x - 3 = 5 & \text{or} & x - 3 = -5 + x \\
2x = 8 & \text{or} & x - 3 - x = -5 + x - x \\
x = 4 & \text{or} & -3 = -5 \qquad \text{False}
\end{array}
$$

Recall from Section 2.3 that when an equation simplifies to a false statement, the equation has no solution. Thus, the only solution for the original absolute value equation is 4.

PRACTICE
9   Solve: $|x - 2| = |8 - x|$.

✓CONCEPT CHECK
True or false? Absolute value equations always have two solutions. Explain your answer.

The following box summarizes the methods shown for solving absolute value equations.

Absolute Value Equations	
$|X| = a$	If a is positive, then solve $X = a$ or $X = -a$.
	If a is 0, solve $X = 0$.
	If a is negative, the equation $|X| = a$ has no solution.
$|X| = |Y|$	Solve $X = Y$ or $X = -Y$.

Answer to Concept Check:
false; answers may vary

Vocabulary, Readiness & Video Check

Match each absolute value equation with an equivalent statement.

1. $|x - 2| = 5$
2. $|x - 2| = 0$
3. $|x - 2| = |x + 3|$
4. $|x + 3| = 5$
5. $|x + 3| = -5$

A. $x - 2 = 0$
B. $x - 2 = x + 3$ or $x - 2 = -(x + 3)$
C. $x - 2 = 5$ or $x - 2 = -5$
D. $\varnothing$
E. $x + 3 = 5$ or $x + 3 = -5$

Martin-Gay Interactive Videos

See Video 9.2

Watch the section lecture videos and answer the following question.

OBJECTIVE
1

6. As explained in Example 3, why is *a* positive in the rule "$|X| = a$ is equivalent to $X = a$ or $X = -a$"?

9.2 Exercise Set MyMathLab®

Solve each absolute value equation. See Examples 1 through 7.

1. $|x| = 7$
2. $|y| = 15$
3. $|3x| = 12.6$
4. $|6n| = 12.6$
5. $|2x - 5| = 9$
6. $|6 + 2n| = 4$
7. $\left|\dfrac{x}{2} - 3\right| = 1$
8. $\left|\dfrac{n}{3} + 2\right| = 4$
9. $|z| + 4 = 9$
10. $|x| + 1 = 3$
11. $|3x| + 5 = 14$
12. $|2x| - 6 = 4$
13. $|2x| = 0$
14. $|7z| = 0$
15. $|4n + 1| + 10 = 4$
16. $|3z - 2| + 8 = 1$
17. $|5x - 1| = 0$
18. $|3y + 2| = 0$

Solve. See Examples 8 and 9.

19. $|5x - 7| = |3x + 11|$
20. $|9y + 1| = |6y + 4|$
21. $|z + 8| = |z - 3|$
22. $|2x - 5| = |2x + 5|$

MIXED PRACTICE

Solve each absolute value equation. See Examples 1 through 9.

23. $|x| = 4$
24. $|x| = 1$
25. $|y| = 0$
26. $|y| = 8$
27. $|z| = -2$
28. $|y| = -9$
29. $|7 - 3x| = 7$
30. $|4m + 5| = 5$
31. $|6x| - 1 = 11$
32. $|7z| + 1 = 22$
33. $|4p| = -8$
34. $|5m| = -10$

35. $|x - 3| + 3 = 7$
36. $|x + 4| - 4 = 1$
37. $\left|\dfrac{z}{4} + 5\right| = -7$
38. $\left|\dfrac{c}{5} - 1\right| = -2$
39. $|9v - 3| = -8$
40. $|1 - 3b| = -7$
41. $|8n + 1| = 0$
42. $|5x - 2| = 0$
43. $|1 + 6c| - 7 = -3$
44. $|2 + 3m| - 9 = -7$
45. $|5x + 1| = 11$
46. $|8 - 6c| = 1$
47. $|4x - 2| = |-10|$
48. $|3x + 5| = |-4|$
49. $|5x + 1| = |4x - 7|$
50. $|3 + 6n| = |4n + 11|$
51. $|6 + 2x| = -|-7|$
52. $|4 - 5y| = -|-3|$
53. $|2x - 6| = |10 - 2x|$
54. $|4n + 5| = |4n + 3|$
55. $\left|\dfrac{2x - 5}{3}\right| = 7$
56. $\left|\dfrac{1 + 3n}{4}\right| = 4$
57. $2 + |5n| = 17$
58. $8 + |4m| = 24$
59. $\left|\dfrac{2x - 1}{3}\right| = |-5|$
60. $\left|\dfrac{5x + 2}{2}\right| = |-6|$
61. $|2y - 3| = |9 - 4y|$
62. $|5z - 1| = |7 - z|$
63. $\left|\dfrac{3n + 2}{8}\right| = |-1|$
64. $\left|\dfrac{2r - 6}{5}\right| = |-2|$
65. $|x + 4| = |7 - x|$
66. $|8 - y| = |y + 2|$
67. $\left|\dfrac{8c - 7}{3}\right| = -|-5|$
68. $\left|\dfrac{5d + 1}{6}\right| = -|-9|$

REVIEW AND PREVIEW

The circle graph shows the types of cheese produced in the United States in 2010. Use this graph to answer Exercises 69 through 72. See Section 2.6.

U.S. Cheese¹ Production by Variety, 2010

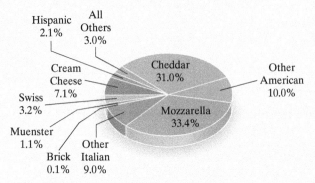

¹Excludes Cottage Cheese

Source: USDA, *Dairy Products Annual Survey*

69. In 2010, cheddar cheese made up what percent of U.S. cheese production?

70. Which cheese had the highest U.S. production in 2010?

71. A circle contains 360°. Find the number of degrees found in the 9% sector for Other Italian Cheese.

72. In 2010, the total production of cheese in the United States was 10,109,293,000 pounds. Find the amount of cream cheese produced during that year.

List five integer solutions of each inequality. See Sections 1.2 and 1.4.

73. $|x| \le 3$

74. $|x| \ge -2$

75. $|y| > -10$

76. $|y| < 0$

CONCEPT EXTENSIONS

Without going through a solution procedure, determine the solution of each absolute value equation or inequality.

77. $|x - 7| = -4$

78. $|x - 7| < -4$

79. Write an absolute value equation representing all numbers x whose distance from 0 is 5 units.

80. Write an absolute value equation representing all numbers x whose distance from 0 is 2 units.

81. Explain why some absolute value equations have two solutions.

82. Explain why some absolute value equations have one solution.

83. Write an absolute value equation representing all numbers x whose distance from 1 is 5 units.

84. Write an absolute value equation representing all numbers x whose distance from 7 is 2 units.

85. Describe how solving an absolute value equation such as $|2x - 1| = 3$ is similar to solving an absolute value equation such as $|2x - 1| = |x - 5|$.

86. Describe how solving an absolute value equation such as $|2x - 1| = 3$ is different from solving an absolute value equation such as $|2x - 1| = |x - 5|$.

Write each as an equivalent absolute value equation.

87. $x = 6$ or $x = -6$

88. $2x - 1 = 4$ or $2x - 1 = -4$

89. $x - 2 = 3x - 4$ or $x - 2 = -(3x - 4)$

90. For what value(s) of c will an absolute value equation of the form $|ax + b| = c$ have

a. one solution?

b. no solution?

c. two solutions?

9.3 | Absolute Value Inequalities

OBJECTIVES

1 Solve Absolute Value Inequalities of the Form $|X| < a$.

2 Solve Absolute Value Inequalities of the Form $|X| > a$.

OBJECTIVE

1 Solving Absolute Value Inequalities of the Form $|X| < a$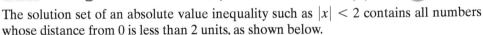

The solution set of an absolute value inequality such as $|x| < 2$ contains all numbers whose distance from 0 is less than 2 units, as shown below.

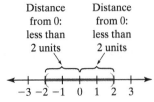

The solution set is $\{x \,|\, -2 < x < 2\}$, or $(-2, 2)$ in interval notation.

EXAMPLE 1 Solve: $|x| \le 3$ and graph the solution set.

Solution The solution set of this inequality contains all numbers whose distance from 0 is less than or equal to 3. Thus 3, -3, and all numbers between 3 and -3 are in the solution set.

The solution set is $[-3, 3]$.

   1   Solve: $|x| < 5$ and graph the solution set.

In general, we have the following.

> **Solving Absolute Value Inequalities of the Form $|X| < a$**
> If a is a positive number, then $|X| < a$ is equivalent to $-a < X < a$.

This property also holds true for the inequality symbol $\leq$.

EXAMPLE 2   Solve for m: $|m - 6| < 2$. Graph the solution set.

Solution Replace X with $m - 6$ and a with 2 in the preceding property, and we see that

$$|m - 6| < 2 \quad \text{is equivalent to} \quad -2 < m - 6 < 2$$

Solve this compound inequality for m by adding 6 to all three parts.

$$-2 < m - 6 < 2$$
$$-2 + 6 < m - 6 + 6 < 2 + 6 \quad \text{Add 6 to all three parts.}$$
$$4 < m < 8 \quad\quad\quad\quad\quad \text{Simplify.}$$

The solution set is $(4, 8)$, and its graph is shown.

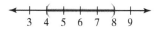

   2   Solve for b: $|b + 1| < 3$. Graph the solution set.

> ▶ **Helpful Hint**
> Before using an absolute value inequality property, isolate the absolute value expression on one side of the inequality.

EXAMPLE 3   Solve for x: $|5x + 1| + 1 \leq 10$. Graph the solution set.

Solution First, isolate the absolute value expression by subtracting 1 from both sides.

$$|5x + 1| + 1 \leq 10$$
$$|5x + 1| \leq 10 - 1 \quad \text{Subtract 1 from both sides.}$$
$$|5x + 1| \leq 9 \quad\quad\quad \text{Simplify.}$$

Since 9 is positive, we apply the absolute value property for $|X| \leq a$.

$$-9 \leq 5x + 1 \leq 9$$
$$-9 - 1 \leq 5x + 1 - 1 \leq 9 - 1 \quad \text{Subtract 1 from all three parts.}$$
$$-10 \leq 5x \leq 8 \quad\quad\quad\quad \text{Simplify.}$$
$$-2 \leq x \leq \frac{8}{5} \quad\quad\quad\quad \text{Divide all three parts by 5.}$$

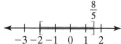

The solution set is $\left[-2, \dfrac{8}{5}\right]$, and the graph is shown above.

   3   Solve for x: $|3x - 2| + 5 \leq 9$. Graph the solution set.

EXAMPLE 4   Solve for x: $\left| 2x - \dfrac{1}{10} \right| < -13$.

Solution   The absolute value of a number is always nonnegative and can never be less than -13. Thus this absolute value inequality has no solution. The solution set is $\{\ \}$ or $\varnothing$.

PRACTICE
4   Solve for x: $\left| 3x + \dfrac{5}{8} \right| < -4$.

EXAMPLE 5   Solve for x: $\left| \dfrac{2(x+1)}{3} \right| \le 0$.

Solution   Recall that "$\le$" means "is less than or equal to." The absolute value of any expression will never be less than 0, but it may be equal to 0. Thus, to solve $\left| \dfrac{2(x+1)}{3} \right| \le 0$, we solve $\left| \dfrac{2(x+1)}{3} \right| = 0$

$$\dfrac{2(x+1)}{3} = 0$$

$$3\left[\dfrac{2(x+1)}{3} \right] = 3(0) \qquad \text{Clear the equation of fractions.}$$

$$2x + 2 = 0 \qquad \text{Apply the distributive property.}$$

$$2x = -2 \qquad \text{Subtract 2 from both sides.}$$

$$x = -1 \qquad \text{Divide both sides by 2.}$$

The solution set is $\{-1\}$.

PRACTICE
5   Solve for x: $\left| \dfrac{3(x-2)}{5} \right| \le 0$.

OBJECTIVE
2   Solving Absolute Value Inequalities of the Form $|X| > a$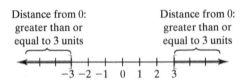

Let us now solve an absolute value inequality of the form $|X| > a$, such as $|x| \ge 3$. The solution set contains all numbers whose distance from 0 is 3 or more units. Thus the graph of the solution set contains 3 and all points to the right of 3 on the number line or -3 and all points to the left of -3 on the number line.

Distance from 0:   Distance from 0:
greater than or   greater than or
equal to 3 units   equal to 3 units

−3 −2 −1 0 1 2 3

This solution set is written as $\{x \mid x \le -3 \text{ or } x \ge 3\}$. In interval notation, the solution is $(-\infty, -3] \cup [3, \infty)$, since "or" means "union." In general, we have the following.

> **Solving Absolute Value Inequalities of the Form $|X| > a$**
>
> If a is a positive number, then $|X| > a$ is equivalent to $X < -a$ or $X > a$.

This property also holds true for the inequality symbol $\ge$.

EXAMPLE 6   Solve for y: $|y - 3| > 7$.

Solution   Since 7 is positive, we apply the property for $|X| > a$.

$$|y - 3| > 7 \text{ is equivalent to } y - 3 < -7 \text{ or } y - 3 > 7$$

Next, solve the compound inequality.

$$y - 3 < -7 \quad \text{or} \quad y - 3 > 7$$
$$y - 3 + 3 < -7 + 3 \quad \text{or} \quad y - 3 + 3 > 7 + 3 \quad \text{Add 3 to both sides.}$$
$$y < -4 \quad \text{or} \quad y > 10 \quad \text{Simplify.}$$

The solution set is $(-\infty, -4) \cup (10, \infty)$, and its graph is shown.

PRACTICE

6 Solve for y: $|y + 4| \geq 6$.

Example 7 illustrates another special case of absolute value inequalities when an isolated absolute value expression is less than, less than or equal to, greater than, or greater than or equal to a negative number or 0.

EXAMPLE 7 Solve: $|2x + 9| + 5 > 3$.

Solution First isolate the absolute value expression by subtracting 5 from both sides.

$$|2x + 9| + 5 > 3$$
$$|2x + 9| + 5 - 5 > 3 - 5 \quad \text{Subtract 5 from both sides.}$$
$$|2x + 9| > -2 \quad \text{Simplify.}$$

The absolute value of any number is always nonnegative and thus is always greater than -2. This inequality and the original inequality are true for all values of x. The solution set is $\{x | x \text{ is a real number}\}$ or $(-\infty, \infty)$, and its graph is shown.

PRACTICE

7 Solve: $|4x + 3| + 5 > 3$. Graph the solution set.

✓ **CONCEPT CHECK**

Without taking any solution steps, how do you know that the absolute value inequality $|3x - 2| > -9$ has a solution? What is its solution?

EXAMPLE 8 Solve: $\left|\dfrac{x}{3} - 1\right| - 7 \geq -5$.

Solution First, isolate the absolute value expression by adding 7 to both sides.

$$\left|\frac{x}{3} - 1\right| - 7 \geq -5$$
$$\left|\frac{x}{3} - 1\right| - 7 + 7 \geq -5 + 7 \quad \text{Add 7 to both sides.}$$
$$\left|\frac{x}{3} - 1\right| \geq 2 \quad \text{Simplify.}$$

Next, write the absolute value inequality as an equivalent compound inequality and solve.

$$\frac{x}{3} - 1 \leq -2 \qquad \text{or} \qquad \frac{x}{3} - 1 \geq 2$$
$$3\left(\frac{x}{3} - 1\right) \leq 3(-2) \qquad \text{or} \qquad 3\left(\frac{x}{3} - 1\right) \geq 3(2) \quad \text{Clear the inequalities of fractions.}$$
$$x - 3 \leq -6 \qquad \text{or} \qquad x - 3 \geq 6 \quad \text{Apply the distributive property.}$$
$$x \leq -3 \qquad \text{or} \qquad x \geq 9 \quad \text{Add 3 to both sides.}$$

Answer to Concept Check:
$(-\infty, \infty)$ since the absolute value is always nonnegative

(Continued on next page)

The solution set is $(-\infty, -3] \cup [9, \infty)$, and its graph is shown.

```
        -3                    9
  ←──+─┤─+─+─+─+─+─+─┤─+─+─→
    -6 -4 -2  0  2  4  6  8 10 12
```

PRACTICE
8 Solve: $\left|\dfrac{x}{2} - 3\right| - 5 > -2$. Graph the solution set.

The following box summarizes the types of absolute value equations and inequalities.

Solving Absolute Value Equations and Inequalities with $a > 0$

Algebraic Solution	**Solution Graph**

$|X| = a$ is equivalent to $X = a$ or $X = -a$.

$|X| < a$ is equivalent to $-a < X < a$.

$|X| > a$ is equivalent to $X < -a$ or $X > a$.

Vocabulary, Readiness & Video Check

Match each absolute value statement with an equivalent statement.

1. $|2x + 1| = 3$
2. $|2x + 1| \le 3$
3. $|2x + 1| < 3$
4. $|2x + 1| \ge 3$
5. $|2x + 1| > 3$

A. $2x + 1 > 3$ or $2x + 1 < -3$
B. $2x + 1 \ge 3$ or $2x + 1 \le -3$
C. $-3 < 2x + 1 < 3$
D. $2x + 1 = 3$ or $2x + 1 = -3$
E. $-3 \le 2x + 1 \le 3$

Martin-Gay Interactive Videos

Watch the section lecture video and answer the following questions.

OBJECTIVE 1
6. In Example 3, how can you reason that the inequality has no solution even if you don't know the rule?

OBJECTIVE 2
7. In Example 4, why is the union symbol used when the solution is written in interval notation?

See Video 9.3

9.3 Exercise Set

Solve each inequality. Then graph the solution set and write it in interval notation. See Examples 1 through 4.

1. $|x| \le 4$
2. $|x| < 6$
3. $|x - 3| < 2$
4. $|y - 7| \le 5$
5. $|x + 3| < 2$
6. $|x + 4| < 6$
7. $|2x + 7| \le 13$
8. $|5x - 3| \le 18$
9. $|x| + 7 \le 12$
10. $|x| + 6 \le 7$
11. $|3x - 1| < -5$
12. $|8x - 3| < -2$
13. $|x - 6| - 7 \le -1$
14. $|z + 2| - 7 < -3$

Solve each inequality. Graph the solution set and write it in interval notation. See Examples 6 through 8.

15. $|x| > 3$
16. $|y| \ge 4$
17. $|x + 10| \ge 14$
18. $|x - 9| \ge 2$
19. $|x| + 2 > 6$
20. $|x| - 1 > 3$
21. $|5x| > -4$
22. $|4x - 11| > -1$
23. $|6x - 8| + 3 > 7$
24. $|10 + 3x| + 1 > 2$

Solve each inequality. Graph the solution set and write it in interval notation. See Example 5.

25. $|x| \le 0$

26. $|x| \ge 0$

27. $|8x + 3| > 0$

28. $|5x - 6| < 0$

MIXED PRACTICE

Solve each inequality. Graph the solution set and write it in interval notation. See Examples 1 through 8.

29. $|x| \le 2$

30. $|z| < 8$

31. $|y| > 1$

32. $|x| \ge 10$

33. $|x - 3| < 8$

34. $|-3 + x| \le 10$

35. $|0.6x - 3| > 0.6$

36. $|1 + 0.3x| \ge 0.1$

37. $5 + |x| \le 2$

38. $8 + |x| < 1$

39. $|x| > -4$

40. $|x| \le -7$

41. $|2x - 7| \le 11$

42. $|5x + 2| < 8$

43. $|x + 5| + 2 \ge 8$

44. $|-1 + x| - 6 > 2$

45. $|x| > 0$

46. $|x| < 0$

47. $9 + |x| > 7$

48. $5 + |x| \ge 4$

49. $6 + |4x - 1| \le 9$

50. $-3 + |5x - 2| \le 4$

51. $\left|\dfrac{2}{3}x + 1\right| > 1$

52. $\left|\dfrac{3}{4}x - 1\right| \ge 2$

53. $|5x + 3| < -6$

54. $|4 + 9x| \ge -6$

55. $\left|\dfrac{8x - 3}{4}\right| \le 0$

56. $\left|\dfrac{5x + 6}{2}\right| \le 0$

57. $|1 + 3x| + 4 < 5$

58. $|7x - 3| - 1 \le 10$

59. $\left|\dfrac{x + 6}{3}\right| > 2$

60. $\left|\dfrac{7 + x}{2}\right| \ge 4$

61. $-15 + |2x - 7| \le -6$

62. $-9 + |3 + 4x| < -4$

63. $\left|2x + \dfrac{3}{4}\right| - 7 \le -2$

64. $\left|\dfrac{3}{5} + 4x\right| - 6 < -1$

MIXED PRACTICE

Solve each equation or inequality for x. (Sections 9.2, 9.3)

65. $|2x - 3| < 7$

66. $|2x - 3| > 7$

67. $|2x - 3| = 7$

68. $|5 - 6x| = 29$

69. $|x - 5| \ge 12$

70. $|x + 4| \ge 20$

71. $|9 + 4x| = 0$

72. $|9 + 4x| \ge 0$

73. $|2x + 1| + 4 < 7$

74. $8 + |5x - 3| \ge 11$

75. $|3x - 5| + 4 = 5$

76. $|5x - 3| + 2 = 4$

77. $|x + 11| = -1$

78. $|4x - 4| = -3$

79. $\left|\dfrac{2x - 1}{3}\right| = 6$

80. $\left|\dfrac{6 - x}{4}\right| = 5$

81. $\left|\dfrac{3x - 5}{6}\right| > 5$

82. $\left|\dfrac{4x - 7}{5}\right| < 2$

MIXED PRACTICE

Solve. See Section 2.4.

Many companies predict the growth or decline of various technologies. The following data is based on information from Techcrunchies, a technological information site. Notice that the first table is the estimated increase in the number of Wi-Fi-enabled cell phones (in millions), and the second is the estimated percent increase in the number of Wi-Fi-enabled cell phones in the United States.

83. Use the middle column in the table to find the estimated number of Wi-Fi-enabled cell phones for each year.

Year	Increase in Wi-Fi-Enabled Cell Phones	Estimated Number
2010	$2x - 21$	
2012	$\dfrac{5}{2}x + 2$	
2014	$3x + 24$	
Total	290 million	

84. Use the middle column in the table to find the estimated percent increase in the number of Wi-Fi-enabled cell phones for each year.

Year	Percent Increase in Wi-Fi-Enabled Cell Phones since 2009	Estimated Percent Increase
2010	x	
2011	$2x + 10$	
2012	$4x - 25$	
	300%	

Consider the equation $3x - 4y = 12$. For each value of x or y given, find the corresponding value of the other variable that makes the statement true. See Section 3.1.

85. If $x = 2$, find y.

86. If $y = -1$, find x.

87. If $y = -3$, find x.

88. If $x = 4$, find y.

CONCEPT EXTENSIONS

89. Write an absolute value inequality representing all numbers x whose distance from 0 is less than 7 units.

90. Write an absolute value inequality representing all numbers x whose distance from 0 is greater than 4 units.

91. Write $-5 \leq x \leq 5$ as an equivalent inequality containing an absolute value.

92. Write $x > 1$ or $x < -1$ as an equivalent inequality containing an absolute value.

93. Describe how solving $|x - 3| = 5$ is different from solving $|x - 3| < 5$.

94. Describe how solving $|x + 4| = 0$ is similar to solving $|x + 4| \leq 0$.

The expression $|x_T - x|$ is defined to be the absolute error in x, where x_T is the true value of a quantity and x is the measured value or value as stored in a computer.

95. If the true value of a quantity is 3.5 and the absolute error must be less than 0.05, find the acceptable measured values.

96. If the true value of a quantity is 0.2 and the approximate value stored in a computer is $\dfrac{51}{256}$, find the absolute error.

Integrated Review SOLVING COMPOUND INEQUALITIES AND ABSOLUTE VALUE EQUATIONS AND INEQUALITIES

Solve each equation or inequality. Write inequality solution sets in interval rotation. For inequalities containing "and" or "or", also graph the solution set and write it in interval rotation.

1. $x < 7$ and $x > -5$

2. $x < 7$ or $x > -5$

3. $|4x - 3| = 1$

4. $|2x + 1| < 5$

5. $|6x| - 9 \geq -3$

6. $|x - 7| = |2x + 11|$

7. $-5 \leq \dfrac{3x - 8}{2} \leq 2$

8. $|9x - 1| = -3$

9. $3x + 2 \leq 5$ or $-3x \geq 0$

10. $3x + 2 \leq 5$ and $-3x \geq 0$

11. $|3 - x| - 5 \leq -2$

12. $\left| \dfrac{4x + 1}{5} \right| = |-1|$

Match each equation or inequality on the left with an equivalent statement on the right.

13. $|2x + 1| = 5$

A. $2x + 1 > 5$ or $2x + 1 < -5$

14. $|2x + 1| < 5$

B. $2x + 1 = 5$ or $2x + 1 = -5$

15. $|2x + 1| > 5$

C. $x < 5$

16. $x < 3$ or $x < 5$

D. $x < 3$

17. $x < 3$ and $x < 5$

E. $-5 < 2x + 1 < 5$

9.4 Graphing Linear Inequalities in Two Variables and Systems of Linear Inequalities

OBJECTIVE

1 Graph a Linear Inequality in Two Variables.

2 Solve a System of Linear Inequalities.

In this section, we first learn to graph a single linear inequality in two variables. Then we solve systems of linear inequalities.

Recall that a linear equation in two variables is an equation that can be written in the form $Ax + By = C$ where $A, B,$ and C are real numbers and A and B are not both 0. The definition of a linear inequality is the same except that the equal sign is replaced with an inequality sign.

A **linear inequality in two variables** is an inequality that can be written in one of the forms:

$$Ax + By < C \qquad Ax + By \leq C$$
$$Ax + By > C \qquad Ax + By \geq C$$

where A, B, and C are real numbers and A and B are not both 0. Just as for linear equations in x and y, an ordered pair is a **solution** of an inequality in x and y if replacing the variables by coordinates of the ordered pair results in a true statement.

OBJECTIVE

1   Graphing Linear Inequalities in Two Variables

The linear equation $x - y = 1$ is graphed next. Recall that all points on the line correspond to ordered pairs that satisfy the equation $x - y = 1$.

   Notice the line defined by $x - y = 1$ divides the rectangular coordinate system plane into 2 sides. All points on one side of the line satisfy the inequality $x - y < 1$ and all points on the other side satisfy the inequality $x - y > 1$. The graph below shows a few examples of this.

Check	$x - y < 1$
$(1, 3)$	$1 - 3 < 1$ True
$(-2, 1)$	$-2 - 1 < 1$ True
$(-4, -4)$	$-4 - (-4) < 1$ True

Check	$x - y > 1$
$(4, 1)$	$4 - 1 > 1$ True
$(2, -2)$	$2 - (-2) > 1$ True
$(0, -4)$	$0 - (-4) > 1$ True

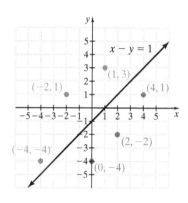

The graph of $x - y < 1$ is the region shaded blue, and the graph of $x - y > 1$ is the region shaded red below.

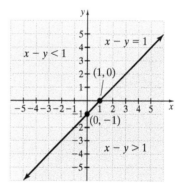

The region to the left of the line and the region to the right of the line are called **half-planes.** Every line divides the plane (similar to a sheet of paper extending indefinitely in all directions) into two half-planes; the line is called the **boundary.**

   Recall that the inequality $x - y \leq 1$ means

$$x - y = 1 \quad \text{or} \quad x - y < 1$$

Thus, the graph of $x - y \leq 1$ is the half-plane $x - y < 1$ along with the boundary line $x - y = 1$.

Graphing a Linear Inequality in Two Variables

Step 1. Graph the boundary line found by replacing the inequality sign with an equal sign. If the inequality sign is > or <, graph a dashed boundary line (indicating that the points on the line are not solutions of the inequality). If the inequality sign is ≥ or ≤, graph a solid boundary line (indicating that the points on the line are solutions of the inequality).

Step 2. Choose a point, *not* on the boundary line, as a test point. Substitute the coordinates of this test point into the *original* inequality.

Step 3. If a true statement is obtained in Step 2, shade the half-plane that contains the test point. If a false statement is obtained, shade the half-plane that does not contain the test point.

EXAMPLE 1 Graph: $x + y < 7$

Solution

Step 1. First we graph the boundary line by graphing the equation $x + y = 7$. We graph this boundary as a dashed line because the inequality sign is <, and thus the points on the line are not solutions of the inequality $x + y < 7$.

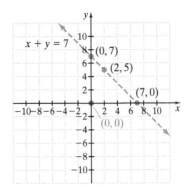

Step 2. Next, we choose a test point, being careful not to choose a point on the boundary line. We choose $(0, 0)$. Substitute the coordinates of $(0, 0)$ into $x + y < 7$.

$$x + y < 7 \quad \text{Original inequality}$$
$$0 + 0 \overset{?}{<} 7 \quad \text{Replace } x \text{ with 0 and } y \text{ with 0.}$$
$$0 < 7 \quad \text{True}$$

Step 3. Since the result is a true statement, $(0, 0)$ is a solution of $x + y < 7$, and every point in the same half-plane as $(0, 0)$ is also a solution. To indicate this, shade the entire half-plane containing $(0, 0)$, as shown.

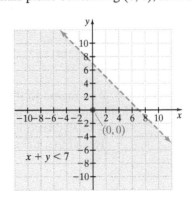

PRACTICE

1 Graph: $x + y > 5$

✓CONCEPT CHECK
Determine whether $(0, 0)$ is included in the graph of
  a. $y \geq 2x + 3$ **b.** $x < 7$ **c.** $2x - 3y < 6$

EXAMPLE 2   Graph: $2x - y \geq 3$

Solution

Step 1. We graph the boundary line by graphing $2x - y = 3$. We draw this line as a solid line because the inequality sign is $\geq$, and thus the points on the line are solutions of $2x - y \geq 3$.

Step 2. Once again, $(0, 0)$ is a convenient test point since it is not on the boundary line. We substitute 0 for x and 0 for y into the original inequality.

$$2x - y \geq 3$$
$$2(0) - 0 \geq 3 \quad \text{Let } x = 0 \text{ and } y = 0.$$
$$0 \geq 3 \quad \text{False}$$

Step 3. Since the statement is false, no point in the half-plane containing $(0, 0)$ is a solution. Therefore, we shade the half-plane that does not contain $(0, 0)$. Every point in the shaded half-plane and every point on the boundary line is a solution of $2x - y \geq 3$.

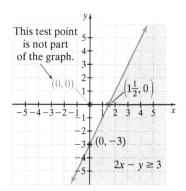

PRACTICE
2   Graph: $3x - y \geq 4$

▶ Helpful Hint

When graphing an inequality, make sure the test point is substituted into the **original inequality.** For Example 2, we substituted the test point $(0, 0)$ into the **original inequality** $2x - y \geq 3$, *not* $2x - y = 3$.

EXAMPLE 3   Graph: $x > 2y$

Solution

Step 1. We find the boundary line by graphing $x = 2y$. The boundary line is a dashed line since the inequality symbol is $>$.

Step 2. We cannot use $(0, 0)$ as a test point because it is a point on the boundary line. We choose instead $(0, 2)$.

$$x > 2y$$
$$0 > 2(2) \quad \text{Let } x = 0 \text{ and } y = 2.$$
$$0 > 4 \quad \text{False}$$

Answers to Concept Check:
a. no   **b.** yes   **c.** yes

(Continued on next page)

Step 3. Since the statement is false, we shade the half-plane that does not contain the test point $(0, 2)$, as shown.

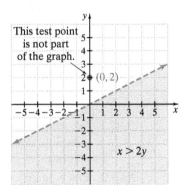

PRACTICE

3 Graph: $x > 3y$

EXAMPLE 4 Graph: $5x + 4y \leq 20$

Solution We graph the solid boundary line $5x + 4y = 20$ and choose $(0, 0)$ as the test point.

$$5x + 4y \leq 20$$
$$5(0) + 4(0) \overset{?}{\leq} 20 \quad \text{Let } x = 0 \text{ and } y = 0.$$
$$0 \leq 20 \quad \text{True}$$

We shade the half-plane that contains $(0, 0)$, as shown.

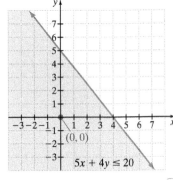

PRACTICE

4 Graph: $3x + 4y \geq 12$

EXAMPLE 5 Graph: $y > 3$

Solution We graph the dashed boundary line $y = 3$ and choose $(0, 0)$ as the test point. (Recall that the graph of $y = 3$ is a horizontal line with y-intercept 3.)

$$y > 3$$
$$0 \overset{?}{>} 3 \quad \text{Let } y = 0.$$
$$0 > 3 \quad \text{False}$$

We shade the half-plane that does not contain $(0, 0)$, as shown.

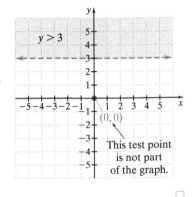

PRACTICE

5 Graph: $x > 3$

OBJECTIVE

2   Solving Systems of Linear Inequalities

Just as two linear equations make a system of linear equations, two linear inequalities make a **system of linear inequalities.** Systems of inequalities are very important in a process called linear programming. Many businesses use linear programming to find the most profitable way to use limited resources such as employees, machines, or buildings.

A **solution of a system of linear inequalities** is an ordered pair that satisfies each inequality in the system. The set of all such ordered pairs is the solution set of the system. Graphing this set gives us a picture of the solution set. We can graph a system of inequalities by graphing each inequality in the system and identifying the region of overlap.

EXAMPLE 6   Graph the solution of the system: $\begin{cases} 3x \ge y \\ x + 2y \le 8 \end{cases}$

Solution   We begin by graphing each inequality on the same set of axes. The graph of the solution region of the system is the region contained in the graphs of both inequalities. It is their intersection.

First, graph $3x \ge y$. The boundary line is the graph of $3x = y$. Sketch a solid boundary line since the inequality $3x \ge y$ means $3x > y$ or $3x = y$. The test point $(1, 0)$ satisfies the inequality, so shade the half-plane that includes $(1, 0)$.

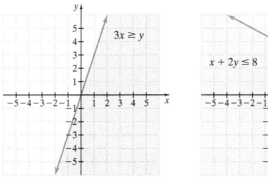 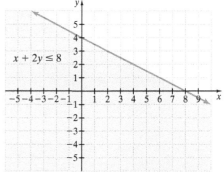

Next, sketch a solid boundary line $x + 2y = 8$ on the same set of axes. The test point $(0, 0)$ satisfies the inequality $x + 2y \le 8$, so shade the half-plane that includes $(0, 0)$. (For clarity, the graph of $x + 2y \le 8$ is shown on a separate set of axes.)

An ordered pair solution of the system must satisfy both inequalities. These solutions are points that lie in both shaded regions. The solution region of the system is the purple shaded region as seen below. This solution region includes parts of both boundary lines.

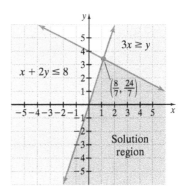

PRACTICE

6   Graph the solution of the system: $\begin{cases} 4x \le y \\ x + 3y \ge 9 \end{cases}$

In linear programming, it is sometimes necessary to find the coordinates of the **corner point:** the point at which the two boundary lines intersect. To find the point of intersection, solve the related linear system

$$\begin{cases} 3x = y \\ x + 2y = 8 \end{cases}$$

by the substitution method or the addition method. The lines intersect at $\left(\dfrac{8}{7}, \dfrac{24}{7}\right)$, the corner point of the graph.

Graphing the Solution Region of a System of Linear Inequalities

Step 1. Graph each inequality in the system on the same set of axes.

Step 2. The solutions (or solution region) of the system are the points common to the graphs of all the inequalities in the system.

EXAMPLE 7 Graph the solution of the system: $\begin{cases} x - y < 2 \\ x + 2y > -1 \end{cases}$

Solution Graph both inequalities on the same set of axes. Both boundary lines are dashed lines since the inequality symbols are $<$ and $>$. The solution region of the system is the region shown by the purple shading. In this example, the boundary lines are not a part of the solution.

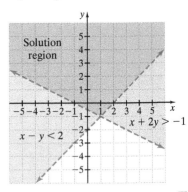

PRACTICE
7 Graph the solution of the system: $\begin{cases} x - y > 4 \\ x + 3y < -4 \end{cases}$

EXAMPLE 8 Graph the solution of the system: $\begin{cases} -3x + 4y < 12 \\ x \geq 2 \end{cases}$

Solution Graph both inequalities on the same set of axes.

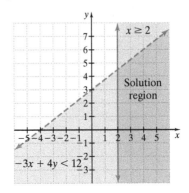

The solution region of the system is the purple shaded region, including a portion of the line $x = 2$.

PRACTICE
8 Graph the solution of the system: $\begin{cases} y \leq 6 \\ -2x + 5y > 10 \end{cases}$

Vocabulary, Readiness & Video Check

Use the choices below to fill in each blank. Some choices may be used more than once and some not at all.

true	$x < 3$	$y < 3$	half-planes	yes
false	$x \le 3$	$y \le 3$	linear inequality in two variables	no

1. The statement $5x - 6y < 7$ is an example of a(n) _____.
2. A boundary line divides a plane into two regions called _____.
3. True or false: The graph of $5x - 6y < 7$ includes its corresponding boundary line. _____
4. True or false: When graphing a linear inequality, to determine which side of the boundary line to shade, choose a point *not* on the boundary line. _____
5. True or false: The boundary line for the inequality $5x - 6y < 7$ is the graph of $5x - 6y = 7$.
   _____

6. The graph of _____ is

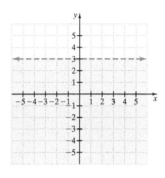

State whether the graph of each inequality includes its corresponding boundary line. Answer yes or no.

7. $y \ge x + 4$ **8.** $x - y > -7$ **9.** $y \ge x$ **10.** $x > 0$

Martin-Gay Interactive Videos

See Video 9.4

Watch the section lecture video and answer the following questions.

OBJECTIVE
1

11. From Example 1, how do you find the equation of the boundary line? How do you determine if the points on the boundary line are solutions of the inequality?

OBJECTIVE
2

12. In Example 2, did the graph of the first inequality of the system limit where we could choose the test point for the second inequality? Why or why not?

9.4 Exercise Set   MyMathLab®

Determine whether the ordered pairs given are solutions of the linear inequality in two variables.

1. $x - y > 3; (2, -1), (5, 1)$
2. $y - x < -2; (2, 1), (5, -1)$
3. $3x - 5y \le -4; (-1, -1), (4, 0)$
4. $2x + y \ge 10; (-1, -4), (5, 0)$
5. $x < -y; (0, 2), (-5, 1)$
6. $y > 3x; (0, 0), (-1, -4)$

MIXED PRACTICE

Graph each inequality. See Examples 1 through 5.

7. $x + y \le 1$ 8. $x + y \ge -2$
9. $2x + y > -4$ 10. $x + 3y \le 3$
11. $x + 6y \le -6$ 12. $7x + y > -14$
13. $2x + 5y > -10$ 14. $5x + 2y \le 10$
15. $x + 2y \le 3$ 16. $2x + 3y > -5$

17. $2x + 7y > 5$

18. $3x + 5y \leq -2$

19. $x - 2y \geq 3$

20. $4x + y \leq 2$

21. $5x + y < 3$

22. $x + 2y > -7$

23. $4x + y < 8$

24. $9x + 2y \geq -9$

25. $y \geq 2x$

26. $x < 5y$

27. $x \geq 0$

28. $y \leq 0$

29. $y \leq -3$

30. $x > -\dfrac{2}{3}$

31. $2x - 7y > 0$

32. $5x + 2y \leq 0$

33. $3x - 7y \geq 0$

34. $-2x - 9y > 0$

35. $x > y$

36. $x \leq -y$

37. $x - y \leq 6$

38. $x - y > 10$

39. $-\dfrac{1}{4}y + \dfrac{1}{3}x > 1$

40. $\dfrac{1}{2}x - \dfrac{1}{3}y \leq -1$

41. $-x < 0.4y$

42. $0.3x \geq 0.1y$

In Exercises 43 through 48, match each inequality with its graph.

a. $x > 2$

b. $y < 2$

c. $y < 2x$

d. $y \leq -3x$

e. $2x + 3y < 6$

f. $3x + 2y > 6$

43.

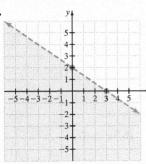

44.

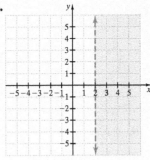

45.

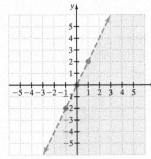

46.

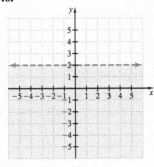

47.

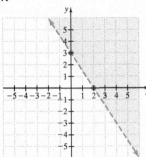

48.

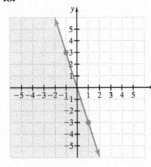

Graph the solution of each system of linear inequalities. See Examples 6 through 8.

49. $\begin{cases} y \geq x + 1 \\ y \geq 3 - x \end{cases}$

50. $\begin{cases} y \geq x - 3 \\ y \geq -1 - x \end{cases}$

51. $\begin{cases} y < 3x - 4 \\ y \leq x + 2 \end{cases}$

52. $\begin{cases} y \leq 2x + 1 \\ y > x + 2 \end{cases}$

53. $\begin{cases} y \leq -2x - 2 \\ y \geq x + 4 \end{cases}$

54. $\begin{cases} y \leq 2x + 4 \\ y \geq -x - 5 \end{cases}$

55. $\begin{cases} y \geq -x + 2 \\ y \leq 2x + 5 \end{cases}$

56. $\begin{cases} y \geq x - 5 \\ y \leq -3x + 3 \end{cases}$

57. $\begin{cases} x \geq 3y \\ x + 3y \leq 6 \end{cases}$

58. $\begin{cases} -2x < y \\ x + 2y < 3 \end{cases}$

59. $\begin{cases} y + 2x \geq 0 \\ 5x - 3y \leq 12 \end{cases}$

60. $\begin{cases} y + 2x \leq 0 \\ 5x + 3y \geq -2 \end{cases}$

61. $\begin{cases} 3x - 4y \geq -6 \\ 2x + y \leq 7 \end{cases}$

62. $\begin{cases} 4x - y \geq -2 \\ 2x + 3y \leq -8 \end{cases}$

63. $\begin{cases} x \leq 2 \\ y \geq -3 \end{cases}$

64. $\begin{cases} x \geq -3 \\ y \geq -2 \end{cases}$

65. $\begin{cases} y \geq 1 \\ x < -3 \end{cases}$

66. $\begin{cases} y > 2 \\ x \geq -1 \end{cases}$

67. $\begin{cases} 2x + 3y < -8 \\ x \geq -4 \end{cases}$

68. $\begin{cases} 3x + 2y \leq 6 \\ x < 2 \end{cases}$

69. $\begin{cases} 2x - 5y \leq 9 \\ y \leq -3 \end{cases}$

70. $\begin{cases} 2x + 5y \leq -10 \\ y \geq 1 \end{cases}$

71. $\begin{cases} y \geq \dfrac{1}{2}x + 2 \\ y \leq \dfrac{1}{2}x - 3 \end{cases}$

72. $\begin{cases} y \geq -\dfrac{3}{2}x + 3 \\ y < -\dfrac{3}{2}x + 6 \end{cases}$

REVIEW AND PREVIEW

Evaluate each expression for the given replacement value. See Section 5.1.

73. x^2 if x is -5

74. x^3 if x is -5

75. $2x^3$ if x is -1

76. $3x^2$ if x is -1

CONCEPT EXTENSIONS

Determine whether $(1,1)$ is included in each graph. See the Concept Check in this section.

77. $3x + 4y < 8$

78. $y > 5x$

79. $y \geq -\dfrac{1}{2}x$

80. $x > 3$

81. Write an inequality whose solutions are all pairs of numbers x and y whose sum is at least 13. Graph the inequality.

82. Write an inequality whose solutions are all the pairs of numbers x and y whose sum is at most -4. Graph the inequality.

83. Explain why a point on the boundary line should not be chosen as the test point.

84. Describe the graph of a linear inequality.

85. The price for a taxi cab in a small city is $2.50 per mile, x, while traveling, and $0.25 every minute, y, while waiting. If you have $20 to spend on a cab ride, the inequality

$$2.5x + 0.25y \leq 20$$

represents your situation. Graph this inequality in the first quadrant only.

86. A word processor charges $22 per hour, x, for typing a first draft, and $15 per hour, y, for making changes and typing a second draft. If you need a document typed and have $100, the inequality

$$22x + 15y \leq 100$$

represents your situation. Graph the inequality in the first quadrant only.

87. In Exercises 85 and 86, why were you instructed to graph each inequality in the first quadrant only?

88. Scott Sambracci and Sara Thygeson are planning their wedding. They have calculated that they want the cost of their wedding ceremony, x, plus the cost of their reception, y, to be no more than $5000.

   a. Write an inequality describing this relationship.

   b. Graph this inequality.

   c. Why should we be interested in only quadrant I of this graph?

89. It's the end of the budgeting period for Dennis Fernandes, and he has $500 left in his budget for car rental expenses. He plans to spend this budget on a sales trip throughout southern Texas. He will rent a car that costs $30 per day and $0.15 per mile, and he can spend no more than $500.

   a. Write an inequality describing this situation. Let x = number of days and let y = number of miles.

   b. Graph this inequality.

   c. Why should we be interested in only quadrant I of this graph?

90. Explain how to decide which region to shade to show the solution region of the following system.

$$\begin{cases} x \geq 3 \\ y \geq -2 \end{cases}$$

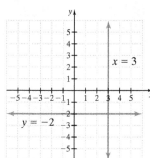

For each system of inequalities, choose the corresponding graph.

91. $\begin{cases} y < 5 \\ x > 3 \end{cases}$ **92.** $\begin{cases} y > 5 \\ x < 3 \end{cases}$ **93.** $\begin{cases} y \leq 5 \\ x < 3 \end{cases}$

94. $\begin{cases} y > 5 \\ x \geq 3 \end{cases}$

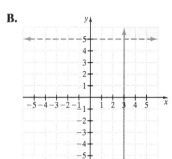

A.   **B.**

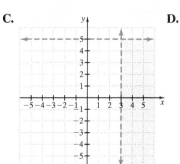

C.   **D.**

95. Graph the solution of $\begin{cases} 2x - y \leq 6 \\ x \geq 3 \\ y > 2 \end{cases}$

96. Graph the solution of $\begin{cases} x + y < 5 \\ y < 2x \\ x \geq 0 \\ y \geq 0 \end{cases}$

97. Describe the location of the solution region of the system

$$\begin{cases} x > 0 \\ y > 0. \end{cases}$$

Chapter 9 **Vocabulary Check**

Fill in each blank with one of the words or phrases listed below.

compound inequality   solution   system of linear inequalities

absolute value   union   intersection

1. The statement "$x < 5$ or $x > 7$" is called a(n) _____ .

2. The _____ of two sets is the set of all elements common to both sets.

3. The _____ of two sets is the set of all elements that belong to either of the sets.

4. A number's distance from 0 is called its _____.

5. When a variable in an equation is replaced by a number and the resulting equation is true, then that number is called a(n) _____ of the equation.

6. Two or more linear inequalities are called a(n) _____ .

Chapter 9 Highlights

DEFINITIONS AND CONCEPTS	EXAMPLES

Section 9.1 Compound Inequalities

Two inequalities joined by the words **and** or **or** are called **compound inequalities.**

Compound inequalities:

$$x - 7 \leq 4 \quad and \quad x \geq -21$$
$$2x + 7 > x - 3 \quad or \quad 5x + 2 > -3$$

The solution set of a compound inequality formed by the word **and** is the **intersection,** ∩, of the solution sets of the two inequalities.

Solve for x:

$x < 5$ and $x < 3$

$\{x | x < 5\}$ (−∞, 5)

$\{x | x < 3\}$ (−∞, 3)

$\{x | x < 3$ and $x < 5\}$ (−∞, 3)

The solution set of a compound inequality formed by the word **or** is the **union,** ∪, of the solution sets of the two inequalities.

Solve for x:

$$x - 2 \geq -3 \quad or \quad 2x \leq -4$$
$$x \geq -1 \quad or \quad x \leq -2$$

$\{x | x \geq -1\}$ [−1, ∞)

$\{x | x \leq -2\}$ (−∞, −2]

$\{x | x \leq -2$ or $x \geq -1\}$ (−∞, −2] ∪ [−1, ∞)

Section 9.2 Absolute Value Equations

If a is a positive number, then $|x| = a$ is equivalent to $x = a$ or $x = -a$.

Solve for y:

$$|5y - 1| - 7 = 4$$

$|5y - 1| = 11$ Add 7.

$5y - 1 = 11$ or $5y - 1 = -11$

$5y = 12$ or $\quad 5y = -10$ Add 1.

$y = \dfrac{12}{5}$ or $\quad y = -2$ Divide by 5.

The solutions are -2 and $\dfrac{12}{5}$.

If a is negative, then $|x| = a$ has no solution.

Solve for x:

$$\left|\frac{x}{2} - 7\right| = -1$$

The solution set is $\{\ \}$ or ∅.

DEFINITIONS AND CONCEPTS	EXAMPLES

Section 9.2   Absolute Value Equations (continued)

If an absolute value equation is of the form $|x| = |y|$, solve $x = y$ or $x = -y$.

Solve for x:

$$|x - 7| = |2x + 1|$$

$$x - 7 = 2x + 1 \quad \text{or} \quad x - 7 = -(2x + 1)$$
$$x = 2x + 8 \qquad\qquad x - 7 = -2x - 1$$
$$-x = 8 \qquad\qquad\qquad x = -2x + 6$$
$$x = -8 \quad \text{or} \quad\; 3x = 6$$
$$x = 2$$

The solutions are -8 and 2.

Section 9.3   Absolute Value Inequalities

If a is a positive number, then $|x| < a$ is equivalent to $-a < x < a$.

Solve for y:

$$|y - 5| \le 3$$
$$-3 \le y - 5 \le 3$$
$$-3 + 5 \le y - 5 + 5 \le 3 + 5 \quad \text{Add 5.}$$
$$2 \le y \le 8$$

The solution set is $[2, 8]$.

If a is a positive number, then $|x| > a$ is equivalent to $x < -a$ or $x > a$.

Solve for x:

$$\left|\frac{x}{2} - 3\right| > 7$$

$$\frac{x}{2} - 3 < -7 \quad \text{or} \quad \frac{x}{2} - 3 > 7$$
$$x - 6 < -14 \quad \text{or} \quad x - 6 > 14 \quad \text{Multiply by 2.}$$
$$x < -8 \quad \text{or} \quad x > 20 \qquad \text{Add 6.}$$

The solution set is $(-\infty, -8) \cup (20, \infty)$.

Section 9.4   Graphing Linear Inequalities in Two Variables and Systems of Linear Inequalities

A **linear inequality in two variables** is an inequality that can be written in one of the forms:

$$Ax + By < C \qquad Ax + By \le C$$
$$Ax + By > C \qquad Ax + By \ge C$$

To graph a linear inequality

1. Graph the boundary line by graphing the related equation. Draw the line solid if the inequality symbol is $\le$ or $\ge$. Draw the line dashed if the inequality symbol is $<$ or $>$.

2. Choose a test point not on the line. Substitute its coordinates into the original inequality.

3. If the resulting inequality is true, shade the half-plane that contains the test point. If the inequality is not true, shade the half-plane that does not contain the test point.

Linear Inequalities

$$2x - 5y < 6 \qquad x \ge -5$$
$$y > -8x \qquad y \le 2$$

Graph $2x - y \le 4$.

1. Graph $2x - y = 4$. Draw a solid line because the inequality symbol is $\le$.

2. Check the test point $(0, 0)$ in the inequality $2x - y \le 4$.

$$2 \cdot 0 - 0 \le 4 \quad \text{Let } x = 0 \text{ and } y = 0.$$
$$0 \le 4 \quad \text{True}$$

3. The inequality is true so we shade the half-plane containing $(0, 0)$.

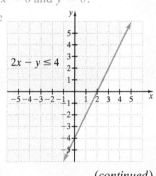

(continued)

DEFINITIONS AND CONCEPTS	EXAMPLES
Section 9.4 Graphing Linear Inequalities in Two Variables and Systems of Linear Inequalities (continued)	

A system of linear inequalities consists of two or more linear inequalities.

To graph a system of inequalities, graph each inequality in the system. The overlapping region is the solution of the system.

System of Linear Inequalities

$$\begin{cases} x - y \geq 3 \\ y \leq -2x \end{cases}$$

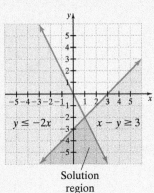

Solution region

Chapter 9 **Review**

(9.1) *Solve each inequality. Write your answers in interval notation.*

1. $-3 < 4(2x - 1) < 12$

2. $-2 \leq 8 + 5x < -1$

3. $\dfrac{1}{6} < \dfrac{4x - 3}{3} \leq \dfrac{4}{5}$

4. $-6 < x - (3 - 4x) < -3$

5. $3x - 5 > 6$ *or* $-x < -5$

6. $x \leq 2$ *and* $x > -5$

(9.2) *Solve each absolute value equation.*

7. $|8 - x| = 3$ **8.** $|x - 7| = 9$

9. $|-3x + 4| = 7$ **10.** $|2x + 9| = 9$

11. $5 + |6x + 1| = 5$ **12.** $|3x - 2| + 6 = 10$

13. $|5 - 6x| + 8 = 3$ **14.** $-5 = |4x - 3|$

15. $\left|\dfrac{3x - 7}{4}\right| = 2$ **16.** $-4 = \left|\dfrac{x - 3}{2}\right| - 5$

17. $|6x + 1| = |15 + 4x|$ **18.** $|x - 3| = |x + 5|$

(9.3) *Solve each absolute value inequality. Graph the solution set and write it in interval notation.*

19. $|5x - 1| < 9$

20. $|6 + 4x| \geq 10$

21. $|3x| - 8 > 1$

22. $9 + |5x| < 24$

23. $|6x - 5| \leq -1$

24. $|6x - 5| \leq 5$

25. $\left|3x + \dfrac{2}{5}\right| \geq 4$

26. $|5x - 3| > 2$

27. $\left|\dfrac{x}{3} + 6\right| - 8 > -5$

28. $\left|\dfrac{4(x - 1)}{7}\right| + 10 < 2$

(9.4) *Graph the following inequalities.*

29. $3x - 4y \leq 0$ **30.** $3x - 4y \geq 0$

31. $x + 6y < 6$ **32.** $y \leq -4$

33. $y \geq -7$ **34.** $x \geq -y$

Graph the solution region of the following systems of linear inequalities.

35. $\begin{cases} y \geq 2x - 3 \\ y \leq -2x + 1 \end{cases}$ **36.** $\begin{cases} y \leq -3x - 3 \\ y \leq 2x + 7 \end{cases}$

37. $\begin{cases} x + 2y > 0 \\ x - y \leq 6 \end{cases}$ **38.** $\begin{cases} 4x - y \leq 0 \\ 3x - 2y \geq -5 \end{cases}$

39. $\begin{cases} 3x - 2y \leq 4 \\ 2x + y \geq 5 \end{cases}$ **40.** $\begin{cases} -2x + 3y > -7 \\ x \geq -2 \end{cases}$

MIXED REVIEW

Solve. If an inequality, write your solutions in interval notation.

41. $0 \leq \dfrac{2(3x + 4)}{5} \leq 3$

42. $x \leq 2$ or $x > -5$

43. $-2x \leq 6$ and $-2x + 3 < -7$

44. $|7x| - 26 = -5$

45. $\left| \dfrac{9 - 2x}{5} \right| = -3$

46. $|x - 3| = |7 + 2x|$

47. $|6x - 5| \geq -1$

48. $\left| \dfrac{4x - 3}{5} \right| < 1$

Graph the solutions.

49. $-x \leq y$

50. $x + y > -2$

51. $\begin{cases} -3x + 2y > -1 \\ y < -2 \end{cases}$

52. $\begin{cases} x - 2y \geq 7 \\ x + y \leq -5 \end{cases}$

Chapter 9 **Test**   MyMathLab®   CHAPTER **Test Prep** VIDEOS   ▶ You Tube™

Solve each equation or inequality.

1. $|6x - 5| - 3 = -2$

2. $|8 - 2t| = -6$

3. $|x - 5| = |x + 2|$

4. $-3 < 2(x - 3) \leq 4$

5. $|3x + 1| > 5$

6. $|x - 5| - 4 < -2$

7. $x \leq -2$ and $x \leq -5$

8. $x \leq -2$ or $x \leq -5$

9. $-x > 1$ and $3x + 3 \geq x - 3$

10. $6x + 1 > 5x + 4$ or $1 - x > -4$

11. $\left| \dfrac{5x - 7}{2} \right| = 4$

12. $\left| 17x - \dfrac{1}{5} \right| > -2$

13. $-1 \leq \dfrac{2x - 5}{3} < 2$

Graph each linear equality.

14. $y > -4x$

15. $2x - 3y > -6$

Graph the solutions of the following systems of linear inequalities.

16. $\begin{cases} y + 2x \leq 4 \\ y \geq 2 \end{cases}$

17. $\begin{cases} 2y - x \geq 1 \\ x + y \geq -4 \end{cases}$

Chapter 9 **Cumulative Review**

1. Find the value of each expression when $x = 2$ and $y = -5$.

  a. $\dfrac{x - y}{12 + x}$ **b.** $x^2 - 3y$

2. Find the value of each expression when $x = -4$ and $y = 7$.

  a. $\dfrac{x - y}{7 - x}$ **b.** $x^2 + 2y$

3. Simplify each expression.

  a. $\dfrac{(-12)(-3) + 3}{-7 - (-2)}$ **b.** $\dfrac{2(-3)^2 - 20}{-5 + 4}$

4. Simplify each expression.

  a. $\dfrac{4(-3) - (-6)}{-8 + 4}$ **b.** $\dfrac{3 + (-3)(-2)^3}{-1 - (-4)}$

5. Simplify each expression by combining like terms.

  a. $2x + 3x + 5 + 2$
  b. $-5a - 3 + a + 2$
  c. $4y - 3y^2$

  d. $2.3x + 5x - 6$
  e. $-\dfrac{1}{2}b + b$

6. Simplify each expression by combining like terms.

  a. $4x - 3 + 7 - 5x$
  b. $-6y + 3y - 8 + 8y$
  c. $2 + 8.1a + a - 6$
  d. $2x^2 - 2x$

7. Solve $2x + 3x - 5 + 7 = 10x + 3 - 6x - 4$.

8. Solve $6y - 11 + 4 + 2y = 8 + 15y - 8y$.

9. Complete the table for the equation $y = 3x$.

x	y
-1	
	0
	-9

10. Complete the table for the equation $2x + y = 6$.

x	y
0	
	-2
3	

11. Identify the *x*- and *y*-intercepts.

a.
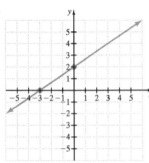

b.
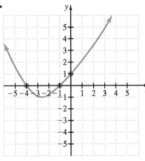

c.
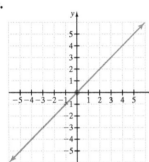

d.
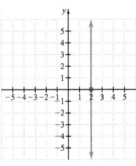

e.
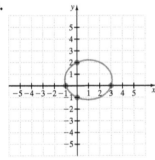

12. Identify the *x*- and *y*-intercepts.

a.
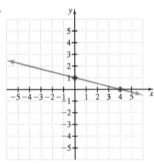

b.
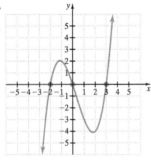

c.
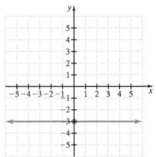

d.
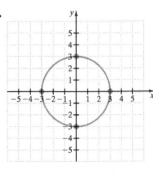

13. Determine whether the graphs of $y = -\dfrac{1}{5}x + 1$ and $2x + 10y = 3$ are parallel lines, perpendicular lines, or neither.

14. Determine whether the graphs of $y = 3x + 7$ and $x + 3y = -15$ are parallel lines, perpendicular lines, or neither.

15. Find an equation of the line with *y*-intercept $(0, -3)$ and slope of $\dfrac{1}{4}$.

16. Find an equation of the line with *y*-intercept $(0, 4)$ and slope of -2.

17. Find an equation of the line parallel to the line $y = 5$ and passing through $(-2, -3)$.

18. Find an equation of the line perpendicular to $y = 2x + 4$ and passing through $(1, 5)$.

19. Which of the following linear equations are functions?

  a. $y = x$
  b. $y = 2x + 1$
  c. $y = 5$
  d. $x = -1$

20. Which of the following linear equations are functions?

  a. $2x + 3 = y$
  b. $x + 4 = 0$
  c. $\dfrac{1}{2}y = 2x$
  d. $y = 0$

21. Determine whether $(12, 6)$ is a solution of the given system.
$$\begin{cases} 2x - 3y = 6 \\ x = 2y \end{cases}$$

22. Which of the following ordered pairs is a solution of the given system?
$$\begin{cases} 2x + y = 4 \\ x + y = 2 \end{cases}$$

  a. $(1, 1)$
  b. $(2, 0)$

23. Add $11x^3 - 12x^2 + x - 3$ and $x^3 - 10x + 5$.

24. Combine like terms to simplify.
$4a^2 + 3a - 2a^2 + 7a - 5$.

25. Factor $x^2 + 7yx + 6y^2$.

26. Factor $3x^2 + 15x + 18$.

27. Divide $\dfrac{3x^3y^7}{40} \div \dfrac{4x^3}{y^2}$.

28. Divide $\dfrac{12x^2y^3}{5} \div \dfrac{3y^2}{x}$.

29. Subtract $\dfrac{2y}{2y - 7} - \dfrac{7}{2y - 7}$.

30. Subtract $\dfrac{-4x^2}{x + 1} - \dfrac{4x}{x + 1}$.

31. Add $\dfrac{2x}{x^2 + 2x + 1} + \dfrac{x}{x^2 - 1}$.

32. Add $\dfrac{3x}{x^2 + 5x + 6} + \dfrac{1}{x^2 + 2x - 3}$.

33. Solve $\dfrac{x}{2} + \dfrac{8}{3} = \dfrac{1}{6}$.

34. Solve $\dfrac{1}{21} + \dfrac{x}{7} = \dfrac{5}{3}$.

35. Solve the following system of equations by graphing.
$$\begin{cases} 2x + y = 7 \\ 2y = -4x \end{cases}$$

36. Solve the following system by graphing.
$$\begin{cases} y = x + 2 \\ 2x + y = 5 \end{cases}$$

37. Solve the system.
$$\begin{cases} 7x - 3y = -14 \\ -3x + y = 6 \end{cases}$$

38. Solve the system.
$$\begin{cases} 5x + y = 3 \\ y = -5x \end{cases}$$

39. Solve the system.
$$\begin{cases} 3x - 2y = 2 \\ -9x + 6y = -6 \end{cases}$$

40. Solve the system.
$$\begin{cases} -2x + y = 7 \\ 6x - 3y = -21 \end{cases}$$

41. Graph the solution of the system
$$\begin{cases} -3x + 4y < 12 \\ x \geq 2 \end{cases}$$

42. Graph the solution of the system.
$$\begin{cases} 2x - y \leq 6 \\ y \geq 2 \end{cases}$$

43. Simplify the following.

   a. $x^7 \cdot x^4$

   b. $\left(\dfrac{t}{2}\right)^4$

   c. $(9y^5)^2$

44. Simplify.

   a. $\left(\dfrac{-6x}{y^3}\right)^3$ **b.** $\dfrac{(2b^2)^5}{a^2b^7}$

   c. $\dfrac{(3y)^2}{y^2}$ **d.** $\dfrac{(x^2y^4)^2}{xy^3}$

45. Solve $(5x - 1)(2x^2 + 15x + 18) = 0$.

46. Solve $(x + 1)(2x^2 - 3x - 5) = 0$.

47. Solve $\dfrac{45}{x} = \dfrac{5}{7}$.

48. Solve $\dfrac{2x + 7}{3} = \dfrac{x - 6}{2}$.

Rational Exponents, Radicals, and Complex Numbers

10.1 Radicals and Radical Functions

10.2 Rational Exponents

10.3 Simplifying Radical Expressions

10.4 Adding, Subtracting, and Multiplying Radical Expressions

10.5 Rationalizing Denominators and Numerators of Radical Expressions

Integrated Review— Radicals and Rational Exponents

10.6 Radical Equations and Problem Solving

10.7 Complex Numbers

In this chapter, radical notation is reviewed, and then rational exponents are introduced. As the name implies, rational exponents are exponents that are rational numbers. We present an interpretation of rational exponents that is consistent with the meaning and rules already established for integer exponents, and we present two forms of notation for roots: radical and exponent. We conclude this chapter with complex numbers, a natural extension of the real number system.

The Google Lunar X PRIZE is an international competition to safely land a robot on the surface of the moon, travel 500 meters over the lunar surface, and send images and data back to Earth. Teams needed to be registered by December 31, 2010. There are multiple prizes and bonuses, but the first team to land on the moon and complete the mission objectives by December 31, 2012, will be awarded $20 million. After this time, the first prize drops to $15 million. The deadline for winning the competition is December 31, 2014, and thus far, 20 teams are competing for the prize.

To reach the moon, these vehicles must first leave the gravity of Earth. In Exercises 115 and 116 of Section 10.1, you will calculate the escape velocity of Earth and the moon, the minimum speed an object must reach to escape the pull of a planet's gravity. (*Source:* X PRIZE Foundation)

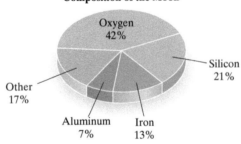

Composition of the Moon

Oxygen 42%

Silicon 21%

Iron 13%

Aluminum 7%

Other 17%

Why the moon? To name a few reasons:

- It is closest to Earth (1.3 seconds for light or radio) so that lunar machines can be directly controlled from Earth.

- It is also the closest source of materials to use for any other space project, and it is 22 times easier to launch from the moon than from Earth.

- The moon is 42% oxygen by weight (see the circle graph to the left) and oxygen is the main ingredient of rocket fuel.

- We can collect energy from the moon's surface and transmit it to Earth.

10.1 | Radicals and Radical Functions

OBJECTIVES

1 Find Square Roots.

2 Approximate Roots.

3 Find Cube Roots.

4 Find nth Roots.

5 Find $\sqrt[n]{a^n}$ Where a Is a Real Number.

6 Graph Square and Cube Root Functions.

OBJECTIVE

1   Finding Square Roots

Recall from Section 8.2 that to find a **square root** of a number a, we find a number that was squared to get a.

Thus, because

$$5^2 = 25 \quad \text{and} \quad (-5)^2 = 25,$$

both 5 and -5 are square roots of 25.

Recall that we denote the **nonnegative,** or **principal, square root** with the **radical sign.**

$$\sqrt{25} = 5$$

We denote the **negative square root** with the **negative radical sign.**

$$-\sqrt{25} = -5$$

An expression containing a radical sign is called a **radical expression.** An expression within, or "under," a radical sign is called a **radicand.**

radical expression: $\sqrt{a}$ ↙radical sign   ↘radicand

> **Principal and Negative Square Roots**
>
> If a is a nonnegative number, then
> $\sqrt{a}$ is the **principal,** or **nonnegative, square root** of a
> $-\sqrt{a}$ is the **negative square root** of a

EXAMPLE 1   Simplify. Assume that all variables represent positive numbers.

a. $\sqrt{36}$ b. $\sqrt{0}$ c. $\sqrt{\dfrac{4}{49}}$ d. $\sqrt{0.25}$

e. $\sqrt{x^6}$ f. $\sqrt{9x^{12}}$ g. $-\sqrt{81}$ h. $\sqrt{-81}$

Solution

a. $\sqrt{36} = 6$ because $6^2 = 36$ and 6 is not negative.

b. $\sqrt{0} = 0$ because $0^2 = 0$ and 0 is not negative.

c. $\sqrt{\dfrac{4}{49}} = \dfrac{2}{7}$ because $\left(\dfrac{2}{7}\right)^2 = \dfrac{4}{49}$ and $\dfrac{2}{7}$ is not negative.

d. $\sqrt{0.25} = 0.5$ because $(0.5)^2 = 0.25$.

e. $\sqrt{x^6} = x^3$ because $(x^3)^2 = x^6$.

f. $\sqrt{9x^{12}} = 3x^6$ because $(3x^6)^2 = 9x^{12}$.

g. $-\sqrt{81} = -9$. The negative in front of the radical indicates the negative square root of 81.

h. $\sqrt{-81}$ is not a real number.

PRACTICE

1   Simplify. Assume that all variables represent positive numbers.

a. $\sqrt{49}$ b. $\sqrt{\dfrac{0}{1}}$ c. $\sqrt{\dfrac{16}{81}}$ d. $\sqrt{0.64}$

e. $\sqrt{z^8}$ f. $\sqrt{16b^4}$ g. $-\sqrt{36}$ h. $\sqrt{-36}$

Recall from Section 8.2 our discussion of the square root of a negative number. For example, can we simplify $\sqrt{-4}$? That is, can we find a real number whose square is -4? No, there is no real number whose square is -4, and we say that $\sqrt{-4}$ is not a real number. In general:

The square root of a negative number is not a real number.

> ▶ Helpful Hint
> - Remember: $\sqrt{0} = 0$.
> - Don't forget that the square root of a negative number is not a real number. For example,
>
> $$\sqrt{-9} \text{ is not a real number}$$
>
> because there is no real number that when multiplied by itself would give a product of -9. In Section 10.7, we will see what kind of a number $\sqrt{-9}$ is.

OBJECTIVE
2 Approximating Roots

Recall that numbers such as 1, 4, 9, and 25 are called **perfect squares,** since $1 = 1^2, 4 = 2^2, 9 = 3^2$, and $25 = 5^2$. Square roots of perfect square radicands simplify to rational numbers. What happens when we try to simplify a root such as $\sqrt{3}$? Since there is no rational number whose square is 3, $\sqrt{3}$ is not a rational number. It is called an **irrational number,** and we can find a decimal **approximation** of it. To find decimal approximations, use a calculator. For example, an approximation for $\sqrt{3}$ is

$$\sqrt{3} \approx 1.732$$
$$\uparrow$$
$$\text{approximation symbol}$$

To see if the approximation is reasonable, notice that since

$$1 < 3 < 4,$$
$$\sqrt{1} < \sqrt{3} < \sqrt{4}, \text{ or}$$
$$1 < \sqrt{3} < 2.$$

We found $\sqrt{3} \approx 1.732$, a number between 1 and 2, so our result is reasonable.

EXAMPLE 2 Use a calculator to approximate $\sqrt{20}$. Round the approximation to 3 decimal places and check to see that your approximation is reasonable.

$$\sqrt{20} \approx 4.472$$

Solution Is this reasonable? Since $16 < 20 < 25$, $\sqrt{16} < \sqrt{20} < \sqrt{25}$, or $4 < \sqrt{20} < 5$. The approximation is between 4 and 5 and thus is reasonable. □

PRACTICE
2 Use a calculator to approximate $\sqrt{45}$. Round the approximation to three decimal places and check to see that your approximation is reasonable.

OBJECTIVE
3 Finding Cube Roots

Finding roots can be extended to other roots such as cube roots. For example, since $2^3 = 8$, we call 2 the **cube root** of 8. In symbols, we write

$$\sqrt[3]{8} = 2$$

> **Cube Root**
>
> The **cube root** of a real number a is written as $\sqrt[3]{a}$, and
>
> $$\sqrt[3]{a} = b \text{ only if } b^3 = a$$

From this definition, we have

$$\sqrt[3]{64} = 4 \text{ since } 4^3 = 64$$
$$\sqrt[3]{-27} = -3 \text{ since } (-3)^3 = -27$$
$$\sqrt[3]{x^3} = x \text{ since } x^3 = x^3$$

Notice that, unlike with square roots, *it is possible to have a negative radicand when finding a cube root.* This is so because the *cube* of a negative number is a negative number. Therefore, the *cube root* of a negative number is a negative number.

EXAMPLE 3   Find the cube roots.

a. $\sqrt[3]{1}$ **b.** $\sqrt[3]{-64}$ **c.** $\sqrt[3]{\dfrac{8}{125}}$ **d.** $\sqrt[3]{x^6}$ **e.** $\sqrt[3]{-27x^9}$

Solution

a. $\sqrt[3]{1} = 1$ because $1^3 = 1$.

b. $\sqrt[3]{-64} = -4$ because $(-4)^3 = -64$.

c. $\sqrt[3]{\dfrac{8}{125}} = \dfrac{2}{5}$ because $\left(\dfrac{2}{5}\right)^3 = \dfrac{8}{125}$.

d. $\sqrt[3]{x^6} = x^2$ because $(x^2)^3 = x^6$.

e. $\sqrt[3]{-27x^9} = -3x^3$ because $(-3x^3)^3 = -27x^9$.

PRACTICE

3   Find the cube roots.

a. $\sqrt[3]{-1}$ **b.** $\sqrt[3]{27}$ **c.** $\sqrt[3]{\dfrac{27}{64}}$ **d.** $\sqrt[3]{x^{12}}$ **e.** $\sqrt[3]{-8x^3}$

OBJECTIVE

4   Finding *n*th Roots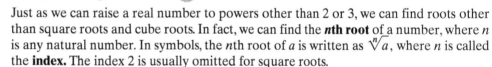

Just as we can raise a real number to powers other than 2 or 3, we can find roots other than square roots and cube roots. In fact, we can find the **nth root** of a number, where n is any natural number. In symbols, the nth root of a is written as $\sqrt[n]{a}$, where n is called the **index.** The index 2 is usually omitted for square roots.

▶ **Helpful Hint**

If the index is even, such as $\sqrt{}$, $\sqrt[4]{}$, $\sqrt[6]{}$, and so on, the radicand must be nonnegative for the root to be a real number. For example,

$$\sqrt[4]{16} = 2, \text{ but } \sqrt[4]{-16} \text{ is not a real number.}$$
$$\sqrt[6]{64} = 2, \text{ but } \sqrt[6]{-64} \text{ is not a real number.}$$

If the index is odd, such as $\sqrt[3]{}$, $\sqrt[5]{}$, and so on, the radicand may be any real number. For example,

$$\sqrt[3]{64} = 4 \quad \text{and} \quad \sqrt[3]{-64} = -4$$
$$\sqrt[5]{32} = 2 \quad \text{and} \quad \sqrt[5]{-32} = -2$$

✔**CONCEPT CHECK**

Which one is not a real number?

a. $\sqrt[3]{-15}$ **b.** $\sqrt[4]{-15}$ **c.** $\sqrt[5]{-15}$ **d.** $\sqrt{(-15)^2}$

Answer to Concept Check: **b**

EXAMPLE 4 Simplify the following expressions.

a. $\sqrt[4]{81}$ **b.** $\sqrt[5]{-243}$ **c.** $-\sqrt{25}$ **d.** $\sqrt[4]{-81}$ **e.** $\sqrt[3]{64x^3}$

Solution

a. $\sqrt[4]{81} = 3$ because $3^4 = 81$ and 3 is positive.

b. $\sqrt[5]{-243} = -3$ because $(-3)^5 = -243$.

c. $-\sqrt{25} = -5$ because -5 is the opposite of $\sqrt{25}$.

d. $\sqrt[4]{-81}$ is not a real number. There is no real number that, when raised to the fourth power, is -81.

e. $\sqrt[3]{64x^3} = 4x$ because $(4x)^3 = 64x^3$.

PRACTICE

  4   Simplify the following expressions.

a. $\sqrt[4]{10{,}000}$ **b.** $\sqrt[5]{-1}$ **c.** $-\sqrt{81}$ **d.** $\sqrt[4]{-625}$ **e.** $\sqrt[3]{27x^9}$

OBJECTIVE

  5   Finding $\sqrt[n]{a^n}$ Where *a* Is a Real Number ▶

Recall that the notation $\sqrt{a^2}$ indicates the positive square root of a^2 only. For example,

$$\sqrt{(-7)^2} = \sqrt{49} = 7$$

When variables are present in the radicand and it is *unclear whether the variable represents a positive number or a negative number*, absolute value bars are sometimes needed to ensure that the result is a positive number. For example,

$$\sqrt{x^2} = |x|$$

This ensures that the result is positive. This same situation may occur when the index is any *even* positive integer. When the index is any *odd* positive integer, absolute value bars are not necessary.

Finding $\sqrt[n]{a^n}$

If *n* is an *even* positive integer, then $\sqrt[n]{a^n} = |a|$.

If *n* is an *odd* positive integer, then $\sqrt[n]{a^n} = a$.

EXAMPLE 5 Simplify.

a. $\sqrt{(-3)^2}$ **b.** $\sqrt{x^2}$ **c.** $\sqrt[4]{(x-2)^4}$ **d.** $\sqrt[3]{(-5)^3}$

e. $\sqrt[5]{(2x-7)^5}$ **f.** $\sqrt{25x^2}$ **g.** $\sqrt{x^2 + 2x + 1}$

Solution

a. $\sqrt{(-3)^2} = |-3| = 3$ When the index is even, the absolute value bars ensure that our result is not negative.

b. $\sqrt{x^2} = |x|$

c. $\sqrt[4]{(x-2)^4} = |x-2|$

d. $\sqrt[3]{(-5)^3} = -5$

e. $\sqrt[5]{(2x-7)^5} = 2x - 7$ Absolute value bars are not needed when the index is odd.

f. $\sqrt{25x^2} = 5|x|$

g. $\sqrt{x^2 + 2x + 1} = \sqrt{(x+1)^2} = |x+1|$

PRACTICE
5   Simplify.

a. $\sqrt{(-4)^2}$ **b.** $\sqrt{x^{14}}$ **c.** $\sqrt[4]{(x+7)^4}$ **d.** $\sqrt[3]{(-7)^3}$

e. $\sqrt[5]{(3x-5)^5}$ **f.** $\sqrt{49x^2}$ **g.** $\sqrt{x^2+16x+64}$

OBJECTIVE
6   Graphing Square and Cube Root Functions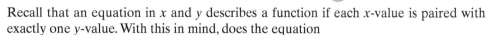

Recall that an equation in x and y describes a function if each x-value is paired with exactly one y-value. With this in mind, does the equation

$$y = \sqrt{x}$$

describe a function? First, notice that replacement values for x must be nonnegative real numbers, since $\sqrt{x}$ is not a real number if $x < 0$. The notation $\sqrt{x}$ denotes the principal square root of x, so for every nonnegative number x, there is exactly one number, $\sqrt{x}$. Therefore, $y = \sqrt{x}$ describes a function, and we may write it as

$$f(x) = \sqrt{x}$$

In general, radical functions are functions of the form

$$f(x) = \sqrt[n]{x}.$$

Recall that the domain of a function in x is the set of all possible replacement values of x. This means that if n is even, the domain is the set of all nonnegative numbers, or $\{x \mid x \geq 0\}$ or $[0, \infty)$. If n is odd, the domain is the set of all real numbers, or $(-\infty, \infty)$. Keep this in mind as we find function values.

EXAMPLE 6   If $f(x) = \sqrt{x-4}$ and $g(x) = \sqrt[3]{x+2}$, find each function value.

a. $f(8)$ **b.** $f(6)$ **c.** $g(-1)$ **d.** $g(1)$

Solution

a. $f(8) = \sqrt{8-4} = \sqrt{4} = 2$ **b.** $f(6) = \sqrt{6-4} = \sqrt{2}$

c. $g(-1) = \sqrt[3]{-1+2} = \sqrt[3]{1} = 1$ **d.** $g(1) = \sqrt[3]{1+2} = \sqrt[3]{3}$

PRACTICE
6   If $f(x) = \sqrt{x+5}$ and $g(x) = \sqrt[3]{x-3}$, find each function value.

a. $f(11)$ **b.** $f(-1)$ **c.** $g(11)$ **d.** $g(-6)$

> ▶ Helpful Hint
>
> Notice that for the function $f(x) = \sqrt{x-4}$, the domain includes all real numbers that make the radicand ≥ 0. To see what numbers these are, solve $x - 4 \geq 0$ and find that $x \geq 4$. The domain is $\{x \mid x \geq 4\}$, or $[4, \infty)$.
>   The domain of the cube root function $g(x) = \sqrt[3]{x+2}$ is the set of real numbers, or $(-\infty, \infty)$.

EXAMPLE 7   Graph the square root function $f(x) = \sqrt{x}$.

Solution   To graph, we identify the domain, evaluate the function for several values of x, plot the resulting points, and connect the points with a smooth curve. Since $\sqrt{x}$ represents the nonnegative square root of x, the domain of this function is the set of all nonnegative numbers, $\{x \mid x \geq 0\}$ or $[0, \infty)$. We have approximated $\sqrt{3}$ in the table on the next page to help us locate the point corresponding to $(3, \sqrt{3})$.

(Continued on next page)

x	$f(x) = \sqrt{x}$
0	0
1	1
3	$\sqrt{3} \approx 1.7$
4	2
9	3

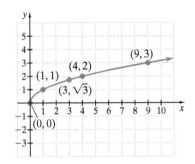

Notice that the graph of this function passes the vertical line test, as expected.

PRACTICE
7 Graph the square root function $h(x) = \sqrt{x + 2}$.

The equation $f(x) = \sqrt[3]{x}$ also describes a function. Here, x may be any real number, so the domain of this function is the set of all real numbers, or $(-\infty, \infty)$. A few function values are given next.

$$f(0) = \sqrt[3]{0} = 0$$
$$f(1) = \sqrt[3]{1} = 1$$
$$f(-1) = \sqrt[3]{-1} = -1$$
$$f(6) = \sqrt[3]{6}$$
$$f(-6) = \sqrt[3]{-6}$$
$$f(8) = \sqrt[3]{8} = 2$$
$$f(-8) = \sqrt[3]{-8} = -2$$

Here, there is no rational number whose cube is 6. Thus, the radicals do not simplify to rational numbers.

EXAMPLE 8 Graph the function $f(x) = \sqrt[3]{x}$.

Solution To graph, we identify the domain, plot points, and connect the points with a smooth curve. The domain of this function is the set of all real numbers. The table comes from the function values obtained earlier. We have approximated $\sqrt[3]{6}$ and $\sqrt[3]{-6}$ for graphing purposes.

x	$f(x) = \sqrt[3]{x}$
0	0
1	1
−1	−1
6	$\sqrt[3]{6} \approx 1.8$
−6	$\sqrt[3]{-6} \approx -1.8$
8	2
−8	−2

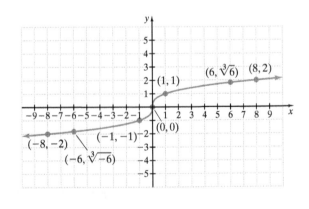

The graph of this function passes the vertical line test, as expected.

PRACTICE
8 Graph the function $f(x) = \sqrt[3]{x} - 4$.

Vocabulary, Readiness & Video Check

Use the choices below to fill in each blank. Not all choices will be used.

is	cubes	$-\sqrt{a}$	radical sign	index
is not	squares	$\sqrt{-a}$	radicand	

1. In the expression $\sqrt[n]{a}$, the n is called the _____, the $\sqrt{}$ is called the _____, and a is called the _____.
2. If $\sqrt{a}$ is the positive square root of a, $a \neq 0$, then _____ is the negative square root of a.
3. The square root of a negative number _____ a real number.
4. Numbers such as $1, 4, 9$, and 25 are called perfect _____, whereas numbers such as $1, 8, 27$, and 125 are called perfect _____.

Fill in the blank.

5. The domain of the function $f(x) = \sqrt{x}$ is _____.
6. The domain of the function $f(x) = \sqrt[3]{x}$ is _____.
7. If $f(16) = 4$, the corresponding ordered pair is _____.
8. If $g(-8) = -2$, the corresponding ordered pair is _____.

Martin-Gay Interactive Videos

See Video 10.1

Watch the section lecture video and answer the following questions.

OBJECTIVE
1
9. From ▱ Examples 5 and 6, when simplifying radicals containing variables with exponents, describe a shortcut you can use.

OBJECTIVE
2
10. From ▱ Example 9, how can you determine a reasonable approximation for a non-perfect square root without using a calculator?

OBJECTIVE
3
11. From ▱ Example 11, what is an important difference between the square root and the cube root of a negative number?

OBJECTIVE
4
12. From ▱ Example 12, what conclusion is made about the even root of a negative number?

OBJECTIVE
5
13. From the lecture before ▱ Example 17, why do you think no absolute value bars are used when n is odd?

OBJECTIVE
6
14. In ▱ Example 19, the domain is found by looking at the graph. How can the domain be found by looking at the function?

10.1 Exercise Set   MyMathLab®

Simplify. Assume that variables represent positive real numbers. See Example 1.

1. $\sqrt{100}$
2. $\sqrt{400}$
3. $\sqrt{\dfrac{1}{4}}$
4. $\sqrt{\dfrac{9}{25}}$
5. $\sqrt{0.0001}$
6. $\sqrt{0.04}$
7. $-\sqrt{36}$
8. $-\sqrt{9}$
9. $\sqrt{x^{10}}$
10. $\sqrt{x^{16}}$
11. $\sqrt{16y^6}$
12. $\sqrt{64y^{20}}$

Use a calculator to approximate each square root to 3 decimal places. Check to see that each approximation is reasonable. See Example 2.

13. $\sqrt{7}$
14. $\sqrt{11}$

▸ 15. $\sqrt{38}$
16. $\sqrt{56}$
17. $\sqrt{200}$
18. $\sqrt{300}$

Find each cube root. See Example 3.

19. $\sqrt[3]{64}$
20. $\sqrt[3]{27}$
▸ 21. $\sqrt[3]{\dfrac{1}{8}}$
22. $\sqrt[3]{\dfrac{27}{64}}$
23. $\sqrt[3]{-1}$
24. $\sqrt[3]{-125}$
25. $\sqrt[3]{x^{12}}$
26. $\sqrt[3]{x^{15}}$
▸ 27. $\sqrt[3]{-27x^9}$
28. $\sqrt[3]{-64x^6}$

Find each root. Assume that all variables represent nonnegative real numbers. See Example 4.

29. $-\sqrt[4]{16}$

30. $\sqrt[5]{-243}$

31. $\sqrt[4]{-16}$

32. $\sqrt{-16}$

33. $\sqrt[5]{-32}$

34. $\sqrt[5]{-1}$

35. $\sqrt[5]{x^{20}}$

36. $\sqrt[4]{x^{20}}$

37. $\sqrt[6]{64x^{12}}$

38. $\sqrt[5]{-32x^{15}}$

39. $\sqrt{81x^4}$

40. $\sqrt[4]{81x^4}$

41. $\sqrt[4]{256x^8}$

42. $\sqrt{256x^8}$

Simplify. Assume that the variables represent any real number. See Example 5.

43. $\sqrt{(-8)^2}$

44. $\sqrt{(-7)^2}$

45. $\sqrt[3]{(-8)^3}$

46. $\sqrt[5]{(-7)^5}$

47. $\sqrt{4x^2}$

48. $\sqrt[4]{16x^4}$

49. $\sqrt[3]{x^3}$

50. $\sqrt[5]{x^5}$

51. $\sqrt{(x-5)^2}$

52. $\sqrt{(y-6)^2}$

53. $\sqrt{x^2+4x+4}$
(*Hint:* Factor the polynomial first.)

54. $\sqrt{x^2-8x+16}$
(*Hint:* Factor the polynomial first.)

MIXED PRACTICE

Simplify each radical. Assume that all variables represent positive real numbers.

55. $-\sqrt{121}$

56. $-\sqrt[3]{125}$

57. $\sqrt[3]{8x^3}$

58. $\sqrt{16x^8}$

59. $\sqrt{y^{12}}$

60. $\sqrt[3]{y^{12}}$

61. $\sqrt{25a^2b^{20}}$

62. $\sqrt{9x^4y^6}$

63. $\sqrt[3]{-27x^{12}y^9}$

64. $\sqrt[3]{-8a^{21}b^6}$

65. $\sqrt[4]{a^{16}b^4}$

66. $\sqrt[4]{x^8y^{12}}$

67. $\sqrt[5]{-32x^{10}y^5}$

68. $\sqrt[5]{-243x^5z^{15}}$

69. $\sqrt{\dfrac{25}{49}}$

70. $\sqrt{\dfrac{4}{81}}$

71. $\sqrt{\dfrac{x^{20}}{4y^2}}$

72. $\sqrt{\dfrac{y^{10}}{9x^6}}$

73. $-\sqrt[3]{\dfrac{z^{21}}{27x^3}}$

74. $-\sqrt[3]{\dfrac{64a^3}{b^9}}$

75. $\sqrt[4]{\dfrac{x^4}{16}}$

76. $\sqrt[4]{\dfrac{y^4}{81x^4}}$

If $f(x) = \sqrt{2x+3}$ and $g(x) = \sqrt[3]{x-8}$, find the following function values. See Example 6.

77. $f(0)$

78. $g(0)$

79. $g(7)$

80. $f(-1)$

81. $g(-19)$

82. $f(3)$

83. $f(2)$

84. $g(1)$

Identify the domain and then graph each function. See Example 7.

85. $f(x) = \sqrt{x} + 2$

86. $f(x) = \sqrt{x} - 2$

87. $f(x) = \sqrt{x-3}$; use the following table.

x	$f(x)$
3	
4	
7	
12	

88. $f(x) = \sqrt{x+1}$; use the following table.

x	$f(x)$
-1	
0	
3	
8	

Identify the domain and then graph each function. See Example 8.

89. $f(x) = \sqrt[3]{x} + 1$

90. $f(x) = \sqrt[3]{x} - 2$

91. $g(x) = \sqrt[3]{x-1}$; use the following table.

x	$g(x)$
1	
2	
0	
9	
-7	

92. $g(x) = \sqrt[3]{x+1}$; use the following table.

x	$g(x)$
-1	
0	
-2	
7	
-9	

REVIEW AND PREVIEW

Simplify each exponential expression. See Sections 5.1 and 5.5.

93. $(-2x^3y^2)^5$

94. $(4y^6z^7)^3$

95. $(-3x^2y^3z^5)(20x^5y^7)$

96. $(-14a^5bc^2)(2abc^4)$

97. $\dfrac{7x^{-1}y}{14(x^5y^2)^{-2}}$

98. $\dfrac{(2a^{-1}b^2)^3}{(8a^2b)^{-2}}$

CONCEPT EXTENSIONS

Determine whether the following are real numbers. See the Concept Check in this section.

99. $\sqrt{-17}$

100. $\sqrt[3]{-17}$

101. $\sqrt[10]{-17}$

102. $\sqrt[15]{-17}$

Choose the correct letter or letters. No pencil is needed, just think your way through these.

103. Which radical is not a real number?
  a. $\sqrt{3}$ **b.** $-\sqrt{11}$ **c.** $\sqrt[3]{-10}$ **d.** $\sqrt{-10}$

104. Which radical(s) simplify to 3?
  a. $\sqrt{9}$ **b.** $\sqrt{-9}$ **c.** $\sqrt[3]{27}$ **d.** $\sqrt[3]{-27}$

105. Which radical(s) simplify to -3?
  a. $\sqrt{9}$ **b.** $\sqrt{-9}$ **c.** $\sqrt[3]{27}$ **d.** $\sqrt[3]{-27}$

106. Which radical does not simplify to a whole number?
  a. $\sqrt{64}$ **b.** $\sqrt[3]{64}$ **c.** $\sqrt{8}$ **d.** $\sqrt[3]{8}$

For Exercises 107 through 110, do not use a calculator.

107. $\sqrt{160}$ is closest to
  a. 10   **b.** 13   **c.** 20   **d.** 40

108. $\sqrt{1000}$ is closest to
  a. 10   **b.** 30   **c.** 100   **d.** 500

109. The perimeter of the triangle is closest to
  a. 12   **b.** 18
  c. 66   **d.** 132

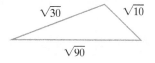

110. The length of the bent wire is closest to
  a. 5   **b.** $\sqrt{28}$
  c. 7   **d.** 14

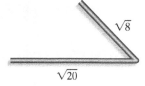

111. Explain why $\sqrt{-64}$ is not a real number.

112. Explain why $\sqrt[3]{-64}$ is a real number.

The Mosteller formula for calculating adult body surface area is $B = \sqrt{\dfrac{hw}{3131}}$, where B is an individual's body surface area in square meters, h is the individual's height in inches, and w is the individual's weight in pounds. Use this information to answer Exercises 113 and 114. Round answers to 2 decimal places.

113. Find the body surface area of an individual who is 66 inches tall and who weighs 135 pounds.

114. Find the body surface area of an individual who is 74 inches tall and who weighs 225 pounds.

115. Escape velocity is the minimum speed that an object must reach to escape the pull of a planet's gravity. Escape velocity v is given by the equation $v = \sqrt{\dfrac{2Gm}{r}}$, where m is the mass of the planet, r is its radius, and G is the universal gravitational constant, which has a value of $G = 6.67 \times 10^{-11}$ m³/kg·s². The mass of Earth is 5.97×10^{24} kg, and its radius is 6.37×10^6 m. Use this information to find the escape velocity for Earth in meters per second. Round to the nearest whole number. (*Source: National Space Science Data Center*)

116. Use the formula from Exercise 115 to determine the escape velocity for the moon. The mass of the moon is 7.35×10^{22} kg, and its radius is 1.74×10^6 m. Round to the nearest whole number. (*Source:* National Space Science Data Center)

117. Suppose a classmate tells you that $\sqrt{13} \approx 5.7$. Without a calculator, how can you convince your classmate that he or she must have made an error?

118. Suppose a classmate tells you that $\sqrt[3]{10} \approx 3.2$. Without a calculator, how can you convince your friend that he or she must have made an error?

Use a graphing calculator to verify the domain of each function and its graph.

119. Exercise 85

120. Exercise 86

121. Exercise 89

122. Exercise 90

10.2 | Rational Exponents

OBJECTIVES

1 Understand the Meaning of $a^{1/n}$.

2 Understand the Meaning of $a^{m/n}$.

3 Understand the Meaning of $a^{-m/n}$.

4 Use Rules for Exponents to Simplify Expressions That Contain Rational Exponents.

5 Use Rational Exponents to Simplify Radical Expressions.

OBJECTIVE

1   Understanding the Meaning of $a^{1/n}$

So far in this text, we have not defined expressions with rational exponents such as $3^{1/2}$, $x^{2/3}$, and $-9^{-1/4}$. We will define these expressions so that the rules for exponents will apply to these rational exponents as well.

Suppose that $x = 5^{1/3}$. Then

$$x^3 = (5^{1/3})^3 = 5^{1/3 \cdot 3} = 5^1 \text{ or } 5$$

using rules for exponents

Since $x^3 = 5$, x is the number whose cube is 5, or $x = \sqrt[3]{5}$. Notice that we also know that $x = 5^{1/3}$. This means

$$5^{1/3} = \sqrt[3]{5}$$

Definition of $a^{1/n}$

If n is a positive integer greater than 1 and $\sqrt[n]{a}$ is a real number, then

$$a^{1/n} = \sqrt[n]{a}$$

Notice that the denominator of the rational exponent corresponds to the index of the radical.

EXAMPLE 1   Use radical notation to write the following. Simplify if possible.

a. $4^{1/2}$ **b.** $64^{1/3}$ **c.** $x^{1/4}$ **d.** $0^{1/6}$ **e.** $-9^{1/2}$ **f.** $(81x^8)^{1/4}$ **g.** $5y^{1/3}$

Solution

a. $4^{1/2} = \sqrt{4} = 2$ **b.** $64^{1/3} = \sqrt[3]{64} = 4$

c. $x^{1/4} = \sqrt[4]{x}$ **d.** $0^{1/6} = \sqrt[6]{0} = 0$

e. $-9^{1/2} = -\sqrt{9} = -3$ **f.** $(81x^8)^{1/4} = \sqrt[4]{81x^8} = 3x^2$

g. $5y^{1/3} = 5\sqrt[3]{y}$

PRACTICE

1   Use radical notation to write the following. Simplify if possible.

a. $36^{1/2}$ **b.** $1000^{1/3}$ **c.** $x^{1/3}$ **d.** $1^{1/4}$

e. $-64^{1/2}$ **f.** $(125x^9)^{1/3}$ **g.** $3x^{1/4}$

OBJECTIVE

2   Understanding the Meaning of $a^{m/n}$

As we expand our use of exponents to include $\dfrac{m}{n}$, we define their meaning so that rules for exponents still hold true. For example, by properties of exponents,

$$8^{2/3} = (8^{1/3})^2 = (\sqrt[3]{8})^2 \quad \text{or}$$
$$8^{2/3} = (8^2)^{1/3} = \sqrt[3]{8^2}$$

Definition of $a^{m/n}$

If m and n are positive integers greater than 1 with $\dfrac{m}{n}$ in simplest form, then

$$a^{m/n} = \sqrt[n]{a^m} = (\sqrt[n]{a})^m$$

as long as $\sqrt[n]{a}$ is a real number.

Notice that the denominator n of the rational exponent corresponds to the index of the radical. The numerator m of the rational exponent indicates that the base is to be raised to the mth power. This means

$$8^{2/3} = \sqrt[3]{8^2} = \sqrt[3]{64} = 4 \quad \text{or}$$

$$8^{2/3} = \left(\sqrt[3]{8}\right)^2 = 2^2 = 4$$

From simplifying $8^{2/3}$, can you see that it doesn't matter whether you raise to a power first and then take the nth root or you take the nth root first and then raise to a power?

> ▶ Helpful Hint
>
> Most of the time, $\left(\sqrt[n]{a}\right)^m$ will be easier to calculate than $\sqrt[n]{a^m}$.

EXAMPLE 2   Use radical notation to write the following. Then simplify if possible.

a. $4^{3/2}$ **b.** $-16^{3/4}$ **c.** $(-27)^{2/3}$

d. $\left(\dfrac{1}{9}\right)^{3/2}$ **e.** $(4x - 1)^{3/5}$

Solution

a. $4^{3/2} = \left(\sqrt{4}\right)^3 = 2^3 = 8$ **b.** $-16^{3/4} = -\left(\sqrt[4]{16}\right)^3 = -(2)^3 = -8$

c. $(-27)^{2/3} = \left(\sqrt[3]{-27}\right)^2 = (-3)^2 = 9$ **d.** $\left(\dfrac{1}{9}\right)^{3/2} = \left(\sqrt{\dfrac{1}{9}}\right)^3 = \left(\dfrac{1}{3}\right)^3 = \dfrac{1}{27}$

e. $(4x - 1)^{3/5} = \sqrt[5]{(4x - 1)^3}$

PRACTICE

2   Use radical notation to write the following. Simplify if possible.

a. $16^{3/2}$ **b.** $-1^{3/5}$ **c.** $-(81)^{3/4}$

d. $\left(\dfrac{1}{25}\right)^{3/2}$ **e.** $(3x + 2)^{5/9}$

> ▶ Helpful Hint
>
> The *denominator* of a rational exponent is the index of the corresponding radical. For example, $x^{1/5} = \sqrt[5]{x}$ and $z^{2/3} = \sqrt[3]{z^2}$, or $z^{2/3} = \left(\sqrt[3]{z}\right)^2$.

OBJECTIVE
3   Understanding the Meaning of $a^{-m/n}$

The rational exponents we have given meaning to exclude negative rational numbers. To complete the set of definitions, we define $a^{-m/n}$.

> **Definition of $a^{-m/n}$**
>
> $$a^{-m/n} = \frac{1}{a^{m/n}}$$
>
> as long as $a^{m/n}$ is a nonzero real number.

EXAMPLE 3   Write each expression with a positive exponent, and then simplify.

a. $16^{-3/4}$ **b.** $(-27)^{-2/3}$

Solution

a. $16^{-3/4} = \dfrac{1}{16^{3/4}} = \dfrac{1}{\left(\sqrt[4]{16}\right)^3} = \dfrac{1}{2^3} = \dfrac{1}{8}$

b. $(-27)^{-2/3} = \dfrac{1}{(-27)^{2/3}} = \dfrac{1}{\left(\sqrt[3]{-27}\right)^2} = \dfrac{1}{(-3)^2} = \dfrac{1}{9}$

(Continued on next page)

3 Write each expression with a positive exponent; then simplify.

a. $9^{-3/2}$ **b.** $(-64)^{-2/3}$

> ▶ **Helpful Hint**
>
> If an expression contains a negative rational exponent, such as $9^{-3/2}$, you may want to first write the expression with a positive exponent and then interpret the rational exponent. Notice that the sign of the base is not affected by the sign of its exponent. For example,
>
> $$9^{-3/2} = \frac{1}{9^{3/2}} = \frac{1}{(\sqrt{9})^3} = \frac{1}{27}$$
>
> Also,
>
> $$(-27)^{-1/3} = \frac{1}{(-27)^{1/3}} = -\frac{1}{3}$$

✓**CONCEPT CHECK**
Which one is correct?

a. $-8^{2/3} = \frac{1}{4}$ **b.** $8^{-2/3} = -\frac{1}{4}$ **c.** $8^{-2/3} = -4$ **d.** $-8^{-2/3} = -\frac{1}{4}$

---

4 Using Rules for Exponents to Simplify Expressions

It can be shown that the properties of integer exponents hold for rational exponents. By using these properties and definitions, we can now simplify expressions that contain rational exponents.

These rules are repeated here for review.

Note: For the remainder of this chapter, we will assume that variables represent positive real numbers. Since this is so, we need not insert absolute value bars when we simplify even roots.

> **Summary of Exponent Rules**
>
> If m and n are rational numbers, and a, b, and c are numbers for which the expressions below exist, then
>
> | | |
> |---|---|
> | Product rule for exponents: | $a^m \cdot a^n = a^{m+n}$ |
> | Power rule for exponents: | $(a^m)^n = a^{m \cdot n}$ |
> | Power rules for products and quotients: | $(ab)^n = a^n b^n$ and |
> | | $\left(\dfrac{a}{c}\right)^n = \dfrac{a^n}{c^n}, c \neq 0$ |
> | Quotient rule for exponents: | $\dfrac{a^m}{a^n} = a^{m-n}, a \neq 0$ |
> | Zero exponent: | $a^0 = 1, a \neq 0$ |
> | Negative exponent: | $a^{-n} = \dfrac{1}{a^n}, a \neq 0$ |

EXAMPLE 4   Use properties of exponents to simplify. Write results with only positive exponents.

a. $b^{1/3} \cdot b^{5/3}$ **b.** $x^{1/2} x^{1/3}$ **c.** $\dfrac{7^{1/3}}{7^{4/3}}$

d. $y^{-4/7} \cdot y^{6/7}$ **e.** $\dfrac{(2x^{2/5} y^{-1/3})^5}{x^2 y}$

Solution

a. $b^{1/3} \cdot b^{5/3} = b^{(1/3+5/3)} = b^{6/3} = b^2$

b. $x^{1/2}x^{1/3} = x^{(1/2+1/3)} = x^{3/6+2/6} = x^{5/6}$ Use the product rule.

c. $\dfrac{7^{1/3}}{7^{4/3}} = 7^{1/3-4/3} = 7^{-3/3} = 7^{-1} = \dfrac{1}{7}$ Use the quotient rule.

d. $y^{-4/7} \cdot y^{6/7} = y^{-4/7+6/7} = y^{2/7}$ Use the product rule.

e. We begin by using the power rule $(ab)^m = a^m b^m$ to simplify the numerator.

$$\dfrac{(2x^{2/5}y^{-1/3})^5}{x^2 y} = \dfrac{2^5(x^{2/5})^5(y^{-1/3})^5}{x^2 y} = \dfrac{32x^2 y^{-5/3}}{x^2 y}$$ Use the power rule and simplify

$$= 32x^{2-2}y^{-5/3-3/3}$$ Apply the quotient rule.

$$= 32x^0 y^{-8/3}$$

$$= \dfrac{32}{y^{8/3}}$$

PRACTICE
4   Use properties of exponents to simplify.

a. $y^{2/3} \cdot y^{8/3}$ **b.** $x^{3/5} \cdot x^{1/4}$ **c.** $\dfrac{9^{2/7}}{9^{9/7}}$

d. $b^{4/9} \cdot b^{-2/9}$ **e.** $\dfrac{(3x^{1/4}y^{-2/3})^4}{x^4 y}$

EXAMPLE 5   Multiply.

a. $z^{2/3}(z^{1/3} - z^5)$ **b.** $(x^{1/3} - 5)(x^{1/3} + 2)$

Solution

a. $z^{2/3}(z^{1/3} - z^5) = z^{2/3}z^{1/3} - z^{2/3}z^5$ Apply the distributive property.

$$= z^{(2/3+1/3)} - z^{(2/3+5)}$$ Use the product rule.

$$= z^{3/3} - z^{(2/3+15/3)}$$

$$= z - z^{17/3}$$

b. $(x^{1/3} - 5)(x^{1/3} + 2) = x^{2/3} + 2x^{1/3} - 5x^{1/3} - 10$ Think of $(x^{1/3} - 5)$ and $(x^{1/3} + 2)$ as 2 binomials, and FOIL.

$$= x^{2/3} - 3x^{1/3} - 10$$

PRACTICE
5   Multiply.

a. $x^{3/5}(x^{1/3} - x^2)$ **b.** $(x^{1/2} + 6)(x^{1/2} - 2)$

EXAMPLE 6   Factor $x^{-1/2}$ from the expression $3x^{-1/2} - 7x^{5/2}$. Assume that all variables represent positive numbers.

Solution

$$3x^{-1/2} - 7x^{5/2} = (x^{-1/2})(3) - (x^{-1/2})(7x^{6/2})$$

$$= x^{-1/2}(3 - 7x^3)$$

To check, multiply $x^{-1/2}(3 - 7x^3)$ to see that the product is $3x^{-1/2} - 7x^{5/2}$.

PRACTICE
6   Factor $x^{-1/5}$ from the expression $2x^{-1/5} - 7x^{4/5}$.

OBJECTIVE
> **5** **Using Rational Exponents to Simplify Radical Expressions**

Some radical expressions are easier to simplify when we first write them with rational exponents. Use properties of exponents to simplify, and then convert back to radical notation.

EXAMPLE 7 Use rational exponents to simplify. Assume that variables represent positive numbers.

a. $\sqrt[8]{x^4}$ **b.** $\sqrt[6]{25}$ **c.** $\sqrt[4]{r^2 s^6}$

Solution

a. $\sqrt[8]{x^4} = x^{4/8} = x^{1/2} = \sqrt{x}$

b. $\sqrt[6]{25} = 25^{1/6} = (5^2)^{1/6} = 5^{2/6} = 5^{1/3} = \sqrt[3]{5}$

c. $\sqrt[4]{r^2 s^6} = (r^2 s^6)^{1/4} = r^{2/4} s^{6/4} = r^{1/2} s^{3/2} = (rs^3)^{1/2} = \sqrt{rs^3}$ □

PRACTICE
7 Use rational exponents to simplify. Assume that the variables represent positive numbers.

a. $\sqrt[9]{x^3}$ **b.** $\sqrt[4]{36}$ **c.** $\sqrt[8]{a^4 b^2}$

EXAMPLE 8 Use rational exponents to write as a single radical.

a. $\sqrt{x} \cdot \sqrt[4]{x}$ **b.** $\dfrac{\sqrt{x}}{\sqrt[3]{x}}$ **c.** $\sqrt[3]{3} \cdot \sqrt{2}$

Solution

a. $\sqrt{x} \cdot \sqrt[4]{x} = x^{1/2} \cdot x^{1/4} = x^{1/2 + 1/4}$
$$= x^{3/4} = \sqrt[4]{x^3}$$

b. $\dfrac{\sqrt{x}}{\sqrt[3]{x}} = \dfrac{x^{1/2}}{x^{1/3}} = x^{1/2 - 1/3} = x^{3/6 - 2/6}$
$$= x^{1/6} = \sqrt[6]{x}$$

c. $\sqrt[3]{3} \cdot \sqrt{2} = 3^{1/3} \cdot 2^{1/2}$ Write with rational exponents.
$$= 3^{2/6} \cdot 2^{3/6}$$ Write the exponents so that they have the same denominator.
$$= (3^2 \cdot 2^3)^{1/6}$$ Use $a^n b^n = (ab)^n$
$$= \sqrt[6]{3^2 \cdot 2^3}$$ Write with radical notation.
$$= \sqrt[6]{72}$$ Multiply $3^2 \cdot 2^3$.   □

PRACTICE
8 Use rational expressions to write each of the following as a single radical.

a. $\sqrt[3]{x} \cdot \sqrt[4]{x}$ **b.** $\dfrac{\sqrt[3]{y}}{\sqrt[5]{y}}$ **c.** $\sqrt[3]{5} \cdot \sqrt{3}$

Vocabulary, Readiness & Video Check

Answer each true or false.

1. $9^{-1/2}$ is a positive number. _____

2. $9^{-1/2}$ is a whole number. _____

3. $\dfrac{1}{a^{-m/n}} = a^{m/n}$ (where $a^{m/n}$ is a nonzero real number). _____

Fill in the blank with the correct choice.

4. To simplify $x^{2/3} \cdot x^{1/5}$, _____ the exponents.
    a. add   **b.** subtract   **c.** multiply   **d.** divide

5. To simplify $(x^{2/3})^{1/5}$, _____ the exponents.
    a. add   **b.** subtract   **c.** multiply   **d.** divide

6. To simplify $\dfrac{x^{2/3}}{x^{1/5}}$, _____ the exponents.
    a. add   **b.** subtract   **c.** multiply   **d.** divide

Martin-Gay Interactive Videos

See Video 10.2

Watch the section lecture video and answer the following questions.

OBJECTIVE 1

7. From looking at Example 2, what is $-(3x)^{1/5}$ in radical notation?

OBJECTIVE 2

8. From Examples 3 and 4, in a fractional exponent, what do the numerator and denominator each represent in radical form?

OBJECTIVE 3

9. Based on Example 5, complete the following statements. A negative fractional exponent will move a base from the numerator to the _____ with the fractional exponent becoming _____.

OBJECTIVE 4

10. Based on Examples 7–9, complete the following statements. Assume you have an expression with fractional exponents. If applying the product rule of exponents, you _____ the exponents. If applying the quotient rule of exponents, you _____ the exponents. If applying the power rule of exponents, you _____ the exponents.

OBJECTIVE 5

11. From Example 10, describe a way to simplify a radical of a variable raised to a power if the index and the exponent have a common factor.

10.2 Exercise Set   MyMathLab®

Use radical notation to write each expression. Simplify if possible. See Example 1.

1. $49^{1/2}$ **2.** $64^{1/3}$

3. $27^{1/3}$ **4.** $8^{1/3}$

5. $\left(\dfrac{1}{16}\right)^{1/4}$ **6.** $\left(\dfrac{1}{64}\right)^{1/2}$

7. $169^{1/2}$ **8.** $81^{1/4}$

9. $2m^{1/3}$ **10.** $(2m)^{1/3}$

11. $(9x^4)^{1/2}$ **12.** $(16x^8)^{1/2}$

13. $(-27)^{1/3}$ **14.** $-64^{1/2}$

15. $-16^{1/4}$ **16.** $(-32)^{1/5}$

Use radical notation to write each expression. Simplify if possible. See Example 2.

17. $16^{3/4}$ **18.** $4^{5/2}$

19. $(-64)^{2/3}$ **20.** $(-8)^{4/3}$

21. $(-16)^{3/4}$ **22.** $(-9)^{3/2}$

23. $(2x)^{3/5}$ **24.** $2x^{3/5}$

25. $(7x+2)^{2/3}$ **26.** $(x-4)^{3/4}$

27. $\left(\dfrac{16}{9}\right)^{3/2}$ **28.** $\left(\dfrac{49}{25}\right)^{3/2}$

Write with positive exponents. Simplify if possible. See Example 3.

29. $8^{-4/3}$ **30.** $64^{-2/3}$

31. $(-64)^{-2/3}$ **32.** $(-8)^{-4/3}$

33. $(-4)^{-3/2}$ **34.** $(-16)^{-5/4}$

35. $x^{-1/4}$ **36.** $y^{-1/6}$

37. $\dfrac{1}{a^{-2/3}}$ **38.** $\dfrac{1}{n^{-8/9}}$

39. $\dfrac{5}{7x^{-3/4}}$ **40.** $\dfrac{2}{3y^{-5/7}}$

Use the properties of exponents to simplify each expression. Write with positive exponents. See Example 4.

41. $a^{2/3}a^{5/3}$ **42.** $b^{9/5}b^{8/5}$

43. $x^{-2/5} \cdot x^{7/5}$ **44.** $y^{4/3} \cdot y^{-1/3}$

45. $3^{1/4} \cdot 3^{3/8}$ **46.** $5^{1/2} \cdot 5^{1/6}$

47. $\dfrac{y^{1/3}}{y^{1/6}}$ **48.** $\dfrac{x^{3/4}}{x^{1/8}}$

49. $(4u^2)^{3/2}$ **50.** $(32^{1/5}x^{2/3})^3$

51. $\dfrac{b^{1/2}b^{3/4}}{-b^{1/4}}$ **52.** $\dfrac{a^{1/4}a^{-1/2}}{a^{2/3}}$

53. $\dfrac{(x^3)^{1/2}}{x^{7/2}}$ **54.** $\dfrac{y^{11/3}}{(y^5)^{1/3}}$

55. $\dfrac{(3x^{1/4})^3}{x^{1/12}}$

56. $\dfrac{(2x^{1/5})^4}{x^{3/10}}$

57. $\dfrac{(y^3 z)^{1/6}}{y^{-1/2} z^{1/3}}$

58. $\dfrac{(m^2 n)^{1/4}}{m^{-1/2} n^{5/8}}$

59. $\dfrac{(x^3 y^2)^{1/4}}{(x^{-5} y^{-1})^{-1/2}}$

60. $\dfrac{(a^{-2} b^3)^{1/8}}{(a^{-3} b)^{-1/4}}$

Multiply. See Example 5.

61. $y^{1/2}(y^{1/2} - y^{2/3})$

62. $x^{1/2}(x^{1/2} + x^{3/2})$

63. $x^{2/3}(x - 2)$

64. $3x^{1/2}(x + y)$

65. $(2x^{1/3} + 3)(2x^{1/3} - 3)$

66. $(y^{1/2} + 5)(y^{1/2} + 5)$

Factor the given factor from the expression. See Example 6.

67. $x^{8/3}; \ x^{8/3} + x^{10/3}$

68. $x^{3/2}; \ x^{5/2} - x^{3/2}$

69. $x^{1/5}; \ x^{2/5} - 3x^{1/5}$

70. $x^{2/7}; \ x^{3/7} - 2x^{2/7}$

71. $x^{-1/3}; \ 5x^{-1/3} + x^{2/3}$

72. $x^{-3/4}; \ x^{-3/4} + 3x^{1/4}$

Use rational exponents to simplify each radical. Assume that all variables represent positive numbers. See Example 7.

73. $\sqrt[6]{x^3}$

74. $\sqrt[9]{a^3}$

75. $\sqrt[6]{4}$

76. $\sqrt[4]{36}$

77. $\sqrt[4]{16x^2}$

78. $\sqrt[8]{4y^2}$

79. $\sqrt[8]{x^4 y^4}$

80. $\sqrt[9]{y^6 z^3}$

81. $\sqrt[12]{a^8 b^4}$

82. $\sqrt[10]{a^5 b^5}$

83. $\sqrt[4]{(x+3)^2}$

84. $\sqrt[8]{(y+1)^4}$

Use rational expressions to write as a single radical expression. See Example 8.

85. $\sqrt[3]{y} \cdot \sqrt[5]{y^2}$

86. $\sqrt[3]{y^2} \cdot \sqrt[6]{y}$

87. $\dfrac{\sqrt[3]{b^2}}{\sqrt[4]{b}}$

88. $\dfrac{\sqrt[4]{a}}{\sqrt[5]{a}}$

89. $\sqrt[3]{x} \cdot \sqrt[4]{x} \cdot \sqrt[8]{x^3}$

90. $\sqrt[6]{y} \cdot \sqrt[3]{y} \cdot \sqrt[5]{y^2}$

91. $\dfrac{\sqrt[3]{a^2}}{\sqrt[6]{a}}$

92. $\dfrac{\sqrt[5]{b^2}}{\sqrt[10]{b^3}}$

93. $\sqrt{3} \cdot \sqrt[3]{4}$

94. $\sqrt[3]{5} \cdot \sqrt{2}$

95. $\sqrt[5]{7} \cdot \sqrt[3]{y}$

96. $\sqrt[4]{5} \cdot \sqrt[3]{x}$

97. $\sqrt{5r} \cdot \sqrt[3]{s}$

98. $\sqrt[3]{b} \cdot \sqrt[4]{4a}$

REVIEW AND PREVIEW

Write each integer as a product of two integers such that one of the factors is a perfect square. For example, write 18 as 9 · 2 because 9 is a perfect square.

99. 75

100. 20

101. 48

102. 45

Write each integer as a product of two integers such that one of the factors is a perfect cube. For example, write 24 as 8 · 3 because 8 is a perfect cube.

103. 16

104. 56

105. 54

106. 80

CONCEPT EXTENSIONS

Choose the correct letter for each exercise. Letters will be used more than once. No pencil is needed. Just think about the meaning of each expression.

A = 2, B = −2, C = not a real number

107. $4^{1/2}$ _____

108. $-4^{1/2}$ _____

109. $(-4)^{1/2}$ _____

110. $8^{1/3}$ _____

111. $-8^{1/3}$ _____

112. $(-8)^{1/3}$ _____

Basal metabolic rate (BMR) is the number of calories per day a person needs to maintain life. A person's basal metabolic rate B(w) in calories per day can be estimated with the function $B(w) = 70w^{3/4}$, where w is the person's weight in kilograms. Use this information to answer Exercises 113 and 114.

113. Estimate the BMR for a person who weighs 60 kilograms. Round to the nearest calorie. (*Note:* 60 kilograms is approximately 132 pounds.)

114. Estimate the BMR for a person who weighs 90 kilograms. Round to the nearest calorie. (*Note:* 90 kilograms is approximately 198 pounds.)

The number of cell telephone subscribers in the United States from 1995–2010 can be modeled by $f(x) = 25x^{23/25}$, where f(x) is the number of cellular telephone subscriptions in millions, x years after 1995. (Source: CTIA-Wireless Association, 1995–2010) Use this information to answer Exercises 115 and 116.

115. Use this model to estimate the number of cellular subscriptions in 2010. Round to the nearest tenth of a million.

116. Predict the number of cellular telephone subscriptions in 2015. Round to the nearest tenth of a million.

117. Explain how writing x^{-7} with positive exponents is similar to writing $x^{-1/4}$ with positive exponents.

118. Explain how writing $2x^{-5}$ with positive exponents is similar to writing $2x^{-3/4}$ with positive exponents.

Fill in each box with the correct expression.

119. $\square \cdot a^{2/3} = a^{3/3}$, or a

120. $\square \cdot x^{1/8} = x^{4/8}$, or $x^{1/2}$

121. $\dfrac{\square}{x^{-2/5}} = x^{3/5}$

122. $\dfrac{\square}{y^{-3/4}} = y^{4/4}$, or y

Use a calculator to write a four-decimal-place approximation of each number.

123. $8^{1/4}$

124. $20^{1/5}$

125. $18^{3/5}$

126. $76^{5/7}$

127. In physics, the speed of a wave traveling over a stretched string with tension t and density u is given by the expression $\dfrac{\sqrt{t}}{\sqrt{u}}$. Write this expression with rational exponents.

128. In electronics, the angular frequency of oscillations in a certain type of circuit is given by the expression $(LC)^{-1/2}$. Use radical notation to write this expression.

10.3 Simplifying Radical Expressions

OBJECTIVES

1 Use the Product Rule for Radicals.

2 Use the Quotient Rule for Radicals.

3 Simplify Radicals.

4 Use the Distance and Midpoint Formulas.

OBJECTIVE

1 Using the Product Rule

It is possible to simplify some radicals that do not evaluate to rational numbers. To do so, we use a product rule and a quotient rule for radicals. To discover the product rule, notice the following pattern.

$$\sqrt{9} \cdot \sqrt{4} = 3 \cdot 2 = 6$$
$$\sqrt{9 \cdot 4} = \sqrt{36} = 6$$

Since both expressions simplify to 6, it is true that

$$\sqrt{9} \cdot \sqrt{4} = \sqrt{9 \cdot 4}$$

This pattern suggests the following product rule for radicals.

Product Rule for Radicals

If $\sqrt[n]{a}$ and $\sqrt[n]{b}$ are real numbers, then

$$\sqrt[n]{a} \cdot \sqrt[n]{b} = \sqrt[n]{ab}$$

Notice that the product rule is the relationship $a^{1/n} \cdot b^{1/n} = (ab)^{1/n}$ stated in radical notation.

EXAMPLE 1 Multiply.

a. $\sqrt{3} \cdot \sqrt{5}$

b. $\sqrt{21} \cdot \sqrt{x}$

c. $\sqrt[3]{4} \cdot \sqrt[3]{2}$

d. $\sqrt[4]{5y^2} \cdot \sqrt[4]{2x^3}$

e. $\sqrt{\dfrac{2}{a}} \cdot \sqrt{\dfrac{b}{3}}$

Solution

a. $\sqrt{3} \cdot \sqrt{5} = \sqrt{3 \cdot 5} = \sqrt{15}$

b. $\sqrt{21} \cdot \sqrt{x} = \sqrt{21x}$

c. $\sqrt[3]{4} \cdot \sqrt[3]{2} = \sqrt[3]{4 \cdot 2} = \sqrt[3]{8} = 2$

d. $\sqrt[4]{5y^2} \cdot \sqrt[4]{2x^3} = \sqrt[4]{5y^2 \cdot 2x^3} = \sqrt[4]{10y^2x^3}$

e. $\sqrt{\dfrac{2}{a}} \cdot \sqrt{\dfrac{b}{3}} = \sqrt{\dfrac{2}{a} \cdot \dfrac{b}{3}} = \sqrt{\dfrac{2b}{3a}}$

PRACTICE

1 Multiply.

a. $\sqrt{5} \cdot \sqrt{7}$

b. $\sqrt{13} \cdot \sqrt{z}$

c. $\sqrt[4]{125} \cdot \sqrt[4]{5}$

d. $\sqrt[3]{5y} \cdot \sqrt[3]{3x^2}$

e. $\sqrt{\dfrac{5}{m}} \cdot \sqrt{\dfrac{t}{2}}$

OBJECTIVE

2 Using the Quotient Rule

To discover a quotient rule for radicals, notice the following pattern.

$$\sqrt{\frac{4}{9}} = \frac{2}{3}$$

$$\frac{\sqrt{4}}{\sqrt{9}} = \frac{2}{3}$$

Since both expressions simplify to $\frac{2}{3}$, it is true that

$$\sqrt{\frac{4}{9}} = \frac{\sqrt{4}}{\sqrt{9}}$$

This pattern suggests the following quotient rule for radicals.

Quotient Rule for Radicals

If $\sqrt[n]{a}$ and $\sqrt[n]{b}$ are real numbers and $\sqrt[n]{b}$ is not zero, then

$$\sqrt[n]{\frac{a}{b}} = \frac{\sqrt[n]{a}}{\sqrt[n]{b}}$$

Notice that the quotient rule is the relationship $\left(\dfrac{a}{b}\right)^{1/n} = \dfrac{a^{1/n}}{b^{1/n}}$ stated in radical notation. We can use the quotient rule to simplify radical expressions by reading the rule from left to right or to divide radicals by reading the rule from right to left.

For example,

$$\sqrt{\frac{x}{16}} = \frac{\sqrt{x}}{\sqrt{16}} = \frac{\sqrt{x}}{4} \qquad \text{Using } \sqrt[n]{\frac{a}{b}} = \frac{\sqrt[n]{a}}{\sqrt[n]{b}}$$

$$\frac{\sqrt{75}}{\sqrt{3}} = \sqrt{\frac{75}{3}} = \sqrt{25} = 5 \qquad \text{Using } \frac{\sqrt[n]{a}}{\sqrt[n]{b}} = \sqrt[n]{\frac{a}{b}}$$

Note: *Recall that from Section 10.2 on, we assume that variables represent positive real numbers. Since this is so, we need not insert absolute value bars when we simplify even roots.*

EXAMPLE 2 Use the quotient rule to simplify.

a. $\sqrt{\dfrac{25}{49}}$ b. $\sqrt{\dfrac{x}{9}}$ c. $\sqrt[3]{\dfrac{8}{27}}$ d. $\sqrt[4]{\dfrac{3}{16y^4}}$

Solution

a. $\sqrt{\dfrac{25}{49}} = \dfrac{\sqrt{25}}{\sqrt{49}} = \dfrac{5}{7}$ b. $\sqrt{\dfrac{x}{9}} = \dfrac{\sqrt{x}}{\sqrt{9}} = \dfrac{\sqrt{x}}{3}$

c. $\sqrt[3]{\dfrac{8}{27}} = \dfrac{\sqrt[3]{8}}{\sqrt[3]{27}} = \dfrac{2}{3}$ d. $\sqrt[4]{\dfrac{3}{16y^4}} = \dfrac{\sqrt[4]{3}}{\sqrt[4]{16y^4}} = \dfrac{\sqrt[4]{3}}{2y}$

PRACTICE

2 Use the quotient rule to simplify.

a. $\sqrt{\dfrac{36}{49}}$ b. $\sqrt{\dfrac{z}{16}}$ c. $\sqrt[3]{\dfrac{125}{8}}$ d. $\sqrt[4]{\dfrac{5}{81x^8}}$

OBJECTIVE

3   Simplifying Radicals

Both the product and quotient rules can be used to simplify a radical. If the product rule is read from right to left, we have that

$$\sqrt[n]{ab} = \sqrt[n]{a} \cdot \sqrt[n]{b}.$$

This is used to simplify the following radicals.

EXAMPLE 3   Simplify the following.

a. $\sqrt{50}$ **b.** $\sqrt[3]{24}$ **c.** $\sqrt{26}$ **d.** $\sqrt[4]{32}$

Solution

a. Factor 50 such that one factor is the largest perfect square that divides 50. The largest perfect square factor of 50 is 25, so we write 50 as $25 \cdot 2$ and use the product rule for radicals to simplify.

$$\sqrt{50} = \sqrt{25 \cdot 2} = \sqrt{25} \cdot \sqrt{2} = 5\sqrt{2}$$

⎸ The largest perfect square factor of 50

> **Helpful Hint**
> Don't forget that, for example, $5\sqrt{2}$ means $5 \cdot \sqrt{2}$.

b. $\sqrt[3]{24} = \sqrt[3]{8 \cdot 3} = \sqrt[3]{8} \cdot \sqrt[3]{3} = 2\sqrt[3]{3}$

⎸ The largest perfect cube factor of 24

c. $\sqrt{26}$ The largest perfect square factor of 26 is 1, so $\sqrt{26}$ cannot be simplified further.

d. $\sqrt[4]{32} = \sqrt[4]{16 \cdot 2} = \sqrt[4]{16} \cdot \sqrt[4]{2} = 2\sqrt[4]{2}$

⎸ The largest fourth power factor of 32

PRACTICE

3   Simplify the following.

a. $\sqrt{98}$ **b.** $\sqrt[3]{54}$ **c.** $\sqrt{35}$ **d.** $\sqrt[4]{243}$

After simplifying a radical such as a square root, always check the radicand to see that it contains no other perfect square factors. It may, if the largest perfect square factor of the radicand was not originally recognized. For example,

$$\sqrt{200} = \sqrt{4 \cdot 50} = \sqrt{4} \cdot \sqrt{50} = 2\sqrt{50}$$

Notice that the radicand 50 still contains the perfect square factor 25. This is because 4 is not the largest perfect square factor of 200. We continue as follows.

$$2\sqrt{50} = 2\sqrt{25 \cdot 2} = 2 \cdot \sqrt{25} \cdot \sqrt{2} = 2 \cdot 5 \cdot \sqrt{2} = 10\sqrt{2}$$

The radical is now simplified since 2 contains no perfect square factors (other than 1).

> **Helpful Hint**
> To help you recognize largest perfect power factors of a radicand, it will help if you are familiar with some perfect powers. A few are listed below.
>
> | Perfect Squares | 1, | 4, | 9, | 16, | 25, | 36, | 49, | 64, | 81, | 100, | 121, | 144 |
> |---|---|---|---|---|---|---|---|---|---|---|---|---|
> | | 1^2 | 2^2 | 3^2 | 4^2 | 5^2 | 6^2 | 7^2 | 8^2 | 9^2 | 10^2 | 11^2 | 12^2 |
> | Perfect Cubes | 1, | 8, | 27, | 64, | 125 | | | | | | | |
> | | 1^3 | 2^3 | 3^3 | 4^3 | 5^3 | | | | | | | |
> | Perfect Fourth Powers | 1, | 16, | 81, | 256 | | | | | | | | |
> | | 1^4 | 2^4 | 3^4 | 4^4 | | | | | | | | |

> In general, we say that a radicand of the form $\sqrt[n]{a}$ is simplified when the radicand a contains no factors that are perfect nth powers (other than 1 or -1).

EXAMPLE 4 Use the product rule to simplify.

a. $\sqrt{25x^3}$ **b.** $\sqrt[3]{54x^6y^8}$ **c.** $\sqrt[4]{81z^{11}}$

Solution

a. $\sqrt{25x^3} = \sqrt{25x^2 \cdot x}$ Find the largest perfect square factor.

$\qquad = \sqrt{25x^2} \cdot \sqrt{x}$ Apply the product rule.

$\qquad = 5x\sqrt{x}$ Simplify.

b. $\sqrt[3]{54x^6y^8} = \sqrt[3]{27 \cdot 2 \cdot x^6 \cdot y^6 \cdot y^2}$ Factor the radicand and identify perfect cube factors.

$\qquad = \sqrt[3]{27x^6y^6 \cdot 2y^2}$

$\qquad = \sqrt[3]{27x^6y^6} \cdot \sqrt[3]{2y^2}$ Apply the product rule.

$\qquad = 3x^2y^2\sqrt[3]{2y^2}$ Simplify.

c. $\sqrt[4]{81z^{11}} = \sqrt[4]{81 \cdot z^8 \cdot z^3}$ Factor the radicand and identify perfect fourth power factors.

$\qquad = \sqrt[4]{81z^8} \cdot \sqrt[4]{z^3}$ Apply the product rule.

$\qquad = 3z^2\sqrt[4]{z^3}$ Simplify. $\qquad\square$

PRACTICE

4 Use the product rule to simplify.

a. $\sqrt{36z^7}$ **b.** $\sqrt[3]{32p^4q^7}$ **c.** $\sqrt[4]{16x^{15}}$

EXAMPLE 5 Use the quotient rule to divide, and simplify if possible.

a. $\dfrac{\sqrt{20}}{\sqrt{5}}$ **b.** $\dfrac{\sqrt{50x}}{2\sqrt{2}}$ **c.** $\dfrac{7\sqrt[3]{48x^4y^8}}{\sqrt[3]{6y^2}}$ **d.** $\dfrac{2\sqrt[4]{32a^8b^6}}{\sqrt[4]{a^{-1}b^2}}$

Solution

a. $\dfrac{\sqrt{20}}{\sqrt{5}} = \sqrt{\dfrac{20}{5}}$ Apply the quotient rule.

$\qquad = \sqrt{4}$ Simplify.

$\qquad = 2$ Simplify.

b. $\dfrac{\sqrt{50x}}{2\sqrt{2}} = \dfrac{1}{2} \cdot \sqrt{\dfrac{50x}{2}}$ Apply the quotient rule.

$\qquad = \dfrac{1}{2} \cdot \sqrt{25x}$ Simplify.

$\qquad = \dfrac{1}{2} \cdot \sqrt{25} \cdot \sqrt{x}$ Factor $25x$.

$\qquad = \dfrac{1}{2} \cdot 5 \cdot \sqrt{x}$ Simplify.

$\qquad = \dfrac{5}{2}\sqrt{x}$

c. $\dfrac{7\sqrt[3]{48x^4y^8}}{\sqrt[3]{6y^2}} = 7 \cdot \sqrt[3]{\dfrac{48x^4y^8}{6y^2}}$ Apply the quotient rule.

$\qquad = 7 \cdot \sqrt[3]{8x^4y^6}$ Simplify.

$\qquad = 7\sqrt[3]{8x^3y^6 \cdot x}$ Factor.

$\qquad = 7 \cdot \sqrt[3]{8x^3y^6} \cdot \sqrt[3]{x}$ Apply the product rule.

$$= 7 \cdot 2xy^2 \cdot \sqrt[3]{x} \quad \text{Simplify.}$$
$$= 14xy^2\sqrt[3]{x}$$

d. $\dfrac{2\sqrt[4]{32a^8b^6}}{\sqrt[4]{a^{-1}b^2}} = 2\sqrt[4]{\dfrac{32a^8b^6}{a^{-1}b^2}} = 2\sqrt[4]{32a^9b^4} = 2\sqrt[4]{16 \cdot a^8 \cdot b^4 \cdot 2 \cdot a}$

$$= 2\sqrt[4]{16a^8b^4} \cdot \sqrt[4]{2a} = 2 \cdot 2a^2b \cdot \sqrt[4]{2a} = 4a^2b\sqrt[4]{2a}$$

PRACTICE

5   Use the quotient rule to divide and simplify.

a. $\dfrac{\sqrt{80}}{\sqrt{5}}$ **b.** $\dfrac{\sqrt{98z}}{3\sqrt{2}}$ **c.** $\dfrac{5\sqrt[3]{40x^5y^7}}{\sqrt[3]{5y}}$ **d.** $\dfrac{3\sqrt[5]{64x^9y^8}}{\sqrt[5]{x^{-1}y^2}}$

✓CONCEPT CHECK

Find and correct the error:

$$\dfrac{\sqrt[3]{27}}{\sqrt{9}} = \sqrt[3]{\dfrac{27}{9}} = \sqrt[3]{3}$$

OBJECTIVE

4   **Using the Distance and Midpoint Formulas**

Now that we know how to simplify radicals, we can derive and use the distance formula. The midpoint formula is often confused with the distance formula, so to clarify both, we will also review the midpoint formula.

The Cartesian coordinate system helps us visualize a distance between points. To find the distance between two points, we use the distance formula, which is derived from the Pythagorean theorem.

To find the distance d between two points (x_1, y_1) and (x_2, y_2) as shown to the left, notice that the length of leg a is $x_2 - x_1$ and that the length of leg b is $y_2 - y_1$.

Thus, the Pythagorean theorem tells us that

$$d^2 = a^2 + b^2$$

or

$$d^2 = (x_2 - x_1)^2 + (y_2 - y_1)^2$$

or

$$d = \sqrt{(x_2 - x_1)^2 + (y_2 - y_1)^2}$$

This formula gives us the distance between any two points on the real plane.

Distance Formula

The distance d between two points (x_1, y_1) and (x_2, y_2) is given by

$$d = \sqrt{(x_2 - x_1)^2 + (y_2 - y_1)^2}$$

EXAMPLE 6   Find the distance between $(2, -5)$ and $(1, -4)$. Give an exact distance and a three-decimal-place approximation.

Solution   To use the distance formula, it makes no difference which point we call (x_1, y_1) and which point we call (x_2, y_2). We will let $(x_1, y_1) = (2, -5)$ and $(x_2, y_2) = (1, -4)$.

(Continued on next page)

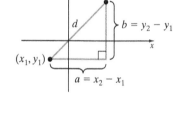
Answer to Concept Check:
$$\dfrac{\sqrt[3]{27}}{\sqrt{9}} = \dfrac{3}{3} = 1$$

$$d = \sqrt{(x_2 - x_1)^2 + (y_2 - y_1)^2}$$
$$= \sqrt{(1 - 2)^2 + [-4 - (-5)]^2}$$
$$= \sqrt{(-1)^2 + (1)^2}$$
$$= \sqrt{1 + 1}$$
$$= \sqrt{2} \approx 1.414$$

The distance between the two points is exactly $\sqrt{2}$ units, or approximately 1.414 units.

PRACTICE

6   Find the distance between $(-3, 7)$ and $(-2, 3)$. Give an exact distance and a three-decimal-place approximation.

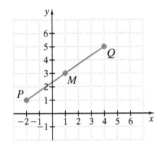

   The **midpoint** of a line segment is the **point** located exactly halfway between the two endpoints of the line segment. On the graph to the left, the point M is the midpoint of line segment PQ. Thus, the distance between M and P equals the distance between M and Q.
   Note: We usually need no knowledge of roots to calculate the midpoint of a line segment. We review midpoint here only because it is often confused with the distance between two points.
   The x-coordinate of M is at half the distance between the x-coordinates of P and Q, and the y-coordinate of M is at half the distance between the y-coordinates of P and Q. That is, the x-coordinate of M is the average of the x-coordinates of P and Q; the y-coordinate of M is the average of the y-coordinates of P and Q.

Midpoint Formula

The midpoint of the line segment whose endpoints are (x_1, y_1) and (x_2, y_2) is the point with coordinates

$$\left(\frac{x_1 + x_2}{2}, \frac{y_1 + y_2}{2} \right)$$

EXAMPLE 7   Find the midpoint of the line segment that joins points $P(-3, 3)$ and $Q(1, 0)$.

Solution   Use the midpoint formula. It makes no difference which point we call (x_1, y_1) or which point we call (x_2, y_2). Let $(x_1, y_1) = (-3, 3)$ and $(x_2, y_2) = (1, 0)$.

$$\text{midpoint} = \left(\frac{x_1 + x_2}{2}, \frac{y_1 + y_2}{2} \right)$$
$$= \left(\frac{-3 + 1}{2}, \frac{3 + 0}{2} \right)$$
$$= \left(\frac{-2}{2}, \frac{3}{2} \right)$$
$$= \left(-1, \frac{3}{2} \right)$$

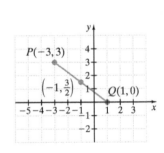

The midpoint of the segment is $\left(-1, \frac{3}{2} \right)$.

PRACTICE

7   Find the midpoint of the line segment that joins points $P(5, -2)$ and $Q(8, -6)$.

> ▶ **Helpful Hint**
>
> The distance between two points is a distance. The midpoint of a line segment is the point halfway between the endpoints of the segment.
>
> distance—measured in units
>
> midpoint—it is a point

Vocabulary, Readiness & Video Check

Use the choices below to fill in each blank. Some choices may be used more than once.

distance   midpoint   point

1. The _____ of a line segment is a _____ exactly halfway between the two endpoints of the line segment.

2. The _____ between two points is a distance, measured in units.

3. The _____ formula is $d = \sqrt{(x_2 - x_1)^2 + (y_2 - y_1)^2}$.

4. The _____ formula is $\left(\dfrac{x_1 + x_2}{2}, \dfrac{y_1 + y_2}{2} \right)$.

Martin-Gay Interactive Videos

See Video 10.3 🍅

Watch the section lecture video and answer the following questions.

OBJECTIVE 1
5. From 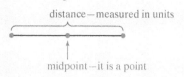 Example 1 and the lecture before, in order to apply the product rule for radicals, what must be true about the indexes of the radicals being multiplied?

OBJECTIVE 2
6. From ⌨ Examples 2–6, when might you apply the quotient rule (in either direction) in order to simplify a fractional radical expression?

OBJECTIVE 3
7. From ⌨ Example 8, we know that an even power of a variable is a perfect square factor of the variable, leaving no factor in the radicand once simplified. Therefore, what must be true about the power of any variable left in the radicand of a simplified square root? Explain.

OBJECTIVE 4
8. From ⌨ Example 10, the formula uses the coordinates of two points similar to the slope formula. What caution should you take when replacing values in the formula?

OBJECTIVE 4
9. Based on ⌨ Example 11, complete the following statement. The x-value of the midpoint is the _____ of the x-values of the endpoints and the y-value of the midpoint is the _____ of the y-values of the endpoints.

10.3 Exercise Set MyMathLab®

Use the product rule to multiply. See Example 1.

1. $\sqrt{7} \cdot \sqrt{2}$

2. $\sqrt{11} \cdot \sqrt{10}$

3. $\sqrt[4]{8} \cdot \sqrt[4]{2}$

4. $\sqrt[4]{27} \cdot \sqrt[4]{3}$

5. $\sqrt[3]{4} \cdot \sqrt[3]{9}$

6. $\sqrt[3]{10} \cdot \sqrt[3]{5}$

▶ 7. $\sqrt{2} \cdot \sqrt{3x}$

8. $\sqrt{3y} \cdot \sqrt{5x}$

9. $\sqrt{\dfrac{7}{x}} \cdot \sqrt{\dfrac{2}{y}}$

10. $\sqrt{\dfrac{6}{m}} \cdot \sqrt{\dfrac{n}{5}}$

11. $\sqrt[4]{4x^3} \cdot \sqrt[4]{5}$

12. $\sqrt[4]{ab^2} \cdot \sqrt[4]{27ab}$

Use the quotient rule to simplify. See Examples 2 and 3.

▶ 13. $\sqrt{\dfrac{6}{49}}$

14. $\sqrt{\dfrac{8}{81}}$

15. $\sqrt{\dfrac{2}{49}}$

16. $\sqrt{\dfrac{5}{121}}$

▶ 17. $\sqrt[4]{\dfrac{x^3}{16}}$

18. $\sqrt[4]{\dfrac{y}{81x^4}}$

19. $\sqrt[3]{\dfrac{4}{27}}$

20. $\sqrt[3]{\dfrac{3}{64}}$

21. $\sqrt[4]{\dfrac{8}{x^8}}$

22. $\sqrt[4]{\dfrac{a^3}{81}}$

23. $\sqrt[3]{\dfrac{2x}{81y^{12}}}$

24. $\sqrt[3]{\dfrac{3}{8x^6}}$

25. $\sqrt{\dfrac{x^2y}{100}}$

26. $\sqrt{\dfrac{y^2z}{36}}$

▶ **27.** $\sqrt{\dfrac{5x^2}{4y^2}}$

28. $\sqrt{\dfrac{y^{10}}{9x^6}}$

29. $-\sqrt[3]{\dfrac{z^7}{27x^3}}$

30. $-\sqrt[3]{\dfrac{64a}{b^9}}$

Simplify. See Examples 3 and 4.

▶ **31.** $\sqrt{32}$

32. $\sqrt{27}$

33. $\sqrt[3]{192}$

34. $\sqrt[3]{108}$

35. $5\sqrt{75}$

36. $3\sqrt{8}$

37. $\sqrt{24}$

38. $\sqrt{20}$

39. $\sqrt{100x^5}$

40. $\sqrt{64y^9}$

41. $\sqrt[3]{16y^7}$

42. $\sqrt[3]{64y^9}$

43. $\sqrt[4]{a^8b^7}$

44. $\sqrt[5]{32z^{12}}$

45. $\sqrt{y^5}$

46. $\sqrt[3]{y^5}$

▶ **47.** $\sqrt{25a^2b^3}$

48. $\sqrt{9x^5y^7}$

▶ **49.** $\sqrt[5]{-32x^{10}y}$

50. $\sqrt[5]{-243z^9}$

51. $\sqrt[3]{50x^{14}}$

52. $\sqrt[3]{40y^{10}}$

53. $-\sqrt{32a^8b^7}$

54. $-\sqrt{20ab^6}$

55. $\sqrt{9x^7y^9}$

56. $\sqrt{12r^9s^{12}}$

57. $\sqrt[3]{125r^9s^{12}}$

58. $\sqrt[3]{8a^6b^9}$

59. $\sqrt[4]{32x^{12}y^5}$

60. $\sqrt[4]{162x^7y^{20}}$

Use the quotient rule to divide. Then simplify if possible. See Example 5.

▶ **61.** $\dfrac{\sqrt{14}}{\sqrt{7}}$

62. $\dfrac{\sqrt{45}}{\sqrt{9}}$

63. $\dfrac{\sqrt[3]{24}}{\sqrt[3]{3}}$

64. $\dfrac{\sqrt[3]{10}}{\sqrt[3]{2}}$

65. $\dfrac{5\sqrt[4]{48}}{\sqrt[4]{3}}$

66. $\dfrac{7\sqrt[4]{162}}{\sqrt[4]{2}}$

▶ **67.** $\dfrac{\sqrt{x^5y^3}}{\sqrt{xy}}$

68. $\dfrac{\sqrt{a^7b^6}}{\sqrt{a^3b^2}}$

69. $\dfrac{8\sqrt[3]{54m^7}}{\sqrt[3]{2m}}$

70. $\dfrac{\sqrt[3]{128x^3}}{-3\sqrt[3]{2x}}$

71. $\dfrac{3\sqrt{100x^2}}{2\sqrt{2x^{-1}}}$

72. $\dfrac{\sqrt{270y^2}}{5\sqrt{3y^{-4}}}$

73. $\dfrac{\sqrt[4]{96a^{10}b^3}}{\sqrt[4]{3a^2b^3}}$

74. $\dfrac{\sqrt[4]{160x^{10}y^5}}{\sqrt[4]{2x^2y^2}}$

75. $\dfrac{\sqrt[5]{64x^{10}y^3}}{\sqrt[5]{2x^3y^{-7}}}$

76. $\dfrac{\sqrt[5]{192x^6y^{12}}}{\sqrt[5]{2x^{-1}y^{-3}}}$

Find the distance between each pair of points. Give an exact distance and a three-decimal-place approximation. See Example 6.

77. $(5,1)$ and $(8,5)$

78. $(2,3)$ and $(14,8)$

▶ **79.** $(-3,2)$ and $(1,-3)$

80. $(3,-2)$ and $(-4,1)$

81. $(-9,4)$ and $(-8,1)$

82. $(-5,-2)$ and $(-6,-6)$

83. $(0,-\sqrt{2})$ and $(\sqrt{3},0)$

84. $(-\sqrt{5},0)$ and $(0,\sqrt{7})$

85. $(1.7,-3.6)$ and $(-8.6,5.7)$

86. $(9.6,2.5)$ and $(-1.9,-3.7)$

Find the midpoint of the line segment whose endpoints are given. See Example 7.

87. $(6,-8),(2,4)$

88. $(3,9),(7,11)$

▶ **89.** $(-2,-1),(-8,6)$

90. $(-3,-4),(6,-8)$

91. $(7,3),(-1,-3)$

92. $(-2,5),(-1,6)$

93. $\left(\dfrac{1}{2},\dfrac{3}{8}\right),\left(-\dfrac{3}{2},\dfrac{5}{8}\right)$

94. $\left(-\dfrac{2}{5},\dfrac{7}{15}\right),\left(-\dfrac{2}{5},-\dfrac{4}{15}\right)$

95. $(\sqrt{2},3\sqrt{5}),(\sqrt{2},-2\sqrt{5})$

96. $(\sqrt{8},-\sqrt{12}),(3\sqrt{2},7\sqrt{3})$

97. $(4.6,-3.5),(7.8,-9.8)$

98. $(-4.6,2.1),(-6.7,1.9)$

REVIEW AND PREVIEW

Perform each indicated operation. See Sections 2.1, 5.3 and 5.4.

99. $6x+8x$

100. $(6x)(8x)$

101. $(2x+3)(x-5)$

102. $(2x+3)+(x-5)$

103. $9y^2-8y^2$

104. $(9y^2)(-8y^2)$

105. $-3(x+5)$

106. $-3+x+5$

107. $(x-4)^2$

108. $(2x+1)^2$

CONCEPT EXTENSIONS

Answer true or false. Assume all radicals represent nonzero real numbers.

109. $\sqrt[n]{a}\cdot\sqrt[n]{b}=\sqrt[n]{ab}$, _____

110. $\sqrt[3]{7}\cdot\sqrt[3]{11}=\sqrt[3]{18}$, _____

111. $\sqrt[3]{7}\cdot\sqrt{11}=\sqrt{77}$, _____

112. $\sqrt{x^7y^8}=\sqrt{x^7}\cdot\sqrt{y^8}$, _____

113. $\dfrac{\sqrt[n]{a}}{\sqrt[n]{b}}=\sqrt[n]{\dfrac{a}{b}}$, _____

114. $\dfrac{\sqrt[3]{12}}{\sqrt[3]{4}}=\sqrt[3]{8}$, _____

Find and correct the error. See the Concept Check in this section.

115. $\dfrac{\sqrt[3]{64}}{\sqrt{64}} = \sqrt[3]{\dfrac{64}{64}} = \sqrt[3]{1} = 1$

116. $\dfrac{\sqrt[4]{16}}{\sqrt{4}} = \sqrt[4]{\dfrac{16}{4}} = \sqrt[4]{4}$

Simplify. See the Concept Check in this section. Assume variables represent positive numbers.

117. $\sqrt[5]{x^{35}}$ **118.** $\sqrt[6]{y^{48}}$

119. $\sqrt[4]{a^{12}b^4c^{20}}$ **120.** $\sqrt[3]{a^9b^{21}c^3}$

121. $\sqrt[3]{z^{32}}$ **122.** $\sqrt[5]{x^{49}}$

123. $\sqrt[7]{q^{17}r^{40}s^7}$ **124.** $\sqrt[4]{p^{11}q^4r^{45}}$

125. The formula for the radius r of a sphere with surface area A is given by $r = \sqrt{\dfrac{A}{4\pi}}$. Calculate the radius of a standard zorb, whose outside surface area is 32.17 sq m. Round to the nearest tenth. (A zorb is a large inflated ball within a ball in which a person, strapped inside, may choose to roll down a hill. *Source:* Zorb, Ltd.)

126. The owner of Knightime Classic Movie Rentals has determined that the demand equation for renting older released DVDs is $F(x) = 0.6\sqrt{49 - x^2}$, where x is the price in dollars per two-day rental and $F(x)$ is the number of times the DVD is demanded per week.

    a. Approximate to one decimal place the demand per week of an older released DVD if the rental price is $3 per two-day rental.

    b. Approximate to one decimal place the demand per week of an older released DVD if the rental price is $5 per two-day rental.

    c. Explain how the owner of the store can use this equation to predict the number of copies of each DVD that should be in stock.

127. The formula for the lateral surface area A of a cone with height h and radius r is given by

$$A = \pi r \sqrt{r^2 + h^2}$$

    a. Find the lateral surface area of a cone whose height is 3 centimeters and whose radius is 4 centimeters.

    b. Approximate to two decimal places the lateral surface area of a cone whose height is 7.2 feet and whose radius is 6.8 feet.

128. Before Mount Vesuvius, a volcano in Italy, erupted violently in 79 C.E., its height was 4190 feet. Vesuvius was roughly cone-shaped, and its base had a radius of approximately 25,200 feet. Use the formula for the lateral surface area of a cone, given in Exercise 127, to approximate the surface area this volcano had before it erupted. (*Source:* Global Volcanism Network)

10.4   Adding, Subtracting, and Multiplying Radical Expressions

OBJECTIVES

1 Add or Subtract Radical Expressions.

2 Multiply Radical Expressions.

OBJECTIVE

1   Adding or Subtracting Radical Expressions

We have learned that sums or differences of like terms can be simplified. To simplify these sums or differences, we use the distributive property. For example,

$$2x + 3x = (2 + 3)x = 5x \quad \text{and} \quad 7x^2y - 4x^2y = (7 - 4)x^2y = 3x^2y$$

The distributive property can also be used to add **like radicals.**

Like Radicals

Radicals with the same index and the same radicand are like radicals.

For example, $2\sqrt{7} + 3\sqrt{7} = (2 + 3)\sqrt{7} = 5\sqrt{7}$. Also,

$$\underbrace{}_{\text{Like radicals}}$$

$$5\sqrt{3x} - 7\sqrt{3x} = (5 - 7)\sqrt{3x} = -2\sqrt{3x}$$

The expression $2\sqrt{7} + 2\sqrt[3]{7}$ cannot be simplified further since $2\sqrt{7}$ and $2\sqrt[3]{7}$ are not like radicals.

$$\underbrace{}_{\text{Unlike radicals}}$$

EXAMPLE 1   Add or subtract as indicated. Assume all variables represent positive real numbers.

a. $4\sqrt{11} + 8\sqrt{11}$ **b.** $5\sqrt[3]{3x} - 7\sqrt[3]{3x}$ **c.** $4\sqrt{5} + 4\sqrt[3]{5}$

Solution

a. $4\sqrt{11} + 8\sqrt{11} = (4 + 8)\sqrt{11} = 12\sqrt{11}$

b. $5\sqrt[3]{3x} - 7\sqrt[3]{3x} = (5 - 7)\sqrt[3]{3x} = -2\sqrt[3]{3x}$

c. $4\sqrt{5} + 4\sqrt[3]{5}$

This expression cannot be simplified since $4\sqrt{5}$ and $4\sqrt[3]{5}$ do not contain like radicals.

PRACTICE

1   Add or subtract as indicated.

a. $3\sqrt{17} + 5\sqrt{17}$ **b.** $7\sqrt[3]{5z} - 12\sqrt[3]{5z}$ **c.** $3\sqrt{2} + 5\sqrt[3]{2}$

When adding or subtracting radicals, always check first to see whether any radicals can be simplified.

✓CONCEPT CHECK

True or false?

$$\sqrt{a} + \sqrt{b} = \sqrt{a + b}$$

Explain.

EXAMPLE 2   Add or subtract. Assume that variables represent positive real numbers.

a. $\sqrt{20} + 2\sqrt{45}$ **b.** $\sqrt[3]{54} - 5\sqrt[3]{16} + \sqrt[3]{2}$ **c.** $\sqrt{27x} - 2\sqrt{9x} + \sqrt{72x}$

d. $\sqrt[3]{98} + \sqrt{98}$ **e.** $\sqrt[3]{48y^4} + \sqrt[3]{6y^4}$

Solution   First, simplify each radical. Then add or subtract any like radicals.

a. $\sqrt{20} + 2\sqrt{45} = \sqrt{4 \cdot 5} + 2\sqrt{9 \cdot 5}$ Factor 20 and 45.

$\phantom{\sqrt{20} + 2\sqrt{45}} = \sqrt{4} \cdot \sqrt{5} + 2 \cdot \sqrt{9} \cdot \sqrt{5}$ Use the product rule.

$\phantom{\sqrt{20} + 2\sqrt{45}} = 2 \cdot \sqrt{5} + 2 \cdot 3 \cdot \sqrt{5}$ Simplify $\sqrt{4}$ and $\sqrt{9}$.

$\phantom{\sqrt{20} + 2\sqrt{45}} = 2\sqrt{5} + 6\sqrt{5}$

$\phantom{\sqrt{20} + 2\sqrt{45}} = 8\sqrt{5}$ Add like radicals.

b. $\sqrt[3]{54} - 5\sqrt[3]{16} + \sqrt[3]{2}$

$ = \sqrt[3]{27} \cdot \sqrt[3]{2} - 5 \cdot \sqrt[3]{8} \cdot \sqrt[3]{2} + \sqrt[3]{2}$ Factor and use the product rule.

$ = 3 \cdot \sqrt[3]{2} - 5 \cdot 2 \cdot \sqrt[3]{2} + \sqrt[3]{2}$ Simplify $\sqrt[3]{27}$ and $\sqrt[3]{8}$.

$ = 3\sqrt[3]{2} - 10\sqrt[3]{2} + \sqrt[3]{2}$ Write $5 \cdot 2$ as 10.

$ = -6\sqrt[3]{2}$ Combine like radicals.

Answer to Concept Check:
false; answers may vary

c. $\sqrt{27x} - 2\sqrt{9x} + \sqrt{72x}$

$= \sqrt{9} \cdot \sqrt{3x} - 2 \cdot \sqrt{9} \cdot \sqrt{x} + \sqrt{36} \cdot \sqrt{2x}$ Factor and use the product rule.

$= 3 \cdot \sqrt{3x} - 2 \cdot 3 \cdot \sqrt{x} + 6 \cdot \sqrt{2x}$ Simplify $\sqrt{9}$ and $\sqrt{36}$.

$= 3\sqrt{3x} - 6\sqrt{x} + 6\sqrt{2x}$ Write $2 \cdot 3$ as 6.

> ▶ **Helpful Hint**
> None of these terms contain like radicals. We can simplify no further.

d. $\sqrt[3]{98} + \sqrt{98} = \sqrt[3]{98} + \sqrt{49} \cdot \sqrt{2}$ Factor and use the product rule.

$= \sqrt[3]{98} + 7\sqrt{2}$ No further simplification is possible.

e. $\sqrt[3]{48y^4} + \sqrt[3]{6y^4} = \sqrt[3]{8y^3} \cdot \sqrt[3]{6y} + \sqrt[3]{y^3} \cdot \sqrt[3]{6y}$ Factor and use the product rule.

$= 2y\sqrt[3]{6y} + y\sqrt[3]{6y}$ Simplify $\sqrt[3]{8y^3}$ and $\sqrt[3]{y^3}$.

$= 3y\sqrt[3]{6y}$ Combine like radicals. ☐

PRACTICE
2   Add or subtract.

a. $\sqrt{24} + 3\sqrt{54}$ **b.** $\sqrt[3]{24} - 4\sqrt[3]{81} + \sqrt[3]{3}$ **c.** $\sqrt{75x} - 3\sqrt{27x} + \sqrt{12x}$
d. $\sqrt{40} + \sqrt[3]{40}$ **e.** $\sqrt[3]{81x^4} + \sqrt[3]{3x^4}$

Let's continue to assume that variables represent positive real numbers.

EXAMPLE 3   Add or subtract as indicated.

a. $\dfrac{\sqrt{45}}{4} - \dfrac{\sqrt{5}}{3}$ **b.** $\sqrt[3]{\dfrac{7x}{8}} + 2\sqrt[3]{7x}$

Solution

a. $\dfrac{\sqrt{45}}{4} - \dfrac{\sqrt{5}}{3} = \dfrac{3\sqrt{5}}{4} - \dfrac{\sqrt{5}}{3}$ To subtract, notice that the LCD is 12.

$= \dfrac{3\sqrt{5} \cdot 3}{4 \cdot 3} - \dfrac{\sqrt{5} \cdot 4}{3 \cdot 4}$ Write each expression as an equivalent expression with a denominator of 12.

$= \dfrac{9\sqrt{5}}{12} - \dfrac{4\sqrt{5}}{12}$ Multiply factors in the numerator and the denominator.

$= \dfrac{5\sqrt{5}}{12}$ Subtract.

b. $\sqrt[3]{\dfrac{7x}{8}} + 2\sqrt[3]{7x} = \dfrac{\sqrt[3]{7x}}{\sqrt[3]{8}} + 2\sqrt[3]{7x}$ Apply the quotient rule for radicals.

$= \dfrac{\sqrt[3]{7x}}{2} + 2\sqrt[3]{7x}$ Simplify.

$= \dfrac{\sqrt[3]{7x}}{2} + \dfrac{2\sqrt[3]{7x} \cdot 2}{2}$ Write each expression as an equivalent expression with a denominator of 2.

$= \dfrac{\sqrt[3]{7x}}{2} + \dfrac{4\sqrt[3]{7x}}{2}$

$= \dfrac{5\sqrt[3]{7x}}{2}$ Add. ☐

PRACTICE
3   Add or subtract as indicated.

a. $\dfrac{\sqrt{28}}{3} - \dfrac{\sqrt{7}}{4}$ **b.** $\sqrt[3]{\dfrac{6y}{64}} + 3\sqrt[3]{6y}$

OBJECTIVE

2 Multiplying Radical Expressions

We can multiply radical expressions by using many of the same properties used to multiply polynomial expressions. For instance, to multiply $\sqrt{2}(\sqrt{6} - 3\sqrt{2})$, we use the distributive property and multiply $\sqrt{2}$ by each term inside the parentheses.

$$\sqrt{2}(\sqrt{6} - 3\sqrt{2}) = \sqrt{2}(\sqrt{6}) - \sqrt{2}(3\sqrt{2}) \qquad \text{Use the distributive property.}$$
$$= \sqrt{2 \cdot 6} - 3\sqrt{2 \cdot 2}$$
$$= \sqrt{2 \cdot 2 \cdot 3} - 3 \cdot 2 \qquad \text{Use the product rule for radicals.}$$
$$= 2\sqrt{3} - 6$$

EXAMPLE 4 Multiply.

a. $\sqrt{3}(5 + \sqrt{30})$ **b.** $(\sqrt{5} - \sqrt{6})(\sqrt{7} + 1)$ **c.** $(7\sqrt{x} + 5)(3\sqrt{x} - \sqrt{5})$

d. $(4\sqrt{3} - 1)^2$ **e.** $(\sqrt{2x} - 5)(\sqrt{2x} + 5)$ **f.** $(\sqrt{x-3} + 5)^2$

Solution

a. $\sqrt{3}(5 + \sqrt{30}) = \sqrt{3}(5) + \sqrt{3}(\sqrt{30})$
$$= 5\sqrt{3} + \sqrt{3 \cdot 30}$$
$$= 5\sqrt{3} + \sqrt{3 \cdot 3 \cdot 10}$$
$$= 5\sqrt{3} + 3\sqrt{10}$$

b. To multiply, we can use the FOIL method.

$$\begin{array}{cccc} \text{First} & \text{Outer} & \text{Inner} & \text{Last} \end{array}$$
$$(\sqrt{5} - \sqrt{6})(\sqrt{7} + 1) = \sqrt{5} \cdot \sqrt{7} + \sqrt{5} \cdot 1 - \sqrt{6} \cdot \sqrt{7} - \sqrt{6} \cdot 1$$
$$= \sqrt{35} + \sqrt{5} - \sqrt{42} - \sqrt{6}$$

c. $(7\sqrt{x} + 5)(3\sqrt{x} - \sqrt{5}) = 7\sqrt{x}(3\sqrt{x}) - 7\sqrt{x}(\sqrt{5}) + 5(3\sqrt{x}) - 5(\sqrt{5})$
$$= 21x - 7\sqrt{5x} + 15\sqrt{x} - 5\sqrt{5}$$

d. $(4\sqrt{3} - 1)^2 = (4\sqrt{3} - 1)(4\sqrt{3} - 1)$
$$= 4\sqrt{3}(4\sqrt{3}) - 4\sqrt{3}(1) - 1(4\sqrt{3}) - 1(-1)$$
$$= 16 \cdot 3 - 4\sqrt{3} - 4\sqrt{3} + 1$$
$$= 48 - 8\sqrt{3} + 1$$
$$= 49 - 8\sqrt{3}$$

e. $(\sqrt{2x} - 5)(\sqrt{2x} + 5) = \sqrt{2x} \cdot \sqrt{2x} + 5\sqrt{2x} - 5\sqrt{2x} - 5 \cdot 5$
$$= 2x - 25$$

f. $(\underbrace{\sqrt{x-3}}_{a} + \underbrace{5}_{b})^2 = \underbrace{(\sqrt{x-3})^2}_{a^2} + \underbrace{2 \cdot}_{+2 \cdot} \underbrace{\sqrt{x-3}}_{a} \cdot \underbrace{5}_{\cdot b} + \underbrace{5^2}_{+ b^2}$

$$= x - 3 + 10\sqrt{x-3} + 25 \qquad \text{Simplify.}$$
$$= x + 22 + 10\sqrt{x-3} \qquad \text{Combine like terms.} \qquad \square$$

PRACTICE

4 Multiply.

a. $\sqrt{5}(2 + \sqrt{15})$ **b.** $(\sqrt{2} - \sqrt{5})(\sqrt{6} + 2)$

c. $(3\sqrt{z} - 4)(2\sqrt{z} + 3)$ **d.** $(\sqrt{6} - 3)^2$

e. $(\sqrt{5x} + 3)(\sqrt{5x} - 3)$ **f.** $(\sqrt{x+2} + 3)^2$

Vocabulary, Readiness & Video Check

Complete the table with "Like" or "Unlike."

Terms	Like or Unlike Radical Terms?
1. $\sqrt{7}, \sqrt[3]{7}$	
2. $\sqrt[3]{x^2 y}, \sqrt[3]{yx^2}$	
3. $\sqrt[3]{abc}, \sqrt[3]{cba}$	
4. $2x\sqrt{5}, 2x\sqrt{10}$	

Simplify. Assume that all variables represent positive real numbers.

5. $2\sqrt{3} + 4\sqrt{3} =$ _____

6. $5\sqrt{7} + 3\sqrt{7} =$ _____

7. $8\sqrt{x} - \sqrt{x} =$ _____

8. $3\sqrt{y} - \sqrt{y} =$ _____

9. $7\sqrt[3]{x} + \sqrt[3]{x} =$ _____

10. $8\sqrt[3]{z} + \sqrt[3]{z} =$ _____

Martin-Gay Interactive Videos

See Video 10.4

Watch the section lecture video and answer the following questions.

OBJECTIVE
1

11. From Examples 1 and 2, why should you always check to see if all terms in your expression are simplified before attempting to add or subtract radicals?

OBJECTIVE
2

12. In Example 4, what are you told to remember about the square root of a positive number?

10.4 Exercise Set   MyMathLab®

Add or subtract. See Examples 1 through 3.

1. $\sqrt{8} - \sqrt{32}$

2. $\sqrt{27} - \sqrt{75}$

3. $2\sqrt{2x^3} + 4x\sqrt{8x}$

4. $3\sqrt{45x^3} + x\sqrt{5x}$

5. $2\sqrt{50} - 3\sqrt{125} + \sqrt{98}$

6. $4\sqrt{32} - \sqrt{18} + 2\sqrt{128}$

7. $\sqrt[3]{16x} - \sqrt[3]{54x}$

8. $2\sqrt[3]{3a^4} - 3a\sqrt[3]{81a}$

9. $\sqrt{9b^3} - \sqrt{25b^3} + \sqrt{49b^3}$

10. $\sqrt{4x^7} + 9x^2\sqrt{x^3} - 5x\sqrt{x^5}$

11. $\dfrac{5\sqrt{2}}{3} + \dfrac{2\sqrt{2}}{5}$

12. $\dfrac{\sqrt{3}}{2} + \dfrac{4\sqrt{3}}{3}$

13. $\sqrt[3]{\dfrac{11}{8}} - \dfrac{\sqrt[3]{11}}{6}$

14. $\dfrac{2\sqrt[3]{4}}{7} - \dfrac{\sqrt[3]{4}}{14}$

15. $\dfrac{\sqrt{20x}}{9} + \sqrt{\dfrac{5x}{9}}$

16. $\dfrac{3x\sqrt{7}}{5} + \sqrt{\dfrac{7x^2}{100}}$

17. $7\sqrt{9} - 7 + \sqrt{3}$

18. $\sqrt{16} - 5\sqrt{10} + 7$

19. $2 + 3\sqrt{y^2} - 6\sqrt{y^2} + 5$

20. $3\sqrt{7} - \sqrt[3]{x} + 4\sqrt{7} - 3\sqrt[3]{x}$

21. $3\sqrt{108} - 2\sqrt{18} - 3\sqrt{48}$

22. $-\sqrt{75} + \sqrt{12} - 3\sqrt{3}$

23. $-5\sqrt[3]{625} + \sqrt[3]{40}$

24. $-2\sqrt[3]{108} - \sqrt[3]{32}$

25. $a^3\sqrt{9ab^3} - \sqrt{25a^7b^3} + \sqrt{16a^7b^3}$

26. $\sqrt{4x^7y^5} + 9x^2\sqrt{x^3y^5} - 5xy\sqrt{x^5y^3}$

27. $5y\sqrt{8y} + 2\sqrt{50y^3}$

28. $3\sqrt{8x^2y^3} - 2x\sqrt{32y^3}$

29. $\sqrt[3]{54xy^3} - 5\sqrt[3]{2xy^3} + y\sqrt[3]{128x}$

30. $2\sqrt[3]{24x^3y^4} + 4x\sqrt[3]{81y^4}$

31. $6\sqrt[3]{11} + 8\sqrt{11} - 12\sqrt{11}$

32. $3\sqrt[3]{5} + 4\sqrt{5} - 8\sqrt{5}$

33. $-2\sqrt[4]{x^7} + 3\sqrt[4]{16x^7} - x\sqrt[4]{x^3}$

34. $6\sqrt[3]{24x^3} - 2\sqrt[3]{81x^3} - x\sqrt[3]{3}$

35. $\dfrac{4\sqrt{3}}{3} - \dfrac{\sqrt{12}}{3}$

36. $\dfrac{\sqrt{45}}{10} + \dfrac{7\sqrt{5}}{10}$

37. $\dfrac{\sqrt[3]{8x^4}}{7} + \dfrac{3x\sqrt[3]{x}}{7}$

38. $\dfrac{\sqrt[4]{48}}{5x} - \dfrac{2\sqrt[4]{3}}{10x}$

39. $\sqrt{\dfrac{28}{x^2}} + \sqrt{\dfrac{7}{4x^2}}$

40. $\dfrac{\sqrt{99}}{5x} - \sqrt{\dfrac{44}{x^2}}$

41. $\sqrt[3]{\dfrac{16}{27}} - \dfrac{\sqrt[3]{54}}{6}$

42. $\dfrac{\sqrt[3]{3}}{10} + \sqrt[3]{\dfrac{24}{125}}$

43. $-\dfrac{\sqrt[3]{2x^4}}{9} + \sqrt[3]{\dfrac{250x^4}{27}}$

44. $\dfrac{\sqrt[3]{y^5}}{8} + \dfrac{5y\sqrt[3]{y^2}}{4}$

△ **45.** Find the perimeter of the trapezoid.

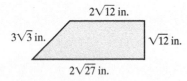

△ **46.** Find the perimeter of the triangle.

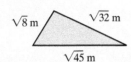

Multiply and then simplify if possible. See Example 4.

▶ **47.** $\sqrt{7}(\sqrt{5} + \sqrt{3})$

48. $\sqrt{5}(\sqrt{15} - \sqrt{35})$

49. $(\sqrt{5} - \sqrt{2})^2$

50. $(3x - \sqrt{2})(3x - \sqrt{2})$

51. $\sqrt{3x}(\sqrt{3} - \sqrt{x})$

52. $\sqrt{5y}(\sqrt{y} + \sqrt{5})$

53. $(2\sqrt{x} - 5)(3\sqrt{x} + 1)$

54. $(8\sqrt{y} + z)(4\sqrt{y} - 1)$

55. $(\sqrt[3]{a} - 4)(\sqrt[3]{a} + 5)$

56. $(\sqrt[3]{a} + 2)(\sqrt[3]{a} + 7)$

57. $6(\sqrt{2} - 2)$

58. $\sqrt{5}(6 - \sqrt{5})$

59. $\sqrt{2}(\sqrt{2} + x\sqrt{6})$

60. $\sqrt{3}(\sqrt{3} - 2\sqrt{5x})$

▶ **61.** $(2\sqrt{7} + 3\sqrt{5})(\sqrt{7} - 2\sqrt{5})$

62. $(\sqrt{6} - 4\sqrt{2})(3\sqrt{6} + \sqrt{2})$

63. $(\sqrt{x} - y)(\sqrt{x} + y)$

64. $(\sqrt{3x} + 2)(\sqrt{3x} - 2)$

65. $(\sqrt{3} + x)^2$

66. $(\sqrt{y} - 3x)^2$

67. $(\sqrt{5x} - 2\sqrt{3x})(\sqrt{5x} - 3\sqrt{3x})$

68. $(5\sqrt{7x} - \sqrt{2x})(4\sqrt{7x} + 6\sqrt{2x})$

69. $(\sqrt[3]{4} + 2)(\sqrt[3]{2} - 1)$

70. $(\sqrt[3]{3} + \sqrt[3]{2})(\sqrt[3]{9} - \sqrt[3]{4})$

71. $(\sqrt[3]{x} + 1)(\sqrt[3]{x^2} - \sqrt[3]{x} + 1)$

72. $(\sqrt[3]{3x} + 2)(\sqrt[3]{9x^2} - 2\sqrt[3]{3x} + 4)$

73. $(\sqrt{x - 1} + 5)^2$

74. $(\sqrt{3x + 1} + 2)^2$

75. $(\sqrt{2x + 5} - 1)^2$

76. $(\sqrt{x - 6} - 7)^2$

REVIEW AND PREVIEW

Factor each numerator and denominator. Then simplify if possible. See Section 7.1.

77. $\dfrac{2x - 14}{2}$

78. $\dfrac{8x - 24y}{4}$

79. $\dfrac{7x - 7y}{x^2 - y^2}$

80. $\dfrac{x^3 - 8}{4x - 8}$

81. $\dfrac{6a^2b - 9ab}{3ab}$

82. $\dfrac{14r - 28r^2s^2}{7rs}$

83. $\dfrac{-4 + 2\sqrt{3}}{6}$

84. $\dfrac{-5 + 10\sqrt{7}}{5}$

CONCEPT EXTENSIONS

△ **85.** Find the perimeter and area of the rectangle.

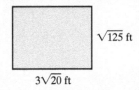

86. Find the area and perimeter of the trapezoid. (*Hint:* The area of a trapezoid is the product of half the height $6\sqrt{3}$ meters and the sum of the bases $2\sqrt{63}$ and $7\sqrt{7}$ meters.)

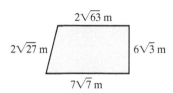

2√63 m

2√27 m   6√3 m

7√7 m

87. a. Add: $\sqrt{3} + \sqrt{3}$.

   b. Multiply: $\sqrt{3} \cdot \sqrt{3}$.

   c. Describe the differences in parts (a) and (b).

88. a. Add: $2\sqrt{5} + \sqrt{5}$

   b. Multiply: $2\sqrt{5} \cdot \sqrt{5}$

   c. Describe the differences in parts (a) and (b).

89. Multiply: $\left(\sqrt{2} + \sqrt{3} - 1\right)^2$.

90. Multiply: $\left(\sqrt{5} - \sqrt{2} + 1\right)^2$

91. Explain how simplifying $2x + 3x$ is similar to simplifying $2\sqrt{x} + 3\sqrt{x}$.

92. Explain how multiplying $(x - 2)(x + 3)$ is similar to multiplying $\left(\sqrt{x} - \sqrt{2}\right)\left(\sqrt{x} + 3\right)$.

10.5 Rationalizing Denominators and Numerators of Radical Expressions

OBJECTIVES

1 Rationalize Denominators.

2 Rationalize Denominators Having Two Terms.

3 Rationalize Numerators.

OBJECTIVE

1   Rationalizing Denominators of Radical Expressions

Often in mathematics, it is helpful to write a radical expression such as $\dfrac{\sqrt{3}}{\sqrt{2}}$ either without a radical in the denominator or without a radical in the numerator. The process of writing this expression as an equivalent expression but without a radical in the denominator is called **rationalizing the denominator.** To rationalize the denominator of $\dfrac{\sqrt{3}}{\sqrt{2}}$, we use the fundamental principle of fractions and multiply the numerator and the denominator by $\sqrt{2}$. Recall that this is the same as multiplying by $\dfrac{\sqrt{2}}{\sqrt{2}}$, which simplifies to 1.

$$\frac{\sqrt{3}}{\sqrt{2}} = \frac{\sqrt{3} \cdot \sqrt{2}}{\sqrt{2} \cdot \sqrt{2}} = \frac{\sqrt{6}}{\sqrt{4}} = \frac{\sqrt{6}}{2}$$

In this section, we continue to assume that variables represent positive real numbers.

EXAMPLE 1   Rationalize the denominator of each expression.

a. $\dfrac{2}{\sqrt{5}}$ **b.** $\dfrac{2\sqrt{16}}{\sqrt{9x}}$ **c.** $\sqrt[3]{\dfrac{1}{2}}$

Solution

a. To rationalize the denominator, we multiply the numerator and denominator by a factor that makes the radicand in the denominator a perfect square.

$$\frac{2}{\sqrt{5}} = \frac{2 \cdot \sqrt{5}}{\sqrt{5} \cdot \sqrt{5}} = \frac{2\sqrt{5}}{5} \quad \text{The denominator is now rationalized.}$$

b. First, we simplify the radicals and then rationalize the denominator.

$$\frac{2\sqrt{16}}{\sqrt{9x}} = \frac{2(4)}{3\sqrt{x}} = \frac{8}{3\sqrt{x}}$$

To rationalize the denominator, multiply the numerator and denominator by $\sqrt{x}$. Then

$$\frac{8}{3\sqrt{x}} = \frac{8 \cdot \sqrt{x}}{3\sqrt{x} \cdot \sqrt{x}} = \frac{8\sqrt{x}}{3x}$$

(Continued on next page)

c. $\sqrt[3]{\dfrac{1}{2}} = \dfrac{\sqrt[3]{1}}{\sqrt[3]{2}} = \dfrac{1}{\sqrt[3]{2}}$. Now we rationalize the denominator. Since $\sqrt[3]{2}$ is a cube root, we want to multiply by a value that will make the radicand 2 a perfect cube. If we multiply $\sqrt[3]{2}$ by $\sqrt[3]{2^2}$, we get $\sqrt[3]{2^3} = \sqrt[3]{8} = 2$.

$$\dfrac{1 \cdot \sqrt[3]{2^2}}{\sqrt[3]{2} \cdot \sqrt[3]{2^2}} = \dfrac{\sqrt[3]{4}}{\sqrt[3]{2^3}} = \dfrac{\sqrt[3]{4}}{2} \quad \begin{array}{l}\text{Multiply the numerator and denominator}\\ \text{by } \sqrt[3]{2^2} \text{ and then simplify.}\end{array}$$

PRACTICE
1 Rationalize the denominator of each expression.

a. $\dfrac{5}{\sqrt{3}}$ **b.** $\dfrac{3\sqrt{25}}{\sqrt{4x}}$ **c.** $\sqrt[3]{\dfrac{2}{9}}$

✓**CONCEPT CHECK**
Determine by which number both the numerator and denominator can be multiplied to rationalize the denominator of the radical expression.

a. $\dfrac{1}{\sqrt[3]{7}}$ **b.** $\dfrac{1}{\sqrt[4]{8}}$

EXAMPLE 2 Rationalize the denominator of $\sqrt{\dfrac{7x}{3y}}$.

Solution $\sqrt{\dfrac{7x}{3y}} = \dfrac{\sqrt{7x}}{\sqrt{3y}}$ Use the quotient rule. No radical may be simplified further.

$= \dfrac{\sqrt{7x} \cdot \sqrt{3y}}{\sqrt{3y} \cdot \sqrt{3y}}$ Multiply numerator and denominator by $\sqrt{3y}$ so that the radicand in the denominator is a perfect square.

$= \dfrac{\sqrt{21xy}}{3y}$ Use the product rule in the numerator and denominator. Remember that $\sqrt{3y} \cdot \sqrt{3y} = 3y$.

PRACTICE
2 Rationalize the denominator of $\sqrt{\dfrac{3z}{5y}}$.

EXAMPLE 3 Rationalize the denominator of $\dfrac{\sqrt[4]{x}}{\sqrt[4]{81y^5}}$.

Solution First, simplify each radical if possible.

$\dfrac{\sqrt[4]{x}}{\sqrt[4]{81y^5}} = \dfrac{\sqrt[4]{x}}{\sqrt[4]{81y^4} \cdot \sqrt[4]{y}}$ Use the product rule in the denominator.

$= \dfrac{\sqrt[4]{x}}{3y\sqrt[4]{y}}$ Write $\sqrt[4]{81y^4}$ as $3y$.

$= \dfrac{\sqrt[4]{x} \cdot \sqrt[4]{y^3}}{3y\sqrt[4]{y} \cdot \sqrt[4]{y^3}}$ Multiply numerator and denominator by $\sqrt[4]{y^3}$ so that the radicand in the denominator is a perfect fourth power.

$= \dfrac{\sqrt[4]{xy^3}}{3y\sqrt[4]{y^4}}$ Use the product rule in the numerator and denominator.

$= \dfrac{\sqrt[4]{xy^3}}{3y^2}$ In the denominator, $\sqrt[4]{y^4} = y$ and $3y \cdot y = 3y^2$.

PRACTICE
3 Rationalize the denominator of $\dfrac{\sqrt[3]{z^2}}{\sqrt[3]{27x^4}}$.

Answer to Concept Check:
a. $\sqrt[3]{7^2}$ or $\sqrt[3]{49}$ **b.** $\sqrt[4]{2}$

OBJECTIVE
2   Rationalizing Denominators Having Two Terms

Remember the product of the sum and difference of two terms?

$$(a + b)(a - b) = a^2 - b^2$$

These two expressions are called **conjugates** of each other.

To rationalize a numerator or denominator that is a sum or difference of two terms, we use conjugates. To see how and why this works, let's rationalize the denominator of the expression $\dfrac{5}{\sqrt{3} - 2}$. To do so, we multiply both the numerator and the denominator by $\sqrt{3} + 2$, the **conjugate** of the denominator $\sqrt{3} - 2$, and see what happens.

$$\frac{5}{\sqrt{3} - 2} = \frac{5(\sqrt{3} + 2)}{(\sqrt{3} - 2)(\sqrt{3} + 2)}$$

$$= \frac{5(\sqrt{3} + 2)}{(\sqrt{3})^2 - 2^2} \quad \text{Multiply the sum and difference of two terms: } (a + b)(a - b) = a^2 - b^2.$$

$$= \frac{5(\sqrt{3} + 2)}{3 - 4}$$

$$= \frac{5(\sqrt{3} + 2)}{-1}$$

$$= -5(\sqrt{3} + 2) \quad \text{or} \quad -5\sqrt{3} - 10$$

Notice in the denominator that the product of $(\sqrt{3} - 2)$ and its conjugate, $(\sqrt{3} + 2)$, is -1. In general, the product of an expression and its conjugate will contain no radical terms. This is why, when rationalizing a denominator or a numerator containing two terms, we multiply by its conjugate. Examples of conjugates are

$$\sqrt{a} - \sqrt{b} \quad \text{and} \quad \sqrt{a} + \sqrt{b}$$
$$x + \sqrt{y} \quad \text{and} \quad x - \sqrt{y}$$

EXAMPLE 4   Rationalize each denominator.

a. $\dfrac{2}{3\sqrt{2} + 4}$ **b.** $\dfrac{\sqrt{6} + 2}{\sqrt{5} - \sqrt{3}}$ **c.** $\dfrac{2\sqrt{m}}{3\sqrt{x} + \sqrt{m}}$

Solution

a. Multiply the numerator and denominator by the conjugate of the denominator, $3\sqrt{2} + 4$.

$$\frac{2}{3\sqrt{2} + 4} = \frac{2(3\sqrt{2} - 4)}{(3\sqrt{2} + 4)(3\sqrt{2} - 4)}$$

$$= \frac{2(3\sqrt{2} - 4)}{(3\sqrt{2})^2 - 4^2}$$

$$= \frac{2(3\sqrt{2} - 4)}{18 - 16}$$

$$= \frac{2(3\sqrt{2} - 4)}{2}, \quad \text{or} \quad 3\sqrt{2} - 4$$

It is often useful to leave a numerator in factored form to help determine whether the expression can be simplified.

(Continued on next page)

b. Multiply the numerator and denominator by the conjugate of $\sqrt{5} - \sqrt{3}$.

$$\frac{\sqrt{6} + 2}{\sqrt{5} - \sqrt{3}} = \frac{(\sqrt{6} + 2)(\sqrt{5} + \sqrt{3})}{(\sqrt{5} - \sqrt{3})(\sqrt{5} + \sqrt{3})}$$

$$= \frac{\sqrt{6}\sqrt{5} + \sqrt{6}\sqrt{3} + 2\sqrt{5} + 2\sqrt{3}}{(\sqrt{5})^2 - (\sqrt{3})^2}$$

$$= \frac{\sqrt{30} + \sqrt{18} + 2\sqrt{5} + 2\sqrt{3}}{5 - 3}$$

$$= \frac{\sqrt{30} + 3\sqrt{2} + 2\sqrt{5} + 2\sqrt{3}}{2}$$

c. Multiply by the conjugate of $3\sqrt{x} + \sqrt{m}$ to eliminate the radicals from the denominator.

$$\frac{2\sqrt{m}}{3\sqrt{x} + \sqrt{m}} = \frac{2\sqrt{m}(3\sqrt{x} - \sqrt{m})}{(3\sqrt{x} + \sqrt{m})(3\sqrt{x} - \sqrt{m})} = \frac{6\sqrt{mx} - 2m}{(3\sqrt{x})^2 - (\sqrt{m})^2}$$

$$= \frac{6\sqrt{mx} - 2m}{9x - m}$$

PRACTICE
4   Rationalize the denominator.

a. $\dfrac{5}{3\sqrt{5} + 2}$

b. $\dfrac{\sqrt{2} + 5}{\sqrt{3} - \sqrt{5}}$

c. $\dfrac{3\sqrt{x}}{2\sqrt{x} + \sqrt{y}}$

OBJECTIVE
3   **Rationalizing Numerators**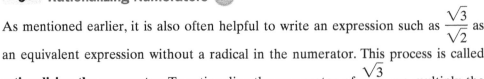

As mentioned earlier, it is also often helpful to write an expression such as $\dfrac{\sqrt{3}}{\sqrt{2}}$ as an equivalent expression without a radical in the numerator. This process is called **rationalizing the numerator.** To rationalize the numerator of $\dfrac{\sqrt{3}}{\sqrt{2}}$, we multiply the numerator and the denominator by $\sqrt{3}$.

$$\frac{\sqrt{3}}{\sqrt{2}} = \frac{\sqrt{3} \cdot \sqrt{3}}{\sqrt{2} \cdot \sqrt{3}} = \frac{\sqrt{9}}{\sqrt{6}} = \frac{3}{\sqrt{6}}$$

EXAMPLE 5   Rationalize the numerator of $\dfrac{\sqrt{7}}{\sqrt{45}}$.

Solution   First we simplify $\sqrt{45}$.

$$\frac{\sqrt{7}}{\sqrt{45}} = \frac{\sqrt{7}}{\sqrt{9 \cdot 5}} = \frac{\sqrt{7}}{3\sqrt{5}}$$

Next we rationalize the numerator by multiplying the numerator and the denominator by $\sqrt{7}$.

$$\frac{\sqrt{7}}{3\sqrt{5}} = \frac{\sqrt{7} \cdot \sqrt{7}}{3\sqrt{5} \cdot \sqrt{7}} = \frac{7}{3\sqrt{5} \cdot 7} = \frac{7}{3\sqrt{35}}$$

PRACTICE
5   Rationalize the numerator of $\dfrac{\sqrt{32}}{\sqrt{80}}$.

EXAMPLE 6   Rationalize the numerator of $\dfrac{\sqrt[3]{2x^2}}{\sqrt[3]{5y}}$.

Solution   The numerator and the denominator of this expression are already simplified. To rationalize the numerator, $\sqrt[3]{2x^2}$, we multiply the numerator and denominator by a factor that will make the radicand a perfect cube. If we multiply $\sqrt[3]{2x^2}$ by $\sqrt[3]{4x}$, we get $\sqrt[3]{8x^3} = 2x$.

$$\frac{\sqrt[3]{2x^2}}{\sqrt[3]{5y}} = \frac{\sqrt[3]{2x^2} \cdot \sqrt[3]{4x}}{\sqrt[3]{5y} \cdot \sqrt[3]{4x}} = \frac{\sqrt[3]{8x^3}}{\sqrt[3]{20xy}} = \frac{2x}{\sqrt[3]{20xy}}$$

PRACTICE
6   Rationalize the numerator of $\dfrac{\sqrt[3]{5b}}{\sqrt[3]{2a}}$.

EXAMPLE 7   Rationalize the numerator of $\dfrac{\sqrt{x} + 2}{5}$.

Solution   We multiply the numerator and the denominator by the conjugate of the numerator, $\sqrt{x} + 2$.

$$\frac{\sqrt{x} + 2}{5} = \frac{(\sqrt{x} + 2)(\sqrt{x} - 2)}{5(\sqrt{x} - 2)} \quad \text{Multiply by } \sqrt{x} - 2, \text{ the conjugate of } \sqrt{x} + 2.$$

$$= \frac{(\sqrt{x})^2 - 2^2}{5(\sqrt{x} - 2)} \qquad (a + b)(a - b) = a^2 - b^2$$

$$= \frac{x - 4}{5(\sqrt{x} - 2)}$$

PRACTICE
7   Rationalize the numerator of $\dfrac{\sqrt{x} - 3}{4}$.

Vocabulary, Readiness & Video Check

Use the choices below to fill in each blank. Not all choices will be used.

rationalizing the numerator   conjugate $\dfrac{\sqrt{3}}{\sqrt{3}}$

rationalizing the denominator $\dfrac{5}{5}$

1. The _____ of $a + b$ is $a - b$.

2. The process of writing an equivalent expression, but without a radical in the denominator, is called _____.

3. The process of writing an equivalent expression, but without a radical in the numerator, is called _____.

4. To rationalize the denominator of $\dfrac{5}{\sqrt{3}}$, we multiply by _____.

Martin-Gay Interactive Videos

See Video 10.5

Watch the section lecture video and answer the following questions.

OBJECTIVE
1   5. From Examples 1–3, what is the goal of rationalizing a denominator?

OBJECTIVE
2   6. From Example 4, why will multiplying a denominator by its conjugate always rationalize the denominator?

OBJECTIVE
3   7. From Example 5, is the process of rationalizing a numerator any different from rationalizing a denominator?

10.5 **Exercise Set** MyMathLab®

Rationalize each denominator. See Examples 1 through 3.

1. $\dfrac{\sqrt{2}}{\sqrt{7}}$
2. $\dfrac{\sqrt{3}}{\sqrt{2}}$

3. $\sqrt{\dfrac{1}{5}}$
4. $\sqrt{\dfrac{1}{2}}$

5. $\sqrt{\dfrac{4}{x}}$
6. $\sqrt{\dfrac{25}{y}}$

7. $\dfrac{4}{\sqrt[3]{3}}$
8. $\dfrac{6}{\sqrt[3]{9}}$

9. $\dfrac{3}{\sqrt{8x}}$
10. $\dfrac{5}{\sqrt{27a}}$

11. $\dfrac{3}{\sqrt[3]{4x^2}}$
12. $\dfrac{5}{\sqrt[3]{3y}}$

13. $\dfrac{9}{\sqrt{3a}}$
14. $\dfrac{x}{\sqrt{5}}$

15. $\dfrac{3}{\sqrt[3]{2}}$
16. $\dfrac{5}{\sqrt[3]{9}}$

17. $\dfrac{2\sqrt{3}}{\sqrt{7}}$
18. $\dfrac{-5\sqrt{2}}{\sqrt{11}}$

19. $\sqrt{\dfrac{2x}{5y}}$
20. $\sqrt{\dfrac{13a}{2b}}$

21. $\sqrt[3]{\dfrac{3}{5}}$
22. $\sqrt[3]{\dfrac{7}{10}}$

23. $\sqrt{\dfrac{3x}{50}}$
24. $\sqrt{\dfrac{11y}{45}}$

25. $\dfrac{1}{\sqrt{12z}}$
26. $\dfrac{1}{\sqrt{32x}}$

27. $\dfrac{\sqrt[3]{2y^2}}{\sqrt[3]{9x^2}}$
28. $\dfrac{\sqrt[3]{3x}}{\sqrt[3]{4y^4}}$

29. $\sqrt[4]{\dfrac{81}{8}}$
30. $\sqrt[4]{\dfrac{1}{9}}$

31. $\sqrt[4]{\dfrac{16}{9x^7}}$
32. $\sqrt[5]{\dfrac{32}{m^6 n^{13}}}$

33. $\dfrac{5a}{\sqrt[5]{8a^9 b^{11}}}$
34. $\dfrac{9y}{\sqrt[4]{4y^9}}$

Write the conjugate of each expression.

35. $\sqrt{2} + x$
36. $\sqrt{3} + y$
37. $5 - \sqrt{a}$
38. $6 - \sqrt{b}$
39. $-7\sqrt{5} + 8\sqrt{x}$
40. $-9\sqrt{2} - 6\sqrt{y}$

Rationalize each denominator. See Example 4.

41. $\dfrac{6}{2 - \sqrt{7}}$
42. $\dfrac{3}{\sqrt{7} - 4}$

43. $\dfrac{-7}{\sqrt{x} - 3}$
44. $\dfrac{-8}{\sqrt{y} + 4}$

45. $\dfrac{\sqrt{2} - \sqrt{3}}{\sqrt{2} + \sqrt{3}}$
46. $\dfrac{\sqrt{3} + \sqrt{4}}{\sqrt{2} - \sqrt{3}}$

47. $\dfrac{\sqrt{a} + 1}{2\sqrt{a} - \sqrt{b}}$
48. $\dfrac{2\sqrt{a} - 3}{2\sqrt{a} + \sqrt{b}}$

49. $\dfrac{8}{1 + \sqrt{10}}$
50. $\dfrac{-3}{\sqrt{6} - 2}$

51. $\dfrac{\sqrt{x}}{\sqrt{x} + \sqrt{y}}$
52. $\dfrac{2\sqrt{a}}{2\sqrt{x} - \sqrt{y}}$

53. $\dfrac{2\sqrt{3} + \sqrt{6}}{4\sqrt{3} - \sqrt{6}}$
54. $\dfrac{4\sqrt{5} + \sqrt{2}}{2\sqrt{5} - \sqrt{2}}$

Rationalize each numerator. See Examples 5 and 6.

55. $\sqrt{\dfrac{5}{3}}$
56. $\sqrt{\dfrac{3}{2}}$

57. $\sqrt{\dfrac{18}{5}}$
58. $\sqrt{\dfrac{12}{7}}$

59. $\dfrac{\sqrt{4x}}{7}$
60. $\dfrac{\sqrt{3x^5}}{6}$

61. $\dfrac{\sqrt[3]{5y^2}}{\sqrt[3]{4x}}$
62. $\dfrac{\sqrt[3]{4x}}{\sqrt[3]{z^4}}$

63. $\sqrt{\dfrac{2}{5}}$
64. $\sqrt{\dfrac{3}{7}}$

65. $\dfrac{\sqrt{2x}}{11}$
66. $\dfrac{\sqrt{y}}{7}$

67. $\sqrt[3]{\dfrac{7}{8}}$
68. $\sqrt[3]{\dfrac{25}{2}}$

69. $\dfrac{\sqrt[3]{3x^5}}{10}$
70. $\sqrt[3]{\dfrac{9y}{7}}$

71. $\sqrt{\dfrac{18x^4 y^6}{3z}}$
72. $\sqrt{\dfrac{8x^5 y}{2z}}$

Rationalize each numerator. See Example 7.

73. $\dfrac{2 - \sqrt{11}}{6}$
74. $\dfrac{\sqrt{15} + 1}{2}$

75. $\dfrac{2 - \sqrt{7}}{-5}$
76. $\dfrac{\sqrt{5} + 2}{\sqrt{2}}$

77. $\dfrac{\sqrt{x} + 3}{\sqrt{x}}$
78. $\dfrac{5 + \sqrt{2}}{\sqrt{2x}}$

79. $\dfrac{\sqrt{2} - 1}{\sqrt{2} + 1}$
80. $\dfrac{\sqrt{8} - \sqrt{3}}{\sqrt{2} + \sqrt{3}}$

81. $\dfrac{\sqrt{x} + 1}{\sqrt{x} - 1}$
82. $\dfrac{\sqrt{x} + \sqrt{y}}{\sqrt{x} - \sqrt{y}}$

REVIEW AND PREVIEW

Solve each equation. See Sections 2.3 and 6.6.

83. $2x - 7 = 3(x - 4)$ **84.** $9x - 4 = 7(x - 2)$

85. $(x - 6)(2x + 1) = 0$ **86.** $(y + 2)(5y + 4) = 0$

87. $x^2 - 8x = -12$ **88.** $x^3 = x$

CONCEPT EXTENSIONS

△ **89.** The formula of the radius r of a sphere with surface area A is

$$r = \sqrt{\frac{A}{4\pi}}$$

Rationalize the denominator of the radical expression in this formula.

△ **90.** The formula for the radius r of a cone with height 7 centimeters and volume V is

$$r = \sqrt{\frac{3V}{7\pi}}$$

Rationalize the numerator of the radical expression in this formula.

7 cm

r

91. Given $\dfrac{\sqrt{5y^3}}{\sqrt{12x^3}}$, rationalize the denominator by following parts (a) and (b).

  a. Multiply the numerator and denominator by $\sqrt{12x^3}$.

  b. Multiply the numerator and denominator by $\sqrt{3x}$.

  c. What can you conclude from parts (a) and (b)?

92. Given $\dfrac{\sqrt[3]{5y}}{\sqrt[3]{4}}$, rationalize the denominator by following parts (a) and (b).

  a. Multiply the numerator and denominator by $\sqrt[3]{16}$.

  b. Multiply the numerator and denominator by $\sqrt[3]{2}$.

  c. What can you conclude from parts (a) and (b)?

Determine the smallest number both the numerator and denominator should be multiplied by to rationalize the denominator of the radical expression. See the Concept Check in this section.

93. $\dfrac{9}{\sqrt[3]{5}}$ **94.** $\dfrac{5}{\sqrt{27}}$

95. When rationalizing the denominator of $\dfrac{\sqrt{5}}{\sqrt{7}}$, explain why both the numerator and the denominator must be multiplied by $\sqrt{7}$.

96. When rationalizing the numerator of $\dfrac{\sqrt{5}}{\sqrt{7}}$, explain why both the numerator and the denominator must be multiplied by $\sqrt{5}$.

97. Explain why rationalizing the denominator does not change the value of the original expression.

98. Explain why rationalizing the numerator does not change the value of the original expression.

Integrated Review RADICALS AND RATIONAL EXPONENTS

Sections 10.1–10.5

Throughout this review, assume that all variables represent positive real numbers.

Find each root.

1. $\sqrt{81}$ **2.** $\sqrt[3]{-8}$ **3.** $\sqrt[4]{\dfrac{1}{16}}$ **4.** $\sqrt{x^6}$

5. $\sqrt[3]{y^9}$ **6.** $\sqrt{4y^{10}}$ **7.** $\sqrt[5]{-32y^5}$ **8.** $\sqrt[4]{81b^{12}}$

Use radical notation to write each expression. Simplify if possible.

9. $36^{1/2}$ **10.** $(3y)^{1/4}$ **11.** $64^{-2/3}$ **12.** $(x + 1)^{3/5}$

Use the properties of exponents to simplify each expression. Write with positive exponents.

13. $y^{-1/6} \cdot y^{7/6}$ **14.** $\dfrac{(2x^{1/3})^4}{x^{5/6}}$ **15.** $\dfrac{x^{1/4}x^{3/4}}{x^{-1/4}}$ **16.** $4^{1/3} \cdot 4^{2/5}$

Use rational exponents to simplify each radical.

17. $\sqrt[3]{8x^6}$ **18.** $\sqrt[12]{a^9b^6}$

Use rational exponents to write each as a single radical expression.

19. $\sqrt[4]{x} \cdot \sqrt{x}$

20. $\sqrt{5} \cdot \sqrt[3]{2}$

Simplify.

21. $\sqrt{40}$

22. $\sqrt[4]{16x^7y^{10}}$

23. $\sqrt[3]{54x^4}$

24. $\sqrt[5]{-64b^{10}}$

Multiply or divide. Then simplify if possible.

25. $\sqrt{5} \cdot \sqrt{x}$

26. $\sqrt[3]{8x} \cdot \sqrt[3]{8x^2}$

27. $\dfrac{\sqrt{98y^6}}{\sqrt{2y}}$

28. $\dfrac{\sqrt[4]{48a^9b^3}}{\sqrt[4]{ab^3}}$

Perform each indicated operation.

29. $\sqrt{20} - \sqrt{75} + 5\sqrt{7}$

30. $\sqrt[3]{54y^4} - y\sqrt[3]{16y}$

31. $\sqrt{3}(\sqrt{5} - \sqrt{2})$

32. $(\sqrt{7} + \sqrt{3})^2$

33. $(2x - \sqrt{5})(2x + \sqrt{5})$

34. $(\sqrt{x+1} - 1)^2$

Rationalize each denominator.

35. $\sqrt{\dfrac{7}{3}}$

36. $\dfrac{5}{\sqrt[3]{2x^2}}$

37. $\dfrac{\sqrt{3} - \sqrt{7}}{2\sqrt{3} + \sqrt{7}}$

Rationalize each numerator.

38. $\sqrt{\dfrac{7}{3}}$

39. $\sqrt[3]{\dfrac{9y}{11}}$

40. $\dfrac{\sqrt{x} - 2}{\sqrt{x}}$

10.6 Radical Equations and Problem Solving

OBJECTIVES

1 Solve Equations That Contain Radical Expressions. ▶

2 Use the Pythagorean Theorem to Model Problems. ▶

OBJECTIVE

1 Solving Equations That Contain Radical Expressions ▶

In this section, we present techniques to solve equations containing radical expressions such as

$$\sqrt{2x - 3} = 9$$

We use the power rule to help us solve these radical equations.

Power Rule

If both sides of an equation are raised to the same power, **all** solutions of the original equation are **among** the solutions of the new equation.

This property *does not* say that raising both sides of an equation to a power yields an equivalent equation. A solution of the new equation *may or may not* be a solution of the original equation. For example, $(-2)^2 = 2^2$, but $-2 \neq 2$. Thus, *each solution of the new equation must be checked* to make sure it is a solution of the original equation. Recall that a proposed solution that is not a solution of the original equation is called an **extraneous solution**.

EXAMPLE 1 Solve: $\sqrt{2x - 3} = 9$.

Solution We use the power rule to square both sides of the equation to eliminate the radical.

$$\sqrt{2x - 3} = 9$$
$$(\sqrt{2x - 3})^2 = 9^2$$
$$2x - 3 = 81$$
$$2x = 84$$
$$x = 42$$

Now we check the solution in the original equation.

Check:

$$\sqrt{2x - 3} = 9$$

$$\sqrt{2(42) - 3} \stackrel{?}{=} 9 \quad \text{Let } x = 42.$$

$$\sqrt{84 - 3} \stackrel{?}{=} 9$$

$$\sqrt{81} \stackrel{?}{=} 9$$

$$9 = 9 \quad \text{True}$$

The solution checks, so we conclude that the solution is 42, or the solution set is $\{42\}$. ☐

PRACTICE
1   Solve: $\sqrt{3x - 5} = 7$.

To solve a radical equation, first isolate a radical on one side of the equation.

EXAMPLE 2   Solve: $\sqrt{-10x - 1} + 3x = 0$.

Solution   First, isolate the radical on one side of the equation. To do this, we subtract $3x$ from both sides.

$$\sqrt{-10x - 1} + 3x = 0$$

$$\sqrt{-10x - 1} + 3x - 3x = 0 - 3x$$

$$\sqrt{-10x - 1} = -3x$$

Next we use the power rule to eliminate the radical.

$$(\sqrt{-10x - 1})^2 = (-3x)^2$$

$$-10x - 1 = 9x^2$$

Since this is a quadratic equation, we can set the equation equal to 0 and try to solve by factoring.

$$9x^2 + 10x + 1 = 0$$

$$(9x + 1)(x + 1) = 0 \quad \text{Factor.}$$

$$9x + 1 = 0 \quad \text{or} \quad x + 1 = 0 \quad \text{Set each factor equal to 0.}$$

$$x = -\frac{1}{9} \quad \text{or} \quad x = -1$$

Check: Let $x = -\frac{1}{9}$.   Let $x = -1$.

$$\sqrt{-10x - 1} + 3x = 0 \qquad\qquad \sqrt{-10x - 1} + 3x = 0$$

$$\sqrt{-10\left(-\frac{1}{9}\right) - 1} + 3\left(-\frac{1}{9}\right) \stackrel{?}{=} 0 \qquad \sqrt{-10(-1) - 1} + 3(-1) \stackrel{?}{=} 0$$

$$\sqrt{\frac{10}{9} - \frac{9}{9}} - \frac{3}{9} \stackrel{?}{=} 0 \qquad\qquad \sqrt{10 - 1} - 3 \stackrel{?}{=} 0$$

$$\sqrt{\frac{1}{9}} - \frac{1}{3} \stackrel{?}{=} 0 \qquad\qquad\qquad \sqrt{9} - 3 \stackrel{?}{=} 0$$

$$\frac{1}{3} - \frac{1}{3} = 0 \quad \text{True} \qquad\qquad 3 - 3 = 0 \quad \text{True}$$

Both solutions check. The solutions are $-\frac{1}{9}$ and -1, or the solution set is $\left\{-\frac{1}{9}, -1\right\}$. ☐

PRACTICE
2   Solve: $\sqrt{16x - 3} - 4x = 0$.

The following steps may be used to solve a radical equation.

Solving a Radical Equation

Step 1. Isolate one radical on one side of the equation.

Step 2. Raise each side of the equation to a power equal to the index of the radical and simplify.

Step 3. If the equation still contains a radical term, repeat Steps 1 and 2. If not, solve the equation.

Step 4. Check all proposed solutions in the original equation.

EXAMPLE 3   Solve: $\sqrt[3]{x + 1} + 5 = 3$.

Solution   First we isolate the radical by subtracting 5 from both sides of the equation.

$$\sqrt[3]{x + 1} + 5 = 3$$
$$\sqrt[3]{x + 1} = -2$$

Next we raise both sides of the equation to the third power to eliminate the radical.

$$\left(\sqrt[3]{x + 1}\right)^3 = (-2)^3$$
$$x + 1 = -8$$
$$x = -9$$

The solution checks in the original equation, so the solution is -9.   □

PRACTICE
3   Solve: $\sqrt[3]{x - 2} + 1 = 3$.

....

EXAMPLE 4   Solve: $\sqrt{4 - x} = x - 2$.

Solution

$$\sqrt{4 - x} = x - 2$$
$$\left(\sqrt{4 - x}\right)^2 = (x - 2)^2$$
$$4 - x = x^2 - 4x + 4$$
$$x^2 - 3x = 0 \qquad \text{Write the quadratic equation in standard form.}$$
$$x(x - 3) = 0 \qquad \text{Factor.}$$
$$x = 0 \quad \text{or} \quad x - 3 = 0 \qquad \text{Set each factor equal to 0.}$$
$$x = 3$$

Check:

$$\sqrt{4 - x} = x - 2 \qquad\qquad\qquad \sqrt{4 - x} = x - 2$$
$$\sqrt{4 - 0} \stackrel{?}{=} 0 - 2 \quad \text{Let } x = 0. \qquad \sqrt{4 - 3} \stackrel{?}{=} 3 - 2 \quad \text{Let } x = 3.$$
$$2 = -2 \quad \text{False} \qquad\qquad\qquad 1 = 1 \quad \text{True}$$

The proposed solution 3 checks, but 0 does not. Since 0 is an extraneous solution, the only solution is 3.   □

PRACTICE
4   Solve: $\sqrt{16 + x} = x - 4$.

....

▶ **Helpful Hint**

In Example 4, notice that $(x - 2)^2 = x^2 - 4x + 4$. Make sure binomials are squared correctly.

✓CONCEPT CHECK
How can you immediately tell that the equation $\sqrt{2y + 3} = -4$ has no real solution?

EXAMPLE 5   Solve: $\sqrt{2x + 5} + \sqrt{2x} = 3$.

Solution   We get one radical alone by subtracting $\sqrt{2x}$ from both sides.

$$\sqrt{2x + 5} + \sqrt{2x} = 3$$
$$\sqrt{2x + 5} = 3 - \sqrt{2x}$$

Now we use the power rule to begin eliminating the radicals. First we square both sides.

$$\left(\sqrt{2x + 5}\right)^2 = \left(3 - \sqrt{2x}\right)^2$$
$$2x + 5 = 9 - 6\sqrt{2x} + 2x \quad \text{Multiply } (3 - \sqrt{2x})(3 - \sqrt{2x}).$$

There is still a radical in the equation, so we get a radical alone again. Then we square both sides.

$$2x + 5 = 9 - 6\sqrt{2x} + 2x$$
$$6\sqrt{2x} = 4 \qquad \text{Get the radical alone.}$$
$$36(2x) = 16 \qquad \text{Square both sides of the equation to eliminate the radical.}$$
$$72x = 16 \qquad \text{Multiply.}$$
$$x = \frac{16}{72} \qquad \text{Solve.}$$
$$x = \frac{2}{9} \qquad \text{Simplify.}$$

The proposed solution, $\frac{2}{9}$, checks in the original equation. The solution is $\frac{2}{9}$.   □

PRACTICE
5   Solve: $\sqrt{8x + 1} + \sqrt{3x} = 2$.

▶ **Helpful Hint**
Make sure expressions are squared correctly. In Example 5, we squared $(3 - \sqrt{2x})$ as

$$\left(3 - \sqrt{2x}\right)^2 = \left(3 - \sqrt{2x}\right)\left(3 - \sqrt{2x}\right)$$
$$= 3 \cdot 3 - 3\sqrt{2x} - 3\sqrt{2x} + \sqrt{2x} \cdot \sqrt{2x}$$
$$= 9 - 6\sqrt{2x} + 2x$$

✓CONCEPT CHECK
What is wrong with the following solution?

$$\sqrt{2x + 5} + \sqrt{4 - x} = 8$$
$$\left(\sqrt{2x + 5} + \sqrt{4 - x}\right)^2 = 8^2$$
$$(2x + 5) + (4 - x) = 64$$
$$x + 9 = 64$$
$$x = 55$$

Answers to Concept Checks:
answers may vary;
$\left(\sqrt{2x + 5} + \sqrt{4 - x}\right)^2$ is not $(2x + 5) + (4 - x)$.

OBJECTIVE
2   Using the Pythagorean Theorem

Recall that the Pythagorean theorem states that in a right triangle, the length of the hypotenuse squared equals the sum of the lengths of each of the legs squared.

Pythagorean Theorem

If a and b are the lengths of the legs of a right triangle and c is the length of the hypotenuse, then $a^2 + b^2 = c^2$.

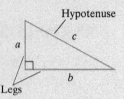

Hypotenuse

c

a

b

Legs

⚠ **EXAMPLE 6** Find the length of the unknown leg of the right triangle.

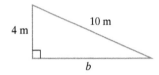

10 m

4 m

b

Solution In the formula $a^2 + b^2 = c^2$, c is the hypotenuse. Here, $c = 10$, the length of the hypotenuse, and $a = 4$. We solve for b. Then $a^2 + b^2 = c^2$ becomes

$$4^2 + b^2 = 10^2$$
$$16 + b^2 = 100$$
$$b^2 = 84 \quad \text{Subtract 16 from both sides.}$$
$$b = \pm\sqrt{84} = \pm\sqrt{4 \cdot 21} = \pm 2\sqrt{21}$$

Since b is a length and thus is positive, we will use the positive value only. The unknown leg of the triangle is $2\sqrt{21}$ meters long. ☐

PRACTICE

6 Find the length of the unknown leg of the right triangle.

12 m

6 m

a

- ▨

⚠ **EXAMPLE 7** **Calculating Placement of a Wire**

A 50-foot supporting wire is to be attached to a 75-foot antenna. Because of surrounding buildings, sidewalks, and roadways, the wire must be anchored exactly 20 feet from the base of the antenna.

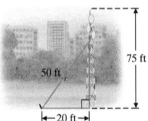

75 ft

50 ft

⊢—20 ft—⊣

a. How high from the base of the antenna is the wire attached?

b. Local regulations require that a supporting wire be attached at a height no less than $\dfrac{3}{5}$ of the total height of the antenna. From part (a), have local regulations been met?

Solution

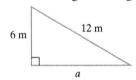

50 ft x ft

⊢—20 ft—⊣

1. UNDERSTAND. Read and reread the problem. From the diagram, we notice that a right triangle is formed with hypotenuse 50 feet and one leg 20 feet. Let x be the height from the base of the antenna to the attached wire.

2. TRANSLATE. Use the Pythagorean theorem.

$$a^2 + b^2 = c^2$$
$$20^2 + x^2 = 50^2 \quad a = 20, c = 50$$

3. SOLVE.

$$20^2 + x^2 = 50^2$$
$$400 + x^2 = 2500$$
$$x^2 = 2100 \qquad \text{Subtract 400 from both sides.}$$
$$x = \pm\sqrt{2100}$$
$$= \pm 10\sqrt{21}$$

4. INTERPRET. *Check* the work and *state* the solution.

Check: We will use only the positive value, $x = 10\sqrt{21}$, because x represents length. The wire is attached exactly $10\sqrt{21}$ feet from the base of the pole, or approximately 45.8 feet.

State: The supporting wire must be attached at a height no less than $\frac{3}{5}$ of the total height of the antenna. This height is $\frac{3}{5}$ (75 feet), or 45 feet. Since we know from part (a) that the wire is to be attached at a height of approximately 45.8 feet, local regulations have been met.   □

PRACTICE
7   Keith Robinson bought two Siamese fighting fish, but when he got home, he found he only had one rectangular tank that was 12 in. long, 7 in. wide, and 5 in. deep. Since the fish must be kept separated, he needed to insert a plastic divider in the diagonal of the tank. He already has a piece that is 5 in. in one dimension, but how long must it be to fit corner to corner in the tank?

- -

Graphing Calculator Explorations

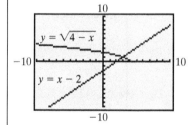

We can use a graphing calculator to solve radical equations. For example, to use a graphing calculator to approximate the solutions of the equation solved in Example 4, we graph the following.

$$Y_1 = \sqrt{4 - x} \quad \text{and} \quad Y_2 = x - 2$$

The x-value of the point of intersection is the solution. Use the Intersect feature or the Zoom and Trace features of your graphing calculator to see that the solution is 3.

Use a graphing calculator to solve each radical equation. Round all solutions to the nearest hundredth.

1. $\sqrt{x + 7} = x$ **2.** $\sqrt{3x + 5} = 2x$

3. $\sqrt{2x + 1} = \sqrt{2x + 2}$ **4.** $\sqrt{10x - 1} = \sqrt{-10x + 10} - 1$

5. $1.2x = \sqrt{3.1x + 5}$ **6.** $\sqrt{1.9x^2 - 2.2} = -0.8x + 3$

Vocabulary, Readiness & Video Check

Use the choices below to fill in each blank. Not all choices will be used.

hypotenuse	right	$x^2 + 25$	$16 - 8\sqrt{7x} + 7x$
extraneous solution	legs	$x^2 - 10x + 25$	$16 + 7x$

1. A proposed solution that is not a solution of the original equation is called a(n) _____.

2. The Pythagorean theorem states that $a^2 + b^2 = c^2$ where a and b are the lengths of the _____ of a(n) _____ triangle and c is the length of the _____.

3. The square of $x - 5$, or $(x - 5)^2 =$ _____.

4. The square of $4 - \sqrt{7x}$, or $(4 - \sqrt{7x})^2 =$ _____.

Martin-Gay Interactive Videos

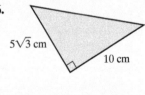

See Video 10.6

Watch the section lecture video and answer the following questions.

OBJECTIVE
1

5. From Examples 1–4, why must you be careful and check your proposed solution(s) in the original equation?

OBJECTIVE
2

6. From Example 5, when solving problems using the Pythagorean theorem, what two things must you remember?

OBJECTIVE
2

7. What important reminder is given as the final answer to Example 5 is being found?

10.6 Exercise Set   MyMathLab®

Solve. See Examples 1 and 2.

1. $\sqrt{2x} = 4$

2. $\sqrt{3x} = 3$

3. $\sqrt{x - 3} = 2$

4. $\sqrt{x + 1} = 5$

5. $\sqrt{2x} = -4$

6. $\sqrt{5x} = -5$

7. $\sqrt{4x - 3} - 5 = 0$

8. $\sqrt{x - 3} - 1 = 0$

9. $\sqrt{2x - 3} - 2 = 1$

10. $\sqrt{3x + 3} - 4 = 8$

Solve. See Example 3.

11. $\sqrt[3]{6x} = -3$

12. $\sqrt[3]{4x} = -2$

13. $\sqrt[3]{x - 2} - 3 = 0$

14. $\sqrt[3]{2x - 6} - 4 = 0$

Solve. See Examples 4 and 5.

15. $\sqrt{13 - x} = x - 1$

16. $\sqrt{2x - 3} = 3 - x$

17. $x - \sqrt{4 - 3x} = -8$

18. $2x + \sqrt{x + 1} = 8$

19. $\sqrt{y + 5} = 2 - \sqrt{y - 4}$

20. $\sqrt{x + 3} + \sqrt{x - 5} = 3$

21. $\sqrt{x - 3} + \sqrt{x + 2} = 5$

22. $\sqrt{2x - 4} - \sqrt{3x + 4} = -2$

MIXED PRACTICE

Solve. See Examples 1 through 5.

23. $\sqrt{3x - 2} = 5$

24. $\sqrt{5x - 4} = 9$

25. $-\sqrt{2x} + 4 = -6$

26. $-\sqrt{3x + 9} = -12$

27. $\sqrt{3x + 1} + 2 = 0$

28. $\sqrt{3x + 1} - 2 = 0$

29. $\sqrt[4]{4x + 1} - 2 = 0$

30. $\sqrt[4]{2x - 9} - 3 = 0$

31. $\sqrt{4x - 3} = 7$

32. $\sqrt{3x + 9} = 6$

33. $\sqrt[3]{6x - 3} - 3 = 0$

34. $\sqrt[3]{3x + 4} = 7$

35. $\sqrt[3]{2x - 3} - 2 = -5$

36. $\sqrt[3]{x - 4} - 5 = -7$

37. $\sqrt{x + 4} = \sqrt{2x - 5}$

38. $\sqrt{3y + 6} = \sqrt{7y - 6}$

39. $x - \sqrt{1 - x} = -5$

40. $x - \sqrt{x - 2} = 4$

41. $\sqrt[3]{-6x - 1} = \sqrt[3]{-2x - 5}$

42. $\sqrt[3]{-4x - 3} = \sqrt[3]{-x - 15}$

43. $\sqrt{5x - 1} - \sqrt{x + 2} = 3$

44. $\sqrt{2x - 1} - 4 = -\sqrt{x - 4}$

45. $\sqrt{2x - 1} = \sqrt{1 - 2x}$

46. $\sqrt{7x - 4} = \sqrt{4 - 7x}$

47. $\sqrt{3x + 4} - 1 = \sqrt{2x + 1}$

48. $\sqrt{x - 2} + 3 = \sqrt{4x + 1}$

49. $\sqrt{y + 3} - \sqrt{y - 3} = 1$

50. $\sqrt{x + 1} - \sqrt{x - 1} = 2$

Find the length of the unknown side of each triangle. See Example 6.

51.

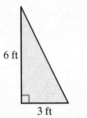

6 ft

3 ft

52.   7 in.

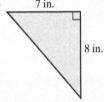

8 in.

53.

3 m

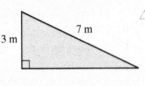

7 m

54.   4 cm

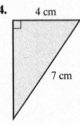

7 cm

Find the length of the unknown side of each triangle. Give the exact length and a one-decimal-place approximation. See Example 6.

55.

9 m

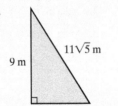

$11\sqrt{5}$ m

56.

$5\sqrt{3}$ cm

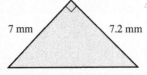

10 cm

57.

7 mm

7.2 mm

58.

2.7 in.

2.3 in.

Solve. Give exact answers and two-decimal-place approximations where appropriate. For Exercises 59 and 60, the solutions have been started for you. See Example 7.

59. A wire is needed to support a vertical pole 15 feet tall. The cable will be anchored to a stake 8 feet from the base of the pole. How much cable is needed?

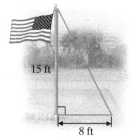

15 ft

8 ft

Start the solution:

1. UNDERSTAND the problem. Reread it as many times as needed. Notice that a right triangle is formed with legs of length 8 ft and 15 ft.
   Since we are looking for how much cable is needed, let

$$x = \text{amount of cable needed}$$

2. TRANSLATE into an equation. We use the Pythagorean theorem. (Fill in the blanks below.)

$$a^2 \quad + \quad b^2 \quad = \quad c^2$$
$$\underline{\quad}^2 \quad + \quad \underline{\quad}^2 \quad = \quad x^2$$

Finish with:

3. SOLVE and 4. INTERPRET

60. The tallest structure in the United States is a TV tower in Blanchard, North Dakota. Its height is 2063 feet. A 2382-foot length of wire is to be used as a guy wire attached to the top of the tower. Approximate to the nearest foot how far from the base of the tower the guy wire must be anchored. (*Source:* U.S. Geological Survey)

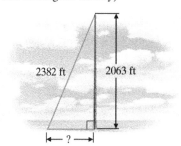

2382 ft   2063 ft

?

Start the solution:

1. UNDERSTAND the problem. Reread it as many times as needed. Notice that a right triangle is formed with hypotenuse 2382 ft and one leg 2063 ft.
   Since we are looking for how far from the base of the tower the guy wire is anchored, let

$$x = \text{distance from base of tower to where guy wire is anchored.}$$

2. TRANSLATE into an equation. We use the Pythagorean theorem. (Fill in the blanks below.)

$$a^2 \quad + \quad b^2 \quad = \quad c^2$$
$$\underline{\quad}^2 \quad + \quad x^2 \quad = \quad \underline{\quad}^2$$

Finish with:

3. SOLVE and 4. INTERPRET

61. A spotlight is mounted on the eaves of a house 12 feet above the ground. A flower bed runs between the house and the sidewalk, so the closest a ladder can be placed to the house is 5 feet. How long of a ladder is needed so that an electrician can reach the place where the light is mounted?

12 ft

5 ft

62. A wire is to be attached to support a telephone pole. Because of surrounding buildings, sidewalks, and roadways, the wire must be anchored exactly 15 feet from the base of the pole. Telephone company workers have only 30 feet of cable, and 2 feet of that must be used to attach the cable to the pole and to the stake on the ground. How high from the base of the pole can the wire be attached?

15 ft

63. The radius of the moon is 1080 miles. Use the formula for the radius r of a sphere given its surface area A,

$$r = \sqrt{\frac{A}{4\pi}}$$

to find the surface area of the moon. Round to the nearest square mile. (*Source:* National Space Science Data Center)

64. Police departments find it very useful to be able to approximate the speed of a car when they are given the distance that the car skidded before it came to a stop. If the road surface is wet concrete, the function $S(x) = \sqrt{10.5x}$ is used, where $S(x)$ is the speed of the car in miles per hour and x is the distance skidded in feet. Find how fast a car was moving if it skidded 280 feet on wet concrete.

65. The formula $v = \sqrt{2gh}$ gives the velocity v, in feet per second, of an object when it falls h feet accelerated by gravity g, in feet per second squared. If g is approximately 32 feet per second squared, find how far an object has fallen if its velocity is 80 feet per second.

66. Two tractors are pulling a tree stump from a field. If two forces A and B pull at right angles (90°) to each other, the size of the resulting force R is given by the formula $R = \sqrt{A^2 + B^2}$. If tractor A is exerting 600 pounds of force and the resulting force is 850 pounds, find how much force tractor B is exerting.

600 lb

In psychology, it has been suggested that the number S of nonsense syllables that a person can repeat consecutively depends on his or her IQ score I according to the equation $S = 2\sqrt{I} - 9$.

67. Use this relationship to estimate the IQ of a person who can repeat 11 nonsense syllables consecutively.

68. Use this relationship to estimate the IQ of a person who can repeat 15 nonsense syllables consecutively.

*The **period** of a pendulum is the time it takes for the pendulum to make one full back-and-forth swing. The period of a pendulum depends on the length of the pendulum. The formula for the period P, in seconds, is $P = 2\pi\sqrt{\dfrac{l}{32}}$, where l is the length of the pendulum in feet. Use this formula for Exercises 69 through 74.*

69. Find the period of a pendulum whose length is 2 feet. Give an exact answer and a two-decimal-place approximation.

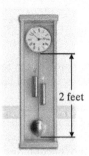
2 feet

70. Klockit sells a 43-inch lyre pendulum. Find the period of this pendulum. Round your answer to 2 decimal places. (*Hint:* First convert inches to feet.)

71. Find the length of a pendulum whose period is 4 seconds. Round your answer to 2 decimal places.

72. Find the length of a pendulum whose period is 3 seconds. Round your answer to 2 decimal places.

73. Study the relationship between period and pendulum length in Exercises 69 through 72 and make a conjecture about this relationship.

74. Galileo experimented with pendulums. He supposedly made conjectures about pendulums of equal length with different bob weights. Try this experiment. Make two pendulums 3 feet long. Attach a heavy weight (lead) to one and a light weight (a cork) to the other. Pull both pendulums back the same angle measure and release. Make a conjecture from your observations.

If the three lengths of the sides of a triangle are known, Heron's formula can be used to find its area. If a, b, and c are the lengths of the three sides, Heron's formula for area is

$$A = \sqrt{s(s - a)(s - b)(s - c)}$$

where s is half the perimeter of the triangle, or $s = \dfrac{1}{2}(a + b + c)$.

Use this formula to find the area of each triangle. Give an exact answer and then a two-decimal-place approximation.

△ **75.**   △ **76.**

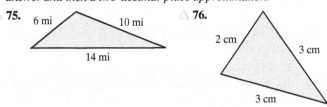
6 mi   10 mi   2 cm   3 cm
14 mi   3 cm

77. Describe when Heron's formula might be useful.

78. In your own words, explain why you think s in Heron's formula is called the *semiperimeter*.

The maximum distance $D(h)$ in kilometers that a person can see from a height h kilometers above the ground is given by the function $D(h) = 111.7\sqrt{h}$. Use this function for Exercises 79 and 80. Round your answers to two decimal places.

79. Find the height that would allow a person to see 80 kilometers.

80. Find the height that would allow a person to see 40 kilometers.

REVIEW AND PREVIEW

Use the vertical line test to determine whether each graph represents the graph of a function. See Section 3.6.

81.   **82.**

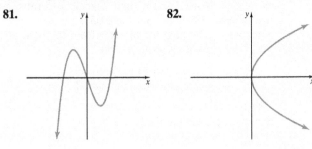

83.
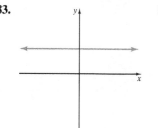

84.
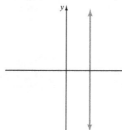

85.
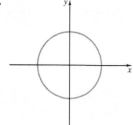

86.
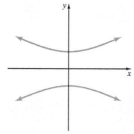

Simplify. See Section 7.7.

87. $\dfrac{\dfrac{x}{6}}{\dfrac{2x}{3} + \dfrac{1}{2}}$

88. $\dfrac{\dfrac{1}{y} + \dfrac{4}{5}}{\dfrac{3}{20}}$

89. $\dfrac{\dfrac{z}{5} + \dfrac{1}{10}}{\dfrac{z}{20} - \dfrac{z}{5}}$

90. $\dfrac{\dfrac{1}{y} + \dfrac{1}{x}}{\dfrac{1}{y} - \dfrac{1}{x}}$

CONCEPT EXTENSIONS

Find the error in each solution and correct. See the second Concept Check in this section.

91.
$$\sqrt{5x - 1} + 4 = 7$$
$$(\sqrt{5x - 1} + 4)^2 = 7^2$$
$$5x - 1 + 16 = 49$$
$$5x = 34$$
$$x = \frac{34}{5}$$

92.
$$\sqrt{2x + 3} + 4 = 1$$
$$\sqrt{2x + 3} = 5$$
$$(\sqrt{2x + 3})^2 = 5^2$$
$$2x + 3 = 25$$
$$2x = 22$$
$$x = 11$$

93. Solve: $\sqrt{\sqrt{x + 3}} + \sqrt{x} = \sqrt{3}$

94. The cost $C(x)$ in dollars per day to operate a small delivery service is given by $C(x) = 80\sqrt[3]{x} + 500$, where x is the number of deliveries per day. In July, the manager decides that it is necessary to keep delivery costs below \$1620.00. Find the greatest number of deliveries this company can make per day and still keep overhead below \$1620.00.

95. Consider the equations $\sqrt{2x} = 4$ and $\sqrt[3]{2x} = 4$.
   a. Explain the difference in solving these equations.
   b. Explain the similarity in solving these equations.

96. Explain why proposed solutions of radical equations must be checked.

Example

For Exercises 97 through 100, see the example below.

Solve $(t^2 - 3t) - 2\sqrt{t^2 - 3t} = 0$.

Solution

Substitution can be used to make this problem somewhat simpler. Since $t^2 - 3t$ occurs more than once, let $x = t^2 - 3t$.

$$(t^2 - 3t) - 2\sqrt{t^2 - 3t} = 0$$
$$x - 2\sqrt{x} = 0$$
$$x = 2\sqrt{x}$$
$$x^2 = (2\sqrt{x})^2$$
$$x^2 = 4x$$
$$x^2 - 4x = 0$$
$$x(x - 4) = 0$$
$$x = 0 \quad \text{or} \quad x - 4 = 0$$
$$x = 4$$

Now we "undo" the substitution.
$x = 0$ Replace x with $t^2 - 3t$.

$$t^2 - 3t = 0$$
$$t(t - 3) = 0$$
$$t = 0 \quad \text{or} \quad t - 3 = 0$$
$$t = 3$$

$x = 4$ Replace x with $t^2 - 3t$.

$$t^2 - 3t = 4$$
$$t^2 - 3t - 4 = 0$$
$$(t - 4)(t + 1) = 0$$
$$t - 4 = 0 \quad \text{or} \quad t + 1 = 0$$
$$t = 4 \qquad\qquad t = -1$$

In this problem, we have four possible solutions: $0, 3, 4,$ and -1. All four solutions check in the original equation, so the solutions are $-1, 0, 3, 4$.

Solve. See the preceding example.

97. $3\sqrt{x^2 - 8x} = x^2 - 8x$

98. $\sqrt{(x^2 - x) + 7} = 2(x^2 - x) - 1$

99. $7 - (x^2 - 3x) = \sqrt{(x^2 - 3x) + 5}$

100. $x^2 + 6x = 4\sqrt{x^2 + 6x}$

10.7 Complex Numbers

OBJECTIVES

1 Write Square Roots of Negative Numbers in the Form bi.

2 Add or Subtract Complex Numbers.

3 Multiply Complex Numbers.

4 Divide Complex Numbers.

5 Raise i to Powers.

OBJECTIVE

1 Writing Numbers in the Form bi

Our work with radical expressions has excluded expressions such as $\sqrt{-16}$ because $\sqrt{-16}$ is not a real number; there is no real number whose square is -16. In this section, we discuss a number system that includes roots of negative numbers. This number system is the **complex number system,** and it includes the set of real numbers as a subset. The complex number system allows us to solve equations such as $x^2 + 1 = 0$ that have no real number solutions. The set of complex numbers includes the **imaginary unit.**

> **Imaginary Unit**
>
> The imaginary unit, written i, is the number whose square is -1. That is,
> $$i^2 = -1 \quad \text{and} \quad i = \sqrt{-1}$$

To write the square root of a negative number in terms of i, use the property that if a is a positive number, then

$$\sqrt{-a} = \sqrt{-1} \cdot \sqrt{a}$$
$$= i \cdot \sqrt{a}$$

Using i, we can write $\sqrt{-16}$ as

$$\sqrt{-16} = \sqrt{-1 \cdot 16} = \sqrt{-1} \cdot \sqrt{16} = i \cdot 4, \text{ or } 4i$$

EXAMPLE 1 Write with i notation.

a. $\sqrt{-36}$ **b.** $\sqrt{-5}$ **c.** $-\sqrt{-20}$

Solution

a. $\sqrt{-36} = \sqrt{-1 \cdot 36} = \sqrt{-1} \cdot \sqrt{36} = i \cdot 6, \text{ or } 6i$

b. $\sqrt{-5} = \sqrt{-1(5)} = \sqrt{-1} \cdot \sqrt{5} = i\sqrt{5}$.

c. $-\sqrt{-20} = -\sqrt{-1 \cdot 20} = -\sqrt{-1} \cdot \sqrt{4 \cdot 5} = -i \cdot 2\sqrt{5} = -2i\sqrt{5}$

> ▶ **Helpful Hint**
> Since $\sqrt{5}i$ can easily be confused with $\sqrt{5i}$, we write $\sqrt{5}i$ as $i\sqrt{5}$.

PRACTICE

1 Write with i notation.

a. $\sqrt{-4}$ **b.** $\sqrt{-7}$ **c.** $-\sqrt{-18}$

The product rule for radicals does not necessarily hold true for imaginary numbers. *To multiply square roots of negative numbers, first we write each number in terms of the imaginary unit i.* For example, to multiply $\sqrt{-4}$ and $\sqrt{-9}$, we first write each number in the form bi.

$$\sqrt{-4}\sqrt{-9} = 2i(3i) = 6i^2 = 6(-1) = -6 \quad \text{Correct}$$

We will also use this method to simplify quotients of square roots of negative numbers. Why? The product rule does not work for this example. In other words,

$$\sqrt{-4} \cdot \sqrt{-9} = \sqrt{(-4)(-9)} = \sqrt{36} = 6 \quad \text{Incorrect}$$

EXAMPLE 2   Multiply or divide as indicated.

a. $\sqrt{-3} \cdot \sqrt{-5}$ **b.** $\sqrt{-36} \cdot \sqrt{-1}$ **c.** $\sqrt{8} \cdot \sqrt{-2}$ **d.** $\dfrac{\sqrt{-125}}{\sqrt{5}}$

Solution

a. $\sqrt{-3} \cdot \sqrt{-5} = i\sqrt{3}(i\sqrt{5}) = i^2\sqrt{15} = -1\sqrt{15} = -\sqrt{15}$

b. $\sqrt{-36} \cdot \sqrt{-1} = 6i(i) = 6i^2 = 6(-1) = -6$

c. $\sqrt{8} \cdot \sqrt{-2} = 2\sqrt{2}(i\sqrt{2}) = 2i(\sqrt{2}\sqrt{2}) = 2i(2) = 4i$

d. $\dfrac{\sqrt{-125}}{\sqrt{5}} = \dfrac{i\sqrt{125}}{\sqrt{5}} = i\sqrt{25} = 5i$

PRACTICE

2   Multiply or divide as indicated.

a. $\sqrt{-5} \cdot \sqrt{-6}$ **b.** $\sqrt{-9} \cdot \sqrt{-1}$ **c.** $\sqrt{125} \cdot \sqrt{-5}$ **d.** $\dfrac{\sqrt{-27}}{\sqrt{3}}$

Now that we have practiced working with the imaginary unit, we define complex numbers.

> **Complex Numbers**
>
> A **complex number** is a number that can be written in the form $a + bi$, where a and b are real numbers.

Notice that the set of real numbers is a subset of the complex numbers since any real number can be written in the form of a complex number. For example,

$$16 = 16 + 0i$$

In general, a complex number $a + bi$ is a real number if $b = 0$. Also, a complex number is called a **pure imaginary number** or an imaginary number if $a = 0$ and $b \neq 0$. For example,

$$3i = 0 + 3i \quad \text{and} \quad i\sqrt{7} = 0 + i\sqrt{7}$$

are pure imaginary numbers.

The following diagram shows the relationship between complex numbers and their subsets.

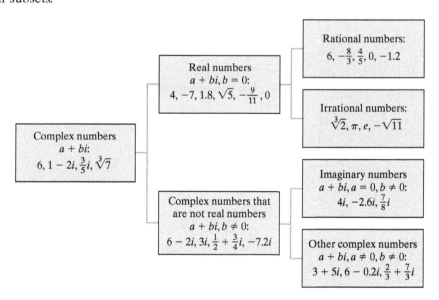

> ✓CONCEPT CHECK
> True or false? Every complex number is also a real number.

2 Adding or Subtracting Complex Numbers

Two complex numbers $a + bi$ and $c + di$ are equal if and only if $a = c$ and $b = d$. Complex numbers can be added or subtracted by adding or subtracting their real parts and then adding or subtracting their imaginary parts.

Sum or Difference of Complex Numbers

If $a + bi$ and $c + di$ are complex numbers, then their sum is

$$(a + bi) + (c + di) = (a + c) + (b + d)i$$

Their difference is

$$(a + bi) - (c + di) = a + bi - c - di = (a - c) + (b - d)i$$

EXAMPLE 3 Add or subtract the complex numbers. Write the sum or difference in the form $a + bi$.

a. $(2 + 3i) + (-3 + 2i)$　　**b.** $5i - (1 - i)$　　**c.** $(-3 - 7i) - (-6)$

Solution

a. $(2 + 3i) + (-3 + 2i) = (2 - 3) + (3 + 2)i = -1 + 5i$

b. $5i - (1 - i) = 5i - 1 + i$
$$= -1 + (5 + 1)i$$
$$= -1 + 6i$$

c. $(-3 - 7i) - (-6) = -3 - 7i + 6$
$$= (-3 + 6) - 7i$$
$$= 3 - 7i$$

PRACTICE
3 Add or subtract the complex numbers. Write the sum or difference in the form $a + bi$.

a. $(3 - 5i) + (-4 + i)$　　**b.** $4i - (3 - i)$　　**c.** $(-5 - 2i) - (-8)$

3 Multiplying Complex Numbers

To multiply two complex numbers of the form $a + bi$, we multiply as though they are binomials. Then we use the relationship $i^2 = -1$ to simplify.

EXAMPLE 4 Multiply the complex numbers. Write the product in the form $a + bi$.

a. $-7i \cdot 3i$　　　　　**b.** $3i(2 - i)$　　　　　**c.** $(2 - 5i)(4 + i)$
d. $(2 - i)^2$　　　　　**e.** $(7 + 3i)(7 - 3i)$

Solution

a. $-7i \cdot 3i = -21i^2$
$$= -21(-1) \quad \text{Replace } i^2 \text{ with } -1.$$
$$= 21 + 0i$$

b. $3i(2 - i) = 3i \cdot 2 - 3i \cdot i$ Use the distributive property.

$\qquad = 6i - 3i^2$ Multiply.

$\qquad = 6i - 3(-1)$ Replace i^2 with -1.

$\qquad = 6i + 3$

$\qquad = 3 + 6i$

$\qquad\qquad$ Use the FOIL order below. (First, Outer, Inner, Last)

c. $(2 - 5i)(4 + i) = 2(4) + 2(i) - 5i(4) - 5i(i)$

$\qquad\qquad\qquad\quad$ F $\quad$ O $\quad$ I $\quad$ L

$\qquad\qquad = 8 + 2i - 20i - 5i^2$

$\qquad\qquad = 8 - 18i - 5(-1)$ $\qquad\qquad\qquad i^2 = -1$

$\qquad\qquad = 8 - 18i + 5$

$\qquad\qquad = 13 - 18i$

d. $(2 - i)^2 = (2 - i)(2 - i)$

$\qquad\qquad = 2(2) - 2(i) - 2(i) + i^2$

$\qquad\qquad = 4 - 4i + (-1)$ $\qquad\qquad i^2 = -1$

$\qquad\qquad = 3 - 4i$

e. $(7 + 3i)(7 - 3i) = 7(7) - 7(3i) + 3i(7) - 3i(3i)$

$\qquad\qquad\qquad\quad = 49 - 21i + 21i - 9i^2$

$\qquad\qquad\qquad\quad = 49 - 9(-1)$ $\qquad\qquad\qquad i^2 = -1$

$\qquad\qquad\qquad\quad = 49 + 9$

$\qquad\qquad\qquad\quad = 58 + 0i$

PRACTICE

4 $\quad$ Multiply the complex numbers. Write the product in the form $a + bi$.

a. $-4i \cdot 5i$ $\qquad\qquad$ **b.** $5i(2 + i)$ $\qquad\qquad$ **c.** $(2 + 3i)(6 - i)$

d. $(3 - i)^2$ $\qquad\qquad$ **e.** $(9 + 2i)(9 - 2i)$

Notice that if you add, subtract, or multiply two complex numbers, just like real numbers, the result is a complex number.

OBJECTIVE

4 $\quad$ **Dividing Complex Numbers**

From Example 4e, notice that the product of $7 + 3i$ and $7 - 3i$ is a real number. These two complex numbers are called **complex conjugates** of one another. In general, we have the following definition.

Complex Conjugates

The complex numbers $(a + bi)$ and $(a - bi)$ are called **complex conjugates** of each other, and

$$(a + bi)(a - bi) = a^2 + b^2.$$

To see that the product of a complex number $a + bi$ and its conjugate $a - bi$ is the real number $a^2 + b^2$, we multiply.

$$(a + bi)(a - bi) = a^2 - abi + abi - b^2 i^2$$
$$= a^2 - b^2(-1)$$
$$= a^2 + b^2$$

We use complex conjugates to divide by a complex number.

EXAMPLE 5   Divide. Write in the form $a + bi$.

a. $\dfrac{2 + i}{1 - i}$ **b.** $\dfrac{7}{3i}$

Solution

a. Multiply the numerator and denominator by the complex conjugate of $1 - i$ to eliminate the imaginary number in the denominator.

$$\dfrac{2 + i}{1 - i} = \dfrac{(2 + i)(1 + i)}{(1 - i)(1 + i)}$$

$$= \dfrac{2(1) + 2(i) + 1(i) + i^2}{1^2 - i^2}$$

$$= \dfrac{2 + 3i - 1}{1 + 1} \qquad \text{Here, } i^2 = -1.$$

$$= \dfrac{1 + 3i}{2} \quad \text{or} \quad \dfrac{1}{2} + \dfrac{3}{2}i$$

b. Multiply the numerator and denominator by the conjugate of $3i$. Note that $3i = 0 + 3i$, so its conjugate is $0 - 3i$ or $-3i$.

$$\dfrac{7}{3i} = \dfrac{7(-3i)}{(3i)(-3i)} = \dfrac{-21i}{-9i^2} = \dfrac{-21i}{-9(-1)} = \dfrac{-21i}{9} = \dfrac{-7i}{3} \quad \text{or} \quad 0 - \dfrac{7}{3}i \qquad \square$$

PRACTICE
5   Divide. Write in the form $a + bi$.

a. $\dfrac{4 - i}{3 + i}$ **b.** $\dfrac{5}{2i}$

> ▶ **Helpful Hint**
>
> Recall that division can be checked by multiplication.
>
> To check that $\dfrac{2 + i}{1 - i} = \dfrac{1}{2} + \dfrac{3}{2}i$, in Example 5a, multiply $\left(\dfrac{1}{2} + \dfrac{3}{2}i\right)(1 - i)$ to verify that the product is $2 + i$.

OBJECTIVE
5   Finding Powers of I ▶

We can use the fact that $i^2 = -1$ to find higher powers of i. To find i^3, we rewrite it as the product of i^2 and i.

$$i^3 = i^2 \cdot i = (-1)i = -i$$

$$i^4 = i^2 \cdot i^2 = (-1) \cdot (-1) = 1$$

We continue this process and use the fact that $i^4 = 1$ and $i^2 = -1$ to simplify i^5 and i^6.

$$i^5 = i^4 \cdot i = 1 \cdot i = i$$

$$i^6 = i^4 \cdot i^2 = 1 \cdot (-1) = -1$$

If we continue finding powers of i, we generate the following pattern. Notice that the values $i, -1, -i,$ and 1 repeat as i is raised to higher and higher powers.

$i^1 = i$	$i^5 = i$	$i^9 = i$
$i^2 = -1$	$i^6 = -1$	$i^{10} = -1$
$i^3 = -i$	$i^7 = -i$	$i^{11} = -i$
$i^4 = 1$	$i^8 = 1$	$i^{12} = 1$

This pattern allows us to find other powers of i. To do so, we will use the fact that $i^4 = 1$ and rewrite a power of i in terms of i^4. For example,

$$i^{22} = i^{20} \cdot i^2 = (i^4)^5 \cdot i^2 = 1^5 \cdot (-1) = 1 \cdot (-1) = -1.$$

EXAMPLE 6 Find the following powers of i.

a. i^7　　　　**b.** i^{20}　　　　**c.** i^{46}　　　　**d.** i^{-12}

Solution

a. $i^7 = i^4 \cdot i^3 = 1(-i) = -i$

b. $i^{20} = (i^4)^5 = 1^5 = 1$

c. $i^{46} = i^{44} \cdot i^2 = (i^4)^{11} \cdot i^2 = 1^{11}(-1) = -1$

d. $i^{-12} = \dfrac{1}{i^{12}} = \dfrac{1}{(i^4)^3} = \dfrac{1}{(1)^3} = \dfrac{1}{1} = 1$

PRACTICE

6 Find the following powers of i.

a. i^9　　　　**b.** i^{16}　　　　**c.** i^{34}　　　　**d.** i^{-24}

Vocabulary, Readiness & Video Check

Use the choices below to fill in each blank. Not all choices will be used.

-1	$\sqrt{-1}$	real	imaginary unit
1	$\sqrt{1}$	complex	pure imaginary

1. A _____ number is one that can be written in the form $a + bi$, where a and b are real numbers.

2. In the complex number system, i denotes the _____.

3. $i^2 = $ _____

4. $i = $ _____

5. A complex number, $a + bi$, is a _____ number if $b = 0$.

6. A complex number, $a + bi$, is a _____ number if $a = 0$ and $b \neq 0$.

Martin-Gay Interactive Videos

See Video 10.7

Watch the section lecture video and answer the following questions.

OBJECTIVE 1

7. From ▭ Example 4, with what rule must you be especially careful when working with imaginary numbers and why?

OBJECTIVE 2

8. In ▭ Examples 5 and 6, what is the process of adding and subtracting complex numbers compared to? What important reminder is given about i?

OBJECTIVE 3

9. In ▭ Examples 7 and 8, what part of the definition of the imaginary unit i may be used during the multiplication of complex numbers to help simplify products?

OBJECTIVE 4

10. In ▭ Example 9, using complex conjugates to divide complex numbers is compared to what process?

OBJECTIVE 5

11. From the lecture before ▭ Example 10, what are the first four powers of i whose values keep repeating?

10.7 Exercise Set MyMathLab®

Simplify. See Example 1.

1. $\sqrt{-81}$　　　　**2.** $\sqrt{-49}$　　　　**3.** $\sqrt{-7}$

4. $\sqrt{-3}$　　　　**5.** $-\sqrt{16}$　　　　**6.** $-\sqrt{4}$

7. $\sqrt{-64}$　　　　**8.** $\sqrt{-100}$

Write in terms of i. See Example 1.

9. $\sqrt{-24}$　　　　　　**10.** $\sqrt{-32}$

11. $-\sqrt{-36}$　　　　　**12.** $-\sqrt{-121}$

13. $8\sqrt{-63}$　　　　　**14.** $4\sqrt{-20}$

15. $-\sqrt{54}$　　　　　**16.** $\sqrt{-63}$

Multiply or divide. See Example 2.

17. $\sqrt{-2} \cdot \sqrt{-7}$　　　　**18.** $\sqrt{-11} \cdot \sqrt{-3}$

19. $\sqrt{-5} \cdot \sqrt{-10}$　　　　**20.** $\sqrt{-2} \cdot \sqrt{-6}$

21. $\sqrt{16} \cdot \sqrt{-1}$　　　　**22.** $\sqrt{3} \cdot \sqrt{-27}$

23. $\dfrac{\sqrt{-9}}{\sqrt{3}}$　　　　**24.** $\dfrac{\sqrt{49}}{\sqrt{-10}}$

25. $\dfrac{\sqrt{-80}}{\sqrt{-10}}$　　　　**26.** $\dfrac{\sqrt{-40}}{\sqrt{-8}}$

Add or subtract. Write the sum or difference in the form a + bi. See Example 3.

27. $(4 - 7i) + (2 + 3i)$　　　**28.** $(2 - 4i) - (2 - i)$

29. $(6 + 5i) - (8 - i)$　　　**30.** $(8 - 3i) + (-8 + 3i)$

31. $6 - (8 + 4i)$　　　　　**32.** $(9 - 4i) - 9$

Multiply. Write the product in the form a + bi. See Example 4.

33. $-10i \cdot -4i$　　　　**34.** $-2i \cdot -11i$

35. $6i(2 - 3i)$　　　　　**36.** $5i(4 - 7i)$

37. $(\sqrt{3} + 2i)(\sqrt{3} - 2i)$　　**38.** $(\sqrt{5} - 5i)(\sqrt{5} + 5i)$

39. $(4 - 2i)^2$　　　　　**40.** $(6 - 3i)^2$

Write each quotient in the form a + bi. See Example 5.

41. $\dfrac{4}{i}$　　　　　**42.** $\dfrac{5}{6i}$

43. $\dfrac{7}{4 + 3i}$　　　　**44.** $\dfrac{9}{1 - 2i}$

45. $\dfrac{3 + 5i}{1 + i}$　　　　**46.** $\dfrac{6 + 2i}{4 - 3i}$

47. $\dfrac{5 - i}{3 - 2i}$　　　　**48.** $\dfrac{6 - i}{2 + i}$

MIXED PRACTICE

Perform each indicated operation. Write the result in the form a + bi.

49. $(7i)(-9i)$　　　　　**50.** $(-6i)(-4i)$

51. $(6 - 3i) - (4 - 2i)$　　**52.** $(-2 - 4i) - (6 - 8i)$

53. $-3i(-1 + 9i)$　　　　**54.** $-5i(-2 + i)$

55. $\dfrac{4 - 5i}{2i}$　　　　**56.** $\dfrac{6 + 8i}{3i}$

57. $(4 + i)(5 + 2i)$　　　**58.** $(3 + i)(2 + 4i)$

59. $(6 - 2i)(3 + i)$　　　**60.** $(2 - 4i)(2 - i)$

61. $(8 - 3i) + (2 + 3i)$　　**62.** $(7 + 4i) + (4 - 4i)$

63. $(1 - i)(1 + i)$　　　　**64.** $(6 + 2i)(6 - 2i)$

65. $\dfrac{16 + 15i}{-3i}$　　　　**66.** $\dfrac{2 - 3i}{-7i}$

67. $(9 + 8i)^2$　　　　　**68.** $(4 - 7i)^2$

69. $\dfrac{2}{3 + i}$　　　　　**70.** $\dfrac{5}{3 - 2i}$

71. $(5 - 6i) - 4i$　　　　**72.** $(6 - 2i) + 7i$

73. $\dfrac{2 - 3i}{2 + i}$　　　　**74.** $\dfrac{6 + 5i}{6 - 5i}$

75. $(2 + 4i) + (6 - 5i)$　　**76.** $(5 - 3i) + (7 - 8i)$

77. $(\sqrt{6} + i)(\sqrt{6} - i)$　　**78.** $(\sqrt{14} - 4i)(\sqrt{14} + 4i)$

79. $4(2 - i)^2$　　　　　**80.** $9(2 - i)^2$

Find each power of i. See Example 6.

81. i^8　　**82.** i^{10}　　**83.** i^{21}　　**84.** i^{15}

85. i^{11}　　**86.** i^{40}　　**87.** i^{-6}　　**88.** i^{-9}

89. $(2i)^6$　　**90.** $(5i)^4$　　**91.** $(-3i)^5$　　**92.** $(-2i)^7$

REVIEW AND PREVIEW

Recall that the sum of the measures of the angles of a triangle is 180°. Find the unknown angle in each triangle.

△ **93.**　　　　　　　　　　△ **94.**

Use synthetic division to divide the following. See Section 5.7.

95. $(x^3 - 6x^2 + 3x - 4) \div (x - 1)$

96. $(5x^4 - 3x^2 + 2) \div (x + 2)$

Thirty people were recently polled about the average monthly balance in their checking accounts. The results of this poll are shown in the following histogram. Use this graph to answer Exercises 97 through 102. See Section 3.1.

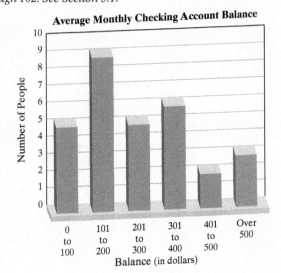

97. How many people polled reported an average checking balance of $201 to $300?

98. How many people polled reported an average checking balance of $0 to $100?

99. How many people polled reported an average checking balance of $200 or less?

100. How many people polled reported an average checking balance of $301 or more?

101. What percent of people polled reported an average checking balance of $201 to $300? Round to the nearest tenth of a percent.

102. What percent of people polled reported an average checking balance of $0 to $100? Round to the nearest tenth of a percent.

CONCEPT EXTENSIONS

Write in the form a + bi.

103. $i^3 - i^4$

104. $i^8 - i^7$

105. $i^6 + i^8$

106. $i^4 + i^{12}$

107. $2 + \sqrt{-9}$

108. $5 - \sqrt{-16}$

109. $\dfrac{6 + \sqrt{-18}}{3}$

110. $\dfrac{4 - \sqrt{-8}}{2}$

111. $\dfrac{5 - \sqrt{-75}}{10}$

112. $\dfrac{7 + \sqrt{-98}}{14}$

113. Describe how to find the conjugate of a complex number.

114. Explain why the product of a complex number and its complex conjugate is a real number.

Simplify.

115. $\left(8 - \sqrt{-3}\right) - \left(2 + \sqrt{-12}\right)$

116. $\left(8 - \sqrt{-4}\right) - \left(2 + \sqrt{-16}\right)$

117. Determine whether $2i$ is a solution of $x^2 + 4 = 0$.

118. Determine whether $-1 + i$ is a solution of $x^2 + 2x = -2$.

Chapter 10 Vocabulary Check

Fill in each blank with one of the words or phrases listed below.

index	rationalizing	conjugate	principal square root	cube root	midpoint
complex number	like radicals	radicand	imaginary unit	distance	

1. The _____ of $\sqrt{3} + 2$ is $\sqrt{3} - 2$.

2. The _____ of a nonnegative number a is written as $\sqrt{a}$.

3. The process of writing a radical expression as an equivalent expression but without a radical in the denominator is called _____ the denominator.

4. The _____, written i, is the number whose square is -1.

5. The _____ of a number is written as $\sqrt[3]{a}$.

6. In the notation $\sqrt[n]{a}$, n is called the _____ and a is called the _____.

7. Radicals with the same index and the same radicand are called _____.

8. A(n) _____ is a number that can be written in the form $a + bi$, where a and b are real numbers.

9. The _____ formula is $d = \sqrt{(x_2 - x_1)^2 + (y_2 - y_1)^2}$.

10. The _____ formula is $\left(\dfrac{x_1 + x_2}{2}, \dfrac{y_1 + y_2}{2}\right)$.

Chapter 10 Highlights

DEFINITIONS AND CONCEPTS	EXAMPLES
Section 10.1 Radicals and Radical Functions	
The **positive**, or **principal**, **square root** of a nonnegative number a is written as $\sqrt{a}$. $\sqrt{a} = b$ only if $b^2 = a$ and $b \geq 0$ The **negative square root of** a is written as $-\sqrt{a}$.	$\sqrt{36} = 6 \qquad \sqrt{\dfrac{9}{100}} = \dfrac{3}{10}$ $-\sqrt{36} = -6 \quad -\sqrt{0.04} = -0.2$

(continued)

DEFINITIONS AND CONCEPTS	EXAMPLES

Section 10.1   Radicals and Radical Functions (continued)

The **cube root** of a real number a is written as $\sqrt[3]{a}$.

$$\sqrt[3]{a} = b \text{ only if } b^3 = a$$

If n is an even positive integer, then $\sqrt[n]{a^n} = |a|$.

If n is an odd positive integer, then $\sqrt[n]{a^n} = a$.

A **radical function** in x is a function defined by an expression containing a root of x.

$$\sqrt[3]{27} = 3 \qquad \sqrt[3]{-\frac{1}{8}} = -\frac{1}{2}$$

$$\sqrt[3]{y^6} = y^2 \qquad \sqrt[3]{64x^9} = 4x^3$$

$$\sqrt{(-3)^2} = |-3| = 3$$

$$\sqrt[3]{(-7)^3} = -7$$

If $f(x) = \sqrt{x} + 2$,

$$f(1) = \sqrt{(1)} + 2 = 1 + 2 = 3$$

$$f(3) = \sqrt{(3)} + 2 \approx 3.73$$

Section 10.2   Rational Exponents

$a^{1/n} = \sqrt[n]{a}$ if $\sqrt[n]{a}$ is a real number.

If m and n are positive integers greater than 1 with $\dfrac{m}{n}$ in lowest terms and $\sqrt[n]{a}$ is a real number, then

$$a^{m/n} = (a^{1/n})^m = (\sqrt[n]{a})^m$$

$a^{-m/n} = \dfrac{1}{a^{m/n}}$ as long as $a^{m/n}$ is a nonzero number.

Exponent rules are true for rational exponents.

$$81^{1/2} = \sqrt{81} = 9$$

$$(-8x^3)^{1/3} = \sqrt[3]{-8x^3} = -2x$$

$$4^{5/2} = (\sqrt{4})^5 = 2^5 = 32$$

$$27^{2/3} = (\sqrt[3]{27})^2 = 3^2 = 9$$

$$16^{-3/4} = \frac{1}{16^{3/4}} = \frac{1}{(\sqrt[4]{16})^3} = \frac{1}{2^3} = \frac{1}{8}$$

$$x^{2/3} \cdot x^{-5/6} = x^{2/3-5/6} = x^{-1/6} = \frac{1}{x^{1/6}}$$

$$(8^4)^{1/2} = 8^2 = 64$$

$$\frac{a^{4/5}}{a^{-2/5}} = a^{4/5-(-2/5)} = a^{6/5}$$

Section 10.3   Simplifying Radical Expressions

Product and Quotient Rules

If $\sqrt[n]{a}$ and $\sqrt[n]{b}$ are real numbers,

$$\sqrt[n]{a} \cdot \sqrt[n]{b} = \sqrt[n]{a \cdot b}$$

$$\frac{\sqrt[n]{a}}{\sqrt[n]{b}} = \sqrt[n]{\frac{a}{b}}, \text{ provided } \sqrt[n]{b} \neq 0$$

A radical of the form $\sqrt[n]{a}$ is **simplified** when a contains no factors that are perfect nth powers.

Distance Formula

The distance d between two points (x_1, y_1) and (x_2, y_2) is given by

$$d = \sqrt{(x_2 - x_1)^2 + (y_2 - y_1)^2}$$

Multiply or divide as indicated:

$$\sqrt{11} \cdot \sqrt{3} = \sqrt{33}$$

$$\frac{\sqrt[3]{40x}}{\sqrt[3]{5x}} = \sqrt[3]{8} = 2$$

$$\sqrt{40} = \sqrt{4 \cdot 10} = 2\sqrt{10}$$

$$\sqrt{36x^5} = \sqrt{36x^4 \cdot x} = 6x^2\sqrt{x}$$

$$\sqrt[3]{24x^7y^3} = \sqrt[3]{8x^6y^3 \cdot 3x} = 2x^2y\sqrt[3]{3x}$$

Find the distance between points $(-1, 6)$ and $(-2, -4)$. Let $(x_1, y_1) = (-1, 6)$ and $(x_2, y_2) = (-2, -4)$.

$$d = \sqrt{(x_2 - x_1)^2 + (y_2 - y_1)^2}$$

$$= \sqrt{(-2 - (-1))^2 + (-4 - 6)^2}$$

$$= \sqrt{1 + 100} = \sqrt{101}$$

DEFINITIONS AND CONCEPTS	EXAMPLES

Section 10.3 Simplifying Radical Expressions (continued)

Midpoint Formula

The midpoint of the line segment whose endpoints are (x_1, y_1) and (x_2, y_2) is the point with coordinates

$$\left(\frac{x_1 + x_2}{2}, \frac{y_1 + y_2}{2} \right)$$

Find the midpoint of the line segment whose endpoints are $(-1, 6)$ and $(-2, -4)$.

$$\left(\frac{-1 + (-2)}{2}, \frac{6 + (-4)}{2} \right)$$

The midpoint is $\left(-\dfrac{3}{2}, 1 \right)$.

Section 10.4 Adding, Subtracting, and Multiplying Radical Expressions

Radicals with the same index and the same radicand are **like radicals.**

The distributive property can be used to add like radicals.

$$5\sqrt{6} + 2\sqrt{6} = (5 + 2)\sqrt{6} = 7\sqrt{6}$$

$$\sqrt[3]{3x} - 10\sqrt[3]{3x} + 3\sqrt[3]{10x}$$

$$= (-1 - 10)\sqrt[3]{3x} + 3\sqrt[3]{10x}$$

$$= -11\sqrt[3]{3x} + 3\sqrt[3]{10x}$$

Radical expressions are multiplied by using many of the same properties used to multiply polynomials.

Multiply:

$$(\sqrt{5} - \sqrt{2x})(\sqrt{2} + \sqrt{2x})$$

$$= \sqrt{10} + \sqrt{10x} - \sqrt{4x} - 2x$$

$$= \sqrt{10} + \sqrt{10x} - 2\sqrt{x} - 2x$$

$$(2\sqrt{3} - \sqrt{8x})(2\sqrt{3} + \sqrt{8x})$$

$$= 4(3) - 8x = 12 - 8x$$

Section 10.5 Rationalizing Denominators and Numerators of Radical Expressions

The **conjugate** of $a + b$ is $a - b$.

The conjugate of $\sqrt{7} + \sqrt{3}$ is $\sqrt{7} - \sqrt{3}$.

The process of writing the denominator of a radical expression without a radical is called **rationalizing the denominator.**

Rationalize each denominator.

$$\frac{\sqrt{5}}{\sqrt{3}} = \frac{\sqrt{5} \cdot \sqrt{3}}{\sqrt{3} \cdot \sqrt{3}} = \frac{\sqrt{15}}{3}$$

$$\frac{6}{\sqrt{7} + \sqrt{3}} = \frac{6(\sqrt{7} - \sqrt{3})}{(\sqrt{7} + \sqrt{3})(\sqrt{7} - \sqrt{3})}$$

$$= \frac{6(\sqrt{7} - \sqrt{3})}{7 - 3}$$

$$= \frac{6(\sqrt{7} - \sqrt{3})}{4} = \frac{3(\sqrt{7} - \sqrt{3})}{2}$$

(continued)

DEFINITIONS AND CONCEPTS	EXAMPLES

Section 10.5 Rationalizing Denominators and Numerators of Radical Expressions (continued)

The process of writing the numerator of a radical expression without a radical is called **rationalizing the numerator.**

Rationalize each numerator:

$$\frac{\sqrt[3]{9}}{\sqrt[3]{5}} = \frac{\sqrt[3]{9}\cdot\sqrt[3]{3}}{\sqrt[3]{5}\cdot\sqrt[3]{3}} = \frac{\sqrt[3]{27}}{\sqrt[3]{15}} = \frac{3}{\sqrt[3]{15}}$$

$$\frac{\sqrt{9}+\sqrt{3x}}{12} = \frac{(\sqrt{9}+\sqrt{3x})(\sqrt{9}-\sqrt{3x})}{12(\sqrt{9}-\sqrt{3x})}$$

$$= \frac{9-3x}{12(\sqrt{9}-\sqrt{3x})}$$

$$= \frac{3(3-x)}{3\cdot4(3-\sqrt{3x})} = \frac{3-x}{4(3-\sqrt{3x})}$$

Section 10.6 Radical Equations and Problem Solving

To Solve a Radical Equation

Step 1. Write the equation so that one radical is by itself on one side of the equation.

Step 2. Raise each side of the equation to a power equal to the index of the radical and simplify.

Step 3. If the equation still contains a radical, repeat Steps 1 and 2. If not, solve the equation.

Step 4. Check all proposed solutions in the original equation.

Solve: $x = \sqrt{4x+9} + 3$.

1. $\quad x - 3 = \sqrt{4x+9}$

2. $\quad (x-3)^2 = (\sqrt{4x+9})^2$
   $\quad x^2 - 6x + 9 = 4x + 9$

3. $\quad x^2 - 10x = 0$
   $\quad x(x-10) = 0$
   $\quad\quad x = 0 \quad\text{or}\quad x = 10$

4. The proposed solution 10 checks, but 0 does not. The solution is 10.

Section 10.7 Complex Numbers

$i^2 = -1$ and $i = \sqrt{-1}$

A **complex number** is a number that can be written in the form $a + bi$, where a and b are real numbers.

Simplify: $\sqrt{-9}$.

$$\sqrt{-9} = \sqrt{-1\cdot9} = \sqrt{-1}\cdot\sqrt{9} = i\cdot3 \text{ or } 3i$$

Complex Numbers	***Written in Form a + bi***
12	$12 + 0i$
$-5i$	$0 + (-5)i$
$-2 - 3i$	$-2 + (-3)i$

Multiply.

$$\sqrt{-3}\cdot\sqrt{-7} = i\sqrt{3}\cdot i\sqrt{7}$$
$$= i^2\sqrt{21}$$
$$= -\sqrt{21}$$

To add or subtract complex numbers, add or subtract their real parts and then add or subtract their imaginary parts.

To multiply complex numbers, multiply as though they are binomials.

Perform each indicated operation.

$$(-3 + 2i) - (7 - 4i) = -3 + 2i - 7 + 4i$$
$$= -10 + 6i$$

$$(-7 - 2i)(6 + i) = -42 - 7i - 12i - 2i^2$$
$$= -42 - 19i - 2(-1)$$
$$= -42 - 19i + 2$$
$$= -40 - 19i$$

DEFINITIONS AND CONCEPTS	EXAMPLES

Section 10.7   Complex Numbers (continued)

The complex numbers $(a + bi)$ and $(a - bi)$ are called **complex conjugates.**

The complex conjugate of
$$(3 + 6i) \text{ is } (3 - 6i).$$
Their product is a real number:
$$(3 - 6i)(3 + 6i) = 9 - 36i^2$$
$$= 9 - 36(-1) = 9 + 36 = 45$$

To divide complex numbers, multiply the numerator and the denominator by the conjugate of the denominator.

Divide.
$$\frac{4}{2 - i} = \frac{4(2 + i)}{(2 - i)(2 + i)}$$
$$= \frac{4(2 + i)}{4 - i^2}$$
$$= \frac{4(2 + i)}{5}$$
$$= \frac{8 + 4i}{5} = \frac{8}{5} + \frac{4}{5}i$$

Chapter 10 **Review**

(10.1) Find the root. Assume that all variables represent positive numbers.

1. $\sqrt{81}$

2. $\sqrt[4]{81}$

3. $\sqrt[3]{-8}$

4. $\sqrt[4]{-16}$

5. $-\sqrt{\dfrac{1}{49}}$

6. $\sqrt{x^{64}}$

7. $-\sqrt{36}$

8. $\sqrt[3]{64}$

9. $\sqrt[3]{-a^6 b^9}$

10. $\sqrt{16a^4 b^{12}}$

11. $\sqrt[5]{32a^5 b^{10}}$

12. $\sqrt[5]{-32x^{15} y^{20}}$

13. $\sqrt{\dfrac{x^{12}}{36y^2}}$

14. $\sqrt[3]{\dfrac{27y^3}{z^{12}}}$

Simplify. Use absolute value bars when necessary.

15. $\sqrt{(-x)^2}$

16. $\sqrt[4]{(x^2 - 4)^4}$

17. $\sqrt[3]{(-27)^3}$

18. $\sqrt[5]{(-5)^5}$

19. $-\sqrt[5]{x^5}$

20. $-\sqrt[3]{x^3}$

21. $\sqrt[4]{16(2y + z)^4}$

22. $\sqrt{25(x - y)^2}$

23. $\sqrt[5]{y^5}$

24. $\sqrt[6]{x^6}$

25. Let $f(x) = \sqrt{x} + 3$.

   a. Find $f(0)$ and $f(9)$.

   b. Find the domain of $f(x)$.

   c. Graph $f(x)$.

26. Let $g(x) = \sqrt[3]{x} - 3$.

   a. Find $g(11)$ and $g(20)$.

   b. Find the domain of $g(x)$.

   c. Graph $g(x)$.

(10.2) Evaluate.

27. $\left(\dfrac{1}{81}\right)^{1/4}$

28. $\left(-\dfrac{1}{27}\right)^{1/3}$

29. $(-27)^{-1/3}$

30. $(-64)^{-1/3}$

31. $-9^{3/2}$

32. $64^{-1/3}$

33. $(-25)^{5/2}$

34. $\left(\dfrac{25}{49}\right)^{-3/2}$

35. $\left(\dfrac{8}{27}\right)^{-2/3}$

36. $\left(-\dfrac{1}{36}\right)^{-1/4}$

Write with rational exponents.

37. $\sqrt[3]{x^2}$

38. $\sqrt[5]{5x^2 y^3}$

Write using radical notation.

39. $y^{4/5}$

40. $5(xy^2 z^5)^{1/3}$

41. $(x + 2)^{-1/3}$

42. $(x + 2y)^{-1/2}$

Simplify each expression. Assume that all variables represent positive real numbers. Write with only positive exponents.

43. $a^{1/3} a^{4/3} a^{1/2}$

44. $\dfrac{b^{1/3}}{b^{4/3}}$

45. $(a^{1/2} a^{-2})^3$

46. $(x^{-3} y^6)^{1/3}$

47. $\left(\dfrac{b^{3/4}}{a^{-1/2}}\right)^8$

48. $\dfrac{x^{1/4} x^{-1/2}}{x^{2/3}}$

49. $\left(\dfrac{49c^{5/3}}{a^{-1/4} b^{5/6}}\right)^{-1}$

50. $a^{-1/4}(a^{5/4} - a^{9/4})$

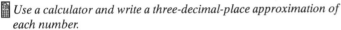 *Use a calculator and write a three-decimal-place approximation of each number.*

51. $\sqrt{20}$

52. $\sqrt[3]{-39}$

53. $\sqrt[4]{726}$

54. $56^{1/3}$

55. $-78^{3/4}$

56. $105^{-2/3}$

Use rational exponents to write each as a single radical.

57. $\sqrt[3]{2} \cdot \sqrt{7}$

58. $\sqrt[3]{3} \cdot \sqrt[4]{x}$

(10.3) Perform each indicated operation and then simplify if possible. Assume that all variables represent positive real numbers.

59. $\sqrt{3} \cdot \sqrt{8}$

60. $\sqrt[3]{7y} \cdot \sqrt[3]{x^2 z}$

61. $\dfrac{\sqrt{44x^3}}{\sqrt{11x}}$

62. $\dfrac{\sqrt[4]{a^6 b^{13}}}{\sqrt[4]{a^2 b}}$

Simplify.

63. $\sqrt{60}$

64. $-\sqrt{75}$

65. $\sqrt[3]{162}$

66. $\sqrt[3]{-32}$

67. $\sqrt{36x^7}$

68. $\sqrt[3]{24a^5 b^7}$

69. $\sqrt{\dfrac{p^{17}}{121}}$

70. $\sqrt[3]{\dfrac{y^5}{27x^6}}$

71. $\sqrt[4]{\dfrac{xy^6}{81}}$

72. $\sqrt{\dfrac{2x^3}{49y^4}}$

△ *The formula for the radius r of a circle of area A is* $r = \sqrt{\dfrac{A}{\pi}}$. *Use this for Exercises 73 and 74.*

73. Find the exact radius of a circle whose area is 25 square meters.

74. Approximate to two decimal places the radius of a circle whose area is 104 square inches.

Find the distance between each pair of points. Give an exact value and a three-decimal-place approximation.

75. $(-6, 3)$ and $(8, 4)$

76. $(-4, -6)$ and $(-1, 5)$

77. $(-1, 5)$ and $(2, -3)$

78. $(-\sqrt{2}, 0)$ and $(0, -4\sqrt{6})$

79. $(-\sqrt{5}, -\sqrt{11})$ and $(-\sqrt{5}, -3\sqrt{11})$

80. $(7.4, -8.6)$ and $(-1.2, 5.6)$

Find the midpoint of each line segment whose endpoints are given.

81. $(2, 6); (-12, 4)$

82. $(-6, -5); (-9, 7)$

83. $(4, -6); (-15, 2)$

84. $\left(0, -\dfrac{3}{8}\right); \left(\dfrac{1}{10}, 0\right)$

85. $\left(\dfrac{3}{4}, -\dfrac{1}{7}\right); \left(-\dfrac{1}{4}, -\dfrac{3}{7}\right)$

86. $(\sqrt{3}, -2\sqrt{6}); (\sqrt{3}, -4\sqrt{6})$

(10.4) Perform each indicated operation. Assume that all variables represent positive real numbers.

87. $\sqrt{20} + \sqrt{45} - 7\sqrt{5}$

88. $x\sqrt{75x} - \sqrt{27x^3}$

89. $\sqrt[3]{128} + \sqrt[3]{250}$

90. $3\sqrt[4]{32a^5} - a\sqrt[4]{162a}$

91. $\dfrac{5}{\sqrt{4}} + \dfrac{\sqrt{3}}{3}$

92. $\sqrt{\dfrac{8}{x^2}} - \sqrt{\dfrac{50}{16x^2}}$

93. $2\sqrt{50} - 3\sqrt{125} + \sqrt{98}$

94. $2a\sqrt[4]{32b^5} - 3b\sqrt[4]{162a^4 b} + \sqrt[4]{2a^4 b^5}$

Multiply and then simplify if possible. Assume that all variables represent positive real numbers.

95. $\sqrt{3}(\sqrt{27} - \sqrt{3})$

96. $(\sqrt{x} - 3)^2$

97. $(\sqrt{5} - 5)(2\sqrt{5} + 2)$

98. $(2\sqrt{x} - 3\sqrt{y})(2\sqrt{x} + 3\sqrt{y})$

99. $(\sqrt{a} + 3)(\sqrt{a} - 3)$

100. $(\sqrt[3]{a} + 2)^2$

101. $(\sqrt[3]{5x} + 9)(\sqrt[3]{5x} - 9)$

102. $(\sqrt[3]{a} + 4)(\sqrt[3]{a^2} - 4\sqrt[3]{a} + 16)$

(10.5) Rationalize each denominator. Assume that all variables represent positive real numbers.

103. $\dfrac{3}{\sqrt{7}}$

104. $\sqrt{\dfrac{x}{12}}$

105. $\dfrac{5}{\sqrt[3]{4}}$

106. $\sqrt{\dfrac{24x^5}{3y}}$

107. $\sqrt[3]{\dfrac{15x^6 y^7}{z^2}}$

108. $\sqrt[4]{\dfrac{81}{8x^{10}}}$

109. $\dfrac{3}{\sqrt{y} - 2}$

110. $\dfrac{\sqrt{2} - \sqrt{3}}{\sqrt{2} + \sqrt{3}}$

Rationalize each numerator. Assume that all variables represent positive real numbers.

111. $\dfrac{\sqrt{11}}{3}$

112. $\sqrt{\dfrac{18}{y}}$

113. $\dfrac{\sqrt[3]{9}}{7}$

114. $\sqrt{\dfrac{24x^5}{3y^2}}$

115. $\sqrt[3]{\dfrac{xy^2}{10z}}$

116. $\dfrac{\sqrt{x} + 5}{-3}$

(10.6) Solve each equation.

117. $\sqrt{y - 7} = 5$

118. $\sqrt{2x} + 10 = 4$

119. $\sqrt[3]{2x - 6} = 4$

120. $\sqrt{x + 6} = \sqrt{x + 2}$

121. $2x - 5\sqrt{x} = 3$

122. $\sqrt{x + 9} = 2 + \sqrt{x - 7}$

Find each unknown length.

△ **123.**

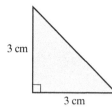

△ **124.**

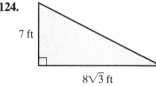

△ **125.** Craig and Daniel Cantwell want to determine the distance *x* across a pond on their property. They are able to measure the distances shown on the following diagram. Find how wide the pond is at the crossing point indicated by the triangle to the nearest tenth of a foot.

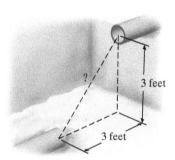

△ **126.** Andrea Roberts, a pipefitter, needs to connect two underground pipelines that are offset by 3 feet, as pictured in the diagram. Neglecting the joints needed to join the pipes, find the length of the shortest possible connecting pipe rounded to the nearest hundredth of a foot.

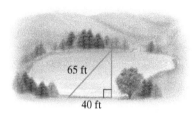

(10.7) *Perform each indicated operation and simplify. Write the results in the form a + bi.*

127. $\sqrt{-8}$

128. $-\sqrt{-6}$

129. $\sqrt{-4} + \sqrt{-16}$

130. $\sqrt{-2} \cdot \sqrt{-5}$

131. $(12 - 6i) + (3 + 2i)$

132. $(-8 - 7i) - (5 - 4i)$

133. $(2i)^6$

134. $(3i)^4$

135. $-3i(6 - 4i)$

136. $(3 + 2i)(1 + i)$

137. $(2 - 3i)^2$

138. $(\sqrt{6} - 9i)(\sqrt{6} + 9i)$

139. $\dfrac{2 + 3i}{2i}$

140. $\dfrac{1 + i}{-3i}$

MIXED REVIEW

Simplify. Use absolute value bars when necessary.

141. $\sqrt[3]{x^3}$

142. $\sqrt{(x + 2)^2}$

Simplify. Assume that all variables represent positive real numbers. If necessary, write answers with positive exponents only.

143. $-\sqrt{100}$

144. $\sqrt[3]{-x^{12}y^3}$

145. $\sqrt[4]{\dfrac{y^{20}}{16x^{12}}}$

146. $9^{1/2}$

147. $64^{-1/2}$

148. $\left(\dfrac{27}{64}\right)^{-2/3}$

149. $\dfrac{(x^{2/3}x^{-3})^3}{x^{-1/2}}$

150. $\sqrt{200x^9}$

151. $\sqrt{\dfrac{3n^3}{121m^{10}}}$

152. $3\sqrt{20} - 7x\sqrt[3]{40} + 3\sqrt[3]{5x^3}$

153. $(2\sqrt{x} - 5)^2$

154. Find the distance between $(-3, 5)$ and $(-8, 9)$.

155. Find the midpoint of the line segment joining $(-3, 8)$ and $(11, 24)$.

Rationalize each denominator.

156. $\dfrac{7}{\sqrt{13}}$

157. $\dfrac{2}{\sqrt{x} + 3}$

Solve.

158. $\sqrt{x + 2} = x$

159. $\sqrt{2x - 1} + 2 = x$

Chapter 10 Test   MyMathLab®    **Test Prep** VIDEOS   You **Tube**

Raise to the power or find the root. Assume that all variables represent positive numbers. Write with only positive exponents.

▶ **1.** $\sqrt{216}$

▶ **2.** $-\sqrt[4]{x^{64}}$

▶ **3.** $\left(\dfrac{1}{125}\right)^{1/3}$

▶ **4.** $\left(\dfrac{1}{125}\right)^{-1/3}$

▶ **5.** $\left(\dfrac{8x^3}{27}\right)^{2/3}$

▶ **6.** $\sqrt[3]{-a^{18}b^9}$

▶ **7.** $\left(\dfrac{64c^{4/3}}{a^{-2/3}b^{5/6}}\right)^{1/2}$

▶ **8.** $a^{-2/3}(a^{5/4} - a^3)$

Find the root. Use absolute value bars when necessary.

▶ **9.** $\sqrt[4]{(4xy)^4}$

▶ **10.** $\sqrt[3]{(-27)^3}$

Rationalize the denominator. Assume that all variables represent positive numbers.

▶ **11.** $\sqrt{\dfrac{9}{y}}$

▶ **12.** $\dfrac{4 - \sqrt{x}}{4 + 2\sqrt{x}}$

▶ **13.** $\dfrac{\sqrt[3]{ab}}{\sqrt[3]{ab^2}}$

▶ **14.** Rationalize the numerator of $\dfrac{\sqrt{6} + x}{8}$ and simplify.

Perform the indicated operations. Assume that all variables represent positive numbers.

▶ **15.** $\sqrt{125x^3} - 3\sqrt{20x^3}$

▶ **16.** $\sqrt{3}(\sqrt{16} - \sqrt{2})$

▶ **17.** $(\sqrt{x} + 1)^2$

▶ **18.** $(\sqrt{2} - 4)(\sqrt{3} + 1)$

▶ **19.** $(\sqrt{5} + 5)(\sqrt{5} - 5)$

Use a calculator to approximate each to three decimal places.

▶ **20.** $\sqrt{561}$

▶ **21.** $386^{-2/3}$

Solve.

▶ **22.** $x = \sqrt{x - 2} + 2$

▶ **23.** $\sqrt{x^2 - 7} + 3 = 0$

▶ **24.** $\sqrt[3]{x + 5} = \sqrt[3]{2x - 1}$

Perform the indicated operation and simplify. Write the result in the form a + bi.

▶ **25.** $\sqrt{-2}$

▶ **26.** $-\sqrt{-8}$

▶ **27.** $(12 - 6i) - (12 - 3i)$

▶ **28.** $(6 - 2i)(6 + 2i)$

▶ **29.** $(4 + 3i)^2$

▶ **30.** $\dfrac{1 + 4i}{1 - i}$

▶ **31.** Find x.

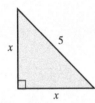

▶ **32.** Identify the domain of $g(x)$. Then complete the accompanying table and graph $g(x)$.

$$g(x) = \sqrt{x} + 2$$

x	-2	-1	2	7
$g(x)$				

▶ **33.** Find the distance between the points $(-6, 3)$ and $(-8, -7)$.

▶ **34.** Find the distance between the points $(-2\sqrt{5}, \sqrt{10})$ and $(-\sqrt{5}, 4\sqrt{10})$.

▶ **35.** Find the midpoint of the line segment whose endpoints are $(-2, -5)$ and $(-6, 12)$.

▶ **36.** Find the midpoint of the line segment whose endpoints are $\left(-\dfrac{2}{3}, -\dfrac{1}{5}\right)$ and $\left(-\dfrac{1}{3}, \dfrac{4}{5}\right)$.

Solve.

▶ **37.** The function $V(r) = \sqrt{2.5r}$ can be used to estimate the maximum safe velocity V in miles per hour at which a car can travel if it is driven along a curved road with a *radius of curvature r* in feet. To the nearest whole number, find the maximum safe speed if a cloverleaf exit on an expressway has a radius of curvature of 300 feet.

▶ **38.** Use the formula from Exercise 37 to find the radius of curvature if the safe velocity is 30 mph.

Chapter 10 **Cumulative Review**

1. Simplify each expression.

   a. $-3 + [(-2 - 5) - 2]$

   b. $2^3 - |10| + [-6 - (-5)]$

2. Simplify each expression.

   a. $2(x - 3) + (5x + 3)$

   b. $4(3x + 2) - 3(5x - 1)$

   c. $7x + 2(x - 7) - 3x$

3. Solve: $\dfrac{x}{2} - 1 = \dfrac{2}{3}x - 3$

4. Solve: $\dfrac{a - 1}{2} + a = 2 - \dfrac{2a + 7}{8}$

5. A 48-inch balsa wood stick is to be cut into two pieces so that the longer piece is 3 times the shorter. Find the length of each piece.

6. The Smith family owns a lake house 121.5 miles from home. If it takes them $4\dfrac{1}{2}$ hours to drive round-trip from their house to their lake house, find their average speed.

7. Without graphing, determine the number of solutions of the system.

$$\begin{cases} 3x - y = 4 \\ x + 2y = 8 \end{cases}$$

8. Solve: $|3x - 2| + 5 = 5$

9. Solve the system: $\begin{cases} x + 2y = 7 \\ 2x + 2y = 13 \end{cases}$

10. Solve: $\left|\dfrac{x}{2} - 1\right| \le 0$.

11. Solve the system: $\begin{cases} 2x - y = 7 \\ 8x - 4y = 1 \end{cases}$

12. Graph $y = |x - 2|$.

13. Lynn Pike, a pharmacist, needs 70 liters of a 50% alcohol solution. She has available a 30% alcohol solution and an 80% alcohol solution. How many liters of each solution should she mix to obtain 70 liters of a 50% alcohol solution?

14. Find the domain and the range of each relation. Use the vertical line test to determine whether each graph is the graph of a function.

a.

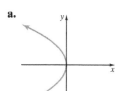

b.

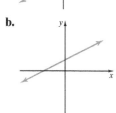

c.

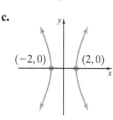

15. If $P(x) = 3x^2 - 2x - 5$, find the following.
   a. $P(1)$ **b.** $P(-2)$

16. Graph $f(x) = -2$.

17. Divide $6m^2 + 2m$ by $2m$.

18. Find the slope of $y = -3$.

19. Use synthetic division to divide $2x^3 - x^2 - 13x + 1$ by $x - 3$.

20. Solve the system.
$$\begin{cases} \dfrac{x}{6} - \dfrac{y}{2} = 1 \\ \dfrac{x}{3} - \dfrac{y}{4} = 2 \end{cases}$$

21. Factor $40 - 13t + t^2$.

22. At a seasonal clearance sale, Nana Long spent $33.75. She paid $3.50 for tee-shirts and $4.25 for shorts. If she bought 9 items, how many of each item did she buy?

23. Simplify each rational expression.
   a. $\dfrac{x^3 + 8}{2 + x}$

   b. $\dfrac{2y^2 + 2}{y^3 - 5y^2 + y - 5}$

24. Use scientific notation to simplify and write the answer in scientific notation. $\dfrac{0.0000035 \times 4000}{0.28}$

25. Solve: $|x - 3| = |5 - x|$

26. Subtract $(2x - 5)$ from the sum of $(5x^2 - 3x + 6)$ and $(4x^2 + 5x - 3)$.

27. Subtract: $\dfrac{3x^2 + 2x}{x - 1} - \dfrac{10x - 5}{x - 1}$

28. Multiply and simplify the product if possible.
   a. $(y - 2)(3y + 4)$
   b. $(3y - 1)(2y^2 + 3y - 1)$

29. Add: $1 + \dfrac{m}{m + 1}$

30. Factor. $x^3 - x^2 + 4x - 4$

31. Simply each complex fraction.
   a. $\dfrac{\dfrac{5x}{x + 2}}{\dfrac{10}{x - 2}}$

   b. $\dfrac{\dfrac{x}{y^2} + \dfrac{1}{y}}{\dfrac{y}{x^2} + \dfrac{1}{x}}$

32. Simplify each rational expression.
   a. $\dfrac{a^3 - 8}{2 - a}$

   b. $\dfrac{3a^2 - 3}{a^3 + 5a^2 - a - 5}$

33. Solve: $|5x + 1| + 1 \le 10$

34. Perform the indicated operations.
   a. $\dfrac{3}{xy^2} - \dfrac{2}{3x^2y}$

   b. $\dfrac{5x}{x + 3} - \dfrac{2x}{x - 3}$

   c. $\dfrac{x}{x - 2} - \dfrac{5}{2 - x}$

35. If the following two triangles are similar, find the missing length x.

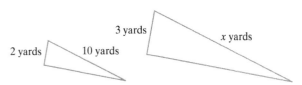

36. Simplify each complex fraction.
   a. $\dfrac{\dfrac{y - 2}{16}}{\dfrac{2y + 3}{12}}$

   b. $\dfrac{\dfrac{x}{16} - \dfrac{1}{x}}{1 - \dfrac{4}{x}}$

37. Find the cube roots.

    a. $\sqrt[3]{1}$ **b.** $\sqrt[3]{-64}$

    c. $\sqrt[3]{\dfrac{8}{125}}$ **d.** $\sqrt[3]{x^6}$

    e. $\sqrt[3]{-27x^9}$

38. Divide $x^3 - 2x^2 + 3x - 6$ by $x - 2$.

39. Write each expression with a positive exponent, and then simplify.

    a. $16^{-3/4}$

    b. $(-27)^{-2/3}$

40. Use synthetic division to divide $4y^3 - 12y^2 - y + 12$ by $y - 3$.

41. Rationalize the numerator of $\dfrac{\sqrt{x} + 2}{5}$

42. Solve: $\dfrac{28}{9 - a^2} = \dfrac{2a}{a - 3} + \dfrac{6}{a + 3}$

43. Suppose that u varies inversely as w. If u is 3 when w is 5, find the constant of variation and the inverse variation equation.

44. Suppose that y varies directly as x. If $y = 0.51$ when $x = 3$, find the constant of variation and the direct variation equation.

Quadratic Equations and Functions

11.1 Solving Quadratic Equations by Completing the Square

11.2 Solving Quadratic Equations by the Quadratic Formula

11.3 Solving Equations by Using Quadratic Methods

Integrated Review— Summary on Solving Quadratic Equations

11.4 Nonlinear Inequalities in One Variable

11.5 Quadratic Functions and Their Graphs

11.6 Further Graphing of Quadratic Functions

Man has always desired to reach the stars, and some buildings seem to be trying to do just that. As populations expand and land becomes scarcer, ever taller and more spectacular buildings are being constructed. As of 2010, the tallest building in the world was the Burj Khalifa, in Dubai. In Exercise 80, Section 11.1, you will explore the height of the Burj Khalifa. (*Source:* Council on Tall Buildings and Urban Habitat, *Fast Company*)

An important part of the study of algebra is learning to model and solve problems. Often, the model of a problem is a quadratic equation or a function containing a second-degree polynomial. In this chapter, we continue the work begun in Chapter 6, when we solved polynomial equations in one variable by factoring. Two additional methods of solving quadratic equations are analyzed as well as methods of solving nonlinear inequalities in one variable.

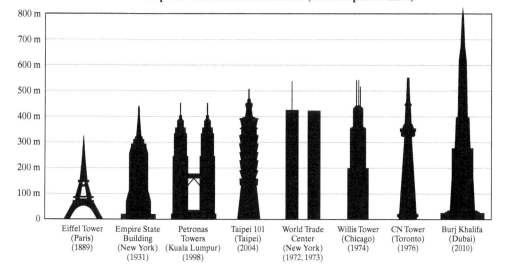

Snapshot of Selected Tall Structures (with completion dates)

Source: Council on Tall Buildings and Urban Habitat, (*Fast Company*)

Solving Quadratic Equations by Completing the Square

OBJECTIVES

1 Use the Square Root Property to Solve Quadratic Equations.

2 Solve Quadratic Equations by Completing the Square.

3 Use Quadratic Equations to Solve Problems.

OBJECTIVE

1 Using the Square Root Property

In Chapter 6, we solved quadratic equations by factoring. Recall that a **quadratic, or second-degree, equation** is an equation that can be written in the form $ax^2 + bx + c = 0$, where a, b, and c are real numbers and a is not 0. To solve a quadratic equation such as $x^2 = 9$ by factoring, we use the zero factor theorem. To use the zero factor theorem, the equation must first be written in standard form, $ax^2 + bx + c = 0$.

$$x^2 = 9$$
$$x^2 - 9 = 0 \qquad \text{Subtract 9 from both sides.}$$
$$(x + 3)(x - 3) = 0 \qquad \text{Factor.}$$
$$x + 3 = 0 \quad \text{or} \quad x - 3 = 0 \quad \text{Set each factor equal to 0.}$$
$$x = -3 \qquad\qquad x = 3 \quad \text{Solve.}$$

The solution set is $\{-3, 3\}$, the positive and negative square roots of 9. Not all quadratic equations can be solved by factoring, so we need to explore other methods. Notice that the solutions of the equation $x^2 = 9$ are two numbers whose square is 9.

$$3^2 = 9 \qquad \text{and} \qquad (-3)^2 = 9$$

Thus, we can solve the equation $x^2 = 9$ by taking the square root of both sides. Be sure to include both $\sqrt{9}$ and $-\sqrt{9}$ as solutions since both $\sqrt{9}$ and $-\sqrt{9}$ are numbers whose square is 9.

$$x^2 = 9$$
$$\sqrt{x^2} = \pm\sqrt{9} \quad \text{The notation } \pm\sqrt{9} \text{ (read as "plus or minus } \sqrt{9}\text{")}$$
$$x = \pm 3 \qquad \text{indicates the pair of numbers } +\sqrt{9} \text{ and } -\sqrt{9}.$$

This illustrates the square root property.

Square Root Property

If b is a real number and if $a^2 = b$, then $a = \pm\sqrt{b}$.

▶ **Helpful Hint**

The notation ± 3, for example, is read as "plus or minus 3." It is a shorthand notation for the pair of numbers $+3$ and -3.

EXAMPLE 1 Use the square root property to solve $x^2 = 50$.

Solution
$$x^2 = 50$$
$$x = \pm\sqrt{50} \quad \text{Use the square root property.}$$
$$x = \pm 5\sqrt{2} \quad \text{Simplify the radical.}$$

Check:

Let $x = 5\sqrt{2}$.	Let $x = -5\sqrt{2}$.
$x^2 = 50$	$x^2 = 50$
$(5\sqrt{2})^2 \stackrel{?}{=} 50$	$(-5\sqrt{2})^2 \stackrel{?}{=} 50$
$25 \cdot 2 \stackrel{?}{=} 50$	$25 \cdot 2 \stackrel{?}{=} 50$
$50 = 50$ True	$50 = 50$ True

The solutions are $5\sqrt{2}$ and $-5\sqrt{2}$, or the solution set is $\{-5\sqrt{2}, 5\sqrt{2}\}$. □

PRACTICE

1 Use the square root property to solve $x^2 = 32$.

EXAMPLE 2   Use the square root property to solve $2x^2 - 14 = 0$.

Solution   First we get the squared variable alone on one side of the equation.

$$2x^2 - 14 = 0$$
$$2x^2 = 14 \qquad \text{Add 14 to both sides.}$$
$$x^2 = 7 \qquad \text{Divide both sides by 2.}$$
$$x = \pm\sqrt{7} \qquad \text{Use the square root property.}$$

Check to see that the solutions are $\sqrt{7}$ and $-\sqrt{7}$, or the solution set is $\{-\sqrt{7}, \sqrt{7}\}$. □

PRACTICE
2   Use the square root property to solve $5x^2 - 50 = 0$.

EXAMPLE 3   Use the square root property to solve $(x + 1)^2 = 12$.

Solution

$$(x + 1)^2 = 12$$
$$x + 1 = \pm\sqrt{12} \qquad \text{Use the square root property.}$$
$$x + 1 = \pm2\sqrt{3} \qquad \text{Simplify the radical.}$$
$$x = \underbrace{-1 \pm 2\sqrt{3}}_{} \qquad \text{Subtract 1 from both sides.}$$

▶ **Helpful Hint**
Don't forget that $-1 \pm 2\sqrt{3}$, for example, means $-1 + 2\sqrt{3}$ and $-1 - 2\sqrt{3}$. In other words, the equation in Example 3 has two solutions.

Check: Below is a check for $-1 + 2\sqrt{3}$. The check for $-1 - 2\sqrt{3}$ is almost the same and is left for you to do on your own.

$$(x + 1)^2 = 12$$
$$\left(-1 + 2\sqrt{3} + 1\right)^2 \overset{?}{=} 12$$
$$\left(2\sqrt{3}\right)^2 \overset{?}{=} 12$$
$$4 \cdot 3 \overset{?}{=} 12$$
$$12 = 12 \quad \text{True}$$

The solutions are $-1 + 2\sqrt{3}$ and $-1 - 2\sqrt{3}$. □

PRACTICE
3   Use the square root property to solve $(x + 3)^2 = 20$.

EXAMPLE 4   Use the square root property to solve $(2x - 5)^2 = -16$.

Solution

$$(2x - 5)^2 = -16$$
$$2x - 5 = \pm\sqrt{-16} \qquad \text{Use the square root property.}$$
$$2x - 5 = \pm4i \qquad \text{Simplify the radical.}$$
$$2x = 5 \pm 4i \qquad \text{Add 5 to both sides.}$$
$$x = \frac{5 \pm 4i}{2} \qquad \text{Divide both sides by 2.}$$

The solutions are $\dfrac{5 + 4i}{2}$ and $\dfrac{5 - 4i}{2}$, or in standard form $a + bi$ for complex numbers, $\dfrac{5}{2} + 2i$ and $\dfrac{5}{2} - 2i$. □

PRACTICE
4   Use the square root property to solve $(5x - 2)^2 = -9$.

✓CONCEPT CHECK
How do you know just by looking that $(x - 2)^2 = -4$ has complex but not real solutions?

OBJECTIVE
2 Solving by Completing the Square

Notice from Examples 3 and 4 that, if we write a quadratic equation so that one side is the square of a binomial, we can solve by using the square root property. To write the square of a binomial, we write perfect square trinomials. Recall that a perfect square trinomial is a trinomial that can be factored into two identical binomial factors.

Perfect Square Trinomials	*Factored Form*
$x^2 + 8x + 16$	$(x + 4)^2$
$x^2 - 6x + 9$	$(x - 3)^2$
$x^2 + 3x + \dfrac{9}{4}$	$\left(x + \dfrac{3}{2}\right)^2$

Notice that for each perfect square trinomial in x, **the constant term of the trinomial is the square of half the coefficient of the x-term.** For example,

$$x^2 + 8x + 16 \qquad\qquad x^2 - 6x + 9$$

$$\frac{1}{2}(8) = 4 \text{ and } 4^2 = 16 \qquad \frac{1}{2}(-6) = -3 \text{ and } (-3)^2 = 9$$

The process of writing a quadratic equation so that one side is a perfect square trinomial is called **completing the square.**

EXAMPLE 5 Solve $p^2 + 2p = 4$ by completing the square.

Solution First, add the square of half the coefficient of p to both sides so that the resulting trinomial will be a perfect square trinomial. The coefficient of p is 2.

$$\frac{1}{2}(2) = 1 \quad \text{and} \quad 1^2 = 1$$

Add 1 to both sides of the original equation.

$$p^2 + 2p = 4$$
$$p^2 + 2p + 1 = 4 + 1 \quad \text{Add 1 to both sides.}$$
$$(p + 1)^2 = 5 \quad \text{Factor the trinomial; simplify the right side.}$$

We may now use the square root property and solve for p.

$$p + 1 = \pm\sqrt{5} \quad \text{Use the square root property.}$$
$$p = -1 \pm \sqrt{5} \quad \text{Subtract 1 from both sides.}$$

Notice that there are two solutions: $-1 + \sqrt{5}$ and $-1 - \sqrt{5}$. ☐

PRACTICE
5 Solve $b^2 + 4b = 3$ by completing the square.

EXAMPLE 6 Solve $m^2 - 7m - 1 = 0$ for m by completing the square.

Solution First, add 1 to both sides of the equation so that the left side has no constant term.

$$m^2 - 7m - 1 = 0$$
$$m^2 - 7m = 1$$

Answer to Concept Check:
answers may vary

Now find the constant term that makes the left side a perfect square trinomial by squaring half the coefficient of m. Add this constant to both sides of the equation.

$$\frac{1}{2}(-7) = -\frac{7}{2} \quad \text{and} \quad \left(-\frac{7}{2}\right)^2 = \frac{49}{4}$$

$$m^2 - 7m + \frac{49}{4} = 1 + \frac{49}{4} \qquad \text{Add } \frac{49}{4} \text{ to both sides of the equation.}$$

$$\left(m - \frac{7}{2}\right)^2 = \frac{53}{4} \qquad \text{Factor the perfect square trinomial and simplify the right side.}$$

$$m - \frac{7}{2} = \pm\sqrt{\frac{53}{4}} \qquad \text{Apply the square root property.}$$

$$m = \frac{7}{2} \pm \frac{\sqrt{53}}{2} \qquad \text{Add } \frac{7}{2} \text{ to both sides and simplify } \sqrt{\frac{53}{4}}.$$

$$m = \frac{7 \pm \sqrt{53}}{2} \qquad \text{Simplify.}$$

The solutions are $\dfrac{7 + \sqrt{53}}{2}$ and $\dfrac{7 - \sqrt{53}}{2}$. □

PRACTICE

6 Solve $p^2 - 3p + 1 = 0$ by completing the square.

The following steps may be used to solve a quadratic equation such as $ax^2 + bx + c = 0$ by completing the square. This method may be used whether or not the polynomial $ax^2 + bx + c$ is factorable.

Solving a Quadratic Equation in x by Completing the Square

Step 1. If the coefficient of x^2 is 1, go to Step 2. Otherwise, divide both sides of the equation by the coefficient of x^2.

Step 2. Isolate all variable terms on one side of the equation.

Step 3. Complete the square for the resulting binomial by adding the square of half of the coefficient of x to both sides of the equation.

Step 4. Factor the resulting perfect square trinomial and write it as the square of a binomial.

Step 5. Use the square root property to solve for x.

EXAMPLE 7 Solve: $2x^2 - 8x + 3 = 0$.

Solution Our procedure for finding the constant term to complete the square works only if the coefficient of the squared variable term is 1. Therefore, to solve this equation, the first step is to divide both sides by 2, the coefficient of x^2.

$$2x^2 - 8x + 3 = 0$$

Step 1. $x^2 - 4x + \dfrac{3}{2} = 0 \qquad$ Divide both sides by 2.

Step 2. $x^2 - 4x = -\dfrac{3}{2} \qquad$ Subtract $\dfrac{3}{2}$ from both sides.

Next find the square of half of -4.

$$\frac{1}{2}(-4) = -2 \quad \text{and} \quad (-2)^2 = 4$$

Add 4 to both sides of the equation to complete the square.

Step 3. $x^2 - 4x + 4 = -\dfrac{3}{2} + 4$

(Continued on next page)

656 CHAPTER 11   Quadratic Equations and Functions

Step 4. $(x - 2)^2 = \dfrac{5}{2}$ Factor the perfect square and simplify the right side.

Step 5. $x - 2 = \pm\sqrt{\dfrac{5}{2}}$ Apply the square root property.

$x - 2 = \pm\dfrac{\sqrt{10}}{2}$ Rationalize the denominator.

$x = 2 \pm \dfrac{\sqrt{10}}{2}$ Add 2 to both sides.

$= \dfrac{4}{2} \pm \dfrac{\sqrt{10}}{2}$ Find a common denominator.

$= \dfrac{4 \pm \sqrt{10}}{2}$ Simplify.

The solutions are $\dfrac{4 + \sqrt{10}}{2}$ and $\dfrac{4 - \sqrt{10}}{2}$.

PRACTICE
7   Solve: $3x^2 - 12x + 1 = 0$.

EXAMPLE 8   Solve $3x^2 - 9x + 8 = 0$ by completing the square.

Solution $3x^2 - 9x + 8 = 0$

Step 1. $x^2 - 3x + \dfrac{8}{3} = 0$ Divide both sides of the equation by 3.

Step 2. $x^2 - 3x = -\dfrac{8}{3}$ Subtract $\dfrac{8}{3}$ from both sides.

Since $\dfrac{1}{2}(-3) = -\dfrac{3}{2}$ and $\left(-\dfrac{3}{2}\right)^2 = \dfrac{9}{4}$, we add $\dfrac{9}{4}$ to both sides of the equation.

Step 3. $x^2 - 3x + \dfrac{9}{4} = \underbrace{-\dfrac{8}{3} + \dfrac{9}{4}}$

Step 4. $\left(x - \dfrac{3}{2}\right)^2 = -\dfrac{5}{12}$ Factor the perfect square trinomial.

Step 5. $x - \dfrac{3}{2} = \pm\sqrt{-\dfrac{5}{12}}$ Apply the square root property.

$x - \dfrac{3}{2} = \pm\dfrac{i\sqrt{5}}{2\sqrt{3}}$ Simplify the radical.

$x - \dfrac{3}{2} = \pm\dfrac{i\sqrt{15}}{6}$ Rationalize the denominator.

$x = \dfrac{3}{2} \pm \dfrac{i\sqrt{15}}{6}$ Add $\dfrac{3}{2}$ to both sides.

$= \dfrac{9}{6} \pm \dfrac{i\sqrt{15}}{6}$ Find a common denominator.

$= \dfrac{9 \pm i\sqrt{15}}{6}$ Simplify.

The solutions are $\dfrac{9 + i\sqrt{15}}{6}$ and $\dfrac{9 - i\sqrt{15}}{6}$, or in $a + bi$ form, $\dfrac{3}{2} + \dfrac{\sqrt{15}}{6}i$ and $\dfrac{3}{2} - \dfrac{\sqrt{15}}{6}i$.

PRACTICE
8   Solve $2x^2 - 5x + 7 = 0$ by completing the square.

OBJECTIVE

3 **Solving Problems Modeled by Quadratic Equations**

Recall the **simple interest** formula $I = Prt$, where I is the interest earned, P is the principal, r is the rate of interest, and t is time in years. If \$100 is invested at a simple interest rate of 5% annually, at the end of 3 years the total interest I earned is

$$I = P \cdot r \cdot t$$

or

$$I = 100 \cdot 0.05 \cdot 3 = \$15$$

and the new principal is

$$\$100 + \$15 = \$115$$

Most of the time, the interest computed on money borrowed or money deposited is **compound interest.** Compound interest, unlike simple interest, is computed on original principal *and* on interest already earned. To see the difference between simple interest and compound interest, suppose that \$100 is invested at a rate of 5% compounded annually. To find the total amount of money at the end of 3 years, we calculate as follows.

$$I = P \cdot r \cdot t$$

First year: Interest = \$100 · 0.05 · 1 = \$5.00
New principal = \$100.00 + \$5.00 = \$105.00

Second year: Interest = \$105.00 · 0.05 · 1 = \$5.25
New principal = \$105.00 + \$5.25 = \$110.25

Third year: Interest = \$110.25 · 0.05 · 1 ≈ \$5.51
New principal = \$110.25 + \$5.51 = \$115.76

At the end of the third year, the total compound interest earned is \$15.76, whereas the total simple interest earned is \$15.

It is tedious to calculate compound interest as we did above, so we use a compound interest formula. The formula for calculating the total amount of money when interest is compounded annually is

$$A = P(1 + r)^t$$

where P is the original investment, r is the interest rate per compounding period, and t is the number of periods. For example, the amount of money A at the end of 3 years if \$100 is invested at 5% compounded annually is

$$A = \$100(1 + 0.05)^3 \approx \$100(1.1576) = \$115.76$$

as we previously calculated.

EXAMPLE 9   **Finding Interest Rates**

Use the formula $A = P(1 + r)^t$ to find the interest rate r if \$2000 compounded annually grows to \$2420 in 2 years.

Solution

1. UNDERSTAND the problem. Since the \$2000 is compounded annually, we use the compound interest formula. For this example, make sure that you understand the formula for compounding interest annually.

2. TRANSLATE. We substitute the given values into the formula.

$$A = P(1 + r)^t$$

$$2420 = 2000(1 + r)^2 \quad \text{Let } A = 2420, P = 2000, \text{ and } t = 2.$$

(Continued on next page)

3. SOLVE. Solve the equation for r.

$$2420 = 2000(1 + r)^2$$

$$\frac{2420}{2000} = (1 + r)^2 \qquad \text{Divide both sides by 2000.}$$

$$\frac{121}{100} = (1 + r)^2 \qquad \text{Simplify the fraction.}$$

$$\pm\sqrt{\frac{121}{100}} = 1 + r \qquad \text{Use the square root property.}$$

$$\pm\frac{11}{10} = 1 + r \qquad \text{Simplify.}$$

$$-1 \pm \frac{11}{10} = r$$

$$-\frac{10}{10} \pm \frac{11}{10} = r$$

$$\frac{1}{10} = r \quad \text{or} \quad -\frac{21}{10} = r$$

4. INTERPRET. The rate cannot be negative, so we reject $-\dfrac{21}{10}$.

Check: $\dfrac{1}{10} = 0.10 = 10\%$ per year. If we invest \$2000 at 10% compounded annually, in 2 years the amount in the account would be $2000(1 + 0.10)^2 = 2420$ dollars, the desired amount.

State: The interest rate is 10% compounded annually. $\square$

PRACTICE

9 Use the formula from Example 9 to find the interest rate r if \$5000 compounded annually grows to \$5618 in 2 years.

Graphing Calculator Explorations

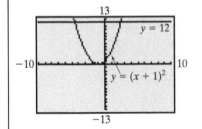

In Section 6.6, we showed how we can use a grapher to approximate real number solutions of a quadratic equation written in standard form. We can also use a grapher to solve a quadratic equation when it is not written in standard form. For example, to solve $(x + 1)^2 = 12$, the quadratic equation in Example 3, we graph the following on the same set of axes. Use Xmin $= -10$, Xmax $= 10$, Ymin $= -13$, and Ymax $= 13$.

$$Y_1 = (x + 1)^2 \quad \text{and} \quad Y_2 = 12$$

Use the Intersect feature or the Zoom and Trace features to locate the points of intersection of the graphs. (See your manuals for specific instructions.) The x-values of these points are the solutions of $(x + 1)^2 = 12$. The solutions, rounded to two decimal places, are 2.46 and -4.46.

Check to see that these numbers are approximations of the exact solutions $-1 \pm 2\sqrt{3}$.

Use a graphing calculator to solve each quadratic equation. Round all solutions to the nearest hundredth.

1. $x(x - 5) = 8$ **2.** $x(x + 2) = 5$

3. $x^2 + 0.5x = 0.3x + 1$ **4.** $x^2 - 2.6x = -2.2x + 3$

5. Use a graphing calculator and solve $(2x - 5)^2 = -16$, Example 4 in this section, using the window

$$\text{Xmin} = -20$$
$$\text{Xmax} = 20$$
$$\text{Xscl} = 1$$
$$\text{Ymin} = -20$$
$$\text{Ymax} = 20$$
$$\text{Yscl} = 1$$

Explain the results. Compare your results with the solution found in Example 4.

6. What are the advantages and disadvantages of using a graphing calculator to solve quadratic equations?

Vocabulary, Readiness & Video Check

Use the choices below to fill in each blank. Not all choices will be used.

binomial	$\sqrt{b}$	$\pm\sqrt{b}$	b^2	9	25	completing the square
quadratic	$-\sqrt{b}$	$\dfrac{b}{2}$	$\left(\dfrac{b}{2}\right)^2$	3	5	

1. By the square root property, if b is a real number, and $a^2 = b$, then $a = $ _____.

2. A _____ equation can be written in the form $ax^2 + bx + c = 0, a \neq 0$.

3. The process of writing a quadratic equation so that one side is a perfect square trinomial is called _____.

4. A perfect square trinomial is one that can be factored as a _____ squared.

5. To solve $x^2 + 6x = 10$ by completing the square, add _____ to both sides.

6. To solve $x^2 + bx = c$ by completing the square, add _____ to both sides.

Martin-Gay Interactive Videos

See Video 11.1

Watch the section lecture video and answer the following questions.

OBJECTIVE 1

7. From ▭ Examples 2 and 3, explain a step you can perform so that you may easily apply the square root property to $2x^2 = 16$. Explain why you perform this step.

OBJECTIVE 2

8. In ▭ Example 5, why is the equation first divided through by 3?

OBJECTIVE 3

9. In ▭ Example 6, why is the negative solution not considered?

11.1 Exercise Set   MyMathLab®

Use the square root property to solve each equation. These equations have real number solutions. See Examples 1 through 3.

1. $x^2 = 16$

2. $x^2 = 49$

3. $x^2 - 7 = 0$

4. $x^2 - 11 = 0$

5. $x^2 = 18$

6. $y^2 = 20$

7. $3z^2 - 30 = 0$

8. $2x^2 - 4 = 0$

9. $(x + 5)^2 = 9$

10. $(y - 3)^2 = 4$

11. $(z - 6)^2 = 18$

12. $(y + 4)^2 = 27$

13. $(2x - 3)^2 = 8$

14. $(4x + 9)^2 = 6$

Use the square root property to solve each equation. See Examples 1 through 4.

15. $x^2 + 9 = 0$

16. $x^2 + 4 = 0$

17. $x^2 - 6 = 0$

18. $y^2 - 10 = 0$

19. $2z^2 + 16 = 0$

20. $3p^2 + 36 = 0$

21. $(3x - 1)^2 = -16$

22. $(4y + 2)^2 = -25$

23. $(z + 7)^2 = 5$

24. $(x + 10)^2 = 11$

25. $(x + 3)^2 + 8 = 0$

26. $(y - 4)^2 + 18 = 0$

Add the proper constant to each binomial so that the resulting trinomial is a perfect square trinomial. Then factor the trinomial.

27. $x^2 + 16x +$ _____

28. $y^2 + 2y +$ _____

29. $z^2 - 12z +$ _____

30. $x^2 - 8x +$ _____

31. $p^2 + 9p +$ _____

32. $n^2 + 5n +$ _____

33. $x^2 + x +$ _____

34. $y^2 - y +$ _____

MIXED PRACTICE

Solve each equation by completing the square. These equations have real number solutions. See Examples 5 through 7.

35. $x^2 + 8x = -15$

36. $y^2 + 6y = -8$

37. $x^2 + 6x + 2 = 0$

38. $x^2 - 2x - 2 = 0$

39. $x^2 + x - 1 = 0$

40. $x^2 + 3x - 2 = 0$

41. $x^2 + 2x - 5 = 0$

42. $x^2 - 6x + 3 = 0$

43. $y^2 + y - 7 = 0$

44. $x^2 - 7x - 1 = 0$

45. $3p^2 - 12p + 2 = 0$

46. $2x^2 + 14x - 1 = 0$

47. $4y^2 - 2 = 12y$

48. $6x^2 - 3 = 6x$

49. $2x^2 + 7x = 4$

50. $3x^2 - 4x = 4$

51. $x^2 + 8x + 1 = 0$

52. $x^2 - 10x + 2 = 0$

53. $3y^2 + 6y - 4 = 0$

54. $2y^2 + 12y + 3 = 0$

55. $2x^2 - 3x - 5 = 0$ **56.** $5x^2 + 3x - 2 = 0$

Solve each equation by completing the square. See Examples 5 through 8.

57. $y^2 + 2y + 2 = 0$

58. $x^2 + 4x + 6 = 0$

59. $y^2 + 6y - 8 = 0$

60. $y^2 + 10y - 26 = 0$

61. $2a^2 + 8a = -12$

62. $3x^2 + 12x = -14$

63. $5x^2 + 15x - 1 = 0$

64. $16y^2 + 16y - 1 = 0$

65. $2x^2 - x + 6 = 0$

66. $4x^2 - 2x + 5 = 0$

67. $x^2 + 10x + 28 = 0$

68. $y^2 + 8y + 18 = 0$

69. $z^2 + 3z - 4 = 0$

70. $y^2 + y - 2 = 0$

71. $2x^2 - 4x = -3$

72. $9x^2 - 36x = -40$

73. $3x^2 + 3x = 5$

74. $10y^2 - 30y = 2$

Use the formula $A = P(1 + r)^t$ to solve Exercises 75 through 78. See Example 9.

75. Find the rate r at which \$3000 compounded annually grows to \$4320 in 2 years.

76. Find the rate r at which \$800 compounded annually grows to \$882 in 2 years.

77. Find the rate at which \$15,000 compounded annually grows to \$16,224 in 2 years.

78. Find the rate at which \$2000 compounded annually grows to \$2880 in 2 years.

Neglecting air resistance, the distance $s(t)$ in feet traveled by a freely falling object is given by the function $s(t) = 16t^2$, where t is time in seconds. Use this formula to solve Exercises 79 through 82. Round answers to two decimal places.

79. The Petronas Towers in Kuala Lumpur, completed in 1998, are the tallest buildings in Malaysia. Each tower is 1483 feet tall. How long would it take an object to fall to the ground from the top of one of the towers? (*Source:* Council on Tall Buildings and Urban Habitat, Lehigh University)

80. The Burj Khalifa, the tallest building in the world, was completed in 2010 in Dubai. It is estimated to be 2717 feet tall. How long would it take an object to fall to the ground from the top of the building? (*Source:* Council on Tall Buildings and Urban Habitat)

81. The Rogun Dam in Tajikistan (part of the former USSR that borders Afghanistan) is the tallest dam in the world at 1100 feet. How long would it take an object to fall from the top to the base of the dam? (*Source:* U.S. Committee on Large Dams of the International Commission on Large Dams)

82. The Hoover Dam, located on the Colorado River on the border of Nevada and Arizona near Las Vegas, is 725 feet tall. How long would it take an object to fall from the top to the base of the dam? (*Source:* U.S. Committee on Large Dams of the International Commission on Large Dams)

Solve.

83. The area of a square room is 225 square feet. Find the dimensions of the room.

84. The area of a circle is 36π square inches. Find the radius of the circle.

85. An isosceles right triangle has legs of equal length. If the hypotenuse is 20 centimeters long, find the length of each leg.

86. The top of a square coffee table has a diagonal that measures 30 inches. Find the length of each side of the top of the coffee table.

REVIEW AND PREVIEW

Simplify each expression. See Section 10.1

87. $\dfrac{1}{2} - \sqrt{\dfrac{9}{4}}$

88. $\dfrac{9}{10} - \sqrt{\dfrac{49}{100}}$

Simplify each expression. See Section 10.5.

89. $\dfrac{6 + 4\sqrt{5}}{2}$

90. $\dfrac{10 - 20\sqrt{3}}{2}$

91. $\dfrac{3 - 9\sqrt{2}}{6}$

92. $\dfrac{12 - 8\sqrt{7}}{16}$

Evaluate $\sqrt{b^2 - 4ac}$ for each set of values. See Section 10.3.

93. $a = 2, b = 4, c = -1$

94. $a = 1, b = 6, c = 2$

95. $a = 3, b = -1, c = -2$

96. $a = 1, b = -3, c = -1$

CONCEPT EXTENSIONS

Without solving, determine whether the solutions of each equation are real numbers or complex but not real numbers. See the Concept Check in this section.

97. $(x + 1)^2 = -1$

98. $(y - 5)^2 = -9$

99. $3z^2 = 10$

100. $4x^2 = 17$

101. $(2y - 5)^2 + 7 = 3$

102. $(3m + 2)^2 + 4 = 1$

Find two possible missing terms so that each is a perfect square trinomial.

103. $x^2 + + 16$

104. $y^2 + + 9$

105. $z^2 + + \dfrac{25}{4}$

106. $x^2 + + \dfrac{1}{4}$

107. In your own words, explain how to calculate the number that will complete the square on an expression such as $x^2 - 5x$.

108. In your own words, what is the difference between simple interest and compound interest?

109. If you are depositing money in an account that pays 4%, would you prefer the interest to be simple or compound? Explain your answer.

110. If you are borrowing money at a rate of 10%, would you prefer the interest to be simple or compound? Explain your answer.

A common equation used in business is a demand equation. It expresses the relationship between the unit price of some commodity and the quantity demanded. For Exercises 111 and 112, p represents the unit price and x represents the quantity demanded in thousands.

111. A manufacturing company has found that the demand equation for a certain type of scissors is given by the equation $p = -x^2 + 47$. Find the demand for the scissors if the price is $11 per pair.

112. Acme, Inc., sells desk lamps and has found that the demand equation for a certain style of desk lamp is given by the equation $p = -x^2 + 15$. Find the demand for the desk lamp if the price is $7 per lamp.

11.2 Solving Quadratic Equations by the Quadratic Formula

OBJECTIVES

1 Solve Quadratic Equations by Using the Quadratic Formula.

2 Determine the Number and Type of Solutions of a Quadratic Equation by Using the Discriminant.

3 Solve Problems Modeled by Quadratic Equations.

OBJECTIVE

1   Solving Quadratic Equations by Using the Quadratic Formula

Any quadratic equation can be solved by completing the square. Since the same sequence of steps is repeated each time we complete the square, let's complete the square for a general quadratic equation, $ax^2 + bx + c = 0, a \neq 0$. By doing so, we find a pattern for the solutions of a quadratic equation known as the **quadratic formula.**

Recall that to complete the square for an equation such as $ax^2 + bx + c = 0$, we first divide both sides by the coefficient of x^2.

$$ax^2 + bx + c = 0$$

$$x^2 + \frac{b}{a}x + \frac{c}{a} = 0 \qquad \text{Divide both sides by } a, \text{ the coefficient of } x^2.$$

$$x^2 + \frac{b}{a}x = -\frac{c}{a} \qquad \text{Subtract the constant } \frac{c}{a} \text{ from both sides.}$$

Next, find the square of half $\frac{b}{a}$, the coefficient of x.

$$\frac{1}{2}\left(\frac{b}{a}\right) = \frac{b}{2a} \quad \text{and} \quad \left(\frac{b}{2a}\right)^2 = \frac{b^2}{4a^2}$$

Add this result to both sides of the equation.

$$x^2 + \frac{b}{a}x + \frac{b^2}{4a^2} = -\frac{c}{a} + \frac{b^2}{4a^2} \qquad \text{Add } \frac{b^2}{4a^2} \text{ to both sides.}$$

$$x^2 + \frac{b}{a}x + \frac{b^2}{4a^2} = \frac{-c \cdot 4a}{a \cdot 4a} + \frac{b^2}{4a^2} \qquad \begin{array}{l}\text{Find a common denominator} \\ \text{on the right side.}\end{array}$$

$$x^2 + \frac{b}{a}x + \frac{b^2}{4a^2} = \frac{b^2 - 4ac}{4a^2} \qquad \text{Simplify the right side.}$$

$$\left(x + \frac{b}{2a}\right)^2 = \frac{b^2 - 4ac}{4a^2} \qquad \begin{array}{l}\text{Factor the perfect square} \\ \text{trinomial on the left side.}\end{array}$$

$$x + \frac{b}{2a} = \pm\sqrt{\frac{b^2 - 4ac}{4a^2}} \qquad \text{Apply the square root property.}$$

$$x + \frac{b}{2a} = \pm\frac{\sqrt{b^2 - 4ac}}{2a} \qquad \text{Simplify the radical.}$$

$$x = -\frac{b}{2a} \pm \frac{\sqrt{b^2 - 4ac}}{2a} \qquad \text{Subtract } \frac{b}{2a} \text{ from both sides.}$$

$$x = \frac{-b \pm \sqrt{b^2 - 4ac}}{2a} \qquad \text{Simplify.}$$

This equation identifies the solutions of the general quadratic equation in standard form and is called the quadratic formula. It can be used to solve any equation written in standard form $ax^2 + bx + c = 0$ as long as a is not 0.

Quadratic Formula

A quadratic equation written in the form $ax^2 + bx + c = 0$ has the solutions

$$x = \frac{-b \pm \sqrt{b^2 - 4ac}}{2a}$$

EXAMPLE 1   Solve $3x^2 + 16x + 5 = 0$ for x.

Solution   This equation is in standard form, so $a = 3$, $b = 16$, and $c = 5$. Substitute these values into the quadratic formula.

$$x = \frac{-b \pm \sqrt{b^2 - 4ac}}{2a} \qquad \text{Quadratic formula}$$

$$= \frac{-16 \pm \sqrt{16^2 - 4(3)(5)}}{2 \cdot 3} \qquad \text{Use } a = 3, b = 16, \text{ and } c = 5.$$

$$= \frac{-16 \pm \sqrt{256 - 60}}{6}$$

$$= \frac{-16 \pm \sqrt{196}}{6} = \frac{-16 \pm 14}{6}$$

$$x = \frac{-16 + 14}{6} = -\frac{1}{3} \quad \text{or} \quad x = \frac{-16 - 14}{6} = -\frac{30}{6} = -5$$

The solutions are $-\dfrac{1}{3}$ and -5, or the solution set is $\left\{-\dfrac{1}{3}, -5\right\}$.

PRACTICE
1   Solve $3x^2 - 5x - 2 = 0$ for x.

▶ Helpful Hint

To replace a, b, and c correctly in the quadratic formula, write the quadratic equation in standard form $ax^2 + bx + c = 0$.

EXAMPLE 2   Solve: $2x^2 - 4x = 3$.

Solution   First write the equation in standard form by subtracting 3 from both sides.

$$2x^2 - 4x - 3 = 0$$

Now $a = 2$, $b = -4$, and $c = -3$. Substitute these values into the quadratic formula.

$$x = \frac{-b \pm \sqrt{b^2 - 4ac}}{2a}$$

$$= \frac{-(-4) \pm \sqrt{(-4)^2 - 4(2)(-3)}}{2 \cdot 2}$$

$$= \frac{4 \pm \sqrt{16 + 24}}{4}$$

$$= \frac{4 \pm \sqrt{40}}{4} = \frac{4 \pm 2\sqrt{10}}{4}$$

$$= \frac{2(2 \pm \sqrt{10})}{2 \cdot 2} = \frac{2 \pm \sqrt{10}}{2}$$

The solutions are $\dfrac{2 + \sqrt{10}}{2}$ and $\dfrac{2 - \sqrt{10}}{2}$, or the solution set is $\left\{\dfrac{2 - \sqrt{10}}{2}, \dfrac{2 + \sqrt{10}}{2}\right\}$.

PRACTICE
2   Solve: $3x^2 - 8x = 2$.

▶ Helpful Hint

To simplify the expression $\dfrac{4 \pm 2\sqrt{10}}{4}$ in the preceding example, note that 2 is factored out of both terms of the numerator *before* simplifying.

$$\frac{4 \pm 2\sqrt{10}}{4} = \frac{2(2 \pm \sqrt{10})}{2 \cdot 2} = \frac{2 \pm \sqrt{10}}{2}$$

EXAMPLE 3   Solve: $\frac{1}{4}m^2 - m + \frac{1}{2} = 0$.

Solution We could use the quadratic formula with $a = \frac{1}{4}$, $b = -1$, and $c = \frac{1}{2}$. Instead, we find a simpler, equivalent standard form equation whose coefficients are not fractions.
Multiply both sides of the equation by the LCD 4 to clear fractions.

$$4\left(\frac{1}{4}m^2 - m + \frac{1}{2}\right) = 4 \cdot 0$$

$$m^2 - 4m + 2 = 0 \qquad \text{Simplify.}$$

Substitute $a = 1, b = -4$, and $c = 2$ into the quadratic formula and simplify.

$$m = \frac{-(-4) \pm \sqrt{(-4)^2 - 4(1)(2)}}{2 \cdot 1} = \frac{4 \pm \sqrt{16 - 8}}{2}$$

$$= \frac{4 \pm \sqrt{8}}{2} = \frac{4 \pm 2\sqrt{2}}{2} = \frac{2(2 \pm \sqrt{2})}{2}$$

$$= 2 \pm \sqrt{2}$$

The solutions are $2 + \sqrt{2}$ and $2 - \sqrt{2}$.

PRACTICE
3   Solve: $\frac{1}{8}x^2 - \frac{1}{4}x - 2 = 0$.

EXAMPLE 4   Solve: $x = -3x^2 - 3$.

Solution The equation in standard form is $3x^2 + x + 3 = 0$. Thus, let $a = 3, b = 1$, and $c = 3$ in the quadratic formula.

$$x = \frac{-1 \pm \sqrt{1^2 - 4(3)(3)}}{2 \cdot 3} = \frac{-1 \pm \sqrt{1 - 36}}{6} = \frac{-1 \pm \sqrt{-35}}{6} = \frac{-1 \pm i\sqrt{35}}{6}$$

The solutions are $\frac{-1 + i\sqrt{35}}{6}$ and $\frac{-1 - i\sqrt{35}}{6}$, or in the form $a + bi$, $-\frac{1}{6} + \frac{\sqrt{35}}{6}i$ and $-\frac{1}{6} - \frac{\sqrt{35}}{6}i$.

PRACTICE
4   Solve: $x = -2x^2 - 2$.

In Example 1, the equation $3x^2 + 16x + 5 = 0$ had 2 real roots, $-\frac{1}{3}$ and -5. In Example 4, the equation $3x^2 + x + 3 = 0$ (written in standard form) had no real roots. How do their related graphs compare? Recall that the x-intercepts of

$f(x) = 3x^2 + 16x + 5$ occur where $f(x) = 0$ or where $3x^2 + 16x + 5 = 0$. Since this equation has 2 real roots, the graph has 2 x-intercepts. Similarly, since the equation $3x^2 + x + 3 = 0$ has no real roots, the graph of $f(x) = 3x^2 + x + 3$ has no x-intercepts.

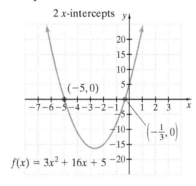

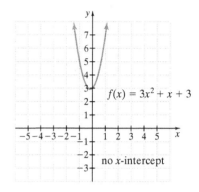

OBJECTIVE

2   Using the Discriminant

In the quadratic formula, $x = \dfrac{-b \pm \sqrt{b^2 - 4ac}}{2a}$, the radicand $b^2 - 4ac$ is called the **discriminant** because, by knowing its value, we can **discriminate** among the possible number and type of solutions of a quadratic equation. Possible values of the discriminant and their meanings are summarized next.

Discriminant

The following table corresponds the discriminant $b^2 - 4ac$ of a quadratic equation of the form $ax^2 + bx + c = 0$ with the number and type of solutions of the equation.

$b^2 - 4ac$	*Number and Type of Solutions*
Positive	Two real solutions
Zero	One real solution
Negative	Two complex but not real solutions

EXAMPLE 5   Use the discriminant to determine the number and type of solutions of each quadratic equation.

a. $x^2 + 2x + 1 = 0$ **b.** $3x^2 + 2 = 0$ **c.** $2x^2 - 7x - 4 = 0$

Solution

a. In $x^2 + 2x + 1 = 0$, $a = 1$, $b = 2$, and $c = 1$. Thus,

$$b^2 - 4ac = 2^2 - 4(1)(1) = 0$$

Since $b^2 - 4ac = 0$, this quadratic equation has one real solution.

b. In this equation, $a = 3$, $b = 0$, $c = 2$. Then $b^2 - 4ac = 0 - 4(3)(2) = -24$. Since $b^2 - 4ac$ is negative, the quadratic equation has two complex but not real solutions.

c. In this equation, $a = 2$, $b = -7$, and $c = -4$. Then

$$b^2 - 4ac = (-7)^2 - 4(2)(-4) = 81$$

Since $b^2 - 4ac$ is positive, the quadratic equation has two real solutions.   □

PRACTICE

5   Use the discriminant to determine the number and type of solutions of each quadratic equation.

a. $x^2 - 6x + 9 = 0$ **b.** $x^2 - 3x - 1 = 0$ **c.** $7x^2 + 11 = 0$

The discriminant helps us determine the number and type of solutions of a quadratic equation, $ax^2 + bx + c = 0$. Recall that the solutions of this equation are the same as the x-intercepts of its related graph $f(x) = ax^2 + bx + c$. This means that the discriminant of $ax^2 + bx + c = 0$ also tells us the number of x-intercepts for the graph of $f(x) = ax^2 + bx + c$ or, equivalently, $y = ax^2 + bx + c$.

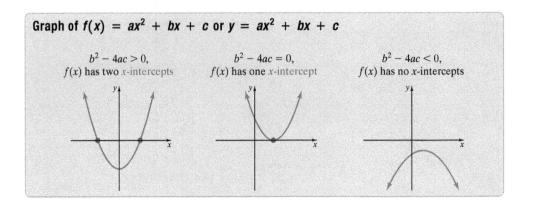

Graph of $f(x) = ax^2 + bx + c$ or $y = ax^2 + bx + c$

| $b^2 - 4ac > 0$, $f(x)$ has two x-intercepts | $b^2 - 4ac = 0$, $f(x)$ has one x-intercept | $b^2 - 4ac < 0$, $f(x)$ has no x-intercepts |

OBJECTIVE

3 **Solving Problems Modeled by Quadratic Equations**

The quadratic formula is useful in solving problems that are modeled by quadratic equations.

⚠ **EXAMPLE 6** **Calculating Distance Saved**

At a local university, students often leave the sidewalk and cut across the lawn to save walking distance. Given the diagram below of a favorite place to cut across the lawn, approximate how many feet of walking distance a student saves by cutting across the lawn instead of walking on the sidewalk.

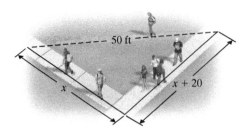

Solution

1. UNDERSTAND. Read and reread the problem. In the diagram, notice that a triangle is formed. Since the corner of the block forms a right angle, we use the Pythagorean theorem for right triangles. You may want to review this theorem.

2. TRANSLATE. By the Pythagorean theorem, we have

$$\text{In words: } (\text{leg})^2 + (\text{leg})^2 = (\text{hypotenuse})^2$$
$$\text{Translate: } x^2 + (x + 20)^2 = 50^2$$

3. SOLVE. Use the quadratic formula to solve.

$$x^2 + x^2 + 40x + 400 = 2500 \quad \text{Square } (x + 20) \text{ and } 50.$$
$$2x^2 + 40x - 2100 = 0 \quad \text{Set the equation equal to } 0.$$
$$x^2 + 20x - 1050 = 0 \quad \text{Divide by } 2.$$

Here, $a = 1, b = 20, c = -1050$. By the quadratic formula,

$$x = \frac{-20 \pm \sqrt{20^2 - 4(1)(-1050)}}{2 \cdot 1}$$

$$= \frac{-20 \pm \sqrt{400 + 4200}}{2} = \frac{-20 \pm \sqrt{4600}}{2}$$

$$= \frac{-20 \pm \sqrt{100 \cdot 46}}{2} = \frac{-20 \pm 10\sqrt{46}}{2}$$

$$= -10 \pm 5\sqrt{46} \quad \text{Simplify.}$$

4. INTERPRET

Check: Your calculations in the quadratic formula. The length of a side of a triangle can't be negative, so we reject $-10 - 5\sqrt{46}$. Since $-10 + 5\sqrt{46} \approx 24$ feet, the walking distance along the sidewalk is

$$x + (x + 20) \approx 24 + (24 + 20) = 68 \text{ feet.}$$

State: A student saves about $68 - 50$ or 18 feet of walking distance by cutting across the lawn.

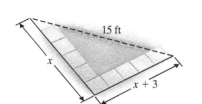

PRACTICE

6   Given the diagram, approximate to the nearest foot how many feet of walking distance a person can save by cutting across the lawn instead of walking on the sidewalk.

EXAMPLE 7   **Calculating Landing Time**

An object is thrown upward from the top of a 200-foot cliff with a velocity of 12 feet per second. The height h in feet of the object after t seconds is

$$h = -16t^2 + 12t + 200$$

How long after the object is thrown will it strike the ground? Round to the nearest tenth of a second.

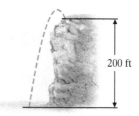

Solution

1. UNDERSTAND. Read and reread the problem.

2. TRANSLATE. Since we want to know when the object strikes the ground, we want to know when the height $h = 0$, or

$$0 = -16t^2 + 12t + 200$$

3. SOLVE. First we divide both sides of the equation by -4.

$$0 = 4t^2 - 3t - 50 \quad \text{Divide both sides by } -4.$$

Here, $a = 4, b = -3$, and $c = -50$. By the quadratic formula,

$$t = \frac{-(-3) \pm \sqrt{(-3)^2 - 4(4)(-50)}}{2 \cdot 4}$$

$$= \frac{3 \pm \sqrt{9 + 800}}{8}$$

$$= \frac{3 \pm \sqrt{809}}{8}$$

(Continued on next page)

4. INTERPRET.

Check: We check our calculations from the quadratic formula. Since the time won't be negative, we reject the proposed solution

$$\frac{3 - \sqrt{809}}{8}.$$

State: The time it takes for the object to strike the ground is exactly

$$\frac{3 + \sqrt{809}}{8} \text{ seconds} \approx 3.9 \text{ seconds}.$$

PRACTICE

7 A toy rocket is shot upward from the top of a building, 45 feet high, with an initial velocity of 20 feet per second. The height h in feet of the rocket after t seconds is

$$h = -16t^2 + 20t + 45$$

How long after the rocket is launched will it strike the ground? Round to the nearest tenth of a second.

Vocabulary, Readiness & Video Check

Fill in each blank.

1. The quadratic formula is _____ .

2. For $2x^2 + x + 1 = 0$, if $a = 2$, then $b =$ _____ and $c =$ _____ .

3. For $5x^2 - 5x - 7 = 0$, if $a = 5$, then $b =$ _____ and $c =$ _____ .

4. For $7x^2 - 4 = 0$, if $a = 7$, then $b =$ _____ and $c =$ _____ .

5. For $x^2 + 9 = 0$, if $c = 9$, then $a =$ _____ and $b =$ _____ .

6. The correct simplified form of $\dfrac{5 \pm 10\sqrt{2}}{5}$ is _____ .

    a. $1 \pm 10\sqrt{2}$ **b.** $2\sqrt{2}$ **c.** $1 \pm 2\sqrt{2}$ **d.** $\pm 5\sqrt{2}$

Martin-Gay Interactive Videos

See Video 11.2

Watch the section lecture video and answer the following questions.

OBJECTIVE
1

7. Based on ⊟ Examples 1–3, answer the following.
  a. Must a quadratic equation be written in standard form in order to use the quadratic formula? Why or why not?
  b. Must fractions be cleared from an equation before using the quadratic formula? Why or why not?

OBJECTIVE
2

8. Based on ⊟ Example 4 and the lecture before, complete the following statements. The discriminant is the _____ in the quadratic formula and can be used to find the number and type of solutions of a quadratic equation without _____ the equation. To use the discriminant, the quadratic equation needs to be written in _____ form.

OBJECTIVE
3

9. In ⊟ Example 5, the value of x is found, which is then used to find the dimensions of the triangle. Yet all this work still does solve the problem. Explain.

11.2 Exercise Set MyMathLab®

Use the quadratic formula to solve each equation. These equations have real number solutions only. See Examples 1 through 3.

1. $m^2 + 5m - 6 = 0$

2. $p^2 + 11p - 12 = 0$

3. $2y = 5y^2 - 3$

4. $5x^2 - 3 = 14x$

5. $x^2 - 6x + 9 = 0$

6. $y^2 + 10y + 25 = 0$

7. $x^2 + 7x + 4 = 0$

8. $y^2 + 5y + 3 = 0$

9. $8m^2 - 2m = 7$

10. $11n^2 - 9n = 1$

11. $3m^2 - 7m = 3$

12. $x^2 - 13 = 5x$

13. $\frac{1}{2}x^2 - x - 1 = 0$

14. $\frac{1}{6}x^2 + x + \frac{1}{3} = 0$

15. $\frac{2}{5}y^2 + \frac{1}{5}y = \frac{3}{5}$

16. $\frac{1}{8}x^2 + x = \frac{5}{2}$

17. $\frac{1}{3}y^2 = y + \frac{1}{6}$

18. $\frac{1}{2}y^2 = y + \frac{1}{2}$

19. $x^2 + 5x = -2$

20. $y^2 - 8 = 4y$

21. $(m + 2)(2m - 6) = 5(m - 1) - 12$

22. $7p(p - 2) + 2(p + 4) = 3$

MIXED PRACTICE

Use the quadratic formula to solve each equation. These equations have real solutions and complex but not real solutions. See Examples 1 through 4.

23. $x^2 + 6x + 13 = 0$

24. $x^2 + 2x + 2 = 0$

25. $(x + 5)(x - 1) = 2$

26. $x(x + 6) = 2$

27. $6 = -4x^2 + 3x$

28. $2 = -9x^2 - x$

29. $\frac{x^2}{3} - x = \frac{5}{3}$

30. $\frac{x^2}{2} - 3 = -\frac{9}{2}x$

31. $10y^2 + 10y + 3 = 0$

32. $3y^2 + 6y + 5 = 0$

33. $x(6x + 2) = 3$

34. $x(7x + 1) = 2$

35. $\frac{2}{5}y^2 + \frac{1}{5}y + \frac{3}{5} = 0$

36. $\frac{1}{8}x^2 + x + \frac{5}{2} = 0$

37. $\frac{1}{2}y^2 = y - \frac{1}{2}$

38. $\frac{2}{3}x^2 - \frac{20}{3}x = -\frac{100}{6}$

39. $(n - 2)^2 = 2n$

40. $\left(p - \frac{1}{2}\right)^2 = \frac{p}{2}$

Use the discriminant to determine the number and types of solutions of each equation. See Example 5.

41. $x^2 - 5 = 0$

42. $x^2 - 7 = 0$

43. $4x^2 + 12x = -9$

44. $9x^2 + 1 = 6x$

45. $3x = -2x^2 + 7$

46. $3x^2 = 5 - 7x$

47. $6 = 4x - 5x^2$

48. $8x = 3 - 9x^2$

49. $9x - 2x^2 + 5 = 0$

50. $5 - 4x + 12x^2 = 0$

Solve. See Examples 7 and 8.

51. Nancy, Thelma, and John Varner live on a corner lot. Often, neighborhood children cut across their lot to save walking distance. Given the diagram below, approximate to the nearest foot how many feet of walking distance is saved by cutting across their property instead of walking around the lot.

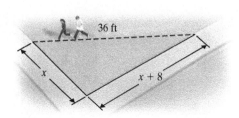

△ **52.** Given the diagram below, approximate to the nearest foot how many feet of walking distance a person saves by cutting across the lawn instead of walking on the sidewalk.

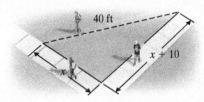

△ **53.** The hypotenuse of an isosceles right triangle is 2 centimeters longer than either of its legs. Find the exact length of each side. (*Hint:* An isosceles right triangle is a right triangle whose legs are the same length.)

△ **54.** The hypotenuse of an isosceles right triangle is one meter longer than either of its legs. Find the length of each side.

△ **55.** Bailey's rectangular dog pen for his Irish setter must have an area of 400 square feet. Also, the length must be 10 feet longer than the width. Find the dimensions of the pen.

△ **56.** An entry in the Peach Festival Poster Contest must be rectangular and have an area of 1200 square inches. Furthermore, its length must be 20 inches longer than its width. Find the dimensions each entry must have.

△ **57.** A holding pen for cattle must be square and have a diagonal length of 100 meters.

    a. Find the length of a side of the pen.

    b. Find the area of the pen.

△ **58.** A rectangle is three times longer than it is wide. It has a diagonal of length 50 centimeters.

    a. Find the dimensions of the rectangle.

    b. Find the perimeter of the rectangle.

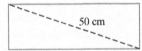

△ **59.** The heaviest reported door in the world is the 708.6 ton radiation shield door in the National Institute for Fusion Science at Toki, Japan. If the height of the door is 1.1 feet longer than its width, and its front area (neglecting depth) is 1439.9 square feet, find its width and height [Interesting note: The door is 6.6 feet thick.] (*Source: Guinness World Records*)

△ **60.** Christi and Robbie Wegmann are constructing a rectangular stained glass window whose length is 7.3 inches longer than its width. If the area of the window is 569.9 square inches, find its width and length.

△ **61.** The base of a triangle is four more than twice its height. If the area of the triangle is 42 square centimeters, find its base and height.

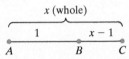

62. If a point B divides a line segment such that the smaller portion is to the larger portion as the larger is to the whole, the whole is the length of the *golden ratio*.

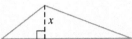

The golden ratio was thought by the Greeks to be the most pleasing to the eye, and many of their buildings contained numerous examples of the golden ratio. The value of the golden ratio is the positive solution of

$$\begin{array}{cc}(\text{smaller}) & x-1 \\ (\text{larger}) & \overline{} \end{array} \frac{x-1}{1} = \frac{1}{x} \begin{array}{c}(\text{larger}) \\ (\text{whole})\end{array}$$

Find this value.

The Wollomombi Falls in Australia have a height of 1100 feet. A pebble is thrown upward from the top of the falls with an initial velocity of 20 feet per second. The height of the pebble h after t seconds is given by the equation $h = -16t^2 + 20t + 1100$. Use this equation for Exercises 63 and 64.

63. How long after the pebble is thrown will it hit the ground? Round to the nearest tenth of a second.

64. How long after the pebble is thrown will it be 550 feet from the ground? Round to the nearest tenth of a second.

A ball is thrown downward from the top of a 180-foot building with an initial velocity of 20 feet per second. The height of the ball h after t seconds is given by the equation $h = -16t^2 - 20t + 180$. Use this equation to answer Exercises 65 and 66.

65. How long after the ball is thrown will it strike the ground? Round the result to the nearest tenth of a second.

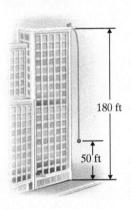

66. How long after the ball is thrown will it be 50 feet from the ground? Round the result to the nearest tenth of a second.

REVIEW AND PREVIEW

Solve each equation. See Sections 7.5 and 10.6.

67. $\sqrt{5x - 2} = 3$

68. $\sqrt{y + 2} + 7 = 12$

69. $\dfrac{1}{x} + \dfrac{2}{5} = \dfrac{7}{x}$

70. $\dfrac{10}{z} = \dfrac{5}{z} - \dfrac{1}{3}$

Factor. See Sections 6.3 through 6.5.

71. $x^4 + x^2 - 20$

72. $2y^4 + 11y^2 - 6$

73. $z^4 - 13z^2 + 36$

74. $x^4 - 1$

CONCEPT EXTENSIONS

For each quadratic equation, choose the correct substitution for a, b, and c in the standard form $ax^2 + bx + c = 0$.

75. $x^2 = -10$

   a. $a = 1, b = 0, c = -10$

   b. $a = 1, b = 0, c = 10$

   c. $a = 0, b = 1, c = -10$

   d. $a = 1, b = 1, c = 10$

76. $x^2 + 5 = -x$

   a. $a = 1, b = 5, c = -1$

   b. $a = 1, b = -1, c = 5$

   c. $a = 1, b = 5, c = 1$

   d. $a = 1, b = 1, c = 5$

77. Solve Exercise 1 by factoring. Explain the result.

78. Solve Exercise 2 by factoring. Explain the result.

Use the quadratic formula and a calculator to approximate each solution to the nearest tenth.

79. $2x^2 - 6x + 3 = 0$

80. $3.6x^2 + 1.8x - 4.3 = 0$

The accompanying graph shows the daily low temperatures for one week in New Orleans, Louisiana.

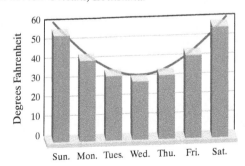

81. Between which days of the week was there the greatest decrease in the low temperature?

82. Between which days of the week was there the greatest increase in the low temperature?

83. Which day of the week had the lowest low temperature?

84. Use the graph to estimate the low temperature on Thursday.

Notice that the shape of the temperature graph is similar to the curve drawn. In fact, this graph can be modeled by the quadratic function $f(x) = 3x^2 - 18x + 56$, where f(x) is the temperature in degrees Fahrenheit and x is the number of days from Sunday. (This graph is shown in blue.) Use this function to answer Exercises 85 and 86.

85. Use the quadratic function given to approximate the temperature on Thursday. Does your answer agree with the graph?

86. Use the function given and the quadratic formula to find when the temperature was 35° F. [*Hint:* Let $f(x) = 35$ and solve for x.] Round your answer to one decimal place and interpret your result. Does your answer agree with the graph?

87. The number of college students in the United States can be modeled by the quadratic function $f(x) = 22x^2 + 274x + 15{,}628$, where $f(x)$ is the number of college students in thousands of students, and x is the number of years after 2000. (*Source:* Based on data from the U.S. Department of Education)

   a. Find the number of college students in the United States in 2010.

   b. If the trend described by this model continues, find the year after 2000 in which the population of American college students reaches 24,500 students.

88. The projected number of Wi-Fi-enabled cell phones in the United States can be modeled by the quadratic function $c(x) = -0.4x^2 + 21x + 35$, where $c(x)$ is the projected number of Wi-Fi-enabled cell phones in millions and x is the number of years after 2009. Round to the nearest million. (*Source:* Techcrunchies.com)

   a. Find the number of Wi-Fi-enabled cell phones in the United States in 2010.

   b. Find the estimated number of Wi-Fi-enabled cell phones in the United States in 2012.

   c. If the trend described by this model continues, find the year in which the projected number of Wi-Fi-enabled cell phones in the United States reaches 150 million.

89. The average total daily supply y of motor gasoline (in thousands of barrels per day) in the United States for the period 2000–2008 can be approximated by the equation $y = -10x^2 + 193x + 8464$, where x is the number of years after 2000. (*Source:* Based on data from the Energy Information Administration)

   a. Find the average total daily supply of motor gasoline in 2004.

   b. According to this model, in what year, from 2000 to 2008, was the average total daily supply of gasoline 9325 thousand barrels per day?

   c. According to this model, in what year, from 2009 on, will the average total supply of gasoline be 9325 thousand barrels per day?

90. The relationship between body weight and the Recommended Dietary Allowance (RDA) for vitamin A in children up to age 10 is modeled by the quadratic equation $y = 0.149x^2 - 4.475x + 406.478$, where y is the RDA for vitamin A in micrograms for a child whose weight is x pounds. (*Source:* Based on data from the Food and Nutrition Board, National Academy of Sciences–Institute of Medicine, 1989)

   a. Determine the vitamin A requirements of a child who weighs 35 pounds.

   b. What is the weight of a child whose RDA of vitamin A is 600 micrograms? Round your answer to the nearest pound.

The solutions of the quadratic equation $ax^2 + bx + c = 0$ are $\dfrac{-b + \sqrt{b^2 - 4ac}}{2a}$ and $\dfrac{-b - \sqrt{b^2 - 4ac}}{2a}$.

91. Show that the sum of these solutions is $\dfrac{-b}{a}$.

92. Show that the product of these solutions is $\dfrac{c}{a}$.

Use the quadratic formula to solve each quadratic equation.

93. $3x^2 - \sqrt{12}x + 1 = 0$
    (*Hint:* $a = 3, b = -\sqrt{12}, c = 1$)

94. $5x^2 + \sqrt{20}x + 1 = 0$

95. $x^2 + \sqrt{2}x + 1 = 0$

96. $x^2 - \sqrt{2}x + 1 = 0$

97. $2x^2 - \sqrt{3}x - 1 = 0$

98. $7x^2 + \sqrt{7}x - 2 = 0$

99. Use a graphing calculator to solve Exercises 63 and 65.

100. Use a graphing calculator to solve Exercises 64 and 66.

Recall that the discriminant also tells us the number of x-intercepts of the related function.

101. Check the results of Exercise 49 by graphing $y = 9x - 2x^2 + 5$.

102. Check the results of Exercise 50 by graphing $y = 5 - 4x + 12x^2$.

11.3   Solving Equations by Using Quadratic Methods

OBJECTIVES

1 Solve Various Equations That Are Quadratic in Form.

2 Solve Problems That Lead to Quadratic Equations.

OBJECTIVE

1   Solving Equations That Are Quadratic in Form

In this section, we discuss various types of equations that can be solved in part by using the methods for solving quadratic equations.

    Once each equation is simplified, you may want to use these steps when deciding which method to use to solve the quadratic equation.

Solving a Quadratic Equation

Step 1.   If the equation is in the form $(ax + b)^2 = c$, use the square root property and solve. If not, go to Step 2.

Step 2.   Write the equation in standard form: $ax^2 + bx + c = 0$.

Step 3.   Try to solve the equation by the factoring method. If not possible, go to Step 4.

Step 4.   Solve the equation by the quadratic formula.

The first example is a radical equation that becomes a quadratic equation once we square both sides.

EXAMPLE 1   Solve: $x - \sqrt{x} - 6 = 0$.

Solution   Recall that to solve a radical equation, first get the radical alone on one side of the equation. Then square both sides.

$$x - 6 = \sqrt{x} \qquad \text{Add } \sqrt{x} \text{ to both sides.}$$
$$(x - 6)^2 = \left(\sqrt{x}\right)^2 \quad \text{Square both sides.}$$
$$x^2 - 12x + 36 = x$$
$$x^2 - 13x + 36 = 0 \qquad \text{Set the equation equal to 0.}$$
$$(x - 9)(x - 4) = 0$$
$$x - 9 = 0 \quad \text{or} \quad x - 4 = 0$$
$$x = 9 \qquad\qquad x = 4$$

Check:

$$\text{Let } x = 9 \qquad\qquad \text{Let } x = 4$$

$$x - \sqrt{x} - 6 = 0 \qquad\qquad x - \sqrt{x} - 6 = 0$$

$$9 - \sqrt{9} - 6 \overset{?}{=} 0 \qquad\qquad 4 - \sqrt{4} - 6 \overset{?}{=} 0$$

$$9 - 3 - 6 \overset{?}{=} 0 \qquad\qquad 4 - 2 - 6 \overset{?}{=} 0$$

$$0 = 0 \quad \text{True} \qquad\qquad -4 = 0 \quad \text{False}$$

The solution is 9 or the solution set is {9}.

PRACTICE
1   Solve: $x - \sqrt{x + 1} - 5 = 0.$

EXAMPLE 2   Solve: $\dfrac{3x}{x - 2} - \dfrac{x + 1}{x} = \dfrac{6}{x(x - 2)}.$

Solution   In this equation, x cannot be either 2 or 0 because these values cause denominators to equal zero. To solve for x, we first multiply both sides of the equation by $x(x - 2)$ to clear the fractions. By the distributive property, this means that we multiply each term by $x(x - 2)$.

$$x(x - 2)\left(\frac{3x}{x - 2}\right) - x(x - 2)\left(\frac{x + 1}{x}\right) = x(x - 2)\left[\frac{6}{x(x - 2)}\right]$$

$$3x^2 - (x - 2)(x + 1) = 6 \quad \text{Simplify.}$$

$$3x^2 - (x^2 - x - 2) = 6 \quad \text{Multiply.}$$

$$3x^2 - x^2 + x + 2 = 6$$

$$2x^2 + x - 4 = 0 \quad \text{Simplify.}$$

This equation cannot be factored using integers, so we solve by the quadratic formula.

$$x = \frac{-1 \pm \sqrt{1^2 - 4(2)(-4)}}{2 \cdot 2} \quad \begin{array}{l}\text{Use } a = 2, b = 1, \text{ and } c = -4 \\ \text{in the quadratic formula.}\end{array}$$

$$= \frac{-1 \pm \sqrt{1 + 32}}{4} \quad \text{Simplify.}$$

$$= \frac{-1 \pm \sqrt{33}}{4}$$

Neither proposed solution will make the denominators 0.

The solutions are $\dfrac{-1 + \sqrt{33}}{4}$ and $\dfrac{-1 - \sqrt{33}}{4}$ or the solution set is $\left\{\dfrac{-1 + \sqrt{33}}{4}, \dfrac{-1 - \sqrt{33}}{4}\right\}.$

PRACTICE
2   Solve: $\dfrac{5x}{x + 1} - \dfrac{x + 4}{x} = \dfrac{3}{x(x + 1)}.$

EXAMPLE 3   Solve: $p^4 - 3p^2 - 4 = 0.$

Solution   First we factor the trinomial.

$$p^4 - 3p^2 - 4 = 0$$

$$(p^2 - 4)(p^2 + 1) = 0 \qquad\qquad \text{Factor.}$$

$$(p - 2)(p + 2)(p^2 + 1) = 0 \qquad\qquad \text{Factor further.}$$

$$p - 2 = 0 \quad \text{or} \quad p + 2 = 0 \quad \text{or} \quad p^2 + 1 = 0 \quad \begin{array}{l}\text{Set each factor equal}\\ \text{to 0 and solve.}\end{array}$$

$$p = 2 \qquad\qquad p = -2 \qquad\qquad p^2 = -1$$

$$p = \pm\sqrt{-1} = \pm i$$

(Continued on next page)

The solutions are 2, -2, i and $-i$.

PRACTICE
3 Solve: $p^4 - 7p^2 - 144 = 0$.

▶ **Helpful Hint**

Example 3 can be solved using substitution also. Think of $p^4 - 3p^2 - 4 = 0$ as

$$(p^2)^2 - 3p^2 - 4 = 0 \quad \text{Then let } x = p^2 \text{ and solve and substitute back.}$$
$$x^2 - 3x - 4 = 0 \qquad \text{The solutions will be the same.}$$

✓**CONCEPT CHECK**
  a. True or false? The maximum number of solutions that a quadratic equation can have is 2.
  b. True or false? The maximum number of solutions that an equation in quadratic form can have is 2.

EXAMPLE 4 Solve: $(x - 3)^2 - 3(x - 3) - 4 = 0$.

Solution Notice that the quantity $(x - 3)$ is repeated in this equation. Sometimes it is helpful to substitute a variable (in this case other than x) for the repeated quantity. We will let $y = x - 3$. Then

$$(x - 3)^2 - 3(x - 3) - 4 = 0$$

becomes

$$y^2 - 3y - 4 = 0 \quad \text{Let } x - 3 = y.$$
$$(y - 4)(y + 1) = 0 \quad \text{Factor.}$$

To solve, we use the zero factor property.

$$y - 4 = 0 \quad \text{or} \quad y + 1 = 0 \quad \text{Set each factor equal to 0.}$$
$$y = 4 \qquad\qquad y = -1 \quad \text{Solve.}$$

▶ **Helpful Hint**

When using substitution, don't forget to substitute back to the original variable.

To find values of x, we substitute back. That is, we substitute $x - 3$ for y.

$$x - 3 = 4 \quad \text{or} \quad x - 3 = -1$$
$$x = 7 \qquad\qquad x = 2$$

Both 2 and 7 check. The solutions are 2 and 7.

PRACTICE
4 Solve: $(x + 2)^2 - 2(x + 2) - 3 = 0$.

EXAMPLE 5 Solve: $x^{2/3} - 5x^{1/3} + 6 = 0$.

Solution The key to solving this equation is recognizing that $x^{2/3} = (x^{1/3})^2$. We replace $x^{1/3}$ with m so that

$$(x^{1/3})^2 - 5x^{1/3} + 6 = 0$$

becomes

$$m^2 - 5m + 6 = 0$$

Now we solve by factoring.

$$m^2 - 5m + 6 = 0$$
$$(m - 3)(m - 2) = 0 \qquad\qquad \text{Factor.}$$
$$m - 3 = 0 \quad \text{or} \quad m - 2 = 0 \quad \text{Set each factor equal to 0.}$$
$$m = 3 \qquad\qquad m = 2$$

Answer to Concept Check:
a. true   **b.** false

Since $m = x^{1/3}$, we have

$$x^{1/3} = 3 \qquad \text{or} \quad x^{1/3} = 2$$
$$x = 3^3 = 27 \quad \text{or} \quad x = 2^3 = 8$$

Both 8 and 27 check. The solutions are 8 and 27.

PRACTICE

5   Solve: $x^{2/3} - 5x^{1/3} + 4 = 0$.

OBJECTIVE

2   Solving Problems That Lead to Quadratic Equations

The next example is a work problem. This problem is modeled by a rational equation that simplifies to a quadratic equation.

EXAMPLE 6   **Finding Work Time**

Together, an experienced word processor and an apprentice word processor can create a word document in 6 hours. Alone, the experienced word processor can create the document 2 hours faster than the apprentice word processor can. Find the time in which each person can create the word document alone.

Solution

1. UNDERSTAND. Read and reread the problem. The key idea here is the relationship between the *time* (hours) it takes to complete the job and the *part of the job* completed in one unit of time (hour). For example, because they can complete the job together in 6 hours, the *part of the job* they can complete in 1 hour is $\frac{1}{6}$.

Let

$x = $ the *time* in hours it takes the apprentice word processor to complete the job alone

$x - 2 = $ the *time* in hours it takes the experienced word processor to complete the job alone

We can summarize in a chart the information discussed

	Total Hours to Complete Job	*Part of Job Completed in 1 Hour*
Apprentice Word Processor	x	$\frac{1}{x}$
Experienced Word Processor	$x - 2$	$\frac{1}{x - 2}$
Together	6	$\frac{1}{6}$

2. TRANSLATE.

	part of job completed by apprentice word processor in 1 hour	added to	part of job completed by experienced word processor in 1 hour	is equal to	part of job completed together in 1 hour
In words:	↓	↓	↓	↓	↓
Translate:	$\frac{1}{x}$	$+$	$\frac{1}{x - 2}$	$=$	$\frac{1}{6}$

(Continued on next page)

3. SOLVE.

$$\frac{1}{x} + \frac{1}{x-2} = \frac{1}{6}$$

$$6x(x-2)\left(\frac{1}{x} + \frac{1}{x-2}\right) = 6x(x-2)\cdot\frac{1}{6}$$ Multiply both sides by the LCD $6x(x-2)$.

$$6x(x-2)\cdot\frac{1}{x} + 6x(x-2)\cdot\frac{1}{x-2} = 6x(x-2)\cdot\frac{1}{6}$$ Use the distributive property.

$$6(x-2) + 6x = x(x-2)$$

$$6x - 12 + 6x = x^2 - 2x$$

$$0 = x^2 - 14x + 12$$

Now we can substitute $a = 1, b = -14$, and $c = 12$ into the quadratic formula and simplify.

$$x = \frac{-(-14) \pm \sqrt{(-14)^2 - 4(1)(12)}}{2\cdot 1} = \frac{14 \pm \sqrt{148}^*}{2}$$

Using a calculator or a square root table, we see that $\sqrt{148} \approx 12.2$ rounded to one decimal place. Thus,

$$x \approx \frac{14 \pm 12.2}{2}$$

$$x \approx \frac{14 + 12.2}{2} = 13.1 \quad \text{or} \quad x \approx \frac{14 - 12.2}{2} = 0.9$$

4. INTERPRET.

Check: If the apprentice word processor completes the job alone in 0.9 hours, the experienced word processor completes the job alone in $x - 2 = 0.9 - 2 = -1.1$ hours. Since this is not possible, we reject the solution of 0.9. The approximate solution thus is 13.1 hours.

State: The apprentice word processor can complete the job alone in approximately 13.1 hours, and the experienced word processor can complete the job alone in approximately

$$x - 2 = 13.1 - 2 = 11.1 \text{ hours.} \qquad \square$$

PRACTICE

6 Together, Katy and Steve can groom all the dogs at the Barkin' Doggie Day Care in 4 hours. Alone, Katy can groom the dogs 1 hour faster than Steve can groom the dogs alone. Find the time in which each of them can groom the dogs alone.

EXAMPLE 7   **Finding Driving Speeds**

Beach and Fargo are about 400 miles apart. A salesperson travels from Fargo to Beach one day at a certain speed. She returns to Fargo the next day and drives 10 mph faster.

Her total travel time was $14\frac{2}{3}$ hours. Find her speed to Beach and the return speed to Fargo.

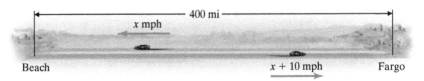

(*This expression can be simplified further, but this will suffice because we are approximating.)

Solution

1. UNDERSTAND. Read and reread the problem. Let

$$x = \text{the speed to Beach, so}$$

$$x + 10 = \text{the return speed to Fargo.}$$

Then organize the given information in a table.

> ▶ Helpful Hint
>
> Since $d = rt$, $t = \dfrac{d}{r}$. The time column was completed using $\dfrac{d}{r}$.

	distance	=	rate	·	time	
To Beach	400		x		$\dfrac{400}{x}$	← distance ← rate
Return to Fargo	400		$x + 10$		$\dfrac{400}{x + 10}$	← distance ← rate

2. TRANSLATE.

In words: $\begin{array}{c}\text{time to} \\ \text{Beach}\end{array}$ + $\begin{array}{c}\text{return} \\ \text{time to} \\ \text{Fargo}\end{array}$ = $\begin{array}{c}14\frac{2}{3} \\ \text{hours}\end{array}$

$$\qquad\qquad\qquad \downarrow \qquad\qquad \downarrow \qquad\qquad \downarrow$$

Translate: $\dfrac{400}{x}$ + $\dfrac{400}{x + 10}$ = $\dfrac{44}{3}$

3. SOLVE.

$$\frac{400}{x} + \frac{400}{x + 10} = \frac{44}{3}$$

$$\frac{100}{x} + \frac{100}{x + 10} = \frac{11}{3} \qquad \text{Divide both sides by 4.}$$

$$3x(x + 10)\left(\frac{100}{x} + \frac{100}{x + 10}\right) = 3x(x + 10) \cdot \frac{11}{3} \qquad \begin{array}{l}\text{Multiply both sides by} \\ \text{the LCD } 3x(x + 10).\end{array}$$

$$3x(x + 10) \cdot \frac{100}{x} + 3x(x + 10) \cdot \frac{100}{x + 10} = 3x(x + 10) \cdot \frac{11}{3} \qquad \begin{array}{l}\text{Use the distributive} \\ \text{property.}\end{array}$$

$$3(x + 10) \cdot 100 + 3x \cdot 100 = x(x + 10) \cdot 11$$

$$300x + 3000 + 300x = 11x^2 + 110x$$

$$0 = 11x^2 - 490x - 3000 \qquad \text{Set equation equal to 0.}$$

$$0 = (11x + 60)(x - 50) \qquad \text{Factor.}$$

$$11x + 60 = 0 \quad \text{or} \quad x - 50 = 0 \qquad \begin{array}{l}\text{Set each factor equal} \\ \text{to 0.}\end{array}$$

$$x = -\frac{60}{11} \text{ or } -5\frac{5}{11}; \quad x = 50$$

4. INTERPRET.

Check: The speed is not negative, so it's not $-5\dfrac{5}{11}$. The number 50 does check.

State: The speed to Beach was 50 mph, and her return speed to Fargo was 60 mph. □

PRACTICE

7   The 36-km S-shaped Hangzhou Bay Bridge is the longest cross-sea bridge in the world, linking Ningbo and Shanghai, China. A merchant drives over the bridge one morning from Ningbo to Shanghai in very heavy traffic and returns home that night driving 50 km per hour faster. The total travel time was 1.3 hours. Find the speed to Shanghai and the return speed to Ningbo.

Vocabulary, Readiness & Video Check

Martin-Gay Interactive Videos

See Video 11.3 🍎

Watch the section lecture video and answer the following questions.

OBJECTIVE 1
1. From Examples 1 and 2, what's the main thing to remember when using a substitution in order to solve an equation by quadratic methods?

OBJECTIVE 2
2. In Example 4, the translated equation is actually a rational equation. Explain how we end up solving it using quadratic methods.

11.3   Exercise Set   MyMathLab®

Solve. See Example 1.

1. $2x = \sqrt{10 + 3x}$

2. $3x = \sqrt{8x + 1}$

3. $x - 2\sqrt{x} = 8$

4. $x - \sqrt{2x} = 4$

5. $\sqrt{9x} = x + 2$

6. $\sqrt{16x} = x + 3$

Solve. See Example 2.

▶ **7.** $\dfrac{2}{x} + \dfrac{3}{x - 1} = 1$

8. $\dfrac{6}{x^2} = \dfrac{3}{x + 1}$

9. $\dfrac{3}{x} + \dfrac{4}{x + 2} = 2$

10. $\dfrac{5}{x - 2} + \dfrac{4}{x + 2} = 1$

11. $\dfrac{7}{x^2 - 5x + 6} = \dfrac{2x}{x - 3} - \dfrac{x}{x - 2}$

12. $\dfrac{11}{2x^2 + x - 15} = \dfrac{5}{2x - 5} - \dfrac{x}{x + 3}$

Solve. See Example 3.

13. $p^4 - 16 = 0$

14. $x^4 + 2x^2 - 3 = 0$

15. $4x^4 + 11x^2 = 3$

16. $z^4 = 81$

17. $z^4 - 13z^2 + 36 = 0$

18. $9x^4 + 5x^2 - 4 = 0$

Solve. See Examples 4 and 5.

▶ **19.** $x^{2/3} - 3x^{1/3} - 10 = 0$

20. $x^{2/3} + 2x^{1/3} + 1 = 0$

21. $(5n + 1)^2 + 2(5n + 1) - 3 = 0$

22. $(m - 6)^2 + 5(m - 6) + 4 = 0$

23. $2x^{2/3} - 5x^{1/3} = 3$

24. $3x^{2/3} + 11x^{1/3} = 4$

25. $1 + \dfrac{2}{3t - 2} = \dfrac{8}{(3t - 2)^2}$

26. $2 - \dfrac{7}{x + 6} = \dfrac{15}{(x + 6)^2}$

27. $20x^{2/3} - 6x^{1/3} - 2 = 0$

28. $4x^{2/3} + 16x^{1/3} = -15$

MIXED PRACTICE

Solve. See Examples 1 through 5.

29. $a^4 - 5a^2 + 6 = 0$

30. $x^4 - 12x^2 + 11 = 0$

31. $\dfrac{2x}{x - 2} + \dfrac{x}{x + 3} = -\dfrac{5}{x + 3}$

32. $\dfrac{5}{x - 3} + \dfrac{x}{x + 3} = \dfrac{19}{x^2 - 9}$

▶ **33.** $(p + 2)^2 = 9(p + 2) - 20$

34. $2(4m - 3)^2 - 9(4m - 3) = 5$

35. $2x = \sqrt{11x + 3}$

36. $4x = \sqrt{2x + 3}$

37. $x^{2/3} - 8x^{1/3} + 15 = 0$

38. $x^{2/3} - 2x^{1/3} - 8 = 0$

39. $y^3 + 9y - y^2 - 9 = 0$

40. $x^3 + x - 3x^2 - 3 = 0$

41. $2x^{2/3} + 3x^{1/3} - 2 = 0$

42. $6x^{2/3} - 25x^{1/3} - 25 = 0$

43. $x^{-2} - x^{-1} - 6 = 0$

44. $y^{-2} - 8y^{-1} + 7 = 0$

45. $x - \sqrt{x} = 2$

46. $x - \sqrt{3x} = 6$

47. $\dfrac{x}{x-1} + \dfrac{1}{x+1} = \dfrac{2}{x^2-1}$

48. $\dfrac{x}{x-5} + \dfrac{5}{x+5} = -\dfrac{1}{x^2-25}$

49. $p^4 - p^2 - 20 = 0$

50. $x^4 - 10x^2 + 9 = 0$

51. $(x+3)(x^2 - 3x + 9) = 0$

52. $(x-6)(x^2 + 6x + 36) = 0$

53. $1 = \dfrac{4}{x-7} + \dfrac{5}{(x-7)^2}$

54. $3 + \dfrac{1}{2p+4} = \dfrac{10}{(2p+4)^2}$

55. $27y^4 + 15y^2 = 2$

56. $8z^4 + 14z^2 = -5$

57. $x - \sqrt{19 - 2x} - 2 = 0$

58. $x - \sqrt{17 - 4x} - 3 = 0$

Solve. For Exercises 59 and 60, the solutions have been started for you. See Examples 6 and 7.

59. Roma Sherry drove 330 miles from her hometown to Tucson. During her return trip, she was able to increase her speed by 11 miles per hour. If her return trip took 1 hour less time, find her original speed and her speed returning home.

Start the solution:

1. UNDERSTAND the problem. Reread it as many times as needed. Let

$$x = \text{original speed}$$
$$x + 11 = \text{return-trip speed}$$

Organize the information in a table.

	distance	=	rate	·	time	
To Tucson	330		x		$\dfrac{330}{x}$	← distance ← rate
Return trip	330		___		$\dfrac{330}{\text{___}}$	← distance ← rate

2. TRANSLATE into an equation. (Fill in the blanks below.)

Time to Tucson	equals	Return trip time	plus	1 hour
↓	↓	↓	↓	↓
___	=	___	+	1

Finish with:

3. SOLVE and **4.** INTERPRET

60. A salesperson drove to Portland, a distance of 300 miles. During the last 80 miles of his trip, heavy rainfall forced him to decrease his speed by 15 miles per hour. If his total driving time was 6 hours, find his original speed and his speed during the rainfall.

Start the solution:

1. UNDERSTAND the problem. Reread it as many times as needed. Let

$$x = \text{original speed}$$
$$x - 15 = \text{rainfall speed}$$

Organize the information in a table.

	distance	=	rate	·	time	
First part of trip	300 − 80, or 220		x		$\dfrac{220}{x}$	← distance ← rate
Heavy rainfall part of trip	80		$x - 15$		$\dfrac{80}{\text{___}}$	← distance ← rate

2. TRANSLATE into an equation. (Fill in the blanks below.)

Time during first part of trip	plus	Time during heavy rainfall	equals	6 hr
↓	↓	↓	↓	↓
___	+	___	=	6

Finish with:

3. SOLVE and **4.** INTERPRET

61. A jogger ran 3 miles, decreased her speed by 1 mile per hour, and then ran another 4 miles. If her total time jogging was $1\dfrac{3}{5}$ hours, find her speed for each part of her run.

62. Mark Keaton's workout consists of jogging for 3 miles and then riding his bike for 5 miles at a speed 4 miles per hour faster than he jogs. If his total workout time is 1 hour, find his jogging speed and his biking speed.

63. A Chinese restaurant in Mandeville, Louisiana, has a large goldfish pond around the restaurant. Suppose that an inlet pipe and a hose together can fill the pond in 8 hours. The inlet pipe alone can complete the job in one hour less time than the hose alone. Find the time that the hose can complete the job alone and the time that the inlet pipe can complete the job alone. Round each to the nearest tenth of an hour.

64. A water tank on a farm in Flatonia, Texas, can be filled with a large inlet pipe and a small inlet pipe in 3 hours. The large inlet pipe alone can fill the tank in 2 hours less time than the small inlet pipe alone. Find the time to the nearest tenth of an hour each pipe can fill the tank alone.

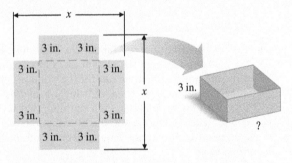

65. Bill Shaughnessy and his son Billy can clean the house together in 4 hours. When the son works alone, it takes him an hour longer to clean than it takes his dad alone. Find how long to the nearest tenth of an hour it takes the son to clean alone.

66. Together, Noodles and Freckles eat a 50-pound bag of dog food in 30 days. Noodles by himself eats a 50-pound bag in 2 weeks less time than Freckles does by himself. How many days to the nearest whole day would a 50-pound bag of dog food last Freckles?

67. The product of a number and 4 less than the number is 96. Find the number.

68. A whole number increased by its square is two more than twice itself. Find the number.

△ **69.** Suppose that an open box is to be made from a square sheet of cardboard by cutting out squares from each corner as shown and then folding along the dotted lines. If the box is to have a volume of 300 cubic inches, find the original dimensions of the sheet of cardboard.

a. The ? in the drawing above will be the length (and the width) of the box as shown. Represent this length in terms of x.

b. Use the formula for volume of a box, $V = l \cdot w \cdot h$, to write an equation in x.

c. Solve the equation for x and give the dimensions of the sheet of cardboard. Check your solution.

△ **70.** Suppose that an open box is to be made from a square sheet of cardboard by cutting out squares from each corner as shown and then folding along the dotted lines. If the box is to have a volume of 128 cubic inches, find the original dimensions of the sheet of cardboard.

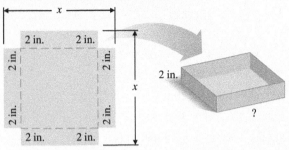

a. The ? in the drawing above will be the length (and the width) of the box as shown. Represent this length in terms of x.

b. Use the formula for volume of a box, $V = l \cdot w \cdot h$, to write an equation in x.

c. Solve the equation for x and give the dimensions of the sheet of cardboard. Check your solution.

△ **71.** A sprinkler that sprays water in a circular pattern is to be used to water a square garden. If the area of the garden is 920 square feet, find the smallest whole number *radius* that the sprinkler can be adjusted to so that the entire garden is watered.

△ **72.** Suppose that a square field has an area of 6270 square feet. See Exercise 71 and find a new sprinkler radius.

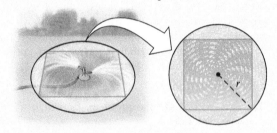

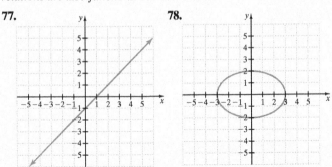

REVIEW AND PREVIEW

Solve each inequality. See Section 2.8.

73. $\dfrac{5x}{3} + 2 \le 7$

74. $\dfrac{2x}{3} + \dfrac{1}{6} \ge 2$

75. $\dfrac{y-1}{15} > -\dfrac{2}{5}$

76. $\dfrac{z-2}{12} < \dfrac{1}{4}$

Find the domain and range of each graphed relation. Decide which relations are also functions. See Section 3.6.

77.

78.

79.

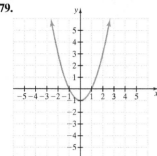

80.

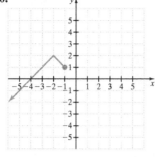

86. $y^3 - 216 = 0$

87. Write a polynomial equation that has three solutions: 2, 5, and -7.

88. Write a polynomial equation that has three solutions: 0, $2i$, and $-2i$.

89. During the seventh stage of the 2010 Paris–Nice bicycle race, Thomas Voeckler posted the fastest average speed, but Alberto Contador won the race. The seventh stage was 119 kilometers long. Voeckler's average speed was 0.0034 meters per second faster than Contador's. Traveling at these average speeds, Contador took 3 seconds longer than Voeckler to complete the race stage. (*Source:* Based on data from cyclingnews.com)

  a. Find Thomas Voeckler's average speed during the seventh stage of the 2010 Paris–Nice cycle race. Round to three decimal places.

  b. Find Alberto Contador's average speed during the seventh stage of the 2010 Paris–Nice cycle race. Round to three decimal places.

  c. Convert Voeckler's average speed to miles per hour. Round to three decimal places.

CONCEPT EXTENSIONS

Solve.

81. $5y^3 + 45y - 5y^2 - 45 = 0$

82. $10x^3 + 10x - 30x^2 - 30 = 0$

83. $3x^{-2} - 3x^{-1} - 18 = 0$

84. $2y^{-2} - 16y^{-1} + 14 = 0$

85. $2x^3 = -54$

 90. Use a graphing calculator to solve Exercise 29. Compare the solution with the solution from Exercise 29. Explain any differences.

Integrated Review SUMMARY ON SOLVING QUADRATIC EQUATIONS

Sections 11.1–11.3

Use the square root property to solve each equation.

1. $x^2 - 10 = 0$

2. $x^2 - 14 = 0$

3. $(x - 1)^2 = 8$

4. $(x + 5)^2 = 12$

Solve each equation by completing the square.

5. $x^2 + 2x - 12 = 0$

6. $x^2 - 12x + 11 = 0$

7. $3x^2 + 3x = 5$

8. $16y^2 + 16y = 1$

Use the quadratic formula to solve each equation

9. $2x^2 - 4x + 1 = 0$

10. $\dfrac{1}{2}x^2 + 3x + 2 = 0$

11. $x^2 + 4x = -7$

12. $x^2 + x = -3$

Solve each equation. Use a method of your choice.

13. $x^2 + 3x + 6 = 0$

14. $2x^2 + 18 = 0$

15. $x^2 + 17x = 0$

16. $4x^2 - 2x - 3 = 0$

17. $(x - 2)^2 = 27$

18. $\dfrac{1}{2}x^2 - 2x + \dfrac{1}{2} = 0$

19. $3x^2 + 2x = 8$

20. $2x^2 = -5x - 1$

21. $x(x - 2) = 5$

22. $x^2 - 31 = 0$

23. $5x^2 - 55 = 0$

24. $5x^2 + 55 = 0$

25. $x(x + 5) = 66$

26. $5x^2 + 6x - 2 = 0$

27. $2x^2 + 3x = 1$

28. $x - \sqrt{13 - 3x} - 3 = 0$

29. $\dfrac{5x}{x - 2} - \dfrac{x + 1}{x} = \dfrac{3}{x(x - 2)}$

△ **30.** The diagonal of a square room measures 20 feet. Find the exact length of a side of the room. Then approximate the length to the nearest tenth of a foot.

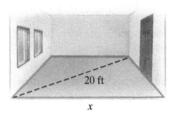

31. Together, Jack and Lucy Hoag can prepare a crawfish boil for a large party in 4 hours. Lucy alone can complete the job in 2 hours less time than Jack alone. Find the time that each person can prepare the crawfish boil alone. Round each time to the nearest tenth of an hour.

32. Diane Gray exercises at Total Body Gym. On the treadmill, she runs 5 miles, then increases her speed by 1 mile per hour and runs an additional 2 miles. If her total time on the treadmill is $1\frac{1}{3}$ hours, find her speed during each part of her run.

11.4 | Nonlinear Inequalities in One Variable

OBJECTIVES

1 Solve Polynomial Inequalities of Degree 2 or Greater.

2 Solve Inequalities That Contain Rational Expressions with Variables in the Denominator.

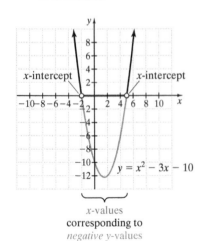

x-values corresponding to *negative y*-values

OBJECTIVE

1 Solving Polynomial Inequalities

Just as we can solve linear inequalities in one variable, so can we also solve quadratic inequalities in one variable. A **quadratic inequality** is an inequality that can be written so that one side is a quadratic expression and the other side is 0. Here are examples of quadratic inequalities in one variable. Each is written in **standard form.**

$$x^2 - 10x + 7 \le 0 \qquad 3x^2 + 2x - 6 > 0$$
$$2x^2 + 9x - 2 < 0 \qquad x^2 - 3x + 11 \ge 0$$

A solution of a quadratic inequality in one variable is a value of the variable that makes the inequality a true statement.

The value of an expression such as $x^2 - 3x - 10$ will sometimes be positive, sometimes negative, and sometimes 0, depending on the value substituted for x. To solve the inequality $x^2 - 3x - 10 < 0$, we are looking for all values of x that make the expression $x^2 - 3x - 10$ *less than 0*, or *negative.* To understand how we find these values, we'll study the graph of the quadratic function $y = x^2 - 3x - 10$.

Notice that the x-values for which y is positive are separated from the x-values for which y is negative by the x-intercepts. (Recall that the x-intercepts correspond to values of x for which $y = 0$.) Thus, the solution set of $x^2 - 3x - 10 < 0$ consists of all real numbers from -2 to 5 or, in interval notation, $(-2, 5)$.

It is not necessary to graph $y = x^2 - 3x - 10$ to solve the related inequality $x^2 - 3x - 10 < 0$. Instead, we can draw a number line representing the x-axis and keep the following in mind: *A region on the number line for which the value of $x^2 - 3x - 10$ is positive is separated from a region on the number line for which the value of $x^2 - 3x - 10$ is negative by a value for which the expression is* 0.

Let's find these values for which the expression is 0 by solving the related equation:

$$x^2 - 3x - 10 = 0$$
$$(x - 5)(x + 2) = 0 \qquad \text{Factor.}$$
$$x - 5 = 0 \quad \text{or} \quad x + 2 = 0 \qquad \text{Set each factor equal to 0.}$$
$$x = 5 \qquad\qquad x = -2 \qquad \text{Solve.}$$

These two numbers, -2 and 5, divide the number line into three regions. We will call the regions A, B, and C. These regions are important because, if the value of $x^2 - 3x - 10$ is negative when a number from a region is substituted for x, then $x^2 - 3x - 10$ is negative when any number in that region is substituted for x. The same is true if the value of $x^2 - 3x - 10$ is positive for a particular value of x in a region.

To see whether the inequality $x^2 - 3x - 10 < 0$ is true or false in each region, we choose a test point from each region and substitute its value for x in the inequality $x^2 - 3x - 10 < 0$. If the resulting inequality is true, the region containing the test point is a solution region.

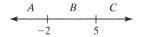

Region	Test Point Value	$(x - 5)(x + 2) < 0$	Result
A	-3	$(-8)(-1) < 0$	False
B	0	$(-5)(2) < 0$	True
C	6	$(1)(8) < 0$	False

The values in region B satisfy the inequality. The numbers -2 and 5 are not included in the solution set since the inequality symbol is $<$. The solution set is $(-2, 5)$, and its graph is shown.

$$
\begin{array}{ccc}
A & B & C \\
\end{array}
$$
F -2 T 5 F

EXAMPLE 1   Solve: $(x + 3)(x - 3) > 0$.

Solution   First we solve the related equation, $(x + 3)(x - 3) = 0$.

$$(x + 3)(x - 3) = 0$$
$$x + 3 = 0 \quad \text{or} \quad x - 3 = 0$$
$$x = -3 \qquad\qquad x = 3$$

The two numbers -3 and 3 separate the number line into three regions, A, B, and C.

$$
\begin{array}{ccc}
A & B & C \\
-3 & & 3
\end{array}
$$

Now we substitute the value of a test point from each region. If the test value satisfies the inequality, every value in the region containing the test value is a solution.

Region	Test Point Value	$(x + 3)(x - 3) > 0$	Result
A	-4	$(-1)(-7) > 0$	True
B	0	$(3)(-3) > 0$	False
C	4	$(7)(1) > 0$	True

The points in regions A and C satisfy the inequality. The numbers -3 and 3 are not included in the solution since the inequality symbol is $>$. The solution set is $(-\infty, -3) \cup (3, \infty)$, and its graph is shown.

$$
\begin{array}{ccc}
A & B & C \\
\end{array}
$$
T -3 F 3 T

PRACTICE

1   Solve: $(x - 4)(x + 3) > 0$.

The following steps may be used to solve a polynomial inequality.

Solving a Polynomial Inequality

Step 1. Write the inequality in standard form and then solve the related equation.

Step 2. Separate the number line into regions with the solutions from Step 1.

Step 3. For each region, choose a test point and determine whether its value satisfies the *original inequality*.

Step 4. The solution set includes the regions whose test point value is a solution. If the inequality symbol is $\leq$ or $\geq$, the values from Step 1 are solutions; if $<$ or $>$, they are not.

✓CONCEPT CHECK

When choosing a test point in Step 3, why would the solutions from Step 1 not make good choices for test points?

EXAMPLE 2 Solve: $x^2 - 4x \leq 0$.

Solution   First we solve the related equation, $x^2 - 4x = 0$.

$$x^2 - 4x = 0$$
$$x(x - 4) = 0$$
$$x = 0 \quad \text{or} \quad x = 4$$

The numbers 0 and 4 separate the number line into three regions, A, B, and C.

We check a test value in each region in the original inequality. Values in region B satisfy the inequality. The numbers 0 and 4 are included in the solution since the inequality symbol is $\leq$. The solution set is $[0, 4]$, and its graph is shown.

PRACTICE
2   Solve: $x^2 - 8x \leq 0$.

EXAMPLE 3 Solve: $(x + 2)(x - 1)(x - 5) \leq 0$.

Solution   First we solve $(x + 2)(x - 1)(x - 5) = 0$. By inspection, we see that the solutions are $-2, 1$, and 5. They separate the number line into four regions, A, B, C, and D. Next we check test points from each region.

Region	Test Point Value	$(x + 2)(x - 1)(x - 5) \leq 0$	Result
A	-3	$(-1)(-4)(-8) \leq 0$	True
B	0	$(2)(-1)(-5) \leq 0$	False
C	2	$(4)(1)(-3) \leq 0$	True
D	6	$(8)(5)(1) \leq 0$	False

Answer to Concept Check:
The solutions found in Step 1 have a value of 0 in the original inequality.

The solution set is $(-\infty, -2] \cup [1, 5]$, and its graph is shown. We include the numbers -2, 1, and 5 because the inequality symbol is $\leq$.

$$
\begin{array}{ccccccc}
& A & & B & C & & D \\
\hline
\text{T} & -2 & \text{F} & 1 & \text{T} & 5 & \text{F}
\end{array}
$$

PRACTICE
3   Solve: $(x + 3)(x - 2)(x + 1) \leq 0$.

OBJECTIVE
2   **Solving Rational Inequalities**

Inequalities containing rational expressions with variables in the denominator are solved by using a similar procedure.

EXAMPLE 4   Solve: $\dfrac{x + 2}{x - 3} \leq 0$.

Solution   First we find all values that make the denominator equal to 0. To do this, we solve $x - 3 = 0$ and find that $x = 3$.

Next, we solve the related equation $\dfrac{x + 2}{x - 3} = 0$.

$$\frac{x + 2}{x - 3} = 0$$

$$x + 2 = 0 \qquad \text{Multiply both sides by the LCD, } x - 3.$$

$$x = -2$$

Now we place these numbers on a number line and proceed as before, checking test point values in the original inequality.

$$
\begin{array}{ccc}
A & B & C \\
\hline
& -2 & 3
\end{array}
$$

Choose -3 from region A.

$$\frac{x + 2}{x - 3} \leq 0$$

$$\frac{-3 + 2}{-3 - 3} \leq 0$$

$$\frac{-1}{-6} \leq 0$$

$$\frac{1}{6} \leq 0 \quad \text{False}$$

Choose 0 from region B.

$$\frac{x + 2}{x - 3} \leq 0$$

$$\frac{0 + 2}{0 - 3} \leq 0$$

$$-\frac{2}{3} \leq 0 \quad \text{True}$$

Choose 4 from region C.

$$\frac{x + 2}{x - 3} \leq 0$$

$$\frac{4 + 2}{4 - 3} \leq 0$$

$$6 \leq 0 \quad \text{False}$$

The solution set is $[-2, 3)$. This interval includes -2 because -2 satisfies the original inequality. This interval does not include 3 because 3 would make the denominator 0.

$$
\begin{array}{ccc}
A & B & C \\
\hline
\text{F} \; -2 & \text{T} & 3 \; \text{F}
\end{array}
$$

PRACTICE
4   Solve: $\dfrac{x - 5}{x + 4} \leq 0$.

The following steps may be used to solve a rational inequality with variables in the denominator.

> **Solving a Rational Inequality**
>
> **Step 1.** Solve for values that make all denominators 0.
>
> **Step 2.** Solve the related equation.
>
> **Step 3.** Separate the number line into regions with the solutions from Steps 1 and 2.
>
> **Step 4.** For each region, choose a test point and determine whether its value satisfies the *original inequality*.
>
> **Step 5.** The solution set includes the regions whose test point value is a solution. Check whether to include values from Step 2. Be sure *not* to include values that make any denominator 0.

EXAMPLE 5 Solve: $\dfrac{5}{x+1} < -2$.

Solution First we find values for x that make the denominator equal to 0.

$$x + 1 = 0$$
$$x = -1$$

Next we solve $\dfrac{5}{x+1} = -2$.

$$(x+1) \cdot \dfrac{5}{x+1} = (x+1) \cdot -2 \quad \text{Multiply both sides by the LCD, } x + 1.$$
$$5 = -2x - 2 \qquad \text{Simplify.}$$
$$7 = -2x$$
$$-\dfrac{7}{2} = x$$

We use these two solutions to divide a number line into three regions and choose test points. Only a test point value from region B satisfies the *original inequality*. The solution set is $\left(-\dfrac{7}{2}, -1\right)$, and its graph is shown.

PRACTICE
5 Solve: $\dfrac{7}{x+3} < 5$.

Vocabulary, Readiness & Video Check

Write the graphed solution set in interval notation.

1.
   _____

2.
   _____

3.

4.
   _____

5.

6.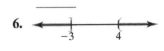
   _____

Martin-Gay Interactive Videos

See Video 11.4

Watch the section lecture video and answer the following questions.

OBJECTIVE
1

7. From ▭ Examples 1–3, how does solving a related equation help you solve a polynomial inequality? Are the solutions to the related equation ever solutions to the inequality?

OBJECTIVE
2

8. In ▭ Example 4, one of the values that separates the number line into regions is 4. The inequality is ≥, so why isn't 4 included in the solution set?

11.4 Exercise Set

MyMathLab®

Solve each polynomial inequality. Write the solution set in interval notation. See Examples 1 through 3.

1. $(x + 1)(x + 5) > 0$

2. $(x + 1)(x + 5) \leq 0$

▶ **3.** $(x - 3)(x + 4) \leq 0$

4. $(x + 4)(x - 1) > 0$

5. $x^2 - 7x + 10 \leq 0$

6. $x^2 + 8x + 15 \geq 0$

7. $3x^2 + 16x < -5$

8. $2x^2 - 5x < 7$

9. $(x - 6)(x - 4)(x - 2) > 0$

10. $(x - 6)(x - 4)(x - 2) \leq 0$

11. $x(x - 1)(x + 4) \leq 0$

12. $x(x - 6)(x + 2) > 0$

13. $(x^2 - 9)(x^2 - 4) > 0$

14. $(x^2 - 16)(x^2 - 1) \leq 0$

Solve each inequality. Write the solution set in interval notation. See Example 4.

15. $\dfrac{x + 7}{x - 2} < 0$

16. $\dfrac{x - 5}{x - 6} > 0$

17. $\dfrac{5}{x + 1} > 0$

18. $\dfrac{3}{y - 5} < 0$

▶ **19.** $\dfrac{x + 1}{x - 4} \geq 0$

20. $\dfrac{x + 1}{x - 4} \leq 0$

Solve each inequality. Write the solution set in interval notation. See Example 5.

21. $\dfrac{3}{x - 2} < 4$

22. $\dfrac{-2}{y + 3} > 2$

23. $\dfrac{x^2 + 6}{5x} \geq 1$

24. $\dfrac{y^2 + 15}{8y} \leq 1$

25. $\dfrac{x + 2}{x - 3} < 1$

26. $\dfrac{x - 1}{x + 4} > 2$

MIXED PRACTICE

Solve each inequality. Write the solution set in interval notation.

27. $(2x - 3)(4x + 5) \leq 0$

28. $(6x + 7)(7x - 12) > 0$

▶ **29.** $x^2 > x$

30. $x^2 < 25$

31. $(2x - 8)(x + 4)(x - 6) \leq 0$

32. $(3x - 12)(x + 5)(2x - 3) \geq 0$

33. $6x^2 - 5x \geq 6$

34. $12x^2 + 11x \leq 15$

35. $4x^3 + 16x^2 - 9x - 36 > 0$

36. $x^3 + 2x^2 - 4x - 8 < 0$

▶ **37.** $x^4 - 26x^2 + 25 \geq 0$

38. $16x^4 - 40x^2 + 9 \leq 0$

39. $(2x - 7)(3x + 5) > 0$

40. $(4x - 9)(2x + 5) < 0$

41. $\dfrac{x}{x - 10} < 0$

42. $\dfrac{x + 10}{x - 10} > 0$

43. $\dfrac{x - 5}{x + 4} \geq 0$

44. $\dfrac{x - 3}{x + 2} \leq 0$

45. $\dfrac{x(x + 6)}{(x - 7)(x + 1)} \geq 0$

46. $\dfrac{(x - 2)(x + 2)}{(x + 1)(x - 4)} \leq 0$

47. $\dfrac{-1}{x - 1} > -1$

48. $\dfrac{4}{y + 2} < -2$

49. $\dfrac{x}{x + 4} \leq 2$

50. $\dfrac{4x}{x - 3} \geq 5$

51. $\dfrac{z}{z - 5} \geq 2z$

52. $\dfrac{p}{p + 4} \leq 3p$

53. $\dfrac{(x + 1)^2}{5x} > 0$

54. $\dfrac{(2x - 3)^2}{x} < 0$

REVIEW AND PREVIEW

Recall that the graph of $f(x) + K$ is the same as the graph of $f(x)$ shifted K units upward if $K > 0$ and $|K|$ units downward if $K < 0$. Use the graph of $f(x) = |x|$ below to sketch the graph of each function. See Section 8.3.

55. $g(x) = |x| + 2$

56. $H(x) = |x| - 2$

57. $f(x) = |x| - 1$

58. $h(x) = |x| + 5$

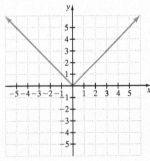

Use the graph of $f(x) = x^2$ below to sketch the graph of each function.

59. $F(x) = x^2 - 3$

60. $h(x) = x^2 - 4$

61. $H(x) = x^2 + 1$

62. $g(x) = x^2 + 3$

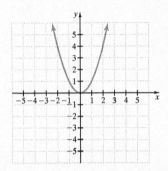

CONCEPT EXTENSIONS

63. Explain why $\dfrac{x + 2}{x - 3} > 0$ and $(x + 2)(x - 3) > 0$ have the same solutions.

64. Explain why $\dfrac{x + 2}{x - 3} \geq 0$ and $(x + 2)(x - 3) \geq 0$ do not have the same solutions.

Find all numbers that satisfy each of the following.

65. A number minus its reciprocal is less than zero. Find the numbers.

66. Twice a number added to its reciprocal is nonnegative. Find the numbers.

67. The total profit function $P(x)$ for a company producing x thousand units is given by

$$P(x) = -2x^2 + 26x - 44$$

Find the values of x for which the company makes a profit. [*Hint:* The company makes a profit when $P(x) > 0$.]

68. A projectile is fired straight up from the ground with an initial velocity of 80 feet per second. Its height $s(t)$ in feet at any time t is given by the function

$$s(t) = -16t^2 + 80t$$

Find the interval of time for which the height of the projectile is greater than 96 feet.

Use a graphing calculator to check each exercise.

69. Exercise 37

70. Exercise 38

71. Exercise 39

72. Exercise 40

11.5 Quadratic Functions and Their Graphs

OBJECTIVES

1 Graph Quadratic Functions of the Form $f(x) = x^2 + k$.

2 Graph Quadratic Functions of the Form $f(x) = (x - h)^2$.

3 Graph Quadratic Functions of the Form $f(x) = (x - h)^2 + k$.

4 Graph Quadratic Functions of the Form $f(x) = ax^2$.

5 Graph Quadratic Functions of the Form $f(x) = a(x - h)^2 + k$.

OBJECTIVE

1 Graphing $f(x) = x^2 + k$

We first graphed the quadratic equation $y = x^2$ in Section 8.2. In Sections 8.2 and 8.3, we learned that this graph defines a function, and we wrote $y = x^2$ as $f(x) = x^2$. In these sections, we discovered that the graph of a quadratic function is a parabola opening upward or downward. In this section, we continue our study of quadratic functions and their graphs. (Much of the contents of this section is a review of shifting and reflecting techniques from Section 8.3, but specific to quadratic functions.)

First, let's recall the definition of a quadratic function.

Quadratic Function

A quadratic function is a function that can be written in the form $f(x) = ax^2 + bx + c$, where a, b, and c are real numbers and $a \neq 0$.

Notice that equations of the form $y = ax^2 + bx + c$, where $a \neq 0$, define quadratic functions, since y is a function of x or $y = f(x)$.

Recall that if $a > 0$, the parabola opens upward and if $a < 0$, the parabola opens downward. Also, the vertex of a parabola is the lowest point if the parabola opens upward and the highest point if the parabola opens downward. The axis of symmetry is the vertical line that passes through the vertex.

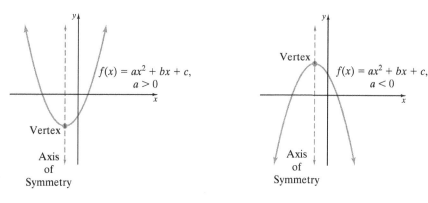

EXAMPLE 1 Graph $f(x) = x^2$ and $g(x) = x^2 + 6$ on the same set of axes.

Solution First we construct a table of values for $f(x)$ and plot the points. Notice that for each x-value, the corresponding value of $g(x)$ must be 6 more than the corresponding value of $f(x)$ since $f(x) = x^2$ and $g(x) = x^2 + 6$. In other words, the graph of $g(x) = x^2 + 6$ is the same as the graph of $f(x) = x^2$ shifted upward 6 units. The axis of symmetry for both graphs is the y-axis.

x	$f(x) = x^2$	$g(x) = x^2 + 6$
-2	4	10
-1	1	7
0	0	6
1	1	7
2	4	10

Each y-value is increased by 6.

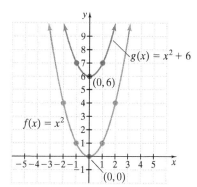

PRACTICE

1 Graph $f(x) = x^2$ and $g(x) = x^2 - 4$ on the same set of axes.

In general, we have the following properties.

Graphing the Parabola Defined by $f(x) = x^2 + k$

If k is positive, the graph of $f(x) = x^2 + k$ is the graph of $y = x^2$ shifted upward k units.

If k is negative, the graph of $f(x) = x^2 + k$ is the graph of $y = x^2$ shifted downward $|k|$ units.

The vertex is $(0, k)$, and the axis of symmetry is the y-axis.

EXAMPLE 2   Graph each function.

a. $F(x) = x^2 + 2$ **b.** $g(x) = x^2 - 3$

Solution

a. $F(x) = x^2 + 2$

The graph of $F(x) = x^2 + 2$ is obtained by shifting the graph of $y = x^2$ upward 2 units.

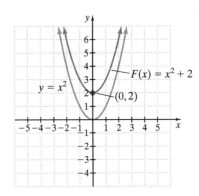

b. $g(x) = x^2 - 3$

The graph of $g(x) = x^2 - 3$ is obtained by shifting the graph of $y = x^2$ downward 3 units.

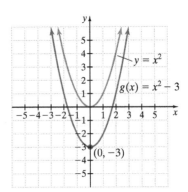

PRACTICE

2   Graph each function.

a. $f(x) = x^2 - 5$ **b.** $g(x) = x^2 + 3$

....

OBJECTIVE

2   **Graphing $f(x) = (x - h)^2$** ▶

Now we will graph functions of the form $f(x) = (x - h)^2$.

EXAMPLE 3   Graph $f(x) = x^2$ and $g(x) = (x - 2)^2$ on the same set of axes.

Solution   By plotting points, we see that for each x-value, the corresponding value of $g(x)$ is the same as the value of $f(x)$ when the x-value is increased by 2. Thus, the graph of $g(x) = (x - 2)^2$ is the graph of $f(x) = x^2$ shifted to the right 2 units. The axis of symmetry for the graph of $g(x) = (x - 2)^2$ is also shifted 2 units to the right and is the line $x = 2$.

x	$f(x) = x^2$	x	$g(x) = (x - 2)^2$
-2	4	0	4
-1	1	1	1
0	0	2	0
1	1	3	1
2	4	4	4

Each x-value increased by 2 corresponds to same y-value.

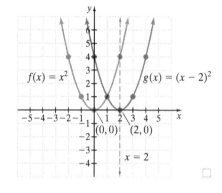

PRACTICE

3   Graph $f(x) = x^2$ and $g(x) = (x + 6)^2$ on the same set of axes.

In general, we have the following properties.

Graphing the Parabola Defined by $f(x) = (x - h)^2$

If h is positive, the graph of $f(x) = (x - h)^2$ is the graph of $y = x^2$ shifted to the right h units.
If h is negative, the graph of $f(x) = (x - h)^2$ is the graph of $y = x^2$ shifted to the left $|h|$ units.
The vertex is $(h, 0)$, and the axis of symmetry is the vertical line $x = h$.

EXAMPLE 4   Graph each function.

a. $G(x) = (x - 3)^2$ **b.** $F(x) = (x + 1)^2$

Solution

a. The graph of $G(x) = (x - 3)^2$ is obtained by shifting the graph of $y = x^2$ to the right 3 units. The graph of $G(x)$ is below on the left.

b. The equation $F(x) = (x + 1)^2$ can be written as $F(x) = [x - (-1)]^2$. The graph of $F(x) = [x - (-1)]^2$ is obtained by shifting the graph of $y = x^2$ to the left 1 unit. The graph of $F(x)$ is below on the right.

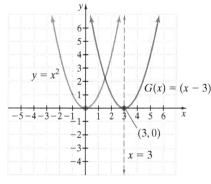
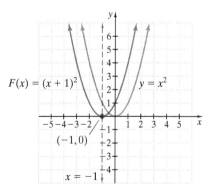

(Continued on next page)

PRACTICE
4   Graph each function.

a. $G(x) = (x + 4)^2$ **b.** $H(x) = (x - 7)^2$

OBJECTIVE

3   Graphing $f(x) = (x - h)^2 + k$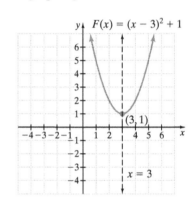

As we will see in graphing functions of the form $f(x) = (x - h)^2 + k$, it is possible to combine vertical and horizontal shifts.

> **Graphing the Parabola Defined by $f(x) = (x - h)^2 + k$**
>
> The parabola has the same shape as $y = x^2$.
> The vertex is (h, k), and the axis of symmetry is the vertical line $x = h$.

EXAMPLE 5   Graph $F(x) = (x - 3)^2 + 1$.

Solution   The graph of $F(x) = (x - 3)^2 + 1$ is the graph of $y = x^2$ shifted 3 units to the right and 1 unit up. The vertex is then $(3, 1)$, and the axis of symmetry is $x = 3$. A few ordered pair solutions are plotted to aid in graphing.

x	$F(x) = (x - 3)^2 + 1$
1	5
2	2
4	2
5	5

PRACTICE
5   Graph $f(x) = (x + 2)^2 + 2$.

OBJECTIVE

4   Graphing $f(x) = ax^2$

Next, we discover the change in the shape of the graph when the coefficient of x^2 is not 1.

EXAMPLE 6   Graph $f(x) = x^2$, $g(x) = 3x^2$, and $h(x) = \frac{1}{2}x^2$ on the same set of axes.

Solution   Comparing the tables of values, we see that for each x-value, the corresponding value of $g(x)$ is triple the corresponding value of $f(x)$. Similarly, the value of $h(x)$ is half the value of $f(x)$.

x	$f(x) = x^2$
-2	4
-1	1
0	0
1	1
2	4

x	$g(x) = 3x^2$
-2	12
-1	3
0	0
1	3
2	12

x	$h(x) = \frac{1}{2}x^2$
-2	2
-1	$\frac{1}{2}$
0	0
1	$\frac{1}{2}$
2	2

The result is that the graph of $g(x) = 3x^2$ is narrower than the graph of $f(x) = x^2$, and the graph of $h(x) = \dfrac{1}{2}x^2$ is wider. The vertex for each graph is $(0, 0)$, and the axis of symmetry is the y-axis.

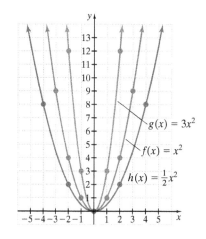

PRACTICE

6   Graph $f(x) = x^2$, $g(x) = 4x^2$, and $h(x) = \dfrac{1}{4}x^2$ on the same set of axes.

Graphing the Parabola Defined by $f(x) = ax^2$

If a is positive, the parabola opens upward, and if a is negative, the parabola opens downward.

If $|a| > 1$, the graph of the parabola is narrower than the graph of $y = x^2$.

If $|a| < 1$, the graph of the parabola is wider than the graph of $y = x^2$.

EXAMPLE 7   Graph $f(x) = -2x^2$.

Solution   Because $a = -2$, a negative value, this parabola opens downward. Since $|-2| = 2$ and $2 > 1$, the parabola is narrower than the graph of $y = x^2$. The vertex is $(0, 0)$, and the axis of symmetry is the y-axis. We verify this by plotting a few points.

x	$f(x) = -2x^2$
-2	-8
-1	-2
0	0
1	-2
2	-8

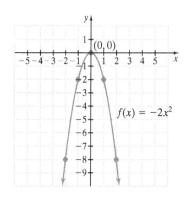

PRACTICE

7   Graph $f(x) = -\dfrac{1}{2}x^2$.

OBJECTIVE

5   **Graphing $f(x) = a(x - h)^2 + k$**

Now we will see the shape of the graph of a quadratic function of the form $f(x) = a(x - h)^2 + k$.

EXAMPLE 8 Graph $g(x) = \frac{1}{2}(x + 2)^2 + 5$. Find the vertex and the axis of symmetry.

Solution The function $g(x) = \frac{1}{2}(x + 2)^2 + 5$ may be written as $g(x) = \frac{1}{2}[x - (-2)]^2 + 5$. Thus, this graph is the same as the graph of $y = x^2$ shifted 2 units to the left and 5 units up, and it is wider because a is $\frac{1}{2}$. The vertex is $(-2, 5)$, and the axis of symmetry is $x = -2$. We plot a few points to verify.

x	$g(x) = \frac{1}{2}(x + 2)^2 + 5$
-4	7
-3	$5\frac{1}{2}$
-2	5
-1	$5\frac{1}{2}$
0	7

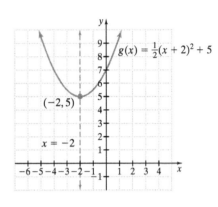

PRACTICE

8 Graph $h(x) = \frac{1}{3}(x - 4)^2 - 3$.

In general, the following holds.

Graph of a Quadratic Function

The graph of a quadratic function written in the form $f(x) = a(x - h)^2 + k$ is a parabola with vertex (h, k).

If $a > 0$, the parabola opens upward.
If $a < 0$, the parabola opens downward.

The axis of symmetry is the line whose equation is $x = h$.

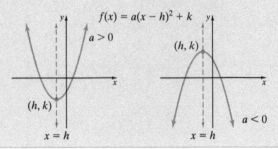

✓CONCEPT CHECK

Which description of the graph of $f(x) = -0.35(x + 3)^2 - 4$ is correct?
a. The graph opens downward and has its vertex at $(-3, 4)$.
b. The graph opens upward and has its vertex at $(-3, 4)$.
c. The graph opens downward and has its vertex at $(-3, -4)$.
d. The graph is narrower than the graph of $y = x^2$.

Answer to Concept Check: c

Graphing Calculator Explorations

Use a graphing calculator to graph the first function of each pair that follows. Then use its graph to predict the graph of the second function. Check your prediction by graphing both on the same set of axes.

1. $F(x) = \sqrt{x}$; $G(x) = \sqrt{x} + 1$

2. $g(x) = x^3$; $H(x) = x^3 - 2$

3. $H(x) = |x|$; $f(x) = |x - 5|$

4. $h(x) = x^3 + 2$; $g(x) = (x - 3)^3 + 2$

5. $f(x) = |x + 4|$; $F(x) = |x + 4| + 3$

6. $G(x) = \sqrt{x} - 2$; $g(x) = \sqrt{x - 4} - 2$

Vocabulary, Readiness & Video Check

Use the choices below to fill in each blank. Some choices will be used more than once.

upward   highest   parabola   downward   lowest   quadratic

1. A(n) _____ function is one that can be written in the form $f(x) = ax^2 + bx + c, a \neq 0$.

2. The graph of a quadratic function is a(n) _____ opening _____ or _____.

3. If $a > 0$, the graph of the quadratic function opens _____.

4. If $a < 0$, the graph of the quadratic function opens _____.

5. The vertex of a parabola is the _____ point if $a > 0$.

6. The vertex of a parabola is the _____ point if $a < 0$.

State the vertex of the graph of each quadratic function.

7. $f(x) = x^2$

8. $f(x) = -5x^2$

9. $g(x) = (x - 2)^2$

10. $g(x) = (x + 5)^2$

11. $f(x) = 2x^2 + 3$

12. $h(x) = x^2 - 1$

13. $g(x) = (x + 1)^2 + 5$

14. $h(x) = (x - 10)^2 - 7$

Martin-Gay Interactive Videos

See Video 11.5

Watch the section lecture video and answer the following questions.

OBJECTIVE
1

15. From ▣ Examples 1 and 2 and the lecture before, how do graphs of the form $f(x) = x^2 + k$ differ from $y = x^2$? Consider the location of the vertex $(0, k)$ on these graphs of the form $f(x) = x^2 + k$—by what other name do we call this point on a graph?

OBJECTIVE
2

16. From ▣ Example 3 and the lecture before, how do graphs of the form $f(x) = (x - h)^2$ differ from $y = x^2$? Consider the location of the vertex $(h, 0)$ on these graphs of the form $f(x) = (x - h)^2$—by what other name do we call this point on a graph?

OBJECTIVE
3

17. From ▣ Example 4 and the lecture before, what general information does the equation $f(x) = (x - h)^2 + k$ tell us about its graph?

OBJECTIVE
4

18. From the lecture before ▣ Example 5, besides the direction a parabola opens, what other graphing information can the value of a tell us?

OBJECTIVE
5

19. In ▣ Examples 6 and 7, what four properties of the graph did we learn from the equation that helped us locate and draw the general shape of the parabola?

11.5 Exercise Set MyMathLab®

MIXED PRACTICE

Sketch the graph of each quadratic function. Label the vertex and sketch and label the axis of symmetry. See Examples 1 through 5.

1. $f(x) = x^2 - 1$
2. $g(x) = x^2 + 3$
3. $h(x) = x^2 + 5$
4. $h(x) = x^2 - 4$
5. $g(x) = x^2 + 7$
6. $f(x) = x^2 - 2$
7. $f(x) = (x - 5)^2$
8. $g(x) = (x + 5)^2$
9. $h(x) = (x + 2)^2$
10. $H(x) = (x - 1)^2$
11. $G(x) = (x + 3)^2$
12. $f(x) = (x - 6)^2$
13. $f(x) = (x - 2)^2 + 5$
14. $g(x) = (x - 6)^2 + 1$
15. $h(x) = (x + 1)^2 + 4$
16. $G(x) = (x + 3)^2 + 3$
17. $g(x) = (x + 2)^2 - 5$
18. $h(x) = (x + 4)^2 - 6$

Sketch the graph of each quadratic function. Label the vertex, and sketch and label the axis of symmetry. See Examples 6 and 7.

19. $H(x) = 2x^2$
20. $f(x) = 5x^2$
21. $h(x) = \frac{1}{3}x^2$
22. $f(x) = -\frac{1}{4}x^2$
23. $g(x) = -x^2$
24. $g(x) = -3x^2$

Sketch the graph of each quadratic function. Label the vertex and sketch and label the axis of symmetry. See Example 8.

25. $f(x) = 2(x - 1)^2 + 3$
26. $g(x) = 4(x - 4)^2 + 2$
27. $h(x) = -3(x + 3)^2 + 1$
28. $f(x) = -(x - 2)^2 - 6$
29. $H(x) = \frac{1}{2}(x - 6)^2 - 3$
30. $G(x) = \frac{1}{5}(x + 4)^2 + 3$

MIXED PRACTICE

Sketch the graph of each quadratic function. Label the vertex and sketch and label the axis of symmetry.

31. $f(x) = -(x - 2)^2$
32. $g(x) = -(x + 6)^2$
33. $F(x) = -x^2 + 4$
34. $H(x) = -x^2 + 10$
35. $F(x) = 2x^2 - 5$
36. $g(x) = \frac{1}{2}x^2 - 2$
37. $h(x) = (x - 6)^2 + 4$
38. $f(x) = (x - 5)^2 + 2$
39. $F(x) = \left(x + \frac{1}{2}\right)^2 - 2$
40. $H(x) = \left(x + \frac{1}{2}\right)^2 - 3$
41. $F(x) = \frac{3}{2}(x + 7)^2 + 1$
42. $g(x) = -\frac{3}{2}(x - 1)^2 - 5$
43. $f(x) = \frac{1}{4}x^2 - 9$
44. $H(x) = \frac{3}{4}x^2 - 2$
45. $G(x) = 5\left(x + \frac{1}{2}\right)^2$
46. $F(x) = 3\left(x - \frac{3}{2}\right)^2$
47. $h(x) = -(x - 1)^2 - 1$
48. $f(x) = -3(x + 2)^2 + 2$
49. $g(x) = \sqrt{3}(x + 5)^2 + \frac{3}{4}$
50. $G(x) = \sqrt{5}(x - 7)^2 - \frac{1}{2}$

51. $h(x) = 10(x + 4)^2 - 6$
52. $h(x) = 8(x + 1)^2 + 9$
53. $f(x) = -2(x - 4)^2 + 5$
54. $G(x) = -4(x + 9)^2 - 1$

REVIEW AND PREVIEW

Add the proper constant to each binomial so that the resulting trinomial is a perfect square trinomial. See Section 11.1.

55. $x^2 + 8x$
56. $y^2 + 4y$
57. $z^2 - 16z$
58. $x^2 - 10x$
59. $y^2 + y$
60. $z^2 - 3z$

Solve by completing the square. See Section 11.1.

61. $x^2 + 4x = 12$
62. $y^2 + 6y = -5$
63. $z^2 + 10z - 1 = 0$
64. $x^2 + 14x + 20 = 0$
65. $z^2 - 8z = 2$
66. $y^2 - 10y = 3$

CONCEPT EXTENSIONS

Solve. See the Concept Check in this section.

67. Which description of $f(x) = -213(x - 0.1)^2 + 3.6$ is correct?

Graph Opens	Vertex
a. upward	$(0.1, 3.6)$
b. upward	$(-213, 3.6)$
c. downward	$(0.1, 3.6)$
d. downward	$(-0.1, 3.6)$

68. Which description of $f(x) = 5\left(x + \frac{1}{2}\right)^2 + \frac{1}{2}$ is correct?

Graph Opens	Vertex
a. upward	$\left(\frac{1}{2}, \frac{1}{2}\right)$
b. upward	$\left(-\frac{1}{2}, \frac{1}{2}\right)$
c. downward	$\left(\frac{1}{2}, -\frac{1}{2}\right)$
d. downward	$\left(-\frac{1}{2}, -\frac{1}{2}\right)$

Write the equation of the parabola that has the same shape as $f(x) = 5x^2$ but with the following vertex.

69. $(2, 3)$
70. $(1, 6)$
71. $(-3, 6)$
72. $(4, -1)$

The shifting properties covered in this section apply to the graphs of all functions. Given the graph of $y = f(x)$ below, sketch the graph of each of the following.

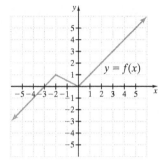

73. $y = f(x) + 1$

74. $y = f(x) - 2$

75. $y = f(x - 3)$

76. $y = f(x + 3)$

77. $y = f(x + 2) + 2$

78. $y = f(x - 1) + 1$

79. The quadratic function $f(x) = 2158x^2 - 10{,}339x + 6731$ approximates the number of text messages sent in the United States each month between 2000 and 2008, where x is the number of years past 2000 and $f(x)$ is the number of text messages sent in the U.S. each month in millions. (*Source:* cellsigns)

  a. Use this function to find the number of text messages sent in the U.S. each month in 2010.

  b. Use this function to predict the number of text messages sent in the U.S. each month in 2014.

80. Use the function in Exercise 79.

  a. Use this function to predict the number of text messages sent in the U.S. each month in 2018.

  b. Look up the current number of cell phone subscribers in the U.S.

  c. Based on your answers for parts **a.** and **b.**, discuss some possible limitations of using this quadratic function to predict data.

11.6 Further Graphing of Quadratic Functions

OBJECTIVES

1 Write Quadratic Functions in the Form $y = a(x - h)^2 + k$.

2 Derive a Formula for Finding the Vertex of a Parabola.

3 Find the Minimum or Maximum Value of a Quadratic Function.

OBJECTIVE

1 Writing Quadratic Functions in the Form $y = a(x - h)^2 + k$

We know that the graph of a quadratic function is a parabola. If a quadratic function is written in the form

$$f(x) = a(x - h)^2 + k$$

we can easily find the vertex (h, k) and graph the parabola. To write a quadratic function in this form, complete the square. (See Section 11.1 for a review of completing the square.)

EXAMPLE 1 Graph $f(x) = x^2 - 4x - 12$. Find the vertex and any intercepts.

Solution The graph of this quadratic function is a parabola. To find the vertex of the parabola, we will write the function in the form $y = (x - h)^2 + k$. To do this, we complete the square on the binomial $x^2 - 4x$. To simplify our work, we let $f(x) = y$.

$$y = x^2 - 4x - 12 \quad \text{Let } f(x) = y.$$
$$y + 12 = x^2 - 4x \quad \text{Add 12 to both sides to get the } x\text{-variable terms alone.}$$

Now we add the square of half of -4 to both sides.

$$\frac{1}{2}(-4) = -2 \quad \text{and} \quad (-2)^2 = 4$$

$$y + 12 + 4 = x^2 - 4x + 4 \quad \text{Add 4 to both sides.}$$
$$y + 16 = (x - 2)^2 \quad \text{Factor the trinomial.}$$
$$y = (x - 2)^2 - 16 \quad \text{Subtract 16 from both sides.}$$
$$f(x) = (x - 2)^2 - 16 \quad \text{Replace } y \text{ with } f(x).$$

From this equation, we can see that the vertex of the parabola is $(2, -16)$, a point in quadrant IV, and the axis of symmetry is the line $x = 2$.

Notice that $a = 1$. Since $a > 0$, the parabola opens upward. This parabola opening upward with vertex $(2, -16)$ will have two x-intercepts and one y-intercept. (See the Helpful Hint after this example.)

(Continued on next page)

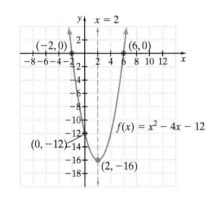

x-intercepts: let y or $f(x) = 0$

$$f(x) = x^2 - 4x - 12$$
$$0 = x^2 - 4x - 12$$
$$0 = (x - 6)(x + 2)$$
$$0 = x - 6 \quad \text{or} \quad 0 = x + 2$$
$$6 = x \qquad\qquad -2 = x$$

y-intercept: let $x = 0$

$$f(x) = x^2 - 4x - 12$$
$$f(0) = 0^2 - 4 \cdot 0 - 12$$
$$= -12$$

The two x-intercepts are $(6, 0)$ and $(-2, 0)$. The y-intercept is $(0, -12)$. The sketch of $f(x) = x^2 - 4x - 12$ is shown.

Notice that the axis of symmetry is always halfway between the x-intercepts. For this example, halfway between -2 and 6 is $\dfrac{-2 + 6}{2} = 2$, and the axis of symmetry is $x = 2$.

PRACTICE

1 Graph $g(x) = x^2 - 2x - 3$. Find the vertex and any intercepts.

───

▶ Helpful Hint

Parabola Opens Upward
Vertex in I or II: no x-intercept
Vertex in III or IV: 2 x-intercepts

Parabola Opens Downward
Vertex in I or II: 2 x-intercepts
Vertex in III or IV: no x-intercept.

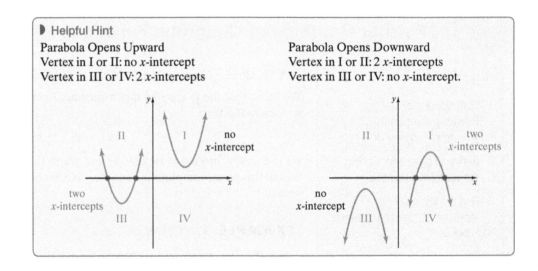

EXAMPLE 2 Graph $f(x) = 3x^2 + 3x + 1$. Find the vertex and any intercepts.

Solution Replace $f(x)$ with y and complete the square on x to write the equation in the form $y = a(x - h)^2 + k$.

$$y = 3x^2 + 3x + 1 \qquad \text{Replace } f(x) \text{ with } y.$$
$$y - 1 = 3x^2 + 3x \qquad \text{Isolate } x\text{-variable terms.}$$

Factor 3 from the terms $3x^2 + 3x$ so that the coefficient of x^2 is 1.

$$y - 1 = 3(x^2 + x) \qquad \text{Factor out 3.}$$

The coefficient of x in the parentheses above is 1. Then $\dfrac{1}{2}(1) = \dfrac{1}{2}$ and $\left(\dfrac{1}{2}\right)^2 = \dfrac{1}{4}$.

Since we are adding $\dfrac{1}{4}$ inside the parentheses, we are really adding $3\left(\dfrac{1}{4}\right)$, so we *must* add $3\left(\dfrac{1}{4}\right)$ to the left side.

$$y - 1 + 3\left(\frac{1}{4}\right) = 3\left(x^2 + x + \frac{1}{4}\right)$$

$$y - \frac{1}{4} = 3\left(x + \frac{1}{2}\right)^2 \qquad \text{Simplify the left side and factor the right side.}$$

$$y = 3\left(x + \frac{1}{2}\right)^2 + \frac{1}{4} \qquad \text{Add } \frac{1}{4} \text{ to both sides.}$$

$$f(x) = 3\left(x + \frac{1}{2}\right)^2 + \frac{1}{4} \qquad \text{Replace } y \text{ with } f(x).$$

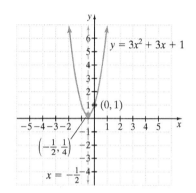

$y = 3x^2 + 3x + 1$

$(0, 1)$

$\left(-\frac{1}{2}, \frac{1}{4}\right)$

$x = -\frac{1}{2}$

Then $a = 3, h = -\frac{1}{2}$, and $k = \frac{1}{4}$. This means that the parabola opens upward with vertex $\left(-\frac{1}{2}, \frac{1}{4}\right)$ and that the axis of symmetry is the line $x = -\frac{1}{2}$.

To find the y-intercept, let $x = 0$. Then

$$f(0) = 3(0)^2 + 3(0) + 1 = 1$$

Thus the y-intercept is $(0, 1)$.

This parabola has no x-intercepts since the vertex is in the second quadrant and the parabola opens upward. Use the vertex, axis of symmetry, and y-intercept to sketch the parabola. □

PRACTICE

2   Graph $g(x) = 4x^2 + 4x + 3$. Find the vertex and any intercepts.

EXAMPLE 3   Graph $f(x) = -x^2 - 2x + 3$. Find the vertex and any intercepts.

Solution   We write $f(x)$ in the form $a(x - h)^2 + k$ by completing the square. First we replace $f(x)$ with y.

$$f(x) = -x^2 - 2x + 3$$

$$y = -x^2 - 2x + 3$$

$$y - 3 = -x^2 - 2x \qquad \text{Subtract 3 from both sides to get the } x\text{-variable terms alone.}$$

$$y - 3 = -1(x^2 + 2x) \qquad \text{Factor } -1 \text{ from the terms } -x^2 - 2x.$$

[handwritten: Replace]
[handwritten: y " $f(t)$]
[handwritten: Keep (−1)]

The coefficient of x is 2. Then $\frac{1}{2}(2) = 1$ and $1^2 = 1$. We add 1 to the right side inside the parentheses and add $-1(1)$ to the left side.

$$y - 3 - 1(1) = -1(x^2 + 2x + 1)$$

$$y - 4 = -1(x + 1)^2 \qquad \text{Simplify the left side and factor the right side.}$$

$$y = -1(x + 1)^2 + 4 \qquad \text{Add 4 to both sides.}$$

$$f(x) = -1(x + 1)^2 + 4 \qquad \text{Replace } y \text{ with } f(x).$$

> ▶ **Helpful Hint**
> This can be written as
> $f(x) = -1[x - (-1)]^2 + 4$.
> Notice that the vertex is $(-1, 4)$.

Since $a = -1$, the parabola opens downward with vertex $(-1, 4)$ and axis of symmetry $x = -1$.

To find the y-intercept, we let $x = 0$ and solve for y. Then

$$f(0) = -0^2 - 2(0) + 3 = 3$$

Thus, $(0, 3)$ is the y-intercept.

To find the x-intercepts, we let y or $f(x) = 0$ and solve for x.

$$f(x) = -x^2 - 2x + 3$$

$$0 = -x^2 - 2x + 3 \qquad \text{Let } f(x) = 0.$$

(Continued on next page)

$x = -1$

$f(x) = -x^2 - 2x + 3$

Now we divide both sides by -1 so that the coefficient of x^2 is 1.

$$\frac{0}{-1} = \frac{-x^2}{-1} - \frac{2x}{-1} + \frac{3}{-1} \qquad \text{Divide both sides by } -1.$$

$$0 = x^2 + 2x - 3 \qquad \text{Simplify.}$$

$$0 = (x + 3)(x - 1) \qquad \text{Factor.}$$

$$x + 3 = 0 \quad \text{or} \quad x - 1 = 0 \qquad \text{Set each factor equal to 0.}$$

$$x = -3 \qquad\qquad x = 1 \qquad \text{Solve.}$$

The x-intercepts are $(-3, 0)$ and $(1, 0)$. Use these points to sketch the parabola.

PRACTICE

3   Graph $g(x) = -x^2 + 5x + 6$. Find the vertex and any intercepts.

Nice →

OBJECTIVE

2   Deriving a Formula for Finding the Vertex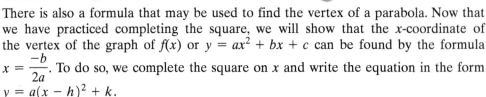

There is also a formula that may be used to find the vertex of a parabola. Now that we have practiced completing the square, we will show that the x-coordinate of the vertex of the graph of $f(x)$ or $y = ax^2 + bx + c$ can be found by the formula $x = \dfrac{-b}{2a}$. To do so, we complete the square on x and write the equation in the form $y = a(x - h)^2 + k$.

First, isolate the x-variable terms by subtracting c from both sides.

$$y = ax^2 + bx + c$$

$$y - c = ax^2 + bx$$

Next, factor a from the terms $ax^2 + bx$.

$$y - c = a\left(x^2 + \frac{b}{a}x\right)$$

Next, add the square of half of $\dfrac{b}{a}$, or $\left(\dfrac{b}{2a}\right)^2 = \dfrac{b^2}{4a^2}$, to the right side inside the parentheses. Because of the factor a, what we really added was $a\left(\dfrac{b^2}{4a^2}\right)$, and this must be added to the left side.

$$y - c + a\left(\frac{b^2}{4a^2}\right) = a\left(x^2 + \frac{b}{a}x + \frac{b^2}{4a^2}\right)$$

$$y - c + \frac{b^2}{4a} = a\left(x + \frac{b}{2a}\right)^2 \qquad \begin{array}{l}\text{Simplify the left side and} \\ \text{factor the right side.}\end{array}$$

$$y = a\left(x + \frac{b}{2a}\right)^2 + c - \frac{b^2}{4a} \qquad \begin{array}{l}\text{Add } c \text{ to both sides and subtract } \dfrac{b^2}{4a} \\ \text{from both sides.}\end{array}$$

Compare this form with $f(x)$ or $y = a(x - h)^2 + k$ and see that h is $\dfrac{-b}{2a}$, which means that the x-coordinate of the vertex of the graph of $f(x) = ax^2 + bx + c$ is $\dfrac{-b}{2a}$.

Vertex Formula

The graph of $f(x) = ax^2 + bx + c$, when $a \neq 0$, is a parabola with vertex

$$\left(\frac{-b}{2a}, f\left(\frac{-b}{2a}\right)\right)$$

Let's use this formula to find the vertex of the parabola we graphed in Example 1.

EXAMPLE 4   Find the vertex of the graph of $f(x) = x^2 - 4x - 12$.

Solution   In the quadratic function $f(x) = x^2 - 4x - 12$, notice that $a = 1, b = -4$, and $c = -12$. Then

$$\frac{-b}{2a} = \frac{-(-4)}{2(1)} = 2 \qquad \text{Nice} \quad \text{}$$

The x-value of the vertex is 2. To find the corresponding $f(x)$ or y-value, find $f(2)$. Then

$$f(2) = 2^2 - 4(2) - 12 = 4 - 8 - 12 = -16$$

The vertex is $(2, -16)$. These results agree with our findings in Example 1. □

PRACTICE
4   Find the vertex of the graph of $g(x) = x^2 - 2x - 3$.

OBJECTIVE
3   Finding Minimum and Maximum Values ▶

The vertex of a parabola gives us some important information about its corresponding quadratic function. The quadratic function whose graph is a parabola that opens upward has a minimum value, and the quadratic function whose graph is a parabola that opens downward has a maximum value. The $f(x)$ or y-value of the vertex is the minimum or maximum value of the function.

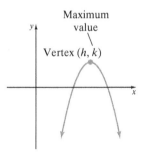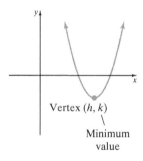

✓CONCEPT CHECK
Without making any calculations, tell whether the graph of $f(x) = 7 - x - 0.3x^2$ has a maximum value or a minimum value. Explain your reasoning.

EXAMPLE 5   **Finding Maximum Height**

A rock is thrown upward from the ground. Its height in feet above ground after t seconds is given by the function $f(t) = -16t^2 + 20t$. Find the maximum height of the rock and the number of seconds it took for the rock to reach its maximum height.

Solution

1. UNDERSTAND. The maximum height of the rock is the largest value of $f(t)$. Since the function $f(t) = -16t^2 + 20t$ is a quadratic function, its graph is a parabola. It opens downward since $-16 < 0$. Thus, the maximum value of $f(t)$ is the $f(t)$ or y-value of the vertex of its graph.

Answer to Concept Check:
$f(x)$ has a maximum value since it opens downward.

(Continued on next page)

2. TRANSLATE. To find the vertex (h, k), notice that for $f(t) = -16t^2 + 20t$, $a = -16, b = 20$, and $c = 0$. We will use these values and the vertex formula

$$\left(\frac{-b}{2a}, f\left(\frac{-b}{2a}\right)\right)$$

3. SOLVE.

$$h = \frac{-b}{2a} = \frac{-20}{-32} = \frac{5}{8}$$

$$f\left(\frac{5}{8}\right) = -16\left(\frac{5}{8}\right)^2 + 20\left(\frac{5}{8}\right)$$

$$= -16\left(\frac{25}{64}\right) + \frac{25}{2}$$

$$= -\frac{25}{4} + \frac{50}{4} = \frac{25}{4}$$

4. INTERPRET. The graph of $f(t)$ is a parabola opening downward with vertex $\left(\frac{5}{8}, \frac{25}{4}\right)$. This means that the rock's maximum height is $\frac{25}{4}$ feet, or $6\frac{1}{4}$ feet, which was reached in $\frac{5}{8}$ second. □

PRACTICE

5 A ball is tossed upward from the ground. Its height in feet above ground after t seconds is given by the function $h(t) = -16t^2 + 24t$. Find the maximum height of the ball and the number of seconds it took for the ball to reach the maximum height.

Vocabulary, Readiness & Video Check

Fill in each blank.

1. If a quadratic function is in the form $f(x) = a(x - h)^2 + k$, the vertex of its graph is _____.

2. The graph of $f(x) = ax^2 + bx + c, a \neq 0$, is a parabola whose vertex has x-value _____.

Martin-Gay Interactive Videos

See Video 11.6

Watch the section lecture video and answer the following questions.

OBJECTIVE
1
3. From ▥ Example 1, how does writing a quadratic function in the form $f(x) = a(x - h)^2 + k$ help us graph the function? What procedure can we use to write a quadratic function in this form?

OBJECTIVE
2
4. From ▥ Example 2, how can locating the vertex and knowing whether the parabola opens upward or downward potentially help save unnecessary work? Explain.

OBJECTIVE
3
5. From ▥ Example 4, when an application involving a quadratic function asks for the maximum or minimum, what part of a parabola should we find?

11.6   Exercise Set   MyMathLab®

Fill in each blank.

	Parabola Opens	*Vertex Location*	*Number of x-intercept(s)*	*Number of y-intercept(s)*
1.	up	Q I		
2.	up	Q III		
3.	down	Q II		
4.	down	Q IV		
5.	up	x-axis		
6.	down	x-axis		
7.		Q III	0	
8.		Q I	2	
9.		Q IV	2	
10.		Q II	0	

Find the vertex of the graph of each quadratic function. See Examples 1 through 4.

11. $f(x) = x^2 + 8x + 7$

12. $f(x) = x^2 + 6x + 5$

13. $f(x) = -x^2 + 10x + 5$

14. $f(x) = -x^2 - 8x + 2$

15. $f(x) = 5x^2 - 10x + 3$

16. $f(x) = -3x^2 + 6x + 4$

17. $f(x) = -x^2 + x + 1$

18. $f(x) = x^2 - 9x + 8$

Match each function with its graph. See Examples 1 through 4.

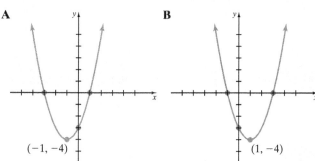

A   (-1, -4)
B   (1, -4)

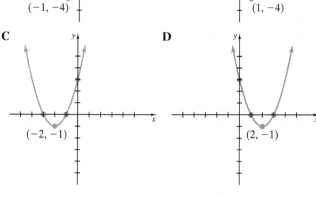

C   (-2, -1)
D   (2, -1)

19. $f(x) = x^2 - 4x + 3$

20. $f(x) = x^2 + 2x - 3$

21. $f(x) = x^2 - 2x - 3$

22. $f(x) = x^2 + 4x + 3$

MIXED PRACTICE

Find the vertex of the graph of each quadratic function. Determine whether the graph opens upward or downward, find any intercepts, and sketch the graph. See Examples 1 through 4.

23. $f(x) = x^2 + 4x - 5$ **24.** $f(x) = x^2 + 2x - 3$

25. $f(x) = -x^2 + 2x - 1$ **26.** $f(x) = -x^2 + 4x - 4$

27. $f(x) = x^2 - 4$ **28.** $f(x) = x^2 - 1$

29. $f(x) = 4x^2 + 4x - 3$ **30.** $f(x) = 2x^2 - x - 3$

31. $f(x) = \frac{1}{2}x^2 + 4x + \frac{15}{2}$ **32.** $f(x) = \frac{1}{5}x^2 + 2x + \frac{9}{5}$

33. $f(x) = x^2 - 6x + 5$ **34.** $f(x) = x^2 - 4x + 3$

35. $f(x) = x^2 - 4x + 5$ **36.** $f(x) = x^2 - 6x + 11$

37. $f(x) = 2x^2 + 4x + 5$ **38.** $f(x) = 3x^2 + 12x + 16$

39. $f(x) = -2x^2 + 12x$ **40.** $f(x) = -4x^2 + 8x$

41. $f(x) = x^2 + 1$ **42.** $f(x) = x^2 + 4$

43. $f(x) = x^2 - 2x - 15$ **44.** $f(x) = x^2 - x - 12$

45. $f(x) = -5x^2 + 5x$ **46.** $f(x) = 3x^2 - 12x$

47. $f(x) = -x^2 + 2x - 12$ **48.** $f(x) = -x^2 + 8x - 17$

49. $f(x) = 3x^2 - 12x + 15$ **50.** $f(x) = 2x^2 - 8x + 11$

51. $f(x) = x^2 + x - 6$ **52.** $f(x) = x^2 + 3x - 18$

53. $f(x) = -2x^2 - 3x + 35$ **54.** $f(x) = 3x^2 - 13x - 10$

Solve. See Example 5.

55. If a projectile is fired straight upward from the ground with an initial speed of 96 feet per second, then its height h in feet after t seconds is given by the equation

$$h(t) = -16t^2 + 96t$$

Find the maximum height of the projectile.

56. If Rheam Gaspar throws a ball upward with an initial speed of 32 feet per second, then its height h in feet after t seconds is given by the equation

$$h(t) = -16t^2 + 32t$$

Find the maximum height of the ball.

57. The cost C in dollars of manufacturing x bicycles at Holladay's Production Plant is given by the function

$$C(x) = 2x^2 - 800x + 92,000.$$

   a. Find the number of bicycles that must be manufactured to minimize the cost.

   b. Find the minimum cost.

58. The Utah Ski Club sells calendars to raise money. The profit P, in cents, from selling x calendars is given by the equation $P(x) = 360x - x^2$.

   a. Find how many calendars must be sold to maximize profit.

   b. Find the maximum profit.

59. Find two numbers whose sum is 60 and whose product is as large as possible. [*Hint:* Let x and $60 - x$ be the two positive numbers. Their product can be described by the function $f(x) = x(60 - x)$.]

60. Find two numbers whose sum is 11 and whose product is as large as possible. (Use the hint for Exercise 59.)

61. Find two numbers whose difference is 10 and whose product is as small as possible. (Use the hint for Exercise 59.)

62. Find two numbers whose difference is 8 and whose product is as small as possible.

△ **63.** The length and width of a rectangle must have a sum of 40. Find the dimensions of the rectangle that will have the maximum area. (Use the hint for Exercise 59.)

△ **64.** The length and width of a rectangle must have a sum of 50. Find the dimensions of the rectangle that will have maximum area.

REVIEW AND PREVIEW

Sketch the graph of each function. See Section 11.5.

65. $f(x) = x^2 + 2$ **66.** $f(x) = (x - 3)^2$

67. $g(x) = x + 2$ **68.** $h(x) = x - 3$

69. $f(x) = (x + 5)^2 + 2$ **70.** $f(x) = 2(x - 3)^2 + 2$

71. $f(x) = 3(x - 4)^2 + 1$ **72.** $f(x) = (x + 1)^2 + 4$

73. $f(x) = -(x - 4)^2 + \dfrac{3}{2}$ **74.** $f(x) = -2(x + 7)^2 + \dfrac{1}{2}$

CONCEPT EXTENSIONS

Without calculating, tell whether each graph has a minimum value or a maximum value. See the Concept Check in the section.

75. $f(x) = 2x^2 - 5$

76. $g(x) = -7x^2 + x + 1$

77. $f(x) = 3 - \dfrac{1}{2}x^2$

78. $G(x) = 3 - \dfrac{1}{2}x + 0.8x^2$

Find the vertex of the graph of each quadratic function. Determine whether the graph opens upward or downward, find the y-intercept, approximate the x-intercepts to one decimal place, and sketch the graph.

79. $f(x) = x^2 + 10x + 15$ **80.** $f(x) = x^2 - 6x + 4$

81. $f(x) = 3x^2 - 6x + 7$ **82.** $f(x) = 2x^2 + 4x - 1$

Find the maximum or minimum value of each function. Approximate to two decimal places.

83. $f(x) = 2.3x^2 - 6.1x + 3.2$

84. $f(x) = 7.6x^2 + 9.8x - 2.1$

85. $f(x) = -1.9x^2 + 5.6x - 2.7$

86. $f(x) = -5.2x^2 - 3.8x + 5.1$

87. The projected number of Wi-Fi-enabled cell phones in the United States can be modeled by the quadratic function $c(x) = -0.4x^2 + 21x + 35$, where $c(x)$ is the projected number of Wi-Fi-enabled cell phones in millions and x is the number of years after 2009. (*Source:* Techcrunchies.com)

   a. Will this function have a maximum or a minimum? How can you tell?

   b. According to this model, in what year will the number of Wi-Fi-enabled cell phones in the United States be at its maximum or minimum?

   c. What is the maximum/minimum number of Wi-Fi-enabled cell phones predicted? Round to the nearest whole million.

88. Methane is a gas produced by landfills, natural gas systems, and coal mining that contributes to the greenhouse effect and global warming. Projected methane emissions in the United States can be modeled by the quadratic function

$$f(x) = -0.072x^2 + 1.93x + 173.9$$

where $f(x)$ is the amount of methane produced in million metric tons and x is the number of years after 2000. (*Source:* Based on data from the U.S. Environmental Protection Agency, 2000–2020)

   a. According to this model, what will U.S. emissions of methane be in 2018? (Round to 2 decimal places.)

   b. Will this function have a maximum or a minimum? How can you tell?

   c. In what year will methane emissions in the United States be at their maximum/minimum? Round to the nearest whole year.

d. What is the level of methane emissions for that year? (Use your rounded answer from part (c).) (Round this answer to 2 decimal places.)

Use a graphing calculator to check each exercise.

89. Exercise 37   **90.** Exercise 38

91. Exercise 47   **92.** Exercise 48

Chapter 11 Vocabulary Check

Fill in each blank with one of the words or phrases listed below.

quadratic formula	quadratic	discriminant	$\pm\sqrt{b}$
completing the square	quadratic inequality	(h, k)	$(0, k)$
$(h, 0)$	$\dfrac{-b}{2a}$		

1. The _____ helps us find the number and type of solutions of a quadratic equation.

2. If $a^2 = b$, then $a =$ _____ .

3. The graph of $f(x) = ax^2 + bx + c$, where a is not 0, is a parabola whose vertex has x-value _____ .

4. A _____ is an inequality that can be written so that one side is a quadratic expression and the other side is 0.

5. The process of writing a quadratic equation so that one side is a perfect square trinomial is called _____ .

6. The graph of $f(x) = x^2 + k$ has vertex _____ .

7. The graph of $f(x) = (x - h)^2$ has vertex _____ .

8. The graph of $f(x) = (x - h)^2 + k$ has vertex _____ .

9. The formula $x = \dfrac{-b \pm \sqrt{b^2 - 4ac}}{2a}$ is called the _____ .

10. A _____ equation is one that can be written in the form $ax^2 + bx + c = 0$ where $a, b,$ and c are real numbers and a is not 0.

Chapter 11 Highlights

DEFINITIONS AND CONCEPTS	EXAMPLES
Section 11.1 Solving Quadratic Equations by Completing the Square	

Square root property If b is a real number and if $a^2 = b$, then $a = \pm\sqrt{b}$.	Solve: $(x + 3)^2 = 14$. $\qquad x + 3 = \pm\sqrt{14}$ $\qquad\qquad x = -3 \pm \sqrt{14}$
To solve a quadratic equation in x by completing the square **Step 1.** If the coefficient of x^2 is not 1, divide both sides of the equation by the coefficient of x^2.	Solve: $3x^2 - 12x - 18 = 0$. **1.** $x^2 - 4x - 6 = 0$
Step 2. Isolate the variable terms.	**2.** $\qquad x^2 - 4x = 6$
Step 3. Complete the square by adding the square of half of the coefficient of x to both sides.	**3.** $\quad \frac{1}{2}(-4) = -2$ and $(-2)^2 = 4$ $\qquad x^2 - 4x + 4 = 6 + 4$
Step 4. Write the resulting trinomial as the square of a binomial.	**4.** $\qquad (x - 2)^2 = 10$
Step 5. Apply the square root property and solve for x.	**5.** $\qquad x - 2 = \pm\sqrt{10}$ $\qquad\qquad x = 2 \pm \sqrt{10}$

DEFINITIONS AND CONCEPTS	EXAMPLES

Section 11.2   Solving Quadratic Equations by the Quadratic Formula

A quadratic equation written in the form $ax^2 + bx + c = 0$ has solutions

$$x = \frac{-b \pm \sqrt{b^2 - 4ac}}{2a}$$

Solve: $x^2 - x - 3 = 0$.

$$a = 1, b = -1, c = -3$$

$$x = \frac{-(-1) \pm \sqrt{(-1)^2 - 4(1)(-3)}}{2 \cdot 1}$$

$$x = \frac{1 \pm \sqrt{13}}{2}$$

Section 11.3   Solving Equations by Using Quadratic Methods

Substitution is often helpful in solving an equation that contains a repeated variable expression.

Solve: $(2x + 1)^2 - 5(2x + 1) + 6 = 0$.

Let $m = 2x + 1$. Then

$$m^2 - 5m + 6 = 0 \qquad \text{Let } m = 2x + 1.$$
$$(m - 3)(m - 2) = 0$$
$$m = 3 \quad \text{or} \quad m = 2$$
$$2x + 1 = 3 \quad \text{or} \quad 2x + 1 = 2 \quad \text{Substitute back.}$$
$$x = 1 \quad \text{or} \qquad x = \frac{1}{2}$$

Section 11.4   Nonlinear Inequalities in One Variable

To solve a polynomial inequality

Step 1. Write the inequality in standard form.

Step 2. Solve the related equation.

Step 3. Use solutions from Step 2 to separate the number line into regions.

Step 4. Use test points to determine whether values in each region satisfy the original inequality.

Step 5. Write the solution set as the union of regions whose test point value is a solution.

Solve: $x^2 \geq 6x$.

1. $x^2 - 6x \geq 0$

2. $x^2 - 6x = 0$

   $x(x - 6) = 0$

   $x = 0 \quad \text{or} \quad x = 6$

3.

Region	Test Point Value	$x^2 \geq 6x$	Result
A	-2	$(-2)^2 \geq 6(-2)$	True
B	1	$1^2 \geq 6(1)$	False
C	7	$7^2 \geq 6(7)$	True

5.

The solution set is $(-\infty, 0] \cup [6, \infty)$.

To solve a rational inequality

Step 1. Solve for values that make all denominators 0.

Step 2. Solve the related equation.

Step 3. Use solutions from Steps 1 and 2 to separate the number line into regions.

Step 4. Use test points to determine whether values in each region satisfy the original inequality.

Step 5. Write the solution set as the union of regions whose test point value is a solution.

Solve: $\dfrac{6}{x - 1} < -2$.

1. $x - 1 = 0$ Set denominator equal to 0.

   $x = 1$

2. $\dfrac{6}{x - 1} = -2$

   $6 = -2(x - 1)$ Multiply by $(x - 1)$.

   $6 = -2x + 2$

   $4 = -2x$

   $-2 = x$

DEFINITIONS AND CONCEPTS	**EXAMPLES**

3.

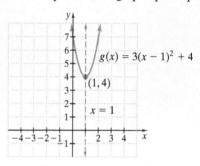

    A B C

-2 1

4. Only a test value from region B satisfies the original inequality.

5. A B C

-2 1

The solution set is $(-2, 1)$.

Graph of a quadratic function

The graph of a quadratic function written in the form $f(x) = a(x - h)^2 + k$ is a parabola with vertex (h, k). If $a > 0$, the parabola opens upward; if $a < 0$, the parabola opens downward. The axis of symmetry is the line whose equation is $x = h$.

$$f(x) = a(x - h)^2 + k$$

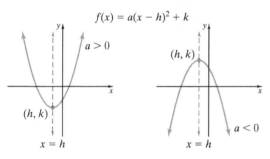

Graph $g(x) = 3(x - 1)^2 + 4$.

The graph is a parabola with vertex $(1, 4)$ and axis of symmetry $x = 1$. Since $a = 3$ is positive, the graph opens upward.

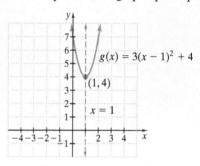

The graph of $f(x) = ax^2 + bx + c$, where $a \neq 0$, is a parabola with vertex

$$\left(\frac{-b}{2a}, f\left(\frac{-b}{2a} \right) \right)$$

Graph $f(x) = x^2 - 2x - 8$. Find the vertex and x- and y-intercepts.

$$\frac{-b}{2a} = \frac{-(-2)}{2 \cdot 1} = 1$$

$$f(1) = 1^2 - 2(1) - 8 = -9$$

The vertex is $(1, -9)$.

$$0 = x^2 - 2x - 8$$

$$0 = (x - 4)(x + 2)$$

$$x = 4 \quad \text{or} \quad x = -2$$

The x-intercepts are $(4, 0)$ and $(-2, 0)$.

$$f(0) = 0^2 - 2 \cdot 0 - 8 = -8$$

The y-intercept is $(0, -8)$.

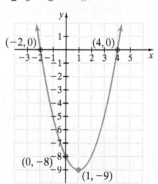

Chapter 11 Review

(11.1) Solve by factoring.

1. $x^2 - 15x + 14 = 0$ **2.** $7a^2 = 29a + 30$

Solve by using the square root property.

3. $4m^2 = 196$ **4.** $(5x - 2)^2 = 2$

Solve by completing the square.

5. $z^2 + 3z + 1 = 0$

6. $(2x + 1)^2 = x$

7. If P dollars are originally invested, the formula $A = P(1 + r)^2$ gives the amount A in an account paying interest rate r compounded annually after 2 years. Find the interest rate r such that \$2500 increases to \$2717 in 2 years. Round the result to the nearest hundredth of a percent.

△ **8.** Two ships leave a port at the same time and travel at the same speed. One ship is traveling due north and the other due east. In a few hours, the ships are 150 miles apart. How many miles has each ship traveled? Give an exact answer and a one-decimal-place approximation.

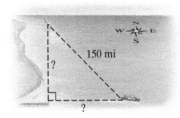

(11.2) If the discriminant of a quadratic equation has the given value, determine the number and type of solutions of the equation.

9. -8 **10.** 48

11. 100 **12.** 0

Solve by using the quadratic formula.

13. $x^2 - 16x + 64 = 0$ **14.** $x^2 + 5x = 0$

15. $2x^2 + 3x = 5$ **16.** $9x^2 + 4 = 2x$

17. $6x^2 + 7 = 5x$ **18.** $(2x - 3)^2 = x$

19. Cadets graduating from military school usually toss their hats high into the air at the end of the ceremony. One cadet threw his hat so that its distance $d(t)$ in feet above the ground t seconds after it was thrown was $d(t) = -16t^2 + 30t + 6$.

a. Find the distance above the ground of the hat 1 second after it was thrown.

b. Find the time it takes the hat to hit the ground. Give an exact time and a one-decimal-place approximation.

△ **20.** The hypotenuse of an isosceles right triangle is 6 centimeters longer than either of the legs. Find the length of the legs.

(11.3) Solve each equation for the variable.

21. $x^3 = 27$

22. $y^3 = -64$

23. $\dfrac{5}{x} + \dfrac{6}{x - 2} = 3$

24. $x^4 - 21x^2 - 100 = 0$

25. $x^{2/3} - 6x^{1/3} + 5 = 0$

26. $5(x + 3)^2 - 19(x + 3) = 4$

27. $a^6 - a^2 = a^4 - 1$

28. $y^{-2} + y^{-1} = 20$

29. Two postal workers, Jerome Grant and Tim Bozik, can sort a stack of mail in 5 hours. Working alone, Tim can sort the mail in 1 hour less time than Jerome can. Find the time that each postal worker can sort the mail alone. Round the result to one decimal place.

30. A negative number decreased by its reciprocal is $-\dfrac{24}{5}$. Find the number.

(11.4) Solve each inequality for x. Write each solution set in interval notation.

31. $2x^2 - 50 \le 0$

32. $\dfrac{1}{4}x^2 < \dfrac{1}{16}$

33. $(x^2 - 4)(x^2 - 25) \le 0$

34. $(x^2 - 16)(x^2 - 1) > 0$

35. $\dfrac{x - 5}{x - 6} < 0$

36. $\dfrac{(4x + 3)(x - 5)}{x(x + 6)} > 0$

37. $(x + 5)(x - 6)(x + 2) \le 0$

38. $x^3 + 3x^2 - 25x - 75 > 0$

39. $\dfrac{x^2 + 4}{3x} \le 1$ **40.** $\dfrac{3}{x - 2} > 2$

(11.5) Sketch the graph of each function. Label the vertex and the axis of symmetry.

41. $f(x) = x^2 - 4$

42. $g(x) = x^2 + 7$

43. $H(x) = 2x^2$

44. $h(x) = -\dfrac{1}{3}x^2$

45. $F(x) = (x - 1)^2$

46. $G(x) = (x + 5)^2$

47. $f(x) = (x - 4)^2 - 2$

48. $f(x) = -3(x - 1)^2 + 1$

(11.6) Sketch the graph of each function. Find the vertex and the intercepts.

49. $f(x) = x^2 + 10x + 25$

50. $f(x) = -x^2 + 6x - 9$

51. $f(x) = 4x^2 - 1$

52. $f(x) = -5x^2 + 5$

53. Find the vertex of the graph of $f(x) = -3x^2 - 5x + 4$. Determine whether the graph opens upward or downward, find the y-intercept, approximate the x-intercepts to one decimal place, and sketch the graph.

54. The function $h(t) = -16t^2 + 120t + 300$ gives the height in feet of a projectile fired from the top of a building after t seconds.

   a. When will the object reach a height of 350 feet? Round your answer to one decimal place.

   b. Explain why part (a) has two answers.

55. Find two numbers whose product is as large as possible, given that their sum is 420.

56. Write an equation of a quadratic function whose graph is a parabola that has vertex $(-3, 7)$. Let the value of a be $-\dfrac{7}{9}$.

MIXED REVIEW

Solve each equation or inequality.

57. $x^2 - x - 30 = 0$

58. $10x^2 = 3x + 4$

59. $9y^2 = 36$

60. $(9n + 1)^2 = 9$

61. $x^2 + x + 7 = 0$

62. $(3x - 4)^2 = 10x$

63. $x^2 + 11 = 0$

64. $x^2 + 7 = 0$

65. $(5a - 2)^2 - a = 0$

66. $\dfrac{7}{8} = \dfrac{8}{x^2}$

67. $x^{2/3} - 6x^{1/3} = -8$

68. $(2x - 3)(4x + 5) \geq 0$

69. $\dfrac{x(x + 5)}{4x - 3} \geq 0$

70. $\dfrac{3}{x - 2} > 2$

71. The busiest airport in the world is the Hartsfield International Airport in Atlanta, Georgia. The total amount of passenger traffic through Atlanta during the period 2000 through 2010 can be modeled by the equation $y = -32x^2 + 1733x + 76{,}362$, where y is the number of passengers enplaned and deplaned in thousands, and x is the number of years after 2000. (*Source:* Based on data from Airports Council International)

   a. Estimate the passenger traffic at Atlanta's Hartsfield International Airport in 2015.

   b. According to this model, in what year will the passenger traffic at Atlanta's Hartsfield International Airport first reach 99,000 thousand passengers?

Chapter 11 **Test**   MyMathLab®    CHAPTER Test Prep VIDEOS   You Tube™

Solve each equation.

1. $5x^2 - 2x = 7$

2. $(x + 1)^2 = 10$

3. $m^2 - m + 8 = 0$

4. $u^2 - 6u + 2 = 0$

5. $7x^2 + 8x + 1 = 0$

6. $y^2 - 3y = 5$

7. $\dfrac{4}{x + 2} + \dfrac{2x}{x - 2} = \dfrac{6}{x^2 - 4}$

8. $x^5 + 3x^4 = x + 3$

9. $x^6 + 1 = x^4 + x^2$

10. $(x + 1)^2 - 15(x + 1) + 56 = 0$

Solve by completing the square.

▶ **11.** $x^2 - 6x = -2$

▶ **12.** $2a^2 + 5 = 4a$

Solve each inequality for x. Write the solution set in interval notation.

▶ **13.** $2x^2 - 7x > 15$

▶ **14.** $(x^2 - 16)(x^2 - 25) \geq 0$

▶ **15.** $\dfrac{5}{x + 3} < 1$

▶ **16.** $\dfrac{7x - 14}{x^2 - 9} \leq 0$

Graph each function. Label the vertex.

▶ **17.** $f(x) = 3x^2$

▶ **18.** $G(x) = -2(x - 1)^2 + 5$

Graph each function. Find and label the vertex, y-intercept, and x-intercepts (if any).

▶ **19.** $h(x) = x^2 - 4x + 4$

▶ **20.** $F(x) = 2x^2 - 8x + 9$

▶ **21.** Dave and Sandy Hartranft can paint a room together in 4 hours. Working alone, Dave can paint the room in 2 hours less time than Sandy can. Find how long it takes Sandy to paint the room alone.

▶ **22.** A stone is thrown upward from a bridge. The stone's height in feet, $s(t)$, above the water t seconds after the stone is thrown is a function given by the equation $s(t) = -16t^2 + 32t + 256$.

 a. Find the maximum height of the stone.

 b. Find the time it takes the stone to hit the water. Round the answer to two decimal places.

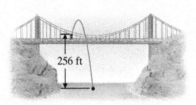

256 ft

△ **23.** Given the diagram shown, approximate to the nearest tenth of a foot how many feet of walking distance a person saves by cutting across the lawn instead of walking on the sidewalk.

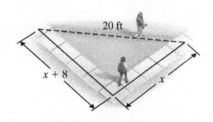

20 ft

$x + 8$

x

Chapter 11 **Cumulative Review**

1. Find the value of each expression when $x = 2$ and $y = -5$.

 a. $\dfrac{x - y}{12 + x}$ **b.** $x^2 - 3y$

2. Solve $|3x - 2| = -5$.

3. Simplify each expression by combining like terms.

 a. $2x + 3x + 5 + 2$

 b. $-5a - 3 + a + 2$

 c. $4y - 3y^2$

 d. $2.3x + 5x - 6$

 e. $-\dfrac{1}{2}b + b$

4. Use the addition method to solve the system.

$$\begin{cases} -6x + y = 5 \\ 4x - 2y = 6 \end{cases}$$

5. Solve the following system of equations by graphing.

$$\begin{cases} 2x + y = 7 \\ 2y = -4x \end{cases}$$

6. Simplify. Use positive exponents to write each answer.

 a. $(a^{-2}bc^3)^{-3}$ **b.** $\left(\dfrac{a^{-4}b^2}{c^3}\right)^{-2}$

 c. $\left(\dfrac{3a^8b^2}{12a^5b^5}\right)^{-2}$

7. Solve the system: $\begin{cases} 7x - 3y = -14 \\ -3x + y = 6 \end{cases}$

8. Multiply.

 a. $(4a - 3)(7a - 2)$

 b. $(2a + b)(3a - 5b)$

9. Simplify each quotient.

 a. $\dfrac{x^5}{x^2}$ **b.** $\dfrac{4^7}{4^3}$

 c. $\dfrac{(-3)^5}{(-3)^2}$ **d.** $\dfrac{s^2}{t^3}$

 e. $\dfrac{2x^5y^2}{xy}$

10. Factor.

 a. $9x^3 + 27x^2 - 15x$

 b. $2x(3y - 2) - 5(3y - 2)$

 c. $2xy + 6x - y - 3$

11. If $P(x) = 2x^3 - 4x^2 + 5$

 a. Find $P(2)$ by substitution.

 b. Use synthetic division to find the remainder when $P(x)$ is divided by $x - 2$.

12. Factor $x^2 - 2x - 48$.

13. Solve $(5x - 1)(2x^2 + 15x + 18) = 0$.

14. Factor. $2ax^2 - 12axy + 18ay^2$

15. Write the rational expression in lowest terms.

$$\frac{2x^2}{10x^3 - 2x^2}$$

16. Solve $2(a^2 + 2) - 8 = -2a(a - 2) - 5$.

17. Simplify. $\dfrac{x^{-1} + 2xy^{-1}}{x^{-2} - x^{-2}y^{-1}}$

18. Find the vertex and any intercepts of $f(x) = x^2 + x - 12$.

19. Factor $4m^4 - 4m^2 + 1$.

20. Simplify. $\dfrac{x^2 - 4x + 4}{2 - x}$

21. The square of a number plus three times the number is 70. Find the number.

22. Subtract. $\dfrac{a + 1}{a^2 - 6a + 8} - \dfrac{3}{16 - a^2}$

23. Use the product rule to simplify.

   a. $\sqrt{25x^3}$ **b.** $\sqrt[3]{54x^6y^8}$

   c. $\sqrt[4]{81z^{11}}$

24. Simplify. $\dfrac{(2a)^{-1} + b^{-1}}{a^{-1} + (2b)^{-1}}$

25. Rationalize the denominator of each expression.

   a. $\dfrac{2}{\sqrt{5}}$

   b. $\dfrac{2\sqrt{16}}{\sqrt{9x}}$

   c. $\sqrt[3]{\dfrac{1}{2}}$

26. Divide $x^3 - 3x^2 - 10x + 24$ by $x + 3$.

27. Solve $\sqrt{2x + 5} + \sqrt{2x} = 3$.

28. If $P(x) = 4x^3 - 2x^2 + 3$,

   a. Find $P(-2)$ by substitution.

   b. Use synthetic division to find the remainder when $P(x)$ is divided by $x + 2$.

29. Solve $\dfrac{x}{2} + \dfrac{8}{3} = \dfrac{1}{6}$.

30. Solve $\dfrac{x + 3}{x^2 + 5x + 6} = \dfrac{3}{2x + 4} - \dfrac{1}{x + 3}$.

31. The quotient of a number and 6, minus $\dfrac{5}{3}$, is the quotient of the number and 2. Find the number.

32. Mr. Briley can roof his house in 24 hours. His son can roof the same house in 40 hours. If they work together, how long will it take to roof the house?

33. Suppose that y varies directly as x. If y is 5 when x is 30, find the constant of variation and the direct variation equation.

34. Suppose that y varies inversely as x. If y is 8 when x is 24, find the constant of variation and the inverse variation equation.

35. Simplify.

   a. $\sqrt{(-3)^2}$ **b.** $\sqrt{x^2}$

   c. $\sqrt[4]{(x - 2)^4}$ **d.** $\sqrt[3]{(-5)^3}$

   e. $\sqrt[5]{(2x - 7)^5}$ **f.** $\sqrt{25x^2}$

   g. $\sqrt{x^2 + 2x + 1}$

36. Simplify. Assume that the variables represent any real number.

   a. $\sqrt{(-2)^2}$

   b. $\sqrt{y^2}$

   c. $\sqrt[4]{(a - 3)^4}$

   d. $\sqrt[3]{(-6)^3}$

   e. $\sqrt[5]{(3x - 1)^5}$

37. Use rational exponents to simplify. Assume that variables represent positive numbers.

   a. $\sqrt[8]{x^4}$

   b. $\sqrt[6]{25}$

   c. $\sqrt[4]{r^2s^6}$

38. Use rational exponents to simplify. Assume that variables represent positive numbers.

   a. $\sqrt[4]{5^2}$

   b. $\sqrt[12]{x^3}$

   c. $\sqrt[6]{x^2y^4}$

39. Divide. Write in the form $a + bi$.

   a. $\dfrac{2 + i}{1 - i}$

   b. $\dfrac{7}{3i}$

40. Write each product in the form of $a + bi$.

   a. $3i(5 - 2i)$

   b. $(6 - 5i)^2$

   c. $\left(\sqrt{3} + 2i\right)\left(\sqrt{3} - 2i\right)$

41. Use the square root property to solve $(x + 1)^2 = 12$.

42. Use the square root property to solve $(y - 1)^2 = 24$.

43. Solve $x - \sqrt{x} - 6 = 0$.

44. Use the quadratic formula to solve $m^2 = 4m + 8$.

CHAPTER 12

Exponential and Logarithmic Functions

12.1 The Algebra of Functions; Composite Functions

12.2 Inverse Functions

12.3 Exponential Functions

12.4 Exponential Growth and Decay Functions

12.5 Logarithmic Functions

12.6 Properties of Logarithms

Integrated Review—Functions and Properties of Logarithms

12.7 Common Logarithms, Natural Logarithms, and Change of Base

12.8 Exponential and Logarithmic Equations and Problem Solving

In this chapter, we discuss two closely related functions: exponential and logarithmic functions. These functions are vital to applications in economics, finance, engineering, the sciences, education, and other fields. Models of tumor growth and learning curves are two examples of the uses of exponential and logarithmic functions.

A compact fluorescent lamp (or light) (CFL) is a type of fluorescent light that is quickly gaining popularity for many reasons. Compared to an incandescent bulb, CFLs use less power and last between 8 and 15 times as long. Although a CFL has a higher price, the savings per bulb are substantial (possibly $30 per life of bulb). Many CFLs are now manufactured to replace an incandescent bulb and can fit into existing fixtures. It should be noted that since CFLs are a type of fluorescent light, they do contain a small amount of mercury.

Although we have no direct applications in this chapter, it should be noted that the light output of a CFL decays exponentially. By the end of their lives, they produce 70–80% of their original output, with the fastest losses occurring soon after the light is first used. Also, it should be noted that the response of the human eye to light is logarithmic.

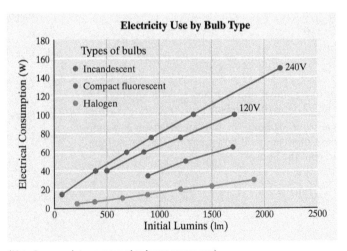

(*Note:* Lower points correspond to lower energy use.)

12.1 The Algebra of Functions; Composite Functions

OBJECTIVES

1 Add, Subtract, Multiply, and Divide Functions.

2 Construct Composite Functions.

OBJECTIVE

1   Adding, Subtracting, Multiplying, and Dividing Functions

As we have seen in earlier chapters, it is possible to add, subtract, multiply, and divide functions. Although we have not stated it as such, the sums, differences, products, and quotients of functions are themselves functions. For example, if $f(x) = 3x$ and $g(x) = x + 1$, their product, $f(x) \cdot g(x) = 3x(x + 1) = 3x^2 + 3x$, is a new function. We can use the notation $(f \cdot g)(x)$ to denote this new function. Finding the sum, difference, product, and quotient of functions to generate new functions is called the **algebra of functions.**

Algebra of Functions

Let f and g be functions. New functions from f and g are defined as follows.

Sum	$(f + g)(x) = f(x) + g(x)$
Difference	$(f - g)(x) = f(x) - g(x)$
Product	$(f \cdot g)(x) = f(x) \cdot g(x)$
Quotient	$\left(\dfrac{f}{g}\right)(x) = \dfrac{f(x)}{g(x)}, \quad g(x) \neq 0$

EXAMPLE 1   If $f(x) = x - 1$ and $g(x) = 2x - 3$, find

a. $(f + g)(x)$ **b.** $(f - g)(x)$ **c.** $(f \cdot g)(x)$ **d.** $\left(\dfrac{f}{g}\right)(x)$

Solution   Use the algebra of functions and replace $f(x)$ by $x - 1$ and $g(x)$ by $2x - 3$. Then we simplify.

a. $(f + g)(x) = f(x) + g(x)$
$$= (x - 1) + (2x - 3) = 3x - 4$$

b. $(f - g)(x) = f(x) - g(x)$
$$= (x - 1) - (2x - 3)$$
$$= x - 1 - 2x + 3$$
$$= -x + 2$$

c. $(f \cdot g)(x) = f(x) \cdot g(x)$
$$= (x - 1)(2x - 3)$$
$$= 2x^2 - 5x + 3$$

d. $\left(\dfrac{f}{g}\right)(x) = \dfrac{f(x)}{g(x)} = \dfrac{x - 1}{2x - 3}$, where $x \neq \dfrac{3}{2}$

PRACTICE

1   If $f(x) = x + 2$ and $g(x) = 3x + 5$, find

a. $(f + g)(x)$ **b.** $(f - g)(x)$ **c.** $(f \cdot g)(x)$ **d.** $\left(\dfrac{f}{g}\right)(x)$

There is an interesting but not surprising relationship between the graphs of functions and the graphs of their sum, difference, product, and quotient. For example, the graph of $(f + g)(x)$ can be found by adding the graph of $f(x)$ to the graph of $g(x)$. We add two graphs by adding y-values of corresponding x-values.

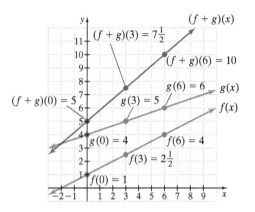

2 Constructing Composite Functions ▶

Another way to combine functions is called **function composition.** To understand this new way of combining functions, study the diagrams below. The right diagram shows an illustration by tables, and the left diagram is the same illustration but by thermometers. In both illustrations, we show degrees Celsius $f(x)$ as a function of degrees Fahrenheit x, then Kelvins $g(x)$ as a function of degrees Celsius x. (The Kelvin scale is a temperature scale devised by Lord Kelvin in 1848.) The first function we will call f, and the second function we will call g.

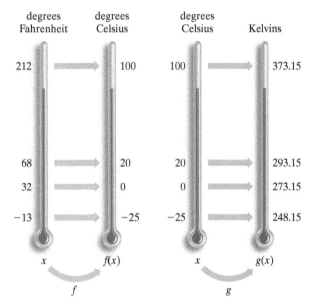

Table Illustration

x = Degrees Fahrenheit (Input)	−13	32	68	212
$f(x)$ = Degrees Celsius (Output)	−25	0	20	100

x = Degrees Celsius (Input)	−25	0	20	100
$g(x)$ = Kelvins (Output)	248.15	273.15	293.15	373.15

Suppose that we want a function that shows a direct conversion from degrees Fahrenheit to Kelvins. In other words, suppose that a function is needed that shows Kelvins as a function of degrees Fahrenheit. This can easily be done because the output of the first function $f(x)$ is the same as the input of the second function. If we use $g(f(x))$ to represent this, then we get the diagrams below.

x = Degrees Fahrenheit (Input)	−13	32	68	212
$g(f(x))$ = Kelvins (Output)	248.15	273.15	293.15	373.15

For example $g(f(-13)) = 248.15$, and so on.

Since the output of the first function is used as the input of the second function, we write the new function as $g(f(x))$. The new function is formed from the composition of the other two functions. The mathematical symbol for this composition is $(g \circ f)(x)$. Thus, $(g \circ f)(x) = g(f(x))$.

It is possible to find an equation for the composition of the two functions f and g. In other words, we can find a function that converts degrees Fahrenheit directly to Kelvins. The function $f(x) = \dfrac{5}{9}(x - 32)$ converts degrees Fahrenheit to degrees Celsius, and the function $g(x) = x + 273.15$ converts degrees Celsius to Kelvins. Thus,

$$(g \circ f)(x) = g(f(x)) = g\left(\frac{5}{9}(x - 32)\right) = \frac{5}{9}(x - 32) + 273.15$$

In general, the notation $g(f(x))$ means "g composed with f" and can be written as $(g \circ f)(x)$. Also $f(g(x))$, or $(f \circ g)(x)$, means "f composed with g."

Composition of Functions

The composition of functions f and g is

$$(f \circ g)(x) = f(g(x))$$

▶ **Helpful Hint**

$(f \circ g)(x)$ does not mean the same as $(f \cdot g)(x)$.

$$(f \circ g)(x) = f(g(x)) \text{ while } (f \cdot g)(x) = f(x) \cdot g(x)$$

        ↑   ↑

Composition of functions   Multiplication of functions

EXAMPLE 2   If $f(x) = x^2$ and $g(x) = x + 3$, find each composition.

a. $(f \circ g)(2)$ and $(g \circ f)(2)$ **b.** $(f \circ g)(x)$ and $(g \circ f)(x)$

Solution

a. $(f \circ g)(2) = f(g(2))$

$\qquad\qquad = f(5)$ Replace $g(2)$ with 5. [Since $g(x) = x + 3$, then

$\qquad\qquad = 5^2 = 25$ $g(2) = 2 + 3 = 5$.]

$\quad (g \circ f)(2) = g(f(2))$

$\qquad\qquad = g(4)$ Since $f(x) = x^2$, then $f(2) = 2^2 = 4$.

$\qquad\qquad = 4 + 3 = 7$

b. $(f \circ g)(x) = f(g(x))$

$\qquad\qquad = f(x + 3)$ Replace $g(x)$ with $x + 3$.

$\qquad\qquad = (x + 3)^2$ $f(x + 3) = (x + 3)^2$

$\qquad\qquad = x^2 + 6x + 9$ Square $(x + 3)$.

$\quad (g \circ f)(x) = g(f(x))$

$\qquad\qquad = g(x^2)$ Replace $f(x)$ with x^2.

$\qquad\qquad = x^2 + 3$ $g(x^2) = x^2 + 3$

PRACTICE

2   If $f(x) = x^2 + 1$ and $g(x) = 3x - 5$, find

a. $(f \circ g)(4)$ **b.** $(f \circ g)(x)$

$\quad (g \circ f)(4)$ $(g \circ f)(x)$

EXAMPLE 3   If $f(x) = |x|$ and $g(x) = x - 2$, find each composition.

a. $(f \circ g)(x)$ **b.** $(g \circ f)(x)$

Solution

a. $(f \circ g)(x) = f(g(x)) = f(x - 2) = |x - 2|$

b. $(g \circ f)(x) = g(f(x)) = g(|x|) = |x| - 2$

▶ **Helpful Hint**

In Examples 2 and 3, notice that $(g \circ f)(x) \neq (f \circ g)(x)$.   In general, $(g \circ f)(x)$ *may* or *may not* equal $(f \circ g)(x)$.

PRACTICE

3   If $f(x) = x^2 + 5$ and $g(x) = x + 3$, find each composition.

a. $(f \circ g)(x)$ **b.** $(g \circ f)(x)$

EXAMPLE 4   If $f(x) = 5x, g(x) = x - 2,$ and $h(x) = \sqrt{x},$ write each function as a composition using two of the given functions.

a. $F(x) = \sqrt{x - 2}$ **b.** $G(x) = 5x - 2$

Solution

a. Notice the order in which the function F operates on an input value x. First, 2 is subtracted from x. This is the function $g(x) = x - 2$. Then the square root *of that result* is taken. The square root function is $h(x) = \sqrt{x}$. This means that $F = h \circ g$. To check, we find $h \circ g$.

$$F(x) = (h \circ g)(x) = h(g(x)) = h(x - 2) = \sqrt{x - 2}$$

b. Notice the order in which the function G operates on an input value x. First, x is multiplied by 5, and then 2 is subtracted from the result. This means that $G = g \circ f$. To check, we find $g \circ f$.

$$G(x) = (g \circ f)(x) = g(f(x)) = g(5x) = 5x - 2$$

PRACTICE

4   If $f(x) = 3x, g(x) = x - 4,$ and $h(x) = |x|,$ write each function as a composition using two of the given functions.

a. $F(x) = |x - 4|$ **b.** $G(x) = 3x - 4$

Graphing Calculator Explorations

$Y_3 = \frac{1}{3}x^2 + \frac{1}{2}x + 6$

$Y_2 = \frac{1}{3}x^2 + 4$

$Y_1 = \frac{1}{2}x + 2$

If $f(x) = \frac{1}{2}x + 2$ and $g(x) = \frac{1}{3}x^2 + 4,$ then

$$(f + g)(x) = f(x) + g(x)$$
$$= \left(\frac{1}{2}x + 2\right) + \left(\frac{1}{3}x^2 + 4\right)$$
$$= \frac{1}{3}x^2 + \frac{1}{2}x + 6.$$

To visualize this addition of functions with a graphing calculator, graph

$$Y_1 = \frac{1}{2}x + 2, \qquad Y_2 = \frac{1}{3}x^2 + 4, \qquad Y_3 = \frac{1}{3}x^2 + \frac{1}{2}x + 6$$

Use a TABLE feature to verify that for a given x value, $Y_1 + Y_2 = Y_3$. For example, verify that when $x = 0$, $Y_1 = 2$, $Y_2 = 4$, and $Y_3 = 2 + 4 = 6$.

Vocabulary, Readiness & Video Check

Match each function with its definition.

1. $(f \circ g)(x)$ **4.** $(g \circ f)(x)$ **A.** $g(f(x))$ **D.** $\dfrac{f(x)}{g(x)}, g(x) \neq 0$

2. $(f \cdot g)(x)$ **5.** $\left(\dfrac{f}{g}\right)(x)$ **B.** $f(x) + g(x)$ **E.** $f(x) \cdot g(x)$

3. $(f - g)(x)$ **6.** $(f + g)(x)$ **C.** $f(g(x))$ **F.** $f(x) - g(x)$

Martin-Gay Interactive Videos

See Video 12.1

Watch the section lecture video and answer the following questions.

OBJECTIVE 1

7. From Example 1 and the lecture before, we know that $(f + g)(x) = f(x) + g(x)$. Use this fact to explain two ways you can find $(f + g)(2)$.

OBJECTIVE 2

8. From Example 3, given two functions $f(x)$ and $g(x)$, can $f(g(x))$ ever equal $g(f(x))$?

12.1   Exercise Set   MyMathLab®

*For the functions f and g, find **a.** $(f + g)(x)$, **b.** $(f - g)(x)$, **c.** $(f \cdot g)(x)$, and **d.** $\left(\dfrac{f}{g}\right)(x)$. See Example 1.*

1. $f(x) = x - 7, g(x) = 2x + 1$

2. $f(x) = x + 4, g(x) = 5x - 2$

3. $f(x) = x^2 + 1, g(x) = 5x$

4. $f(x) = x^2 - 2, g(x) = 3x$

5. $f(x) = \sqrt[3]{x}, g(x) = x + 5$

6. $f(x) = \sqrt[3]{x}, g(x) = x - 3$

7. $f(x) = -3x, g(x) = 5x^2$

8. $f(x) = 4x^3, g(x) = -6x$

If $f(x) = x^2 - 6x + 2, g(x) = -2x$, and $h(x) = \sqrt{x}$, find each composition. See Example 2.

9. $(f \circ g)(2)$

10. $(h \circ f)(-2)$

11. $(g \circ f)(-1)$

12. $(f \circ h)(1)$

13. $(g \circ h)(0)$

14. $(h \circ g)(0)$

Find $(f \circ g)(x)$ and $(g \circ f)(x)$. See Examples 2 and 3.

15. $f(x) = x^2 + 1, g(x) = 5x$

16. $f(x) = x - 3, g(x) = x^2$

17. $f(x) = 2x - 3, g(x) = x + 7$

18. $f(x) = x + 10, g(x) = 3x + 1$

19. $f(x) = x^3 + x - 2, g(x) = -2x$

20. $f(x) = -4x, g(x) = x^3 + x^2 - 6$

21. $f(x) = |x|; g(x) = 10x - 3$

22. $f(x) = |x|; g(x) = 14x - 8$

23. $f(x) = \sqrt{x}, g(x) = -5x + 2$

24. $f(x) = 7x - 1, g(x) = \sqrt[3]{x}$

If $f(x) = 3x, g(x) = \sqrt{x}$, and $h(x) = x^2 + 2$, write each function as a composition using two of the given functions. See Example 4.

25. $H(x) = \sqrt{x^2 + 2}$

26. $G(x) = \sqrt{3x}$

27. $F(x) = 9x^2 + 2$

28. $H(x) = 3x^2 + 6$

29. $G(x) = 3\sqrt{x}$

30. $F(x) = x + 2$

Find $f(x)$ and $g(x)$ so that the given function $h(x) = (f \circ g)(x)$.

31. $h(x) = (x + 2)^2$

32. $h(x) = |x - 1|$

33. $h(x) = \sqrt{x + 5} + 2$

34. $h(x) = (3x + 4)^2 + 3$

35. $h(x) = \dfrac{1}{2x - 3}$

36. $h(x) = \dfrac{1}{x + 10}$

REVIEW AND PREVIEW

Solve each equation for y. See Section 2.5.

37. $x = y + 2$

38. $x = y - 5$

39. $x = 3y$

40. $x = -6y$

41. $x = -2y - 7$

42. $x = 4y + 7$

CONCEPT EXTENSIONS

Given that $f(-1) = 4 \quad g(-1) = -4$

$\qquad\qquad f(0) = 5 \quad g(0) = -3$

$\qquad\qquad f(2) = 7 \quad g(2) = -1$

$\qquad\qquad f(7) = 1 \quad g(7) = 4$

find each function value.

43. $(f + g)(2)$

44. $(f - g)(7)$

45. $(f \circ g)(2)$

46. $(g \circ f)(2)$

47. $(f \cdot g)(7)$

48. $(f \cdot g)(0)$

49. $\left(\dfrac{f}{g}\right)(-1)$

50. $\left(\dfrac{g}{f}\right)(-1)$

51. If you are given $f(x)$ and $g(x)$, explain in your own words how to find $(f \circ g)(x)$ and then how to find $(g \circ f)(x)$.

52. Given $f(x)$ and $g(x)$, describe in your own words the difference between $(f \circ g)(x)$ and $(f \cdot g)(x)$.

Solve.

53. Business people are concerned with cost functions, revenue functions, and profit functions. Recall that the profit $P(x)$ obtained from x units of a product is equal to the revenue $R(x)$ from selling the x units minus the cost $C(x)$ of manufacturing the x units. Write an equation expressing this relationship among $C(x)$, $R(x)$, and $P(x)$.

54. Suppose the revenue $R(x)$ for x units of a product can be described by $R(x) = 25x$, and the cost $C(x)$ can be described by $C(x) = 50 + x^2 + 4x$. Find the profit $P(x)$ for x units. (See Exercise 53.)

12.2 Inverse Functions

OBJECTIVES

1 Determine Whether a Function Is a One-to-One Function.

2 Use the Horizontal Line Test to Decide Whether a Function Is a One-to-One Function.

3 Find the Inverse of a Function.

4 Find the Equation of the Inverse of a Function.

5 Graph Functions and Their Inverses.

6 Determine Whether Two Functions Are Inverses of Each Other.

OBJECTIVE

1 Determining Whether a Function Is One-to-One

In the next three sections, we begin a study of two new functions: exponential and logarithmic functions. As we learn more about these functions, we will discover that they share a special relation to each other: They are inverses of each other.

Before we study these functions, we need to learn about inverses. We begin by defining one-to-one functions.

Study the following table.

Degrees Fahrenheit (Input)	−31	−13	32	68	149	212
Degrees Celsius (Output)	−35	−25	0	20	65	100

Recall that since each degrees Fahrenheit (input) corresponds to exactly one degrees Celsius (output), this pairing of inputs and outputs does describe a function. Also notice that each output corresponds to exactly one input. This type of function is given a special name—a one-to-one function.

Does the set $f = \{(0, 1), (2, 2), (-3, 5), (7, 6)\}$ describe a one-to-one function? It is a function since each x-value corresponds to a unique y-value. For this particular function f, each y-value also corresponds to a unique x-value. Thus, this function is also a **one-to-one function.**

One-to-One Function

For a **one-to-one function,** each x-value (input) corresponds to only one y-value (output), and each y-value (output) corresponds to only one x-value (input).

EXAMPLE 1   Determine whether each function described is one-to-one.

a. $f = \{(6,2),(5,4),(-1,0),(7,3)\}$

b. $g = \{(3,9),(-4,2),(-3,9),(0,0)\}$

c. $h = \{(1,1),(2,2),(10,10),(-5,-5)\}$

d.

Mineral (Input)	Talc	Gypsum	Diamond	Topaz	Stibnite
Hardness on the Mohs Scale (Output)	1	2	10	8	2

e.

f.

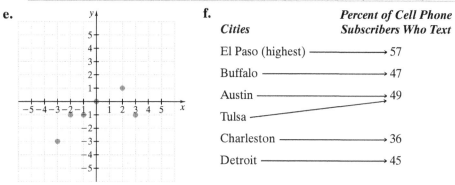

Percent of Cell Phone

| *Cities* | *Subscribers Who Text* |

El Paso (highest) ————————→ 57

Buffalo ————————→ 47

Austin ————————→ 49

Tulsa ————

Charleston ————————→ 36

Detroit ————————→ 45

Solution

a. *f* is one-to-one since each *y*-value corresponds to only one *x*-value.

b. *g* is not one-to-one because the *y*-value 9 in $(3, 9)$ and $(-3, 9)$ corresponds to different *x*-values.

c. *h* is a one-to-one function since each *y*-value corresponds to only one *x*-value.

d. This table does not describe a one-to-one function since the output 2 corresponds to two inputs, gypsum and stibnite.

e. This graph does not describe a one-to-one function since the *y*-value -1 corresponds to three *x*-values, -2, -1, and 3. (See the graph to the left.)

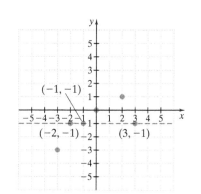

f. The mapping is not one-to-one since 49% corresponds to Austin and Tulsa.

PRACTICE

1   Determine whether each function described is one-to-one.

a. $f = \{(4,-3),(3,-4),(2,7),(5,0)\}$

b. $g = \{(8,4),(-2,0),(6,4),(2,6)\}$

c. $h = \{(2,4),(1,3),(4,6),(-2,4)\}$

d.

Year	1950	1963	1968	1975	1997	2008
Federal Minimum Wage	$0.75	$1.25	$1.60	$2.10	$5.15	$6.55

e.

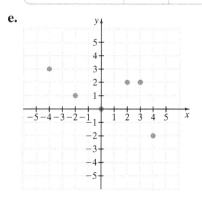

f.

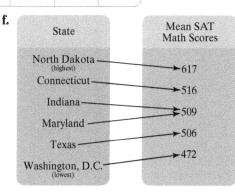

| State | Mean SAT Math Scores |

North Dakota (highest) ————→ 617

Connecticut ————→ 516

Indiana ————→ 509

Maryland ————→ 506

Texas ————→ 472

Washington, D.C. (lowest)

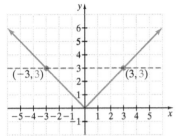

Not a one-to-one function.

OBJECTIVE
2 Using the Horizontal Line Test ▶

Recall that we recognize the graph of a function when it passes the vertical line test. Since every x-value of the function corresponds to exactly one y-value, each vertical line intersects the function's graph at most once. The graph shown (left), for instance, is the graph of a function.

Is this function a *one-to-one* function? The answer is no. To see why not, notice that the y-value of the ordered pair $(-3, 3)$, for example, is the same as the y-value of the ordered pair $(3, 3)$. In other words, the y-value 3 corresponds to two x-values, -3 and 3. This function is therefore not one-to-one.

To test whether a graph is the graph of a one-to-one function, apply the vertical line test to see if it is a function and then apply a similar **horizontal line test** to see if it is a one-to-one function.

Horizontal Line Test

If every horizontal line intersects the graph of a function at most once, then the function is a one-to-one function.

EXAMPLE 2   Determine whether each graph is the graph of a one-to-one function.

a.

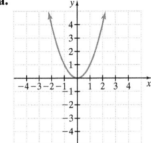

b.

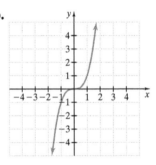

c.

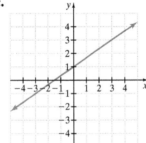

d.

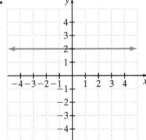

e.

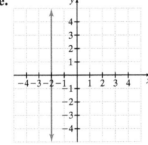

**Solution**   Graphs **a, b, c,** and **d** all pass the vertical line test, so only these graphs are graphs of functions. But, of these, only **b** and **c** pass the horizontal line test, so only **b** and **c** are graphs of one-to-one functions.   □

PRACTICE
2   Determine whether each graph is the graph of a one-to-one function.

a.

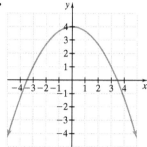

b.

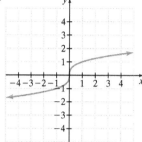

c.

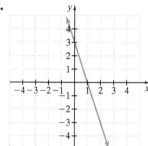

d.

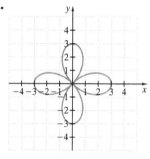

e.

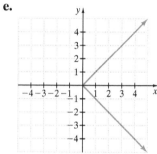

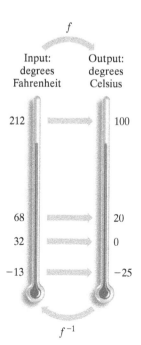

▶ **Helpful Hint**

All linear equations are one-to-one functions except those whose graphs are horizontal or vertical lines. A vertical line does not pass the vertical line test and hence is not the graph of a function. A horizontal line is the graph of a function but does not pass the horizontal line test and hence is not the graph of a one-to-one function.

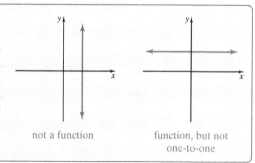

not a function   function, but not one-to-one

OBJECTIVE
3   **Finding the Inverse of a Function** ▶

One-to-one functions are special in that their graphs pass both the vertical and horizontal line tests. They are special, too, in another sense: For each one-to-one function, we can find its **inverse function** by switching the coordinates of the ordered pairs of the function, or the inputs and the outputs. For example, the inverse of the one-to-one function

Degrees Fahrenheit (Input)	−31	−13	32	68	149	212
Degrees Celsius (Output)	−35	−25	0	20	65	100

is the function

Degrees Celsius (Input)	−35	−25	0	20	65	100
Degrees Fahrenheit (Output)	−31	−13	32	68	149	212

Notice that the ordered pair $(-31, -35)$ of the function, for example, becomes the ordered pair $(-35, -31)$ of its inverse.

Also, the inverse of the one-to-one function $f = \{(2, -3), (5, 10), (9, 1)\}$ is $\{(-3, 2), (10, 5), (1, 9)\}$. For a function f, we use the notation f^{-1}, read "f inverse," to denote its inverse function. Notice that since the coordinates of each ordered pair have been switched, the domain (set of inputs) of f is the range (set of outputs) of f^{-1}, and the range of f is the domain of f^{-1}.

> **Inverse Function**
>
> The inverse of a one-to-one function f is the one-to-one function f^{-1} that consists of the set of all ordered pairs (y, x) where (x, y) belongs to f.

> ▶ **Helpful Hint**
>
> If a function is not one-to-one, it does not have an inverse function.

EXAMPLE 3   Find the inverse of the one-to-one function.
$$f = \{(0, 1), (-2, 7), (3, -6), (4, 4)\}$$

Solution $f^{-1} = \{(1, 0), (7, -2), (-6, 3), (4, 4)\}$
Switch coordinates of each ordered pair.

PRACTICE
3   Find the inverse of the one-to-one function.
$$f = \{(3, 4), (-2, 0), (2, 8), (6, 6)\}$$

> ▶ **Helpful Hint**
>
> The symbol f^{-1} is the single symbol that denotes the inverse of the function f.
>
> It is read as "f inverse." This symbol *does not mean* $\frac{1}{f}$.

✓**CONCEPT CHECK**
Suppose that f is a one-to-one function and that $f(1) = 5$.
a. Write the corresponding ordered pair.
b. Write one point that we know must belong to the inverse function f^{-1}.

OBJECTIVE
4   Finding the Equation of the Inverse of a Function

If a one-to-one function f is defined as a set of ordered pairs, we can find f^{-1} by interchanging the x- and y-coordinates of the ordered pairs. If a one-to-one function f is given in the form of an equation, we can find f^{-1} by using a similar procedure.

Answer to Concept Check:
a. $(1, 5)$,   **b.** $(5, 1)$

> **Finding the Inverse of a One-to-One Function f(x)**
>
> **Step 1.** Replace $f(x)$ with y.
> **Step 2.** Interchange x and y.
> **Step 3.** Solve the equation for y.
> **Step 4.** Replace y with the notation $f^{-1}(x)$.

EXAMPLE 4 Find an equation of the inverse of $f(x) = x + 3$.

Solution $f(x) = x + 3$

Step 1. $y = x + 3$ Replace $f(x)$ with y.
Step 2. $x = y + 3$ Interchange x and y.
Step 3. $x - 3 = y$ Solve for y.
Step 4. $f^{-1}(x) = x - 3$ Replace y with $f^{-1}(x)$.

The inverse of $f(x) = x + 3$ is $f^{-1}(x) = x - 3$. Notice that, for example,

$$f(1) = 1 + 3 = 4 \quad \text{and} \quad f^{-1}(4) = 4 - 3 = 1$$

Ordered pair: $(1, 4)$ Ordered pair: $(4, 1)$
The coordinates are
switched, as expected.

PRACTICE
4 Find the equation of the inverse of $f(x) = 6 - x$.

EXAMPLE 5 Find the equation of the inverse of $f(x) = 3x - 5$. Graph f and f^{-1} on the same set of axes.

Solution $f(x) = 3x - 5$

Step 1. $y = 3x - 5$ Replace $f(x)$ with y.
Step 2. $x = 3y - 5$ Interchange x and y.
Step 3. $3y = x + 5$ Solve for y.

$$y = \frac{x + 5}{3}$$

Step 4. $f^{-1}(x) = \dfrac{x + 5}{3}$ Replace y with $f^{-1}(x)$.

Now we graph $f(x)$ and $f^{-1}(x)$ on the same set of axes. Both $f(x) = 3x - 5$ and $f^{-1}(x) = \dfrac{x + 5}{3}$ are linear functions, so each graph is a line.

$f(x) = 3x - 5$	
x	$y = f(x)$
1	-2
0	-5
$\dfrac{5}{3}$	0

$f^{-1}(x) = \dfrac{x + 5}{3}$	
x	$y = f^{-1}(x)$
-2	1
-5	0
0	$\dfrac{5}{3}$

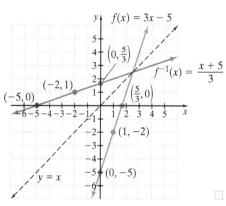

(Continued on next page)

5 Find the equation of the inverse of $f(x) = 5x + 2$. Graph f and f^{-1} on the same set of axes.

OBJECTIVE
5 Graphing Inverse Functions

Notice that the graphs of f and f^{-1} in Example 5 are mirror images of each other, and the "mirror" is the dashed line $y = x$. This is true for every function and its inverse. For this reason, we say that *the graphs of f and f^{-1} are symmetric about the line $y = x$.*

To see why this happens, study the graph of a few ordered pairs and their switched coordinates in the diagram below.

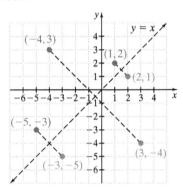

EXAMPLE 6 Graph the inverse of each function.

Solution The function is graphed in blue and the inverse is graphed in red.

a.

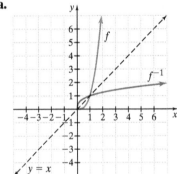

b.

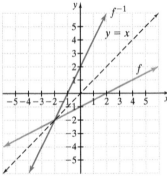

PRACTICE
6 Graph the inverse of each function.

a.

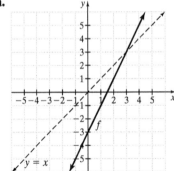

b.

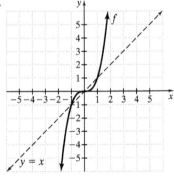

OBJECTIVE
6 Determining Whether Functions Are Inverses of Each Other

Notice in the table of values in Example 5 that $f(0) = -5$ and $f^{-1}(-5) = 0$, as expected. Also, for example, $f(1) = -2$ and $f^{-1}(-2) = 1$. In words, we say that for some input x, the function f^{-1} takes the output of x, called $f(x)$, back to x.

$$x \rightarrow f(x) \quad \text{and} \quad f^{-1}(f(x)) \rightarrow x$$
$$\downarrow \quad \downarrow \qquad \qquad \downarrow \quad \downarrow$$
$$f(0) = -5 \quad \text{and} \quad f^{-1}(-5) = 0$$
$$f(1) = -2 \quad \text{and} \quad f^{-1}(-2) = 1$$

In general,

> If f is a one-to-one function, then the inverse of f is the function f^{-1} such that
> $$(f^{-1} \circ f)(x) = x \quad \text{and} \quad (f \circ f^{-1})(x) = x$$

EXAMPLE 7 Show that if $f(x) = 3x + 2$, then $f^{-1}(x) = \dfrac{x-2}{3}$.

Solution See that $(f^{-1} \circ f)(x) = x$ and $(f \circ f^{-1})(x) = x$.

$$(f^{-1} \circ f)(x) = f^{-1}(f(x))$$
$$= f^{-1}(3x + 2) \qquad \text{Replace } f(x) \text{ with } 3x + 2.$$
$$= \frac{3x + 2 - 2}{3}$$
$$= \frac{3x}{3}$$
$$= x$$

$$(f \circ f^{-1})(x) = f(f^{-1}(x))$$
$$= f\left(\frac{x-2}{3}\right) \qquad \text{Replace } f^{-1}(x) \text{ with } \frac{x-2}{3}.$$
$$= 3\left(\frac{x-2}{3}\right) + 2$$
$$= x - 2 + 2$$
$$= x$$

PRACTICE
7 Show that if $f(x) = 4x - 1$, then $f^{-1}(x) = \dfrac{x+1}{4}$.

Graphing Calculator Explorations

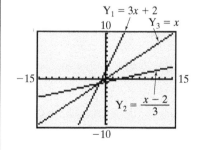

A graphing calculator can be used to visualize the results of Example 7. Recall that the graph of a function f and its inverse f^{-1} are mirror images of each other across the line $y = x$. To see this for the function from Example 7, use a square window and graph

the given function: $\quad Y_1 = 3x + 2$

its inverse: $\qquad\qquad Y_2 = \dfrac{x-2}{3}$

and the line: $\qquad\quad Y_3 = x$

See Exercises 67–70 in Exercise Set 12.2.

Vocabulary, Readiness & Video Check

Use the choices below to fill in each blank. Some choices will not be used, and some will be used more than once.

vertical	$(3,7)$	$(11,2)$	$y = x$	x	true
horizontal	$(7,3)$	$(2,11)$	$\dfrac{1}{f}$	the inverse of f	false

1. If $f(2) = 11$, the corresponding ordered pair is _____.
2. If $(7,3)$ is an ordered pair solution of $f(x)$, and $f(x)$ has an inverse, then an ordered pair solution of $f^{-1}(x)$ is
   _____.
3. The symbol f^{-1} means _____.
4. True or false: The function notation $f^{-1}(x)$ means $\dfrac{1}{f(x)}$. _____
5. To tell whether a graph is the graph of a function, use the _____ line test.
6. To tell whether the graph of a function is also a one-to-one function, use the _____ line test.
7. The graphs of f and f^{-1} are symmetric about the line _____.
8. Two functions are inverses of each other if $(f \circ f^{-1})(x) =$ _____ and $(f^{-1} \circ f)(x) =$ _____.

Martin-Gay Interactive Videos

See Video 12.2

Watch the section lecture video and answer the following questions.

OBJECTIVE 1
9. From ▭ Example 1 and the definition before, what makes a one-to-one function different from other types of functions?

OBJECTIVE 2
10. From ▭ Examples 2 and 3, if a graph passes the horizontal line test, but not the vertical line test, is it a one-to-one function? Explain.

OBJECTIVE 3
11. From ▭ Example 4 and the lecture before, if you find the inverse of a one-to-one function, is this inverse function also a one-to-one function? How do you know?

OBJECTIVE 4
12. From ▭ Examples 5 and 6, explain why the interchanging of x and y when finding an inverse equation makes sense given the definition of an inverse function.

OBJECTIVE 5
13. From ▭ Example 7, if you have the equation or graph of a one-to-one function, how can you graph its inverse without finding the inverse's equation?

OBJECTIVE 6
14. Based on ▭ Example 8 and the lecture before, what's wrong with the following statement? "If f is a one-to-one function, you can prove that f and f^{-1} are inverses of each other by showing that $f(f^{-1}(x)) = f^{-1}(f(x))$."

12.2 Exercise Set MyMathLab®

Determine whether each function is a one-to-one function. If it is one-to-one, list the inverse function by switching coordinates, or inputs and outputs. See Examples 1 and 3.

1. $f = \{(-1, -1), (1, 1), (0, 2), (2, 0)\}$

2. $g = \{(8, 6), (9, 6), (3, 4), (-4, 4)\}$

3. $h = \{(10, 10)\}$

4. $r = \{(1, 2), (3, 4), (5, 6), (6, 7)\}$

5. $f = \{(11, 12), (4, 3), (3, 4), (6, 6)\}$

6. $g = \{(0, 3), (3, 7), (6, 7), (-2, -2)\}$

7.

Month of 2009 (Input)	July	August	September	October	November	December
Unemployment Rate in Percent (Output)	9.4	9.7	9.8	10.1	10.0	10.0

(*Source:* U.S. Bureau of Labor Statistics)

8.

State (Input)	Texas	Massachusetts	Nevada	Idaho	Wisconsin
Number of Two-Year Colleges (Output)	70	22	3	3	31

(*Source:* University of Texas at Austin)

9.

State (Input)	California	Alaska	Indiana	Louisiana	New Mexico	Ohio
Rank in Population (Output)	1	47	16	25	36	7

(*Source:* U.S. Bureau of the Census)

△ 10.

Shape (Input)	Triangle	Pentagon	Quadrilateral	Hexagon	Decagon
Number of Sides (Output)	3	5	4	6	10

Given the one-to-one function $f(x) = x^3 + 2$, find the following.
[Hint: You do not need to find the equation for $f^{-1}(x)$.]

11. a. $f(1)$
  b. $f^{-1}(3)$

12. a. $f(0)$
  b. $f^{-1}(2)$

13. a. $f(-1)$
  b. $f^{-1}(1)$

14. a. $f(-2)$
  b. $f^{-1}(-6)$

Determine whether the graph of each function is the graph of a one-to-one function. See Example 2.

◉ 15.

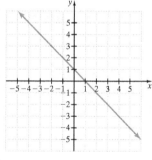

16.

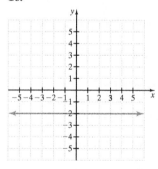

◉ 17.

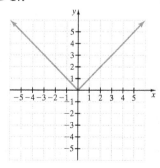

18.

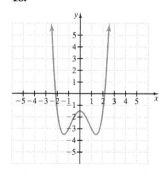

19.

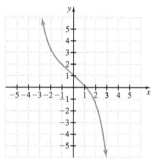

20.

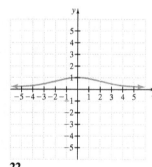

21.

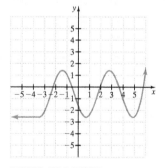

22.

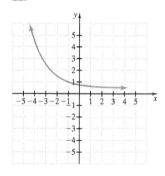

MIXED PRACTICE

Each of the following functions is one-to-one. Find the inverse of each function and graph the function and its inverse on the same set of axes. See Examples 4 and 5.

23. $f(x) = x + 4$

24. $f(x) = x - 5$

◉ 25. $f(x) = 2x - 3$

26. $f(x) = 4x + 9$

27. $f(x) = \frac{1}{2}x - 1$

28. $f(x) = -\frac{1}{2}x + 2$

29. $f(x) = x^3$

30. $f(x) = x^3 - 1$

Find the inverse of each one-to-one function. See Examples 4 and 5.

31. $f(x) = 5x + 2$

32. $f(x) = 6x - 1$

33. $f(x) = \frac{x - 2}{5}$

34. $f(x) = \frac{x - 3}{2}$

35. $f(x) = \sqrt[3]{x}$

36. $f(x) = \sqrt[3]{x + 1}$

▶ 37. $f(x) = \frac{5}{3x + 1}$

38. $f(x) = \frac{7}{2x + 4}$

39. $f(x) = (x + 2)^3$

40. $f(x) = (x - 5)^3$

Graph the inverse of each function on the same set of axes. See Example 6.

41.

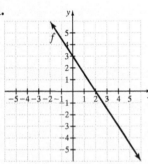

42.

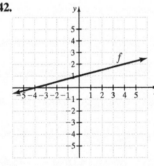

43.

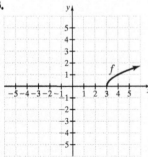

44.

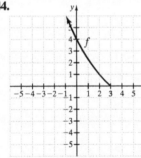

45.

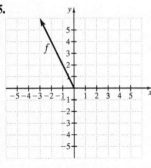

46.

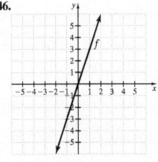

Solve. See Example 7.

▶ 47. If $f(x) = 2x + 1$, show that $f^{-1}(x) = \frac{x - 1}{2}$.

48. If $f(x) = 3x - 10$, show that $f^{-1}(x) = \frac{x + 10}{3}$.

49. If $f(x) = x^3 + 6$, show that $f^{-1}(x) = \sqrt[3]{x - 6}$.

50. If $f(x) = x^3 - 5$, show that $f^{-1}(x) = \sqrt[3]{x + 5}$.

REVIEW AND PREVIEW

Evaluate each of the following. See Section 10.2.

51. $25^{1/2}$ **52.** $49^{1/2}$

53. $16^{3/4}$ **54.** $27^{2/3}$

55. $9^{-3/2}$ **56.** $81^{-3/4}$

If $f(x) = 3^x$, find the following. In Exercises 59 and 60, give an exact answer and a two-decimal-place approximation. See Sections 5.1, 8.2, and 10.2.

57. $f(2)$ **58.** $f(0)$

59. $f\left(\frac{1}{2}\right)$ **60.** $f\left(\frac{2}{3}\right)$

CONCEPT EXTENSIONS

Solve. See the Concept Check in this section.

61. Suppose that f is a one-to-one function and that $f(2) = 9$.

    a. Write the corresponding ordered pair.

    b. Name one ordered pair that we know is a solution of the inverse of f, or f^{-1}.

62. Suppose that F is a one-to-one function and that $F\left(\frac{1}{2}\right) = -0.7$.

    a. Write the corresponding ordered pair.

    b. Name one ordered pair that we know is a solution of the inverse of F, or F^{-1}.

For Exercises 63 and 64,

a. *Write the ordered pairs for $f(x)$ whose points are highlighted. (Include the points whose coordinates are given.)*

b. *Write the corresponding ordered pairs for the inverse of f, f^{-1}.*

c. *Graph the ordered pairs for f^{-1} found in part b.*

d. *Graph $f^{-1}(x)$ by drawing a smooth curve through the plotted points.*

63.

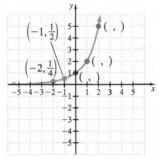

64.

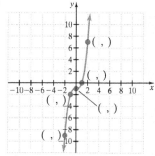

65. If you are given the graph of a function, describe how you can tell from the graph whether a function has an inverse.

66. Describe the appearance of the graphs of a function and its inverse.

Find the inverse of each given one-to-one function. Then use a graphing calculator to graph the function and its inverse on a square window.

67. $f(x) = 3x + 1$

68. $f(x) = -2x - 6$

69. $f(x) = \sqrt[3]{x + 1}$

70. $f(x) = x^3 - 3$

12.3 Exponential Functions

OBJECTIVES

1 Graph Exponential Functions.

2 Solve Equations of the Form $b^x = b^y$.

3 Solve Problems Modeled by Exponential Equations.

OBJECTIVE
1 **Graphing Exponential Functions**

In earlier chapters, we gave meaning to exponential expressions such as 2^x, where x is a rational number. For example,

$$2^3 = 2 \cdot 2 \cdot 2 \qquad \text{Three factors; each factor is 2}$$

$$2^{3/2} = (2^{1/2})^3 = \sqrt{2} \cdot \sqrt{2} \cdot \sqrt{2} \qquad \text{Three factors; each factor is } \sqrt{2}$$

When x is an irrational number (for example, $\sqrt{3}$), what meaning can we give to $2^{\sqrt{3}}$?

It is beyond the scope of this book to give precise meaning to 2^x if x is irrational. We can confirm your intuition and say that $2^{\sqrt{3}}$ is a real number and, since $1 < \sqrt{3} < 2$, $2^1 < 2^{\sqrt{3}} < 2^2$. We can also use a calculator and approximate $2^{\sqrt{3}}$: $2^{\sqrt{3}} \approx 3.321997$. In fact, as long as the base b is positive, b^x is a real number for all real numbers x. Finally, the rules of exponents apply whether x is rational or irrational as long as b is positive. In this section, we are interested in functions of the form $f(x) = b^x$, where $b > 0$. A function of this form is called an **exponential function.**

Exponential Function

A function of the form

$$f(x) = b^x$$

is called an **exponential function** if $b > 0$, b is not 1, and x is a real number.

Next, we practice graphing exponential functions.

EXAMPLE 1 Graph the exponential functions defined by $f(x) = 2^x$ and $g(x) = 3^x$ on the same set of axes.

Solution Graph each function by plotting points. Set up a table of values for each of the two functions.

(Continued on next page)

If each set of points is plotted and connected with a smooth curve, the following graphs result.

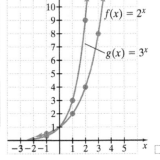

$f(x) = 2^x$	x	0	1	2	3	-1	-2
	$f(x)$	1	2	4	8	$\frac{1}{2}$	$\frac{1}{4}$

$g(x) = 3^x$	x	0	1	2	3	-1	-2
	$g(x)$	1	3	9	27	$\frac{1}{3}$	$\frac{1}{9}$

PRACTICE

1 Graph the exponential functions defined by $f(x) = 2^x$ and $g(x) = 7^x$ on the same set of axes.

A number of things should be noted about the two graphs of exponential functions in Example 1. First, the graphs show that $f(x) = 2^x$ and $g(x) = 3^x$ are one-to-one functions since each graph passes the vertical and horizontal line tests. The y-intercept of each graph is $(0, 1)$, but neither graph has an x-intercept. From the graph, we can also see that the domain of each function is all real numbers and that the range is $(0, \infty)$. We can also see that as x-values are increasing, y-values are increasing also.

EXAMPLE 2 Graph the exponential functions $y = \left(\frac{1}{2}\right)^x$ and $y = \left(\frac{1}{3}\right)^x$ on the same set of axes.

Solution As before, plot points and connect them with a smooth curve.

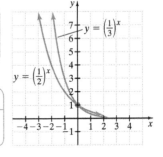

$y = \left(\frac{1}{2}\right)^x$	x	0	1	2	3	-1	-2
	y	1	$\frac{1}{2}$	$\frac{1}{4}$	$\frac{1}{8}$	2	4

$y = \left(\frac{1}{3}\right)^x$	x	0	1	2	3	-1	-2
	y	1	$\frac{1}{3}$	$\frac{1}{9}$	$\frac{1}{27}$	3	9

PRACTICE

2 Graph the exponential functions $f(x) = \left(\frac{1}{3}\right)^x$ and $g(x) = \left(\frac{1}{5}\right)^x$ on the same set of axes.

Each function in Example 2 again is a one-to-one function. The y-intercept of both is $(0, 1)$. The domain is the set of all real numbers, and the range is $(0, \infty)$.

Notice the difference between the graphs of Example 1 and the graphs of Example 2. An exponential function is always increasing if the base is greater than 1.

When the base is between 0 and 1, the graph is always decreasing. The figures on the next page summarize these characteristics of exponential functions.

$$f(x) = b^x, \quad b > 0, \quad b \neq 1$$

- one-to-one function
- *y*-intercept $(0, 1)$
- no *x*-intercept

- domain: $(-\infty, \infty)$
- range: $(0, \infty)$

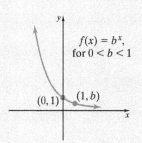

$f(x) = b^x$, for $b > 1$

$(0, 1)$ $(1, b)$

$f(x) = b^x$, for $0 < b < 1$

$(0, 1)$ $(1, b)$

EXAMPLE 3 Graph the exponential function $f(x) = 3^{x+2}$.

Solution As before, we find and plot a few ordered pair solutions. Then we connect the points with a smooth curve.

$f(x) = 3^{x+2}$	
x	$f(x)$
0	9
-1	3
-2	1
-3	$\frac{1}{3}$
-4	$\frac{1}{9}$

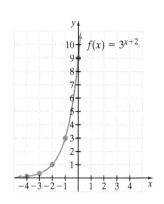

$f(x) = 3^{x+2}$

PRACTICE
3 Graph the exponential function $f(x) = 2^{x-3}$.

✓CONCEPT CHECK
Which functions are exponential functions?

a. $f(x) = x^3$ **b.** $g(x) = \left(\dfrac{2}{3}\right)^x$ **c.** $h(x) = 5^{x-2}$ **d.** $w(x) = (2x)^2$

OBJECTIVE
2 **Solving Equations of the Form $b^x = b^y$**

We have seen that an exponential function $y = b^x$ is a one-to-one function. Another way of stating this fact is a property that we can use to solve exponential equations.

Uniqueness of b^x

Let $b > 0$ and $b \neq 1$. Then $b^x = b^y$ is equivalent to $x = y$.

Thus, one way to solve an exponential equation depends on whether it's possible to write each side of the equation with the same base; that is, $b^x = b^y$. We solve by this method first.

EXAMPLE 4 Solve each equation for x.

a. $2^x = 16$ **b.** $9^x = 27$ **c.** $4^{x+3} = 8^x$

Solution

a. We write 16 as a power of 2 and then use the uniqueness of b^x to solve.

$$2^x = 16$$
$$2^x = 2^4$$

Since the bases are the same and are nonnegative, by the uniqueness of b^x, we then have that the exponents are equal. Thus,

$$x = 4$$

The solution is 4, or the solution set is $\{4\}$.

b. Notice that both 9 and 27 are powers of 3.

$$9^x = 27$$
$$(3^2)^x = 3^3 \quad \text{Write 9 and 27 as powers of 3.}$$
$$3^{2x} = 3^3$$
$$2x = 3 \quad \text{Apply the uniqueness of } b^x.$$
$$x = \frac{3}{2} \quad \text{Divide by 2.}$$

To check, replace x with $\frac{3}{2}$ in the original expression, $9^x = 27$. The solution is $\frac{3}{2}$.

c. Write both 4 and 8 as powers of 2.

$$4^{x+3} = 8^x$$
$$(2^2)^{x+3} = (2^3)^x$$
$$2^{2x+6} = 2^{3x}$$
$$2x + 6 = 3x \quad \text{Apply the uniqueness of } b^x.$$
$$6 = x \quad \text{Subtract } 2x \text{ from both sides.}$$

The solution is 6.

PRACTICE
4 Solve each equation for x.

a. $3^x = 9$ **b.** $8^x = 16$ **c.** $125^x = 25^{x-2}$

....

There is one major problem with the preceding technique. Often the two sides of an equation cannot easily be written as powers of a common base. We explore how to solve an equation such as $4 = 3^x$ with the help of **logarithms** later.

OBJECTIVE
3 **Solving Problems Modeled by Exponential Equations**

The bar graph on the next page shows the increase in the number of cellular phone users. Notice that the graph of the exponential function $y = 136.76(1.107)^x$ approximates the heights of the bars. This is just one example of how the world abounds with patterns that can be modeled by exponential functions. To make these applications realistic, we use numbers that warrant a calculator.

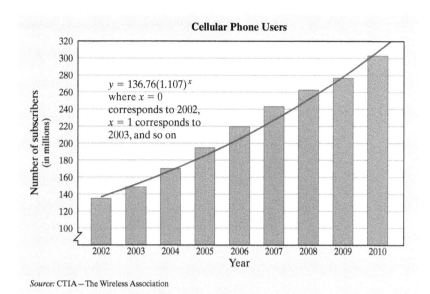

Cellular Phone Users

$y = 136.76(1.107)^x$ where $x = 0$ corresponds to 2002, $x = 1$ corresponds to 2003, and so on

Source: CTIA — The Wireless Association

Another application of an exponential function has to do with interest rates on loans.

The exponential function defined by $A = P\left(1 + \dfrac{r}{n}\right)^{nt}$ models the dollars A accrued (or owed) after P dollars are invested (or loaned) at an annual rate of interest r compounded n times each year for t years. This function is known as the compound interest formula.

EXAMPLE 5   **Using the Compound Interest Formula**

Find the amount owed at the end of 5 years if $1600 is loaned at a rate of 9% compounded monthly.

Solution   We use the formula $A = P\left(1 + \dfrac{r}{n}\right)^{nt}$, with the following values.

$P = \$1600$ (the amount of the loan)

$r = 9\% = 0.09$ (the annual rate of interest)

$n = 12$ (the number of times interest is compounded each year)

$t = 5$ (the duration of the loan, in years)

$$A = P\left(1 + \frac{r}{n}\right)^{nt} \qquad \text{Compound interest formula}$$

$$= 1600\left(1 + \frac{0.09}{12}\right)^{12(5)} \qquad \text{Substitute known values.}$$

$$= 1600(1.0075)^{60}$$

To approximate A, use the $\boxed{y^x}$ or $\boxed{\wedge}$ key on your calculator.

$$\boxed{2505.0896}$$

Thus, the amount A owed is approximately $2505.09.

PRACTICE

5   Find the amount owed at the end of 4 years if $3000 is loaned at a rate of 7% compounded semiannually (twice a year).

EXAMPLE 6 **Estimating Percent of Radioactive Material**

As a result of a nuclear accident, radioactive debris was carried through the atmosphere. One immediate concern was the impact that the debris had on the milk supply. The percent y of radioactive material in raw milk after t days is estimated by $y = 100(2.7)^{-0.1t}$. Estimate the expected percent of radioactive material in the milk after 30 days.

Solution Replace t with 30 in the given equation.

$$y = 100(2.7)^{-0.1t}$$
$$= 100(2.7)^{-0.1(30)} \quad \text{Let } t = 30.$$
$$= 100(2.7)^{-3}$$

To approximate the percent y, the following keystrokes may be used on a scientific calculator.

The display should read

$$\boxed{5.0805263}$$

Thus, approximately 5% of the radioactive material still remained in the milk supply after 30 days. □

PRACTICE

6 The percent p of light that passes through n successive sheets of a particular glass is given approximately by the function $p(n) = 100(2.7)^{-0.05n}$. Estimate the expected percent of light that will pass through the following numbers of sheets of glass. Round each to the nearest hundredth of a percent.

a. 2 sheets of glass   **b.** 10 sheets of glass

Graphing Calculator Explorations

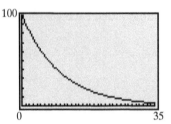

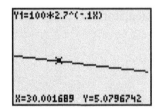

We can use a graphing calculator and its TRACE feature to solve Example 6 graphically.

To estimate the expected percent of radioactive material in the milk after 30 days, enter $Y_1 = 100(2.7)^{-0.1x}$. (The variable t in Example 6 is changed to x here to accommodate our work better on the graphing calculator.) The graph does not appear on a standard viewing window, so we need to determine an appropriate viewing window. Because it doesn't make sense to look at radioactivity *before* the nuclear accident, we use Xmin = 0. We are interested in finding the percent of radioactive material in the milk when $x = 30$, so we choose Xmax = 35 to leave enough space to see the graph at $x = 30$. Because the values of y are percents, it seems appropriate that $0 \le y \le 100$. (We also use Xscl = 1 and Yscl = 10.) Now we graph the function.

We can use the TRACE feature to obtain an approximation of the expected percent of radioactive material in the milk when $x = 30$. (A TABLE feature may also be used to approximate the percent.) To obtain a better approximation, let's use the ZOOM feature several times to zoom in near $x = 30$.

The percent of radioactive material in the milk 30 days after the nuclear accident was 5.08%, accurate to two decimal places.

Use a graphing calculator to find each percent. Approximate your solutions so that they are accurate to two decimal places.

1. Estimate the expected percent of radioactive material in the milk 2 days after the nuclear accident.

2. Estimate the expected percent of radioactive material in the milk 10 days after the nuclear accident.

3. Estimate the expected percent of radioactive material in the milk 15 days after the nuclear accident.

4. Estimate the expected percent of radioactive material in the milk 25 days after the nuclear accident.

Vocabulary, Readiness & Video Check

Use the choices to fill in each blank.

1. A function such as $f(x) = 2^x$ is a(n) _____ function.
   A. linear   **B.** quadratic   **C.** exponential

2. If $7^x = 7^y$, then _____.
   A. $x = 7^y$ **B.** $x = y$ **C.** $y = 7^x$ **D.** $7 = 7^y$

Answer the questions about the graph of $y = 2^x$, shown to the right.

3. Is this a function? _____

4. Is this a one-to-one function? _____

5. Is there an x-intercept? _____ If so, name the coordinates. _____

6. Is there a y-intercept? _____ If so, name the coordinates. _____

7. The domain of this function, in interval notation, is _____.

8. The range of this function, in interval notation, is _____.

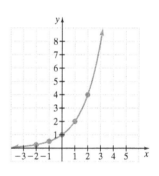

Martin-Gay Interactive Videos

See Video 12.3

Watch the section lecture video and answer the following questions.

OBJECTIVE 1
9. From the lecture before Example 1, what's the main difference between a polynomial function and an exponential function?

OBJECTIVE 2
10. From Examples 2 and 3, you can only apply the uniqueness of b^x to solve an exponential equation if you're able to do what?

OBJECTIVE 3
11. For Example 4, write the equation and find how much uranium will remain after 101 days. Round your answer to the nearest tenth.

12.3   Exercise Set   MyMathLab®

Graph each exponential function. See Examples 1 through 3.

1. $y = 5^x$

2. $y = 4^x$

3. $y = 2^x + 1$

4. $y = 3^x - 1$

5. $y = \left(\dfrac{1}{4}\right)^x$

6. $y = \left(\dfrac{1}{5}\right)^x$

7. $y = \left(\dfrac{1}{2}\right)^x - 2$

8. $y = \left(\dfrac{1}{3}\right)^x + 2$

9. $y = -2^x$

10. $y = -3^x$

11. $y = -\left(\dfrac{1}{4}\right)^x$

12. $y = -\left(\dfrac{1}{5}\right)^x$

13. $f(x) = 2^{x+1}$

14. $f(x) = 3^{x-1}$

15. $f(x) = 4^{x-2}$

16. $f(x) = 2^{x+3}$

Match each exponential equation with its graph below. See Examples 1 through 3.

17. $f(x) = \left(\dfrac{1}{2}\right)^x$

18. $f(x) = \left(\dfrac{1}{4}\right)^x$

19. $f(x) = 2^x$

20. $f(x) = 3^x$

A.

B.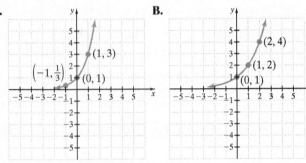

C.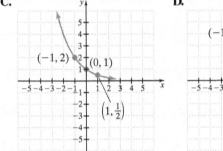

D.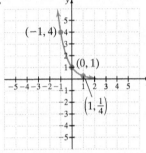

Solve each equation for x. See Example 4.

21. $3^x = 27$

22. $6^x = 36$

23. $16^x = 8$

24. $64^x = 16$

25. $32^{2x-3} = 2$

26. $9^{2x+1} = 81$

27. $\dfrac{1}{4} = 2^{3x}$

28. $\dfrac{1}{27} = 3^{2x}$

29. $5^x = 625$

30. $2^x = 64$

31. $4^x = 8$

32. $32^x = 4$

33. $27^{x+1} = 9$

34. $125^{x-2} = 25$

35. $81^{x-1} = 27^{2x}$

36. $4^{3x-7} = 32^{2x}$

Solve. Unless otherwise indicated, round results to one decimal place. See Example 6.

37. One type of uranium has a radioactive decay rate of 0.4% per day. If 30 pounds of this uranium is available today, how much will still remain after 50 days? Use $y = 30(0.996)^x$ and let x be 50.

38. The nuclear waste from an atomic energy plant decays at a rate of 3% each century. If 150 pounds of nuclear waste is disposed of, how much of it will still remain after 10 centuries? Use $y = 150(0.97)^x$, and let x be 10.

39. Cheese production in the United States is currently growing at a rate of 3% per year. The equation $y = 8.6(1.03)^x$ models the cheese production in the United States from 2003 to 2009. In this equation, y is the amount of cheese produced, in billions of pounds, and x represents the number of years after 2003. Round answers to the nearest tenth of a billion. (*Source:* National Agricultural Statistics Service)

a. Estimate the total cheese production in the United States in 2007.

b. Assuming this equation continues to be valid in the future, use the equation to predict the total amount of cheese produced in the United States in 2015.

40. Retail revenue from shopping on the Internet is currently growing at rate of 26% per year. In 2003, a total of $39 billion in revenue was collected through Internet retail sales. Answer the following questions using $y = 39(1.26)^t$, where y is Internet revenues in billions of dollars and t is the number of years after 2003. Round answers to the nearest tenth of a billion dollars. (*Source:* U.S. Bureau of the Census)

a. According to the model, what level of retail revenues from Internet shopping was expected in 2005?

b. If the given model continues to be valid, predict the level of Internet shopping revenues in 2015.

41. The equation $y = 140{,}242(1.083)^x$ models the number of American college students who studied abroad each year from 2000 through 2009. In the equation, y is the number of American students studying abroad, and x represents the number of years after 2000. Round answers to the nearest whole. (*Source:* Based on data from Institute of International Education, Open Doors)

a. Estimate the number of American students studying abroad in 2004.

b. Assuming this equation continues to be valid in the future, use this equation to predict the number of American students studying abroad in 2015.

42. Carbon dioxide (CO_2) is a greenhouse gas that contributes to global warming. Partially due to the combustion of fossil fuel, the amount of CO_2 in Earth's atmosphere has been increasing by 0.5% annually over the past century. In 2000, the concentration of CO_2 in the atmosphere was 369.4 parts per million by volume. To make the following predictions, use $y = 369.4(1.005)^t$ where y is the concentration of CO_2 in parts per million by volume and t is the number of years after 2000. (*Sources:* Based on data from the United Nations Environment Programme and the Carbon Dioxide Information Analysis Center)

a. Predict the concentration of CO_2 in the atmosphere in the year 2015.

b. Predict the concentration of CO_2 in the atmosphere in the year 2030.

The equation $y = 136.76(1.107)^x$ gives the number of cellular phone users y (in millions) in the United States for the years 2002 through 2010. In this equation, $x = 0$ corresponds to 2002, $x = 1$ corresponds to 2003, and so on. Use this model to solve Exercises 43 and 44. Round answers to the nearest tenth of a million.

43. Estimate the number of cell phone users in the year 2012.

44. Predict the number of cell phone users in 2014.

45. An unusually wet spring has caused the size of the Cape Cod mosquito population to increase by 8% each day. If an estimated 200,000 mosquitoes are on Cape Cod on May 12, find how many mosquitoes will inhabit the Cape on May 25. Use $y = 200{,}000(1.08)^x$ where x is number of days since May 12. Round to the nearest thousand.

46. The atmospheric pressure p, in pascals, on a weather balloon decreases with increasing height. This pressure, measured in millimeters of mercury, is related to the number of kilometers h above sea level by the function $p(h) = 760(2.7)^{-0.145h}$. Round to the nearest tenth of a pascal.

    a. Find the atmospheric pressure at a height of 1 kilometer.

    b. Find the atmospheric pressure at a height of 10 kilometers.

Solve. Use $A = P\left(1 + \dfrac{r}{n}\right)^{nt}$. Round answers to two decimal places. See Example 5.

47. Find the amount Erica owes at the end of 3 years if $6000 is loaned to her at a rate of 8% compounded monthly.

48. Find the amount owed at the end of 5 years if $3000 is loaned at a rate of 10% compounded quarterly.

49. Find the total amount Janina has in a college savings account if $2000 was invested and earned 6% compounded semiannually for 12 years.

50. Find the amount accrued if $500 is invested and earns 7% compounded monthly for 4 years.

REVIEW AND PREVIEW

Solve each equation. See Sections 2.3 and 6.6.

51. $5x - 2 = 18$

52. $3x - 7 = 11$

53. $3x - 4 = 3(x + 1)$

54. $2 - 6x = 6(1 - x)$

55. $x^2 + 6 = 5x$

56. $18 = 11x - x^2$

By inspection, find the value for x that makes each statement true. See Section 5.1.

57. $2^x = 8$

58. $3^x = 9$

59. $5^x = \dfrac{1}{5}$

60. $4^x = 1$

CONCEPT EXTENSIONS

Is the given function an exponential function? See the Concept Check in this section.

61. $f(x) = 1.5x^2$

62. $g(x) = 3^x$

63. $h(x) = \left(\dfrac{1}{2}x\right)^2$

64. $F(x) = 0.4^{x+1}$

Match each exponential function with its graph.

65. $f(x) = 2^{-x}$

66. $f(x) = \left(\dfrac{1}{2}\right)^{-x}$

67. $f(x) = 4^{-x}$

68. $f(x) = \left(\dfrac{1}{3}\right)^{-x}$

A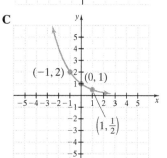

B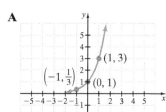

C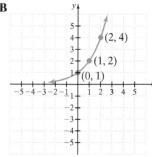

D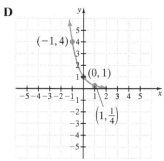

69. Explain why the graph of an exponential function $y = b^x$ contains the point $(1, b)$.

70. Explain why an exponential function $y = b^x$ has a y-intercept of $(0, 1)$.

Graph.

71. $y = |3^x|$

72. $y = \left|\left(\dfrac{1}{3}\right)^x\right|$

73. $y = 3^{|x|}$

74. $y = \left(\dfrac{1}{3}\right)^{|x|}$

75. Graph $y = 2^x$ and $y = \left(\dfrac{1}{2}\right)^{-x}$ on the same set of axes. Describe what you see and why.

76. Graph $y = 2^x$ and $x = 2^y$ on the same set of axes. Describe what you see.

Use a graphing calculator to solve. Estimate your results to two decimal places.

77. Verify the results of Exercise 37.

78. Verify the results of Exercise 38.

79. From Exercise 37, estimate the number of pounds of uranium that will be available after 100 days.

80. From Exercise 37, estimate the number of pounds of uranium that will be available after 120 days.

12.4 Exponential Growth and Decay Functions

OBJECTIVES

1 Model Exponential Growth.

2 Model Exponential Decay.

Now that we can graph exponential functions, let's learn about exponential growth and exponential decay.

A quantity that grows or decays by the same percent at regular time periods is said to have **exponential growth** or **exponential decay.** There are many real-life examples of exponential growth and decay, such as population, bacteria, viruses, and radioactive substances, just to name a few.

Recall the graphs of exponential functions.

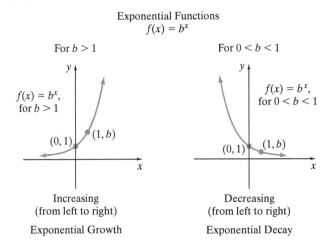

Exponential Functions
$f(x) = b^x$

For $b > 1$

$f(x) = b^x,$
for $b > 1$

(0, 1) (1, b)

Increasing
(from left to right)

Exponential Growth

For $0 < b < 1$

$f(x) = b^x,$
for $0 < b < 1$

(0, 1) (1, b)

Decreasing
(from left to right)

Exponential Decay

OBJECTIVE

1 Modeling Exponential Growth

We begin with exponential growth, as described below.

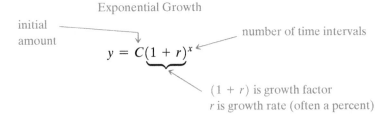

Exponential Growth

initial amount

number of time intervals

$$y = C(1 + r)^x$$

$(1 + r)$ is growth factor
r is growth rate (often a percent)

EXAMPLE 1 In 1995, let's suppose a town named Jackson had a population of 15,500 and was consistently increasing by 10% per year. If this yearly increase continues, predict the city's population in 2015. (Round to the nearest whole.)

Solution: Let's begin to understand by calculating the city's population each year:

Time Interval	$x = 1$	$x = 2$	3	4	5	and so on ...
Year	1996	1997	1998	1999	2000	
Population	17,050	18,755	20,631	22,694	24,963	

$\lfloor 15,500 + 0.10(15,500)\rfloor$ $\lfloor 17,050 + 0.10(17,050)\rfloor$

This is an example of exponential growth, so let's use our formula with

$$C = 15,500; r = 0.10; x = 2015 - 1995 = 20$$

Then,

$$y = C(1 + r)^x$$
$$= 15,500(1 + 0.10)^{20}$$
$$= 15,500(1.1)^{20}$$
$$\approx 104,276$$

In 2015, we predict the population of Jackson to be 104,276.

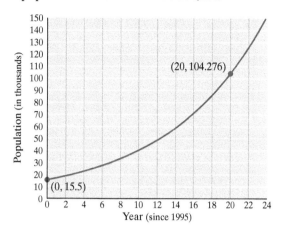

PRACTICE

1   In 2000, the town of Jackson (from Example 1) had a population of 25,000 and started consistently increasing by 12% per year. If this yearly increase continues, predict the city's population in 2015. Round to the nearest whole.

Note: The exponential growth formula, $y = C(1 + r)^x$, should remind you of the compound interest formula from the previous section, $A = P(1 + \frac{r}{n})^{nt}$. In fact, if the number of compoundings per year, n, is 1, the interest formula becomes $A = P(1 + r)^t$, which is the exponential growth formula written with different variables.

OBJECTIVE

2   Modeling Exponential Decay

Now let's study exponential decay.

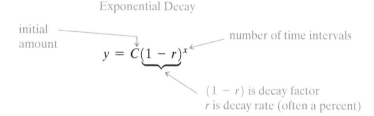

EXAMPLE 2   A large golf country club holds a singles tournament each year. At the start of the tournament for a particular year, there are 512 players. After each round, half the players are eliminated. How many players remain after 6 rounds?

Solution: This is an example of exponential decay.

Let's begin to understand by calculating the number of players after a few rounds.

Round (same as interval)	1	2	3	4	and so on …
Players (at end of round)	256	128	64	32	

$$\underset{512 - 0.50(512)}{\uparrow} \qquad \underset{256 - 0.50(256)}{\uparrow}$$

Here, $C = 512$; $r = \dfrac{1}{2}$ or $50\% = 0.50$; $x = 6$

Thus,

$$
\begin{aligned}
y &= 512(1 - 0.50)^6 \\
&= 512(0.50)^6 \\
&= 8
\end{aligned}
$$

(Continued on next page)

After 6 rounds, there are 8 players remaining.

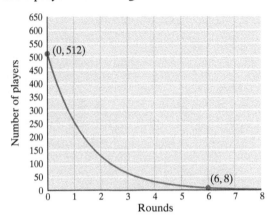

PRACTICE

2 A tournament with 800 persons is played so that after each round, the number of players decreases by 30%. Find the number of players after round 9. Round your answer to the nearest whole.

The **half-life** of a substance is the amount of time it takes for half of the substance to decay.

EXAMPLE 3 A form of DDT pesticide (banned in 1972) has a half-life of approximately 15 years. If a storage unit had 400 pounds of DDT, find how much DDT is remaining after 72 years. Round to the nearest tenth of a pound.

Solution: Here, we need to be careful because each time interval is 15 years, the half-life.

Time Interval	1	2	3	4	5	and so on ...
Years Passed	15	$2 \cdot 15 = 30$	45	60	75	
Pounds of DDT	200	100	50	25	12.5	

From the table, we see that after 72 years, between 4 and 5 intervals, there should be between 12.5 and 25 pounds of DDT remaining.

Let's calculate x, the number of time intervals.

$$x = \frac{72 \, (\text{years})}{15 \, (\text{half-life})} = 4.8$$

Now, using our exponential decay formula and the definition of half-life, for each time interval x, the decay rate r is $\frac{1}{2}$ or 50% or 0.50.

$$y = 400(1 - 0.50)^{4.8} \quad \text{—time intervals for 72 years}$$

original amount   decay rate

$$y = 400(0.50)^{4.8}$$
$$y \approx 14.4$$

In 72 years, 14.4 pounds of DDT remain.

PRACTICE

3 Use the information from Example 3 and calculate how much of a 500-gram sample of DDT will remain after 51 years. Round to the nearest tenth of a gram.

Vocabulary, Readiness & Video Check

Martin-Gay Interactive Videos

See Video 12.4

Watch the section lecture video and answer the following questions.

OBJECTIVE
1

1. Example 1 reviews exponential growth. Explain how you find the growth rate and the correct number of time intervals.

OBJECTIVE
2

2. Explain how you know that ⊟ Example 2 has to do with exponential decay, and not exponential growth.

OBJECTIVE
2

3. For ⊟ Example 3, which has to do with half-life, explain how to calculate the number of time intervals. Also, what is the decay rate for half-life and why?

12.4 Exercise Set   MyMathLab®

Practice using the exponential growth formula by completing the table below. Round final amounts to the nearest whole. See Example 1.

	Original Amount	Growth Rate per Year	Number of Years, x	Final Amount after x Years of Growth
1.	305	5%	8	
2.	402	7%	5	
3.	2000	11%	41	
4.	1000	47%	19	
5.	17	29%	28	
6.	29	61%	12	

Practice using the exponential decay formula by completing the table below. Round final amounts to the nearest whole. See Example 2.

	Original Amount	Decay Rate per Year	Number of Years, x	Final Amount after x Years of Decay
7.	305	5%	8	
8.	402	7%	5	
9.	10,000	12%	15	
10.	15,000	16%	11	
11.	207,000	32%	25	
12.	325,000	29%	31	

MIXED PRACTICE

Solve. Unless noted otherwise, round answers to the nearest whole. See Examples 1 and 2.

13. Suppose a city with population 500,000 has been growing at a rate of 3% per year. If this rate continues, find the population of this city in 12 years.

14. Suppose a city with population 320,000 has been growing at a rate of 4% per year. If this rate continues, find the population of this city in 20 years.

15. The number of employees for a certain company has been decreasing each year by 5%. If the company currently has 640 employees and this rate continues, find the number of employees in 10 years.

16. The number of students attending summer school at a local community college has been decreasing each year by 7%. If 984 students currently attend summer school and this rate continues, find the number of students attending summer school in 5 years.

17. National Park Service personnel are trying to increase the size of the bison population of Theodore Roosevelt National Park. If 260 bison currently live in the park, and if the population's rate of growth is 2.5% annually, find how many bison there should be in 10 years.

18. The size of the rat population of a wharf area grows at a rate of 8% monthly. If there are 200 rats in January, find how many rats should be expected by next January.

19. A rare isotope of a nuclear material is very unstable, decaying at a rate of 15% each second. Find how much isotope remains 10 seconds after 5 grams of the isotope is created.

20. An accidental spill of 75 grams of radioactive material in a local stream has led to the presence of radioactive debris decaying at a rate of 4% each day. Find how much debris still remains after 14 days.

Practice using the exponential decay formula with half-lives by completing the table below. The first row has been completed for you. See Example 3.

	Original Amount	Half-Life (in years)	Number of Years	Time Intervals, $x = \left(\dfrac{\text{Years}}{\text{Half-Life}}\right)$ Rounded to Tenths if Needed	Final Amount after x Time Intervals (rounded to tenths)	Is Your Final Amount Reasonable?
	60	8	10	$\dfrac{10}{8} = 1.25$	25.2	yes
21. **a.**	40	7	14			
b.	40	7	11			
22. **a.**	200	12	36			
b.	200	12	40			
23.	21	152	500			
24.	35	119	500			

Solve. Round answers to the nearest tenth.

25. A form of nickel has a half-life of 96 years. How much of a 30-gram sample is left after 250 years?

26. A form of uranium has a half-life of 72 years. How much of a 100-gram sample is left after 500 years?

REVIEW AND PREVIEW

By inspection, find the value for x that makes each statement true. See Sections 5.1 and 12.3.

27. $2^x = 8$ **28.** $3^x = 9$ **29.** $5^x = \dfrac{1}{5}$ **30.** $4^x = 1$

CONCEPT EXTENSIONS

31. An item is on sale for 40% off its original price. If it is then marked down an additional 60%, does this mean the item is free? Discuss why or why not.

32. Uranium U-232 has a half-life of 72 years. What eventually happens to a 10 gram sample? Does it ever completely decay and disappear? Discuss why or why not.

12.5 Logarithmic Functions

OBJECTIVES

1 Write Exponential Equations with Logarithmic Notation and Write Logarithmic Equations with Exponential Notation.

2 Solve Logarithmic Equations by Using Exponential Notation.

3 Identify and Graph Logarithmic Functions.

OBJECTIVE

1 Using Logarithmic Notation

Since the exponential function $f(x) = 2^x$ is a one-to-one function, it has an inverse.

We can create a table of values for f^{-1} by switching the coordinates in the accompanying table of values for $f(x) = 2^x$.

x	$y = f(x)$
-3	$\dfrac{1}{8}$
-2	$\dfrac{1}{4}$
-1	$\dfrac{1}{2}$
0	1
1	2
2	4
3	8

x	$y = f^{-1}(x)$
$\dfrac{1}{8}$	-3
$\dfrac{1}{4}$	-2
$\dfrac{1}{2}$	-1
1	0
2	1
4	2
8	3

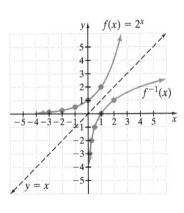

The graphs of $f(x)$ and its inverse are shown on the previous page. Notice that the graphs of f and f^{-1} are symmetric about the line $y = x$, as expected.

Now we would like to be able to write an equation for f^{-1}. To do so, we follow the steps for finding an inverse.

$$f(x) = 2^x$$

Step 1. Replace $f(x)$ by y. $\qquad\qquad y = 2^x$

Step 2. Interchange x and y. $\qquad x = 2^y$

Step 3. Solve for y.

At this point, we are stuck. To solve this equation for y, a new notation, the **logarithmic notation,** is needed.

The symbol $\log_b x$ means "the power to which b is raised to produce a result of x." In other words,

$$\log_b x = y \quad \text{means} \quad b^y = x$$

We say that $\log_b x$ is "the logarithm of x to the base b" or "the log of x to the base b."

Logarithmic Definition

If $b > 0$ and $b \neq 1$, then

$$y = \log_b x \text{ means } x = b^y$$

for every $x > 0$ and every real number y.

▶ Helpful Hint

Notice that a *logarithm* is an *exponent*. In other words, $\log_3 9$ is the *power* that we raise 3 in order to get 9.

Before returning to the function $x = 2^y$ and solving it for y in terms of x, let's practice using the new notation $\log_b x$.

It is important to be able to write exponential equations from logarithmic notation and vice versa. The following table shows examples of both forms.

Logarithmic Equation	Corresponding Exponential Equation
$\log_3 9 = 2$	$3^2 = 9$
$\log_6 1 = 0$	$6^0 = 1$
$\log_2 8 = 3$	$2^3 = 8$
$\log_4 \dfrac{1}{16} = -2$	$4^{-2} = \dfrac{1}{16}$
$\log_8 2 = \dfrac{1}{3}$	$8^{1/3} = 2$

EXAMPLE 1 Write each as an exponential equation.

a. $\log_5 25 = 2$ **b.** $\log_6 \dfrac{1}{6} = -1$ **c.** $\log_2 \sqrt{2} = \dfrac{1}{2}$ **d.** $\log_7 x = 5$

Solution

a. $\log_5 25 = 2$ means $5^2 = 25$

b. $\log_6 \dfrac{1}{6} = -1$ means $6^{-1} = \dfrac{1}{6}$

c. $\log_2 \sqrt{2} = \dfrac{1}{2}$ means $2^{1/2} = \sqrt{2}$

d. $\log_7 x = 5$ means $7^5 = x$

(Continued on next page)

PRACTICE
1 Write each as an exponential equation.

a. $\log_3 81 = 4$ **b.** $\log_5 \frac{1}{5} = -1$ **c.** $\log_7 \sqrt{7} = \frac{1}{2}$ **d.** $\log_{13} y = 4$

EXAMPLE 2 Write each as a logarithmic equation.

a. $9^3 = 729$ **b.** $6^{-2} = \frac{1}{36}$ **c.** $5^{1/3} = \sqrt[3]{5}$ **d.** $\pi^4 = x$

Solution

a. $9^3 = 729$ means $\log_9 729 = 3$

b. $6^{-2} = \frac{1}{36}$ means $\log_6 \frac{1}{36} = -2$

c. $5^{1/3} = \sqrt[3]{5}$ means $\log_5 \sqrt[3]{5} = \frac{1}{3}$

d. $\pi^4 = x$ means $\log_\pi x = 4$

PRACTICE
2 Write each as a logarithmic equation.

a. $4^3 = 64$ **b.** $6^{1/3} = \sqrt[3]{6}$ **c.** $5^{-3} = \frac{1}{125}$ **d.** $\pi^7 = z$

EXAMPLE 3 Find the value of each logarithmic expression.

a. $\log_4 16$ **b.** $\log_{10} \frac{1}{10}$ **c.** $\log_9 3$

Solution

a. $\log_4 16 = 2$ because $4^2 = 16$

b. $\log_{10} \frac{1}{10} = -1$ because $10^{-1} = \frac{1}{10}$

c. $\log_9 3 = \frac{1}{2}$ because $9^{1/2} = \sqrt{9} = 3$

PRACTICE
3 Find the value of each logarithmic expression.

a. $\log_3 9$ **b.** $\log_2 \frac{1}{8}$ **c.** $\log_{49} 7$

▶ **Helpful Hint**

Another method for evaluating logarithms such as those in Example 3 is to set the expression equal to x and then write them in exponential form to find x. For example:

a. $\log_4 16 = x$ means $4^x = 16$. Since $4^2 = 16$, $x = 2$ or $\log_4 16 = 2$.

b. $\log_{10} \frac{1}{10} = x$ means $10^x = \frac{1}{10}$. Since $10^{-1} = \frac{1}{10}$, $x = -1$ or $\log_{10} \frac{1}{10} = -1$.

c. $\log_9 3 = x$ means $9^x = 3$. Since $9^{1/2} = 3$, $x = \frac{1}{2}$ or $\log_9 3 = \frac{1}{2}$.

OBJECTIVE

2   Solving Logarithmic Equations

The ability to interchange the logarithmic and exponential forms of a statement is often the key to solving logarithmic equations.

EXAMPLE 4   Solve each equation for x.

a. $\log_4 \dfrac{1}{4} = x$ **b.** $\log_5 x = 3$ **c.** $\log_x 25 = 2$ **d.** $\log_3 1 = x$ **e.** $\log_b 1 = x$

Solution

a. $\log_4 \dfrac{1}{4} = x$ means $4^x = \dfrac{1}{4}$. Solve $4^x = \dfrac{1}{4}$ for x.

$$4^x = \dfrac{1}{4}$$
$$4^x = 4^{-1}$$

Since the bases are the same, by the uniqueness of b^x, we have that

$$x = -1$$

The solution is -1 or the solution set is $\{-1\}$. To check, see that $\log_4 \dfrac{1}{4} = -1$, since $4^{-1} = \dfrac{1}{4}$.

b. $\log_5 x = 3$

$\quad 5^3 = x$ Write as an exponential equation.

$125 = x$

The solution is 125.

c. $\log_x 25 = 2$

$\quad x^2 = 25$ Write as an exponential equation. Here $x > 0, x \ne 1$.

$\quad x = 5$

Even though $(-5)^2 = 25$, the base b of a logarithm must be positive. The solution is 5.

d. $\log_3 1 = x$

$\quad 3^x = 1$ Write as an exponential equation.

$\quad 3^x = 3^0$ Write 1 as 3^0.

$\quad x = 0$ Use the uniqueness of b^x.

The solution is 0.

e. $\log_b 1 = x$

$\quad b^x = 1$ Write as an exponential equation. Here, $b > 0$ and $b \ne 1$.

$\quad b^x = b^0$ Write 1 as b^0.

$\quad x = 0$ Apply the uniqueness of b^x.

The solution is 0.

PRACTICE

4   Solve each equation for x.

a. $\log_5 \dfrac{1}{25} = x$ **b.** $\log_x 8 = 3$ **c.** $\log_6 x = 2$

d. $\log_{13} 1 = x$ **e.** $\log_h 1 = x$

In Example 4e, we proved an important property of logarithms. That is, $\log_b 1$ is always 0. This property as well as two important others are given next.

Properties of Logarithms

If b is a real number, $b > 0$, and $b \neq 1$, then

1. $\log_b 1 = 0$

2. $\log_b b^x = x$

3. $b^{\log_b x} = x$

To see that **2.** $\log_b b^x = x$, change the logarithmic form to exponential form. Then, $\log_b b^x = x$ means $b^x = b^x$. In exponential form, the statement is true, so in logarithmic form, the statement is also true.

To understand **3.** $b^{\log_b x} = x$, write this exponential equation as an equivalent logarithm.

EXAMPLE 5 Simplify.

a. $\log_3 3^2$ **b.** $\log_7 7^{-1}$ **c.** $5^{\log_5 3}$ **d.** $2^{\log_2 6}$

Solution

a. From Property 2, $\log_3 3^2 = 2$.

b. From Property 2, $\log_7 7^{-1} = -1$.

c. From Property 3, $5^{\log_5 3} = 3$.

d. From Property 3, $2^{\log_2 6} = 6$.

PRACTICE

5 Simplify.

a. $\log_5 5^4$ **b.** $\log_9 9^{-2}$ **c.** $6^{\log_6 5}$ **d.** $7^{\log_7 4}$

. . . .

OBJECTIVE

3 Graphing Logarithmic Functions

Let us now return to the function $f(x) = 2^x$ and write an equation for its inverse, $f^{-1}(x)$. Recall our earlier work.

$$f(x) = 2^x$$

Step 1. Replace $f(x)$ by y. $y = 2^x$

Step 2. Interchange x and y. $x = 2^y$

Having gained proficiency with the notation $\log_b x$, we can now complete the steps for writing the inverse equation by writing $x = 2^y$ as an equivalent logarithm.

Step 3. Solve for y. $y = \log_2 x$

Step 4. Replace y with $f^{-1}(x)$. $f^{-1}(x) = \log_2 x$

Thus, $f^{-1}(x) = \log_2 x$ defines a function that is the inverse function of the function $f(x) = 2^x$. The function $f^{-1}(x)$ or $y = \log_2 x$ is called a **logarithmic function.**

Logarithmic Function

If x is a positive real number, b is a constant positive real number, and b is not 1, then a **logarithmic function** is a function that can be defined by

$$f(x) = \log_b x$$

The domain of f is the set of positive real numbers, and the range of f is the set of real numbers.

✓CONCEPT CHECK

Let $f(x) = \log_3 x$ and $g(x) = 3^x$. These two functions are inverses of each other. Since $(2, 9)$ is an ordered pair solution of $g(x)$ or $g(2) = 9$, what ordered pair do we know to be a solution of $f(x)$? Also, find $f(9)$. Explain why.

We can explore logarithmic functions by graphing them.

EXAMPLE 6   Graph the logarithmic function $y = \log_2 x$.

Solution   First we write the equation with exponential notation as $2^y = x$. Then we find some ordered pair solutions that satisfy this equation. Finally, we plot the points and connect them with a smooth curve. The domain of this function is $(0, \infty)$, and the range is all real numbers.

Since $x = 2^y$ is solved for x, we choose y-values and compute corresponding x-values.

If $y = 0, x = 2^0 = 1$
If $y = 1, x = 2^1 = 2$
If $y = 2, x = 2^2 = 4$
If $y = -1, x = 2^{-1} = \dfrac{1}{2}$

$x = 2^y$	y
1	0
2	1
4	2
$\dfrac{1}{2}$	-1

Notice that the x-intercept is $(1, 0)$ and there is no y-intercept.

PRACTICE

6   Graph the logarithmic function $y = \log_9 x$.

EXAMPLE 7   Graph the logarithmic function $f(x) = \log_{1/3} x$.

Solution   Replace $f(x)$ with y and write the result with exponential notation.

$$f(x) = \log_{1/3} x$$
$$y = \log_{1/3} x \quad \text{Replace } f(x) \text{ with } y.$$
$$\left(\frac{1}{3}\right)^y = x \quad \text{Write in exponential form.}$$

Now we can find ordered pair solutions that satisfy $\left(\dfrac{1}{3}\right)^y = x$, plot these points, and connect them with a smooth curve.

If $y = 0, x = \left(\dfrac{1}{3}\right)^0 = 1$
If $y = 1, x = \left(\dfrac{1}{3}\right)^1 = \dfrac{1}{3}$
If $y = -1, x = \left(\dfrac{1}{3}\right)^{-1} = 3$
If $y = -2, x = \left(\dfrac{1}{3}\right)^{-2} = 9$

$x = \left(\dfrac{1}{3}\right)^y$	y
1	0
$\dfrac{1}{3}$	1
3	-1
9	-2

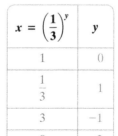
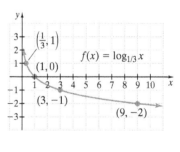

The domain of this function is $(0, \infty)$, and the range is the set of all real numbers. The x-intercept is $(1, 0)$ and there is no y-intercept.

PRACTICE

7   Graph the logarithmic function $y = \log_{1/4} x$.

The following figures summarize characteristics of logarithmic functions.

$$f(x) = \log_b x, b > 0, b \neq 1$$

- one-to-one function
- x-intercept $(1, 0)$
- no y-intercept

- domain: $(0, \infty)$
- range: $(-\infty, \infty)$

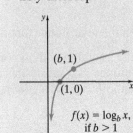

$(b, 1)$

$(1, 0)$

$f(x) = \log_b x,$ if $b > 1$

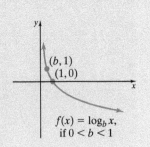

$(b, 1)$
$(1, 0)$

$f(x) = \log_b x,$ if $0 < b < 1$

Vocabulary, Readiness & Video Check

Use the choices to fill in each blank.

1. A function such as $y = \log_2 x$ is a(n) _____ function.

   A. linear   **B.** logarithmic   **C.** quadratic   **D.** exponential

2. If $y = \log_2 x$, then _____.

   A. $x = y$ **B.** $2^x = y$ **C.** $2^y = x$ **D.** $2y = x$

Answer the questions about the graph of $y = \log_2 x$, shown to the left.

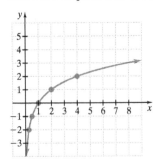

3. Is this a one-to-one function? _____

4. Is there an x-intercept? _____ If so, name the coordinates. _____

5. Is there a y-intercept? _____ If so, name the coordinates. _____

6. The domain of this function, in interval notation, is _____.

7. The range of this function, in interval notation, is _____.

Martin-Gay Interactive Videos

See Video 12.5

Watch the section lecture video and answer the following questions.

OBJECTIVE 1

8. Notice from the definition of a logarithm and from ⊟ Examples 1–4 that a logarithmic statement equals the power in the exponent statement, such as $b^y = x$. What conclusion can you make about logarithms and exponents?

OBJECTIVE 2

9. From ⊟ Examples 8 and 9, how do you solve a logarithmic equation?

OBJECTIVE 3

10. In ⊟ Example 12, why is it easier to choose values for y when finding ordered pairs for the graph?

12.5   Exercise Set   MyMathLab®

Write each as an exponential equation. See Example 1.

1. $\log_6 36 = 2$

2. $\log_2 32 = 5$

3. $\log_3 \frac{1}{27} = -3$

4. $\log_5 \frac{1}{25} = -2$

5. $\log_{10} 1000 = 3$

6. $\log_{10} 10 = 1$

7. $\log_9 x = 4$

8. $\log_8 y = 7$

9. $\log_\pi \frac{1}{\pi^2} = -2$

10. $\log_e \frac{1}{e} = -1$

11. $\log_7 \sqrt{7} = \frac{1}{2}$

12. $\log_{11} \sqrt[4]{11} = \frac{1}{4}$

13. $\log_{0.7} 0.343 = 3$

14. $\log_{1.2} 1.44 = 2$

15. $\log_3 \frac{1}{81} = -4$

16. $\log_{1/4} 16 = -2$

Write each as a logarithmic equation. See Example 2.

17. $2^4 = 16$

18. $5^3 = 125$

19. $10^2 = 100$

20. $10^4 = 10,000$

21. $\pi^3 = x$

22. $\pi^5 = y$

23. $10^{-1} = \frac{1}{10}$

24. $10^{-2} = \frac{1}{100}$

25. $4^{-2} = \frac{1}{16}$

26. $3^{-4} = \frac{1}{81}$

27. $5^{1/2} = \sqrt{5}$

28. $4^{1/3} = \sqrt[3]{4}$

Find the value of each logarithmic expression. See Examples 3 and 5.

29. $\log_2 8$

30. $\log_3 9$

31. $\log_3 \frac{1}{9}$

32. $\log_2 \frac{1}{32}$

33. $\log_{25} 5$

34. $\log_8 \frac{1}{2}$

35. $\log_{1/2} 2$

36. $\log_{2/3} \frac{4}{9}$

37. $\log_6 1$

38. $\log_9 9$

39. $\log_{10} 100$

40. $\log_{10} \frac{1}{10}$

41. $\log_3 81$

42. $\log_2 16$

43. $\log_4 \frac{1}{64}$

44. $\log_3 \frac{1}{9}$

Solve. See Example 4.

45. $\log_3 9 = x$

46. $\log_2 8 = x$

47. $\log_3 x = 4$

48. $\log_2 x = 3$

49. $\log_x 49 = 2$

50. $\log_x 8 = 3$

51. $\log_2 \frac{1}{8} = x$

52. $\log_3 \frac{1}{81} = x$

53. $\log_3 \frac{1}{27} = x$

54. $\log_5 \frac{1}{125} = x$

55. $\log_8 x = \frac{1}{3}$

56. $\log_9 x = \frac{1}{2}$

57. $\log_4 16 = x$

58. $\log_2 16 = x$

59. $\log_{3/4} x = 3$

60. $\log_{2/3} x = 2$

61. $\log_x 100 = 2$

62. $\log_x 27 = 3$

63. $\log_2 2^4 = x$

64. $\log_6 6^{-2} = x$

65. $3^{\log_3 5} = x$

66. $5^{\log_5 7} = x$

67. $\log_x \frac{1}{7} = \frac{1}{2}$

68. $\log_x 2 = -\frac{1}{3}$

Simplify. See Example 5.

69. $\log_5 5^3$

70. $\log_6 6^2$

71. $2^{\log_2 3}$

72. $7^{\log_7 4}$

73. $\log_9 9$

74. $\log_2 2$

75. $\log_8 (8)^{-1}$

76. $\log_{11} (11)^{-1}$

Graph each logarithmic function. Label any intercepts. See Examples 6 and 7.

77. $y = \log_3 x$

78. $y = \log_8 x$

79. $f(x) = \log_{1/4} x$

80. $f(x) = \log_{1/2} x$

81. $f(x) = \log_5 x$

82. $f(x) = \log_6 x$

83. $f(x) = \log_{1/6} x$

84. $f(x) = \log_{1/5} x$

REVIEW AND PREVIEW

Simplify each rational expression. See Section 7.1.

85. $\frac{x + 3}{3 + x}$

86. $\frac{x - 5}{5 - x}$

87. $\frac{x^2 - 8x + 16}{2x - 8}$

88. $\frac{x^2 - 3x - 10}{2 + x}$

Add or subtract as indicated. See Sections 7.3 and 7.4.

89. $\frac{2}{x} + \frac{3}{x^2}$

90. $\frac{5}{y + 1} - \frac{4}{y - 1}$

91. $\frac{3x}{x + 3} + \frac{9}{x + 3}$

92. $\frac{m^2}{m + 1} - \frac{1}{m + 1}$

CONCEPT EXTENSIONS

Solve. See the Concept Check in this section.

93. Let $f(x) = \log_5 x$. Then $g(x) = 5^x$ is the inverse of $f(x)$. The ordered pair $(2, 25)$ is a solution of the function $g(x)$.

   a. Write this solution using function notation.

   b. Write an ordered pair that we know to be a solution of $f(x)$.

   c. Use the answer to part b and write the solution using function notation.

94. Let $f(x) = \log_{0.3} x$. Then $g(x) = 0.3^x$ is the inverse of $f(x)$. The ordered pair $(3, 0.027)$ is a solution of the function $g(x)$.

   a. Write this solution using function notation.

   b. Write an ordered pair that we know to be a solution of $f(x)$.

   c. Use the answer to part b and write the solution using function notation.

95. Explain why negative numbers are not included as logarithmic bases.

96. Explain why 1 is not included as a logarithmic base.

Solve by first writing as an exponent.

97. $\log_7 (5x - 2) = 1$ **98.** $\log_3 (2x + 4) = 2$

99. Simplify: $\log_3(\log_5 125)$

100. Simplify: $\log_7(\log_4(\log_2 16))$

Graph each function and its inverse function on the same set of axes. Label any intercepts.

101. $y = 4^x; y = \log_4 x$

102. $y = 3^x; y = \log_3 x$

103. $y = \left(\dfrac{1}{3}\right)^x; y = \log_{1/3} x$

104. $y = \left(\dfrac{1}{2}\right)^x; y = \log_{1/2} x$

105. Explain why the graph of the function $y = \log_b x$ contains the point $(1, 0)$ no matter what b is.

106. $\log_3 10$ is between which two integers? Explain your answer.

107. The formula $\log_{10}(1 - k) = \dfrac{-0.3}{H}$ models the relationship between the half-life H of a radioactive material and its rate of decay k. Find the rate of decay of the iodine isotope I-131 if its half-life is 8 days. Round to four decimal places.

108. The formula $\text{pH} = -\log_{10}(\text{H}^+)$ provides the pH for a liquid, where H^+ stands for the concentration of hydronium ions. Find the pH of lemonade, whose concentration of hydronium ions is 0.0050 moles/liter. Round to the nearest tenth.

12.6 Properties of Logarithms

In the previous section, we explored some basic properties of logarithms. We now introduce and explore additional properties. Because a logarithm is an exponent, logarithmic properties are just restatements of exponential properties.

OBJECTIVE

1 Using the Product Property

The first of these properties is called the **product property of logarithms** because it deals with the logarithm of a product.

> **Product Property of Logarithms**
>
> If $x, y,$ and b are positive real numbers and $b \neq 1$, then
> $$\log_b xy = \log_b x + \log_b y$$

To prove this, let $\log_b x = M$ and $\log_b y = N$. Now write each logarithm with exponential notation.

$$\log_b x = M \quad \text{is equivalent to} \quad b^M = x$$
$$\log_b y = N \quad \text{is equivalent to} \quad b^N = y$$

When we multiply the left sides and the right sides of the exponential equations, we have that

$$xy = (b^M)(b^N) = b^{M+N}$$

If we write the equation $xy = b^{M+N}$ in equivalent logarithmic form, we have

$$\log_b xy = M + N$$

But since $M = \log_b x$ and $N = \log_b y$, we can write

$$\log_b xy = \log_b x + \log_b y \quad \text{Let } M = \log_b x \text{ and } N = \log_b y.$$

In other words, the logarithm of a product is the sum of the logarithms of the factors. This property is sometimes used to simplify logarithmic expressions.

In the examples that follow, assume that variables represent positive numbers.

EXAMPLE 1   Write each sum as a single logarithm.

a. $\log_{11} 10 + \log_{11} 3$ **b.** $\log_3 \dfrac{1}{2} + \log_3 12$ **c.** $\log_2(x + 2) + \log_2 x$

Solution

In each case, both terms have a common logarithmic base.

a. $\log_{11} 10 + \log_{11} 3 = \log_{11}(10 \cdot 3)$ Apply the product property.
$$= \log_{11} 30$$

b. $\log_3 \dfrac{1}{2} + \log_3 12 = \log_3 \left(\dfrac{1}{2} \cdot 12 \right) = \log_3 6$

c. $\log_2(x + 2) + \log_2 x = \log_2[(x + 2) \cdot x] = \log_2(x^2 + 2x)$

> ▶ **Helpful Hint**
> Check your logarithm properties. Make sure you understand that $\log_2(x + 2)$ *is not* $\log_2 x + \log_2 2$.

PRACTICE
1   Write each sum as a single logarithm.

a. $\log_8 5 + \log_8 3$

b. $\log_2 \dfrac{1}{3} + \log_2 18$

c. $\log_5(x - 1) + \log_5(x + 1)$

OBJECTIVE
2   Using the Quotient Property
The second property is the **quotient property of logarithms.**

> **Quotient Property of Logarithms**
> If x, y, and b are positive real numbers and $b \neq 1$, then
> $$\log_b \dfrac{x}{y} = \log_b x - \log_b y$$

The proof of the quotient property of logarithms is similar to the proof of the product property. Notice that the quotient property says that the logarithm of a quotient is the difference of the logarithms of the dividend and divisor.

✓**CONCEPT CHECK**

Which of the following is the correct way to rewrite $\log_5 \dfrac{7}{2}$?

a. $\log_5 7 - \log_5 2$ **b.** $\log_5(7 - 2)$ **c.** $\dfrac{\log_5 7}{\log_5 2}$ **d.** $\log_5 14$

Answer to Concept Check: a

EXAMPLE 2 Write each difference as a single logarithm.

a. $\log_{10} 27 - \log_{10} 3$ **b.** $\log_5 8 - \log_5 x$ **c.** $\log_3(x^2 + 5) - \log_3(x^2 + 1)$

Solution In each case, both terms have a common logarithmic base.

a. $\log_{10} 27 - \log_{10} 3 = \log_{10} \dfrac{27}{3} = \log_{10} 9$

b. $\log_5 8 - \log_5 x = \log_5 \dfrac{8}{x}$

c. $\log_3(x^2 + 5) - \log_3(x^2 + 1) = \log_3 \dfrac{x^2 + 5}{x^2 + 1}$ Apply the quotient property.   □

PRACTICE

2 Write each difference as a single logarithm.

a. $\log_5 18 - \log_5 6$ **b.** $\log_6 x - \log_6 3$ **c.** $\log_4(x^2 + 1) - \log_4(x^2 + 3)$

OBJECTIVE

3 Using the Power Property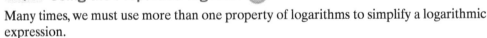

The third and final property we introduce is the **power property of logarithms.**

Power Property of Logarithms

If x and b are positive real numbers, $b \neq 1$, and r is a real number, then

$$\log_b x^r = r \log_b x$$

EXAMPLE 3 Use the power property to rewrite each expression.

a. $\log_5 x^3$ **b.** $\log_4 \sqrt{2}$

Solution

a. $\log_5 x^3 = 3 \log_5 x$ **b.** $\log_4 \sqrt{2} = \log_4 2^{1/2} = \dfrac{1}{2} \log_4 2$ □

PRACTICE

3 Use the power property to rewrite each expression.

a. $\log_7 x^8$ **b.** $\log_5 \sqrt[4]{7}$

OBJECTIVE

4 Using the Properties Together

Many times, we must use more than one property of logarithms to simplify a logarithmic expression.

EXAMPLE 4 Write as a single logarithm.

a. $2 \log_5 3 + 3 \log_5 2$ **b.** $3 \log_9 x - \log_9(x + 1)$ **c.** $\log_4 25 + \log_4 3 - \log_4 5$

Solution In each case, all terms have a common logarithmic base.

a. $2 \log_5 3 + 3 \log_5 2 = \log_5 3^2 + \log_5 2^3$ Apply the power property.

$= \log_5 9 + \log_5 8$

$= \log_5(9 \cdot 8)$ Apply the product property.

$= \log_5 72$

b. $3 \log_9 x - \log_9(x + 1) = \log_9 x^3 - \log_9(x + 1)$ Apply the power property.

$= \log_9 \dfrac{x^3}{x + 1}$ Apply the quotient property.

c. Use both the product and quotient properties.

$$\log_4 25 + \log_4 3 - \log_4 5 = \log_4(25 \cdot 3) - \log_4 5 \quad \text{Apply the product property.}$$
$$= \log_4 75 - \log_4 5 \quad \text{Simplify.}$$
$$= \log_4 \frac{75}{5} \quad \text{Apply the quotient property.}$$
$$= \log_4 15 \quad \text{Simplify.} \qquad \square$$

PRACTICE
4   Write as a single logarithm.

a. $2\log_5 4 + 5\log_5 2$ **b.** $2\log_8 x - \log_8(x + 3)$ **c.** $\log_7 12 + \log_7 5 - \log_7 4$

EXAMPLE 5   Write each expression as sums or differences of multiples of logarithms.

a. $\log_3 \dfrac{5 \cdot 7}{4}$ **b.** $\log_2 \dfrac{x^5}{y^2}$

Solution

a. $\log_3 \dfrac{5 \cdot 7}{4} = \log_3(5 \cdot 7) - \log_3 4 \quad \text{Apply the quotient property.}$
$$= \log_3 5 + \log_3 7 - \log_3 4 \quad \text{Apply the product property.}$$

b. $\log_2 \dfrac{x^5}{y^2} = \log_2(x^5) - \log_2(y^2) \quad \text{Apply the quotient property.}$
$$= 5\log_2 x - 2\log_2 y \quad \text{Apply the power property.} \qquad \square$$

PRACTICE
5   Write each expression as sums or differences of multiples of logarithms.

a. $\log_5 \dfrac{4 \cdot 3}{7}$ **b.** $\log_4 \dfrac{a^2}{b^5}$

> ▶ **Helpful Hint**
> Notice that we are not able to simplify further a logarithmic expression such as $\log_5(2x - 1)$. None of the basic properties gives a way to write the logarithm of a difference (or sum) in some equivalent form.

✓**CONCEPT CHECK**
What is wrong with the following?

$$\log_{10}(x^2 + 5) = \log_{10} x^2 + \log_{10} 5$$
$$= 2\log_{10} x + \log_{10} 5$$

Use a numerical example to demonstrate that the result is incorrect.

EXAMPLE 6   If $\log_b 2 = 0.43$ and $\log_b 3 = 0.68$, use the properties of logarithms to evaluate.

a. $\log_b 6$ **b.** $\log_b 9$ **c.** $\log_b \sqrt{2}$

(Continued on next page)

Solution

a. $\log_b 6 = \log_b(2 \cdot 3)$ Write 6 as $2 \cdot 3$.

       $= \log_b 2 + \log_b 3$ Apply the product property.

       $= 0.43 + 0.68$ Substitute given values.

       $= 1.11$ Simplify.

b. $\log_b 9 = \log_b 3^2$ Write 9 as 3^2.

       $= 2 \log_b 3$

       $= 2(0.68)$ Substitute 0.68 for $\log_b 3$.

       $= 1.36$ Simplify.

c. First, recall that $\sqrt{2} = 2^{1/2}$. Then

     $\log_b \sqrt{2} = \log_b 2^{1/2}$ Write $\sqrt{2}$ as $2^{1/2}$.

            $= \dfrac{1}{2} \log_b 2$ Apply the power property.

            $= \dfrac{1}{2}(0.43)$ Substitute the given value.

            $= 0.215$ Simplify.   ☐

PRACTICE

6   If $\log_b 5 = 0.83$ and $\log_b 3 = 0.56$, use the properties of logarithms to evaluate.

a. $\log_b 15$ **b.** $\log_b 25$ **c.** $\log_b \sqrt{3}$

A summary of the basic properties of logarithms that we have developed so far is given next.

Properties of Logarithms

If x, y, and b are positive real numbers, $b \neq 1$, and r is a real number, then

1. $\log_b 1 = 0$ **2.** $\log_b b^x = x$

3. $b^{\log_b x} = x$ **4.** $\log_b xy = \log_b x + \log_b y$ Product property.

5. $\log_b \dfrac{x}{y} = \log_b x - \log_b y$ Quotient property.   **6.** $\log_b x^r = r \log_b x$ Power property.

Vocabulary, Readiness & Video Check

Select the correct choice.

1. $\log_b 12 + \log_b 3 = \log_b \underline{\quad}$
     a. 36   **b.** 15   **c.** 4   **d.** 9

2. $\log_b 12 - \log_b 3 = \log_b \underline{\quad}$
     a. 36   **b.** 15   **c.** 4   **d.** 9

3. $7 \log_b 2 = \underline{\quad}$
     a. $\log_b 14$ **b.** $\log_b 2^7$ **c.** $\log_b 7^2$ **d.** $(\log_b 2)^7$

4. $\log_b 1 = \underline{\quad}$
     a. b **b.** 1   **c.** 0   **d.** no answer

5. $b^{\log_b x} = \underline{\quad}$
     a. x **b.** b **c.** 1   **d.** 0

6. $\log_5 5^2 = \underline{\quad}$
     a. 25   **b.** 2   **c.** 5^{5^2} **d.** 32

Martin-Gay Interactive Videos

See Video 12.6 🍎

Watch the section lecture video and answer the following questions.

OBJECTIVE 1

7. Can the product property of logarithms be used again on the bottom line of Example 2 to write $\log_{10}(10x^2 + 20)$ as a sum of logarithms, $\log_{10}10x^2 + \log_{10}20$? Explain.

OBJECTIVE 2

8. From Example 3 and the lecture before, what must be true about bases before you can apply the quotient property of logarithms?

OBJECTIVE 3

9. Based on Example 5, explain why $\log_2 \dfrac{1}{x} = -\log_2 x$.

OBJECTIVE 4

10. From the lecture before Example 6, where do the logarithmic properties come from?

12.6 Exercise Set   MyMathLab®

Write each sum as a single logarithm. Assume that variables represent positive numbers. See Example 1.

1. $\log_5 2 + \log_5 7$

2. $\log_3 8 + \log_3 4$

3. $\log_4 9 + \log_4 x$

4. $\log_2 x + \log_2 y$

5. $\log_6 x + \log_6(x + 1)$

6. $\log_5 y^3 + \log_5(y - 7)$

7. $\log_{10} 5 + \log_{10} 2 + \log_{10}(x^2 + 2)$

8. $\log_6 3 + \log_6(x + 4) + \log_6 5$

Write each difference as a single logarithm. Assume that variables represent positive numbers. See Example 2.

9. $\log_5 12 - \log_5 4$

10. $\log_7 20 - \log_7 4$

11. $\log_3 8 - \log_3 2$

12. $\log_5 12 - \log_5 3$

13. $\log_2 x - \log_2 y$

14. $\log_3 12 - \log_3 z$

15. $\log_2(x^2 + 6) - \log_2(x^2 + 1)$

16. $\log_7(x + 9) - \log_7(x^2 + 10)$

Use the power property to rewrite each expression. See Example 3.

17. $\log_3 x^2$

18. $\log_2 x^5$

19. $\log_4 5^{-1}$

20. $\log_6 7^{-2}$

21. $\log_5 \sqrt{y}$

22. $\log_5 \sqrt[3]{x}$

MIXED PRACTICE

Write each as a single logarithm. Assume that variables represent positive numbers. See Example 4.

23. $\log_2 5 + \log_2 x^3$

24. $\log_5 2 + \log_5 y^2$

25. $3\log_4 2 + \log_4 6$

26. $2\log_3 5 + \log_3 2$

27. $3\log_5 x + 6\log_5 z$

28. $2\log_7 y + 6\log_7 z$

29. $\log_4 2 + \log_4 10 - \log_4 5$

30. $\log_6 18 + \log_6 2 - \log_6 9$

31. $\log_7 6 + \log_7 3 - \log_7 4$

32. $\log_8 5 + \log_8 15 - \log_8 20$

33. $\log_{10} x - \log_{10}(x + 1) + \log_{10}(x^2 - 2)$

34. $\log_9(4x) - \log_9(x - 3) + \log_9(x^3 + 1)$

35. $3\log_2 x + \dfrac{1}{2}\log_2 x - 2\log_2(x + 1)$

36. $2\log_5 x + \dfrac{1}{3}\log_5 x - 3\log_5(x + 5)$

37. $2\log_8 x - \dfrac{2}{3}\log_8 x + 4\log_8 x$

38. $5\log_6 x - \dfrac{3}{4}\log_6 x + 3\log_6 x$

MIXED PRACTICE

Write each expression as a sum or difference of multiples of logarithms. Assume that variables represent positive numbers. See Example 5.

39. $\log_3 \dfrac{4y}{5}$

40. $\log_7 \dfrac{5x}{4}$

41. $\log_4 \dfrac{5}{9z}$

42. $\log_9 \dfrac{7}{8y}$

43. $\log_2 \dfrac{x^3}{y}$

44. $\log_5 \dfrac{x}{y^4}$

45. $\log_b \sqrt{7x}$

46. $\log_b \sqrt{\dfrac{3}{y}}$

47. $\log_6 x^4 y^5$

48. $\log_2 y^3 z$

49. $\log_5 x^3(x + 1)$

50. $\log_3 x^2(x - 9)$

51. $\log_6 \dfrac{x^2}{x + 3}$

52. $\log_3 \dfrac{(x + 5)^2}{x}$

If $\log_b 3 = 0.5$ and $\log_b 5 = 0.7$, evaluate each expression. See Example 6.

53. $\log_b 15$

54. $\log_b 25$

55. $\log_b \dfrac{5}{3}$

56. $\log_b \dfrac{3}{5}$

57. $\log_b \sqrt{5}$

58. $\log_b \sqrt[4]{3}$

If $\log_b 2 = 0.43$ and $\log_b 3 = 0.68$, evaluate each expression. See Example 6.

59. $\log_b 8$

60. $\log_b 81$

61. $\log_b \dfrac{3}{9}$

62. $\log_b \dfrac{4}{32}$

63. $\log_b \sqrt{\dfrac{2}{3}}$

64. $\log_b \sqrt{\dfrac{3}{2}}$

REVIEW AND PREVIEW

Graph both functions on the same set of axes. See Sections 12.3 and 12.5.

65. $y = 10^x$

66. $y = \log_{10} x$.

Evaluate each expression. See Section 12.5.

67. $\log_{10} 100$

68. $\log_{10} \dfrac{1}{10}$

69. $\log_7 7^2$

70. $\log_7 \sqrt{7}$

CONCEPT EXTENSIONS

Solve. See the Concept Checks in this section.

71. Which of the following is the correct way to rewrite $\log_3 \dfrac{14}{11}$?

  a. $\dfrac{\log_3 14}{\log_3 11}$

  b. $\log_3 14 - \log_3 11$

  c. $\log_3(14 - 11)$

  d. $\log_3 154$

72. Which of the following is the correct way to rewrite $\log_9 \dfrac{21}{3}$?

  a. $\log_9 7$

  b. $\log_9(21 - 3)$

  c. $\dfrac{\log_9 21}{\log_9 3}$

  d. $\log_9 21 - \log_9 3$

Answer the following true or false. Study your logarithm properties carefully before answering.

73. $\log_2 x^3 = 3\log_2 x$

74. $\log_3(x + y) = \log_3 x + \log_3 y$

75. $\dfrac{\log_7 10}{\log_7 5} = \log_7 2$

76. $\log_7 \dfrac{14}{8} = \log_7 14 - \log_7 8$

77. $\dfrac{\log_7 x}{\log_7 y} = (\log_7 x) - (\log_7 y)$

78. $(\log_3 6) \cdot (\log_3 4) = \log_3 24$

79. It is true that $\log_b 8 = \log_b(8 \cdot 1) = \log_b 8 + \log_b 1$. Explain how $\log_b 8$ can equal $\log_b 8 + \log_b 1$.

80. It is true that $\log_b 7 = \log_b \dfrac{7}{1} = \log_b 7 - \log_b 1$. Explain how $\log_b 7$ can equal $\log_b 7 - \log_b 1$.

Integrated Review FUNCTIONS AND PROPERTIES OF LOGARITHMS

Sections 12.1–12.6

If $f(x) = x - 6$ and $g(x) = x^2 + 1$, find each value.

1. $(f + g)(x)$

2. $(f - g)(x)$

3. $(f \cdot g)(x)$

4. $\left(\dfrac{f}{g}\right)(x)$

If $f(x) = \sqrt{x}$ and $g(x) = 3x - 1$, find each function.

5. $(f \circ g)(x)$

6. $(g \circ f)(x)$

Determine whether each is a one-to-one function. If it is, find its inverse.

7. $f = \{(-2, 6), (4, 8), (2, -6), (3, 3)\}$

8. $g = \{(4, 2), (-1, 3), (5, 3), (7, 1)\}$

Determine from the graph whether each function is one-to-one.

9.

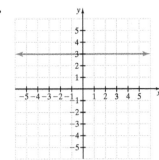

10.

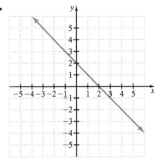

11.

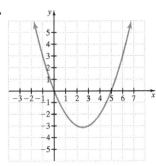

Each function listed is one-to-one. Find the inverse of each function.

12. $f(x) = 3x$

13. $f(x) = x + 4$

14. $f(x) = 5x - 1$

15. $f(x) = 3x + 2$

Graph each function.

16. $y = \left(\dfrac{1}{2}\right)^x$

17. $y = 2^x + 1$

18. $y = \log_3 x$

19. $y = \log_{1/3} x$

Solve.

20. $2^x = 8$

21. $9 = 3^{x-5}$

22. $4^{x-1} = 8^{x+2}$

23. $25^x = 125^{x-1}$

24. $\log_4 16 = x$

25. $\log_{49} 7 = x$

26. $\log_2 x = 5$

27. $\log_x 64 = 3$

28. $\log_x \dfrac{1}{125} = -3$

29. $\log_3 x = -2$

Write each as a single logarithm.

30. $5 \log_2 x$

31. $x \log_2 5$

32. $3 \log_5 x - 5 \log_5 y$

33. $9 \log_5 x + 3 \log_5 y$

34. $\log_2 x + \log_2(x - 3) - \log_2(x^2 + 4)$

35. $\log_3 y - \log_3(y + 2) + \log_3(y^3 + 11)$

Write each expression as sums or differences of multiples of logarithms.

36. $\log_7 \dfrac{9x^2}{y}$

37. $\log_6 \dfrac{5y}{z^2}$

38. An unusually wet spring has caused the size of the mosquito population in a community to increase by 6% each day. If an estimated 100,000 mosquitoes are in the community on April 1, find how many mosquitoes will inhabit the community on April 17. Round to the nearest thousand.

12.7   Common Logarithms, Natural Logarithms, and Change of Base

OBJECTIVES

1 Identify Common Logarithms and Approximate Them by Calculator.

2 Evaluate Common Logarithms of Powers of 10.

3 Identify Natural Logarithms and Approximate Them by Calculator.

4 Evaluate Natural Logarithms of Powers of *e*.

5 Use the Change of Base Formula.

In this section, we look closely at two particular logarithmic bases. These two logarithmic bases are used so frequently that logarithms to their bases are given special names. **Common logarithms** are logarithms to base 10. **Natural logarithms** are logarithms to base *e*, which we introduce in this section. The work in this section is based on the use of a calculator that has both the common "log" $\boxed{\text{LOG}}$ and the natural "log" $\boxed{\text{LN}}$ keys.

OBJECTIVE

1   Approximating Common Logarithms

Logarithms to base 10, common logarithms, are used frequently because our number system is a base 10 decimal system. The notation $\log x$ means the same as $\log_{10} x$.

> **Common Logarithms**
>
> $$\log x \text{ means } \log_{10} x$$

EXAMPLE 1   Use a calculator to approximate log 7 to four decimal places.

Solution   Press the following sequence of keys.

$$\boxed{7}\ \boxed{\text{LOG}}\quad \text{or}\quad \boxed{\text{LOG}}\ \boxed{7}\ \boxed{\text{ENTER}}$$

To four decimal places,

$$\log 7 \approx 0.8451$$

PRACTICE

1   Use a calculator to approximate log 15 to four decimal places.

OBJECTIVE

2 **Evaluating Common Logarithms of Powers of 10**

To evaluate the common log of a power of 10, a calculator is not needed. According to the property of logarithms,

$$\log_b b^x = x$$

It follows that if b is replaced with 10, we have

$$\log 10^x = x$$

> ▶ Helpful Hint
> Remember that the understood base here is 10.

EXAMPLE 2 Find the exact value of each logarithm.

a. $\log 10$ **b.** $\log 1000$ **c.** $\log \dfrac{1}{10}$ **d.** $\log \sqrt{10}$

Solution

a. $\log 10 = \log 10^1 = 1$ **b.** $\log 1000 = \log 10^3 = 3$

c. $\log \dfrac{1}{10} = \log 10^{-1} = -1$ **d.** $\log \sqrt{10} = \log 10^{1/2} = \dfrac{1}{2}$ □

PRACTICE

2 Find the exact value of each logarithm.

a. $\log \dfrac{1}{100}$ **b.** $\log 100{,}000$ **c.** $\log \sqrt[5]{10}$ **d.** $\log 0.001$

As we will soon see, equations containing common logarithms are useful models of many natural phenomena.

EXAMPLE 3 Solve $\log x = 1.2$ for x. Give an exact solution and then approximate the solution to four decimal places.

Solution Remember that the base of a common logarithm is understood to be 10.

$$\log x = 1.2$$

> ▶ Helpful Hint
> The understood base is 10.

$$10^{1.2} = x \qquad \text{Write with exponential notation.}$$

The exact solution is $10^{1.2}$. To four decimal places, $x \approx 15.8489$. □

PRACTICE

3 Solve $\log x = 3.4$ for x. Give an exact solution, and then approximate the solution to four decimal places.

The Richter scale measures the intensity, or magnitude, of an earthquake. The formula for the magnitude R of an earthquake is $R = \log\left(\dfrac{a}{T}\right) + B$, where a is the amplitude in micrometers of the vertical motion of the ground at the recording station, T is the number of seconds between successive seismic waves, and B is an adjustment factor that takes into account the weakening of the seismic wave as the distance increases from the epicenter of the earthquake.

EXAMPLE 4 **Finding the Magnitude of an Earthquake**

Find an earthquake's magnitude on the Richter scale if a recording station measures an amplitude of 300 micrometers and 2.5 seconds between waves. Assume that B is 4.2. Approximate the solution to the nearest tenth.

Solution Substitute the known values into the formula for earthquake intensity.

$$R = \log\left(\frac{a}{T}\right) + B \qquad \text{Richter scale formula}$$

$$= \log\left(\frac{300}{2.5}\right) + 4.2 \qquad \text{Let } a = 300, T = 2.5, \text{ and } B = 4.2.$$

$$= \log(120) + 4.2$$

$$\approx 2.1 + 4.2 \qquad \text{Approximate log 120 by 2.1.}$$

$$= 6.3$$

This earthquake had a magnitude of 6.3 on the Richter scale.

PRACTICE

4 Find an earthquake's magnitude on the Richter scale if a recording station measures an amplitude of 450 micrometers and 4.2 seconds between waves with $B = 3.6$. Approximate the solution to the nearest tenth.

OBJECTIVE

3 Approximating Natural Logarithms

Natural logarithms are also frequently used, especially to describe natural events hence the label "natural logarithm." Natural logarithms are logarithms to the base e, which is a constant approximately equal to 2.7183. The number e is an irrational number, as is π. The notation $\log_e x$ is usually abbreviated to $\ln x$. (The abbreviation ln is read "el en.")

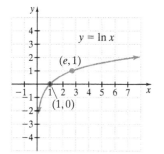

Natural Logarithms

$$\ln x \text{ means } \log_e x$$

The graph of $y = \ln x$ is shown to the left.

EXAMPLE 5 Use a calculator to approximate ln 8 to four decimal places.

Solution Press the following sequence of keys.

$$\boxed{8}\ \boxed{\text{LN}} \quad \text{or} \quad \boxed{\text{LN}}\ \boxed{8}\ \boxed{\text{ENTER}}$$

To four decimal places,

$$\ln 8 \approx 2.0794$$

PRACTICE

5 Use a calculator to approximate ln 13 to four decimal places.

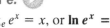

OBJECTIVE

4 Evaluating Natural Logarithms of Powers of e.

As a result of the property $\log_b b^x = x$, we know that $\log_e e^x = x$, or **$\ln e^x = x$.**

Since $\ln e^x = x$, $\ln e^5 = 5$, $\ln e^{22} = 22$, and so on. Also,

$$\ln e^1 = 1 \text{ or simply } \ln e = 1.$$

That is why the graph of $y = \ln x$ shown above in the margin passes through $(e, 1)$.

If $x = e$, then $y = \ln e = 1$, thus the ordered pair is $(e, 1)$.

EXAMPLE 6 Find the exact value of each natural logarithm.

a. $\ln e^3$ **b.** $\ln \sqrt[5]{e}$

Solution

a. $\ln e^3 = 3$ **b.** $\ln \sqrt[5]{e} = \ln e^{1/5} = \dfrac{1}{5}$ □

PRACTICE
6 Find the exact value of each natural logarithm.

a. $\ln e^4$ **b.** $\ln \sqrt[3]{e}$

EXAMPLE 7 Solve $\ln 3x = 5$. Give an exact solution and then approximate the solution to four decimal places.

Solution Remember that the base of a natural logarithm is understood to be e.

$$\ln 3x = 5$$

> **▶ Helpful Hint**
> The understood base is e.

$$e^5 = 3x \quad \text{Write with exponential notation.}$$

$$\frac{e^5}{3} = x \quad \text{Solve for } x.$$

The exact solution is $\dfrac{e^5}{3}$. To four decimal places,

$$x \approx 49.4711.$$ □

PRACTICE
7 Solve $\ln 5x = 8$. Give an exact solution and then approximate the solution to four decimal places.

Recall from Section 12.3 the formula $A = P\left(1 + \dfrac{r}{n}\right)^{nt}$ for compound interest, where n represents the number of compoundings per year. When interest is compounded continuously, the formula $A = Pe^{rt}$ is used, where r is the annual interest rate, and interest is compounded continuously for t years.

EXAMPLE 8 **Finding Final Loan Payment**
Find the amount owed at the end of 5 years if $1600 is loaned at a rate of 9% compounded continuously.

Solution Use the formula $A = Pe^{rt}$, where

$$P = \$1600 \, (\text{the amount of the loan})$$
$$r = 9\% = 0.09 \, (\text{the rate of interest})$$
$$t = 5 \, (\text{the 5-year duration of the loan})$$
$$A = Pe^{rt}$$
$$= 1600e^{0.09(5)} \quad \text{Substitute in known values.}$$
$$= 1600e^{0.45}$$

Now we can use a calculator to approximate the solution.

$$A \approx 2509.30$$

The total amount of money owed is $2509.30. □

PRACTICE
8 Find the amount owed at the end of 4 years if $2400 is borrowed at a rate of 6% compounded continuously.

OBJECTIVE

5   Using the Change of Base Formula

Calculators are handy tools for approximating natural and common logarithms. Unfortunately, some calculators cannot be used to approximate logarithms to bases other than e or 10—at least not directly. In such cases, we use the change of base formula.

Change of Base

If a, b, and c are positive real numbers and neither b nor c is 1, then

$$\log_b a = \frac{\log_c a}{\log_c b}$$

EXAMPLE 9   Approximate $\log_5 3$ to four decimal places.

Solution   Use the change of base property to write $\log_5 3$ as a quotient of logarithms to base 10.

$$\log_5 3 = \frac{\log 3}{\log 5} \qquad \text{Use the change of base property. In the change of base property, we let } a = 3, b = 5, \text{ and } c = 10.$$

$$\approx \frac{0.4771213}{0.69897} \qquad \text{Approximate logarithms by calculator.}$$

$$\approx 0.6826063 \qquad \text{Simplify by calculator.}$$

To four decimal places, $\log_5 3 \approx 0.6826$.

PRACTICE

9   Approximate $\log_8 5$ to four decimal places.

✓**CONCEPT CHECK**

If a graphing calculator cannot directly evaluate logarithms to base 5, describe how you could use the graphing calculator to graph the function $f(x) = \log_5 x$.

Vocabulary, Readiness & Video Check

Use the choices to fill in each blank.

1. The base of $\log 7$ is _____.

 a. e **b.** 7   **c.** 10   **d.** no answer

2. The base of $\ln 7$ is ___.

 a. e **b.** 7   **c.** 10   **d.** no answer

3. $\log_{10} 10^7 =$ _____.

 a. e **b.** 7   **c.** 10   **d.** no answer

4. $\log_7 1 =$ _____.

 a. e **b.** 7   **c.** 10   **d.** 0

5. $\log_e e^5 =$ _____.

 a. e **b.** 5   **c.** 0   **d.** 1

6. Study exercise 5 to the left. Then answer: $\ln e^5 =$ _____.

 a. e **b.** 5   **c.** 0   **d.** 1

7. $\log_2 7 =$ _____   (There may be more than one answer.)

 a. $\dfrac{\log 7}{\log 2}$ **b.** $\dfrac{\ln 7}{\ln 2}$ **c.** $\dfrac{\log 2}{\log 7}$ **d.** $\log \dfrac{7}{2}$

Answer to Concept Check:

$f(x) = \dfrac{\log x}{\log 5}$

Martin-Gay Interactive Videos

See Video 12.7 🍎

Watch the section lecture video and answer the following questions.

OBJECTIVE
1

8. From Example 1 and the lecture before, what is the understood base of a common logarithm?

OBJECTIVE
2

9. From Example 2, why can you find exact values of common logarithms of powers of 10?

OBJECTIVE
3

10. From ▣ Example 4 and the lecture before, what is the understood base of a natural logarithm?

OBJECTIVE
4

11. In ▣ Examples 5 and 6, consider how the expression is rewritten and the resulting answer. What logarithm property is actually used here?

OBJECTIVE
5

12. From ▣ Example 8, what two equivalent fractions will give you the exact value of $\log_6 4$?

12.7 Exercise Set   MyMathLab®

MIXED PRACTICE

Use a calculator to approximate each logarithm to four decimal places. See Examples 1 and 5.

1. $\log 8$
2. $\log 6$

3. $\log 2.31$
4. $\log 4.86$

5. $\ln 2$
6. $\ln 3$

7. $\ln 0.0716$
8. $\ln 0.0032$

9. $\log 12.6$
10. $\log 25.9$

11. $\ln 5$
12. $\ln 7$

13. $\log 41.5$
14. $\ln 41.5$

MIXED PRACTICE

Find the exact value. See Examples 2 and 6.

15. $\log 100$
16. $\log 10{,}000$

17. $\log\dfrac{1}{1000}$
18. $\log\dfrac{1}{100}$

19. $\ln e^2$
20. $\ln e^4$

21. $\ln \sqrt[4]{e}$
22. $\ln \sqrt[5]{e}$

23. $\log 10^3$
24. $\log 10^7$

25. $\ln e^{-7}$
26. $\ln e^{-5}$

27. $\log 0.0001$
28. $\log 0.001$

29. $\ln \sqrt{e}$
30. $\log \sqrt{10}$

Solve each equation for x. Give an exact solution and a four-decimal-place approximation. See Examples 3 and 7.

31. $\ln 2x = 7$
32. $\ln 5x = 9$

33. $\log x = 1.3$
34. $\log x = 2.1$

35. $\log 2x = 1.1$
36. $\log 3x = 1.3$

37. $\ln x = 1.4$
38. $\ln x = 2.1$

39. $\ln(3x - 4) = 2.3$

40. $\ln(2x + 5) = 3.4$

41. $\log x = 2.3$

42. $\log x = 3.1$

43. $\ln x = -2.3$

44. $\ln x = -3.7$

45. $\log(2x + 1) = -0.5$

46. $\log(3x - 2) = -0.8$

47. $\ln 4x = 0.18$

48. $\ln 3x = 0.76$

Approximate each logarithm to four decimal places. See Example 9.

49. $\log_2 3$
50. $\log_3 2$

51. $\log_{1/2} 5$
52. $\log_{1/3} 2$

53. $\log_4 9$
54. $\log_9 4$

55. $\log_3 \dfrac{1}{6}$
56. $\log_6 \dfrac{2}{3}$

57. $\log_8 6$
58. $\log_6 8$

Use the formula $R = \log\left(\dfrac{a}{T}\right) + B$ to find the intensity R on the Richter scale of the earthquakes that fit the descriptions given. Round answers to one decimal place. See Example 4.

59. Amplitude a is 200 micrometers, time T between waves is 1.6 seconds, and B is 2.1.

60. Amplitude a is 150 micrometers, time T between waves is 3.6 seconds, and B is 1.9.

61. Amplitude a is 400 micrometers, time T between waves is 2.6 seconds, and B is 3.1.

62. Amplitude a is 450 micrometers, time T between waves is 4.2 seconds, and B is 2.7.

Use the formula $A = Pe^{rt}$ to solve. See Example 8.

63. Find how much money Dana Jones has after 12 years if $1400 is invested at 8% interest compounded continuously.

64. Determine the amount in an account in which $3500 earns 6% interest compounded continuously for 1 year.

65. Find the amount of money Barbara Mack owes at the end of 4 years if 6% interest is compounded continuously on her $2000 debt.

66. Find the amount of money for which a $2500 certificate of deposit is redeemable if it has been paying 10% interest compounded continuously for 3 years.

REVIEW AND PREVIEW

Solve each equation for x. See Sections 2.3 and 6.6.

67. $6x - 3(2 - 5x) = 6$ **68.** $2x + 3 = 5 - 2(3x - 1)$

69. $2x + 3y = 6x$ **70.** $4x - 8y = 10x$

71. $x^2 + 7x = -6$ **72.** $x^2 + 4x = 12$

Solve each system of equations. See Section 4.1.

73. $\begin{cases} x + 2y = -4 \\ 3x - y = 9 \end{cases}$ **74.** $\begin{cases} 5x + y = 5 \\ -3x - 2y = -10 \end{cases}$

CONCEPT EXTENSIONS

 75. Use a calculator to try to approximate log 0. Describe what happens and explain why.

76. Use a calculator to try to approximate ln 0. Describe what happens and explain why.

77. Without using a calculator, explain which of log 50 or ln 50 must be larger and why.

78. Without using a calculator, explain which of $\log 50^{-1}$ or $\ln 50^{-1}$ must be larger and why.

Graph each function by finding ordered pair solutions, plotting the solutions, and then drawing a smooth curve through the plotted points.

79. $f(x) = e^x$ **80.** $f(x) = e^{2x}$

81. $f(x) = e^{-3x}$ **82.** $f(x) = e^{-x}$

83. $f(x) = e^x + 2$ **84.** $f(x) = e^x - 3$

85. $f(x) = e^{x-1}$ **86.** $f(x) = e^{x+4}$

87. $f(x) = 3e^x$ **88.** $f(x) = -2e^x$

89. $f(x) = \ln x$ **90.** $f(x) = \log x$

91. $f(x) = -2 \log x$ **92.** $f(x) = 3 \ln x$

93. $f(x) = \log (x + 2)$ **94.** $f(x) = \log (x - 2)$

95. $f(x) = \ln x - 3$ **96.** $f(x) = \ln x + 3$

97. Graph $f(x) = e^x$ (Exercise 79), $f(x) = e^x + 2$ (Exercise 83), and $f(x) = e^x - 3$ (Exercise 84) on the same screen. Discuss any trends shown on the graphs.

98. Graph $f(x) = \ln x$ (Exercise 89), $f(x) = \ln x - 3$ (Exercise 95), and $f(x) = \ln x + 3$ (Exercise 96) on the same screen. Discuss any trends shown on the graphs.

12.8 | Exponential and Logarithmic Equations and Problem Solving

OBJECTIVES

1 Solve Exponential Equations.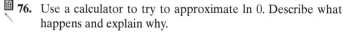

2 Solve Logarithmic Equations.

3 Solve Problems That Can Be Modeled by Exponential and Logarithmic Equations.

OBJECTIVE

1   Solving Exponential Equations

In Section 12.3 we solved exponential equations such as $2^x = 16$ by writing 16 as a power of 2 and applying the uniqueness of b^x.

$$2^x = 16$$
$$2^x = 2^4 \quad \text{Write 16 as } 2^4.$$
$$x = 4 \quad \text{Use the uniqueness of } b^x.$$

Solving the equation in this manner is possible since 16 is a power of 2. If solving an equation such as $2^x = a \ number$, where the number is not a power of 2, we use logarithms. For example, to solve an equation such as $3^x = 7$, we use the fact that $f(x) = \log_b x$ is a one-to-one function. Another way of stating this fact is as a property of equality.

> **Logarithm Property of Equality**
>
> Let a, b, and c be real numbers such that $\log_b a$ and $\log_b c$ are real numbers and b is not 1. Then
>
> $$\log_b a = \log_b c \text{ is equivalent to } a = c$$

EXAMPLE 1   Solve: $3^x = 7$.

Solution   To solve, we use the logarithm property of equality and take the logarithm of both sides. For this example, we use the common logarithm.

$$3^x = 7$$
$$\log 3^x = \log 7 \quad \text{Take the common logarithm of both sides.}$$
$$x \log 3 = \log 7 \quad \text{Apply the power property of logarithms.}$$
$$x = \frac{\log 7}{\log 3} \quad \text{Divide both sides by log 3.}$$

(Continued on next page)

The exact solution is $\dfrac{\log 7}{\log 3}$. If a decimal approximation is preferred,

$$\frac{\log 7}{\log 3} \approx \frac{0.845098}{0.4771213} \approx 1.7712 \text{ to four decimal places.}$$

The solution is $\dfrac{\log 7}{\log 3}$, or *approximately* 1.7712.

PRACTICE
1   Solve: $5^x = 9$.

OBJECTIVE
2   **Solving Logarithmic Equations**

By applying the appropriate properties of logarithms, we can solve a broad variety of logarithmic equations.

EXAMPLE 2   Solve: $\log_4(x - 2) = 2$.

Solution   Notice that $x - 2$ must be positive, so x must be greater than 2. With this in mind, we first write the equation with exponential notation.

$$\log_4(x - 2) = 2$$
$$4^2 = x - 2$$
$$16 = x - 2$$
$$18 = x \qquad \text{Add 2 to both sides.}$$

Check: To check, we replace x with 18 in the original equation.

$$\log_4(x - 2) = 2$$
$$\log_4(18 - 2) \stackrel{?}{=} 2 \qquad \text{Let } x = 18.$$
$$\log_4 16 \stackrel{?}{=} 2$$
$$4^2 = 16 \qquad \text{True}$$

The solution is 18.

PRACTICE
2   Solve: $\log_2(x - 1) = 5$.

EXAMPLE 3   Solve: $\log_2 x + \log_2(x - 1) = 1$.

Solution   Notice that $x - 1$ must be positive, so x must be greater than 1. We use the product property on the left side of the equation.

$$\log_2 x + \log_2(x - 1) = 1$$
$$\log_2 x(x - 1) = 1 \qquad \text{Apply the product property.}$$
$$\log_2(x^2 - x) = 1$$

Next we write the equation with exponential notation and solve for x.

$$2^1 = x^2 - x$$
$$0 = x^2 - x - 2 \qquad\qquad \text{Subtract 2 from both sides.}$$
$$0 = (x - 2)(x + 1) \qquad\qquad \text{Factor.}$$
$$0 = x - 2 \quad \text{or} \quad 0 = x + 1 \quad \text{Set each factor equal to 0.}$$
$$2 = x \qquad\qquad -1 = x$$

Recall that -1 cannot be a solution because x must be greater than 1. If we forgot this, we would still reject -1 after checking. To see this, we replace x with -1 in the original equation.

$$\log_2 x + \log_2(x - 1) = 1$$
$$\log_2(-1) + \log_2(-1 - 1) \stackrel{?}{=} 1 \quad \text{Let } x = -1.$$

Because the logarithm of a negative number is undefined, -1 is rejected. Check to see that the solution is 2. ☐

PRACTICE

3 Solve: $\log_5 x + \log_5 (x + 4) = 1$.

EXAMPLE 4 Solve: $\log(x + 2) - \log x = 2$.

We use the quotient property of logarithms on the left side of the equation.

Solution $\log(x + 2) - \log x = 2$

$$\log \frac{x + 2}{x} = 2 \qquad \text{Apply the quotient property.}$$

$$10^2 = \frac{x + 2}{x} \qquad \text{Write using exponential notation.}$$

$$100 = \frac{x + 2}{x} \qquad \text{Simplify.}$$

$$100x = x + 2 \qquad \text{Multiply both sides by } x.$$

$$99x = 2 \qquad \text{Subtract } x \text{ from both sides.}$$

$$x = \frac{2}{99} \qquad \text{Divide both sides by 99.}$$

Verify that the solution is $\dfrac{2}{99}$. ☐

PRACTICE

4 Solve: $\log(x + 3) - \log x = 1$.

OBJECTIVE

3 **Solving Problems Modeled by Exponential and Logarithmic Equations**

Logarithmic and exponential functions are used in a variety of scientific, technical, and business settings. A few examples follow.

EXAMPLE 5 **Estimating Population Size**

The population size y of a community of lemmings varies according to the relationship $y = y_0 e^{0.15t}$. In this formula, t is time in months, and y_0 is the initial population at time 0. Estimate the population after 6 months if there were originally 5000 lemmings.

Solution We substitute 5000 for y_0 and 6 for t.

$$y = y_0 e^{0.15t}$$
$$= 5000 e^{0.15(6)} \qquad \text{Let } t = 6 \text{ and } y_0 = 5000.$$
$$= 5000 e^{0.9} \qquad \text{Multiply.}$$

Using a calculator, we find that $y \approx 12{,}298.016$. In 6 months, the population will be approximately 12,300 lemmings. ☐

PRACTICE

5 The population size y of a group of rabbits varies according to the relationship $y = y_0 e^{0.916t}$. In this formula, t is time in years and y_0 is the initial population at time $t = 0$. Estimate the population in three years if there were originally 60 rabbits.

EXAMPLE 6   Doubling an Investment

How long does it take an investment of $2000 to double if it is invested at 5% interest compounded quarterly? The necessary formula is $A = P\left(1 + \dfrac{r}{n}\right)^{nt}$, where A is the accrued (or owed) amount, P is the principal invested, r is the annual rate of interest, n is the number of compounding periods per year, and t is the number of years.

Solution   We are given that $P = \$2000$ and $r = 5\% = 0.05$. Compounding quarterly means 4 times a year, so $n = 4$. The investment is to double, so A must be $4000. Substitute these values and solve for t.

$$A = P\left(1 + \frac{r}{n}\right)^{nt}$$

$$4000 = 2000\left(1 + \frac{0.05}{4}\right)^{4t} \qquad \text{Substitute in known values.}$$

$$4000 = 2000(1.0125)^{4t} \qquad \text{Simplify } 1 + \frac{0.05}{4}.$$

$$2 = (1.0125)^{4t} \qquad \text{Divide both sides by 2000.}$$

$$\log 2 = \log 1.0125^{4t} \qquad \text{Take the logarithm of both sides.}$$

$$\log 2 = 4t(\log 1.0125) \qquad \text{Apply the power property.}$$

$$\frac{\log 2}{4 \log 1.0125} = t \qquad \text{Divide both sides by } 4 \log 1.0125.$$

$$13.949408 \approx t \qquad \text{Approximate by calculator.}$$

Thus, it takes nearly 14 years for the money to double in value.   ☐

PRACTICE

6   How long does it take for an investment of $3000 to double if it is invested at 7% interest compounded monthly? Round to the nearest year.

Graphing Calculator Explorations

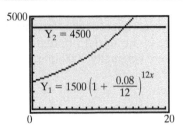

Use a graphing calculator to find how long it takes an investment of $1500 to triple if it is invested at 8% interest compounded monthly.

First, let $P = \$1500$, $r = 0.08$, and $n = 12$ (for 12 months) in the formula

$$A = P\left(1 + \frac{r}{n}\right)^{nt}$$

Notice that when the investment has tripled, the accrued amount A is $4500. Thus,

$$4500 = 1500\left(1 + \frac{0.08}{12}\right)^{12t}$$

Determine an appropriate viewing window and enter and graph the equations

$$Y_1 = 1500\left(1 + \frac{0.08}{12}\right)^{12x}$$

and

$$Y_2 = 4500$$

The point of intersection of the two curves is the solution. The x-coordinate tells how long it takes for the investment to triple.

Use a TRACE feature or an INTERSECT feature to approximate the coordinates of the point of intersection of the two curves. It takes approximately 13.78 years, or 13 years and 9 months, for the investment to triple in value to $4500.

Use this graphical solution method to solve each problem. Round each answer to the nearest hundredth.

1. Find how long it takes an investment of $5000 to grow to $6000 if it is invested at 5% interest compounded quarterly.

2. Find how long it takes an investment of $1000 to double if it is invested at 4.5% interest compounded daily. (Use 365 days in a year.)

3. Find how long it takes an investment of $10,000 to quadruple if it is invested at 6% interest compounded monthly.

4. Find how long it takes $500 to grow to $800 if it is invested at 4% interest compounded semiannually.

Vocabulary, Readiness & Video Check

Martin-Gay Interactive Videos

See Video 12.8

Watch the section lecture video and answer the following questions.

OBJECTIVE 1

1. From the lecture before Example 1, explain why $\ln(4x - 2) = \ln 3$ is equivalent to $4x - 2 = 3$.

OBJECTIVE 2

2. Why is the possible solution of -8 rejected in Example 3?

OBJECTIVE 3

3. For Example 4, write the equation and find the number of years it takes $1000 to double at 7% interest compounded monthly. Explain the similarity to the answer to Example 4. Round your answer to the nearest tenth.

12.8 Exercise Set   MyMathLab®

Solve each equation. Give an exact solution and approximate the solution to four decimal places. See Example 1.

1. $3^x = 6$

2. $4^x = 7$

3. $3^{2x} = 3.8$

4. $5^{3x} = 5.6$

5. $2^{x-3} = 5$

6. $8^{x-2} = 12$

7. $9^x = 5$

8. $3^x = 11$

9. $4^{x+7} = 3$

10. $6^{x+3} = 2$

MIXED PRACTICE

Solve each equation. See Examples 1 through 4.

11. $\log_2(x + 5) = 4$

12. $\log_2(x - 5) = 3$

13. $\log_4 2 + \log_4 x = 0$

14. $\log_3 5 + \log_3 x = 1$

15. $\log_2 6 - \log_2 x = 3$

16. $\log_4 10 - \log_4 x = 2$

17. $\log_6(x^2 - x) = 1$

18. $\log_2(x^2 + x) = 1$

19. $\log_4 x + \log_4(x + 6) = 2$

20. $\log_3 x + \log_3(x + 6) = 3$

21. $\log_5(x + 3) - \log_5 x = 2$

22. $\log_6(x + 2) - \log_6 x = 2$

23. $7^{3x-4} = 11$

24. $5^{2x-6} = 12$

25. $\log_4(x^2 - 3x) = 1$

26. $\log_8(x^2 - 2x) = 1$

27. $e^{6x} = 5$

28. $e^{2x} = 8$

29. $\log_3 x^2 = 4$

30. $\log_2 x^2 = 6$

31. $\ln 5 + \ln x = 0$

32. $\ln 3 + \ln(x - 1) = 0$

33. $3 \log x - \log x^2 = 2$

34. $2 \log x - \log x = 3$

35. $\log_4 x - \log_4(2x - 3) = 3$

36. $\log_2 x - \log_2(3x + 5) = 4$

37. $\log_2 x + \log_2(3x + 1) = 1$

38. $\log_3 x + \log_3(x - 8) = 2$

39. $\log_2 x + \log_2(x + 5) = 1$

40. $\log_4 x + \log_4(x + 7) = 1$

Solve. See Example 5.

41. The size of the wolf population at Isle Royale National Park increases according to the formula $y = y_0 e^{0.043t}$. In this formula, t is time in years and y_0 is the initial population at time 0. If the size of the current population is 83 wolves, find how many there should be in 5 years. Round to the nearest whole number.

42. The number of victims of a flu epidemic is increasing according to the formula $y = y_0 e^{0.075t}$. In this formula, t is time in weeks and y_0 is the given population at time 0. If 20,000 people are currently infected, how many might be infected in 3 weeks? Round to the nearest whole number.

43. The population of the Cook Islands is decreasing according to the formula $y = y_0 e^{-0.0277t}$. In this formula, t is the time in years and y_0 is the initial population at time 0. If the size of the population in 2010 was 11,488, use the formula to predict the population of the Cook Islands in the year 2025. Round to the nearest whole number. (*Source: The World Almanac*)

44. The population of Saint Barthelemy is decreasing according to the formula $y = y_0 e^{-0.0034t}$. In this formula, t is the time in years and y_0 is the initial population at time 0. If the size of the population in 2010 was 6852, use the formula to predict the population of Saint Barthelemy in the year 2025. Round to the nearest whole number. (*Source: The World Almanac*)

Use the formula $A = P\left(1 + \dfrac{r}{n}\right)^{nt}$ *to solve these compound interest problems. Round to the nearest tenth. See Example 6.*

45. Find how long it takes $600 to double if it is invested at 7% interest compounded monthly.

46. Find how long it takes $600 to double if it is invested at 12% interest compounded monthly.

47. Find how long it takes a $1200 investment to earn $200 interest if it is invested at 9% interest compounded quarterly.

48. Find how long it takes a $1500 investment to earn $200 interest if it is invested at 10% compounded semiannually.

49. Find how long it takes $1000 to double if it is invested at 8% interest compounded semiannually.

50. Find how long it takes $1000 to double if it is invested at 8% interest compounded monthly.

The formula $w = 0.00185 h^{2.67}$ *is used to estimate the normal weight w of a boy h inches tall. Use this formula to solve the height–weight problems. Round to the nearest tenth.*

51. Find the expected weight of a boy who is 35 inches tall.

52. Find the expected weight of a boy who is 43 inches tall.

53. Find the expected height of a boy who weighs 85 pounds.

54. Find the expected height of a boy who weighs 140 pounds.

The formula $P = 14.7 e^{-0.21x}$ *gives the average atmospheric pressure P, in pounds per square inch, at an altitude x, in miles above sea level. Use this formula to solve these pressure problems. Round answers to the nearest tenth.*

55. Find the average atmospheric pressure of Denver, which is 1 mile above sea level.

56. Find the average atmospheric pressure of Pikes Peak, which is 2.7 miles above sea level.

57. Find the elevation of a Delta jet if the atmospheric pressure outside the jet is 7.5 lb/sq in.

58. Find the elevation of a remote Himalayan peak if the atmospheric pressure atop the peak is 6.5 lb/sq in.

Psychologists call the graph of the formula $t = \dfrac{1}{c}\ln\left(\dfrac{A}{A - N}\right)$ *the learning curve, since the formula relates time t passed, in weeks, to a measure N of learning achieved, to a measure A of maximum learning possible, and to a measure c of an individual's learning style. Round to the nearest week.*

59. Norman is learning to type. If he wants to type at a rate of 50 words per minute (N is 50) and his expected maximum rate is 75 words per minute (A is 75), find how many weeks it should take him to achieve his goal. Assume that c is 0.09.

60. An experiment with teaching chimpanzees sign language shows that a typical chimp can master a maximum of 65 signs. Find how many weeks it should take a chimpanzee to master 30 signs if c is 0.03.

61. Janine is working on her dictation skills. She wants to take dictation at a rate of 150 words per minute and believes that the maximum rate she can hope for is 210 words per minute. Find how many weeks it should take her to achieve the 150 words per minute level if c is 0.07.

62. A psychologist is measuring human capability to memorize nonsense syllables. Find how many weeks it should take a subject to learn 15 nonsense syllables if the maximum possible to learn is 24 syllables and c is 0.17.

REVIEW AND PREVIEW

If $x = -2$, $y = 0$, and $z = 3$, find the value of each expression. See Section 1.7.

63. $\dfrac{x^2 - y + 2z}{3x}$

64. $\dfrac{x^3 - 2y + z}{2z}$

65. $\dfrac{3z - 4x + y}{x + 2z}$

66. $\dfrac{4y - 3x + z}{2x + y}$

Find the inverse function of each one-to-one function. See Section 12.2.

67. $f(x) = 5x + 2$

68. $f(x) = \dfrac{x - 3}{4}$

CONCEPT EXTENSIONS

The formula $y = y_0 e^{kt}$ gives the population size y of a population that experiences an annual rate of population growth k (given as a decimal). In this formula, t is time in years and y_0 is the initial population at time 0. Use this formula to solve Exercises 69 and 70.

69. In 2010, the population of Michigan was approximately 9,939,000 and decreasing according to the formula $y = y_0 e^{-0.003t}$. Assume that the population continues to decrease according to the given formula and predict how many years after which the population of Michigan will be 9,500,000. (*Hint*: Let $y_0 = 9{,}939{,}000$; $y = 9{,}500{,}000$, and solve for *t*.) (*Source*: U.S. Bureau of the Census)

70. In 2010, the population of Illinois was approximately 12,830,000 and increasing according to the formula $y = y_0 e^{0.005t}$. Assume that the population continues to increase according to the given formula and predict how many years after which the population of Illinois will be 13,500,000. (See the Hint for Exercise 69.) (*Source*: U.S. Bureau of the Census)

71. When solving a logarithmic equation, explain why you must check possible solutions in the original equation.

72. Solve $5^x = 9$ by taking the common logarithm of both sides of the equation. Next, solve this equation by taking the natural logarithm of both sides. Compare your solutions. Are they the same? Why or why not?

Use a graphing calculator to solve each equation. For example, to solve Exercise 73, let $Y_1 = e^{0.3x}$ and $Y_2 = 8$ and graph the equations. The x-value of the point of intersection is the solution. Round all solutions to two decimal places.

73. $e^{0.3x} = 8$

74. $10^{0.5x} = 7$

75. $2\log(-5.6x + 1.3) + x + 1 = 0$

76. $\ln(1.3x - 2.1) + 3.5x - 5 = 0$

77. Check Exercise 23.

78. Check Exercise 24.

79. Check Exercise 31.

80. Check Exercise 32.

Chapter 12 Vocabulary Check

Fill in each blank with one of the words or phrases listed below. Some words or phrases may be used more than once.

inverse	common	composition	symmetric	exponential
vertical	logarithmic	natural	half-life	horizontal

1. For a one-to-one function, we can find its _____ function by switching the coordinates of the ordered pairs of the function.

2. The _____ of functions f and g is $(f \circ g)(x) = f(g(x))$.

3. A function of the form $f(x) = b^x$ is called a(n) _____ function if $b > 0$, b is not 1, and x is a real number.

4. The graphs of f and f^{-1} are _____ about the line $y = x$.

5. _____ logarithms are logarithms to base *e*.

6. _____ logarithms are logarithms to base 10.

7. To see whether a graph is the graph of a one-to-one function, apply the _____ line test to see whether it is a function and then apply the _____ line test to see whether it is a one-to-one function.

8. A(n) _____ function is a function that can be defined by $f(x) = \log_b x$ where x is a positive real number, b is a constant positive real number, and b is not 1.

9. _____ is the amount of time it takes for half of the amount of a substance to decay.

10. A quantity that grows or decays by the same percent at regular time periods is said to have _____ growth or decay.

Chapter 12 Highlights

DEFINITIONS AND CONCEPTS	EXAMPLES

Section 12.1 The Algebra of Functions; Composite Functions

Algebra of Functions

Sum $\quad (f + g)(x) = f(x) + g(x)$

Difference $\quad (f - g)(x) = f(x) - g(x)$

Product $\quad (f \cdot g)(x) = f(x) \cdot g(x)$

Quotient $\quad \left(\dfrac{f}{g}\right)(x) = \dfrac{f(x)}{g(x)}, g(x) \neq 0$

If $f(x) = 7x$ and $g(x) = x^2 + 1$,

$$(f + g)(x) = f(x) + g(x) = 7x + x^2 + 1$$

$$(f - g)(x) = f(x) - g(x) = 7x - (x^2 + 1)$$

$$= 7x - x^2 - 1$$

$$(f \cdot g)(x) = f(x) \cdot g(x) = 7x(x^2 + 1)$$

$$= 7x^3 + 7x$$

$$\left(\dfrac{f}{g}\right)(x) = \dfrac{f(x)}{g(x)} = \dfrac{7x}{x^2 + 1}$$

Composite Functions

The notation $(f \circ g)(x)$ means "f composed with g."

$$(f \circ g)(x) = f(g(x))$$

$$(g \circ f)(x) = g(f(x))$$

If $f(x) = x^2 + 1$ and $g(x) = x - 5$, find $(f \circ g)(x)$.

$$(f \circ g)(x) = f(g(x))$$

$$= f(x - 5)$$

$$= (x - 5)^2 + 1$$

$$= x^2 - 10x + 26$$

Section 12.2 Inverse Functions

If f is a function, then f is a **one-to-one function** only if each y-value (output) corresponds to only one x-value (input).

Horizontal Line Test

If every horizontal line intersects the graph of a function at most once, then the function is a one-to-one function.

Determine whether each graph is a one-to-one function.

A   **B**

C

Graphs **A** and **C** pass the vertical line test, so only these are graphs of functions. Of graphs **A** and **C**, only graph **A** passes the horizontal line test, so only graph **A** is the graph of a one-to-one function.

The **inverse** of a one-to-one function f is the one-to-one function f^{-1} that is the set of all ordered pairs (b, a) such that (a, b) belongs to f.

To Find the Inverse of a One-to-One Function f(x)

Step 1. Replace $f(x)$ with y.

Step 2. Interchange x and y.

Step 3. Solve for y.

Step 4. Replace y with $f^{-1}(x)$.

Find the inverse of $f(x) = 2x + 7$.

$$y = 2x + 7 \quad \text{Replace } f(x) \text{ with } y.$$

$$x = 2y + 7 \quad \text{Interchange } x \text{ and } y.$$

$$2y = x - 7 \quad \text{Solve for } y.$$

$$y = \dfrac{x - 7}{2}$$

$$f^{-1}(x) = \dfrac{x - 7}{2} \quad \text{Replace } y \text{ with } f^{-1}(x).$$

The inverse of $f(x) = 2x + 7$ is $f^{-1}(x) = \dfrac{x - 7}{2}$.

DEFINITIONS AND CONCEPTS	EXAMPLES

Section 12.3   Exponential Functions

A function of the form $f(x) = b^x$ is an **exponential function,** where $b > 0$, $b \neq 1$, and x is a real number.

Graph the exponential function $y = 4^x$.

x	y
-2	$\dfrac{1}{16}$
-1	$\dfrac{1}{4}$
0	1
1	4
2	16

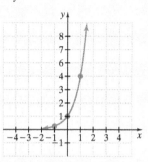

Uniqueness of b^x

If $b > 0$ and $b \neq 1$, then $b^x = b^y$ is equivalent to $x = y$.

Solve $2^{x+5} = 8$.

$2^{x+5} = 2^3$ Write 8 as 2^3.

$x + 5 = 3$ Use the uniqueness of b^x.

$x = -2$ Subtract 5 from both sides.

Section 12.4   Exponential Growth and Decay Functions

A quantity that grows or decays by the same percent at regular time periods is said to have **exponential growth** or **exponential decay.**

Exponential Growth

initial amount

number of time intervals

$$y = C(1 + r)^x$$

$(1 + r)$ is growth factor
r is growth rate (often a percent)

Exponential Decay

initial amount

number of time intervals

$$y = C(1 - r)^x$$

$(1 - r)$ is decay factor
r is decay rate (often a percent)

A city has a current population of 37,000 that has been increasing at a rate of 3% per year. At this rate, find the city's population in 20 years.

$$y = C(1 + r)^x$$
$$y = 37{,}000(1 + 0.03)^{20}$$
$$y \approx 66{,}826.12$$

In 20 years, the predicted population of the city is 66,826.

A city has a current population of 37,000 that has been decreasing at a rate of 3% per year. At this rate, find the city's population in 20 years.

$$y = C(1 - r)^x$$
$$y = 37{,}000(1 - 0.03)^{20}$$
$$y \approx 20{,}120.39$$

In 20 years, predicted population of the city is 20,120.

Section 12.5   Logarithmic Functions

Logarithmic Definition

If $b > 0$ and $b \neq 1$, then

$$y = \log_b x \quad \text{means} \quad x = b^y$$

for any positive number x and real number y.

Logarithmic Form	Corresponding Exponential Statement
$\log_5 25 = 2$	$5^2 = 25$
$\log_9 3 = \dfrac{1}{2}$	$9^{1/2} = 3$

Properties of Logarithms

If b is a real number, $b > 0$, and $b \neq 1$, then

$$\log_b 1 = 0, \quad \log_b b^x = x, \quad b^{\log_b x} = x$$

$$\log_5 1 = 0, \quad \log_7 7^2 = 2, \quad 3^{\log_3 6} = 6$$

(continued)

DEFINITIONS AND CONCEPTS	EXAMPLES

Section 12.5 Logarithmic Functions (continued)

Logarithmic Function

If $b > 0$ and $b \neq 1$, then a **logarithmic function** is a function that can be defined as

$$f(x) = \log_b x$$

The domain of f is the set of positive real numbers, and the range of f is the set of real numbers.

Graph $y = \log_3 x$.

Write $y = \log_3 x$ as $3^y = x$. Plot the ordered pair solutions listed in the table and connect them with a smooth curve.

x	y
3	1
1	0
$\frac{1}{3}$	-1
$\frac{1}{9}$	-2

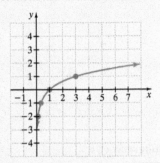

Section 12.6 Properties of Logarithms

Let x, y, and b be positive numbers and $b \neq 1$.

Product Property

$$\log_b xy = \log_b x + \log_b y$$

Quotient Property

$$\log_b \frac{x}{y} = \log_b x - \log_b y$$

Power Property

$$\log_b x^r = r \log_b x$$

Write as a single logarithm.

$$2 \log_5 6 + \log_5 x - \log_5(y + 2)$$

$= \log_5 6^2 + \log_5 x - \log_5(y + 2)$ Power property

$= \log_5 36 \cdot x - \log_5(y + 2)$ Product property

$= \log_5 \dfrac{36x}{y + 2}$ Quotient property

Section 12.7 Common Logarithms, Natural Logarithms, and Change of Base

Common Logarithms

$$\log x \quad \text{means} \quad \log_{10} x$$

Natural Logarithms

$$\ln x \quad \text{means} \quad \log_e x$$

Continuously Compounded Interest Formula

$$A = Pe^{rt}$$

where r is the annual interest rate for P dollars invested for t years.

$\log 5 = \log_{10} 5 \approx 0.69897$

$\ln 7 = \log_e 7 \approx 1.94591$

Find the amount in an account at the end of 3 years if \$1000 is invested at an interest rate of 4% compounded continuously.

Here, $t = 3$ years, $P = \$1000$, and $r = 0.04$.

$$A = Pe^{rt}$$

$$= 1000e^{0.04(3)}$$

$$\approx \$1127.50$$

Section 12.8 Exponential and Logarithmic Equations and Problem Solving

Logarithm Property of Equality

Let $\log_b a$ and $\log_b c$ be real numbers and $b \neq 1$. Then

$$\log_b a = \log_b c \text{ is equivalent to } a = c$$

Solve $2^x = 5$.

$\log 2^x = \log 5$ Logarithm property of equality

$x \log 2 = \log 5$ Power property

$x = \dfrac{\log 5}{\log 2}$ Divide both sides by log 2.

$x \approx 2.3219$ Use a calculator.

Chapter 12 **Review**

(12.1) *If* $f(x) = x - 5$ *and* $g(x) = 2x + 1$, *find*

1. $(f + g)(x)$

2. $(f - g)(x)$

3. $(f \cdot g)(x)$

4. $\left(\dfrac{g}{f}\right)(x)$

If $f(x) = x^2 - 2$, $g(x) = x + 1$, *and* $h(x) = x^3 - x^2$, *find each composition.*

5. $(f \circ g)(x)$

6. $(g \circ f)(x)$

7. $(h \circ g)(2)$

8. $(f \circ f)(x)$

9. $(f \circ g)(-1)$

10. $(h \circ h)(2)$

(12.2) *Determine whether each function is a one-to-one function. If it is one-to-one, list the elements of its inverse.*

11. $h = \{(-9, 14), (6, 8), (-11, 12), (15, 15)\}$

12. $f = \{(-5, 5), (0, 4), (13, 5), (11, -6)\}$

13.

U.S. Region (Input)	Northeast	Midwest	South	West
Rank in Housing Starts for 2009 (Output)	4	3	1	2

△ **14.**

Shape (Input)	Square	Triangle	Parallelogram	Rectangle
Number of Sides (Output)	4	3	4	4

Given that $f(x) = \sqrt{x + 2}$ *is a one-to-one function, find the following.*

15. a. $f(7)$

b. $f^{-1}(3)$

16. a. $f(-1)$

b. $f^{-1}(1)$

Determine whether each function is a one-to-one function.

17.

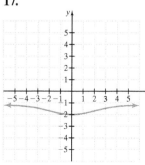

18.

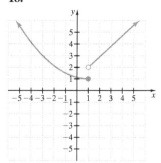

19.

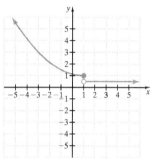

20.

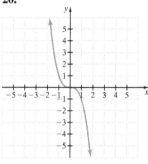

Find an equation defining the inverse function of the given one-to-one function.

21. $f(x) = x - 9$

22. $f(x) = x + 8$

23. $f(x) = 6x + 11$

24. $f(x) = 12x - 1$

25. $f(x) = x^3 - 5$

26. $f(x) = \sqrt[3]{x + 2}$

27. $g(x) = \dfrac{12x - 7}{6}$

28. $r(x) = \dfrac{13x - 5}{2}$

Graph each one-to-one function and its inverse on the same set of axes.

29. $f(x) = -2x + 3$

30. $f(x) = 5x - 5$

(12.3) *Solve each equation for x.*

31. $4^x = 64$

32. $3^x = \dfrac{1}{9}$

33. $2^{3x} = \dfrac{1}{16}$

34. $5^{2x} = 125$

35. $9^{x+1} = 243$

36. $8^{3x-2} = 4$

Graph each exponential function.

37. $y = 3^x$

38. $y = \left(\dfrac{1}{3}\right)^x$

39. $y = 2^{x-4}$

40. $y = 2^x + 4$

Use the formula $A = P\left(1 + \dfrac{r}{n}\right)^{nt}$ *to solve the interest problems. In this formula,*

A = amount accrued (or owed)

P = principal invested (or loaned)

r = rate of interest

n = number of compounding periods per year

t = time in years

41. Find the amount accrued if \$1600 is invested at 9% interest compounded semiannually for 7 years.

42. A total of \$800 is invested in a 7% certificate of deposit for which interest is compounded quarterly. Find the value that this certificate will have at the end of 5 years.

(12.4) Solve. Round each answer to the nearest whole.

43. The city of Henderson, Nevada, has been growing at a rate of 4.4% per year since the year 2000. If the population of Henderson was 79,087 in 2000 and this rate continues, predict the city's population in 2020.

44. The city of Raleigh, North Carolina, has been growing at a rate of 4.2% per year since the year 2000. If the population of Raleigh was 287,370 in 2000 and this rate continues, predict the city's population in 2018.

45. A summer camp tournament starts with 1024 players. After each round, half the players are eliminated. How many players remain after 7 rounds?

46. The bear population in a certain national park is decreasing by 11% each year. If this rate continues, and there is currently an estimated bear population of 1280, find the bear population in 6 years.

(12.5) Write each equation with logarithmic notation.

47. $49 = 7^2$

48. $2^{-4} = \dfrac{1}{16}$

Write each logarithmic equation with exponential notation.

49. $\log_{1/2} 16 = -4$

50. $\log_{0.4} 0.064 = 3$

Solve for x.

51. $\log_4 x = -3$

52. $\log_3 x = 2$

53. $\log_3 1 = x$

54. $\log_4 64 = x$

55. $\log_4 4^5 = x$

56. $\log_7 7^{-2} = x$

57. $5^{\log_5 4} = x$

58. $2^{\log_2 9} = x$

59. $\log_2(3x - 1) = 4$

60. $\log_3(2x + 5) = 2$

61. $\log_4(x^2 - 3x) = 1$

62. $\log_8(x^2 + 7x) = 1$

Graph each pair of equations on the same coordinate system.

63. $y = 2^x$ and $y = \log_2 x$

64. $y = \left(\dfrac{1}{2}\right)^x$ and $y = \log_{1/2} x$

(12.6) Write each of the following as single logarithms.

65. $\log_3 8 + \log_3 4$

66. $\log_2 6 + \log_2 3$

67. $\log_7 15 - \log_7 20$

68. $\log 18 - \log 12$

69. $\log_{11} 8 + \log_{11} 3 - \log_{11} 6$

70. $\log_5 14 + \log_5 3 - \log_5 21$

71. $2 \log_5 x - 2 \log_5(x + 1) + \log_5 x$

72. $4 \log_3 x - \log_3 x + \log_3(x + 2)$

Use properties of logarithms to write each expression as a sum or difference of multiples of logarithms.

73. $\log_3 \dfrac{x^3}{x + 2}$

74. $\log_4 \dfrac{x + 5}{x^2}$

75. $\log_2 \dfrac{3x^2 y}{z}$

76. $\log_7 \dfrac{yz^3}{x}$

If $\log_b 2 = 0.36$ and $\log_b 5 = 0.83$, find the following.

77. $\log_b 50$

78. $\log_b \dfrac{4}{5}$

(12.7) Use a calculator to approximate the logarithm to four decimal places.

79. $\log 3.6$

80. $\log 0.15$

81. $\ln 1.25$

82. $\ln 4.63$

Find the exact value.

83. $\log 1000$

84. $\log \dfrac{1}{10}$

85. $\ln \dfrac{1}{e}$

86. $\ln e^4$

Solve each equation for x.

87. $\ln(2x) = 2$

88. $\ln(3x) = 1.6$

89. $\ln(2x - 3) = -1$

90. $\ln(3x + 1) = 2$

Use the formula $\ln \dfrac{I}{I_0} = -kx$ to solve the radiation problems in Exercises 91 and 92. In this formula,

  x = depth in millimeters
  I = intensity of radiation
  I_0 = initial intensity
  k = a constant measure dependent on the material

Round answers to two decimal places.

91. Find the depth at which the intensity of the radiation passing through a lead shield is reduced to 3% of the original intensity if the value of k is 2.1.

92. If k is 3.2, find the depth at which 2% of the original radiation will penetrate.

Approximate the logarithm to four decimal places.

93. $\log_5 1.6$

94. $\log_3 4$

Use the formula $A = Pe^{rt}$ to solve the interest problems in which interest is compounded continuously. In this formula,

  A = amount accrued (or owed)
  P = principal invested (or loaned)
  r = rate of interest
  t = time in years

95. Bank of New York offers a 5-year, 3% continuously compounded investment option. Find the amount accrued if $1450 is invested.

96. Find the amount to which a $940 investment grows if it is invested at 4% compounded continuously for 3 years.

(12.8) Solve each exponential equation for x. Give an exact solution and approximate the solution to four decimal places.

97. $3^{2x} = 7$

98. $6^{3x} = 5$

99. $3^{2x+1} = 6$

100. $4^{3x+2} = 9$

101. $5^{3x-5} = 4$

102. $8^{4x-2} = 3$

103. $5^{x-1} = \dfrac{1}{2}$

104. $4^{x+5} = \dfrac{2}{3}$

Solve the equation for x.

105. $\log_5 2 + \log_5 x = 2$

106. $\log_3 x + \log_3 10 = 2$

107. $\log(5x) - \log(x + 1) = 4$

108. $-\log_6(4x + 7) + \log_6 x = 1$

109. $\log_2 x + \log_2 2x - 3 = 1$

110. $\log_3(x^2 - 8x) = 2$

Use the formula $y = y_0 e^{kt}$ to solve the population growth problems. In this formula,

y = size of population

y_0 = initial count of population

k = rate of growth written as a decimal

t = time

Round each answer to the nearest tenth.

111. In 1987, the population of California condors was only 27 birds. They were all brought in from the wild and an intensive breeding program was instituted. If we assume a yearly growth rate of 11.4%, how long did it take the condor population to reach 347 California condors? (*Source:* California Department of Fish and Game)

112. France is experiencing an annual growth rate of 0.4%. In 2010, the population of France was approximately 65,822,000. How long will it take for the population to reach 70,000,000? Round to the nearest tenth. (*Source:* Population Reference Bureau)

113. In 2010, the population of Australia was approximately 22,600,000. How long will it take Australia to double its population if its growth rate is 0.7% annually? Round to the nearest tenth. (*Source:* Population Reference Bureau)

114. Israel's population is increasing in size at a rate of 1.6% per year. How long will it take for its population of 7,746,400 to double in size? Round to the nearest tenth. (*Source:* Population Reference Bureau)

Use the compound interest equation $A = P\left(1 + \dfrac{r}{n}\right)^{nt}$ to solve the following. (See the directions for Exercises 41 and 42 for an explanation of this formula.) Round answers to the nearest tenth.

115. Find how long it will take a $5000 investment to grow to $10,000 if it is invested at 8% interest compounded quarterly.

116. An investment of $6000 has grown to $10,000 while the money was invested at 6% interest compounded monthly. Find how long it was invested.

Use a graphing calculator to solve each equation. Round all solutions to two decimal places.

117. $e^x = 2$

118. $10^{0.3x} = 7$

MIXED REVIEW

Solve each equation.

119. $3^x = \dfrac{1}{81}$

120. $7^{4x} = 49$

121. $8^{3x-2} = 32$

122. $9^{x-2} = 27$

123. $\log_4 4 = x$

124. $\log_3 x = 4$

125. $\log_5(x^2 - 4x) = 1$

126. $\log_4(3x - 1) = 2$

127. $\ln x = -3.2$

128. $\log_5 x + \log_5 10 = 2$

129. $\ln x - \ln 2 = 1$

130. $\log_6 x - \log_6(4x + 7) = 1$

 Chapter 12 **Test** MyMathLab®  Test Prep VIDEOS ▶ You Tube

If $f(x) = x$ and $g(x) = 2x - 3$, find the following.

▶ **1.** $(f \cdot g)(x)$

▶ **2.** $(f - g)(x)$

If $f(x) = x$, $g(x) = x - 7$, and $h(x) = x^2 - 6x + 5$, find the following.

▶ **3.** $(f \circ h)(0)$

▶ **4.** $(g \circ f)(x)$

▶ **5.** $(g \circ h)(x)$

On the same set of axes, graph the given one-to-one function and its inverse.

▶ **6.** $f(x) = 7x - 14$

Determine whether the given graph is the graph of a one-to-one function.

▶ **7.**

▶ **8.**

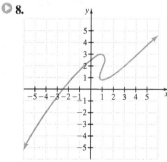

Determine whether each function is one-to-one. If it is one-to-one, find an equation or a set of ordered pairs that defines the inverse function of the given function.

9. $f(x) = 6 - 2x$

10. $f = \{(0,0), (2,3), (-1,5)\}$

11.

Word (Input)	Dog	Cat	House	Desk	Circle
First Letter of Word (Output)	d	c	h	d	c

Use the properties of logarithms to write each expression as a single logarithm.

12. $\log_3 6 + \log_3 4$

13. $\log_5 x + 3\log_5 x - \log_5(x + 1)$

14. Write the expression $\log_6 \dfrac{2x}{y^3}$ as the sum or difference of multiples of logarithms.

15. If $\log_b 3 = 0.79$ and $\log_b 5 = 1.16$, find the value of $\log_b \dfrac{3}{25}$.

16. Approximate $\log_7 8$ to four decimal places.

17. Solve $8^{x-1} = \dfrac{1}{64}$ for x. Give an exact solution.

18. Solve $3^{2x+5} = 4$ for x. Give an exact solution and approximate the solution to four decimal places.

Solve each logarithmic equation for x. Give an exact solution.

19. $\log_3 x = -2$

20. $\ln\sqrt{e} = x$

21. $\log_8(3x - 2) = 2$

22. $\log_5 x + \log_5 3 = 2$

23. $\log_4(x + 1) - \log_4(x - 2) = 3$

24. Solve $\ln(3x + 7) = 1.31$ accurate to four decimal places.

25. Graph $y = \left(\dfrac{1}{2}\right)^x + 1$.

26. Graph the functions $y = 3^x$ and $y = \log_3 x$ on the same coordinate system.

Use the formula $A = P\left(1 + \dfrac{r}{n}\right)^{nt}$ to solve Exercises 27–29.

27. Find the amount in an account if $4000 is invested for 3 years at 9% interest compounded monthly.

28. Find how long it will take $2000 to grow to $3000 if the money is invested at 7% interest compounded semiannually. Round to the nearest whole.

29. Suppose you have $3000 to invest. Which investment, rounded to the nearest dollar, yields the greater return over 10 years: 6.5% compounded semiannually or 6% compounded monthly? How much more is yielded by the better investment?

Solve. Round answers to the nearest whole.

30. Suppose a city with population of 150,000 has been decreasing at a rate of 2% per year. If this rate continues, predict the population of the city in 20 years.

31. The prairie dog population of the Grand Forks area now stands at 57,000 animals. If the population is growing at a rate of 2.6% annually, how many prairie dogs will there be in that area 5 years from now?

32. In an attempt to save an endangered species of wood duck, naturalists would like to increase the wood duck population from 400 to 1000 ducks. If the annual population growth rate is 6.2%, how long will it take the naturalists to reach their goal? Round to the nearest whole year.

The reliability of a new model of CD player can be described by the exponential function $R(t) = 2.7^{-(1/3)t}$, where the reliability R is the probability (as a decimal) that the CD player is still working t years after it is manufactured. Round answers to the nearest hundredth. Then write your answers as percents.

33. What is the probability that the CD player will still work half a year after it is manufactured?

34. What is the probability that the CD player will still work 2 years after it is manufactured?

Chapter 12 **Cumulative Review**

1. Divide. Simplify all quotients if possible.
   a. $\dfrac{4}{5} \div \dfrac{5}{16}$

   b. $\dfrac{7}{10} \div 14$

   c. $\dfrac{3}{8} \div \dfrac{3}{10}$

2. Solve $\dfrac{1}{3}(x - 2) = \dfrac{1}{4}(x + 1)$

3. Graph $f(x) = x^2$.

4. Find an equation of the line through $(-2, 6)$ and perpendicular to $f(x) = -3x + 4$. Write the equation using function notation.

5. Solve the system.
$$\begin{cases} x - 5y - 2z = 6 \\ -2x + 10y + 4z = -12 \\ \dfrac{1}{2}x - \dfrac{5}{2}y - z = 3 \end{cases}$$

6. Line l and line m are parallel lines cut by transversal t. Find the values of x and y.

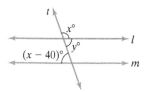

7. Simplify each expression.
   a. $-3 + [(-2 - 5) - 2]$
   b. $2^3 - |10| + [-6 - (-5)]$

8. Use the power rules to simplify the following. Use positive exponents to write all results.
   a. $(4a^3)^2$
   b. $\left(-\dfrac{2}{3}\right)^3$
   c. $\left(\dfrac{4a^5}{b^3}\right)^3$
   d. $\left(\dfrac{3^{-2}}{x}\right)^{-3}$
   e. $(a^{-2}b^3c^{-4})^{-2}$

9. For the ICL Production Company, the rational function $C(x) = \dfrac{2.6x + 10,000}{x}$ describes the company's cost per disc of pressing x compact discs. Find the cost per disc for pressing:
   a. 100 compact discs
   b. 1000 compact discs

10. Multiply.
    a. $(3x - 1)^2$
    b. $\left(\dfrac{1}{2}x + 3\right)\left(\dfrac{1}{2}x - 3\right)$
    c. $(2x - 5)(6x + 7)$

11. Solve $12a - 8a = 10 + 2a - 13 - 7$.

12. Perform the indicated operations and simplify if possible.
    $$\dfrac{5}{x - 2} + \dfrac{3}{x^2 + 4x + 4} - \dfrac{6}{x + 2}$$

13. Divide $\dfrac{8x^2y^2 - 16xy + 2x}{4xy}$.

14. Simplify each complex fraction.
    a. $\dfrac{\dfrac{a}{5}}{\dfrac{a - 1}{10}}$
    b. $\dfrac{\dfrac{3}{2 + a} + \dfrac{6}{2 - a}}{\dfrac{5}{a + 2} - \dfrac{1}{a - 2}}$
    c. $\dfrac{x^{-1} + y^{-1}}{xy}$

15. Factor $3m^2 - 24m - 60$.

16. Factor $5x^2 - 85x + 350$.

17. Subtract $\dfrac{3x^2 + 2x}{x - 1} - \dfrac{10x - 5}{x - 1}$.

18. Use synthetic division to divide: $(8x^2 - 12x - 7) \div (x - 2)$

19. Simplify the following expressions.
    a. $\sqrt[4]{81}$
    b. $\sqrt[5]{-243}$
    c. $-\sqrt{25}$
    d. $\sqrt[4]{-81}$
    e. $\sqrt[3]{64x^3}$

20. Solve $\dfrac{1}{a + 5} = \dfrac{1}{3a + 6} - \dfrac{a + 2}{a^2 + 7a + 10}$

21. Use rational exponents to write as a single radical.
    a. $\sqrt{x} \cdot \sqrt[4]{x}$
    b. $\dfrac{\sqrt{x}}{\sqrt[3]{x}}$
    c. $\sqrt[3]{3} \cdot \sqrt{2}$

22. Suppose that y varies directly as x. If $y = \dfrac{1}{2}$ when $x = 12$, find the constant of variation and the direct variation equation.

23. Multiply.
    a. $\sqrt{3}(5 + \sqrt{30})$
    b. $(\sqrt{5} - \sqrt{6})(\sqrt{7} + 1)$
    c. $(7\sqrt{x} + 5)(3\sqrt{x} - \sqrt{5})$
    d. $(4\sqrt{3} - 1)^2$
    e. $(\sqrt{2x} - 5)(\sqrt{2x} + 5)$
    f. $(\sqrt{x - 3} + 5)^2$

24. Find each root. Assume that all variables represent nonnegative real numbers.
    a. $\sqrt{9}$
    b. $\sqrt[3]{-27}$
    c. $\sqrt{\dfrac{9}{64}}$
    d. $\sqrt[4]{x^{12}}$
    e. $\sqrt[3]{-125y^6}$

25. Rationalize the denominator of $\dfrac{\sqrt[4]{x}}{\sqrt[4]{81y^5}}$.

26. Multiply.
    a. $a^{1/4}(a^{3/4} - a^8)$
    b. $(x^{1/2} - 3)(x^{1/2} + 5)$

27. Solve $\sqrt{4 - x} = x - 2$.

28. Use the quotient rule to divide and simplify if possible.

a. $\dfrac{\sqrt{54}}{\sqrt{6}}$

b. $\dfrac{\sqrt{108a^2}}{3\sqrt{3}}$

c. $\dfrac{3\sqrt[3]{81a^5b^{10}}}{\sqrt[3]{3b^4}}$

29. Solve $3x^2 - 9x + 8 = 0$ by completing the square.

30. Add or subtract as indicated.

a. $\dfrac{\sqrt{20}}{3} + \dfrac{\sqrt{5}}{4}$

b. $\sqrt[3]{\dfrac{24x}{27}} - \dfrac{\sqrt[3]{3x}}{2}$

31. Solve $\dfrac{3x}{x - 2} - \dfrac{x + 1}{x} = \dfrac{6}{x(x - 2)}$.

32. Rationalize the denominator. $\sqrt[3]{\dfrac{27}{m^4n^8}}$

33. Solve $x^2 - 4x \leq 0$.

34. Find the length of the unknown side of the triangle.

8 in.   4 in.

35. Graph $F(x) = (x - 3)^2 + 1$.

36. Find the following powers of i.

a. i^8

b. i^{21}

c. i^{42}

d. i^{-13}

37. Solve $\dfrac{45}{x} = \dfrac{5}{7}$.

38. Solve $4x^2 + 8x - 1 = 0$ by completing the square.

39. Find an equation of the inverse of $f(x) = x + 3$.

40. Solve by using the quadratic formula.

$$\left(x - \frac{1}{2}\right)^2 = \frac{x}{2}$$

41. Find the value of each logarithmic expression.

a. $\log_4 16$

b. $\log_{10} \dfrac{1}{10}$

c. $\log_9 3$

42. Graph $f(x) = -(x + 1)^2 + 1$.

13.1 The Parabola and the Circle

13.2 The Ellipse and the Hyperbola

Integrated Review— Graphing Conic Sections

13.3 Solving Nonlinear Systems of Equations

13.4 Nonlinear Inequalities and Systems of Inequalities

In Chapter 11, we analyzed some of the important connections between a parabola and its equation. Parabolas are interesting in their own right but are more interesting still because they are part of a collection of curves known as conic sections. This chapter is devoted to quadratic equations in two variables and their conic section graphs: the parabola, circle, ellipse, and hyperbola.

The original Ferris wheel was named after its designer, George Washington Gale Ferris, Jr., a trained engineer who produced the first Ferris wheel for the 1893 World's Columbian Exposition in Chicago. This very first wheel was 264 feet high and was the Columbian Exposition's most noticeable attraction. Since then, Ferris wheels have gotten ever taller, have been built with ever greater capacities, and have changed their designations from Ferris wheels to giant observation wheels because of their closed capsules. In Exercise 92 of Section 13.1, you will explore the dimensions of the Singapore Flyer, the current record-breaking giant observation wheel.

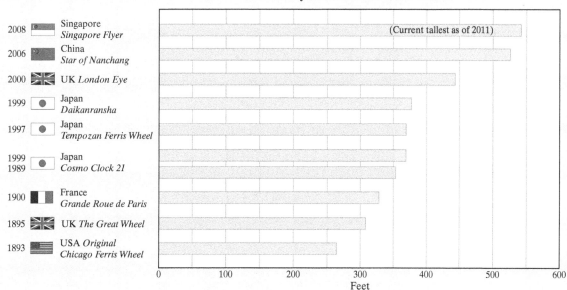

History of World's Tallest Ferris Wheels

Year	Country / Name	
2008	Singapore *Singapore Flyer*	(Current tallest as of 2011)
2006	China *Star of Nanchang*	
2000	UK *London Eye*	
1999	Japan *Daikanransha*	
1997	Japan *Tempozan Ferris Wheel*	
1999 1989	Japan *Cosmo Clock 21*	
1900	France *Grande Roue de Paris*	
1895	UK *The Great Wheel*	
1893	USA *Original Chicago Ferris Wheel*	

0   100   200   300   400   500   600
Feet

13.1 The Parabola and the Circle

OBJECTIVES

1 Graph Parabolas of the Form $x = a(y - k)^2 + h$ and $y = a(x - h)^2 + k$.

2 Graph Circles of the Form $(x - h)^2 + (y - k)^2 = r^2$.

3 Find the Center and the Radius of a Circle, Given Its Equation.

4 Write an Equation of a Circle, Given Its Center and Radius.

Conic sections are named so because each conic section is the intersection of a right circular cone and a plane. The circle, parabola, ellipse, and hyperbola are the conic sections.

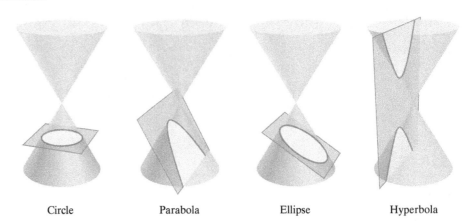

| Circle | Parabola | Ellipse | Hyperbola |

OBJECTIVE
1 Graphing Parabolas

Thus far, we have seen that $f(x)$ or $y = a(x - h)^2 + k$ is the equation of a parabola that opens upward if $a > 0$ or downward if $a < 0$. Parabolas can also open left or right or even on a slant. Equations of these parabolas are not functions of x, of course, since a parabola opening any way other than upward or downward fails the vertical line test. In this section, we introduce parabolas that open to the left and to the right. Parabolas opening on a slant will not be developed in this book.

Just as $y = a(x - h)^2 + k$ is the equation of a parabola that opens upward or downward, $x = a(y - k)^2 + h$ is the equation of a parabola that opens to the right or to the left. The parabola opens to the right if $a > 0$ and to the left if $a < 0$. The parabola has vertex (h, k), and its axis of symmetry is the line $y = k$.

Parabolas

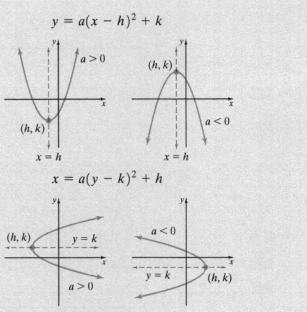

The equations $y = a(x - h)^2 + k$ and $x = a(y - k)^2 + h$ are called **standard forms**.

✓CONCEPT CHECK
Does the graph of the parabola given by the equation $x = -3y^2$ open to the left, to the right, upward, or downward?

EXAMPLE 1   Graph the parabola $x = 2y^2$.

Solution   Written in standard form, the equation $x = 2y^2$ is $x = 2(y - 0)^2 + 0$ with $a = 2, k = 0$, and $h = 0$. Its graph is a parabola with vertex $(0, 0)$, and its axis of symmetry is the line $y = 0$. Since $a > 0$, this parabola opens to the right. The table shows a few more ordered pair solutions of $x = 2y^2$. Its graph is also shown.

x	y
8	-2
2	-1
0	0
2	1
8	2

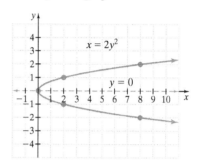

PRACTICE
1   Graph the parabola $x = \dfrac{1}{2}y^2$.

EXAMPLE 2   Graph the parabola $x = -3(y - 1)^2 + 2$.

Solution   The equation $x = -3(y - 1)^2 + 2$ is in the form $x = a(y - k)^2 + h$ with $a = -3, k = 1$, and $h = 2$. Since $a < 0$, the parabola opens to the left. The vertex (h, k) is $(2, 1)$, and the axis of symmetry is the line $y = 1$. When $y = 0, x = -1$, so the x-intercept is $(-1, 0)$. Again, we obtain a few ordered pair solutions and then graph the parabola.

x	y
2	1
-1	0
-1	2
-10	3
-10	-1

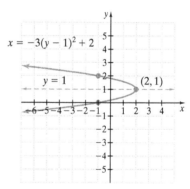

PRACTICE
2   Graph the parabola $x = -2(y + 4)^2 - 1$.

EXAMPLE 3   Graph $y = -x^2 - 2x + 15$.

Solution   Complete the square on x to write the equation in standard form.

$$y - 15 = -x^2 - 2x \qquad \text{Subtract 15 from both sides.}$$
$$y - 15 = -1(x^2 + 2x) \qquad \text{Factor } -1 \text{ from the terms } -x^2 - 2x.$$

(Continued on next page)

Answer to Concept Check:
to the left

The coefficient of x is 2. Find the square of half of 2.

$$\frac{1}{2}(2) = 1 \quad \text{and} \quad 1^2 = 1$$

$$y - 15 - 1(1) = -1(x^2 + 2x + 1) \qquad \text{Add } -1(1) \text{ to both sides.}$$

$$y - 16 = -1(x + 1)^2 \qquad \begin{array}{l}\text{Simplify the left side and} \\ \text{factor the right side.}\end{array}$$

$$y = -(x + 1)^2 + 16 \qquad \text{Add 16 to both sides.}$$

The equation is now in standard form $y = a(x - h)^2 + k$ with $a = -1, h = -1$, and $k = 16$.

   The vertex is then (h, k), or $(-1, 16)$.

A second method for finding the vertex is by using the formula $\dfrac{-b}{2a}$.

$$x = \frac{-(-2)}{2(-1)} = \frac{2}{-2} = -1$$

$$y = -(-1)^2 - 2(-1) + 15 = -1 + 2 + 15 = 16$$

Again, we see that the vertex is $(-1, 16)$, and the axis of symmetry is the vertical line $x = -1$. The y-intercept is $(0, 15)$. Now we can use a few more ordered pair solutions to graph the parabola.

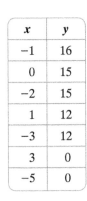

x	y
-1	16
0	15
-2	15
1	12
-3	12
3	0
-5	0

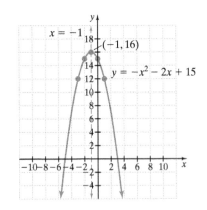

PRACTICE

3   Graph $y = -x^2 + 4x + 6$.

EXAMPLE 4   Graph $x = 2y^2 + 4y + 5$.

Solution   Notice that this equation is quadratic in y, so its graph is a parabola that opens to the left or the right. We can complete the square on y, or we can use the formula $\dfrac{-b}{2a}$ to find the vertex.

   Since the equation is quadratic in y, the formula gives us the y-value of the vertex.

$$y = \frac{-4}{2 \cdot 2} = \frac{-4}{4} = -1$$

$$x = 2(-1)^2 + 4(-1) + 5 = 2 \cdot 1 - 4 + 5 = 3$$

The vertex is $(3, -1)$, and the axis of symmetry is the line $y = -1$. The parabola opens to the right since $a > 0$. The x-intercept is $(5, 0)$.

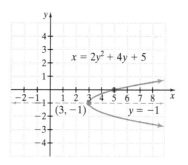

PRACTICE
4   Graph $x = 3y^2 + 6y + 4$.

OBJECTIVE
2   Graphing Circles

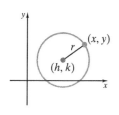

Another conic section is the **circle.** A circle is the set of all points in a plane that are the same distance from a fixed point called the **center.** The distance is called the **radius** of the circle. To find a standard equation for a circle, let (h, k) represent the center of the circle and let (x, y) represent any point on the circle. The distance between (h, k) and (x, y) is defined to be the circle's radius, r units. We can find this distance r by using the distance formula.

$$r = \sqrt{(x - h)^2 + (y - k)^2}$$
$$r^2 = (x - h)^2 + (y - k)^2 \qquad \text{Square both sides.}$$

Circle

The graph of $(x - h)^2 + (y - k)^2 = r^2$ is a circle with center (h, k) and radius r.

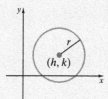

The equation $(x - h)^2 + (y - k)^2 = r^2$ is called **standard form.**

If an equation can be written in the standard form

$$(x - h)^2 + (y - k)^2 = r^2$$

then its graph is a circle, which we can draw by graphing the center (h, k) and using the radius r.

▶ Helpful Hint

Notice that the radius is the *distance* from the center of the circle to any point of the circle. Also notice that the *midpoint* of a diameter of a circle is the center of the circle.

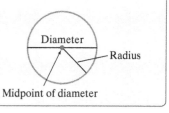

EXAMPLE 5   Graph $x^2 + y^2 = 4$.

Solution   The equation can be written in standard form as

$$(x - 0)^2 + (y - 0)^2 = 2^2$$

The center of the circle is $(0, 0)$, and the radius is 2. Its graph is shown.

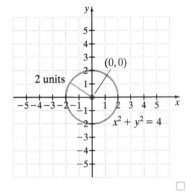

PRACTICE

5   Graph $x^2 + y^2 = 25$.

▶ **Helpful Hint**

Notice the difference between the equation of a circle and the equation of a parabola. The equation of a circle contains both x^2 and y^2 terms on the same side of the equation with equal coefficients. The equation of a parabola has either an x^2 term or a y^2 term but not both.

EXAMPLE 6   Graph $(x + 1)^2 + y^2 = 8$.

Solution   The equation can be written as $(x + 1)^2 + (y - 0)^2 = 8$ with $h = -1$, $k = 0$, and $r = \sqrt{8}$. The center is $(-1, 0)$, and the radius is $\sqrt{8} = 2\sqrt{2} \approx 2.8$.

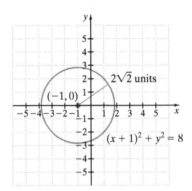

PRACTICE

6   Graph $(x - 3)^2 + (y + 2)^2 = 4$.

✓**CONCEPT CHECK**

In the graph of the equation $(x - 3)^2 + (y - 2)^2 = 5$, what is the distance between the center of the circle and any point on the circle?

OBJECTIVE

3   Finding the Center and the Radius of a Circle

To find the center and the radius of a circle from its equation, write the equation in standard form. To write the equation of a circle in standard form, we complete the square on both x and y.

Answer to Concept Check:
$\sqrt{5}$ units

EXAMPLE 7   Graph $x^2 + y^2 + 4x - 8y = 16$.

Solution   Since this equation contains x^2 and y^2 terms on the same side of the equation with equal coefficients, its graph is a circle. To write the equation in standard form, group the terms involving x and the terms involving y and then complete the square on each variable.

$$(x^2 + 4x) + (y^2 - 8y) = 16$$

Thus, $\frac{1}{2}(4) = 2$ and $2^2 = 4$. Also, $\frac{1}{2}(-8) = -4$ and $(-4)^2 = 16$. Add 4 and then 16 to both sides.

$$(x^2 + 4x + 4) + (y^2 - 8y + 16) = 16 + 4 + 16$$

$$(x + 2)^2 + (y - 4)^2 = 36 \qquad \text{Factor.}$$

This circle the center $(-2, 4)$ and radius 6, as shown.

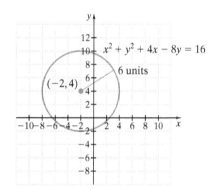

PRACTICE
7   Graph $x^2 + y^2 + 6x - 2y = 6$.

OBJECTIVE
4   Writing Equations of Circles

Since a circle is determined entirely by its center and radius, this information is all we need to write an equation of a circle.

EXAMPLE 8   Find an equation of the circle with center $(-7, 3)$ and radius 10.

Solution   Using the given values $h = -7, k = 3$, and $r = 10$, we write the equation

$$(x - h)^2 + (y - k)^2 = r^2$$

or

$$[x - (-7)]^2 + (y - 3)^2 = 10^2 \qquad \text{Substitute the given values.}$$

or

$$(x + 7)^2 + (y - 3)^2 = 100$$

PRACTICE
8   Find an equation of the circle with center $(-2, -5)$ and radius 9.

Graphing Calculator Explorations

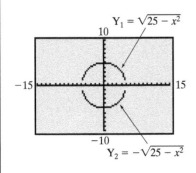

$Y_1 = \sqrt{25 - x^2}$

$Y_2 = -\sqrt{25 - x^2}$

$Y_1 = \sqrt{25 - x^2}$

$Y_2 = -\sqrt{25 - x^2}$

To graph an equation such as $x^2 + y^2 = 25$ with a graphing calculator, we first solve the equation for y.

$$x^2 + y^2 = 25$$
$$y^2 = 25 - x^2$$
$$y = \pm\sqrt{25 - x^2}$$

The graph of $y = \sqrt{25 - x^2}$ will be the top half of the circle, and the graph of $y = -\sqrt{25 - x^2}$ will be the bottom half of the circle.

To graph, press $\boxed{Y=}$ and enter $Y_1 = \sqrt{25 - x^2}$ and $Y_2 = -\sqrt{25 - x^2}$.

Insert parentheses around $25 - x^2$ so that $\sqrt{25 - x^2}$ and not $\sqrt{25} - x^2$ is graphed.

The top graph to the left does not appear to be a circle because we are currently using a standard window and the screen is rectangular. This causes the tick marks on the x-axis to be farther apart than the tick marks on the y-axis and, thus, creates the distorted circle. If we want the graph to appear circular, we must define a square window by using a feature of the graphing calculator or by redefining the window to show the x-axis from -15 to 15 and the y-axis from -10 to 10. Using a square window, the graph appears as shown on the bottom to the left.

Use a graphing calculator to graph each circle.

1. $x^2 + y^2 = 55$

2. $x^2 + y^2 = 20$

3. $5x^2 + 5y^2 = 50$

4. $6x^2 + 6y^2 = 105$

5. $2x^2 + 2y^2 - 34 = 0$

6. $4x^2 + 4y^2 - 48 = 0$

7. $7x^2 + 7y^2 - 89 = 0$

8. $3x^2 + 3y^2 - 35 = 0$

Vocabulary, Readiness & Video Check

Use the choices below to fill in each blank. Some choices may be used more than once.

radius　　　center　　　vertex

diameter　　circle　　　conic sections

1. The circle, parabola, ellipse, and hyperbola are called the _____.

2. For a parabola that opens upward, the lowest point is the _____.

3. A _____ is the set of all points in a plane that are the same distance from a fixed point. The fixed point is called the _____.

4. The midpoint of a diameter of a circle is the _____.

5. The distance from the center of a circle to any point of the circle is called the _____.

6. Twice a circle's radius is its _____.

Martin-Gay Interactive Videos

See Video 13.1

Watch the section lecture video and answer the following questions.

OBJECTIVE
1

7. Based on ▢ Example 1 and the lecture before, would you say that parabolas of the form $x = a(y - k)^2 + h$ are functions? Why or why not?

OBJECTIVE
2

8. Based on the lecture before ▢ Example 2, what would be the standard form of a circle with its center at the origin? Simplify your answer.

OBJECTIVE
3

9. From ▢ Example 3, if you know the center and radius of a circle, how can you write that circle's equation?

OBJECTIVE
4

10. From ▢ Example 4, why do we need to complete the square twice when writing this equation of a circle in standard form?

13.1 Exercise Set   MyMathLab®

The graph of each equation is a parabola. Determine whether the parabola opens upward, downward, to the left, or to the right. Do not graph. See Examples 1 through 4.

1. $y = x^2 - 7x + 5$

2. $y = -x^2 + 16$

3. $x = -y^2 - y + 2$

4. $x = 3y^2 + 2y - 5$

5. $y = -x^2 + 2x + 1$

6. $x = -y^2 + 2y - 6$

The graph of each equation is a parabola. Find the vertex of the parabola and then graph it. See Examples 1 through 4.

7. $x = 3y^2$

8. $x = 5y^2$

9. $x = -2y^2$

10. $x = -4y^2$

11. $y = -4x^2$

12. $y = -2x^2$

13. $x = (y - 2)^2 + 3$

14. $x = (y - 4)^2 - 1$

15. $y = -3(x - 1)^2 + 5$

16. $y = -4(x - 2)^2 + 2$

17. $x = y^2 + 6y + 8$

18. $x = y^2 - 6y + 6$

19. $y = x^2 + 10x + 20$

20. $y = x^2 + 4x - 5$

21. $x = -2y^2 + 4y + 6$

22. $x = 3y^2 + 6y + 7$

The graph of each equation is a circle. Find the center and the radius and then graph the circle. See Examples 5 through 7.

23. $x^2 + y^2 = 9$

24. $x^2 + y^2 = 25$

25. $x^2 + (y - 2)^2 = 1$

26. $(x - 3)^2 + y^2 = 9$

27. $(x - 5)^2 + (y + 2)^2 = 1$

28. $(x + 3)^2 + (y + 3)^2 = 4$

29. $x^2 + y^2 + 6y = 0$

30. $x^2 + 10x + y^2 = 0$

31. $x^2 + y^2 + 2x - 4y = 4$

32. $x^2 + y^2 + 6x - 4y = 3$

33. $(x + 2)^2 + (y - 3)^2 = 7$

34. $(x + 1)^2 + (y - 2)^2 = 5$

35. $x^2 + y^2 - 4x - 8y - 2 = 0$

36. $x^2 + y^2 - 2x - 6y - 5 = 0$

Hint: For Exercises 37 through 42, first divide the equation through by the coefficient of x^2 (or y^2).

37. $3x^2 + 3y^2 = 75$

38. $2x^2 + 2y^2 = 18$

39. $6(x - 4)^2 + 6(y - 1)^2 = 24$

40. $7(x - 1)^2 + 7(y - 3)^2 = 63$

41. $4(x + 1)^2 + 4(y - 3)^2 = 12$

42. $5(x - 2)^2 + 5(y + 1) = 50$

Write an equation of the circle with the given center and radius. See Example 8.

43. $(2, 3); 6$

44. $(-7, 6); 2$

45. $(0, 0); \sqrt{3}$

46. $(0, -6); \sqrt{2}$

47. $(-5, 4); 3\sqrt{5}$

48. the origin; $4\sqrt{7}$

MIXED PRACTICE

Sketch the graph of each equation. If the graph is a parabola, find its vertex. If the graph is a circle, find its center and radius.

49. $x = y^2 - 3$

50. $x = y^2 + 2$

51. $y = (x - 2)^2 - 2$

52. $y = (x + 3)^2 + 3$

53. $x^2 + y^2 = 1$

54. $x^2 + y^2 = 49$

55. $x = (y + 3)^2 - 1$

56. $x = (y - 1)^2 + 4$

57. $(x - 2)^2 + (y - 2)^2 = 16$

58. $(x + 3)^2 + (y - 1)^2 = 9$

59. $x = -(y - 1)^2$

60. $x = -2(y + 5)^2$

61. $(x - 4)^2 + y^2 = 7$

62. $x^2 + (y + 5)^2 = 5$

63. $y = 5(x + 5)^2 + 3$

64. $y = 3(x - 4)^2 + 2$

65. $\dfrac{x^2}{8} + \dfrac{y^2}{8} = 2$

66. $2x^2 + 2y^2 = \dfrac{1}{2}$

67. $y = x^2 + 7x + 6$

68. $y = x^2 - 2x - 15$

69. $x^2 + y^2 + 2x + 12y - 12 = 0$

70. $x^2 + y^2 + 6x + 10y - 2 = 0$

71. $x = y^2 + 8y - 4$

72. $x = y^2 + 6y + 2$

73. $x^2 - 10y + y^2 + 4 = 0$

74. $x^2 + y^2 - 8y + 5 = 0$

75. $x = -3y^2 + 30y$

76. $x = -2y^2 - 4y$

77. $5x^2 + 5y^2 = 25$

78. $\dfrac{x^2}{3} + \dfrac{y^2}{3} = 2$

79. $y = 5x^2 - 20x + 16$

80. $y = 4x^2 - 40x + 105$

REVIEW AND PREVIEW

Graph each equation. See Sections 3.2 and 3.3.

81. $y = 2x + 5$

82. $y = -3x + 3$

83. $y = 3$

84. $x = -2$

Rationalize each denominator and simplify if possible. See Section 10.5.

85. $\dfrac{1}{\sqrt{3}}$

86. $\dfrac{\sqrt{5}}{\sqrt{8}}$

87. $\dfrac{4\sqrt{7}}{\sqrt{6}}$

88. $\dfrac{10}{\sqrt{5}}$

CONCEPT EXTENSIONS

For Exercises 89 and 90, explain the error in each statement.

89. The graph of $x = 5(y + 5)^2 + 1$ is a parabola with vertex $(-5, 1)$ and opening to the right.

90. The graph of $x^2 + (y + 3)^2 = 10$ is a circle with center $(0, -3)$ and radius 5.

91. *The Sarsen Circle* The first image that comes to mind when one thinks of Stonehenge is the very large sandstone blocks with sandstone lintels across the top. The Sarsen Circle of Stonehenge is the outer circle of the sandstone blocks, each of which weighs up to 50 tons. There were originally 30 of these monolithic blocks, but only 17 remain upright to this day. The "altar stone" lies at the center of this circle, which has a diameter of 33 meters.

a. What is the radius of the Sarsen Circle?

b. What is the circumference of the Sarsen Circle? Round your result to 2 decimal places.

c. Since there were originally 30 Sarsen stones located on the circumference, how far apart would the centers of the stones have been? Round to the nearest tenth of a meter.

d. Using the axes in the drawing, what are the coordinates of the center of the circle?

e. Use parts (a) and (d) to write the equation of the Sarsen Circle.

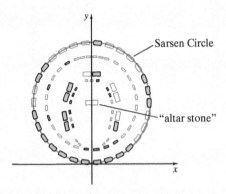

Sarsen Circle

"altar stone"

92. Although there are many larger observation wheels on the horizon, as of this writing the largest observation wheel in the world is the Singapore Flyer. From the Flyer, you can see up to 45 km away. Each of the 28 enclosed capsules holds 28 passengers and completes a full rotation every 32 minutes. Its diameter is 150 meters, and the height of this giant wheel is 165 meters. (*Source:* singaporeflyer.com)

a. What is the radius of the Singapore Flyer?

b. How close is the wheel to the ground?

c. How high is the center of the wheel from the ground?

d. Using the axes in the drawing, what are the coordinates of the center of the wheel?

e. Use parts (a) and (d) to write an equation of the Singapore Flyer.

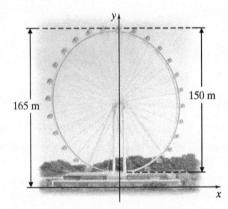

165 m

150 m

93. In 1893, Pittsburgh bridge builder George Ferris designed and built a gigantic revolving steel wheel whose height was 264 feet and diameter was 250 feet. This Ferris wheel opened at the 1893 exposition in Chicago. It had 36 wooden cars, each capable of holding 60 passengers. (*Source: The Handy Science Answer Book*)

a. What was the radius of this Ferris wheel?

b. How close was the wheel to the ground?

c. How high was the center of the wheel from the ground?

d. Using the axes in the drawing, what are the coordinates of the center of the wheel?

e. Use parts (a) and (d) to write an equation of the wheel.

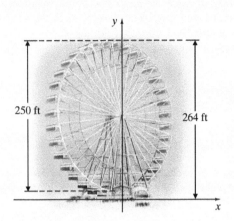

250 ft

264 ft

94. The world's largest-diameter Ferris wheel currently operating is the Cosmo Clock 21 at Yokohama City, Japan. It has a 60-armed wheel, its diameter is 100 meters, and it has a height of 105 meters. (*Source: The Handy Science Answer Book*)

a. What is the radius of this Ferris wheel?

b. How close is the wheel to the ground?

c. How high is the center of the wheel from the ground?

d. Using the axes in the drawing, what are the coordinates of the center of the wheel?

e. Use parts (a) and (d) to write an equation of the wheel.

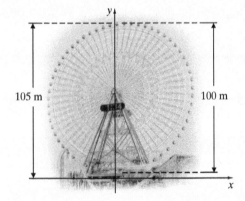

105 m

100 m

95. If you are given a list of equations of circles and parabolas and none are in standard form, explain how you would determine which is an equation of a circle and which is an equation of a parabola. Explain also how you would distinguish the upward or downward parabolas from the left-opening or right-opening parabolas.

96. Determine whether the triangle with vertices $(2, 6)$, $(0, -2)$, and $(5, 1)$ is an isosceles triangle.

Solve.

97. Two surveyors need to find the distance across a lake. They place a reference pole at point *A* in the diagram. Point *B* is 3 meters east and 1 meter north of the reference point *A*. Point *C* is 19 meters east and 13 meters north of point *A*. Find the distance across the lake, from *B* to *C*.

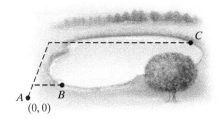

98. A bridge constructed over a bayou has a supporting arch in the shape of a parabola. Find an equation of the parabolic arch if the length of the road over the arch is 100 meters and the maximum height of the arch is 40 meters.

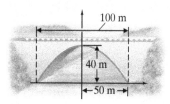

Use a graphing calculator to verify each exercise. Use a square viewing window.

99. Exercise 77.   **100.** Exercise 78.

101. Exercise 79.   **102.** Exercise 80.

13.2 | The Ellipse and the Hyperbola

OBJECTIVES

1 Define and Graph an Ellipse.

2 Define and Graph a Hyperbola.

OBJECTIVE

1   Graphing Ellipses

An **ellipse** can be thought of as the set of points in a plane such that the sum of the distances of those points from two fixed points is constant. Each of the two fixed points is called a **focus**. (The plural of focus is **foci**.) The point midway between the foci is called the **center.**

An ellipse may be drawn by hand by using two thumbtacks, a piece of string, and a pencil. Secure the two thumbtacks in a piece of cardboard, for example, and tie each end of the string to a tack. Use your pencil to pull the string tight and draw the ellipse. The two thumbtacks are the foci of the drawn ellipse.

  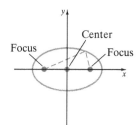

Ellipse with Center (0, 0)

The graph of an equation of the form $\dfrac{x^2}{a^2} + \dfrac{y^2}{b^2} = 1$ is an ellipse with center $(0,0)$.

The *x*-intercepts are $(a,0)$ and $(-a,0)$, and the *y*-intercepts are $(0,b)$, and $(0,-b)$.

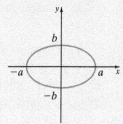

The **standard form** of an ellipse with center $(0, 0)$ is $\dfrac{x^2}{a^2} + \dfrac{y^2}{b^2} = 1.$

EXAMPLE 1 Graph $\dfrac{x^2}{9} + \dfrac{y^2}{16} = 1$.

Solution The equation is of the form $\dfrac{x^2}{a^2} + \dfrac{y^2}{b^2} = 1$, with $a = 3$ and $b = 4$, so its graph is an ellipse with center $(0, 0)$, x-intercepts $(3, 0)$ and $(-3, 0)$, and y-intercepts $(0, 4)$ and $(0, -4)$.

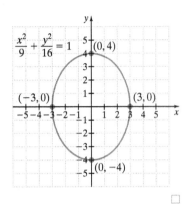

PRACTICE
1 Graph $\dfrac{x^2}{25} + \dfrac{y^2}{4} = 1$.

EXAMPLE 2 Graph $4x^2 + 16y^2 = 64$.

Solution Although this equation contains a sum of squared terms in x and y on the same side of the equation, this is not the equation of a circle since the coefficients of x^2 and y^2 are not the same. The graph of this equation is an ellipse. Since the standard form of the equation of an ellipse has 1 on one side, divide both sides of this equation by 64.

$$4x^2 + 16y^2 = 64$$

$$\frac{4x^2}{64} + \frac{16y^2}{64} = \frac{64}{64} \qquad \text{Divide both sides by 64.}$$

$$\frac{x^2}{16} + \frac{y^2}{4} = 1 \qquad \text{Simplify.}$$

We now recognize the equation of an ellipse with $a = 4$ and $b = 2$. This ellipse has center $(0, 0)$, x-intercepts $(4, 0)$ and $(-4, 0)$, and y-intercepts $(0, 2)$ and $(0, -2)$.

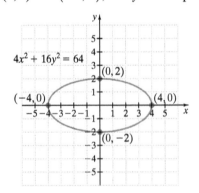

PRACTICE
2 Graph $9x^2 + 4y^2 = 36$.

The center of an ellipse is not always $(0, 0)$, as shown in the next example.

Ellipse with Center (h, k)

The standard form of the equation of an ellipse with center (h, k) is

$$\frac{(x - h)^2}{a^2} + \frac{(y - k)^2}{b^2} = 1$$

EXAMPLE 3   Graph $\dfrac{(x+3)^2}{25} + \dfrac{(y-2)^2}{36} = 1$.

Solution   The center of this ellipse is found in a way that is similar to finding the center of a circle. This ellipse has center $(-3, 2)$. Notice that $a = 5$ and $b = 6$. To find four points on the graph of the ellipse, first graph the center, $(-3, 2)$. Since $a = 5$, count 5 units right and then 5 units left of the point with coordinates $(-3, 2)$. Next, since $b = 6$, start at $(-3, 2)$ and count 6 units up and then 6 units down to find two more points on the ellipse.

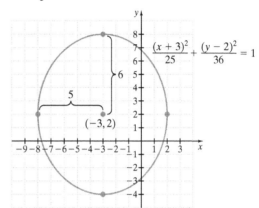

$$\frac{(x+3)^2}{25} + \frac{(y-2)^2}{36} = 1$$

PRACTICE
3   Graph $\dfrac{(x-4)^2}{49} + \dfrac{(y+1)^2}{81} = 1$.

✓**CONCEPT CHECK**

In the graph of the equation $\dfrac{x^2}{64} + \dfrac{y^2}{36} = 1$, which distance is longer: the distance between the x-intercepts or the distance between the y-intercepts? How much longer? Explain.

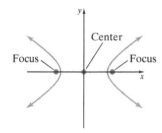

OBJECTIVE
2   **Graphing Hyperbolas**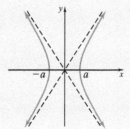

The final conic section is the **hyperbola**. A hyperbola is the set of points in a plane such that the absolute value of the difference of the distances from two fixed points is constant. Each of the two fixed points is called a **focus.** The point midway between the foci is called the **center.**

Using the distance formula, we can show that the graph of $\dfrac{x^2}{a^2} - \dfrac{y^2}{b^2} = 1$ is a hyperbola with center $(0, 0)$ and x-intercepts $(a, 0)$ and $(-a, 0)$. Also, the graph of $\dfrac{y^2}{b^2} - \dfrac{x^2}{a^2} = 1$ is a hyperbola with center $(0,0)$ and y-intercepts $(0, b)$ and $(0, -b)$.

Hyperbola with Center (0, 0)

The graph of an equation of the form $\dfrac{x^2}{a^2} - \dfrac{y^2}{b^2} = 1$ is a hyperbola with center $(0,0)$ and x-intercepts $(a, 0)$ and $(-a, 0)$.

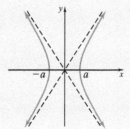

Answer to Concept Check:
x-intercepts, by 4 units

(Continued on next page)

The graph of an equation of the form $\dfrac{y^2}{b^2} - \dfrac{x^2}{a^2} = 1$ is a hyperbola with center $(0,0)$ and y-intercepts $(0,b)$ and $(0,-b)$.

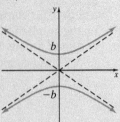

The equations $\dfrac{x^2}{a^2} - \dfrac{y^2}{b^2} = 1$ and $\dfrac{y^2}{b^2} - \dfrac{x^2}{a^2} = 1$ are the **standard forms** for the equation of a hyperbola.

> ▶ **Helpful Hint**
>
> Notice the difference between the equation of an ellipse and a hyperbola. The equation of the ellipse contains x^2 and y^2 terms on the same side of the equation with same-sign coefficients. For a hyperbola, the coefficients on the same side of the equation have different signs.

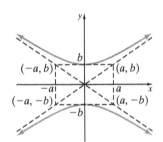

Graphing a hyperbola such as $\dfrac{y^2}{b^2} - \dfrac{x^2}{a^2} = 1$ is made easier by recognizing one of its important characteristics. Examining the figure to the left, notice how the sides of the branches of the hyperbola extend indefinitely and seem to approach the dashed lines in the figure. These dashed lines are called the **asymptotes** of the hyperbola.

To sketch these lines, or asymptotes, draw a rectangle with vertices (a, b), $(-a, b)$, $(a, -b)$ and $(-a, -b)$. The asymptotes of the hyperbola are the extended diagonals of this rectangle.

EXAMPLE 4 Graph $\dfrac{x^2}{16} - \dfrac{y^2}{25} = 1$.

Solution This equation has the form $\dfrac{x^2}{a^2} - \dfrac{y^2}{b^2} = 1$, with $a = 4$ and $b = 5$. Thus, its graph is a hyperbola that opens to the left and right. It has center $(0,0)$ and x-intercepts $(4, 0)$ and $(-4, 0)$. To aid in graphing the hyperbola, we first sketch its asymptotes. The extended diagonals of the rectangle with corners $(4, 5)$, $(4, -5)$, $(-4, 5)$, and $(-4, -5)$ are the asymptotes of the hyperbola. Then we use the asymptotes to aid in sketching the hyperbola.

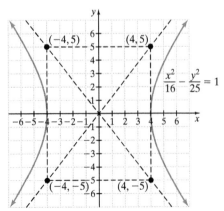

PRACTICE
4 Graph $\dfrac{x^2}{9} - \dfrac{y^2}{16} = 1$.

EXAMPLE 5   Graph $4y^2 - 9x^2 = 36$.

Solution   Since this is a difference of squared terms in x and y on the same side of the equation, its graph is a hyperbola as opposed to an ellipse or a circle. The standard form of the equation of a hyperbola has a 1 on one side, so divide both sides of the equation by 36.

$$4y^2 - 9x^2 = 36$$

$$\frac{4y^2}{36} - \frac{9x^2}{36} = \frac{36}{36} \quad \text{Divide both sides by 36.}$$

$$\frac{y^2}{9} - \frac{x^2}{4} = 1 \quad \text{Simplify.}$$

The equation is of the form $\dfrac{y^2}{b^2} - \dfrac{x^2}{a^2} = 1$, with $a = 2$ and $b = 3$, so the hyperbola is centered at $(0, 0)$ with y-intercepts $(0, 3)$ and $(0, -3)$. The sketch of the hyperbola is shown.

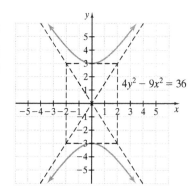

PRACTICE
5   Graph $9y^2 - 25x^2 = 225$.

Although this is beyond the scope of this text, the standard forms of the equations of hyperbolas with center (h, k) are given below. The Concept Extensions section in Exercise Set 13.2 contains some hyperbolas of this form.

Hyperbola with Center (h, k)

Standard forms of the equations of hyperbolas with center (h, k) are:

$$\frac{(x - h)^2}{a^2} - \frac{(y - k)^2}{b^2} = 1 \qquad \frac{(y - k)^2}{b^2} - \frac{(x - h)^2}{a^2} = 1$$

Graphing Calculator Explorations

To graph an ellipse by using a graphing calculator, use the same procedure as for graphing a circle. For example, to graph $x^2 + 3y^2 = 22$, first solve for y.

$$3y^2 = 22 - x^2$$

$$y^2 = \frac{22 - x^2}{3}$$

$$y = \pm\sqrt{\frac{22 - x^2}{3}}$$

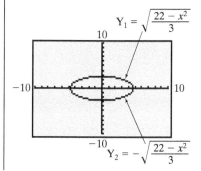

Next, press the $\boxed{Y =}$ key and enter $Y_1 = \sqrt{\dfrac{22 - x^2}{3}}$ and $Y_2 = -\sqrt{\dfrac{22 - x^2}{3}}$.

(Insert two sets of parentheses in the radicand as $\sqrt{((22 - x^2)/3)}$ so that the desired graph is obtained.) The graph appears as shown to the left.

Use a graphing calculator to graph each ellipse.

1. $10x^2 + y^2 = 32$

2. $x^2 + 6y^2 = 35$

3. $20x^2 + 5y^2 = 100$

4. $4y^2 + 12x^2 = 48$

5. $7.3x^2 + 15.5y^2 = 95.2$

6. $18.8x^2 + 36.1y^2 = 205.8$

Vocabulary, Readiness & Video Check

Use the choices below to fill in each blank. Some choices will be used more than once and some not at all.

ellipse	$(0,0)$	x	$(a,0)$ and $(-a,0)$	$(0,a)$ and $(0,-a)$	focus
hyperbola	center	y	$(b,0)$ and $(-b,0)$	$(0,b)$ and $(0,-b)$	

1. A(n) _____ is the set of points in a plane such that the absolute value of the differences of their distances from two fixed points is constant.

2. A(n) _____ is the set of points in a plane such that the sum of their distances from two fixed points is constant.

For exercises 1 and 2 above,

3. The two fixed points are each called a _____ .

4. The point midway between the foci is called the _____ .

5. The graph of $\dfrac{x^2}{a^2} - \dfrac{y^2}{b^2} = 1$ is a(n) _____ with center _____ and _____ -intercepts of _____ .

6. The graph of $\dfrac{x^2}{a^2} + \dfrac{y^2}{b^2} = 1$ is a(n) _____ with center _____ and x-intercepts of _____ .

Martin-Gay Interactive Videos

See Video 13.2 🍎

Watch the section lecture video and answer the following questions.

OBJECTIVE 1

7. From Example 1, what information do the values of a and b give us about the graph of an ellipse? Answer this same question for Example 2.

OBJECTIVE 2

8. From Example 3, we know the points (a,b), $(a,-b)$, $(-a,b)$, and $(-a,-b)$ are not part of the graph. Explain the role of these points.

13.2 Exercise Set   MyMathLab®

Identify the graph of each equation as an ellipse or a hyperbola. Do not graph. See Examples 1 through 5.

1. $\dfrac{x^2}{16} + \dfrac{y^2}{4} = 1$

2. $\dfrac{x^2}{16} - \dfrac{y^2}{4} = 1$

3. $x^2 - 5y^2 = 3$

4. $-x^2 + 5y^2 = 3$

5. $-\dfrac{y^2}{25} + \dfrac{x^2}{36} = 1$

6. $\dfrac{y^2}{25} + \dfrac{x^2}{36} = 1$

Sketch the graph of each equation. See Examples 1 and 2.

7. $\dfrac{x^2}{4} + \dfrac{y^2}{25} = 1$

8. $\dfrac{x^2}{16} + \dfrac{y^2}{9} = 1$

9. $\dfrac{x^2}{9} + y^2 = 1$

10. $x^2 + \dfrac{y^2}{4} = 1$

11. $9x^2 + y^2 = 36$

12. $x^2 + 4y^2 = 16$

13. $4x^2 + 25y^2 = 100$

14. $36x^2 + y^2 = 36$

Sketch the graph of each equation. See Example 3.

15. $\dfrac{(x+1)^2}{36} + \dfrac{(y-2)^2}{49} = 1$

16. $\dfrac{(x-3)^2}{9} + \dfrac{(y+3)^2}{16} = 1$

17. $\dfrac{(x-1)^2}{4} + \dfrac{(y-1)^2}{25} = 1$

18. $\dfrac{(x+3)^2}{16} + \dfrac{(y+2)^2}{4} = 1$

Sketch the graph of each equation. See Examples 4 and 5.

19. $\dfrac{x^2}{4} - \dfrac{y^2}{9} = 1$ **20.** $\dfrac{x^2}{36} - \dfrac{y^2}{36} = 1$

21. $\dfrac{y^2}{25} - \dfrac{x^2}{16} = 1$ **22.** $\dfrac{y^2}{25} - \dfrac{x^2}{49} = 1$

23. $x^2 - 4y^2 = 16$ **24.** $4x^2 - y^2 = 36$

25. $16y^2 - x^2 = 16$ **26.** $4y^2 - 25x^2 = 100$

MIXED PRACTICE

Graph each equation. See Examples 1 through 5.

27. $\dfrac{y^2}{36} = 1 - x^2$ **28.** $\dfrac{x^2}{36} = 1 - y^2$

29. $4(x - 1)^2 + 9(y + 2)^2 = 36$

30. $25(x + 3)^2 + 4(y - 3)^2 = 100$

31. $8x^2 + 2y^2 = 32$ **32.** $3x^2 + 12y^2 = 48$

33. $25x^2 - y^2 = 25$ **34.** $x^2 - 9y^2 = 9$

MIXED PRACTICE–SECTIONS 13.1, 13.2

Identify whether each equation, when graphed, will be a parabola, circle, ellipse, or hyperbola. Sketch the graph of each equation.

If a parabola, label the vertex.
If a circle, label the center and note the radius.
If an ellipse, label the center.
If a hyperbola, label the x- or y-intercepts.

35. $(x - 7)^2 + (y - 2)^2 = 4$ **36.** $y = x^2 + 4$

37. $y = x^2 + 12x + 36$ **38.** $\dfrac{x^2}{4} + \dfrac{y^2}{9} = 1$

39. $\dfrac{y^2}{9} - \dfrac{x^2}{9} = 1$ **40.** $\dfrac{x^2}{16} - \dfrac{y^2}{4} = 1$

41. $\dfrac{x^2}{16} + \dfrac{y^2}{4} = 1$ **42.** $x^2 + y^2 = 16$

43. $x = y^2 + 4y - 1$ **44.** $x = -y^2 + 6y$

45. $9x^2 - 4y^2 = 36$ ▶ **46.** $9x^2 + 4y^2 = 36$

47. $\dfrac{(x - 1)^2}{49} + \dfrac{(y + 2)^2}{25} = 1$ ▶ **48.** $y^2 = x^2 + 16$

49. $\left(x + \dfrac{1}{2}\right)^2 + \left(y - \dfrac{1}{2}\right)^2 = 1$ **50.** $y = -2x^2 + 4x - 3$

REVIEW AND PREVIEW

Perform the indicated operations. See Sections 5.1 and 5.2.

51. $(2x^3)(-4x^2)$ **52.** $2x^3 - 4x^3$

53. $-5x^2 + x^2$ **54.** $(-5x^2)(x^2)$

CONCEPT EXTENSIONS

The graph of each equation is an ellipse. Determine which distance is longer, the distance between the x-intercepts or the distance between the y-intercepts. How much longer? See the Concept Check in this section.

55. $\dfrac{x^2}{16} + \dfrac{y^2}{25} = 1$ **56.** $\dfrac{x^2}{100} + \dfrac{y^2}{49} = 1$

57. $4x^2 + y^2 = 16$ **58.** $x^2 + 4y^2 = 36$

59. If you are given a list of equations of circles, parabolas, ellipses, and hyperbolas, explain how you could distinguish the different conic sections from their equations.

60. We know that $x^2 + y^2 = 25$ is the equation of a circle. Rewrite the equation so that the right side is equal to 1. Which type of conic section does this equation form resemble? In fact, the circle is a special case of this type of conic section. Describe the conditions under which this type of conic section is a circle.

The orbits of stars, planets, comets, asteroids, and satellites all have the shape of one of the conic sections. Astronomers use a measure called eccentricity to describe the shape and elongation of an orbital path. For the circle and ellipse, eccentricity e is calculated with the formula $e = \dfrac{c}{d}$, where $c^2 = |a^2 - b^2|$ and d is the larger value of a or b. For a hyperbola, eccentricity e is calculated with the formula $e = \dfrac{c}{d}$, where $c^2 = a^2 + b^2$ and the value of d is equal to a if the hyperbola has x-intercepts or equal to b if the hyperbola has y-intercepts. Use equations A–H to answer Exercises 61–70.

A. $\dfrac{x^2}{36} - \dfrac{y^2}{13} = 1$ **B.** $\dfrac{x^2}{4} + \dfrac{y^2}{4} = 1$ **C.** $\dfrac{x^2}{25} + \dfrac{y^2}{16} = 1$

D. $\dfrac{y^2}{25} - \dfrac{x^2}{39} = 1$ **E.** $\dfrac{x^2}{17} + \dfrac{y^2}{81} = 1$ **F.** $\dfrac{x^2}{36} + \dfrac{y^2}{36} = 1$

G. $\dfrac{x^2}{16} - \dfrac{y^2}{65} = 1$ **H.** $\dfrac{x^2}{144} + \dfrac{y^2}{140} = 1$

61. Identify the type of conic section represented by each of the equations A–H.

62. For each of the equations A–H, identify the values of a^2 and b^2.

63. For each of the equations A–H, calculate the values of c^2 and c.

64. For each of the equations A–H, find the value of d.

65. For each of the equations A–H, calculate the eccentricity e.

66. What do you notice about the values of e for the equations you identified as ellipses?

67. What do you notice about the values of e for the equations you identified as circles?

68. What do you notice about the values of e for the equations you identified as hyperbolas?

69. The eccentricity of a parabola is exactly 1. Use this information and the observations you made in Exercises 66, 67, and 68 to describe a way that could be used to identify the type of conic section based on its eccentricity value.

70. Graph each of the conic sections given in equations A–H. What do you notice about the shape of the ellipses for increasing values of eccentricity? Which is the most elliptical? Which is the least elliptical, that is, the most circular?

71. A planet's orbit about the sun can be described as an ellipse. Consider the sun as the origin of a rectangular coordinate system. Suppose that the x-intercepts of the elliptical path of the planet are $\pm130{,}000{,}000$ and that the y-intercepts are $\pm125{,}000{,}000$. Write the equation of the elliptical path of the planet.

72. Comets orbit the sun in elongated ellipses. Consider the sun as the origin of a rectangular coordinate system. Suppose that the equation of the path of the comet is

$$\frac{(x - 1{,}782{,}000{,}000)^2}{3.42 \times 10^{23}} + \frac{(y - 356{,}400{,}000)^2}{1.368 \times 10^{22}} = 1$$

Find the center of the path of the comet.

73. Use a graphing calculator to verify Exercise 46.

74. Use a graphing calculator to verify Exercise 12.

For Exercises 75 through 80, see the example below.

Example

Sketch the graph of $\dfrac{(x - 2)^2}{25} - \dfrac{(y - 1)^2}{9} = 1$.

Solution

This hyperbola has center $(2, 1)$. Notice that $a = 5$ and $b = 3$.

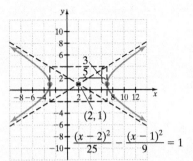

$$\frac{(x - 2)^2}{25} - \frac{(x - 1)^2}{9} = 1$$

Sketch the graph of each equation.

75. $\dfrac{(x - 1)^2}{4} - \dfrac{(y + 1)^2}{25} = 1$ **76.** $\dfrac{(x + 2)^2}{9} - \dfrac{(y - 1)^2}{4} = 1$

77. $\dfrac{y^2}{16} - \dfrac{(x + 3)^2}{9} = 1$ **78.** $\dfrac{(y + 4)^2}{4} - \dfrac{x^2}{25} = 1$

79. $\dfrac{(x + 5)^2}{16} - \dfrac{(y + 2)^2}{25} = 1$ **80.** $\dfrac{(x - 3)^2}{9} - \dfrac{(y - 2)^2}{4} = 1$

Integrated Review — GRAPHING CONIC SECTIONS

Following is a summary of conic sections.

Conic Sections	Standard Form	Graph
Parabola	$y = a(x - h)^2 + k$	
Parabola	$x = a(y - k)^2 + h$	
Circle	$(x - h)^2 + (y - k)^2 = r^2$	
Ellipse center $(0, 0)$	$\dfrac{x^2}{a^2} + \dfrac{y^2}{b^2} = 1$	
Hyperbola center $(0, 0)$	$\dfrac{x^2}{a^2} - \dfrac{y^2}{b^2} = 1$	
Hyperbola center $(0, 0)$	$\dfrac{y^2}{b^2} - \dfrac{x^2}{a^2} = 1$	

Identify whether each equation, when graphed, will be a parabola, circle, ellipse, or hyperbola. Then graph each equation.

1. $(x - 7)^2 + (y - 2)^2 = 4$

2. $y = x^2 + 4$

3. $y = x^2 + 12x + 36$

4. $\dfrac{x^2}{4} + \dfrac{y^2}{9} = 1$

5. $\dfrac{y^2}{9} - \dfrac{x^2}{9} = 1$

6. $\dfrac{x^2}{16} - \dfrac{y^2}{4} = 1$

7. $\dfrac{x^2}{16} + \dfrac{y^2}{4} = 1$

8. $x^2 + y^2 = 16$

9. $x = y^2 + 4y - 1$

10. $x = -y^2 + 6y$

11. $9x^2 - 4y^2 = 36$

12. $9x^2 + 4y^2 = 36$

13. $\dfrac{(x - 1)^2}{49} + \dfrac{(y + 2)^2}{25} = 1$

14. $y^2 = x^2 + 16$

15. $\left(x + \dfrac{1}{2}\right)^2 + \left(y - \dfrac{1}{2}\right)^2 = 1$

13.3 Solving Nonlinear Systems of Equations

OBJECTIVES

1 Solve a Nonlinear System by Substitution.

2 Solve a Nonlinear System by Elimination.

In Chapter 4, we used graphing, substitution, and elimination methods to find solutions of systems of linear equations in two variables. We now apply these same methods to nonlinear systems of equations in two variables. A **nonlinear system of equations** is a system of equations at least one of which is not linear. Since we will be graphing the equations in each system, we are interested in real number solutions only.

OBJECTIVE

1   Solving Nonlinear Systems by Substitution

First, nonlinear systems are solved by the substitution method.

EXAMPLE 1   Solve the system

$$\begin{cases} x^2 - 3y = 1 \\ x - y = 1 \end{cases}$$

Solution   We can solve this system by substitution if we solve one equation for one of the variables. Solving the first equation for x is not the best choice since doing so introduces a radical. Also, solving for y in the first equation introduces a fraction. We solve the second equation for y.

$$x - y = 1 \quad \text{Second equation}$$
$$x - 1 = y \quad \text{Solve for } y.$$

Replace y with $x - 1$ in the first equation, and then solve for x.

$$x^2 - 3y = 1 \quad \text{First equation}$$
$$x^2 - 3(x - 1) = 1 \quad \text{Replace } y \text{ with } x - 1.$$
$$x^2 - 3x + 3 = 1$$
$$x^2 - 3x + 2 = 0$$
$$(x - 2)(x - 1) = 0$$
$$x = 2 \quad \text{or} \quad x = 1$$

Let $x = 2$ and then let $x = 1$ in the equation $y = x - 1$ to find corresponding y-values.

Let $x = 2$.	Let $x = 1$.
$y = x - 1$	$y = x - 1$
$y = 2 - 1 = 1$	$y = 1 - 1 = 0$

The solutions are $(2, 1)$ and $(1, 0)$, or the solution set is $\{(2, 1), (1, 0)\}$. Check both solutions in both equations. Both solutions satisfy both equations, so both are solutions

(Continued on next page)

of the system. The graph of each equation in the system is shown next. Intersections of the graphs are at $(2, 1)$ and $(1, 0)$.

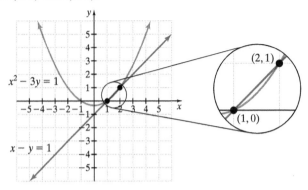

PRACTICE 1 Solve the system $\begin{cases} x^2 - 4y = 4 \\ x + y = -1 \end{cases}$.

EXAMPLE 2 Solve the system

$$\begin{cases} y = \sqrt{x} \\ x^2 + y^2 = 6 \end{cases}$$

Solution This system is ideal for substitution since y is expressed in terms of x in the first equation. Notice that if $y = \sqrt{x}$, then both x and y must be nonnegative if they are real numbers. Substitute $\sqrt{x}$ for y in the second equation, and solve for x.

$$x^2 + y^2 = 6$$
$$x^2 + (\sqrt{x})^2 = 6 \quad \text{Let } y = \sqrt{x}$$
$$x^2 + x = 6$$
$$x^2 + x - 6 = 0$$
$$(x + 3)(x - 2) = 0$$
$$x = -3 \quad \text{or} \quad x = 2$$

The solution -3 is discarded because we have noted that x must be nonnegative. To see this, let $x = -3$ in the first equation. Then let $x = 2$ in the first equation to find a corresponding y-value.

Let $x = -3$.
$$y = \sqrt{x}$$
$$y = \sqrt{-3} \quad \text{Not a real number}$$

Let $x = 2$.
$$y = \sqrt{x}$$
$$y = \sqrt{2}$$

Since we are interested only in real number solutions, the only solution is $\left(2, \sqrt{2}\right)$. Check to see that this solution satisfies both equations. The graph of each equation in the system is shown to the right.

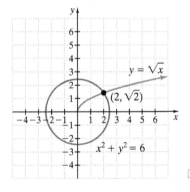

PRACTICE 2 Solve the system $\begin{cases} y = -\sqrt{x} \\ x^2 + y^2 = 20 \end{cases}$.

EXAMPLE 3   Solve the system

$$\begin{cases} x^2 + y^2 = 4 \\ x + y = 3 \end{cases}$$

Solution   We use the substitution method and solve the second equation for x.

$$x + y = 3 \qquad \text{Second equation}$$
$$x = 3 - y$$

Now we let $x = 3 - y$ in the first equation.

$$x^2 + y^2 = 4 \qquad \text{First equation}$$
$$(3 - y)^2 + y^2 = 4 \qquad \text{Let } x = 3 - y.$$
$$9 - 6y + y^2 + y^2 = 4$$
$$2y^2 - 6y + 5 = 0$$

By the quadratic formula, where $a = 2$, $b = -6$, and $c = 5$, we have

$$y = \frac{6 \pm \sqrt{(-6)^2 - 4 \cdot 2 \cdot 5}}{2 \cdot 2} = \frac{6 \pm \sqrt{-4}}{4}$$

Since $\sqrt{-4}$ is not a real number, there is no real solution, or $\varnothing$. Graphically, the circle and the line do not intersect, as shown below.

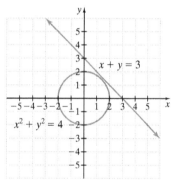

PRACTICE
3   Solve the system $\begin{cases} x^2 + y^2 = 9 \\ x - y = 5 \end{cases}$.

✓**CONCEPT CHECK**
Without solving, how can you tell that $x^2 + y^2 = 9$ and $x^2 + y^2 = 16$ do not have any points of intersection?

OBJECTIVE
2   **Solving Nonlinear Systems by Elimination** ▶

Some nonlinear systems may be solved by the elimination method.

EXAMPLE 4   Solve the system

$$\begin{cases} x^2 + 2y^2 = 10 \\ x^2 - y^2 = 1 \end{cases}$$

Answer to Concept Check:
$x^2 + y^2 = 9$ is a circle inside the circle $x^2 + y^2 = 16$, therefore they do not have any points of intersection.

(Continued on next page)

Solution We will use the elimination, or addition, method to solve this system. To eliminate x^2 when we add the two equations, multiply both sides of the second equation by -1. Then

$$\begin{cases} x^2 + 2y^2 = 10 \\ (-1)(x^2 - y^2) = -1 \cdot 1 \end{cases} \text{ is equivalent to } \begin{cases} x^2 + 2y^2 = 10 \\ -x^2 + y^2 = -1 \end{cases}$$

$$\begin{aligned} 3y^2 &= 9 &&\text{Add.} \\ y^2 &= 3 &&\text{Divide both} \\ y &= \pm\sqrt{3} &&\text{sides by 3.} \end{aligned}$$

To find the corresponding x-values, we let $y = \sqrt{3}$ and $y = -\sqrt{3}$ in either original equation. We choose the second equation.

Let $y = \sqrt{3}$.

$$\begin{aligned} x^2 - y^2 &= 1 \\ x^2 - (\sqrt{3})^2 &= 1 \\ x^2 - 3 &= 1 \\ x^2 &= 4 \\ x &= \pm\sqrt{4} = \pm 2 \end{aligned}$$

Let $y = -\sqrt{3}$.

$$\begin{aligned} x^2 - y^2 &= 1 \\ x^2 - (-\sqrt{3})^2 &= 1 \\ x^2 - 3 &= 1 \\ x^2 &= 4 \\ x &= \pm\sqrt{4} = \pm 2 \end{aligned}$$

The solutions are $(2, \sqrt{3})$, $(-2, \sqrt{3})$, $(2, -\sqrt{3})$, and $(-2, -\sqrt{3})$. Check all four ordered pairs in both equations of the system. The graph of each equation in this system is shown.

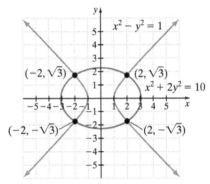

PRACTICE

4 Solve the system $\begin{cases} x^2 + 4y^2 = 16 \\ x^2 - y^2 = 1 \end{cases}$.

Vocabulary, Readiness & Video Check

Martin-Gay Interactive Videos

Watch the section lecture video and answer the following questions.

OBJECTIVE
1
1. In Example 1, why do we choose not to solve either equation for y?

OBJECTIVE
2
2. In Example 2, what important reminder is made as the second equation is multiplied by a number to get opposite coefficients of x?

See Video 13.3

13.3 Exercise Set   MyMathLab®

MIXED PRACTICE

Solve each nonlinear system of equations for real solutions. See Examples 1 through 4.

1. $\begin{cases} x^2 + y^2 = 25 \\ 4x + 3y = 0 \end{cases}$

2. $\begin{cases} x^2 + y^2 = 25 \\ 3x + 4y = 0 \end{cases}$

3. $\begin{cases} x^2 + 4y^2 = 10 \\ y = x \end{cases}$

4. $\begin{cases} 4x^2 + y^2 = 10 \\ y = x \end{cases}$

⊙ 5. $\begin{cases} y^2 = 4 - x \\ x - 2y = 4 \end{cases}$

6. $\begin{cases} x^2 + y^2 = 4 \\ x + y = -2 \end{cases}$

7. $\begin{cases} x^2 + y^2 = 9 \\ 16x^2 - 4y^2 = 64 \end{cases}$

8. $\begin{cases} 4x^2 + 3y^2 = 35 \\ 5x^2 + 2y^2 = 42 \end{cases}$

9. $\begin{cases} x^2 + 2y^2 = 2 \\ x - y = 2 \end{cases}$

10. $\begin{cases} x^2 + 2y^2 = 2 \\ x^2 - 2y^2 = 6 \end{cases}$

11. $\begin{cases} y = x^2 - 3 \\ 4x - y = 6 \end{cases}$

12. $\begin{cases} y = x + 1 \\ x^2 - y^2 = 1 \end{cases}$

13. $\begin{cases} y = x^2 \\ 3x + y = 10 \end{cases}$

14. $\begin{cases} 6x - y = 5 \\ xy = 1 \end{cases}$

15. $\begin{cases} y = 2x^2 + 1 \\ x + y = -1 \end{cases}$

16. $\begin{cases} x^2 + y^2 = 9 \\ x + y = 5 \end{cases}$

17. $\begin{cases} y = x^2 - 4 \\ y = x^2 - 4x \end{cases}$

18. $\begin{cases} x = y^2 - 3 \\ x = y^2 - 3y \end{cases}$

⊙ 19. $\begin{cases} 2x^2 + 3y^2 = 14 \\ -x^2 + y^2 = 3 \end{cases}$

20. $\begin{cases} 4x^2 - 2y^2 = 2 \\ -x^2 + y^2 = 2 \end{cases}$

21. $\begin{cases} x^2 + y^2 = 1 \\ x^2 + (y + 3)^2 = 4 \end{cases}$

22. $\begin{cases} x^2 + 2y^2 = 4 \\ x^2 - y^2 = 4 \end{cases}$

23. $\begin{cases} y = x^2 + 2 \\ y = -x^2 + 4 \end{cases}$

24. $\begin{cases} x = -y^2 - 3 \\ x = y^2 - 5 \end{cases}$

25. $\begin{cases} 3x^2 + y^2 = 9 \\ 3x^2 - y^2 = 9 \end{cases}$

26. $\begin{cases} x^2 + y^2 = 25 \\ x = y^2 - 5 \end{cases}$

27. $\begin{cases} x^2 + 3y^2 = 6 \\ x^2 - 3y^2 = 10 \end{cases}$

28. $\begin{cases} x^2 + y^2 = 1 \\ y = x^2 - 9 \end{cases}$

29. $\begin{cases} x^2 + y^2 = 36 \\ y = \dfrac{1}{6}x^2 - 6 \end{cases}$

30. $\begin{cases} x^2 + y^2 = 16 \\ y = -\dfrac{1}{4}x^2 + 4 \end{cases}$

31. $\begin{cases} y = \sqrt{x} \\ x^2 + y^2 = 12 \end{cases}$

32. $\begin{cases} y = \sqrt{x} \\ x^2 + y^2 = 20 \end{cases}$

REVIEW AND PREVIEW

Graph each inequality in two variables. See Section 9.4.

33. $x > -3$

34. $y \le 1$

35. $y < 2x - 1$

36. $3x - y \le 4$

Find the perimeter of each geometric figure. See Section 5.2.

△ 37.

x inches
$(2x - 5)$ inches
$(5x - 20)$ inches

△ 38.
$(3x + 2)$ centimeters

△ 39.
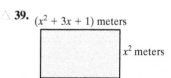
$(x^2 + 3x + 1)$ meters
x^2 meters

△ 40.
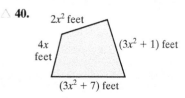
$2x^2$ feet
$4x$ feet
$(3x^2 + 1)$ feet
$(3x^2 + 7)$ feet

CONCEPT EXTENSIONS

For the exercises below, see the Concept Check in this section.

41. Without graphing, how can you tell that the graph of $x^2 + y^2 = 1$ and $x^2 + y^2 = 4$ do not have any points of intersection?

42. Without solving, how can you tell that the graphs of $y = 2x + 3$ and $y = 2x + 7$ do not have any points of intersection?

43. How many real solutions are possible for a system of equations whose graphs are a circle and a parabola? Draw diagrams to illustrate each possibility.

44. How many real solutions are possible for a system of equations whose graphs are an ellipse and a line? Draw diagrams to illustrate each possibility.

Solve.

45. The sum of the squares of two numbers is 130. The difference of the squares of the two numbers is 32. Find the two numbers.

46. The sum of the squares of two numbers is 20. Their product is 8. Find the two numbers.

47. During the development stage of a new rectangular keypad for a security system, it was decided that the area of the rectangle should be 285 square centimeters and the perimeter should be 68 centimeters. Find the dimensions of the keypad.

48. A rectangular holding pen for cattle is to be designed so that its perimeter is 92 feet and its area is 525 feet. Find the dimensions of the holding pen.

*Recall that in business, a demand function expresses the quantity of a commodity demanded as a function of the commodity's unit price. A supply function expresses the quantity of a commodity supplied as a function of the commodity's unit price. When the quantity produced and supplied is equal to the quantity demanded, then we have what is called **market equilibrium.***

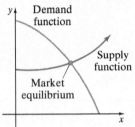

49. The demand function for a certain compact disc is given by the function
$$p = -0.01x^2 - 0.2x + 9$$
and the corresponding supply function is given by
$$p = 0.01x^2 - 0.1x + 3$$
where p is in dollars and x is in thousands of units. Find the equilibrium quantity and the corresponding price by solving the system consisting of the two given equations.

50. The demand function for a certain style of picture frame is given by the function
$$p = -2x^2 + 90$$
and the corresponding supply function is given by
$$p = 9x + 34$$
where p is in dollars and x is in thousands of units. Find the equilibrium quantity and the corresponding price by solving the system consisting of the two given equations.

Use a graphing calculator to verify the results of each exercise.

51. Exercise 3.   52. Exercise 4.

53. Exercise 23.   54. Exercise 24.

13.4 Nonlinear Inequalities and Systems of Inequalities

OBJECTIVES

1 Graph a Nonlinear Inequality.

2 Graph a System of Nonlinear Inequalities.

OBJECTIVE

1 Graphing Nonlinear Inequalities

We can graph a nonlinear inequality in two variables such as $\dfrac{x^2}{9} + \dfrac{y^2}{16} \le 1$ in a way similar to the way we graphed a linear inequality in two variables in Section 9.4. First, graph the related equation $\dfrac{x^2}{9} + \dfrac{y^2}{16} = 1$. The graph of the equation is our boundary. Then, using test points, we determine and shade the region whose points satisfy the inequality.

EXAMPLE 1 Graph $\dfrac{x^2}{9} + \dfrac{y^2}{16} \le 1$.

Solution First, graph the equation $\dfrac{x^2}{9} + \dfrac{y^2}{16} = 1$. Sketch a solid curve since the graph of $\dfrac{x^2}{9} + \dfrac{y^2}{16} \le 1$ includes the graph of $\dfrac{x^2}{9} + \dfrac{y^2}{16} = 1$. The graph is an ellipse, and it divides the plane into two regions, the "inside" and the "outside" of the ellipse. To determine which region contains the solutions, select a test point in either region and determine whether the coordinates of the point satisfy the inequality. We choose $(0, 0)$ as the test point.

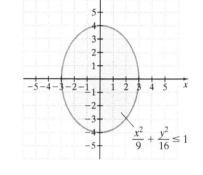

$$\frac{x^2}{9} + \frac{y^2}{16} \le 1$$

$$\frac{0^2}{9} + \frac{0^2}{16} \le 1 \quad \text{Let } x = 0 \text{ and } y = 0.$$

$$0 \le 1 \quad \text{True}$$

Since this statement is true, the solution set is the region containing $(0, 0)$. The graph of the solution set includes the points on and inside the ellipse, as shaded in the figure.

PRACTICE
1   Graph $\dfrac{x^2}{36} + \dfrac{y^2}{16} \ge 1$.

EXAMPLE 2   Graph $4y^2 > x^2 + 16$.

Solution   The related equation is $4y^2 = x^2 + 16$. Subtract x^2 from both sides and divide both sides by 16, and we have $\dfrac{y^2}{4} - \dfrac{x^2}{16} = 1$, which is a hyperbola. Graph the hyperbola as a dashed curve since the graph of $4y^2 > x^2 + 16$ does *not* include the graph of $4y^2 = x^2 + 16$. The hyperbola divides the plane into three regions. Select a test point in each region—not on a boundary line—to determine whether that region contains solutions of the inequality.

Test Region A with $(0, 4)$	*Test Region B with* $(0, 0)$	*Test Region C with* $(0, -4)$
$4y^2 > x^2 + 16$	$4y^2 > x^2 + 16$	$4y^2 > x^2 + 16$
$4(4)^2 > 0^2 + 16$	$4(0)^2 > 0^2 + 16$	$4(-4)^2 > 0^2 + 16$
$64 > 16$ True	$0 > 16$ False	$64 > 16$ True

The graph of the solution set includes the shaded regions A and C only, not the boundary.

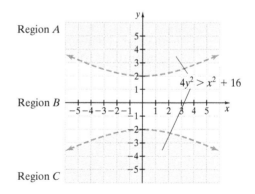

PRACTICE
2   Graph $16y^2 > 9x^2 + 144$.

OBJECTIVE
2   **Graphing Systems of Nonlinear Inequalities** ▶

In Section 9.4 we graphed systems of linear inequalities. Recall that the graph of a system of inequalities is the intersection of the graphs of the inequalities.

EXAMPLE 3 Graph the system

$$\begin{cases} x \le 1 - 2y \\ y \le x^2 \end{cases}$$

Solution We graph each inequality on the same set of axes. The intersection is shown in the third graph below. It is the darkest shaded (appears purple) region along with its boundary lines. The coordinates of the points of intersection can be found by solving the related system.

$$\begin{cases} x = 1 - 2y \\ y = x^2 \end{cases}$$

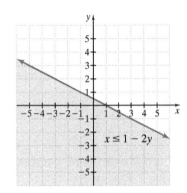 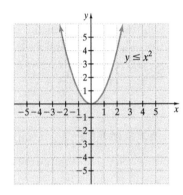 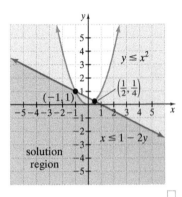

PRACTICE
3 Graph the system $\begin{cases} y \ge x^2 \\ y \le -3x + 2 \end{cases}$.

EXAMPLE 4 Graph the system

$$\begin{cases} x^2 + y^2 < 25 \\ \dfrac{x^2}{9} - \dfrac{y^2}{25} < 1 \\ y < x + 3 \end{cases}$$

Solution We graph each inequality. The graph of $x^2 + y^2 < 25$ contains points "inside" the circle that has center $(0, 0)$ and radius 5. The graph of $\dfrac{x^2}{9} - \dfrac{y^2}{25} < 1$ is the region between the two branches of the hyperbola with x-intercepts -3 and 3 and center $(0, 0)$. The graph of $y < x + 3$ is the region "below" the line with slope 1 and y-intercept $(0, 3)$. The graph of the solution set of the system is the intersection of all the graphs, the darkest shaded region shown. The boundary of this region is not part of the solution.

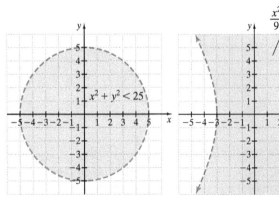 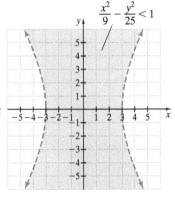 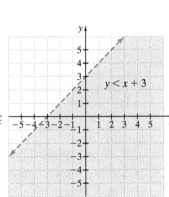 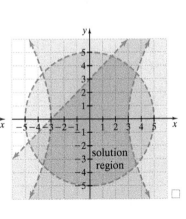

PRACTICE
4   Graph the system $\begin{cases} x^2 + y^2 < 16 \\ \dfrac{x^2}{4} - \dfrac{y^2}{9} < 1 \\ y < x + 3 \end{cases}$.

Vocabulary, Readiness & Video Check

Martin-Gay Interactive Videos

Watch the section lecture video and answer the following questions.

OBJECTIVE
1   1. From ▭ Example 1, explain the similarities between graphing linear inequalities and graphing nonlinear inequalities.

OBJECTIVE
2   2. From ▭ Example 2, describe one possible illustration of graphs of two circle inequalities in which the system has no solution—that is, the graph of the inequalities in the system do not overlap.

See Video 13.4 🍎

13.4   Exercise Set   MyMathLab®

Graph each inequality. See Examples 1 and 2.

1. $y < x^2$
2. $y < -x^2$
3. $x^2 + y^2 \geq 16$
4. $x^2 + y^2 < 36$
5. $\dfrac{x^2}{4} - y^2 < 1$
6. $x^2 - \dfrac{y^2}{9} \geq 1$
7. $y > (x - 1)^2 - 3$
8. $y > (x + 3)^2 + 2$
9. $x^2 + y^2 \leq 9$
10. $x^2 + y^2 > 4$
11. $y > -x^2 + 5$
12. $y < -x^2 + 5$
▶ **13.** $\dfrac{x^2}{4} + \dfrac{y^2}{9} \leq 1$
14. $\dfrac{x^2}{25} + \dfrac{y^2}{4} \geq 1$
15. $\dfrac{y^2}{4} - x^2 \leq 1$
16. $\dfrac{y^2}{16} - \dfrac{x^2}{9} > 1$
17. $y < (x - 2)^2 + 1$
18. $y > (x - 2)^2 + 1$
19. $y \leq x^2 + x - 2$
20. $y > x^2 + x - 2$

Graph each system. See Examples 3 and 4.

21. $\begin{cases} 4x + 3y \geq 12 \\ x^2 + y^2 < 16 \end{cases}$
22. $\begin{cases} 3x - 4y \leq 12 \\ x^2 + y^2 < 16 \end{cases}$
23. $\begin{cases} x^2 + y^2 \leq 9 \\ x^2 + y^2 \geq 1 \end{cases}$
24. $\begin{cases} x^2 + y^2 \geq 9 \\ x^2 + y^2 \geq 16 \end{cases}$
25. $\begin{cases} y > x^2 \\ y \geq 2x + 1 \end{cases}$
26. $\begin{cases} y \leq -x^2 + 3 \\ y \leq 2x - 1 \end{cases}$
▶ **27.** $\begin{cases} x^2 + y^2 > 9 \\ y > x^2 \end{cases}$
28. $\begin{cases} x^2 + y^2 \leq 9 \\ y < x^2 \end{cases}$
29. $\begin{cases} \dfrac{x^2}{4} + \dfrac{y^2}{9} \geq 1 \\ x^2 + y^2 \geq 4 \end{cases}$
30. $\begin{cases} x^2 + (y - 2)^2 \geq 9 \\ \dfrac{x^2}{4} + \dfrac{y^2}{25} < 1 \end{cases}$

31. $\begin{cases} x^2 - y^2 \geq 1 \\ y \geq 0 \end{cases}$
32. $\begin{cases} x^2 - y^2 \geq 1 \\ x \geq 0 \end{cases}$
33. $\begin{cases} x + y \geq 1 \\ 2x + 3y < 1 \\ x > -3 \end{cases}$
34. $\begin{cases} x - y < -1 \\ 4x - 3y > 0 \\ y > 0 \end{cases}$
35. $\begin{cases} x^2 - y^2 < 1 \\ \dfrac{x^2}{16} + y^2 \leq 1 \\ x \geq -2 \end{cases}$
36. $\begin{cases} x^2 - y^2 \geq 1 \\ \dfrac{x^2}{16} + \dfrac{y^2}{4} \leq 1 \\ y \geq 1 \end{cases}$

REVIEW AND PREVIEW

Determine whether each graph is the graph of a function. See Section 3.6.

37.
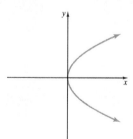

38.
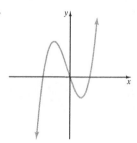

39.

40.
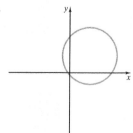

Find each function value if $f(x) = 3x^2 - 2$. See Section 3.6.

41. $f(-1)$ **42.** $f(-3)$

43. $f(a)$ **44.** $f(b)$

47. Graph the system $\begin{cases} y \le x^2 \\ y \ge x + 2 \\ x \ge 0 \\ y \ge 0 \end{cases}$.

CONCEPT EXTENSIONS

45. Discuss how graphing a linear inequality such as $x + y < 9$ is similar to graphing a nonlinear inequality such as $x^2 + y^2 < 9$.

46. Discuss how graphing a linear inequality such as $x + y < 9$ is different from graphing a nonlinear inequality such as $x^2 + y^2 < 9$.

48. Graph the system: $\begin{cases} x \ge 0 \\ y \ge 0 \\ y \ge x^2 + 1 \\ y \le 4 - x \end{cases}$

Chapter 13 Vocabulary Check

Fill in each blank with one of the words or phrases listed below.

circle   ellipse   hyperbola

conic sections   vertex   diameter

center   radius   nonlinear system of equations

1. A(n) _____ is the set of all points in a plane that are the same distance from a fixed point,

called the _____.

2. A(n) _____ is a system of equations at least one of which is not linear.

3. A(n) _____ is the set of points in a plane such that the sum of the distances of those points from two fixed

points is a constant.

4. In a circle, the distance from the center to a point of the circle is called its _____.

5. A(n) _____ is the set of points in a plane such that the absolute value of the difference of the

distance from two fixed points is constant.

6. The circle, parabola, ellipse, and hyperbola are called the _____.

7. For a parabola that opens upward, the lowest point is the _____.

8. Twice a circle's radius is its _____.

Chapter 13 Highlights

DEFINITIONS AND CONCEPTS	EXAMPLES

Section 13.1   The Parabola and the Circle

Parabolas

$$y = a(x - h)^2 + k$$

Graph

$$x = 3y^2 - 12y + 13.$$
$$x - 13 = 3y^2 - 12y$$
$$x - 13 + 3(4) = 3(y^2 - 4y + 4) \quad \text{Add } 3(4) \text{ to both sides.}$$
$$x = 3(y - 2)^2 + 1$$

Since $a = 3$, this parabola opens to the right with vertex $(1, 2)$. Its axis of symmetry is $y = 2$. The x-intercept is $(13, 0)$.

DEFINITIONS AND CONCEPTS	EXAMPLES

Section 13.1   The Parabola and the Circle (continued)

$$x = a(y - k)^2 + h$$

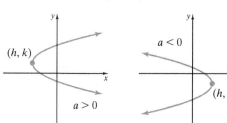

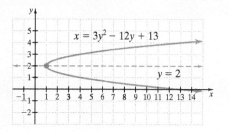

Circle

The graph of $(x - h)^2 + (y - k)^2 = r^2$ is a circle with center (h, k) and radius r.

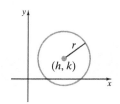

Graph $x^2 + (y + 3)^2 = 5$.

This equation can be written as

$$(x - 0)^2 + (y + 3)^2 = 5 \text{ with } h = 0,$$
$$k = -3, \text{ and } r = \sqrt{5}.$$

The center of this circle is $(0, -3)$, and the radius is $\sqrt{5}$.

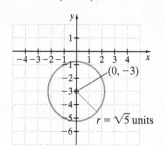

Section 13.2   The Ellipse and the Hyperbola

Ellipse with center $(0, 0)$

The graph of an equation of the form $\dfrac{x^2}{a^2} + \dfrac{y^2}{b^2} = 1$ is an ellipse with center $(0, 0)$. The x-intercepts are $(a, 0)$ and $(-a, 0)$, and the y-intercepts are $(0, b)$ and $(0, -b)$.

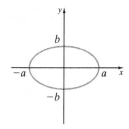

Graph $4x^2 + 9y^2 = 36$.

$$\frac{x^2}{9} + \frac{y^2}{4} = 1 \quad \text{Divide by 36.}$$
$$\frac{x^2}{3^2} + \frac{y^2}{2^2} = 1$$

The ellipse has center $(0, 0)$, x-intercepts $(3, 0)$ and $(-3, 0)$, and y-intercepts $(0, 2)$ and $(0, -2)$.

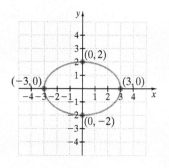

Hyperbola with center $(0, 0)$

The graph of an equation of the form $\dfrac{x^2}{a^2} - \dfrac{y^2}{b^2} = 1$ is a hyperbola with center $(0, 0)$ and x-intercepts $(a, 0)$ and $(-a, 0)$.

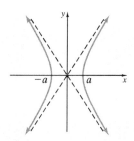

(continued)

DEFINITIONS AND CONCEPTS	EXAMPLES

Section 13.2   The Ellipse and the Hyperbola (continued)

The graph of an equation of the form

$\dfrac{y^2}{b^2} - \dfrac{x^2}{a^2} = 1$ is a hyperbola with

center $(0,0)$ and y-intercepts $(0, b)$ and $(0, -b)$.

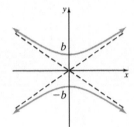

Graph $\dfrac{x^2}{9} - \dfrac{y^2}{4} = 1$. Here $a = 3$ and $b = 2$.

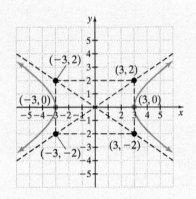

Section 13.3   Solving Nonlinear Systems of Equations

A **nonlinear system of equations** is a system of equations at least one of which is not linear. Both the substitution method and the elimination method may be used to solve a nonlinear system of equations.

Solve the nonlinear system $\begin{cases} y = x + 2 \\ 2x^2 + y^2 = 3 \end{cases}$.

Substitute $x + 2$ for y in the second equation.

$$2x^2 + y^2 = 3$$
$$2x^2 + (x + 2)^2 = 3$$
$$2x^2 + x^2 + 4x + 4 = 3$$
$$3x^2 + 4x + 1 = 0$$
$$(3x + 1)(x + 1) = 0$$
$$x = -\frac{1}{3}, x = -1$$

If $x = -\dfrac{1}{3}, y = x + 2 = -\dfrac{1}{3} + 2 = \dfrac{5}{3}$.

If $x = -1, y = x + 2 = -1 + 2 = 1$.

The solutions are $\left(-\dfrac{1}{3}, \dfrac{5}{3}\right)$ and $(-1, 1)$.

Section 13.4   Nonlinear Inequalities and Systems of Inequalities

The graph of a system of inequalities is the intersection of the graphs of the inequalities.

Graph the system $\begin{cases} x \geq y^2 \\ x + y \leq 4 \end{cases}$.

The graph of the system is the purple shaded region along with its boundary lines.

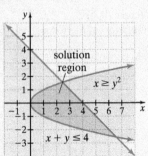

Chapter 13 **Review**

(13.1) *Write an equation of the circle with the given center and radius.*

1. center $(-4, 4)$, radius 3

2. center $(5, 0)$, radius 5

3. center $(-7, -9)$, radius $\sqrt{11}$

4. center $(0, 0)$, radius $\dfrac{7}{2}$

Sketch the graph of the equation. If the graph is a circle, find its center. If the graph is a parabola, find its vertex.

5. $x^2 + y^2 = 7$

6. $x = 2(y - 5)^2 + 4$

7. $x = -(y + 2)^2 + 3$

8. $(x - 1)^2 + (y - 2)^2 = 4$

9. $y = -x^2 + 4x + 10$

10. $x = -y^2 - 4y + 6$

11. $x = \dfrac{1}{2}y^2 + 2y + 1$

12. $y = -3x^2 + \dfrac{1}{2}x + 4$

13. $x^2 + y^2 + 2x + y = \dfrac{3}{4}$

14. $x^2 + y^2 - 3y = \dfrac{7}{4}$

15. $4x^2 + 4y^2 + 16x + 8y = 1$

16. $3x^2 + 3y^2 + 18x - 12y = -12$

(13.1, 13.2) *Graph each equation.*

17. $x^2 - \dfrac{y^2}{4} = 1$

18. $x^2 + \dfrac{y^2}{4} = 1$

19. $4y^2 + 9x^2 = 36$

20. $-5x^2 + 25y^2 = 125$

21. $x^2 - y^2 = 1$

22. $\dfrac{(x + 3)^2}{9} + \dfrac{(y - 4)^2}{25} = 1$

23. $y = x^2 + 9$

24. $36y^2 - 49x^2 = 1764$

25. $x = 4y^2 - 16$

26. $y = x^2 + 4x + 6$

27. $y^2 + 2(x - 1)^2 = 8$

28. $x - 4y = y^2$

29. $x^2 - 4 = y^2$

30. $x^2 = 4 - y^2$

31. $36y^2 = 576 + 16x^2$

32. $3(x - 7)^2 + 3(y + 4)^2 = 1$

(13.3) *Solve each system of equations.*

33. $\begin{cases} y = 2x - 4 \\ y^2 = 4x \end{cases}$

34. $\begin{cases} x^2 + y^2 = 4 \\ x - y = 4 \end{cases}$

35. $\begin{cases} y = x + 2 \\ y = x^2 \end{cases}$

36. $\begin{cases} 4x - y^2 = 0 \\ 2x^2 + y^2 = 16 \end{cases}$

37. $\begin{cases} x^2 + 4y^2 = 16 \\ x^2 + y^2 = 4 \end{cases}$

38. $\begin{cases} x^2 + 2y = 9 \\ 5x - 2y = 5 \end{cases}$

39. $\begin{cases} y = 3x^2 + 5x - 4 \\ y = 3x^2 - x + 2 \end{cases}$

40. $\begin{cases} x^2 - 3y^2 = 1 \\ 4x^2 + 5y^2 = 21 \end{cases}$

41. Find the length and the width of a room whose area is 150 square feet and whose perimeter is 50 feet.

42. What is the greatest number of real number solutions possible for a system of two equations whose graphs are an ellipse and a hyperbola?

(13.4) *Graph each inequality or system of inequalities.*

43. $y \le -x^2 + 3$

44. $x < y^2 - 1$

45. $x^2 + y^2 < 9$

46. $\dfrac{x^2}{4} + \dfrac{y^2}{9} \ge 1$

47. $\begin{cases} 3x + 4y \le 12 \\ x - 2y > 6 \end{cases}$

48. $\begin{cases} x^2 + y^2 \le 16 \\ x^2 + y^2 \ge 4 \end{cases}$

49. $\begin{cases} x^2 + y^2 < 4 \\ x^2 - y^2 \le 1 \end{cases}$

50. $\begin{cases} x^2 + y^2 < 4 \\ y \ge x^2 - 1 \\ x \ge 0 \end{cases}$

MIXED REVIEW

51. Write an equation of the circle with center $(-7, 8)$ and radius 5.

Graph each equation.

52. $y = x^2 + 6x + 9$

53. $x = y^2 + 6y + 9$

54. $\dfrac{y^2}{4} - \dfrac{x^2}{16} = 1$

55. $\dfrac{y^2}{4} + \dfrac{x^2}{16} = 1$

56. $\dfrac{(x - 2)^2}{4} + (y - 1)^2 = 1$

57. $y^2 = x^2 + 6$

58. $y^2 + (x - 2)^2 = 10$

59. $3x^2 + 6x + 3y^2 = 9$

60. $x^2 + y^2 - 8y = 0$

61. $6(x - 2)^2 + 9(y + 5)^2 = 36$

62. $\dfrac{x^2}{16} - \dfrac{y^2}{25} = 1$

Solve each system of equations.

63. $\begin{cases} y = x^2 - 5x + 1 \\ y = -x + 6 \end{cases}$

64. $\begin{cases} x^2 + y^2 = 10 \\ 9x^2 + y^2 = 18 \end{cases}$

Graph each inequality or system of inequalities.

65. $x^2 - y^2 < 1$

66. $\begin{cases} y > x^2 \\ x + y \ge 3 \end{cases}$

Chapter 13 **Test** | MyMathLab® | CHAPTER Test Prep VIDEOS |  | You Tube™

Sketch the graph of each equation.

1. $x^2 + y^2 = 36$

2. $x^2 - y^2 = 36$

3. $16x^2 + 9y^2 = 144$

4. $y = x^2 - 8x + 16$

5. $x^2 + y^2 + 6x = 16$

6. $x = y^2 + 8y - 3$

7. $\dfrac{(x-4)^2}{16} + \dfrac{(y-3)^2}{9} = 1$

8. $y^2 - x^2 = 1$

Solve each system.

9. $\begin{cases} x^2 + y^2 = 169 \\ 5x + 12y = 0 \end{cases}$

10. $\begin{cases} x^2 + y^2 = 26 \\ x^2 - 2y^2 = 23 \end{cases}$

11. $\begin{cases} y = x^2 - 5x + 6 \\ y = 2x \end{cases}$

12. $\begin{cases} x^2 + 4y^2 = 5 \\ y = x \end{cases}$

Graph each system.

13. $\begin{cases} 2x + 5y \geq 10 \\ y \geq x^2 + 1 \end{cases}$

14. $\begin{cases} \dfrac{x^2}{4} + y^2 \leq 1 \\ x + y > 1 \end{cases}$

15. $\begin{cases} x^2 + y^2 > 1 \\ \dfrac{x^2}{4} - y^2 \geq 1 \end{cases}$

16. $\begin{cases} x^2 + y^2 \geq 4 \\ x^2 + y^2 < 16 \\ y \geq 0 \end{cases}$

17. Which graph in the next column best resembles the graph of $x = a(y-k)^2 + h$ if $a > 0, h < 0,$ and $k > 0$?

A.
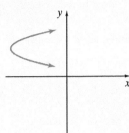

B.
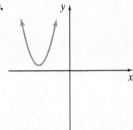

C.
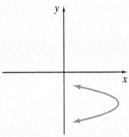

D.

18. A bridge has an arch in the shape of half an ellipse. If the equation of the ellipse, measured in feet, is $100x^2 + 225y^2 = 22{,}500$, find the height of the arch from the road and the width of the arch.

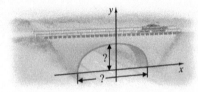

Chapter 13 **Cumulative Review**

1. Solve $2x \geq 0$ *and* $4x - 1 \leq -9$.

2. Solve $3x + 4 > 1$ *and* $2x - 5 \leq 9$. Write the solution in interval notation.

3. Solve $5x - 3 \leq 10$ *or* $x + 1 \geq 5$.

4. Find the slope of the line that goes through $(3, 2)$ and $(1, -4)$.

Solve.

5. $|5w + 3| = 7$

6. Two planes leave Greensboro, one traveling north and the other south. After 2 hours they are 650 miles apart. If one plane is flying 25 mph faster than the other, what is the speed of each?

7. $\left| \dfrac{x}{2} - 1 \right| = 11$

8. Use the quotient rule to simplify.

   a. $\dfrac{4^8}{4^3}$ b. $\dfrac{y^{11}}{y^5}$

   c. $\dfrac{32x^7}{4x^6}$ d. $\dfrac{18a^{12}b^6}{12a^8b^6}$

9. Solve $|3x + 2| = |5x - 8|$.

10. Factor.

   a. $3y^2 + 14y + 15$

   b. $20a^5 + 54a^4 + 10a^3$

   c. $(y - 3)^2 - 2(y - 3) - 8$

11. Solve for m: $|m - 6| < 2$.

12. Perform the indicated operation and simplify if possible.

$$\dfrac{2}{3a - 15} - \dfrac{a}{25 - a^2}$$

13. Simplify $\dfrac{x^{-1} + 2xy^{-1}}{x^{-2} - x^{-2}y^{-1}}$.

14. Simplify each complex fraction.

   a. $(a^{-1} - b^{-1})^{-1}$ b. $\dfrac{2 - \dfrac{1}{x}}{4x - \dfrac{1}{x}}$

15. Solve $|2x + 9| + 5 > 3$.

16. Solve $\dfrac{2}{x + 3} = \dfrac{1}{x^2 - 9} - \dfrac{1}{x - 3}$.

17. Use the remainder theorem and synthetic division to find $P(4)$ if

$$P(x) = 4x^6 - 25x^5 + 35x^4 + 17x^2.$$

18. Suppose that y varies inversely as x. If $y = 3$ when $x = \dfrac{2}{3}$, find the constant of variation and the inverse variation equation.

19. Find the cube roots.

   a. $\sqrt[3]{1}$ **b.** $\sqrt[3]{-64}$ **c.** $\sqrt[3]{\dfrac{8}{125}}$

   d. $\sqrt[3]{x^6}$ **e.** $\sqrt[3]{-27x^9}$

20. Multiply and simplify if possible.

   a. $\sqrt{5}(2 + \sqrt{15})$

   b. $(\sqrt{3} - \sqrt{5})(\sqrt{7} - 1)$

   c. $(2\sqrt{5} - 1)^2$

   d. $(3\sqrt{2} + 5)(3\sqrt{2} - 5)$

21. Multiply.

   a. $z^{2/3}(z^{1/3} - z^5)$

   b. $(x^{1/3} - 5)(x^{1/3} + 2)$

22. Rationalize the denominator $\dfrac{-2}{\sqrt{3} + 3}$.

23. Use the quotient rule to divide, and simplify if possible.

   a. $\dfrac{\sqrt{20}}{\sqrt{5}}$ **b.** $\dfrac{\sqrt{50x}}{2\sqrt{2}}$

   c. $\dfrac{7\sqrt[3]{48x^4y^8}}{\sqrt[3]{6y^2}}$ **d.** $\dfrac{2\sqrt[4]{32a^8 b^6}}{\sqrt[4]{a^{-1}b^2}}$

24. Solve $\sqrt{2x - 3} = x - 3$.

25. Add or subtract as indicated.

   a. $\dfrac{\sqrt{45}}{4} - \dfrac{\sqrt{5}}{3}$ **b.** $\sqrt[3]{\dfrac{7x}{8}} + 2\sqrt[3]{7x}$

26. Use the discriminant to determine the number and type of solutions for $9x^2 - 6x = -4$.

27. Rationalize the denominator of $\sqrt{\dfrac{7x}{3y}}$.

28. Solve $\dfrac{4}{x - 2} - \dfrac{x}{x + 2} = \dfrac{16}{x^2 - 4}$.

29. Solve $\sqrt{2x - 3} = 9$.

30. Solve $x^3 + 2x^2 - 4x \geq 8$.

31. Find the following powers of i.

   a. i^7 **b.** i^{20} **c.** i^{46} **d.** i^{-12}

32. Graph $f(x) = (x + 2)^2 - 1$.

33. Solve $p^2 + 2p = 4$ by completing the square.

34. Find the maximum value of $f(x) = -x^2 - 6x + 4$.

35. Solve: $\dfrac{1}{4}m^2 - m + \dfrac{1}{2} = 0$.

36. Find the inverse of $f(x) = \dfrac{x + 1}{2}$.

37. Solve: $p^4 - 3p^2 - 4 = 0$.

38. Use the quotient rule to simplify.

   a. $\dfrac{\sqrt{32}}{\sqrt{4}}$ **b.** $\dfrac{\sqrt[3]{240y^2}}{5\sqrt[3]{3y^{-4}}}$

   c. $\dfrac{\sqrt[5]{64x^9y^2}}{\sqrt[5]{2x^2y^{-8}}}$

39. Solve $\dfrac{x + 2}{x - 3} \leq 0$.

40. Graph $4x^2 + 9y^2 = 36$.

41. Graph $g(x) = \dfrac{1}{2}(x + 2)^2 + 5$. Find the vertex and the axis of symmetry.

42. Solve each equation for x.

   a. $64^x = 4$ **b.** $125^{x-3} = 25$ **c.** $\dfrac{1}{81} = 3^{2x}$

43. Find the vertex of the graph of $f(x) = x^2 - 4x - 12$.

44. Graph the system: $\begin{cases} x + 2y < 8 \\ y \geq x^2 \end{cases}$

45. Find the distance between $(2, -5)$ and $(1, -4)$. Give an exact distance and a three-decimal-place approximation.

46. Solve the system $\begin{cases} x^2 + y^2 = 36 \\ y = x + 6 \end{cases}$

Sequences, Series, and the Binomial Theorem

14.1 Sequences

14.2 Arithmetic and Geometric Sequences

14.3 Series

Integrated Review— Sequences and Series

14.4 Partial Sums of Arithmetic and Geometric Sequences

14.5 The Binomial Theorem

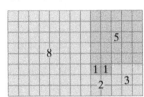

A tiling with squares whose sides are successive Fibonacci numbers in length

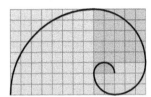

A Fibonacci spiral, created by drawing arcs connecting the opposite corners of squares in the Fibonacci tiling

Having explored in some depth the concept of function, we turn now in this final chapter to *sequences*. In one sense, a sequence is simply an ordered list of numbers. In another sense, a sequence is itself a function. Phenomena modeled by such functions are everywhere around us. The starting place for all mathematics is the sequence of natural numbers: 1, 2, 3, 4, and so on.

Sequences lead us to *series,* which are a sum of ordered numbers. Through series, we gain new insight, for example about the expansion of a binomial $(a + b)^n$, the concluding topic of this book.

The Fibonacci sequence is a special sequence in which the first two terms are 1 and each term thereafter is the sum of the two previous terms:

$$1, 1, 2, 3, 5, 8, 13, 21, \ldots$$

The Fibonacci numbers are named after Leonardo of Pisa, known as Fibonacci, although there is some evidence that these numbers had been described earlier in India.

There are numerous interesting facts about this sequence, and some are shown on the diagrams on this page. In Section 14.1, Exercise 46, you will have the opportunity to check a formula for this sequence.

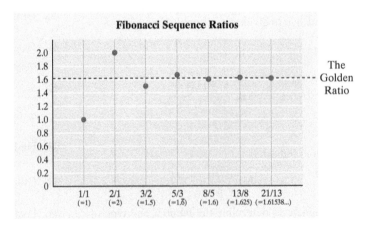

The ratio of successive numbers in the Fibonacci sequence approaches a number called the golden ratio or golden number, which is approximately 1.618034.

14.1 | Sequences

OBJECTIVES

1 Write the Terms of a Sequence Given Its General Term.

2 Find the General Term of a Sequence.

3 Solve Applications That Involve Sequences.

Suppose that a town's present population of 100,000 is growing by 5% each year. After the first year, the town's population will be

$$100{,}000 + 0.05(100{,}000) = 105{,}000$$

After the second year, the town's population will be

$$105{,}000 + 0.05(105{,}000) = 110{,}250$$

After the third year, the town's population will be

$$110{,}250 + 0.05(110{,}250) \approx 115{,}763$$

If we continue to calculate, the town's yearly population can be written as the **infinite sequence** of numbers

$$105{,}000, 110{,}250, 115{,}763, \ldots$$

If we decide to stop calculating after a certain year (say, the fourth year), we obtain the **finite sequence**

$$105{,}000, \quad 110{,}250, \quad 115{,}763, \quad 121{,}551$$

> **Sequences**
>
> An infinite sequence is a function whose domain is the set of natural numbers $\{1, 2, 3, 4, \ldots\}$.
>   A finite sequence is a function whose domain is the set of natural numbers $\{1, 2, 3, 4, \ldots, n\}$, where n is some natural number.

OBJECTIVE

1   Writing the Terms of a Sequence

Given the sequence $2, 4, 8, 16, \ldots$, we say that each number is a **term** of the sequence. Because a sequence is a function, we could describe it by writing $f(n) = 2^n$, where n is a natural number. Instead, we use the notation

$$a_n = 2^n$$

Some function values are

$$
\begin{aligned}
a_1 &= 2^1 = 2 &&\text{First term of the sequence} \\
a_2 &= 2^2 = 4 &&\text{Second term} \\
a_3 &= 2^3 = 8 &&\text{Third term} \\
a_4 &= 2^4 = 16 &&\text{Fourth term} \\
a_{10} &= 2^{10} = 1024 &&\text{Tenth term}
\end{aligned}
$$

The nth term of the sequence a_n is called the **general term.**

> ▶ **Helpful Hint**
>
> If it helps, think of a sequence as simply a list of values in which a position is assigned. For the sequence directly above,
>
> Value: 2,   4,   8,   16, ..., 1024
>   ↑   ↑   ↑   ↑   ↑
> Position 1st 2nd 3rd 4th   10th

EXAMPLE 1   Write the first five terms of the sequence whose general term is given by

$$a_n = n^2 - 1$$

Solution   Evaluate a_n, where n is $1, 2, 3, 4,$ and 5.

$$a_n = n^2 - 1$$
$$a_1 = 1^2 - 1 = 0 \quad \text{Replace } n \text{ with 1.}$$

(Continued on next page)

$$a_2 = 2^2 - 1 = 3 \quad \text{Replace } n \text{ with 2.}$$
$$a_3 = 3^2 - 1 = 8 \quad \text{Replace } n \text{ with 3.}$$
$$a_4 = 4^2 - 1 = 15 \quad \text{Replace } n \text{ with 4.}$$
$$a_5 = 5^2 - 1 = 24 \quad \text{Replace } n \text{ with 5.}$$

Thus, the first five terms of the sequence $a_n = n^2 - 1$ are 0, 3, 8, 15, and 24. □

PRACTICE

1   Write the first five terms of the sequence whose general term is given by $a_n = 5 + n^2$.

EXAMPLE 2   If the general term of a sequence is given by $a_n = \dfrac{(-1)^n}{3n}$, find

a. the first term of the sequence
b. a_8
c. the one-hundredth term of the sequence
d. a_{15}

Solution

a. $a_1 = \dfrac{(-1)^1}{3(1)} = -\dfrac{1}{3}$ Replace n with 1.

b. $a_8 = \dfrac{(-1)^8}{3(8)} = \dfrac{1}{24}$ Replace n with 8.

c. $a_{100} = \dfrac{(-1)^{100}}{3(100)} = \dfrac{1}{300}$ Replace n with 100.

d. $a_{15} = \dfrac{(-1)^{15}}{3(15)} = -\dfrac{1}{45}$ Replace n with 15.   □

PRACTICE

2   If the general term of a sequence is given by $a_n = \dfrac{(-1)^n}{5n}$, find

a. the first term of the sequence
b. a_4
c. The thirtieth term of the sequence
d. a_{19}

OBJECTIVE

2   Finding the General Term of a Sequence

Suppose we know the first few terms of a sequence and want to find a general term that fits the pattern of the first few terms.

EXAMPLE 3   Find a general term a_n of the sequence whose first few terms are given.

a. 1, 4, 9, 16, . . .

b. $\dfrac{1}{1}, \dfrac{1}{2}, \dfrac{1}{3}, \dfrac{1}{4}, \dfrac{1}{5}, \ldots$

c. −3, −6, −9, −12, . . .

d. $\dfrac{1}{2}, \dfrac{1}{4}, \dfrac{1}{8}, \dfrac{1}{16}, \ldots$

Solution

a. These numbers are the squares of the first four natural numbers, so a general term might be $a_n = n^2$.

b. These numbers are the reciprocals of the first five natural numbers, so a general term might be $a_n = \dfrac{1}{n}$.

c. These numbers are the product of −3 and the first four natural numbers, so a general term might be $a_n = -3n$.

d. Notice that the denominators double each time.

$$\frac{1}{2}, \quad \frac{1}{2\cdot 2}, \quad \frac{1}{2(2\cdot 2)}, \quad \frac{1}{2(2\cdot 2\cdot 2)}$$

or

$$\frac{1}{2^1}, \quad \frac{1}{2^2}, \quad \frac{1}{2^3}, \quad \frac{1}{2^4}$$

We might then suppose that the general term is $a_n = \dfrac{1}{2^n}$.

PRACTICE
3   Find the general term a_n of the sequence whose first few terms are given.

a. $1, 3, 5, 7, \ldots$

b. $3, 9, 27, 81, \ldots$

c. $\dfrac{1}{2}, \dfrac{2}{3}, \dfrac{3}{4}, \dfrac{4}{5}, \ldots$

d. $-\dfrac{1}{2}, -\dfrac{1}{3}, -\dfrac{1}{4}, -\dfrac{1}{5}, \ldots$

OBJECTIVE
3   Solving Applications Modeled by Sequences

Sequences model many phenomena of the physical world, as illustrated by the following example.

EXAMPLE 4   **Finding a Puppy's Weight Gain**

The amount of weight, in pounds, a puppy gains in each month of its first year is modeled by a sequence whose general term is $a_n = n + 4$, where n is the number of the month. Write the first five terms of the sequence and find how much weight the puppy should gain in its fifth month.

Solution   Evaluate $a_n = n + 4$ when n is 1, 2, 3, 4, and 5.

$$a_1 = 1 + 4 = 5$$
$$a_2 = 2 + 4 = 6$$
$$a_3 = 3 + 4 = 7$$
$$a_4 = 4 + 4 = 8$$
$$a_5 = 5 + 4 = 9$$

The puppy should gain 9 pounds in its fifth month.

PRACTICE
4   The value v, in dollars, of an office copier depreciates according to the sequence $v_n = 3950(0.8)^n$, where n is the time in years. Find the value of the copier after three years.

Vocabulary, Readiness & Video Check

Use the choices below to fill in each blank.

infinite   finite   general

1. The nth term of the sequence a_n is called the _____ term.

2. A(n) _____ sequence is a function whose domain is $\{1, 2, 3, 4, \ldots, n\}$ where n is some natural number.

3. A(n) _____ sequence is a function whose domain is $\{1, 2, 3, 4, \ldots\}$.

Write the first term of each sequence.

4. $a_n = 7^n; a_1 =$ _____.

5. $a_n = \dfrac{(-1)^n}{n}; a_1 =$ _____.

6. $a_n = (-1)^n \cdot n^4; a_1 =$ _____.

Martin-Gay Interactive Videos

Watch the section lecture video and answer the following questions.

See Video 14.1

OBJECTIVE 1
7. Based on the lecture before Example 1, complete the following statements. A sequence is a _____ whose _____ is the set of natural numbers. We use _____ to mean the general term of a sequence.

OBJECTIVE 2
8. In Example 3, why can't the general term be $a_n = (-2)^n$?

OBJECTIVE 3
9. For Example 4, write the equation for the specific term and find the allowance amount for day 9 of the vacation.

14.1 Exercise Set   MyMathLab®

Write the first five terms of each sequence, whose general term is given. See Example 1.

1. $a_n = n + 4$

2. $a_n = 5 - n$

3. $a_n = (-1)^n$

4. $a_n = (-2)^n$

5. $a_n = \dfrac{1}{n + 3}$

6. $a_n = \dfrac{1}{7 - n}$

7. $a_n = 2n$

8. $a_n = -6n$

9. $a_n = -n^2$

10. $a_n = n^2 + 2$

11. $a_n = 2^n$

12. $a_n = 3^{n-2}$

13. $a_n = 2n + 5$

14. $a_n = 1 - 3n$

15. $a_n = (-1)^n n^2$

16. $a_n = (-1)^{n+1}(n - 1)$

Find the indicated term for each sequence, whose general term is given. See Example 2.

17. $a_n = 3n^2; a_5$

18. $a_n = -n^2; a_{15}$

19. $a_n = 6n - 2; a_{20}$

20. $a_n = 100 - 7n; a_{50}$

21. $a_n = \dfrac{n + 3}{n}; a_{15}$

22. $a_n = \dfrac{n}{n + 4}; a_{24}$

23. $a_n = (-3)^n; a_6$

24. $a_n = 5^{n+1}; a_3$

25. $a_n = \dfrac{n - 2}{n + 1}; a_6$

26. $a_n = \dfrac{n + 3}{n + 4}; a_8$

27. $a_n = \dfrac{(-1)^n}{n}; a_8$

28. $a_n = \dfrac{(-1)^n}{2n}; a_{100}$

29. $a_n = -n^2 + 5; a_{10}$

30. $a_n = 8 - n^2; a_{20}$

31. $a_n = \dfrac{(-1)^n}{n + 6}; a_{19}$

32. $a_n = \dfrac{n - 4}{(-2)^n}; a_6$

Find a general term a_n for each sequence, whose first four terms are given. See Example 3.

33. $3, 7, 11, 15$

34. $2, 7, 12, 17$

35. $-2, -4, -8, -16$

36. $-4, 16, -64, 256$

37. $\dfrac{1}{3}, \dfrac{1}{9}, \dfrac{1}{27}, \dfrac{1}{81}$

38. $\dfrac{2}{5}, \dfrac{2}{25}, \dfrac{2}{125}, \dfrac{2}{625}$

Solve. See Example 4.

39. The distance, in feet, that a Thermos dropped from a cliff falls in each consecutive second is modeled by a sequence whose general term is $a_n = 32n - 16$, where n is the number of seconds. Find the distance the Thermos falls in the second, third, and fourth seconds.

40. The population size of a culture of bacteria triples every hour such that its size is modeled by the sequence $a_n = 50(3)^{n-1}$, where n is the number of the hour just beginning. Find the size of the culture at the beginning of the fourth hour and the size of the culture at the beginning of the first hour.

41. Mrs. Laser agrees to give her son Mark an allowance of $0.10 on the first day of his 14-day vacation, $0.20 on the second day, $0.40 on the third day, and so on. Write an equation of a sequence whose terms correspond to Mark's allowance. Find the allowance Mark will receive on the last day of his vacation.

42. A small theater has 10 rows with 12 seats in the first row, 15 seats in the second row, 18 seats in the third row, and so on. Write an equation of a sequence whose terms correspond to the seats in each row. Find the number of seats in the eighth row.

43. The number of cases of a new infectious disease is doubling every year such that the number of cases is modeled by a sequence whose general term is $a_n = 75(2)^{n-1}$, where n is the number of the year just beginning. Find how many cases there will be at the beginning of the sixth year. Find how many cases there were at the beginning of the first year.

44. A new college had an initial enrollment of 2700 students in 2000, and each year the enrollment increases by 150 students. Find the enrollment for each of 5 years, beginning with 2000.

45. An endangered species of sparrow had an estimated population of 800 in 2000, and scientists predicted that its population would decrease by half each year. Estimate the population in 2004. Estimate the year the sparrow was extinct.

46. A **Fibonacci sequence** is a special type of sequence in which the first two terms are 1, and each term thereafter is the sum of the two previous terms: $1, 1, 2, 3, 5, 8$, etc. The formula for the nth Fibonacci term is $a_n = \dfrac{1}{\sqrt{5}}\left[\left(\dfrac{1 + \sqrt{5}}{2}\right)^n - \left(\dfrac{1 - \sqrt{5}}{2}\right)^n\right]$.

Verify that the first two terms of the Fibonacci sequence are each 1.

REVIEW AND PREVIEW

Sketch the graph of each quadratic function. See Section 11.5.

47. $f(x) = (x - 1)^2 + 3$ **48.** $f(x) = (x - 2)^2 + 1$

49. $f(x) = 2(x + 4)^2 + 2$ **50.** $f(x) = 3(x - 3)^2 + 4$

Find the distance between each pair of points. See Section 10.3.

51. $(-4, -1)$ and $(-7, -3)$

52. $(-2, -1)$ and $(-1, 5)$

53. $(2, -7)$ and $(-3, -3)$

54. $(10, -14)$ and $(5, -11)$

CONCEPT EXTENSIONS

Find the first five terms of each sequence. Round each term after the first to four decimal places.

55. $a_n = \dfrac{1}{\sqrt{n}}$

56. $\dfrac{\sqrt{n}}{\sqrt{n} + 1}$

57. $a_n = \left(1 + \dfrac{1}{n}\right)^n$

58. $a_n = \left(1 + \dfrac{0.05}{n}\right)^n$

14.2 | Arithmetic and Geometric Sequences

OBJECTIVES

1 Identify Arithmetic Sequences and Their Common Differences.

2 Identify Geometric Sequences and Their Common Ratios.

OBJECTIVE

1   Identifying Arithmetic Sequences

Find the first four terms of the sequence whose general term is $a_n = 5 + (n - 1)3$.

$$a_1 = 5 + (1 - 1)3 = 5 \qquad \text{Replace } n \text{ with 1.}$$
$$a_2 = 5 + (2 - 1)3 = 8 \qquad \text{Replace } n \text{ with 2.}$$
$$a_3 = 5 + (3 - 1)3 = 11 \qquad \text{Replace } n \text{ with 3.}$$
$$a_4 = 5 + (4 - 1)3 = 14 \qquad \text{Replace } n \text{ with 4.}$$

The first four terms are $5, 8, 11$, and 14. Notice that the difference of any two successive terms is 3.

$$8 - 5 = 3$$
$$11 - 8 = 3$$
$$14 - 11 = 3$$
$$\vdots$$
$$a_n - a_{n-1} = 3$$

nth term   previous term

Because the difference of any two successive terms is a constant, we call the sequence an **arithmetic sequence,** or an **arithmetic progression.** The constant difference d in successive terms is called the **common difference.** In this example, d is 3.

> **Arithmetic Sequence and Common Difference**
>
> An **arithmetic sequence** is a sequence in which each term (after the first) differs from the preceding term by a constant amount d. The constant d is called the **common difference** of the sequence.

The sequence $2, 6, 10, 14, 18, \ldots$ is an arithmetic sequence. Its common difference is 4. Given the first term a_1 and the common difference d of an arithmetic sequence, we can find any term of the sequence.

EXAMPLE 1 Write the first five terms of the arithmetic sequence whose first term is 7 and whose common difference is 2.

Solution

$$a_1 = 7$$
$$a_2 = 7 + 2 = 9$$
$$a_3 = 9 + 2 = 11$$
$$a_4 = 11 + 2 = 13$$
$$a_5 = 13 + 2 = 15$$

The first five terms are $7, 9, 11, 13, 15$. □

PRACTICE
1 Write the first five terms of the arithmetic sequence whose first term is 4 and whose common difference is 5.

Notice the general pattern of the terms in Example 1.

$$a_1 = 7$$
$$a_2 = 7 + 2 = 9 \quad \text{or} \quad a_2 = a_1 + d$$
$$a_3 = 9 + 2 = 11 \quad \text{or} \quad a_3 = a_2 + d = (a_1 + d) + d = a_1 + 2d$$
$$a_4 = 11 + 2 = 13 \quad \text{or} \quad a_4 = a_3 + d = (a_1 + 2d) + d = a_1 + 3d$$
$$a_5 = 13 + 2 = 15 \quad \text{or} \quad a_5 = a_4 + d = (a_1 + 3d) + d = a_1 + 4d$$

$\longrightarrow$ (subscript $- 1$) is multiplier $\longrightarrow$

The pattern on the right suggests that the general term a_n of an arithmetic sequence is given by

$$a_n = a_1 + (n - 1)d$$

General Term of an Arithmetic Sequence

The general term a_n of an arithmetic sequence is given by

$$a_n = a_1 + (n - 1)d$$

where a_1 is the first term and d is the common difference.

EXAMPLE 2 Consider the arithmetic sequence whose first term is 3 and whose common difference is -5.

a. Write an expression for the general term a_n.
b. Find the twentieth term of this sequence.

Solution

a. Since this is an arithmetic sequence, the general term a_n is given by $a_n = a_1 + (n - 1)d$. Here, $a_1 = 3$ and $d = -5$, so

$$a_n = 3 + (n - 1)(-5) \quad \text{Let } a_1 = 3 \text{ and } d = -5.$$
$$= 3 - 5n + 5 \quad \text{Multiply.}$$
$$= 8 - 5n \quad \text{Simplify.}$$

b. $a_n = 8 - 5n$
$$a_{20} = 8 - 5 \cdot 20 \quad \text{Let } n = 20.$$
$$= 8 - 100 = -92$$ □

PRACTICE

2   Consider the arithmetic sequence whose first term is 2 and whose common difference is −3.

a. Write an expression for the general term a_n.

b. Find the twelfth term of the sequence.

EXAMPLE 3   Find the eleventh term of the arithmetic sequence whose first three terms are 2, 9, and 16.

Solution   Since the sequence is arithmetic, the eleventh term is

$$a_{11} = a_1 + (11 - 1)d = a_1 + 10d$$

We know a_1 is the first term of the sequence, so $a_1 = 2$. Also, d is the constant difference of terms, so $d = a_2 - a_1 = 9 - 2 = 7$. Thus,

$$a_{11} = a_1 + 10d$$
$$= 2 + 10 \cdot 7 \quad \text{Let } a_1 = 2 \text{ and } d = 7.$$
$$= 72$$

PRACTICE

3   Find the ninth term of the arithmetic sequence whose first three terms are 3, 9, and 15.

EXAMPLE 4   If the third term of an arithmetic sequence is 12 and the eighth term is 27, find the fifth term.

Solution   We need to find a_1 and d to write the general term, which then enables us to find a_5, the fifth term. The given facts about terms a_3 and a_8 lead to a system of linear equations.

$$\begin{cases} a_3 = a_1 + (3 - 1)d \\ a_8 = a_1 + (8 - 1)d \end{cases} \quad \text{or} \quad \begin{cases} 12 = a_1 + 2d \\ 27 = a_1 + 7d \end{cases}$$

Next, we solve the system $\begin{cases} 12 = a_1 + 2d \\ 27 = a_1 + 7d \end{cases}$ by elimination. Multiply both sides of the second equation by −1 so that

$$\begin{cases} 12 = a_1 + 2d \\ -1(27) = -1(a_1 + 7d) \end{cases} \quad \begin{matrix} \text{simplifies} \\ \text{to} \end{matrix} \quad \begin{cases} 12 = a_1 + 2d \\ \underline{-27 = -a_1 - 7d} \\ \quad -15 = \qquad -5d \quad \text{Add the equations.} \\ \qquad\quad 3 = d \qquad \text{Divide both sides by } -5. \end{cases}$$

To find a_1, let $d = 3$ in $12 = a_1 + 2d$. Then

$$12 = a_1 + 2(3)$$
$$12 = a_1 + 6$$
$$6 = a_1$$

Thus, $a_1 = 6$ and $d = 3$, so

$$a_n = 6 + (n - 1)(3)$$
$$= 6 + 3n - 3$$
$$= 3 + 3n$$

and

$$a_5 = 3 + 3 \cdot 5 = 18$$

PRACTICE

4   If the third term of an arithmetic sequence is 23 and the eighth term is 63, find the sixth term.

EXAMPLE 5 **Finding Salary**

Donna Theime has an offer for a job starting at $40,000 per year and guaranteeing her a raise of $1600 per year for the next 5 years. Write the general term for the arithmetic sequence that models Donna's potential annual salaries and find her salary for the fourth year.

Solution The first term, a_1, is 40,000, and d is 1600. So

$$a_n = 40,000 + (n - 1)(1600) = 38,400 + 1600n$$
$$a_4 = 38,400 + 1600 \cdot 4 = 44,800$$

Her salary for the fourth year will be $44,800. □

PRACTICE

5 A starting salary for a consulting company is $57,000 per year with guaranteed annual increases of $2200 for the next 4 years. Write the general term for the arithmetic sequence that models the potential annual salaries and find the salary for the third year.

OBJECTIVE

2 **Identifying Geometric Sequences**

We now investigate a **geometric sequence,** also called a **geometric progression.** In the sequence 5, 15, 45, 135, . . . , each term after the first is the *product* of 3 and the preceding term. This pattern of multiplying by a constant to get the next term defines a geometric sequence. The constant is called the **common ratio** because it is the ratio of any term (after the first) to its preceding term.

$$\frac{15}{5} = 3$$

$$\frac{45}{15} = 3$$

$$\frac{135}{45} = 3$$

$$\vdots$$

nth term $\longrightarrow$ $\dfrac{a_n}{a_{n-1}} = 3$
previous term $\longrightarrow$

> **Geometric Sequence and Common Ratio**
>
> A **geometric sequence** is a sequence in which each term (after the first) is obtained by multiplying the preceding term by a constant r. The constant r is called the **common ratio** of the sequence.

The sequence $12, 6, 3, \dfrac{3}{2}, \ldots$ is geometric since each term after the first is the product of the previous term and $\dfrac{1}{2}$.

EXAMPLE 6 Write the first five terms of a geometric sequence whose first term is 7 and whose common ratio is 2.

Solution

$$a_1 = 7$$
$$a_2 = 7(2) = 14$$
$$a_3 = 14(2) = 28$$
$$a_4 = 28(2) = 56$$
$$a_5 = 56(2) = 112$$

The first five terms are 7, 14, 28, 56, and 112. □

PRACTICE

6   Write the first four terms of a geometric sequence whose first term is 8 and whose common ratio is -3

Notice the general pattern of the terms in Example 6.

$$a_1 = 7$$
$$a_2 = 7(2) = 14 \quad \text{or} \quad a_2 = a_1(r)$$
$$a_3 = 14(2) = 28 \quad \text{or} \quad a_3 = a_2(r) = (a_1 \cdot r) \cdot r = a_1 r^2$$
$$a_4 = 28(2) = 56 \quad \text{or} \quad a_4 = a_3(r) = (a_1 \cdot r^2) \cdot r = a_1 r^3$$
$$a_5 = 56(2) = 112 \quad \text{or} \quad a_5 = a_4(r) = (a_1 \cdot r^3) \cdot r = a_1 r^4$$

$$\longrightarrow (\text{subscript} - 1) \text{ is power} \longrightarrow$$

The pattern on the right above suggests that the general term of a geometric sequence is given by $a_n = a_1 r^{n-1}$.

> **General Term of a Geometric Sequence**
>
> The general term a_n of a geometric sequence is given by
>
> $$a_n = a_1 r^{n-1}$$
>
> where a_1 is the first term and r is the common ratio.

EXAMPLE 7   Find the eighth term of the geometric sequence whose first term is 12 and whose common ratio is $\frac{1}{2}$.

Solution   Since this is a geometric sequence, the general term a_n is given by

$$a_n = a_1 r^{n-1}$$

Here $a_1 = 12$ and $r = \frac{1}{2}$, so $a_n = 12\left(\frac{1}{2}\right)^{n-1}$. Evaluate a_n for $n = 8$.

$$a_8 = 12\left(\frac{1}{2}\right)^{8-1} = 12\left(\frac{1}{2}\right)^7 = 12\left(\frac{1}{128}\right) = \frac{3}{32}$$

PRACTICE

7   Find the seventh term of the geometric sequence whose first term is 64 and whose common ratio is $\frac{1}{4}$.

EXAMPLE 8   Find the fifth term of the geometric sequence whose first three terms are 2, -6, and 18.

Solution   Since the sequence is geometric and $a_1 = 2$, the fifth term must be $a_1 r^{5-1}$, or $2r^4$. We know that r is the common ratio of terms, so r must be $\frac{-6}{2}$, or -3. Thus,

$$a_5 = 2r^4$$
$$a_5 = 2(-3)^4 = 162$$

PRACTICE

8   Find the seventh term of the geometric sequence whose first three terms are $-3, 6$, and -12.

EXAMPLE 9 If the second term of a geometric sequence is $\frac{5}{4}$ and the third term is $\frac{5}{16}$, find the first term and the common ratio.

Solution Notice that $\frac{5}{16} \div \frac{5}{4} = \frac{1}{4}$, so $r = \frac{1}{4}$. Then

$$a_2 = a_1\left(\frac{1}{4}\right)^{2-1}$$

$$\frac{5}{4} = a_1\left(\frac{1}{4}\right)^1, \quad \text{or} \quad a_1 = 5 \quad \text{Replace } a_2 \text{ with } \frac{5}{4}.$$

The first term is 5.

PRACTICE
9 If the second term of a geometric sequence is $\frac{9}{2}$ and the third term is $\frac{27}{4}$, find the first term and the common ratio.

EXAMPLE 10 Predicting Population of a Bacterial Culture

The population size of a bacterial culture growing under controlled conditions is doubling each day. Predict how large the culture will be at the beginning of day 7 if it measures 10 units at the beginning of day 1.

Solution Since the culture doubles in size each day, the population sizes are modeled by a geometric sequence. Here $a_1 = 10$ and $r = 2$. Thus,

$$a_n = a_1 r^{n-1} = 10(2)^{n-1} \quad \text{and} \quad a_7 = 10(2)^{7-1} = 640$$

The bacterial culture should measure 640 units at the beginning of day 7.

PRACTICE
10 After applying a test antibiotic, the population of a bacterial culture is reduced by one-half every day. Predict how large the culture will be at the start of day 7 if it measures 4800 units at the beginning of day 1.

Vocabulary, Readiness & Video Check

Use the choices below to fill in each blank. Some choices may be used more than once and some not at all.

first	arithmetic	difference
last	geometric	ratio

1. A(n) _____ sequence is one in which each term (after the first) is obtained by multiplying the preceding term by a constant r. The constant r is called the common _____.

2. A(n) _____ sequence is one in which each term (after the first) differs from the preceding term by a constant amount d. The constant d is called the common _____.

3. The general term of an arithmetic sequence is $a_n = a_1 + (n-1)d$ where a_1 is the _____ term and d is the common _____.

4. The general term of a geometric sequence is $a_n = a_1 r^{n-1}$ where a_1 is the _____ term and r is the common _____.

Martin-Gay Interactive Videos

See Video 14.2

Watch the section lecture video and answer the following questions.

OBJECTIVE 1

5. From the lecture before Example 1, what makes a sequence an arithmetic sequence?

OBJECTIVE 2

6. From the lecture before Example 3, what's the difference between an arithmetic and a geometric sequence?

14.2   Exercise Set   MyMathLab®

Write the first five terms of the arithmetic or geometric sequence, whose first term, a_1, and common difference, d, or common ratio, r, are given. See Examples 1 and 6.

1. $a_1 = 4; d = 2$
2. $a_1 = 3; d = 10$
3. $a_1 = 6; d = -2$
4. $a_1 = -20; d = 3$
5. $a_1 = 1; r = 3$
6. $a_1 = -2; r = 2$
7. $a_1 = 48; r = \dfrac{1}{2}$
8. $a_1 = 1; r = \dfrac{1}{3}$

Find the indicated term of each sequence. See Examples 2 and 7.

9. The eighth term of the arithmetic sequence whose first term is 12 and whose common difference is 3
10. The twelfth term of the arithmetic sequence whose first term is 32 and whose common difference is −4
11. The fourth term of the geometric sequence whose first term is 7 and whose common ratio is −5
12. The fifth term of the geometric sequence whose first term is 3 and whose common ratio is 3
13. The fifteenth term of the arithmetic sequence whose first term is −4 and whose common difference is −4
14. The sixth term of the geometric sequence whose first term is 5 and whose common ratio is −4

Find the indicated term of each sequence. See Examples 3 and 8.

15. The ninth term of the arithmetic sequence 0, 12, 24, . . .
16. The thirteenth term of the arithmetic sequence −3, 0, 3, . . .
17. The twenty-fifth term of the arithmetic sequence 20, 18, 16, . . .
18. The ninth term of the geometric sequence 5, 10, 20, . . .
19. The fifth term of the geometric sequence 2, −10, 50, . . .
20. The sixth term of the geometric sequence $\dfrac{1}{2}, \dfrac{3}{2}, \dfrac{9}{2}, \ldots$

Find the indicated term of each sequence. See Examples 4 and 9.

21. The eighth term of the arithmetic sequence whose fourth term is 19 and whose fifteenth term is 52

22. If the second term of an arithmetic sequence is 6 and the tenth term is 30, find the twenty-fifth term.
23. If the second term of an arithmetic progression is −1 and the fourth term is 5, find the ninth term.
24. If the second term of a geometric progression is 15 and the third term is 3, find a_1 and r.
25. If the second term of a geometric progression is $-\dfrac{4}{3}$ and the third term is $\dfrac{8}{3}$, find a_1 and r.
26. If the third term of a geometric sequence is 4 and the fourth term is −12, find a_1 and r.
27. Explain why 14, 10, and 6 may be the first three terms of an arithmetic sequence when it appears we are subtracting instead of adding to get the next term.
28. Explain why 80, 20, and 5 may be the first three terms of a geometric sequence when it appears we are dividing instead of multiplying to get the next term.

MIXED PRACTICE

Given are the first three terms of a sequence that is either arithmetic or geometric. If the sequence is arithmetic, find a_1 and d. If a sequence is geometric, find a_1 and r.

29. 2, 4, 6
30. 8, 16, 24
31. 5, 10, 20
32. 2, 6, 18
33. $\dfrac{1}{2}, \dfrac{1}{10}, \dfrac{1}{50}$
34. $\dfrac{2}{3}, \dfrac{4}{3}, 2$
35. $x, 5x, 25x$
36. $y, -3y, 9y$
37. $p, p + 4, p + 8$
38. $t, t - 1, t - 2$

Find the indicated term of each sequence.

39. The twenty-first term of the arithmetic sequence whose first term is 14 and whose common difference is $\dfrac{1}{4}$
40. The fifth term of the geometric sequence whose first term is 8 and whose common ratio is −3
41. The fourth term of the geometric sequence whose first term is 3 and whose common ratio is $-\dfrac{2}{3}$

42. The fourth term of the arithmetic sequence whose first term is 9 and whose common difference is 5

43. The fifteenth term of the arithmetic sequence $\frac{3}{2}, 2, \frac{5}{2}, \ldots$

44. The eleventh term of the arithmetic sequence $2, \frac{5}{3}, \frac{4}{3}, \ldots$

45. The sixth term of the geometric sequence $24, 8, \frac{8}{3}, \ldots$

46. The eighteenth term of the arithmetic sequence $5, 2, -1, \ldots$

47. If the third term of an arithmetic sequence is 2 and the seventeenth term is -40, find the tenth term.

48. If the third term of a geometric sequence is -28 and the fourth term is -56, find a_1 and r.

Solve. See Examples 5 and 10.

49. An auditorium has 54 seats in the first row, 58 seats in the second row, 62 seats in the third row, and so on. Find the general term of this arithmetic sequence and the number of seats in the twentieth row.

50. A triangular display of cans in a grocery store has 20 cans in the first row, 17 cans in the next row, and so on, in an arithmetic sequence. Find the general term and the number of cans in the fifth row. Find how many rows there are in the display and how many cans are in the top row.

51. The initial size of a virus culture is 6 units, and it triples its size every day. Find the general term of the geometric sequence that models the culture's size.

52. A real estate investment broker predicts that a certain property will increase in value 15% each year. Thus, the yearly property values can be modeled by a geometric sequence whose common ratio r is 1.15. If the initial property value was $500,000, write the first four terms of the sequence and predict the value at the end of the third year.

53. A rubber ball is dropped from a height of 486 feet, and it continues to bounce one-third the height from which it last fell. Write out the first five terms of this geometric sequence and find the general term. Find how many bounces it takes for the ball to rebound less than 1 foot.

54. On the first swing, the length of the arc through which a pendulum swings is 50 inches. The length of each successive swing is 80% of the preceding swing. Determine whether this sequence is arithmetic or geometric. Find the length of the fourth swing.

55. Jose takes a job that offers a monthly starting salary of $4000 and guarantees him a monthly raise of $125 during his first year of training. Find the general term of this arithmetic sequence and his monthly salary at the end of his training.

56. At the beginning of Claudia Schaffer's exercise program, she rides 15 minutes on the Lifecycle. Each week, she increases her riding time by 5 minutes. Write the general term of this arithmetic sequence, and find her riding time after 7 weeks. Find how many weeks it takes her to reach a riding time of 1 hour.

57. If a radioactive element has a half-life of 3 hours, then x grams of the element dwindles to $\frac{x}{2}$ grams after 3 hours. If a nuclear reactor has 400 grams of that radioactive element, find the amount of radioactive material after 12 hours.

REVIEW AND PREVIEW

Evaluate. See Sections 1.5 and 1.6.

58. $5(1) + 5(2) + 5(3) + 5(4)$

59. $\frac{1}{3(1)} + \frac{1}{3(2)} + \frac{1}{3(3)}$

60. $2(2 - 4) + 3(3 - 4) + 4(4 - 4)$

61. $3^0 + 3^1 + 3^2 + 3^3$

62. $\frac{1}{4(1)} + \frac{1}{4(2)} + \frac{1}{4(3)}$

63. $\frac{8 - 1}{8 + 1} + \frac{8 - 2}{8 + 2} + \frac{8 - 3}{8 + 3}$

CONCEPT EXTENSIONS

Write the first four terms of the arithmetic or geometric sequence, whose first term, a_1, and common difference, d, or common ratio, r, are given.

64. $a_1 = \$3720, d = -\$268.50$

65. $a_1 = \$11,782.40, r = 0.5$

66. $a_1 = 26.8, r = 2.5$

67. $a_1 = 19.652; d = -0.034$

68. Describe a situation in your life that can be modeled by a geometric sequence. Write an equation for the sequence.

69. Describe a situation in your life that can be modeled by an arithmetic sequence. Write an equation for the sequence.

14.3 | Series

OBJECTIVES

1 Identify Finite and Infinite Series and Use Summation Notation.

2 Find Partial Sums.

OBJECTIVE

1   Identifying Finite and Infinite Series and Using Summation Notation

A person who conscientiously saves money by saving first $100 and then saving $10 more each month than he saved the preceding month is saving money according to the arithmetic sequence

$$a_n = 100 + 10(n - 1)$$

Following this sequence, he can predict how much money he should save for any particular month. But if he also wants to know how much money *in total* he has saved, say, by the fifth month, he must find the *sum* of the first five terms of the sequence

$$\underbrace{100}_{a_1} + \underbrace{100 + 10}_{a_2} + \underbrace{100 + 20}_{a_3} + \underbrace{100 + 30}_{a_4} + \underbrace{100 + 40}_{a_5}$$

A sum of the terms of a sequence is called a **series** (the plural is also "series"). As our example here suggests, series are frequently used to model financial and natural phenomena.

A series is a **finite series** if it is the sum of a finite number of terms. A series is an **infinite series** if it is the sum of all the terms of an infinite sequence. For example,

Sequence	*Series*	
$5, 9, 13$	$5 + 9 + 13$	Finite; sum of 3 terms
$5, 9, 13, \ldots$	$5 + 9 + 13 + \cdots$	Infinite
$4, -2, 1, -\dfrac{1}{2}, \dfrac{1}{4}$	$4 + (-2) + 1 + \left(-\dfrac{1}{2}\right) + \left(\dfrac{1}{4}\right)$	Finite; sum of 5 terms
$4, -2, 1, \ldots$	$4 + (-2) + 1 + \cdots$	Infinite
$3, 6, \ldots, 99$	$3 + 6 + \cdots + 99$	Finite; sum of 33 terms

A shorthand notation for denoting a series when the general term of the sequence is known is called **summation notation.** The Greek uppercase letter **sigma, Σ**, is used to mean "sum." The expression $\displaystyle\sum_{n=1}^{5}(3n + 1)$ is read "the sum of $3n + 1$ as n goes from 1 to 5"; this expression means the sum of the first five terms of the sequence whose general term is $a_n = 3n + 1$. Often, the variable i is used instead of n in summation notation: $\displaystyle\sum_{i=1}^{5}(3i + 1)$. Whether we use n, i, k, or some other variable, the variable is called the **index of summation.** The notation $i = 1$ below the symbol Σ indicates the beginning value of i, and the number 5 above the symbol Σ indicates the ending value of i. Thus, the terms of the sequence are found by successively replacing i with the natural numbers $1, 2, 3, 4, 5$. To find the sum, we write out the terms and then add.

$$\sum_{i=1}^{5}(3i + 1) = (3 \cdot 1 + 1) + (3 \cdot 2 + 1) + (3 \cdot 3 + 1)$$
$$+ (3 \cdot 4 + 1) + (3 \cdot 5 + 1)$$
$$= 4 + 7 + 10 + 13 + 16 = 50$$

EXAMPLE 1   Evaluate.

a. $\displaystyle\sum_{i=0}^{6}\frac{i - 2}{2}$ **b.** $\displaystyle\sum_{i=3}^{5}2^i$

(Continued on next page)

Solution

a. $\displaystyle\sum_{i=0}^{6}\frac{i-2}{2} = \frac{0-2}{2} + \frac{1-2}{2} + \frac{2-2}{2} + \frac{3-2}{2} + \frac{4-2}{2} + \frac{5-2}{2} + \frac{6-2}{2}$

$$= (-1) + \left(-\frac{1}{2}\right) + 0 + \frac{1}{2} + 1 + \frac{3}{2} + 2$$

$$= \frac{7}{2}, \text{ or } 3\frac{1}{2}$$

b. $\displaystyle\sum_{i=3}^{5} 2^i = 2^3 + 2^4 + 2^5$

$$= 8 + 16 + 32$$

$$= 56$$

PRACTICE

1 Evaluate.

a. $\displaystyle\sum_{i=0}^{4}\frac{i-3}{4}$ **b.** $\displaystyle\sum_{i=2}^{5} 3^i$

EXAMPLE 2 Write each series with summation notation.

a. $3 + 6 + 9 + 12 + 15$ **b.** $\dfrac{1}{2} + \dfrac{1}{4} + \dfrac{1}{8} + \dfrac{1}{16}$

Solution

a. Since the *difference* of each term and the preceding term is 3, the terms correspond to the first five terms of the arithmetic sequence $a_n = a_1 + (n-1)d$ with $a_1 = 3$ and $d = 3$. So $a_n = 3 + (n-1)3 = 3n$ when simplified. Thus, in summation notation,

$$3 + 6 + 9 + 12 + 15 = \sum_{i=1}^{5} 3i.$$

b. Since each term is the *product* of the preceding term and $\dfrac{1}{2}$, these terms correspond to the first four terms of the geometric sequence $a_n = a_1 r^{n-1}$. Here $a_1 = \dfrac{1}{2}$ and $r = \dfrac{1}{2}$, so $a_n = \left(\dfrac{1}{2}\right)\left(\dfrac{1}{2}\right)^{n-1} = \left(\dfrac{1}{2}\right)^{1+(n-1)} = \left(\dfrac{1}{2}\right)^{n}$. In summation notation,

$$\frac{1}{2} + \frac{1}{4} + \frac{1}{8} + \frac{1}{16} = \sum_{i=1}^{4}\left(\frac{1}{2}\right)^{i}$$

PRACTICE

2 Write each series with summation notation.

a. $5 + 10 + 15 + 20 + 25 + 30$ **b.** $\dfrac{1}{5} + \dfrac{1}{25} + \dfrac{1}{125} + \dfrac{1}{625}$

OBJECTIVE

2 **Finding Partial Sums**

The sum of the first n terms of a sequence is a finite series known as a **partial sum,** S_n. Thus, for the sequence $a_1, a_2, \ldots, a_n$, the first three partial sums are

$$S_1 = a_1$$
$$S_2 = a_1 + a_2$$
$$S_3 = a_1 + a_2 + a_3$$

In general, S_n is the sum of the first n terms of a sequence.

$$S_n = \sum_{i=1}^{n} a_n$$

EXAMPLE 3   Find the sum of the first three terms of the sequence whose general term is $a_n = \dfrac{n + 3}{2n}$.

Solution

$$S_3 = \sum_{i=1}^{3} \frac{i + 3}{2i} = \frac{1 + 3}{2 \cdot 1} + \frac{2 + 3}{2 \cdot 2} + \frac{3 + 3}{2 \cdot 3}$$

$$= 2 + \frac{5}{4} + 1 = 4\frac{1}{4}$$

PRACTICE
3   Find the sum of the first four terms of the sequence whose general term is $a_n = \dfrac{2 + 3n}{n^2}$.

The next example illustrates how these sums model real-life phenomena.

EXAMPLE 4   **Number of Baby Gorillas Born**

The number of baby gorillas born at the San Diego Zoo is a sequence defined by $a_n = n(n - 1)$, where n is the number of years the zoo has owned gorillas. Find the *total* number of baby gorillas born in the *first 4 years*.

Solution   To solve, find the sum

$$S_4 = \sum_{i=1}^{4} i(i - 1)$$

$$= 1(1 - 1) + 2(2 - 1) + 3(3 - 1) + 4(4 - 1)$$

$$= 0 + 2 + 6 + 12 = 20$$

Twenty gorillas were born in the first 4 years.

PRACTICE
4   The number of new strawberry plants growing in a garden each year is a sequence defined by $a_n = n(2n - 1)$, where n is the number of years after planting a strawberry plant. Find the total number of strawberry plants after 5 years.

Vocabulary, Readiness & Video Check

Use the choices below to fill in each blank. Not all choices may be used.

index of summation	infinite	sigma	1	7
partial sum	finite	summation	5	

1. A series is a(n) _____ series if it is the sum of all the terms of an infinite sequence.

2. A series is a(n) _____ series if it is the sum of a finite number of terms.

3. A shorthand notation for denoting a series when the general term of the sequence is known is called _____ notation.

4. In the notation $\displaystyle\sum_{i=1}^{7}(5i - 2)$, the Σ is the Greek uppercase letter _____ and the i is called the _____.

5. The sum of the first n terms of a sequence is a finite series known as a _____.

6. For the notation in Exercise 4 above, the beginning value of i is _____ and the ending value of i is _____.

Martin-Gay Interactive Videos

Watch the section lecture video and answer the following questions.

OBJECTIVE 1

7. From the lecture before Example 1, for the series with the summation notation $\sum_{i=2}^{10} \frac{(-1)^i}{i}$, identify/explain each piece of the notation:

$\Sigma, i, 2, 10, \frac{(-1)^i}{i}$.

OBJECTIVE 2

8. From Example 2 and the lecture before, if you're finding the series S_7 of a sequence, what are you actually finding?

See Video 14.3

14.3 Exercise Set   MyMathLab®

Evaluate. See Example 1.

1. $\sum_{i=1}^{4}(i-3)$

2. $\sum_{i=1}^{5}(i+6)$

3. $\sum_{i=4}^{7}(2i+4)$

4. $\sum_{i=2}^{3}(5i-1)$

5. $\sum_{i=2}^{4}(i^2-3)$

6. $\sum_{i=3}^{5}i^3$

7. $\sum_{i=1}^{3}\left(\frac{1}{i+5}\right)$

8. $\sum_{i=2}^{4}\left(\frac{2}{i+3}\right)$

9. $\sum_{i=1}^{3}\frac{1}{6i}$

10. $\sum_{i=1}^{3}\frac{1}{3i}$

11. $\sum_{i=2}^{6}3i$

12. $\sum_{i=3}^{6}-4i$

13. $\sum_{i=3}^{5}i(i+2)$

14. $\sum_{i=2}^{4}i(i-3)$

15. $\sum_{i=1}^{5}2^i$

16. $\sum_{i=1}^{4}3^{i-1}$

17. $\sum_{i=1}^{4}\frac{4i}{i+3}$

18. $\sum_{i=2}^{5}\frac{6-i}{6+i}$

Write each series with summation notation. See Example 2.

19. $1+3+5+7+9$

20. $4+7+10+13$

21. $4+12+36+108$

22. $5+10+20+40+80+160$

23. $12+9+6+3+0+(-3)$

24. $5+1+(-3)+(-7)$

25. $12+4+\frac{4}{3}+\frac{4}{9}$

26. $80+20+5+\frac{5}{4}+\frac{5}{16}$

27. $1+4+9+16+25+36+49$

28. $1+(-4)+9+(-16)$

Find each partial sum. See Example 3.

29. Find the sum of the first two terms of the sequence whose general term is $a_n=(n+2)(n-5)$.

30. Find the sum of the first two terms of the sequence whose general term is $a_n=n(n-6)$.

31. Find the sum of the first six terms of the sequence whose general term is $a_n=(-1)^n$.

32. Find the sum of the first seven terms of the sequence whose general term is $a_n=(-1)^{n-1}$.

33. Find the sum of the first four terms of the sequence whose general term is $a_n=(n+3)(n+1)$.

34. Find the sum of the first five terms of the sequence whose general term is $a_n=\frac{(-1)^n}{2n}$.

35. Find the sum of the first four terms of the sequence whose general term is $a_n=-2n$.

36. Find the sum of the first five terms of the sequence whose general term is $a_n=(n-1)^2$.

37. Find the sum of the first three terms of the sequence whose general term is $a_n=-\frac{n}{3}$.

38. Find the sum of the first three terms of the sequence whose general term is $a_n=(n+4)^2$.

Solve. See Example 4.

39. A gardener is making a triangular planting with 1 tree in the first row, 2 trees in the second row, 3 trees in the third row, and so on for 10 rows. Write the sequence that describes the number of trees in each row. Find the total number of trees planted.

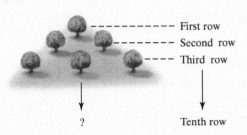

First row
Second row
Third row

?

Tenth row

40. Some surfers at the beach form a human pyramid with 2 surfers in the top row, 3 surfers in the second row, 4 surfers in the third row, and so on. If there are 6 rows in the pyramid, write the sequence that describes the number of surfers in each row of the pyramid. Find the total number of surfers.

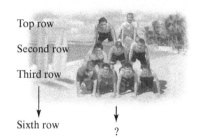

41. A culture of fungus starts with 6 units and grows according to the sequence defined by $a_n = 6 \cdot 2^{n-1}$, where n is the number of fungus units at the end of the day. Find the total number of fungus units there will be at the end of the fifth day.

42. A bacterial colony begins with 100 bacteria and grows according to the sequence defined by $a_n = 100 \cdot 2^{n-1}$, where n is the number of 6-hour periods. Find the total number of bacteria there will be after 24 hours.

43. The number of species born each year in a new aquarium forms a sequence whose general term is $a_n = (n + 1)(n + 3)$. Find the number of species born in the fourth year, and find the total number born in the first four years.

44. The number of otters born each year in a new aquarium forms a sequence whose general term is $a_n = (n - 1)(n + 3)$. Find the number of otters born in the third year and find the total number of otters born in the first three years.

45. The number of opossums killed each month on a new highway forms the sequence whose general term is $a_n = (n + 1)(n + 2)$, where n is the number of the month. Find the number of opossums killed in the fourth month and find the total number killed in the first four months.

46. In 2007, the population of the Northern Spotted Owl continued to decline, and the owl remained on the endangered species list as old-growth Northwest forests were logged. The size of the decrease in the population in a given year can be estimated by $200 - 6n$ pairs of birds. Find the decrease in population in 2010 if year 1 is 2007. Find the estimated total decrease in the spotted owl population for the years 2007 through 2010. (*Source: United States Forest Service*)

47. The amount of decay in pounds of a radioactive isotope each year is given by the sequence whose general term is $a_n = 100(0.5)^n$, where n is the number of the year. Find the amount of decay in the fourth year and find the total amount of decay in the first four years.

48. A person has a choice between two job offers. Job A has an annual starting salary of \$30,000 with guaranteed annual raises of \$1200 for the next four years, whereas job B has an annual starting salary of \$28,000 with guaranteed annual raises of \$2500 for the next four years. Compare the fifth partial sums for each sequence to determine which job would pay more money over the next 5 years.

49. A pendulum swings a length of 40 inches on its first swing. Each successive swing is $\frac{4}{5}$ of the preceding swing. Find the length of the fifth swing and the total length swung during the first five swings. (Round to the nearest tenth of an inch.)

50. Explain the difference between a sequence and a series.

REVIEW AND PREVIEW

Evaluate. See Sections 1.7 and 7.7.

51. $\dfrac{5}{1 - \dfrac{1}{2}}$

52. $\dfrac{-3}{1 - \dfrac{1}{7}}$

53. $\dfrac{\dfrac{1}{3}}{1 - \dfrac{1}{10}}$

54. $\dfrac{\dfrac{6}{11}}{1 - \dfrac{1}{10}}$

55. $\dfrac{3(1 - 2^4)}{1 - 2}$

56. $\dfrac{2(1 - 5^3)}{1 - 5}$

57. $\dfrac{10}{2}(3 + 15)$

58. $\dfrac{12}{2}(2 + 19)$

CONCEPT EXTENSIONS

59. a. Write the sum $\displaystyle\sum_{i=1}^{7}(i + i^2)$ without summation notation.

b. Write the sum $\displaystyle\sum_{i=1}^{7}i + \sum_{i=1}^{7}i^2$ without summation notation.

c. Compare the results of parts (a) and (b).

d. Do you think the following is true or false? Explain your answer.

$$\sum_{i=1}^{n}(a_n + b_n) = \sum_{i=1}^{n}a_n + \sum_{i=1}^{n}b_n$$

60. a. Write the sum $\displaystyle\sum_{i=1}^{6}5i^3$ without summation notation.

b. Write the expression $5 \cdot \displaystyle\sum_{i=1}^{6}i^3$ without summation notation.

c. Compare the results of parts (a) and (b).

d. Do you think the following is true or false? Explain your answer.

$$\sum_{i=1}^{n}c \cdot a_n = c \cdot \sum_{i=1}^{n}a_n, \text{ where } c \text{ is a constant}$$

Integrated Review SEQUENCES AND SERIES

Write the first five terms of each sequence, whose general term is given.

1. $a_n = n - 3$

2. $a_n = \dfrac{7}{1 + n}$

3. $a_n = 3^{n-1}$

4. $a_n = n^2 - 5$

Find the indicated term for each sequence.

5. $(-2)^n; a_6$

6. $-n^2 + 2; a_4$

7. $\dfrac{(-1)^n}{n}; a_{40}$

8. $\dfrac{(-1)^n}{2n}; a_{41}$

Write the first five terms of the arithmetic or geometric sequence, whose first term is a_1 and whose common difference, d, or common ratio, r, is given.

9. $a_1 = 7; d = -3$

10. $a_1 = -3; r = 5$

11. $a_1 = 45; r = \dfrac{1}{3}$

12. $a_1 = -12; d = 10$

Find the indicated term of each sequence.

13. The tenth term of the arithmetic sequence whose first term is 20 and whose common difference is 9

14. The sixth term of the geometric sequence whose first term is 64 and whose common ratio is $\dfrac{3}{4}$

15. The seventh term of the geometric sequence $6, -12, 24, \ldots$

16. The twentieth term of the arithmetic sequence $-100, -85, -70, \ldots$

17. The fifth term of the arithmetic sequence whose fourth term is -5 and whose tenth term is -35

18. The fifth term of a geometric sequence whose fourth term is 1 and whose seventh term is $\dfrac{1}{8}$

Evaluate.

19. $\displaystyle\sum_{i=1}^{4} 5i$

20. $\displaystyle\sum_{i=1}^{7} (3i + 2)$

21. $\displaystyle\sum_{i=3}^{7} 2^{i-4}$

22. $\displaystyle\sum_{i=2}^{5} \dfrac{i}{i + 1}$

Find each partial sum.

23. Find the sum of the first three terms of the sequence whose general term is $a_n = n(n - 4)$.

24. Find the sum of the first ten terms of the sequence whose general term is $a_n = (-1)^n(n + 1)$.

14.4 Partial Sums of Arithmetic and Geometric Sequences

OBJECTIVES

1 Find the Partial Sum of an Arithmetic Sequence.

2 Find the Partial Sum of a Geometric Sequence.

3 Find the Sum of the Terms of an Infinite Geometric Sequence.

OBJECTIVE

1 Finding Partial Sums of Arithmetic Sequences

Partial sums S_n are relatively easy to find when n is small—that is, when the number of terms to add is small. But when n is large, finding S_n can be tedious. For a large n, S_n is still relatively easy to find if the addends are terms of an arithmetic sequence or a geometric sequence.

For an arithmetic sequence, $a_n = a_1 + (n - 1)d$ for some first term a_1 and some common difference d. So S_n, the sum of the first n terms, is

$$S_n = a_1 + (a_1 + d) + (a_1 + 2d) + \cdots + (a_1 + (n - 1)d)$$

We might also find S_n by working backward from the nth term a_n, finding the preceding term a_{n-1}, by subtracting d each time.

$$S_n = a_n + (a_n - d) + (a_n - 2d) + \cdots + (a_n - (n - 1)d)$$

Now add the left sides of these two equations and add the right sides.

$$2S_n = (a_1 + a_n) + (a_1 + a_n) + (a_1 + a_n) + \cdots + (a_1 + a_n)$$

The d terms subtract out, leaving n sums of the first term, a_1, and last term, a_n. Thus, we write

$$2S_n = n(a_1 + a_n)$$

or

$$S_n = \frac{n}{2}(a_1 + a_n)$$

> **Partial Sum S_n of an Arithmetic Sequence**
>
> The partial sum S_n of the first n terms of an arithmetic sequence is given by
>
> $$S_n = \frac{n}{2}(a_1 + a_n)$$
>
> where a_1 is the first term of the sequence and a_n is the nth term.

EXAMPLE 1   Use the partial sum formula to find the sum of the first six terms of the arithmetic sequence $2, 5, 8, 11, 14, 17, \ldots$.

Solution   Use the formula for S_n of an arithmetic sequence, replacing n with 6, a_1 with 2, and a_n with 17.

$$S_n = \frac{n}{2}(a_1 + a_n)$$

$$S_6 = \frac{6}{2}(2 + 17) = 3(19) = 57 \qquad \square$$

PRACTICE

1   Use the partial sum formula to find the sum of the first five terms of the arithmetic sequence $2, 9, 16, 23, 30, \ldots$.

··

EXAMPLE 2   Find the sum of the first 30 positive integers.

Solution   Because $1, 2, 3, \ldots, 30$ is an arithmetic sequence, use the formula for S_n with $n = 30$, $a_1 = 1$, and $a_n = 30$. Thus,

$$S_n = \frac{n}{2}(a_1 + a_n)$$

$$S_{30} = \frac{30}{2}(1 + 30) = 15(31) = 465 \qquad \square$$

PRACTICE

2   Find the sum of the first 50 positive integers.

··

EXAMPLE 3   **Stacking Rolls of Carpet**

Rolls of carpet are stacked in 20 rows with 3 rolls in the top row, 4 rolls in the next row, and so on, forming an arithmetic sequence. Find the total number of carpet rolls if there are 22 rolls in the bottom row.

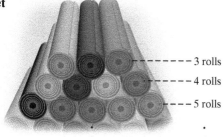
3 rolls
4 rolls
5 rolls

Solution   The list $3, 4, 5, \ldots, 22$ is the first 20 terms of an arithmetic sequence. Use the formula for S_n with $a_1 = 3$, $a_n = 22$, and $n = 20$ terms. Thus,

$$S_{20} = \frac{20}{2}(3 + 22) = 10(25) = 250$$

There are a total of 250 rolls of carpet. $\square$

PRACTICE

3   An ice sculptor is creating a gigantic castle-facade ice sculpture for First Night festivities in Boston. To get the volume of ice necessary, large blocks of ice were stacked atop each other in 10 rows. The topmost row comprised 6 blocks of ice, the next row 7 blocks of ice, and so on, forming an arithmetic sequence. Find the total number of ice blocks needed if there were 15 blocks in the bottom row.

OBJECTIVE

2 Finding Partial Sums of Geometric Sequences ▶

We can also derive a formula for the partial sum S_n of the first n terms of a geometric series. If $a_n = a_1 r^{n-1}$, then

$$S_n = a_1 + a_1 r + a_1 r^2 + \cdots + a_1 r^{n-1}$$

$$\uparrow \quad \uparrow \quad \uparrow \qquad\qquad \uparrow$$

1st   2nd   3rd nth
term   term   term   term

Multiply each side of the equation by $-r$.

$$-rS_n = -a_1 r - a_1 r^2 - a_1 r^3 - \cdots - a_1 r^n$$

Add the two equations.

$$S_n - rS_n = a_1 + (a_1 r - a_1 r) + (a_1 r^2 - a_1 r^2) + (a_1 r^3 - a_1 r^3) + \cdots - a_1 r^n$$

$$S_n - rS_n = a_1 - a_1 r^n$$

Now factor each side.

$$S_n(1 - r) = a_1(1 - r^n)$$

Solve for S_n by dividing both sides by $1 - r$. Thus,

$$S_n = \frac{a_1(1 - r^n)}{1 - r}$$

as long as r is not 1.

Partial Sum S_n of a Geometric Sequence

The partial sum S_n of the first n terms of a geometric sequence is given by

$$S_n = \frac{a_1(1 - r^n)}{1 - r}$$

where a_1 is the first term of the sequence, r is the common ratio, and $r \neq 1$.

EXAMPLE 4   Find the sum of the first six terms of the geometric sequence $5, 10, 20, 40, 80, 160$.

Solution   Use the formula for the partial sum S_n of the terms of a geometric sequence. Here, $n = 6$, the first term $a_1 = 5$, and the common ratio $r = 2$.

$$S_n = \frac{a_1(1 - r^n)}{1 - r}$$

$$S_6 = \frac{5(1 - 2^6)}{1 - 2} = \frac{5(-63)}{-1} = 315$$ □

PRACTICE

4   Find the sum of the first five terms of the geometric sequence $32, 8, 2, \frac{1}{2}, \frac{1}{8}$.

EXAMPLE 5   **Finding Amount of Donation**

A grant from an alumnus to a university specified that the university was to receive $800,000 during the first year and 75% of the preceding year's donation during each of the following 5 years. Find the total amount donated during the 6 years.

Solution   The donations are modeled by the first six terms of a geometric sequence. Evaluate S_n when $n = 6$, $a_1 = 800,000$, and $r = 0.75$.

$$S_6 = \frac{800,000[1 - (0.75)^6]}{1 - 0.75}$$

$$= \$2,630,468.75$$

The total amount donated during the 6 years is $2,630,468.75.   □

PRACTICE

5   A new youth center is being established in a downtown urban area. A philanthropic charity has agreed to help it get off the ground. The charity has pledged to donate $250,000 in the first year, with 80% of the preceding year's donation for each of the following 6 years. Find the total amount donated during the 7 years.

OBJECTIVE

3   Finding Sums of Terms of Infinite Geometric Sequences

Is it possible to find the sum of all the terms of an infinite sequence? Examine the partial sums of the geometric sequence $\frac{1}{2}, \frac{1}{4}, \frac{1}{8}, \ldots$.

$$S_1 = \frac{1}{2}$$

$$S_2 = \frac{1}{2} + \frac{1}{4} = \frac{3}{4}$$

$$S_3 = \frac{1}{2} + \frac{1}{4} + \frac{1}{8} = \frac{7}{8}$$

$$S_4 = \frac{1}{2} + \frac{1}{4} + \frac{1}{8} + \frac{1}{16} = \frac{15}{16}$$

$$S_5 = \frac{1}{2} + \frac{1}{4} + \frac{1}{8} + \frac{1}{16} + \frac{1}{32} = \frac{31}{32}$$

$$\vdots$$

$$S_{10} = \frac{1}{2} + \frac{1}{4} + \frac{1}{8} + \cdots + \frac{1}{2^{10}} = \frac{1023}{1024}$$

Even though each partial sum is larger than the preceding partial sum, we see that each partial sum is closer to 1 than the preceding partial sum. If n gets larger and larger, then S_n gets closer and closer to 1. We say that 1 is the **limit** of S_n and that 1 is the sum of the terms of this infinite sequence. In general, if $|r| < 1$, the following formula gives the sum of the terms of an infinite geometric sequence.

Sum of the Terms of an Infinite Geometric Sequence

The sum S_∞ of the terms of an infinite geometric sequence is given by

$$S_\infty = \frac{a_1}{1 - r}$$

where a_1 is the first term of the sequence, r is the common ratio, and $|r| < 1$. If $|r| \geq 1$, S_∞ does not exist.

What happens for other values of r? For example, in the following geometric sequence, $r = 3$.

$$6, 18, 54, 162, \ldots$$

Here, as n increases, the sum S_n increases also. This time, though, S_n does not get closer and closer to a fixed number but instead increases without bound.

EXAMPLE 6 Find the sum of the terms of the geometric sequence $2, \dfrac{2}{3}, \dfrac{2}{9}, \dfrac{2}{27}, \ldots$

Solution For this geometric sequence, $r = \dfrac{1}{3}$. Since $|r| < 1$, we may use the formula for S_∞ of a geometric sequence with $a_1 = 2$ and $r = \dfrac{1}{3}$.

$$S_\infty = \frac{a_1}{1 - r} = \frac{2}{1 - \dfrac{1}{3}} = \frac{2}{\dfrac{2}{3}} = 3$$

PRACTICE
6 Find the sum of the terms of the geometric sequence $7, \dfrac{7}{4}, \dfrac{7}{16}, \dfrac{7}{64}, \ldots$

The formula for the sum of the terms of an infinite geometric sequence can be used to write a repeating decimal as a fraction. For example,

$$0.33\overline{3} = \frac{3}{10} + \frac{3}{100} + \frac{3}{1000} + \cdots$$

This sum is the sum of the terms of an infinite geometric sequence whose first term a_1 is $\dfrac{3}{10}$ and whose common ratio r is $\dfrac{1}{10}$. Using the formula for S_∞,

$$S_\infty = \frac{a_1}{1 - r} = \frac{\dfrac{3}{10}}{1 - \dfrac{1}{10}} = \frac{1}{3}$$

So, $0.33\overline{3} = \dfrac{1}{3}$.

EXAMPLE 7 **Distance Traveled by a Pendulum**

On its first pass, a pendulum swings through an arc whose length is 24 inches. On each pass thereafter, the arc length is 75% of the arc length on the preceding pass. Find the total distance the pendulum travels before it comes to rest.

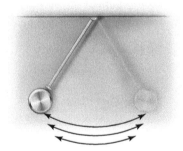

Solution We must find the sum of the terms of an infinite geometric sequence whose first term, a_1, is 24 and whose common ratio, r, is 0.75. Since $|r| < 1$, we may use the formula for S_∞.

$$S_\infty = \frac{a_1}{1 - r} = \frac{24}{1 - 0.75} = \frac{24}{0.25} = 96$$

The pendulum travels a total distance of 96 inches before it comes to rest.

PRACTICE
7 The manufacturers of the "perpetual bouncing ball" claim that the ball rises to 96% of its dropped height on each bounce of the ball. Find the total distance the ball travels before it comes to rest if it is dropped from a height of 36 inches.

Vocabulary, Readiness & Video Check

Decide whether each sequence is geometric or arithmetic.

1. $5, 10, 15, 20, 25, \ldots;$ _____

2. $5, 10, 20, 40, 80, \ldots;$ _____

3. $-1, 3, -9, 27, -81 \ldots;$ _____

4. $-1, 1, 3, 5, 7, \ldots;$ _____

5. $-7, 0, 7, 14, 21, \ldots;$ _____

6. $-7, 7, -7, 7, -7, \ldots;$ _____

Martin-Gay Interactive Videos

See Video 14.4

Watch the section lecture video and answer the following questions.

OBJECTIVE 1

7. From ▭ Example 1, suppose you are asked to find the sum of the first 100 terms of an arithmetic sequence in which you are given only the first few terms. You need the 100th term for the partial sum formula—how can you find this term without actually writing down the first 100 terms?

OBJECTIVE 2

8. From the lecture before ▭ Example 2, we know $r \neq 1$ in the partial sum formula because it would make the denominator 0. What would a geometric sequence with $r = 1$ look like? How could the partial sum of such a sequence be found (without the given formula)?

OBJECTIVE 3

9. From the lecture before ▭ Example 3, why can't you find S_∞ for the geometric sequence $-1, -3, -9, -27, \ldots$?

14.4 Exercise Set   MyMathLab®

Use the partial sum formula to find the partial sum of the given arithmetic or geometric sequence. See Examples 1 and 4.

1. Find the sum of the first six terms of the arithmetic sequence $1, 3, 5, 7, \ldots$.

2. Find the sum of the first seven terms of the arithmetic sequence $-7, -11, -15, \ldots$.

3. Find the sum of the first five terms of the geometric sequence $4, 12, 36, \ldots$.

4. Find the sum of the first eight terms of the geometric sequence $-1, 2, -4, \ldots$.

5. Find the sum of the first six terms of the arithmetic sequence $3, 6, 9, \ldots$.

6. Find the sum of the first four terms of the arithmetic sequence $-4, -8, -12, \ldots$.

7. Find the sum of the first four terms of the geometric sequence $2, \dfrac{2}{5}, \dfrac{2}{25}, \ldots$.

8. Find the sum of the first five terms of the geometric sequence $\dfrac{1}{3}, -\dfrac{2}{3}, \dfrac{4}{3}, \ldots$.

Solve. See Example 2.

9. Find the sum of the first ten positive integers.

10. Find the sum of the first eight negative integers.

11. Find the sum of the first four positive odd integers.

12. Find the sum of the first five negative odd integers.

Find the sum of the terms of each infinite geometric sequence. See Example 6.

13. $12, 6, 3, \ldots$

14. $45, 15, 5, \ldots$

15. $\dfrac{1}{10}, \dfrac{1}{100}, \dfrac{1}{1000}, \ldots$

16. $\dfrac{3}{5}, \dfrac{3}{20}, \dfrac{3}{80}, \ldots$

17. $-10, -5, -\dfrac{5}{2}, \ldots$

18. $-16, -4, -1, \ldots$

19. $2, -\dfrac{1}{4}, \dfrac{1}{32}, \ldots$

20. $-3, \dfrac{3}{5}, -\dfrac{3}{25}, \ldots$

21. $\dfrac{2}{3}, -\dfrac{1}{3}, \dfrac{1}{6}, \ldots$

22. $6, -4, \dfrac{8}{3}, \ldots$

MIXED PRACTICE

Solve.

23. Find the sum of the first ten terms of the sequence $-4, 1, 6, \ldots, 41$ where 41 is the tenth term.

24. Find the sum of the first twelve terms of the sequence $-3, -13, -23, \ldots, -113$ where -113 is the twelfth term.

25. Find the sum of the first seven terms of the sequence $3, \dfrac{3}{2}, \dfrac{3}{4}, \ldots$.

26. Find the sum of the first five terms of the sequence $-2, -6, -18, \ldots$.

27. Find the sum of the first five terms of the sequence $-12, 6, -3, \ldots$.

28. Find the sum of the first four terms of the sequence $-\frac{1}{4}$, $-\frac{3}{4}$, $-\frac{9}{4}$, ...

29. Find the sum of the first twenty terms of the sequence $\frac{1}{2}$, $\frac{1}{4}$, 0, . . . , $-\frac{17}{4}$ where $-\frac{17}{4}$ is the twentieth term.

30. Find the sum of the first fifteen terms of the sequence $-5, -9, -13, \ldots, -61$ where -61 is the fifteenth term.

31. If a_1 is 8 and r is $-\frac{2}{3}$, find S_3.

32. If a_1 is 10, a_{18} is $\frac{3}{2}$, and d is $-\frac{1}{2}$, find S_{18}.

Solve. See Example 3.

33. Modern Car Company has come out with a new car model. Market analysts predict that 4000 cars will be sold in the first month and that sales will drop by 50 cars per month after that during the first year. Write out the first five terms of the sequence and find the number of sold cars predicted for the twelfth month. Find the total predicted number of sold cars for the first year.

34. A company that sends faxes charges \$3 for the first page sent and \$0.10 less than the preceding page for each additional page sent. The cost per page forms an arithmetic sequence. Write the first five terms of this sequence and use a partial sum to find the cost of sending a nine-page document.

35. Sal has two job offers: Firm A starts at \$22,000 per year and guarantees raises of \$1000 per year, whereas Firm B starts at \$20,000 and guarantees raises of \$1200 per year. Over a 10-year period, determine the more profitable offer.

36. The game of pool uses 15 balls numbered 1 to 15. In the variety called rotation, a player who sinks a ball receives as many points as the number on the ball. Use an arithmetic series to find the score of a player who sinks all 15 balls.

Solve. See Example 5.

37. A woman made \$30,000 during the first year she owned her business and made an additional 10% over the previous year in each subsequent year. Find how much she made during her fourth year of business. Find her total earnings during the first four years.

38. In free fall, a parachutist falls 16 feet during the first second, 48 feet during the second second, 80 feet during the third second, and so on. Find how far she falls during the eighth second. Find the total distance she falls during the first 8 seconds.

39. A trainee in a computer company takes 0.9 times as long to assemble each computer as he took to assemble the preceding computer. If it took him 30 minutes to assemble the first computer, find how long it takes him to assemble the fifth computer. Find the total time he takes to assemble the first five computers (round to the nearest minute).

40. On a gambling trip to Reno, Carol doubled her bet each time she lost. If her first losing bet was \$5 and she lost six consecutive bets, find how much she lost on the sixth bet. Find the total amount lost on these six bets.

Solve. See Example 7.

41. A ball is dropped from a height of 20 feet and repeatedly rebounds to a height that is $\frac{4}{5}$ of its previous height. Find the total distance the ball covers before it comes to rest.

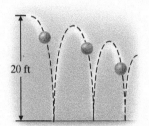

42. A rotating flywheel coming to rest makes 300 revolutions in the first minute and in each minute thereafter makes $\frac{2}{5}$ as many revolutions as in the preceding minute. Find how many revolutions the wheel makes before it comes to rest.

MIXED PRACTICE

Solve.

43. In the pool game of rotation, player A sinks balls numbered 1 to 9, and player B sinks the rest of the balls. Use an arithmetic series to find each player's score (see Exercise 36).

44. A godfather deposited \$250 in a savings account on the day his godchild was born. On each subsequent birthday, he deposited \$50 more than he deposited the previous year. Find how much money he deposited on his godchild's twenty-first birthday. Find the total amount deposited over the 21 years.

45. During the holiday rush, a business can rent a computer system for \$200 the first day, with the rental fee decreasing \$5 for each additional day. Find the fee paid for 20 days during the holiday rush.

46. The spraying of a field with insecticide killed 6400 weevils the first day, 1600 the second day, 400 the third day, and so on. Find the total number of weevils killed during the first 5 days.

47. A college student humorously asks his parents to charge him room and board according to this geometric sequence: \$0.01 for the first day of the month, \$0.02 for the second day, \$0.04 for the third day, and so on. Find the total room and board he would pay for 30 days.

48. Following its television advertising campaign, a bank attracted 80 new customers the first day, 120 the second day, 160 the third day, and so on in an arithmetic sequence. Find how many new customers were attracted during the first 5 days following its television campaign.

REVIEW AND PREVIEW

Evaluate. See Section 1.7.

49. $6 \cdot 5 \cdot 4 \cdot 3 \cdot 2 \cdot 1$

50. $8 \cdot 7 \cdot 6 \cdot 5 \cdot 4 \cdot 3 \cdot 2 \cdot 1$

51. $\dfrac{3 \cdot 2 \cdot 1}{2 \cdot 1}$

52. $\dfrac{5 \cdot 4 \cdot 3 \cdot 2 \cdot 1}{3 \cdot 2 \cdot 1}$

Multiply. See Section 5.4.

53. $(x + 5)^2$

54. $(x - 2)^2$

55. $(2x - 1)^3$

56. $(3x + 2)^3$

CONCEPT EXTENSIONS

57. Write $0.88\overline{8}$ as an infinite geometric series and use the formula for S_∞ to write it as a rational number.

58. Write $0.54\overline{54}$ as an infinite geometric series and use the formula S_∞ to write it as a rational number.

59. Explain whether the sequence $5, 5, 5, \ldots$ is arithmetic, geometric, neither, or both.

60. Describe a situation in everyday life that can be modeled by an infinite geometric series.

14.5   The Binomial Theorem

OBJECTIVES

1 Use Pascal's Triangle to Expand Binomials.

2 Evaluate Factorials.

3 Use the Binomial Theorem to Expand Binomials.

4 Find the *n*th Term in the Expansion of a Binomial Raised to a Positive Power.

In this section, we learn how to **expand** binomials of the form $(a + b)^n$ easily. Expanding a binomial such as $(a + b)^n$ means to write the factored form as a sum. First, we review the patterns in the expansions of $(a + b)^n$.

$$(a + b)^0 = 1 \qquad\qquad \text{1 term}$$
$$(a + b)^1 = a + b \qquad\qquad \text{2 terms}$$
$$(a + b)^2 = a^2 + 2ab + b^2 \qquad\qquad \text{3 terms}$$
$$(a + b)^3 = a^3 + 3a^2b + 3ab^2 + b^3 \qquad\qquad \text{4 terms}$$
$$(a + b)^4 = a^4 + 4a^3b + 6a^2b^2 + 4ab^3 + b^4 \qquad\qquad \text{5 terms}$$
$$(a + b)^5 = a^5 + 5a^4b + 10a^3b^2 + 10a^2b^3 + 5ab^4 + b^5 \qquad \text{6 terms}$$

Notice the following patterns.

1. The expansion of $(a + b)^n$ contains $n + 1$ terms. For example, for $(a + b)^3$, $n = 3$, and the expansion contains $3 + 1$ terms, or 4 terms.

2. The first term of the expansion of $(a + b)^n$ is a^n, and the last term is b^n.

3. The powers of a decrease by 1 for each term, whereas the powers of b increase by 1 for each term.

4. For each term of the expansion of $(a + b)^n$, the sum of the exponents of a and b is n. (For example, the sum of the exponents of $5a^4b$ is $4 + 1$, or 5, and the sum of the exponents of $10a^3b^2$ is $3 + 2$, or 5.)

OBJECTIVE

1   Using Pascal's Triangle

There are patterns in the coefficients of the terms as well. Written in a triangular array, the coefficients are called **Pascal's triangle.**

$$
\begin{array}{llccccccccc}
(a + b)^0: & & & & & & 1 & & & & & n = 0 \\
(a + b)^1: & & & & & 1 & & 1 & & & & n = 1 \\
(a + b)^2: & & & & 1 & & 2 & & 1 & & & n = 2 \\
(a + b)^3: & & & 1 & & 3 & & 3 & & 1 & & n = 3 \\
(a + b)^4: & & 1 & & 4 & & 6 & & 4 & & 1 & n = 4 \\
(a + b)^5: & 1 & & 5 & & 10 & & 10 & & 5 & & 1 \quad n = 5
\end{array}
$$

Each row in Pascal's triangle begins and ends with 1. Any other number in a row is the sum of the two closest numbers above it. Using this pattern, we can write the next row, for $n = 6$, by first writing the number 1. Then we can add the consecutive numbers in the row for $n = 5$ and write each sum between and below the pair. We complete the row by writing a 1.

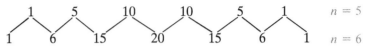

We can use Pascal's triangle and the patterns noted to expand $(a + b)^n$ without actually multiplying any terms.

EXAMPLE 1 Expand $(a + b)^6$.

Solution Using the $n = 6$ row of Pascal's triangle as the coefficients and following the patterns noted, $(a + b)^6$ can be expanded as

$$a^6 + 6a^5b + 15a^4b^2 + 20a^3b^3 + 15a^2b^4 + 6ab^5 + b^6$$

PRACTICE
1 Expand $(p + r)^7$.

OBJECTIVE
2 Evaluating Factorials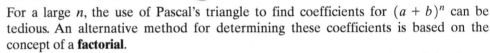

For a large n, the use of Pascal's triangle to find coefficients for $(a + b)^n$ can be tedious. An alternative method for determining these coefficients is based on the concept of a **factorial**.

The **factorial of n,** written $n!$ (read "n factorial"), is the product of the first n consecutive natural numbers.

> **Factorial of n: $n!$**
>
> If n is a natural number, then $n! = n(n - 1)(n - 2)(n - 3) \cdots 3 \cdot 2 \cdot 1$. The factorial of 0, written 0!, is defined to be 1.

For example, $3! = 3 \cdot 2 \cdot 1 = 6$, $5! = 5 \cdot 4 \cdot 3 \cdot 2 \cdot 1 = 120$, and $0! = 1$.

EXAMPLE 2 Evaluate each expression.

a. $\dfrac{5!}{6!}$ **b.** $\dfrac{10!}{7!3!}$ **c.** $\dfrac{3!}{2!1!}$ **d.** $\dfrac{7!}{7!0!}$

Solution

a. $\dfrac{5!}{6!} = \dfrac{5 \cdot 4 \cdot 3 \cdot 2 \cdot 1}{6 \cdot 5 \cdot 4 \cdot 3 \cdot 2 \cdot 1} = \dfrac{1}{6}$

b. $\dfrac{10!}{7!3!} = \dfrac{10 \cdot 9 \cdot 8 \cdot 7!}{7! \cdot 3 \cdot 2 \cdot 1} = \dfrac{10 \cdot 9 \cdot 8}{3 \cdot 2 \cdot 1} = 10 \cdot 3 \cdot 4 = 120$

c. $\dfrac{3!}{2!1!} = \dfrac{3 \cdot 2 \cdot 1}{2 \cdot 1 \cdot 1} = 3$

d. $\dfrac{7!}{7!0!} = \dfrac{7!}{7! \cdot 1} = 1$

PRACTICE
2 Evaluate each expression.

a. $\dfrac{6!}{7!}$ **b.** $\dfrac{8!}{4!2!}$ **c.** $\dfrac{5!}{4!1!}$ **d.** $\dfrac{9!}{9!0!}$

> ▶ Helpful Hint
> We can use a calculator with a factorial key to evaluate a factorial. A calculator uses scientific notation for large results.

OBJECTIVE

3   Using the Binomial Theorem ▶

It can be proved, although we won't do so here, that the coefficients of terms in the expansion of $(a + b)^n$ can be expressed in terms of factorials. Following patterns 1 through 4 given earlier and using the factorial expressions of the coefficients, we have what is known as the **binomial theorem.**

Binomial Theorem

If n is a positive integer, then

$$(a + b)^n = a^n + \frac{n}{1!}a^{n-1}b^1 + \frac{n(n-1)}{2!}a^{n-2}b^2$$

$$+ \frac{n(n-1)(n-2)}{3!}a^{n-3}b^3 + \cdots + b^n$$

We call the formula for $(a + b)^n$ given by the binomial theorem the **binomial formula.**

EXAMPLE 3   Use the binomial theorem to expand $(x + y)^{10}$.

Solution   Let $a = x, b = y$, and $n = 10$ in the binomial formula.

$$(x + y)^{10} = x^{10} + \frac{10}{1!}x^9y + \frac{10 \cdot 9}{2!}x^8y^2 + \frac{10 \cdot 9 \cdot 8}{3!}x^7y^3 + \frac{10 \cdot 9 \cdot 8 \cdot 7}{4!}x^6y^4$$

$$+ \frac{10 \cdot 9 \cdot 8 \cdot 7 \cdot 6}{5!}x^5y^5 + \frac{10 \cdot 9 \cdot 8 \cdot 7 \cdot 6 \cdot 5}{6!}x^4y^6$$

$$+ \frac{10 \cdot 9 \cdot 8 \cdot 7 \cdot 6 \cdot 5 \cdot 4}{7!}x^3y^7$$

$$+ \frac{10 \cdot 9 \cdot 8 \cdot 7 \cdot 6 \cdot 5 \cdot 4 \cdot 3}{8!}x^2y^8$$

$$+ \frac{10 \cdot 9 \cdot 8 \cdot 7 \cdot 6 \cdot 5 \cdot 4 \cdot 3 \cdot 2}{9!}xy^9 + y^{10}$$

$$= x^{10} + 10x^9y + 45x^8y^2 + 120x^7y^3 + 210x^6y^4 + 252x^5y^5 + 210x^4y^6$$

$$+ 120x^3y^7 + 45x^2y^8 + 10xy^9 + y^{10}$$

PRACTICE

3   Use the binomial theorem to expand $(a + b)^9$.

EXAMPLE 4   Use the binomial theorem to expand $(x + 2y)^5$.

Solution   Let $a = x$ and $b = 2y$ in the binomial formula.

$$(x + 2y)^5 = x^5 + \frac{5}{1!}x^4(2y) + \frac{5 \cdot 4}{2!}x^3(2y)^2 + \frac{5 \cdot 4 \cdot 3}{3!}x^2(2y)^3$$

$$+ \frac{5 \cdot 4 \cdot 3 \cdot 2}{4!}x(2y)^4 + (2y)^5$$

$$= x^5 + 10x^4y + 40x^3y^2 + 80x^2y^3 + 80xy^4 + 32y^5$$

PRACTICE

4   Use the binomial theorem to expand $(a + 5b)^3$.

EXAMPLE 5 Use the binomial theorem to expand $(3m - n)^4$.

Solution Let $a = 3m$ and $b = -n$ in the binomial formula.

$$(3m - n)^4 = (3m)^4 + \frac{4}{1!}(3m)^3(-n) + \frac{4 \cdot 3}{2!}(3m)^2(-n)^2$$

$$+ \frac{4 \cdot 3 \cdot 2}{3!}(3m)(-n)^3 + (-n)^4$$

$$= 81m^4 - 108m^3n + 54m^2n^2 - 12mn^3 + n^4 \qquad \square$$

PRACTICE
5 Use the binomial theorem to expand $(3x - 2y)^3$.

OBJECTIVE
4 Finding the *n*th Term of a Binomial Expansion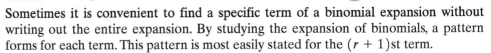

Sometimes it is convenient to find a specific term of a binomial expansion without writing out the entire expansion. By studying the expansion of binomials, a pattern forms for each term. This pattern is most easily stated for the $(r + 1)$st term.

(r + 1)st Term in a Binomial Expansion

The $(r + 1)$st term of the expansion of $(a + b)^n$ is $\dfrac{n!}{r!(n - r)!}a^{n-r}b^r$.

EXAMPLE 6 Find the eighth term in the expansion of $(2x - y)^{10}$.

Solution Use the formula with $n = 10$, $a = 2x$, $b = -y$, and $r + 1 = 8$. Notice that, since $r + 1 = 8$, $r = 7$.

$$\frac{n!}{r!(n - r)!}a^{n-r}b^r = \frac{10!}{7!3!}(2x)^3(-y)^7$$

$$= 120(8x^3)(-y^7)$$

$$= -960x^3y^7 \qquad \square$$

PRACTICE
6 Find the seventh term in the expansion of $(x - 4y)^{11}$.

Vocabulary, Readiness & Video Check

Fill in each blank.

1. $0! = $ _____ **2.** $1! = $ _____ **3.** $4! = $ _____ **4.** $2! = $ _____ **5.** $3!0! = $ _____ **6.** $0!2! = $ _____

Martin-Gay Interactive Videos

See Video 14.5

Watch the section lecture video and answer the following questions.

OBJECTIVE
1 **7.** From ▣ Example 1 and the lecture before, when expanding a binomial such as $(x + y)^7$, what does Pascal's triangle tell you? What does the power on the binomial tell you?

OBJECTIVE
2 **8.** From ▣ Example 2 and the lecture before, write the definition of 4! and evaluate it. What is the value of 0!?

OBJECTIVE
3 **9.** From ▣ Example 4, what point is made about the terms of a binomial when applying the binomial theorem?

OBJECTIVE
4 **10.** In ▣ Example 5, we are looking for the 4th term, so why do we let $r = 3$?

14.5 Exercise Set MyMathLab®

Use Pascal's triangle to expand the binomial. See Example 1.

1. $(m + n)^3$
2. $(x + y)^4$
3. $(c + d)^5$
4. $(a + b)^6$
5. $(y - x)^5$
6. $(q - r)^7$
7. Explain how to generate a row of Pascal's triangle.
8. Write the $n = 8$ row of Pascal's triangle.

Evaluate each expression. See Example 2.

9. $\dfrac{8!}{7!}$
10. $\dfrac{6!}{0!}$
11. $\dfrac{7!}{5!}$
12. $\dfrac{8!}{5!}$
13. $\dfrac{10!}{7!2!}$
14. $\dfrac{9!}{5!3!}$
15. $\dfrac{8!}{6!0!}$
16. $\dfrac{10!}{4!6!}$

MIXED PRACTICE

Use the binomial formula to expand each binomial. See Examples 3 through 5.

17. $(a + b)^7$
18. $(x + y)^8$
19. $(a + 2b)^5$
20. $(x + 3y)^6$
21. $(q + r)^9$
22. $(b + c)^6$
23. $(4a + b)^5$
24. $(3m + n)^4$
25. $(5a - 2b)^4$
26. $(m - 4)^6$
27. $(2a + 3b)^3$
28. $(4 - 3x)^5$

29. $(x + 2)^5$
30. $(3 + 2a)^4$

Find the indicated term. See Example 6.

31. The fifth term of the expansion of $(c - d)^5$
32. The fourth term of the expansion of $(x - y)^6$
33. The eighth term of the expansion of $(2c + d)^7$
34. The tenth term of the expansion of $(5x - y)^9$
35. The fourth term of the expansion of $(2r - s)^5$
36. The first term of the expansion of $(3q - 7r)^6$
37. The third term of the expansion of $(x + y)^4$
38. The fourth term of the expansion of $(a + b)^8$
39. The second term of the expansion of $(a + 3b)^{10}$
40. The third term of the expansion of $(m + 5n)^7$

REVIEW AND PREVIEW

Sketch the graph of each function. Decide whether each function is one-to-one. See Sections 3.6 and 12.2.

41. $f(x) = |x|$
42. $g(x) = 3(x - 1)^2$
43. $H(x) = 2x + 3$
44. $F(x) = -2$
45. $f(x) = x^2 + 3$
46. $h(x) = -(x + 1)^2 - 4$

CONCEPT EXTENSIONS

47. Expand the expression $(\sqrt{x} + \sqrt{3})^5$.

48. Find the term containing x^2 in the expansion of $(\sqrt{x} - \sqrt{5})^6$.

Evaluate the following.

The notation $\dbinom{n}{r}$ means $\dfrac{n!}{r!(n - r)!}$. For example,

$$\binom{5}{3} = \frac{5!}{3!(5 - 3)!} = \frac{5!}{3!2!} = \frac{5 \cdot 4 \cdot 3 \cdot 2 \cdot 1}{(3 \cdot 2 \cdot 1) \cdot (2 \cdot 1)} = 10.$$

49. $\dbinom{9}{5}$
50. $\dbinom{4}{3}$
51. $\dbinom{8}{2}$
52. $\dbinom{12}{11}$

53. Show that $\dbinom{n}{n} = 1$ for any whole number n.

Chapter 14 Vocabulary Check

Fill in each blank with one of the words or phrases listed below.

general term	common difference	finite sequence	common ratio	Pascal's triangle
infinite sequence	factorial of n	arithmetic sequence	geometric sequence	series

1. A(n) _____ is a function whose domain is the set of natural numbers $\{1, 2, 3, \ldots, n\}$, where n is some natural number.

2. The _____, written $n!$, is the product of the first n consecutive natural numbers.

3. A(n) _____ is a function whose domain is the set of natural numbers.

4. A(n) _____ is a sequence in which each term (after the first) is obtained by multiplying the preceding term by a constant amount r. The constant r is called the _____ of the sequence.

5. The sum of the terms of a sequence is called a(n) _____.

6. The nth term of the sequence a_n is called the _____.

7. A(n) _____ is a sequence in which each term (after the first) differs from the preceding term by a constant amount d. The constant d is called the _____ of the sequence.

8. A triangular array of the coefficients of the terms of the expansions of $(a + b)^n$ is called _____.

Chapter 14 Highlights

DEFINITIONS AND CONCEPTS	EXAMPLES
Section 14.1 Sequences	
An **infinite sequence** is a function whose domain is the set of natural numbers $\{1, 2, 3, 4, \ldots\}$.	*Infinite Sequence* $$2, 4, 6, 8, 10, \ldots$$
A **finite sequence** is a function whose domain is the set of natural numbers $\{1, 2, 3, 4, \ldots, n\}$, where n is some natural number.	*Finite Sequence* $$1, -2, 3, -4, 5, -6$$
The notation a_n, where n is a natural number, denotes a sequence.	Write the first four terms of the sequence whose general term is $a_n = n^2 + 1$. $$a_1 = 1^2 + 1 = 2$$ $$a_2 = 2^2 + 1 = 5$$ $$a_3 = 3^2 + 1 = 10$$ $$a_4 = 4^2 + 1 = 17$$
Section 14.2 Arithmetic and Geometric Sequences	
An **arithmetic sequence** is a sequence in which each term differs from the preceding term by a constant amount d, called the **common difference**.	*Arithmetic Sequence* $$5, 8, 11, 14, 17, 20, \ldots$$ Here, $a_1 = 5$ and $d = 3$.
The **general term** a_n of an arithmetic sequence is given by $$a_n = a_1 + (n - 1)d$$ where a_1 is the first term and d is the common difference.	The general term is $$a_n = a_1 + (n - 1)d \text{ or}$$ $$a_n = 5 + (n - 1)3$$

DEFINITIONS AND CONCEPTS	EXAMPLES

Section 14.2   Arithmetic and Geometric Sequences (continued)

A **geometric sequence** is a sequence in which each term is obtained by multiplying the preceding term by a constant r, called the **common ratio.**

The **general term** a_n of a geometric sequence is given by

$$a_n = a_1 r^{n-1}$$

where a_1 is the first term and r is the common ratio.

Geometric Sequence

$$12, -6, 3, -\frac{3}{2}, \ldots$$

Here $a_1 = 12$ and $r = -\frac{1}{2}$.

The general term is

$$a_n = a_1 r^{n-1} \text{ or}$$

$$a_n = 12\left(-\frac{1}{2}\right)^{n-1}$$

Section 14.3   Series

A sum of the terms of a sequence is called a **series.**

A shorthand notation for denoting a series is called **summation notation:**

index of summation $\to$ $\sum\limits_{i=1}^{4}$ $\to$ Greek letter sigma used to mean sum

Sequence	*Series*	
$3, 7, 11, 15$	$3 + 7 + 11 + 15$	finite
$3, 7, 11, 15, \ldots$	$3 + 7 + 11 + 15 + \cdots$	infinite

$$\sum_{i=1}^{4} 3^i = 3^1 + 3^2 + 3^3 + 3^4$$

$$= 3 + 9 + 27 + 81$$

$$= 120$$

Section 14.4   Partial Sums of Arithmetic and Geometric Sequences

Partial sum, S_n, of the first n terms of an arithmetic sequence:

$$S_n = \frac{n}{2}(a_1 + a_n)$$

where a_1 is the first term and a_n is the nth term.

Partial sum, S_n, of the first n terms of a geometric sequence:

$$S_n = \frac{a_1(1 - r^n)}{1 - r}$$

where a_1 is the first term, r is the common ratio, and $r \neq 1$.

Sum of the terms of an infinite geometric sequence:

$$S_\infty = \frac{a_1}{1 - r}$$

where a_1 is the first term, r is the common ratio, and $|r| < 1$. (If $|r| \geq 1$, S_∞ does not exist.)

The sum of the first five terms of the arithmetic sequence

$$12, 24, 36, 48, 60, \ldots \text{ is}$$

$$S_5 = \frac{5}{2}(12 + 60) = 180$$

The sum of the first five terms of the geometric sequence

$$15, 30, 60, 120, 240, \ldots \text{ is}$$

$$S_5 = \frac{15(1 - 2^5)}{1 - 2} = 465$$

The sum of the terms of the infinite geometric sequence

$$1, \frac{1}{3}, \frac{1}{9}, \frac{1}{27}, \ldots \text{ is}$$

$$S_\infty = \frac{1}{1 - \frac{1}{3}} = \frac{3}{2}$$

Section 14.5   The Binomial Theorem

The **factorial of n**, written $n!$, is the product of the first n consecutive natural numbers.

Binomial Theorem

If n is a positive integer, then

$$(a + b)^n = a^n + \frac{n}{1!}a^{n-1}b^1 + \frac{n(n-1)}{2!}a^{n-2}b^2$$

$$+ \frac{n(n-1)(n-2)}{3!}a^{n-3}b^3 + \cdots + b^n$$

$$5! = 5 \cdot 4 \cdot 3 \cdot 2 \cdot 1 = 120$$

Expand $(3x + y)^4$.

$$(3x + y)^4 = (3x)^4 + \frac{4}{1!}(3x)^3(y)^1$$

$$+ \frac{4 \cdot 3}{2!}(3x)^2(y)^2 + \frac{4 \cdot 3 \cdot 2}{3!}(3x)^1 y^3 + y^4$$

$$= 81x^4 + 108x^3y + 54x^2y^2 + 12xy^3 + y^4$$

Chapter 14 **Review**

(14.1) Find the indicated term(s) of the given sequence.

1. The first five terms of the sequence $a_n = -3n^2$

2. The first five terms of the sequence $a_n = n^2 + 2n$

3. The one-hundredth term of the sequence $a_n = \dfrac{(-1)^n}{100}$

4. The fiftieth term of the sequence $a_n = \dfrac{2n}{(-1)^n}$

5. The general term a_n of the sequence $\dfrac{1}{6}, \dfrac{1}{12}, \dfrac{1}{18}, \ldots$

6. The general term a_n of the sequence $-1, 4, -9, 16, \ldots$

Solve the following applications.

7. The distance in feet that an olive falling from rest in a vacuum will travel during each second is given by an arithmetic sequence whose general term is $a_n = 32n - 16$, where n is the number of the second. Find the distance the olive will fall during the fifth, sixth, and seventh seconds.

8. A culture of yeast measures 80 and doubles every day in a geometric progression, where n is the number of the day just ending. Write the measure of the yeast culture for the end of the next 5 days. Find how many days it takes the yeast culture to measure at least 10,000.

9. The Colorado Forest Service reported that western pine beetle infestation, which kills trees, affected approximately 660,000 acres of lodgepole forests in Colorado in 2006. The forest service predicted that during the next 5 years, the beetles would infest twice the number of acres per year as the year before. Write out the first 5 terms of this geometric sequence and find the number of acres of infested trees there were in 2010.

10. The first row of an amphitheater contains 50 seats, and each row thereafter contains 8 additional seats. Write the first ten terms of this arithmetic progression and find the number of seats in the tenth row.

(14.2)

11. Find the first five terms of the geometric sequence whose first term is -2 and whose common ratio is $\dfrac{2}{3}$.

12. Find the first five terms of the arithmetic sequence whose first term is 12 and whose common difference is -1.5.

13. Find the thirtieth term of the arithmetic sequence whose first term is -5 and whose common difference is 4.

14. Find the eleventh term of the arithmetic sequence whose first term is 2 and whose common difference is $\dfrac{3}{4}$.

15. Find the twentieth term of the arithmetic sequence whose first three terms are 12, 7, and 2.

16. Find the sixth term of the geometric sequence whose first three terms are 4, 6, and 9.

17. If the fourth term of an arithmetic sequence is 18 and the twentieth term is 98, find the first term and the common difference.

18. If the third term of a geometric sequence is -48 and the fourth term is 192, find the first term and the common ratio.

19. Find the general term of the sequence $\dfrac{3}{10}, \dfrac{3}{100}, \dfrac{3}{1000}, \ldots$

20. Find a general term that satisfies the terms shown for the sequence $50, 58, 66, \ldots$

Determine whether each of the following sequences is arithmetic, geometric, or neither. If a sequence is arithmetic, find a_1 and d. If a sequence is geometric, find a_1 and r.

21. $\dfrac{8}{3}, 4, 6, \ldots$

22. $-10.5, -6.1, -1.7$

23. $7x, -14x, 28x$

24. $3x^2, 9x^4, 81x^8, \ldots$

Solve the following applications.

25. To test the bounce of a racquetball, the ball is dropped from a height of 8 feet. The ball is judged "good" if it rebounds at least 75% of its previous height with each bounce. Write out the first six terms of this geometric sequence (round to the nearest tenth). Determine if a ball is "good" that rebounds to a height of 2.5 feet after the fifth bounce.

26. A display of oil cans in an auto parts store has 25 cans in the bottom row, 21 cans in the next row, and so on, in an arithmetic progression. Find the general term and the number of cans in the top row.

27. Suppose that you save $1 the first day of a month, $2 the second day, $4 the third day, continuing to double your savings each day. Write the general term of this geometric sequence and find the amount you will save on the tenth day. Estimate the amount you will save on the thirtieth day of the month and check your estimate with a calculator.

28. On the first swing, the length of an arc through which a pendulum swings is 30 inches. The length of the arc for each successive swing is 70% of the preceding swing. Find the length of the arc for the fifth swing.

29. Rosa takes a job that has a monthly starting salary of $900 and guarantees her a monthly raise of $150 during her 6-month training period. Find the general term of this sequence and her salary at the end of her training.

30. A sheet of paper is $\dfrac{1}{512}$-inch thick. By folding the sheet in half, the total thickness will be $\dfrac{1}{256}$-inch. A second fold produces a total thickness of $\dfrac{1}{128}$-inch. Estimate the thickness of the stack after 15 folds and then check your estimate with a calculator.

(14.3) *Write out the terms and find the sum for each of the following.*

31. $\sum_{i=1}^{5}(2i-1)$

32. $\sum_{i=1}^{5}i(i+2)$

33. $\sum_{i=2}^{4}\dfrac{(-1)^i}{2i}$

34. $\sum_{i=3}^{5}5(-1)^{i-1}$

Write the sum with Σ notation.

35. $1+3+9+27+81+243$

36. $6+2+(-2)+(-6)+(-10)+(-14)+(-18)$

37. $\dfrac{1}{4}+\dfrac{1}{16}+\dfrac{1}{64}+\dfrac{1}{256}$

38. $1+\left(-\dfrac{3}{2}\right)+\dfrac{9}{4}$

Solve.

39. A yeast colony begins with 20 yeast and doubles every 8 hours. Write the sequence that describes the growth of the yeast and find the total yeast after 48 hours.

40. The number of cranes born each year in a new aviary forms a sequence whose general term is $a_n = n^2 + 2n - 1$. Find the number of cranes born in the fourth year and the total number of cranes born in the first four years.

41. Harold has a choice between two job offers. Job A has an annual starting salary of $39,500 with guaranteed annual raises of $2200 for the next four years, whereas job B has an annual starting salary of $41,000 with guaranteed annual raises of $1400 for the next four years. Compare the salaries for the fifth year under each job offer.

42. A sample of radioactive waste is decaying such that the amount decaying in kilograms during year n is $a_n = 200(0.5)^n$. Find the amount of decay in the third year and the total amount of decay in the first three years.

(14.4) *Find the partial sum of the given sequence.*

43. S_4 of the sequence $a_n = (n-3)(n+2)$

44. S_6 of the sequence $a_n = n^2$

45. S_5 of the sequence $a_n = -8 + (n-1)3$

46. S_3 of the sequence $a_n = 5(4)^{n-1}$

47. The sixth partial sum of the sequence $15, 19, 23, \ldots$

48. The ninth partial sum of the sequence $5, -10, 20, \ldots$

49. The sum of the first 30 odd positive integers

50. The sum of the first 20 positive multiples of 7

51. The sum of the first 20 terms of the sequence $8, 5, 2, \ldots$

52. The sum of the first eight terms of the sequence $\dfrac{3}{4}, \dfrac{9}{4}, \dfrac{27}{4}, \ldots$

53. S_4 if $a_1 = 6$ and $r = 5$

54. S_{100} if $a_1 = -3$ and $d = -6$

Find the sum of each infinite geometric sequence.

55. $5, \dfrac{5}{2}, \dfrac{5}{4}, \ldots$

56. $18, -2, \dfrac{2}{9}, \ldots$

57. $-20, -4, -\dfrac{4}{5}, \ldots$

58. $0.2, 0.02, 0.002, \ldots$

Solve.

59. A frozen yogurt store owner cleared $20,000 the first year he owned his business and made an additional 15% over the previous year in each subsequent year. Find how much he made during his fourth year of business. Find his total earnings during the first 4 years (round to the nearest dollar).

60. On his first morning in a television assembly factory, a trainee takes 0.8 times as long to assemble each television as he took to assemble the one before. If it took him 40 minutes to assemble the first television, find how long it takes him to assemble the fourth television. Find the total time he takes to assemble the first four televisions (round to the nearest minute).

61. During the harvest season, a farmer can rent a combine machine for $100 the first day, with the rental fee decreasing $7 for each additional day. Find how much the farmer pays for the rental on the seventh day. Find how much total rent the farmer pays for 7 days.

62. A rubber ball is dropped from a height of 15 feet and rebounds 80% of its previous height after each bounce. Find the total distance the ball travels before it comes to rest.

63. After a pond was sprayed once with insecticide, 1800 mosquitoes were killed the first day, 600 the second day, 200 the third day, and so on. Find the total number of mosquitoes killed during the first 6 days after the spraying (round to the nearest unit).

64. See Exercise 63. Find the day on which the insecticide is no longer effective and find the total number of mosquitoes killed (round to the nearest mosquito).

65. Use the formula S_∞ to write $0.55\overline{5}$ as a fraction.

66. A movie theater has 27 seats in the first row, 30 seats in the second row, 33 seats in the third row, and so on. Find the total number of seats in the theater if there are 20 rows.

(14.5) *Use Pascal's triangle to expand each binomial.*

67. $(x+z)^5$

68. $(y-r)^6$

69. $(2x+y)^4$

70. $(3y-z)^4$

Use the binomial formula to expand the following.

71. $(b + c)^8$

72. $(x - w)^7$

73. $(4m - n)^4$

74. $(p - 2r)^5$

Find the indicated term.

75. The fourth term of the expansion of $(a + b)^7$

76. The eleventh term of the expansion of $(y + 2z)^{10}$

MIXED REVIEW

77. Evaluate: $\sum_{i=1}^{4} i^2(i + 1)$

78. Find the fifteenth term of the arithmetic sequence whose first three terms are $14, 8$, and 2.

79. Find the sum of the infinite geometric sequence $27, 9, 3, 1, \ldots$

80. Expand: $(2x - 3)^4$

Chapter 14 **Test** MyMathLab®  Test Prep VIDEOS You Tube™

Find the indicated term(s) of the given sequence.

1. The first five terms of the sequence $a_n = \dfrac{(-1)^n}{n + 4}$

2. The eightieth term of the sequence $a_n = 10 + 3(n - 1)$

3. The general term of the sequence $\dfrac{2}{5}, \dfrac{2}{25}, \dfrac{2}{125}, \ldots$

4. The general term of the sequence $-9, 18, -27, 36, \ldots$

Find the partial sum of the given sequence.

5. S_5 of the sequence $a_n = 5(2)^{n-1}$

6. S_{30} of the sequence $a_n = 18 + (n - 1)(-2)$

7. S_∞ of the sequence $a_1 = 24$ and $r = \dfrac{1}{6}$

8. S_∞ of the sequence $\dfrac{3}{2}, -\dfrac{3}{4}, \dfrac{3}{8}, \ldots$

9. $\sum_{i=1}^{4} i(i - 2)$

10. $\sum_{i=2}^{4} 5(2)^i(-1)^{i-1}$

Expand each binomial.

11. $(a - b)^6$

12. $(2x + y)^5$

Solve the following applications.

13. The population of a small town is growing yearly according to the sequence defined by $a_n = 250 + 75(n - 1)$, where n is the number of the year just beginning. Predict the population at the beginning of the tenth year. Find the town's initial population.

14. A gardener is making a triangular planting with one shrub in the first row, three shrubs in the second row, five shrubs in the third row, and so on, for eight rows. Write the finite series of this sequence and find the total number of shrubs planted.

15. A pendulum swings through an arc of length 80 centimeters on its first swing. On each successive swing, the length of the arc is $\dfrac{3}{4}$ the length of the arc on the preceding swing. Find the length of the arc on the fourth swing and find the total arc length for the first four swings.

16. See Exercise 15. Find the total arc length before the pendulum comes to rest.

17. A parachutist in free-fall falls 16 feet during the first second, 48 feet during the second second, 80 feet during the third second, and so on. Find how far he falls during the tenth second. Find the total distance he falls during the first 10 seconds.

18. Use the formula S_∞ to write $0.42\overline{42}$ as a fraction.

Chapter 14 **Cumulative Review**

1. Evaluate.
   a. $(-2)^3$ **b.** -2^3
   c. $(-3)^2$ **d.** -3^2

2. Simplify each expression.
   a. $3a - (4a + 3)$
   b. $(5x - 3) + (2x + 6)$
   c. $4(2x - 5) - 3(5x + 1)$

3. Subtract $4x - 2$ from $2x - 3$. Simplify, if possible.

4. Sara bought a digital camera for $344.50 including tax. If the tax rate is 6%, what was the price of the camera before taxes?

5. Write an equation of the line with y-intercept $(0, -3)$ and slope of $\dfrac{1}{4}$.

6. Find an equation of a line through $(3, -2)$ and parallel to $3x - 2y = 6$. Write the equation using function notation.

7. Find an equation of the line through $(2, 5)$ and $(-3, 4)$. Write the equation in standard form.

8. Solve $y^3 + 5y^2 - y = 5$

9. Use synthetic division to divide $x^4 - 2x^3 - 11x^2 + 5x + 34$ by $x + 2$.

10. Perform the indicated operation and simplify if possible.
$$\frac{5}{3a - 6} - \frac{a}{a - 2} + \frac{3 + 2a}{5a - 10}$$

11. Simplify the following.
   a. $\sqrt{50}$ 　　　　　 **b.** $\sqrt[3]{24}$
   c. $\sqrt{26}$ 　　　　　 **d.** $\sqrt[4]{32}$

12. Solve $\sqrt{3x + 6} - \sqrt{7x - 6} = 0$

13. Use the formula $A = P(1 + r)^t$ to find the interest rate r if \$2000 compounded annually grows to \$2420 in 2 years.

14. Rationalize each denominator.
   a. $\sqrt[3]{\dfrac{4}{3x}}$ 　　　　 **b.** $\dfrac{\sqrt{2} + 1}{\sqrt{2} - 1}$

15. Solve $(x - 3)^2 - 3(x - 3) - 4 = 0$.

16. Solve $\dfrac{10}{(2x + 4)^2} - \dfrac{1}{2x + 4} = 3$

17. Solve $\dfrac{5}{x + 1} < -2$.

18. Graph $f(x) = (x + 2)^2 - 6$. Find the vertex and axis of symmetry.

19. A rock is thrown upward from the ground. Its height in feet above ground after t seconds is given by the function $f(t) = -16t^2 + 20t$. Find the maximum height of the rock and the number of seconds it takes for the rock to reach its maximum height.

20. Find the vertex of $f(x) = x^2 + 3x - 18$.

21. If $f(x) = x^2$ and $g(x) = x + 3$, find each composition.
   a. $(f \circ g)(2)$ and $(g \circ f)(2)$
   b. $(f \circ g)(x)$ and $(g \circ f)(x)$

22. Find the inverse of $f(x) = -2x + 3$.

23. Find the inverse of the one-to-one function.
   $f = \{(0, 1), (-2, 7), (3, -6), (4, 4)\}$.

24. If $f(x) = x^2 - 2$ and $g(x) = x + 1$, find each composition.
   a. $(f \circ g)(2)$ and $(g \circ f)(2)$
   b. $(f \circ g)(x)$ and $(g \circ f)(x)$

25. Solve each equation for x.
   a. $2^x = 16$ 　　 **b.** $9^x = 27$ 　　 **c.** $4^{x+3} = 8^x$

26. Solve each equation.
   a. $\log_2 32 = x$ 　　　　 **b.** $\log_4 \dfrac{1}{64} = x$
   c. $\log_{1/2} x = 5$

27. Simplify.
   a. $\log_3 3^2$ 　　　　 **b.** $\log_7 7^{-1}$
   c. $5^{\log_5 3}$ 　　　　 **d.** $2^{\log_2 6}$

28. Solve each equation for x.
   a. $4^x = 64$ 　　 **b.** $8^x = 32$ 　　 **c.** $9^{x+4} = 243^x$

29. Write each sum as a single logarithm.
   a. $\log_{11} 10 + \log_{11} 3$
   b. $\log_3 \dfrac{1}{2} + \log_3 12$
   c. $\log_2(x + 2) + \log_2 x$

30. Find the exact value.
   a. $\log 100{,}000$ 　　　　 **b.** $\log 10^{-3}$
   c. $\ln \sqrt[5]{e}$ 　　　　 **d.** $\ln e^4$

31. Find the amount owed at the end of 5 years if \$1600 is loaned at a rate of 9% compounded continuously.

32. Write each expression as a single logarithm.
   a. $\log_6 5 + \log_6 4$
   b. $\log_8 12 - \log_8 4$
   c. $2 \log_2 x + 3 \log_2 x - 2 \log_2(x - 1)$

33. Solve: $3^x = 7$.

34. Using $A = P\left(1 + \dfrac{r}{n}\right)^{nt}$, find how long it takes \$5000 to double if it is invested at 2% interest compounded quarterly. Round to the nearest tenth.

35. Solve $\log_4(x - 2) = 2$.

36. Solve $\log_4 10 - \log_4 x = 2$.

37. Graph $\dfrac{x^2}{16} - \dfrac{y^2}{25} = 1$.

38. Find the distance between $(8, 5)$ and $(-2, 4)$.

39. Solve the system $\begin{cases} y = \sqrt{x} \\ x^2 + y^2 = 6 \end{cases}$.

40. Solve the system $\begin{cases} x^2 + y^2 = 36 \\ x - y = 6 \end{cases}$.

41. Graph $\dfrac{x^2}{9} + \dfrac{y^2}{16} \le 1$.

42. Graph $\begin{cases} y \ge x^2 \\ y \le 4 \end{cases}$.

43. Write the first five terms of the sequence whose general term is given by $a_n = n^2 - 1$.

44. If the general term of a sequence is $a_n = \dfrac{n}{n + 4}$, find a_8.

45. Find the eleventh term of the arithmetic sequence whose first three terms are $2, 9,$ and 16.

46. Find the sixth term of the geometric sequence $2, 10, 50, \ldots$.

47. Evaluate.
   a. $\displaystyle\sum_{i=0}^{6} \frac{i - 2}{2}$ 　　　　 **b.** $\displaystyle\sum_{i=3}^{5} 2^i$

48. Evaluate.
   a. $\displaystyle\sum_{i=0}^{4} i(i + 1)$ 　　　　 **b.** $\displaystyle\sum_{i=0}^{3} 2^i$

49. Find the sum of the first 30 positive integers.

50. Find the third term of the expansion of $(x - y)^6$.

Appendix A

Operations on Decimals/Table of Percent, Decimal, and Fraction Equivalents

A.1 Operations on Decimals

To **add** or **subtract** decimals, write the numbers vertically with decimal points lined up. Add or subtract as with whole numbers and place the decimal point in the answer directly below the decimal points in the problem.

EXAMPLE 1 Add $5.87 + 23.279 + 0.003$.

Solution
$$
\begin{array}{r}
5.87 \\
23.279 \\
+\,0.003 \\
\hline
29.152
\end{array}
$$
☐

EXAMPLE 2 Subtract $32.15 - 11.237$.

Solution
$$
\begin{array}{cccccc}
 & 3 & 2.\overset{1}{\cancel{2}} & .\overset{11}{\cancel{1}} & \overset{4}{\cancel{5}} & \overset{10}{\cancel{0}} \\
- & 1 & 1 & . 2 & 3 & 7 \\
\hline
 & 2 & 0 & . 9 & 1 & 3
\end{array}
$$
☐

To **multiply** decimals, multiply the numbers as if they were whole numbers. The decimal point in the product is placed so that the number of decimal places in the product is the same as the sum of the number of decimal places in the factors.

EXAMPLE 3 Multiply 0.072×3.5.

Solution
$$
\begin{array}{rl}
0.072 & \text{3 decimal places} \\
\times \quad 3.5 & \text{1 decimal place} \\
\hline
360 & \\
216 \quad & \\
\hline
0.2520 & \text{4 decimal places}
\end{array}
$$
☐

To **divide** decimals, move the decimal point in the divisor to the right of the last digit. Move the decimal point in the dividend the same number of places that the decimal point in the divisor was moved. The decimal point in the quotient lies directly above the decimal point in the dividend.

EXAMPLE 4 Divide $9.46 \div 0.04$.

Solution
$$
\begin{array}{r}
236.5 \\
04.\overline{)946.0} \\
\underline{-8} \\
14 \\
\underline{-12} \\
26 \\
\underline{-24} \\
20 \\
\underline{-20}
\end{array}
$$
☐

A Exercise Set

MyMathLab®

Perform the indicated operations.

1. 9.076 + 8.004

2.   6.3
    × 0.05

3.   27.004
   −14.2

4.   0.0036
   7.12
   32.502
   + 0.05

5. 107.92
   + 3.04

6. 7.2 ÷ 4

7. 10 − 7.6

8. 40 ÷ 0.25

9. 126.32 − 97.89

10.   3.62
   7.11
   12.36
   4.15
   + 2.29

11.   3.25
   × 70

12. 26.014
   − 7.8

13. 8.1 ÷ 3

14. 1.2366
   0.005
   15.17
   + 0.97

15. 55.405 − 6.1711

16. 8.09 + 0.22

17. 60 ÷ 0.75

18. 20 − 12.29

19. 7.612 ÷ 100

20.   8.72
    1.12
   14.86
    3.98
   + 1.99

21. 12.312 ÷ 2.7

22. 0.443 ÷ 100

23.   569.2
   71.25
   +   8.01

24. 3.706 − 2.91

25. 768 − 0.17

26. 63 ÷ 0.28

27. 12 + 0.062

28. 0.42 + 18

29. 76 − 14.52

30. 1.1092 ÷ 0.47

31. 3.311 ÷ 0.43

32. 7.61 + 0.0004

33.   762.12
   89.7
   + 11.55

34. 444 ÷ 0.6

35. 23.4 − 0.821

36. 3.7 + 5.6

37. 476.12 − 112.97

38. 19.872 ÷ 0.54

39. 0.007 + 7

40.   51.77
   + 3.6

A.2 Table of Percent, Decimal, and Fraction Equivalents

Percent, Decimal, and Fraction Equivalents		
Percent	*Decimal*	*Fraction*
1%	0.01	$\frac{1}{100}$
5%	0.05	$\frac{1}{20}$
10%	0.1	$\frac{1}{10}$
12.5% or $12\frac{1}{2}$%	0.125	$\frac{1}{8}$
$16.\overline{6}$% or $16\frac{2}{3}$%	$0.1\overline{6}$	$\frac{1}{6}$
20%	0.2	$\frac{1}{5}$
25%	0.25	$\frac{1}{4}$
30%	0.3	$\frac{3}{10}$
$33.\overline{3}$% or $33\frac{1}{3}$%	$0.\overline{3}$	$\frac{1}{3}$
37.5% or $37\frac{1}{2}$%	0.375	$\frac{3}{8}$
40%	0.4	$\frac{2}{5}$
50%	0.5	$\frac{1}{2}$
60%	0.6	$\frac{3}{5}$
62.5% or $62\frac{1}{2}$%	0.625	$\frac{5}{8}$
$66.\overline{6}$% or $66\frac{2}{3}$%	$0.\overline{6}$	$\frac{2}{3}$
70%	0.7	$\frac{7}{10}$
75%	0.75	$\frac{3}{4}$
80%	0.8	$\frac{4}{5}$
$83.\overline{3}$% or $83\frac{1}{3}$%	$08.\overline{3}$	$\frac{5}{6}$
87.5% or $87\frac{1}{2}$%	0.875	$\frac{7}{8}$
90%	0.9	$\frac{9}{10}$
100%	1.0	1
110%	1.1	$1\frac{1}{10}$
125%	1.25	$1\frac{1}{4}$
$133.\overline{3}$% or $133\frac{1}{3}$%	$1.\overline{3}$	$1\frac{1}{3}$
150%	1.5	$1\frac{1}{2}$
$166.\overline{6}$% or $166\frac{2}{3}$%	$1.\overline{6}$	$1\frac{2}{3}$
175%	1.75	$1\frac{3}{4}$
200%	2.0	2

Appendix B

Review of Algebra Topics

Recall that equations model many real-life problems. For example, we can use a linear equation to calculate the increase in the number (in millions) of Wi-Fi-enabled cell phones.

Wi-Fi-enabled cell phones let you carry your Internet access with you. There are already several of these smart phones available, and this technology will continue to expand. Predicted numbers of Wi-Fi-enabled cell phones in the United States for various years are shown below.

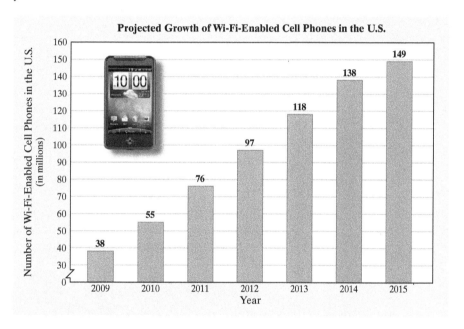

Projected Growth of Wi-Fi-Enabled Cell Phones in the U.S.

To find the projected increase in the number of Wi-Fi-enabled cell phones in the United States from 2014 to 2015, for example, we can use the equation below.

In words:	Increase in cell phones	is	cell phones in 2015	minus	cell phones in 2014
Translate:	x	$=$	149	$-$	138

Since our variable x (increase in Wi-Fi-enabled cell phones) is by itself on one side of the equation, we can find the value of x by simplifying the right side.

$$x = 11$$

The projected increase in the number of Wi-Fi-enabled cell phones from 2014 to 2015 is 11 million.

The **equation** $x = 149 - 138$ is a linear equation in one variable. In this section, we review solving linear equations and quadratic equations that can be solved by factoring. We will learn other methods for solving quadratic equations in Chapter 11.

B.1 Equations (Linear and Quadratic Solved by Factoring)

OBJECTIVE

1 Solving Linear and Quadratic Equations

EXAMPLE 1 Solve: $2(x - 3) = 5x - 9$.

Solution First, use the distributive property.

$$2(x - 3) = 5x - 9$$

$$2x - 6 = 5x - 9 \quad \text{Use the distributive property.}$$

Next, get variable terms on the same side of the equation by subtracting $5x$ from both sides.

$$2x - 6 - 5x = 5x - 9 - 5x \quad \text{Subtract } 5x \text{ from both sides.}$$
$$-3x - 6 = -9 \quad \text{Simplify.}$$
$$-3x - 6 + 6 = -9 + 6 \quad \text{Add 6 to both sides.}$$
$$-3x = -3 \quad \text{Simplify.}$$
$$\frac{-3x}{-3} = \frac{-3}{-3} \quad \text{Divide both sides by } -3.$$
$$x = 1$$

Let $x = 1$ in the original equation to see that 1 is the solution. $\square$

PRACTICE

1 Solve: $3(x - 5) = 6x - 3$.

Don't forget, if an equation contains fractions, you may want to first clear the equation of fractions by multiplying both sides of the equation by the *least common denominator* (LCD) of all fractions in the equation.

EXAMPLE 2 Solve for y: $\dfrac{y}{3} - \dfrac{y}{4} = \dfrac{1}{6}$.

Solution First, clear the equation of fractions by multiplying both sides of the equation by 12, the LCD of denominators 3, 4, and 6.

$$\frac{y}{3} - \frac{y}{4} = \frac{1}{6}$$

$$12\left(\frac{y}{3} - \frac{y}{4}\right) = 12\left(\frac{1}{6}\right) \quad \text{Multiply both sides by the LCD 12.}$$

$$12\left(\frac{y}{3}\right) - 12\left(\frac{y}{4}\right) = 2 \quad \text{Apply the distributive property.}$$

$$4y - 3y = 2 \quad \text{Simplify.}$$

$$y = 2 \quad \text{Simplify.}$$

Check: To check, let $y = 2$ in the original equation.

$$\frac{y}{3} - \frac{y}{4} = \frac{1}{6} \quad \text{Original equation.}$$

$$\frac{2}{3} - \frac{2}{4} \stackrel{?}{=} \frac{1}{6} \quad \text{Let } y = 2.$$

$$\frac{8}{12} - \frac{6}{12} \stackrel{?}{=} \frac{1}{6} \quad \text{Write fractions with the LCD.}$$

$$\frac{2}{12} \stackrel{?}{=} \frac{1}{6} \quad \text{Subtract.}$$

$$\frac{1}{6} = \frac{1}{6} \quad \text{Simplify.}$$

This is a true statement, so the solution is 2.

PRACTICE
2 Solve for y: $\dfrac{y}{2} - \dfrac{y}{5} = \dfrac{1}{4}$.

EXAMPLE 3 Solve: $3(x^2 + 4) + 5 = -6(x^2 + 2x) + 13$.

Solution Rewrite the equation so that one side is 0.

$$3(x^2 + 4) + 5 = -6(x^2 + 2x) + 13$$

$$3x^2 + 12 + 5 = -6x^2 - 12x + 13 \qquad \text{Apply the distributive property.}$$

$$9x^2 + 12x + 4 = 0 \qquad \text{Rewrite the equation so that one side is 0.}$$

$$(3x + 2)(3x + 2) = 0 \qquad \text{Factor.}$$

$$3x + 2 = 0 \quad \text{or} \quad 3x + 2 = 0 \qquad \text{Set each factor equal to 0.}$$

$$3x = -2 \quad \text{or} \qquad 3x = -2$$

$$x = -\frac{2}{3} \quad \text{or} \qquad x = -\frac{2}{3} \qquad \text{Solve each equation.}$$

The solution is $-\dfrac{2}{3}$. Check by substituting $-\dfrac{2}{3}$ into the original equation.

PRACTICE
3 Solve: $8(x^2 + 3) + 4 = -8x(x + 3) + 19$.

EXAMPLE 4 Solve for x: $\dfrac{x + 5}{2} + \dfrac{1}{2} = 2x - \dfrac{x - 3}{8}$.

Solution Multiply both sides of the equation by 8, the LCD of 2 and 8.

$$8\left(\frac{x + 5}{2} + \frac{1}{2}\right) = 8\left(2x - \frac{x - 3}{8}\right) \qquad \text{Multiply both sides by 8.}$$

$$8\left(\frac{x + 5}{2}\right) + 8 \cdot \frac{1}{2} = 8 \cdot 2x - 8\left(\frac{x - 3}{8}\right) \qquad \text{Apply the distributive property.}$$

$$4(x + 5) + 4 = 16x - (x - 3) \qquad \text{Simplify.}$$

$$4x + 20 + 4 = 16x - x + 3 \qquad \text{Use the distributive property to remove parentheses.}$$

$$4x + 24 = 15x + 3 \qquad \text{Combine like terms.}$$

$$-11x + 24 = 3 \qquad \text{Subtract } 15x \text{ from both sides.}$$

$$-11x = -21 \qquad \text{Subtract 24 from both sides.}$$

$$\frac{-11x}{-11} = \frac{-21}{-11} \qquad \text{Divide both sides by } -11.$$

$$x = \frac{21}{11} \qquad \text{Simplify.}$$

> **Helpful Hint**
> When we multiply both sides of an equation by a number, the distributive property tells us that each term of the equation is multiplied by the number.

Check: To check, verify that replacing x with $\dfrac{21}{11}$ makes the original equation true. The solution is $\dfrac{21}{11}$.

PRACTICE
4 Solve for x: $x - \dfrac{x - 2}{12} = \dfrac{x + 3}{4} + \dfrac{1}{4}$.

EXAMPLE 5 Solve: $2x^2 = \dfrac{17}{3}x + 1$.

Solution

$$2x^2 = \dfrac{17}{3}x + 1$$

$$3(2x^2) = 3\left(\dfrac{17}{3}x + 1\right) \qquad \text{Clear the equation of fractions.}$$

$$6x^2 = 17x + 3 \qquad \text{Apply the distributive property.}$$

$$6x^2 - 17x - 3 = 0 \qquad \text{Rewrite the equation in standard form.}$$

$$(6x + 1)(x - 3) = 0 \qquad \text{Factor.}$$

$$6x + 1 = 0 \quad \text{or} \quad x - 3 = 0 \qquad \text{Set each factor equal to zero.}$$

$$6x = -1$$

$$x = -\dfrac{1}{6} \quad \text{or} \qquad x = 3 \qquad \text{Solve each equation.}$$

The solutions are $-\dfrac{1}{6}$ and 3.

PRACTICE
5 Solve: $4x^2 = \dfrac{15}{2}x + 1$.

B.1 Exercise Set MyMathLab®

MIXED PRACTICE

Solve each equation. See Examples 1 through 5.

1. $x^2 + 11x + 24 = 0$
2. $y^2 - 10y + 24 = 0$
3. $3x - 4 - 5x = x + 4 + x$
4. $13x - 15x + 8 = 4x + 2 - 24$
5. $12x^2 + 5x - 2 = 0$
6. $3y^2 - y - 14 = 0$
7. $z^2 + 9 = 10z$
8. $n^2 + n = 72$
9. $5(y + 4) = 4(y + 5)$
10. $6(y - 4) = 3(y - 8)$
11. $0.6x - 10 = 1.4x - 14$
12. $0.3x + 2.4 = 0.1x + 4$
13. $x(5x + 2) = 3$
14. $n(2n - 3) = 2$
15. $6x - 2(x - 3) = 4(x + 1) + 4$
16. $10x - 2(x + 4) = 8(x - 2) + 6$
17. $\dfrac{3}{8} + \dfrac{b}{3} = \dfrac{5}{12}$
18. $\dfrac{a}{2} + \dfrac{7}{4} = 5$
19. $x^2 - 6x = x(8 + x)$
20. $n(3 + n) = n^2 + 4n$
21. $\dfrac{z^2}{6} - \dfrac{z}{2} - 3 = 0$

22. $\dfrac{c^2}{20} - \dfrac{c}{4} + \dfrac{1}{5} = 0$
23. $-z + 3(2 + 4z) = 6(z + 1) + 5z$
24. $4(m - 6) - m = 8(m - 3) - 5m$
25. $\dfrac{x^2}{2} + \dfrac{x}{20} = \dfrac{1}{10}$
26. $\dfrac{y^2}{30} = \dfrac{y}{15} + \dfrac{1}{2}$
27. $\dfrac{4t^2}{5} = \dfrac{t}{5} + \dfrac{3}{10}$
28. $\dfrac{5x^2}{6} - \dfrac{7x}{2} + \dfrac{2}{3} = 0$
29. $\dfrac{3t + 1}{8^-} = \dfrac{5 + 2t}{7} + 2$
30. $4 - \dfrac{2z + 7}{9} = \dfrac{7 - z}{12}$
31. $\dfrac{m - 4}{3} - \dfrac{3m - 1}{5} = 1$
32. $\dfrac{n + 1}{8} - \dfrac{2 - n}{3} = \dfrac{5}{6}$
33. $3x^2 = -x$
34. $y^2 = -5y$
35. $x(x - 3) = x^2 + 5x + 7$
36. $z^2 - 4z + 10 = z(z - 5)$
37. $3(t - 8) + 2t = 7 + t$
38. $7c - 2(3c + 1) = 5(4 - 2c)$
39. $-3(x - 4) + x = 5(3 - x)$

40. $-4(a + 1) - 3a = -7(2a - 3)$

41. $(x - 1)(x + 4) = 24$

42. $(2x - 1)(x + 2) = -3$

43. $\dfrac{x^2}{4} - \dfrac{5}{2}x + 6 = 0$

44. $\dfrac{x^2}{18} + \dfrac{x}{2} + 1 = 0$

45. $y^2 + \dfrac{1}{4} = -y$

46. $\dfrac{x^2}{10} + \dfrac{5}{2} = x$

47. Which solution strategies are incorrect? Why?

    a. Solve $(y - 2)(y + 2) = 4$ by setting each factor equal to 4.

    b. Solve $(x + 1)(x + 3) = 0$ by setting each factor equal to 0.

    c. Solve $z^2 + 5z + 6 = 0$ by factoring $z^2 + 5z + 6$ and setting each factor equal to 0.

    d. Solve $x^2 + 6x + 8 = 10$ by factoring $x^2 + 6x + 8$ and setting each factor equal to 0.

48. Describe two ways a linear equation differs from a quadratic equation.

Find the value of K such that the equations are equivalent.

49. $3.2x + 4 = 5.4x - 7$
$3.2x = 5.4x + K$

50. $-7.6y - 10 = -1.1y + 12$
$-7.6y = -1.1y + K$

51. $\dfrac{x}{6} + 4 = \dfrac{x}{3}$
$x + K = 2x$

52. $\dfrac{5x}{4} + \dfrac{1}{2} = \dfrac{x}{2}$
$5x + K = 2x$

Solve and check.

53. $2.569x = -12.48534$

54. $-9.112y = -47.537304$

55. $2.86z - 8.1258 = -3.75$

56. $1.25x - 20.175 = -8.15$

B.2   Problem Solving

OBJECTIVES

1 Write Algebraic Expressions That Can Be Simplified.

2 Apply the Steps for Problem Solving.

OBJECTIVE

1   **Writing and Simplifying Algebraic Expressions**

In order to prepare for problem solving, we practice writing algebraic expressions that can be simplified.

    Our first example involves consecutive integers and perimeter. Recall that *consecutive integers* are integers that follow one another in order. Study the examples of consecutive, even, and odd integers and their representations.

Consecutive Integers: *Consecutive Even Integers:*   *Consecutive Odd Integers:*

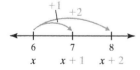 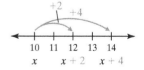 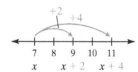

EXAMPLE 1   Write the following as algebraic expressions. Then simplify.

    a. The sum of three consecutive integers, if x is the first consecutive integer.

    b. The perimeter of the triangle with sides of length x, $5x$, and $6x - 3$.

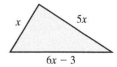

(Continued on next page)

Solution

a. Recall that if x is the first integer, then the next consecutive integer is 1 more, or $x + 1$, and the next consecutive integer is 1 more than $x + 1$, or $x + 2$.

In words:

first integer	plus	next consecutive integer	plus	next consecutive integer
↓	↓	↓	↓	↓

Translate: x $+$ $(x + 1)$ $+$ $(x + 2)$

Then $x + (x + 1) + (x + 2) = x + x + 1 + x + 2$
$$= 3x + 3 \quad \text{Simplify by combining like terms.}$$

b. The perimeter of a triangle is the sum of the lengths of the sides.

In words: side $+$ side $+$ side
      ↓   ↓   ↓

Translate: x $+$ $5x$ $+$ $(6x - 3)$

Then $x + 5x + (6x - 3) = x + 5x + 6x - 3$
$$= 12x - 3 \quad \text{Simplify.} \qquad \square$$

PRACTICE

1   Write the following algebraic expressions. Then simplify.

a. The sum of three consecutive odd integers if x is the first consecutive odd integer

b. The perimeter of a trapezoid with bases x and $2x$ and sides of $x + 2$ and $2x - 3$

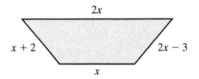

EXAMPLE 2   **Writing Algebraic Expressions Representing Metropolitan Regions**

The most populous metropolitan region in the United States is New York City, although it is only the sixth most populous metropolis in the world. Tokyo is the most populous metropolitan region. Mexico City is the fifth most populous metropolis in the world. Mexico City's population is 0.03 million more than New York's, and Tokyo's is twice that of New York, decreased by 2.19 million. Write the sum of the populations of these three metropolitan regions as an algebraic expression. Let x be the population of New York (in millions). (*Source:* United Nations, Department of Economic and Social Affairs)

Solution:

If x = the population of New York (in millions), then
$$x + 0.03 = \text{the population of Mexico City (in millions) and}$$
$$2x - 2.19 = \text{the population of Tokyo (in millions)}$$

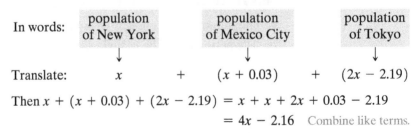

In words:

population of New York		population of Mexico City		population of Tokyo
↓		↓		↓

Translate: x $+$ $(x + 0.03)$ $+$ $(2x - 2.19)$

Then $x + (x + 0.03) + (2x - 2.19) = x + x + 2x + 0.03 - 2.19$
$$= 4x - 2.16 \quad \text{Combine like terms.}$$

In Exercise 57, we will find the actual populations of these cities. $\square$

PRACTICE

2   The three busiest airports in Europe are in London, England; Paris, France; and Frankfurt, Germany. The airport in London has 12.9 million more arrivals and departures than the Frankfurt airport. The Paris airport has 5.2 million more arrivals and departures than the Frankfurt airport. Write the sum of the arrivals and departures from these three cities as a simplified algebraic expression. Let x be the number of arrivals and departures at the Frankfurt airport. (*Source:* Association of European Airlines)

OBJECTIVE

2   Applying Steps for Problem Solving

Our main purpose for studying algebra is to solve problems. The following problem-solving strategy will be used throughout this text and may also be used to solve real-life problems that occur outside the mathematics classroom.

General Strategy for Problem Solving

1. UNDERSTAND the problem. During this step, become comfortable with the problem. Some ways of doing this are to:

Read and reread the problem.

Propose a solution and check. Pay careful attention to how you check your proposed solution. This will help when writing an equation to model the problem.

Construct a drawing.

Choose a variable to represent the unknown. (Very important part)

2. TRANSLATE the problem into an equation.

3. SOLVE the equation.

4. INTERPRET the results: *Check* the proposed solution in the stated problem and *state* your conclusion.

Let's review this strategy by solving a problem involving unknown numbers.

EXAMPLE 3   **Finding Unknown Numbers**

Find three numbers such that the second number is 3 more than twice the first number, and the third number is four times the first number. The sum of the three numbers is 164.

Solution

> **Helpful Hint**
>
> The purpose of guessing a solution is not to guess correctly but to gain confidence and to help understand the problem and how to model it.

1. UNDERSTAND the problem. First let's read and reread the problem and then propose a solution. For example, if the first number is 25, then the second number is 3 more than twice 25, or 53. The third number is four times 25, or 100. The sum of 25, 53, and 100 is 178, not the required sum, but we have gained some valuable information about the problem. First, we know that the first number is less than 25 since our guess led to a sum greater than the required sum. Also, we have gained some information as to how to model the problem.

Next let's assign a variable and use this variable to represent any other unknown quantities. If we let

$$x = \text{the first number, then}$$

$$2x + 3 = \text{the second number}$$

3 more than
twice the first number

$$4x = \text{the third number}$$

(Continued on next page)

2. TRANSLATE the problem into an equation. To do so, we use the fact that the sum of the numbers is 164. First let's write this relationship in words and then translate to an equation.

In words:

first number	added to	second number	added to	third number	is	164
↓	↓	↓	↓	↓	↓	↓

Translate: $\quad x \qquad + \qquad (2x + 3) \qquad + \qquad 4x \qquad = \qquad 164$

3. SOLVE the equation.

$$x + (2x + 3) + 4x = 164$$
$$x + 2x + 4x + 3 = 164 \quad \text{Remove parentheses.}$$
$$7x + 3 = 164 \quad \text{Combine like terms.}$$
$$7x = 161 \quad \text{Subtract 3 from both sides.}$$
$$x = 23 \quad \text{Divide both sides by 7.}$$

4. INTERPRET. Here, we *check* our work and *state* the solution. Recall that if the first number $x = 23$, then the second number $2x + 3 = 2 \cdot 23 + 3 = 49$ and the third number $4x = 4 \cdot 23 = 92$.

Check: Is the second number 3 more than twice the first number? Yes, since 3 more than twice 23 is $46 + 3$, or 49. Also, their sum, $23 + 49 + 92 = 164$, is the required sum.

State: The three numbers are 23, 49, and 92. □

PRACTICE

3 Find three numbers such that the second number is 8 less than triple the first number, the third number is five times the first number, and the sum of the three numbers is 118.

....

Many of today's rates and statistics are given as percents. Interest rates, tax rates, nutrition labeling, and percent of households in a given category are just a few examples. Before we practice solving problems containing percents, let's briefly review the meaning of percent and how to find a percent of a number.

The word *percent* means "per hundred," and the symbol % denotes percent.

This means that 23% is 23 per hundred, or $\dfrac{23}{100}$. Also,

$$41\% = \frac{41}{100} = 0.41$$

To find a percent of a number, we multiply.

$$16\% \text{ of } 25 = 16\% \cdot 25 = 0.16 \cdot 25 = 4$$

Thus, 16% of 25 is 4.

Study the table below. It will help you become more familiar with finding percents.

Percent	*Meaning/Shortcut*	*Example*
50%	$\dfrac{1}{2}$ or half of a number	50% of 60 is 30.
25%	$\dfrac{1}{4}$ or a quarter of a number	25% of 60 is 15.
10%	0.1 or $\dfrac{1}{10}$ of a number (move the decimal point 1 place to the left)	10% of 60 is 6.0 or 6.
1%	0.01 or $\dfrac{1}{100}$ of a number (move the decimal point 2 places to the left)	1% of 60 is 0.60 or 0.6.
100%	1 or all of a number	100% of 60 is 60.
200%	2 or double a number	200% of 60 is 120.

✓CONCEPT CHECK

Suppose you are finding 112% of a number x. Which of the following is a correct description of the result? Explain.

a. The result is less than x.   **b.** The result is equal to x.   **c.** The result is greater than x.

Next, we solve a problem containing a percent.

EXAMPLE 4   **Finding the Original Price of a Computer**

Suppose that a computer store just announced an 8% decrease in the price of a particular computer model. If this computer sells for $2162 after the decrease, find the original price of this computer.

Solution

1. UNDERSTAND. Read and reread the problem. Recall that a percent decrease means a percent of the original price. Let's guess that the original price of the computer is $2500. The amount of decrease is then 8% of $2500, or $(0.08)(\$2500) = \$200$. This means that the new price of the computer is the original price minus the decrease, or $\$2500 - \$200 = \$2300$. Our guess is incorrect, but we now have an idea of how to model this problem. In our model, we will let $x =$ the original price of the computer.

2. TRANSLATE.

In words:	the original price of computer	minus	8% of the original price	is	the new price
	↓	↓	↓	↓	↓
Translate:	x	$-$	$0.08x$	$=$	2162

3. SOLVE the equation.

$$x - 0.08x = 2162$$
$$0.92x = 2162 \qquad \text{Combine like terms.}$$
$$x = \frac{2162}{0.92} = 2350 \quad \text{Divide both sides by 0.92.}$$

4. INTERPRET.

Check: If the original price of the computer was $2350, the new price is
$$\$2350 - (0.08)(\$2350) = \$2350 - \$188$$
$$= \$2162 \qquad \text{The given new price}$$

State: The original price of the computer was $2350.

PRACTICE
4   At the end of the season, the cost of a snowboard was reduced by 40%. If the snowboard sells for $270 after the decrease, find the original price of the board.

Answer to Concept Check:
c; answers may vary

Vocabulary & Readiness Check

Fill in each blank with $<$, $>$, or $=$. (Assume that the unknown number is a positive number.)

1. 130% of a number ___ the number.   **2.** 70% of a number ___ the number.
3. 100% of a number ___ the number.   **4.** 200% of a number ___ the number.

Complete the table. The first row has been completed for you.

	First Integer	All Described Integers
Three consecutive integers	18	18, 19, 20
5. Four consecutive integers	31	
6. Three consecutive odd integers	31	
7. Three consecutive even integers	18	
8. Four consecutive even integers	92	
9. Three consecutive integers	y	
10. Three consecutive even integers	z (z is even)	
11. Four consecutive integers	p	
12. Three consecutive odd integers	s (s is odd)	

B.2 Exercise Set   MyMathLab®

Write the following as algebraic expressions. Then simplify. See Examples 1 and 2.

△ **1.** The perimeter of a square with side length y.

△ **2.** The perimeter of a rectangle with length x and width $x - 5$.

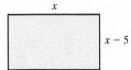

3. The sum of three consecutive integers if the first is z.

4. The sum of three consecutive odd integers if the first integer is z.

5. The total amount of money (in cents) in x nickels, $(x + 3)$ dimes, and $2x$ quarters. (*Hint:* The value of a nickel is 5 cents, the value of a dime is 10 cents, and the value of a quarter is 25 cents.)

6. The total amount of money (in cents) in y quarters, $7y$ dimes, and $(2y - 1)$ nickels. (Use the hint for Exercise 5.)

△ **7.** A piece of land along Bayou Liberty is to be fenced and subdivided as shown so that each rectangle has the same dimensions. Express the total amount of fencing needed as an algebraic expression in x.

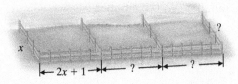

8. A flooded piece of land near the Mississippi River in New Orleans is to be surveyed and divided into 4 rectangles of equal dimension. Express the total amount of fencing needed as an algebraic expression in x.

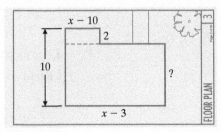

△ **9.** Write the perimeter of the floor plan shown as an algebraic expression in x.

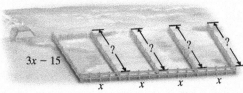

10. Write the perimeter of the floor plan shown as an algebraic expression in x.

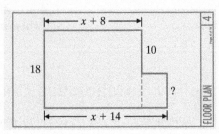

Solve. For Exercises 11 and 12, the solutions have been started for you. See Example 3.

11. Four times the difference of a number and 2 is the same as 2, increased by four times the number, plus twice the number. Find the number.

Start the solution:

1. UNDERSTAND the problem. Reread it as many times as needed.

2. TRANSLATE into an equation. (Fill in the blanks below.)

Four times	the difference of a number and 2	is the same as	2	increased by	four times the number	plus	twice the number
↓	↓	↓	↓	↓	↓	↓	↓
4 ·	$(x - 2)$	=	2	___	___	___	___

Finish with:

3. SOLVE and 4. INTERPRET

12. Twice the sum of a number and 3 is the same as five times the number, minus 1, minus four times the number. Find the number.

Start the solution:

1. UNDERSTAND the problem. Reread it as many times as needed.

2. TRANSLATE into an equation. (Fill in the blanks below.)

Twice	the sum of a number and 3	is the same as	five times the number	minus	1	minus	four times the number
↓	↓	↓	↓	↓	↓	↓	↓
2	$(x + 3)$	=	___	___	1	___	___

Finish with:

3. SOLVE and 4. INTERPRET

13. A second number is five times a first number. A third number is 100 more than the first number. If the sum of the three numbers is 415, find the numbers.

14. A second number is 6 less than a first number. A third number is twice the first number. If the sum of the three numbers is 306, find the numbers.

Solve. See Example 4.

15. The United States consists of 2271 million acres of land. Approximately 29% of this land is federally owned. Find the number of acres that are not federally owned. (*Source:* U.S. General Services Administration)

16. The state of Nevada contains the most federally owned acres of land in the United States. If 90% of the state's 70 million acres of land is federally owned, find the number of acres that are not federally owned. (*Source:* U.S. General Services Administration)

17. In 2010, 8476 earthquakes occurred in the United States. Of these, 91.4% were minor tremors with magnitudes of 3.9 or less on the Richter scale. How many minor earthquakes occurred in the United States in 2010? Round to the nearest whole. (*Source:* U.S. Geological Survey National Earthquake Information Center)

18. Of the 1543 tornadoes that occurred in the United States during 2010, 27.7% occurred during the month of June. How many tornadoes occurred in the United States during June 2010? Round to the nearest whole. (*Source:* Storm Prediction Center)

19. In a recent survey, 15% of online shoppers in the United States say that they prefer to do business only with large, well-known retailers. In a group of 1500 online shoppers, how many are willing to do business with any size retailers? (*Source:* Inc.com)

20. In 2010, the restaurant industry employed 9% of the U.S. workforce. If there are estimated to be 141 million Americans in the workforce, how many people are employed by the restaurant industry? Round to the nearest tenth. (*Source:* National Restaurant Association, U.S. Bureau of Labor Statistics)

The following graph is called a circle graph or a pie chart. The circle represents a whole, or in this case, 100%. This particular graph shows the number of minutes per day that people use email at work. Use this graph to answer Exercises 21 through 24.

Time Spent on Email at Work

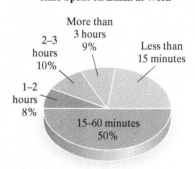

Source: Pew Internet & American Life Project

21. What percent of email users at work spend less than 15 minutes on email per day?

22. Among email users at work, what is the most common time spent on email per day?

23. If it were estimated that a large company has 4633 employees, how many of these would you expect to be using email more than 3 hours per day?

24. If it were estimated that a medium-size company has 250 employees, how many of these would you expect to be using email between 2 and 3 hours per day?

MIXED PRACTICE

Use the diagrams to find the unknown measures of angles or lengths of sides. Recall that the sum of the angle measures of a triangle is 180°.

25.
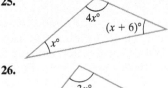

26.
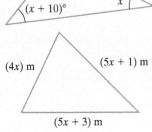

27.
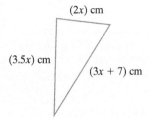

Perimeter is 102 meters.

28. (2x) cm

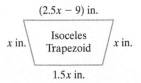

Perimeter is 75 centimeters.

29.
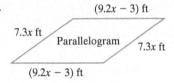

Perimeter is 99 inches.

30.

(9.2x − 3) ft

7.3x ft   Parallelogram   7.3x ft

(9.2x − 3) ft

Perimeter is 324 feet.

Solve.

31. The sum of three consecutive integers is 228. Find the integers.

32. The sum of three consecutive odd integers is 327. Find the integers.

33. The ZIP codes of three Nevada locations—Fallon, Fernley, and Gardnerville Ranchos—are three consecutive even integers. If twice the first integer added to the third is 268,222, find each ZIP code.

34. During a recent year, the average SAT scores in math for the states of Alabama, Louisiana, and Michigan were 3 consecutive integers. If the sum of the first integer, second integer, and three times the third integer is 2637, find each score.

Many companies predict the growth or decline of various technologies. The following data is based on information from Techcrunchies, a technological information site. Notice that the first table is the predicted increase in the number of Wi-Fi-enabled cell phones (in millions), and the second is the predicted percent increase in the number of Wi-Fi-enabled cell phones in the United States.

35. Use the middle column in the table to find the predicted number of Wi-Fi-enabled cell phones for each year.

Year	Increase in Wi-Fi-Enabled Cell Phones	Predicted Number
2010	$2x - 21$	
2012	$\frac{5}{2}x + 2$	
2014	$3x + 24$	
Total	290 million	

36. Use the middle column in the table to find the predicted percent increase in the number of Wi-Fi-enabled cell phones for each year.

Year	Percent Increase in Wi-Fi-Enabled Cell Phones since 2009	Predicted Percent Increase
2010	x	
2011	$2x + 10$	
2012	$4x - 25$	
	300%	

Solve.

37. The occupations of biomedical engineers, skin care specialists, and physician assistants are among the 10 with the largest growth from 2008 to 2018. The number of physician assistant jobs will grow 7 thousand less than three times the number of biomedical engineer jobs. The number of skin care specialist jobs will grow 9 thousand more than half the number of biomedical engineer jobs. If the total growth of these three jobs is predicted to be 56 thousand, find the predicted growth of each job. (*Source:* U.S. Department of Labor, Bureau of Labor Statistics)

38. The occupations of farmer or rancher, file clerk, and telemarketer are among the 10 jobs with the largest decline from 2008 to 2018. The number of file clerk jobs is predicted to decline 11 thousand more than the number of telemarketer jobs. The number of farmer or rancher jobs is predicted to decline 3 thousand more than twice the number of telemarketer jobs. If the total decline of these three jobs is predicted to be 166 thousand, find the predicted decline of each job. (*Source:* U.S. Department of Labor, Bureau of Labor Statistics)

39. The B767-300ER aircraft has 88 more seats than the B737-200 aircraft. The F-100 has 32 fewer seats than the B737-200 aircraft. If their total number of seats is 413, find the number of seats for each aircraft. (*Source:* Air Transport Association of America)

40. Cowboy Stadium, home of the Dallas Cowboys of the NFL, seats approximately 9800 more fans than does Candlestick Park, home of the San Francisco 49ers. Soldier Field, home of the Chicago Bears, seats 8700 fewer fans than Candlestick Park. If the total seats in these three stadiums is 211,700, how many seats are in each of the three stadiums?

41. A new fax machine was recently purchased for an office in Hopedale for $464.40 including tax. If the tax rate in Hopedale is 8%, find the price of the fax machine before tax.

42. A premedical student at a local university was complaining that she had just paid $158.60 for her human anatomy book, including tax. Find the price of the book before taxes if the tax rate at this university is 9%.

43. The median compensation for a U.S. university president was $436,000 for the 2008–2009 academic year. Calculate the salary of a university president who received a 2.3% raise.

44. In 2009, the population of Brazil was 191.5 million. This represented a decrease in population of 3.7% from 2000. What was the population of Brazil in 2000? Round to the nearest tenth of a million. (*Source:* Population Reference Bureau)

45. In 2010, the population of Swaziland was 1,200,000 people. From 2010 to 2050, Swaziland's population is expected to increase by 50%. Find the expected population of Swaziland in 2050. (*Source:* Population Reference Bureau)

46. Dana, an auto parts supplier headquartered in Toledo, Ohio, recently announced it would be cutting 11,000 jobs worldwide. This is equivalent to 15% of Dana's workforce. Find the size of Dana's workforce prior to this round of job layoffs. Round to the nearest whole. (*Source:* Dana Corporation)

Recall that two angles are complements of each other if their sum is 90°. Two angles are supplements of each other if their sum is 180°. Find the measure of each angle.

47. One angle is three times its supplement increased by 20°. Find the measures of the two supplementary angles.

48. One angle is twice its complement increased by 30°. Find the measure of the two complementary angles.

Recall that the sum of the angle measures of a triangle is 180°.

49. Find the measures of the angles of a triangle if the measure of one angle is twice the measure of a second angle and the third angle measures 3 times the second angle decreased by 12.

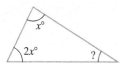

50. Find the angles of an isoceles triangle whose two base angles are equal and whose third angle is 10° less than three times a base angle.

51. Two frames are needed with the same perimeter: one frame in the shape of a square and one in the shape of an equilateral triangle. Each side of the triangle is 6 centimeters longer than each side of the square. Find the dimensions of each frame. (An equilateral triangle has sides that are the same length.)

52. Two frames are needed with the same perimeter: one frame in the shape of a square and one in the shape of a regular pentagon. Each side of the square is 7 inches longer than each side of the pentagon. Find the dimensions of each frame. (A regular polygon has sides that are the same length.)

53. The sum of the first and third of three consecutive even integers is 156. Find the three even integers.

54. The sum of the second and fourth of four consecutive integers is 110. Find the four integers.

55. Daytona International Speedway in Florida has 37,000 more grandstand seats than twice the number of grandstand seats at Darlington Motor Raceway in South Carolina. Together, these two race tracks seat 220,000 NASCAR fans. How many seats does each race track have? (*Source:* NASCAR)

56. For the 2010–2011 National Hockey League season, the payroll for the San Jose Sharks was $5,986,667 more than that for the Montreal Canadiens. The total payroll for these two teams was $113,103,333. What were the payrolls for these two teams for the 2010–2011 NHL season?

57. The sum of the populations of the metropolitan regions of New York, Tokyo, and Mexico City is 75.56 million. Use this information and Example 2 in this section to find the population of each metropolitan region. (*Source:* United Nations Department of Economic and Social Affairs)

58. The airports in London, Paris, and Frankfurt have a total of 177.1 million annual arrivals and departures. Use this information and Practice 2 in this section to find the number from each airport.

59. Suppose the perimeter of the triangle in Example 1b in this section is 483 feet. Find the length of each side.

60. Suppose the perimeter of the trapezoid in Practice 1b in this section is 110 meters. Find the lengths of its sides and bases.

61. Incandescent, fluorescent, and halogen bulbs are lasting longer today than ever before. On average, the number of bulb hours for a fluorescent bulb is 25 times the number of bulb hours for a halogen bulb. The number of bulb hours for an incandescent bulb is 2500 less than the halogen bulb. If the total number of bulb hours for the three types of bulbs is 105,500, find the number of bulb hours for each type. (*Source: Popular Science* magazine)

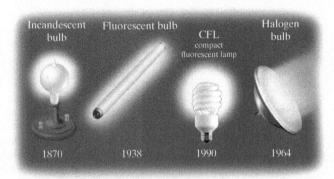

62. Falkland Islands, Iceland, and Norway are the top three countries that have the greatest Internet penetration rate (percent of population) in the world. Falkland Islands has a 6.8 percent greater penetration rate than Iceland. Norway has a 2.3 percent less penetration rate than Iceland. If the sum of the penetration rates is 284.1, find the Internet penetration rate in each of these countries. (*Source*: Internet World Stats)

63. During the 2010 Major League Baseball season, the number of wins for the Milwaukee Brewers, Houston Astros, and Chicago Cubs was three consecutive integers. Of these three teams, the Milwaukee Brewers had the most wins. The Chicago Cubs had the least wins. The total number of wins by these three teams was 228. How many wins did each team have in the 2010 season?

64. In the 2010 Winter Olympics, Austria won more medals than the Russian Federation, which won more medals than South Korea. If the numbers of medals won by these three countries is three consecutive integers whose sum is 45, find the number of medals won by each. (*Source*: Vancouver 2010)

65. The three tallest hospitals in the world are Guy's Tower in London, Queen Mary Hospital in Hong Kong, and Galter Pavilion in Chicago. These buildings have a total height of 1320 feet. Guy's Tower is 67 feet taller than Galter Pavilion, and the Queen Mary Hospital is 47 feet taller than Galter Pavilion. Find the heights of the three hospitals.

△ **66.** The official manual for traffic signs is the *Manual on Uniform Traffic Control Devices* published by the Government Printing Office. The rectangular sign below has a length 12 inches more than twice its height. If the perimeter of the sign is 312 inches, find its dimensions.

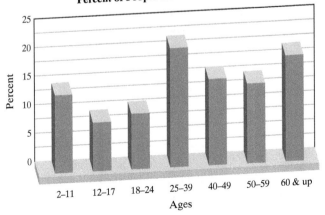

B.3 Graphing

OBJECTIVES

1 Plot Ordered Pairs.
2 Graph Linear Equations.

OBJECTIVE

1 Plotting Ordered Pairs

Graphs are widely used today in newspapers, magazines, and all forms of newsletters. A few examples of graphs are shown here.

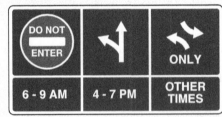

Percent of People Who Go to the Movies

Source: Motion Picture Association of America

**Projected Growth of Wi-Fi-Enabled
Cell Phones in U.S.**

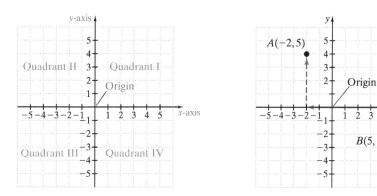

Source: Techcrunchies.com   * (projected)

To review how to read these graphs, we review their origin — the rectangular coordinate system. One way to locate points on a plane is by using a **rectangular coordinate system,** which is also called a **Cartesian coordinate system** after its inventor, René Descartes (1596–1650). The next diagram to the left shows the rectangular coordinate system. For further review of this system, see Section 3.1.

Recall that the location of point A in the figure above is described as 2 units to the left of the origin along the x-axis and 5 units upward parallel to the y-axis. Thus, we identify point A with the ordered pair $(-2, 5)$. Notice that the order of these numbers is *critical.* The x-value -2 is called the **x-coordinate** and is associated with the x-axis. The y-value 5 is called the **y-coordinate** and is associated with the y-axis. Compare the location of point A with the location of point B, which corresponds to the ordered pair $(5, -2)$.

Keep in mind that **each ordered pair corresponds to exactly one point in the real plane and that each point in the plane corresponds to exactly one ordered pair.** Thus, we may refer to the ordered pair (x, y) as the point (x, y).

EXAMPLE 1   Plot each ordered pair on a Cartesian coordinate system and name the quadrant or axis in which the point is located.

a. $(2, -1)$ **b.** $(0, 5)$ **c.** $(-3, 5)$

d. $(-2, 0)$ **e.** $\left(-\dfrac{1}{2}, -4\right)$ **f.** $(1.5, 1.5)$

Solution   The six points are graphed as shown on the next page.

a. $(2, -1)$ is in quadrant IV. **b.** $(0, 5)$ is on the y-axis.

c. $(-3, 5)$ is in quadrant II. **d.** $(-2, 0)$ is on the x-axis.

e. $\left(-\dfrac{1}{2}, -4\right)$ is in quadrant III. **f.** $(1.5, 1.5)$ is in quadrant I.

(Continued on next page)

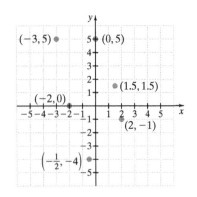

PRACTICE

1 Plot each ordered pair on a Cartesian coordinate system and name the quadrant or axis in which the point is located.

a. $(3, -4)$ **b.** $(0, -2)$ **c.** $(-2, 4)$ **d.** $(4, 0)$ **e.** $\left(-1\frac{1}{2}, -2\right)$ **f.** $(2.5, 3.5)$

Notice that the y-coordinate of any point on the x-axis is 0. For example, the point with coordinates $(-2, 0)$ lies on the x-axis. Also, the x-coordinate of any point on the y-axis is 0. For example, the point with coordinates $(0, 5)$ lies on the y-axis. These points that lie on the axes do not lie in any quadrants.

✓CONCEPT CHECK

Which of the following correctly describes the location of the point $(3, -6)$ in a rectangular coordinate system?

a. 3 units to the left of the y-axis and 6 units above the x-axis
b. 3 units above the x-axis and 6 units to the left of the y-axis
c. 3 units to the right of the y-axis and 6 units below the x-axis
d. 3 units below the x-axis and 6 units to the right of the y-axis

---

OBJECTIVE

2 Graphing Linear Equations

Recall that an equation such as $3x - y = 12$ is called a linear equation in two variables, and **the graph of every linear equation in two variables is a line.**

> **Linear Equation in Two Variables**
>
> A linear equation in two variables is an equation that can be written in the form
>
> $$Ax + By = C$$
>
> where A and B are not both 0. This form is called **standard form.**

Some examples of equations in standard form:

$$3x - y = 12$$
$$-2.1x + 5.6y = 0$$

> ▶ **Helpful Hint**
>
> Remember: A linear equation is written in standard form when all of the variable terms are on one side of the equation and the constant is on the other side.

Answer to Concept Check:
c

EXAMPLE 2   Graph the equation $y = -2x + 3$.

Solution   This is a linear equation. (In standard form it is $2x + y = 3$.) Find three ordered pair solutions, and plot the ordered pairs. The line through the plotted points is the graph. Since the equation is solved for y, let's choose three x-values. We'll choose $0, 2$, and then -1 for x to find our three ordered pair solutions.

Let $x = 0$	Let $x = 2$	Let $x = -1$
$y = -2x + 3$	$y = -2x + 3$	$y = -2x + 3$
$y = -2 \cdot 0 + 3$	$y = -2 \cdot 2 + 3$	$y = -2(-1) + 3$
$y = 3$ Simplify.	$y = -1$ Simplify.	$y = 5$ Simplify.

The three ordered pairs $(0, 3)$, $(2, -1)$, and $(-1, 5)$ are listed in the table and the graph is shown.

x	y
0	3
2	-1
-1	5

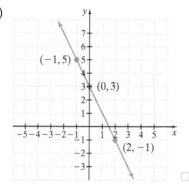

PRACTICE
2   Graph the equation $y = -3x - 2$.

Notice that the graph crosses the y-axis at the point $(0, 3)$. This point is called the **y-intercept.** (You may sometimes see just the number 3 called the y-intercept.) This graph also crosses the x-axis at the point $\left(\dfrac{3}{2}, 0\right)$. This point is called the **x-intercept.** (You may also see just the number $\dfrac{3}{2}$ called the x-intercept.)

Since every point on the y-axis has an x-value of 0, we can find the y-intercept of a graph by letting $x = 0$ and solving for y. Also, every point on the x-axis has a y-value of 0. To find the x-intercept, we let $y = 0$ and solve for x.

Finding x- and y-Intercepts

To find an x-intercept, let $y = 0$ and solve for x.
To find a y-intercept, let $x = 0$ and solve for y.

EXAMPLE 3   Graph the linear equation $y = \dfrac{1}{3}x$.

Solution   To graph, we find ordered pair solutions, plot the ordered pairs, and draw a line through the plotted points. We will choose x-values and substitute in the equation. To avoid fractions, we choose x-values that are multiples of 3. To find the y-intercept, we let $x = 0$.

▶ **Helpful Hint**
Notice that by using multiples of 3 for x, we avoid fractions.

▶ **Helpful Hint**
Since the equation $y = \dfrac{1}{3}x$ is solved for y, we choose x-values for finding points. This way, we simply need to evaluate an expression to find the y-value, as shown.

$$y = \frac{1}{3}x$$

If $x = 0$, then $y = \dfrac{1}{3}(0)$, or 0.

If $x = 6$, then $y = \dfrac{1}{3}(6)$, or 2.

If $x = -3$, then $y = \dfrac{1}{3}(-3)$, or -1.

x	y
0	0
6	2
-3	-1

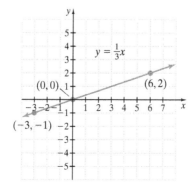

(Continued on next page)

This graph crosses the *x*-axis at $(0, 0)$ and the *y*-axis at $(0, 0)$. This means that the *x*-intercept is $(0, 0)$ and that the *y*-intercept is $(0, 0)$.

PRACTICE
3 Graph the linear equation $y = -\frac{1}{2}x$.

B.3 Exercise Set MyMathLab®

Determine the coordinates of each point on the graph.

1. Point *A*
2. Point *B*
3. Point *C*
4. Point *D*
5. Point *E*
6. Point *F*
7. Point *G*
8. Point *H*

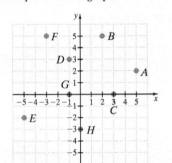

Without graphing, visualize the location of each point. Then give its location by quadrant or x- or y-axis. See Example 1.

9. $(2, 3)$
10. $(0, 5)$
11. $(-2, 7)$
12. $(-3, 0)$
13. $(-1, -4)$
14. $(4, -2)$
15. $(0, -100)$
16. $(10, 30)$
17. $(-10, -30)$
18. $(0, 0)$
19. $(-87, 0)$
20. $(-42, 17)$

Given that x is a positive number and that y is a positive number, determine the quadrant or axis in which each point lies.

21. $(x, -y)$
22. $(-x, y)$
23. $(x, 0)$
24. $(0, -y)$
25. $(-x, -y)$
26. $(0, 0)$

Graph each linear equation. See Examples 2 and 3.

27. $y = -x - 2$
28. $y = -2x + 1$
29. $3x - 4y = 8$
30. $x - 9y = 3$
31. $y = \frac{1}{3}x$
32. $y = \frac{3}{2}x$
33. $y + 4 = 0$
34. $x = -1.5$

Recall that if $f(2) = 7$, for example, this corresponds to the ordered pair $(2, 7)$ on the graph of f. Use this information and the graphs of f and g below to answer Exercises 35 through 42.

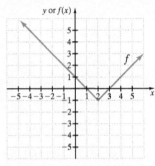 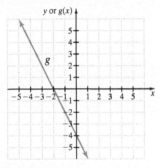

35. $f(4) =$
36. $f(0) =$
37. $g(0) =$
38. $g(-1) =$
39. Find all values for *x* such that $f(x) = 0$.
40. Find all values for *x* such that $g(x) = 0$.
41. If $(-1, -2)$ is a point on the graph of *g*, write this using function notation.
42. If $(-1, 2)$ is a point on the graph of *f*, write this using function notation.

B.4 Polynomials and Factoring

OBJECTIVES

1. Review Operations on Polynomials.
2. Review Factoring Polynomials.

OBJECTIVE
1 Operations on Polynomials

B.4 Exercise Set, Part 1 MyMathLab®

Perform each indicated operation.

1. $(-y^2 + 6y - 1) + (3y^2 - 4y - 10)$
2. $(5z^4 - 6z^2 + z + 1) - (7z^4 - 2z + 1)$
3. Subtract $(x - 5)$ from $(x^2 - 6x + 2)$.
4. $(2x^2 + 6x - 5) + (5x^2 - 10x)$
5. $(5x - 3)^2$
6. $(5x^2 - 14x - 3) \div (5x + 1)$

7. $(2x^4 - 3x^2 + 5x - 2) \div (x + 2)$

8. $(4x - 1)(x^2 - 3x - 2)$

OBJECTIVE
2   Factoring Strategies

The key to proficiency in factoring polynomials is to practice until you are comfortable with each technique. A strategy for factoring polynomials completely is given next.

Factoring a Polynomial

Step 1. Are there any common factors? If so, factor out the greatest common factor.

Step 2. How many terms are in the polynomial?

    a. If there are *two* terms, decide if one of the following formulas may be applied:

        i. Difference of two squares: $a^2 - b^2 = (a - b)(a + b)$

        ii. Difference of two cubes: $a^3 - b^3 = (a - b)(a^2 + ab + b^2)$

        iii. Sum of two cubes: $a^3 + b^3 = (a + b)(a^2 - ab + b^2)$

    b. If there are *three* terms, try one of the following:

        i. Perfect square trinomial: $a^2 + 2ab + b^2 = (a + b)^2$
$$a^2 - 2ab + b^2 = (a - b)^2$$

        ii. If not a perfect square trinomial, factor by using the methods presented in Sections 6.2 through 6.4.

    c. If there are *four* or more terms, try factoring by grouping.

Step 3. See whether any factors in the factored polynomial can be factored further.

A few examples are worked for you below.

EXAMPLE 1   Factor each polynomial completely.

a. $8a^2b - 4ab$ **b.** $36x^2 - 9$ **c.** $2x^2 - 5x - 7$

d. $5p^2 + 5 + qp^2 + q$ **e.** $9x^2 + 24x + 16$ **f.** $y^2 + 25$

Solution

a. Step 1. The terms have a common factor of $4ab$, which we factor out.

$$8a^2b - 4ab = 4ab(2a - 1)$$

  Step 2. There are two terms, but the binomial $2a - 1$ is not the difference of two squares or the sum or difference of two cubes.

  Step 3. The factor $2a - 1$ cannot be factored further.

b. Step 1. Factor out a common factor of 9.

$$36x^2 - 9 = 9(4x^2 - 1)$$

  Step 2. The factor $4x^2 - 1$ has two terms, and it is the difference of two squares.

$$9(4x^2 - 1) = 9(2x + 1)(2x - 1)$$

  Step 3. No factor with more than one term can be factored further.

c. Step 1. The terms of $2x^2 - 5x - 7$ contain no common factor other than 1 or -1.

  Step 2. There are three terms. The trinomial is not a perfect square, so we factor by methods from Section 6.3 or 6.4.

$$2x^2 - 5x - 7 = (2x - 7)(x + 1)$$

  Step 3. No factor with more than one term can be factored further.

(Continued on next page)

d. Step 1. There is no common factor of all terms of $5p^2 + 5 + qp^2 + q$.

Step 2. The polynomial has four terms, so try factoring by grouping.

$$5p^2 + 5 + qp^2 + q = (5p^2 + 5) + (qp^2 + q) \quad \text{Group the terms.}$$
$$= 5(p^2 + 1) + q(p^2 + 1)$$
$$= (p^2 + 1)(5 + q)$$

Step 3. No factor can be factored further.

e. Step 1. The terms of $9x^2 + 24x + 16$ contain no common factor other than 1 or -1.

Step 2. The trinomial $9x^2 + 24x + 16$ is a perfect square trinomial, and $9x^2 + 24x + 16 = (3x + 4)^2$.

Step 3. No factor can be factored further.

f. Step 1. There is no common factor of $y^2 + 25$ other than 1.

Step 2. This binomial is the sum of two squares and is prime.

Step 3. The binomial $y^2 + 25$ cannot be factored further. □

PRACTICE

1 Factor each polynomial completely.

a. $12x^2y - 3xy$ **b.** $49x^2 - 4$

c. $5x^2 + 2x - 3$ **d.** $3x^2 + 6 + x^3 + 2x$

e. $4x^2 + 20x + 25$ **f.** $b^2 + 100$

EXAMPLE 2 Factor each polynomial completely.

a. $27a^3 - b^3$ **b.** $3n^2m^4 - 48m^6$ **c.** $2x^2 - 12x + 18 - 2z^2$

d. $8x^4y^2 + 125xy^2$ **e.** $(x - 5)^2 - 49y^2$

Solution

a. This binomial is the difference of two cubes.

$$27a^3 - b^3 = (3a)^3 - b^3$$
$$= (3a - b)[(3a)^2 + (3a)(b) + b^2]$$
$$= (3a - b)(9a^2 + 3ab + b^2)$$

b. $3n^2m^4 - 48m^6 = 3m^4(n^2 - 16m^2)$ Factor out the GCF $3m^4$.
$$= 3m^4(n + 4m)(n - 4m) \quad \text{Factor the difference of squares.}$$

c. $2x^2 - 12x + 18 - 2z^2 = 2(x^2 - 6x + 9 - z^2)$ The GCF is 2.
$$= 2[(x^2 - 6x + 9) - z^2] \quad \begin{array}{l}\text{Group the first three}\\ \text{terms together.}\end{array}$$
$$= 2[(x - 3)^2 - z^2] \quad \begin{array}{l}\text{Factor the perfect}\\ \text{square trinomial.}\end{array}$$
$$= 2[(x - 3) + z][(x - 3) - z] \quad \begin{array}{l}\text{Factor the difference}\\ \text{of squares.}\end{array}$$
$$= 2(x - 3 + z)(x - 3 - z)$$

d. $8x^4y^2 + 125xy^2 = xy^2(8x^3 + 125)$ The GCF is xy^2.
$$= xy^2[(2x)^3 + 5^3]$$
$$= xy^2(2x + 5)[(2x)^2 - (2x)(5) + 5^2] \quad \text{Factor the sum of cubes.}$$
$$= xy^2(2x + 5)(4x^2 - 10x + 25)$$

e. This binomial is the difference of squares.

$$(x - 5)^2 - 49y^2 = (x - 5)^2 - (7y)^2$$
$$= [(x - 5) + 7y][(x - 5) - 7y]$$
$$= (x - 5 + 7y)(x - 5 - 7y) \quad □$$

PRACTICE
2   Factor each polynomial completely.

a. $64x^3 + y^3$

b. $7x^2y^2 - 63y^4$

c. $3x^2 + 12x + 12 - 3b^2$

d. $x^5y^4 + 27x^2y$

e. $(x + 7)^2 - 81y^2$

B.4   Exercise Set, Part 2   MyMathLab®

Factor completely.

9. $x^2 - 8x + 16 - y^2$

10. $12x^2 - 22x - 20$

11. $x^4 - x$

12. $(2x + 1)^2 - 3(2x + 1) + 2$

13. $14x^2y - 2xy$

14. $24ab^2 - 6ab$

15. $4x^2 - 16$

16. $9x^2 - 81$

17. $3x^2 - 8x - 11$

18. $5x^2 - 2x - 3$

19. $4x^2 + 8x - 12$

20. $6x^2 - 6x - 12$

21. $4x^2 + 36x + 81$

22. $25x^2 + 40x + 16$

23. $8x^3 + 125y^3$

24. $27x^3 - 64y^3$

25. $64x^2y^3 - 8x^2$

26. $27x^5y^4 - 216x^2y$

27. $(x + 5)^3 + y^3$

28. $(y - 1)^3 + 27x^3$

29. $(5a - 3)^2 - 6(5a - 3) + 9$

30. $(4r + 1)^2 + 8(4r + 1) + 16$

31. $7x^2 - 63x$

32. $20x^2 + 23x + 6$

33. $ab - 6a + 7b - 42$

34. $20x^2 - 220x + 600$

35. $x^4 - 1$

36. $15x^2 - 20x$

37. $10x^2 - 7x - 33$

38. $45m^3n^3 - 27m^2n^2$

39. $5a^3b^3 - 50a^3b$

40. $x^4 + x$

41. $16x^2 + 25$

42. $20x^3 + 20y^3$

43. $10x^3 - 210x^2 + 1100x$

44. $9y^2 - 42y + 49$

45. $64a^3b^4 - 27a^3b$

46. $y^4 - 16$

47. $2x^3 - 54$

48. $2sr + 10s - r - 5$

49. $3y^5 - 5y^4 + 6y - 10$

50. $64a^2 + b^2$

51. $100z^3 + 100$

52. $250x^4 - 16x$

53. $4b^2 - 36b + 81$

54. $2a^5 - a^4 + 6a - 3$

55. $(y - 6)^2 + 3(y - 6) + 2$

56. $(c + 2)^2 - 6(c + 2) + 5$

57. Express the area of the shaded region as a polynomial. Factor the polynomial completely.

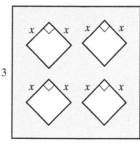

B.5 | Rational Expressions

OBJECTIVE

1 Performing Operations on Rational Expressions and Solving Equations Containing Rational Expressions

It is very important that you understand the difference between an expression and an equation containing rational expressions. An equation contains an equal sign; an expression does not.

Expression to be Simplified	**Equation to be Solved**
$$\frac{x}{2} + \frac{x}{6}$$	$$\frac{x}{2} + \frac{x}{6} = \frac{2}{3}$$
Write both rational expressions with the LCD, 6, as the denominator.	Multiply both sides by the LCD, 6.

$$\frac{x}{2} + \frac{x}{6} = \frac{x \cdot 3}{2 \cdot 3} + \frac{x}{6}$$

$$= \frac{3x}{6} + \frac{x}{6}$$

$$= \frac{4x}{6} = \frac{2x}{3}$$

$$6\left(\frac{x}{2} + \frac{x}{6}\right) = 6\left(\frac{2}{3}\right)$$

$$3x + x = 4$$

$$4x = 4$$

$$x = 1$$

Check to see that the solution is 1.

> ▶ **Helpful Hint**
> Remember: Equations can be cleared of fractions; expressions cannot.

EXAMPLE 1 Multiply. $\dfrac{x^3 - 1}{-3x + 3} \cdot \dfrac{15x^2}{x^2 + x + 1}$

Solution

$$\frac{x^3 - 1}{-3x + 3} \cdot \frac{15x^2}{x^2 + x + 1} = \frac{(x - 1)(x^2 + x + 1)}{-3(x - 1)} \cdot \frac{15x^2}{x^2 + x + 1} \qquad \text{Factor.}$$

$$= \frac{(x - 1)(x^2 + x + 1) \cdot 3 \cdot 5x^2}{-1 \cdot 3(x - 1)(x^2 + x + 1)} \qquad \text{Factor.}$$

$$= \frac{5x^2}{-1} = -5x^2 \qquad \text{Simplest form} \qquad \square$$

PRACTICE

1 Multiply.

a. $\dfrac{2 + 5n}{3n} \cdot \dfrac{6n + 3}{5n^2 - 3n - 2}$

b. $\dfrac{x^3 - 8}{-6x + 12} \cdot \dfrac{6x^2}{x^2 + 2x + 4}$

EXAMPLE 2 Divide. $\dfrac{8m^2}{3m^2 - 12} \div \dfrac{40}{2 - m}$

Solution

$$\frac{8m^2}{3m^2 - 12} \div \frac{40}{2 - m} = \frac{8m^2}{3m^2 - 12} \cdot \frac{2 - m}{40} \qquad \text{Multiply by the reciprocal of the divisor.}$$

$$= \frac{8m^2(2 - m)}{3(m + 2)(m - 2) \cdot 40} \qquad \text{Factor and multiply.}$$

$$= \frac{8 \, m^2 \cdot -1 \, (m - 2)}{3(m + 2) \, (m - 2) \cdot 8 \cdot 5} \qquad \text{Write } (2 - m) \text{ as } -1(m - 2).$$

$$= -\frac{m^2}{15(m + 2)} \qquad \text{Simplify.} \qquad \square$$

PRACTICE
2   Divide.

a. $\dfrac{6y^3}{3y^2 - 27} \div \dfrac{42}{3 - y}$

b. $\dfrac{10x^2 + 23x - 5}{5x^2 - 51x + 10} \div \dfrac{2x^2 + 9x + 10}{7x^2 - 68x - 20}$

EXAMPLE 3   Perform the indicated operation.

$$\frac{3}{x + 2} + \frac{2x}{x - 2}$$

Solution   The LCD is the product of the two denominators: $(x + 2)(x - 2)$.

$\dfrac{3}{x + 2} + \dfrac{2x}{x - 2} = \dfrac{3 \cdot (x - 2)}{(x + 2) \cdot (x - 2)} + \dfrac{2x \cdot (x + 2)}{(x - 2) \cdot (x + 2)}$ Write equivalent rational expressions.

$= \dfrac{3x - 6}{(x + 2)(x - 2)} + \dfrac{2x^2 + 4x}{(x + 2)(x - 2)}$ Multiply in the numerators.

$= \dfrac{3x - 6 + 2x^2 + 4x}{(x + 2)(x - 2)}$ Add the numerators.

$= \dfrac{2x^2 + 7x - 6}{(x + 2)(x - 2)}$ Simplify the numerator.   □

PRACTICE
3   Perform the indicated operation.

a. $\dfrac{4}{p^3 q} + \dfrac{3}{5p^4 q}$

b. $\dfrac{4}{y + 3} + \dfrac{5y}{y - 3}$

c. $\dfrac{3z - 18}{z - 5} - \dfrac{3}{5 - z}$

EXAMPLE 4   Solve: $\dfrac{2x}{x - 3} + \dfrac{6 - 2x}{x^2 - 9} = \dfrac{x}{x + 3}$.

Solution   We factor the second denominator to find that the LCD is $(x + 3)(x - 3)$. We multiply both sides of the equation by $(x + 3)(x - 3)$. By the distributive property, this is the same as multiplying each term by $(x + 3)(x - 3)$.

$$\frac{2x}{x - 3} + \frac{6 - 2x}{x^2 - 9} = \frac{x}{x + 3}$$

$$(x + 3)(x - 3) \cdot \frac{2x}{x - 3} + (x + 3)(x - 3) \cdot \frac{6 - 2x}{(x + 3)(x - 3)}$$

$$= (x + 3)(x - 3)\left(\frac{x}{x + 3}\right)$$

$2x(x + 3) + (6 - 2x) = x(x - 3)$ Simplify.

$2x^2 + 6x + 6 - 2x = x^2 - 3x$ Use the distributive property.

Next we solve this quadratic equation by the factoring method. To do so, we first write the equation so that one side is 0.

$$x^2 + 7x + 6 = 0$$

$$(x + 6)(x + 1) = 0$$ Factor.

$$x = -6 \quad \text{or} \quad x = -1$$ Set each factor equal to 0.

Neither -6 nor -1 makes any denominator 0, so they are both solutions. The solutions are -6 and -1.   □

PRACTICE
4   Solve: $\dfrac{2}{x - 2} - \dfrac{5 + 2x}{x^2 - 4} = \dfrac{x}{x + 2}$.

B.5 Exercise Set

MyMathLab®

Perform each indicated operation and simplify, or solve the equation for the variable.

1. $\dfrac{x}{2} = \dfrac{1}{8} + \dfrac{x}{4}$

2. $\dfrac{x}{4} = \dfrac{3}{2} + \dfrac{x}{10}$

3. $\dfrac{1}{8} + \dfrac{x}{4}$

4. $\dfrac{3}{2} + \dfrac{x}{10}$

5. $\dfrac{4}{x + 2} - \dfrac{2}{x - 1}$

6. $\dfrac{5}{x - 2} - \dfrac{10}{x + 4}$

7. $\dfrac{4}{x + 2} = \dfrac{2}{x - 1}$

8. $\dfrac{5}{x - 2} = \dfrac{10}{x + 4}$

9. $\dfrac{2}{x^2 - 4} = \dfrac{1}{x + 2} - \dfrac{3}{x - 2}$

10. $\dfrac{3}{x^2 - 25} = \dfrac{1}{x + 5} + \dfrac{2}{x - 5}$

11. $\dfrac{5}{x^2 - 3x} + \dfrac{4}{2x - 6}$

12. $\dfrac{5}{x^2 - 3x} \div \dfrac{4}{2x - 6}$

13. $\dfrac{x - 1}{x + 1} + \dfrac{x + 7}{x - 1} = \dfrac{4}{x^2 - 1}$

14. $\left(1 - \dfrac{y}{x}\right) \div \left(1 - \dfrac{x}{y}\right)$

15. $\dfrac{a^2 - 9}{a - 6} \cdot \dfrac{a^2 - 5a - 6}{a^2 - a - 6}$

16. $\dfrac{2}{a - 6} + \dfrac{3a}{a^2 - 5a - 6} - \dfrac{a}{5a + 5}$

17. $\dfrac{2x + 3}{3x - 2} = \dfrac{4x + 1}{6x + 1}$

18. $\dfrac{5x - 3}{2x} = \dfrac{10x + 3}{4x + 1}$

19. $\dfrac{a}{9a^2 - 1} + \dfrac{2}{6a - 2}$

20. $\dfrac{3}{4a - 8} - \dfrac{a + 2}{a^2 - 2a}$

21. $-\dfrac{3}{x^2} - \dfrac{1}{x} + 2 = 0$

22. $\dfrac{x}{2x + 6} + \dfrac{5}{x^2 - 9}$

23. $\dfrac{x - 8}{x^2 - x - 2} + \dfrac{2}{x - 2}$

24. $\dfrac{x - 8}{x^2 - x - 2} + \dfrac{2}{x - 2} = \dfrac{3}{x + 1}$

25. $\dfrac{3}{a} - 5 = \dfrac{7}{a} - 1$

26. $\dfrac{7}{3z - 9} + \dfrac{5}{z}$

Use $\dfrac{x}{5} - \dfrac{x}{4} = \dfrac{1}{10}$ *and* $\dfrac{x}{5} - \dfrac{x}{4} + \dfrac{1}{10}$ *for Exercises 27 and 28.*

27. a. Which one above is an expression?

   b. Describe the first step to simplify this expression.

   c. Simplify the expression.

28. a. Which one above is an equation?

   b. Describe the first step to solve this equation.

   c. Solve the equation.

For each exercise, choose the correct statement.* Each figure represents a real number, and no denominators are 0.

29. a. $\dfrac{\triangle + \square}{\triangle} = \square$ **b.** $\dfrac{\triangle + \square}{\triangle} = 1 + \dfrac{\square}{\triangle}$

   c. $\dfrac{\triangle + \square}{\triangle} = \dfrac{\square}{\triangle}$ **d.** $\dfrac{\triangle + \square}{\triangle} = 1 + \square$

   e. $\dfrac{\triangle + \square}{\triangle - \square} = -1$

*My thanks to Kelly Champagne for permission to use her Exercises for 29 through 33.

▶ Helpful Hint
Remember: Equations can be cleared of fractions; expressions cannot.

30. **a.** $\dfrac{\triangle}{\square} + \dfrac{\square}{\triangle} = \dfrac{\triangle + \square}{\square + \triangle} = 1$

b. $\dfrac{\triangle}{\square} + \dfrac{\square}{\triangle} = \dfrac{\triangle + \square}{\triangle \square}$

c. $\dfrac{\triangle}{\square} + \dfrac{\square}{\triangle} = \triangle \triangle + \square \square$

d. $\dfrac{\triangle}{\square} + \dfrac{\square}{\triangle} = \dfrac{\triangle \triangle + \square \square}{\square \triangle}$

e. $\dfrac{\triangle}{\square} + \dfrac{\square}{\triangle} = \dfrac{\triangle \square}{\square \triangle} = 1$

31. **a.** $\dfrac{\triangle}{\square} \cdot \dfrac{\bigcirc}{\square} = \dfrac{\triangle \bigcirc}{\square}$ **b.** $\dfrac{\triangle}{\square} \cdot \dfrac{\bigcirc}{\square} = \triangle \bigcirc$

c. $\dfrac{\triangle}{\square} \cdot \dfrac{\bigcirc}{\square} = \dfrac{\triangle + \bigcirc}{\square + \square}$ **d.** $\dfrac{\triangle}{\square} \cdot \dfrac{\bigcirc}{\square} = \dfrac{\triangle \bigcirc}{\square \square}$

32. **a.** $\dfrac{\triangle}{\square} \div \dfrac{\bigcirc}{\triangle} = \dfrac{\triangle \triangle}{\square \bigcirc}$ **b.** $\dfrac{\triangle}{\square} \div \dfrac{\bigcirc}{\triangle} = \dfrac{\bigcirc \square}{\triangle \triangle}$

c. $\dfrac{\triangle}{\square} \div \dfrac{\bigcirc}{\triangle} = \dfrac{\bigcirc}{\square}$ **d.** $\dfrac{\triangle}{\square} \div \dfrac{\bigcirc}{\triangle} = \dfrac{\triangle + \triangle}{\square + \bigcirc}$

33. **a.** $\dfrac{\frac{\triangle + \square}{\bigcirc}}{\frac{\triangle}{\bigcirc}} = \square$ **b.** $\dfrac{\frac{\triangle + \square}{\bigcirc}}{\frac{\triangle}{\bigcirc}} = \dfrac{\triangle \triangle + \triangle \square}{\bigcirc \bigcirc}$

c. $\dfrac{\frac{\triangle + \square}{\bigcirc}}{\frac{\triangle}{\bigcirc}} = 1 + \square$ **d.** $\dfrac{\frac{\triangle + \square}{\bigcirc}}{\frac{\triangle}{\bigcirc}} = \dfrac{\triangle + \square}{\triangle}$

Appendix C

An Introduction to Using a Graphing Utility

The Viewing Window and Interpreting Window Settings

In this appendix, we will use the term **graphing utility** to mean a graphing calculator or a computer software graphing package. All graphing utilities graph equations by plotting points on a screen. While plotting several points can be slow and sometimes tedious for us, a graphing utility can quickly and accurately plot hundreds of points. How does a graphing utility show plotted points? A computer or calculator screen is made up of a grid of small rectangular areas called **pixels.** If a pixel contains a point to be plotted, the pixel is turned "on"; otherwise, the pixel remains "off." The graph of an equation is then a collection of pixels turned "on." The graph of $y = 3x + 1$ from a graphing calculator is shown in Figure A-1. Notice the irregular shape of the line caused by the rectangular pixels.

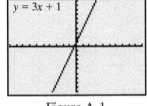
Figure A-1

The portion of the coordinate plane shown on the screen in Figure A-1 is called the **viewing window** or the **viewing rectangle.** Notice the x-axis and the y-axis on the graph. While tick marks are shown on the axes, they are not labeled. This means that from this screen alone, we do not know how many units each tick mark represents. To see what each tick mark represents and the minimum and maximum values on the axes, check the window setting of the graphing utility. It defines the viewing window. The window of the graph of $y = 3x + 1$ shown in Figure A-1 has the following settings (Figure A-2):

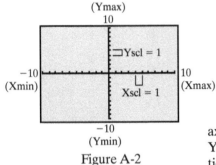
Figure A-2

$$\text{Xmin} = -10 \quad \text{The minimum } x\text{-value is } -10.$$
$$\text{Xmax} = 10 \quad \text{The maximum } x\text{-value is } 10.$$
$$\text{Xscl} = 1 \quad \text{The } x\text{-axis scale is 1 unit per tick mark.}$$
$$\text{Ymin} = -10 \quad \text{The minimum } y\text{-value is } -10.$$
$$\text{Ymax} = 10 \quad \text{The maximum } y\text{-value is } 10.$$
$$\text{Yscl} = 1 \quad \text{The } y\text{-axis scale is 1 unit per tick mark.}$$

By knowing the scale, we can find the minimum and the maximum values on the axes simply by counting tick marks. For example, if both the Xscl (x-axis scale) and the Yscl (y-axis scale) are 1 unit per tick mark on the graph in Figure A-3, we can count the tick marks and find that the minimum x-value is -10 and the maximum x-value is 10. Also, the minimum y-value is -10 and the maximum y-value is 10. If the Xscl changes to 2 units per tick mark (shown in Figure A-4), by counting tick marks, we see that the minimum x-value is now -20 and the maximum x-value is now 20.

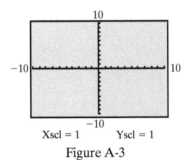

Xscl = 1   Yscl = 1

Figure A-3

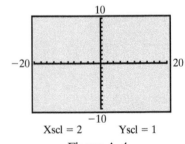

Xscl = 2   Yscl = 1

Figure A-4

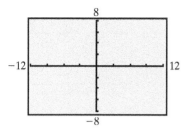

Figure A-5

It is also true that if we know the Xmin and the Xmax values, we can calculate the Xscl by the displayed axes. For example, the Xscl of the graph in Figure A-5 must be 3 units per tick mark for the maximum and minimum x-values to be as shown. Also, the Yscl of that graph must be 2 units per tick mark for the maximum and minimum y-values to be as shown.

We will call the viewing window in Figure A-3 a *standard* viewing window or rectangle. Although a standard viewing window is sufficient for much of this text, special care must be taken to ensure that all key features of a graph are shown. Figures A-6, A-7, and A-8 show the graph of $y = x^2 + 11x - 1$ on three different viewing windows. Note that certain viewing windows for this equation are misleading.

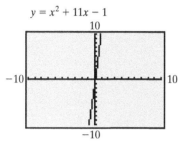

Figure A-6

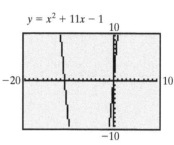

Figure A-7

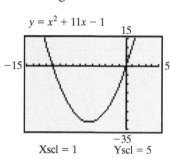

Figure A-8

How do we ensure that all distinguishing features of the graph of an equation are shown? It helps to know about the equation that is being graphed. For example, the equation $y = x^2 + 11x - 1$ is not a linear equation and its graph is not a line. This equation is a quadratic equation and, therefore, its graph is a parabola. By knowing this information, we know that the graph shown in Figure A-6, although correct, is misleading. Of the three viewing rectangles shown, the graph in Figure A-8 is best because it shows more of the distinguishing features of the parabola. Properties of equations needed for graphing will be studied in this text.

The Viewing Window and Interpreting Window Settings Exercise Set

In Exercises 1–4, determine whether all ordered pairs listed will lie within a standard viewing rectangle.

1. $(-9, 0), (5, 8), (1, -8)$
2. $(4, 7), (0, 0), (-8, 9)$
3. $(-11, 0), (2, 2), (7, -5)$
4. $(3, 5), (-3, -5), (15, 0)$

In Exercises 5–10, choose an Xmin, Xmax, Ymin, and Ymax so that all ordered pairs listed will lie within the viewing rectangle.

5. $(-90, 0), (55, 80), (0, -80)$
6. $(4, 70), (20, 20), (-18, 90)$
7. $(-11, 0), (2, 2), (7, -5)$
8. $(3, 5), (-3, -5), (15, 0)$
9. $(200, 200), (50, -50), (70, -50)$
10. $(40, 800), (-30, 500), (15, 0)$

Write the window setting for each viewing window shown. Use the following format:

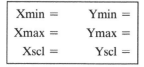

11.

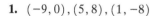

12.

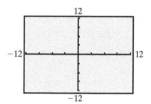

13.

14.

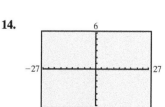

15.

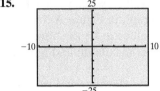

16.

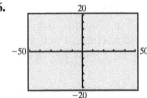

19.

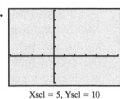

Xscl = 5, Yscl = 10

20.

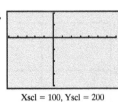

Xscl = 100, Yscl = 200

17.

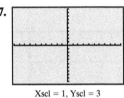

Xscl = 1, Yscl = 3

18.

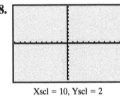

Xscl = 10, Yscl = 2

Graphing Equations and Square Viewing Window

In general, the following steps may be used to graph an equation on a standard viewing window.

> **Graphing an Equation in X and Y with a Graphing Utility on a Standard Viewing Window**
>
> **Step 1:** Solve the equation for y.
>
> **Step 2:** Using your graphing utility, enter the equation in the form
> $Y = expression\ involving\ x$.
>
> **Step 3:** Activate the graphing utility.

Special care must be taken when entering the *expression involving x* in Step 2. You must be sure that the graphing utility you are using interprets the expression as you want it to. For example, let's graph $3y = 4x$. To do so,

Step 1: Solve the equation for y.

$$3y = 4x$$

$$\frac{3y}{3} = \frac{4x}{3}$$

$$y = \frac{4}{3}x$$

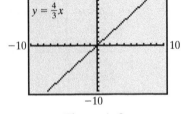

Figure A-9

Step 2: Using your graphing utility, enter the expression $\frac{4}{3}x$ after the $Y =$ prompt. In order for your graphing utility to correctly interpret the expression, you may need to enter $(4/3)x$ or $(4 \div 3)x$.

Step 3: Activate the graphing utility. The graph should appear as in Figure A-9.

Distinguishing features of the graph of a line include showing all the intercepts of the line. For example, the window of the graph of the line in Figure A-10 does not show both intercepts of the line, but the window of the graph of the same line in Figure A-11 does show both intercepts. Notice the notation below each graph. This is a shorthand notation of the range setting of the graph. This notation means [Xmin, Xmax] by [Ymin, Ymax].

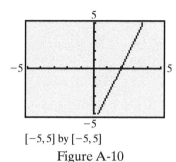

[-5, 5] by [-5, 5]

Figure A-10

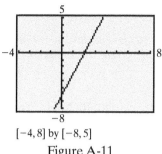

[-4, 8] by [-8, 5]

Figure A-11

On a standard viewing window, the tick marks on the *y*-axis are closer together than the tick marks on the *x*-axis. This happens because the viewing window is a rectangle, and so 10 equally spaced tick marks on the positive *y*-axis will be closer together than 10 equally spaced tick marks on the positive *x*-axis. This causes the appearance of graphs to be distorted.

For example, notice the different appearances of the same line graphed using different viewing windows. The line in Figure A-12 is distorted because the tick marks along the *x*-axis are farther apart than the tick marks along the *y*-axis. The graph of the same line in Figure A-13 is not distorted because the viewing rectangle has been selected so that there is equal spacing between tick marks on both axes.

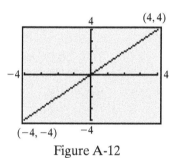

Figure A-12

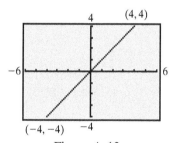

Figure A-13

We say that the line in Figure A-13 is graphed on a *square* setting. Some graphing utilities have a built-in program that, if activated, will automatically provide a square setting. A square setting is especially helpful when we are graphing perpendicular lines, circles, or when a true geometric perspective is desired. Some examples of square screens are shown in Figures A-14 and A-15.

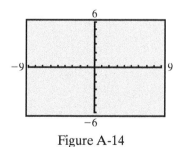

Figure A-14

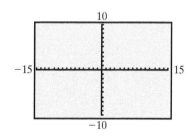

Figure A-15

Other features of a graphing utility such as Trace, Zoom, Intersect, and Table are discussed in appropriate Graphing Calculator Explorations in this text.

Graphing Equations and Square Viewing Window Exercise Set

Graph each linear equation in two variables using the two different range settings given. Determine which setting shows all intercepts of a line.

1. $y = 2x + 12$
Setting A: $[-10, 10]$ by $[-10, 10]$
Setting B: $[-10, 10]$ by $[-10, 15]$

2. $y = -3x + 25$
Setting A: $[-5, 5]$ by $[-30, 10]$
Setting B: $[-10, 10]$ by $[-10, 30]$

3. $y = -x - 41$
Setting A: $[-50, 10]$ by $[-10, 10]$
Setting B: $[-50, 10]$ by $[-50, 15]$

4. $y = 6x - 18$
Setting A: $[-10, 10]$ by $[-20, 10]$
Setting B: $[-10, 10]$ by $[-10, 10]$

5. $y = \dfrac{1}{2}x - 15$
Setting B: $[-10, 10]$ by $[-20, 10]$
Setting B: $[-10, 35]$ by $[-20, 15]$

6. $y = -\dfrac{2}{3}x - \dfrac{29}{3}$
Setting A: $[-10, 10]$ by $[-10, 10]$
Setting B: $[-15, 5]$ by $[-15, 5]$

The graph of each equation is a line. Use a graphing utility and a standard viewing window to graph each equation.

7. $3x = 5y$ **8.** $7y = -3x$ **9.** $9x - 5y = 30$

10. $4x + 6y = 20$ **11.** $y = -7$ **12.** $y = 2$

13. $x + 10y = -5$ **14.** $x - 5y = 9$

Graph the following equations using the square setting given. Some keystrokes that may be helpful are given.

15. $y = \sqrt{x}$ $[-12, 12]$ by $[-8, 8]$
Suggested keystrokes: $\sqrt{\ }x$

16. $y = \sqrt{2x}$ $[-12, 12]$ by $[-8, 8]$
Suggested keystrokes: $\sqrt{\ }(2x)$

17. $y = x^2 + 2x + 1$ $[-15, 15]$ by $[-10, 10]$
Suggested keystrokes: x^2 + 2x + 1

18. $y = x^2 - 5$ $[-15, 15]$ by $[-10, 10]$
Suggested keystrokes: x^2 - 5

19. $y = |x|$ $[-9, 9]$ by $[-6, 6]$
Suggested keystrokes: $ABS(x)$

20. $y = |x - 2|$ $[-9, 9]$ by $[-6, 6]$
Suggested keystrokes: $ABS(x - 2)$

Graph each line. Use a standard viewing window; then, if necessary, change the viewing window so that all intercepts of each line show.

21. $x + 2y = 30$ **22.** $1.5x - 3.7y = 40.3$

Appendix D

Solving Systems of Equations by Matrices

OBJECTIVES

1 Use Matrices to Solve a System of Two Equations.

2 Use Matrices to Solve a System of Three Equations.

By now, you may have noticed that the solution of a system of equations depends on the coefficients of the equations in the system and not on the variables. In this section, we introduce solving a system of equations by a **matrix.**

OBJECTIVE

1 Using Matrices to Solve a System of Two Equations

A matrix (plural: **matrices**) is a rectangular array of numbers. The following are examples of matrices.

$$\begin{bmatrix} 1 & 0 \\ 0 & 1 \end{bmatrix} \qquad \begin{bmatrix} 2 & 1 & 3 & -1 \\ 0 & -1 & 4 & 5 \\ -6 & 2 & 1 & 0 \end{bmatrix} \qquad \begin{bmatrix} a & b & c \\ d & e & f \end{bmatrix}$$

The numbers aligned horizontally in a matrix are in the same **row.** The numbers aligned vertically are in the same **column.**

$$\begin{array}{l} \text{row 1} \rightarrow \\ \text{row 2} \rightarrow \end{array} \begin{bmatrix} 2 & 1 & 0 \\ -1 & 6 & 2 \end{bmatrix}$$

column 1 column 2 column 3

This matrix has 2 rows and 3 columns. It is called a 2×3 (read "two by three") matrix.

To see the relationship between systems of equations and matrices, study the example below.

> **Helpful Hint**
> Before writing the corresponding matrix associated with a system of equations, make sure that the equations are written in standard form.

System of Equations (in standard form)

$$\begin{cases} 2x - 3y = 6 & \text{Equation 1} \\ x + y = 0 & \text{Equation 2} \end{cases}$$

Corresponding Matrix

$$\begin{bmatrix} 2 & -3 & \vdots & 6 \\ 1 & 1 & \vdots & 0 \end{bmatrix} \begin{array}{l} \text{Row 1} \\ \text{Row 2} \end{array}$$

Notice that the rows of the matrix correspond to the equations in the system. The coefficients of each variable are placed to the left of a vertical dashed line. The constants are placed to the right. Each of the numbers in the matrix is called an **element.**

The method of solving systems by matrices is to write this matrix as an equivalent matrix from which we easily identify the solution. Two matrices are equivalent if they represent systems that have the same solution set. The following **row operations** can be performed on matrices, and the result is an equivalent matrix.

> **Helpful Hint**
> Notice that these *row* operations are the same operations that we can perform on *equations* in a system.

Elementary Row Operations

1. Any two rows in a matrix may be interchanged.
2. The elements of any row may be multiplied (or divided) by the same nonzero number.
3. The elements of any row may be multiplied (or divided) by a nonzero number and added to their corresponding elements in any other row.

To solve a system of two equations in x and y by matrices, write the corresponding matrix associated with the system. Then use elementary row operations to write equivalent matrices until you have a matrix of the form

$$\begin{bmatrix} 1 & a & \vdots & b \\ 0 & 1 & \vdots & c \end{bmatrix},$$

where a, b, and c are constants. Why? If a matrix associated with a system of equations is in this form, we can easily solve for x and y. For example,

Matrix		*System of Equations*

$$\begin{bmatrix} 1 & 2 & \vdots & -3 \\ 0 & 1 & \vdots & 5 \end{bmatrix} \quad \text{corresponds to} \quad \begin{cases} 1x + 2y = -3 \\ 0x + 1y = 5 \end{cases} \quad \text{or} \quad \begin{cases} x + 2y = -3 \\ y = 5 \end{cases}$$

In the second equation, we have $y = 5$. Substituting this in the first equation, we have $x + 2(5) = -3$ or $x = -13$. The solution of the system is the ordered pair $(-13, 5)$.

EXAMPLE 1 Use matrices to solve the system.

$$\begin{cases} x + 3y = 5 \\ 2x - y = -4 \end{cases}$$

Solution The corresponding matrix is $\begin{bmatrix} 1 & 3 & \vdots & 5 \\ 2 & -1 & \vdots & -4 \end{bmatrix}$. We use elementary row operations to write an equivalent matrix that looks like $\begin{bmatrix} 1 & a & \vdots & b \\ 0 & 1 & \vdots & c \end{bmatrix}$.

For the matrix given, the element in the first row, first column is already 1, as desired. Next we write an equivalent matrix with a 0 below the 1. To do this, we multiply row 1 by -2 and add to row 2. *We will change only row 2.*

$$\begin{bmatrix} 1 & 3 & \vdots & 5 \\ -2(1) + 2 & -2(3) + (-1) & \vdots & -2(5) + (-4) \end{bmatrix} \quad \text{simplifies to} \quad \begin{bmatrix} 1 & 3 & \vdots & 5 \\ 0 & -7 & \vdots & -14 \end{bmatrix}$$

$$\begin{array}{cccccc} \uparrow & \uparrow & \uparrow & \uparrow & \uparrow & \uparrow \\ \text{row 1} & \text{row 2} & \text{row 1} & \text{row 2} & \text{row 1} & \text{row 2} \\ \text{element} & \text{element} & \text{element} & \text{element} & \text{element} & \text{element} \end{array}$$

Now we change the -7 to a 1 by use of an elementary row operation. We divide row 2 by -7, then

$$\begin{bmatrix} 1 & 3 & \vdots & 5 \\ \dfrac{0}{-7} & \dfrac{-7}{-7} & \vdots & \dfrac{-14}{-7} \end{bmatrix} \quad \text{simplifies to} \quad \begin{bmatrix} 1 & 3 & \vdots & 5 \\ 0 & 1 & \vdots & 2 \end{bmatrix}$$

This last matrix corresponds to the system

$$\begin{cases} x + 3y = 5 \\ y = 2 \end{cases}$$

To find x, we let $y = 2$ in the first equation, $x + 3y = 5$.

$$\begin{aligned} x + 3y &= 5 & \text{First equation} \\ x + 3(2) &= 5 & \text{Let } y = 2. \\ x &= -1 \end{aligned}$$

The ordered pair solution is $(-1, 2)$. Check to see that this ordered pair satisfies both equations. $\square$

PRACTICE

1 Use matrices to solve the system.

$$\begin{cases} x + 4y = -2 \\ 3x - y = 7 \end{cases}$$

EXAMPLE 2   Use matrices to solve the system.

$$\begin{cases} 2x - y = 3 \\ 4x - 2y = 5 \end{cases}$$

Solution   The corresponding matrix is $\begin{bmatrix} 2 & -1 & \vdots & 3 \\ 4 & -2 & \vdots & 5 \end{bmatrix}$. To get 1 in the row 1, column 1 position, we divide the elements of row 1 by 2.

$$\begin{bmatrix} \dfrac{2}{2} & -\dfrac{1}{2} & \vdots & \dfrac{3}{2} \\ 4 & -2 & \vdots & 5 \end{bmatrix} \quad \text{simplifies to} \quad \begin{bmatrix} 1 & -\dfrac{1}{2} & \vdots & \dfrac{3}{2} \\ 4 & -2 & \vdots & 5 \end{bmatrix}$$

To get 0 under the 1, we multiply the elements of row 1 by -4 and add the new elements to the elements of row 2.

$$\begin{bmatrix} 1 & -\dfrac{1}{2} & \vdots & \dfrac{3}{2} \\ -4(1) + 4 & -4\left(-\dfrac{1}{2}\right) - 2 & \vdots & -4\left(\dfrac{3}{2}\right) + 5 \end{bmatrix} \quad \text{simplifies to} \quad \begin{bmatrix} 1 & -\dfrac{1}{2} & \vdots & \dfrac{3}{2} \\ 0 & 0 & \vdots & -1 \end{bmatrix}$$

The corresponding system is $\begin{cases} x - \dfrac{1}{2}y = \dfrac{3}{2} \\ 0 = -1 \end{cases}$. The equation $0 = -1$ is false for all y or x values; hence, the system is inconsistent and has no solution. The solution set is $\{\ \}$ or $\varnothing$. □

PRACTICE

2   Use matrices to solve the system.

$$\begin{cases} x - 3y = 3 \\ -2x + 6y = 4 \end{cases}$$

✓**CONCEPT CHECK**

Consider the system

$$\begin{cases} 2x - 3y = 8 \\ x + 5y = -3 \end{cases}$$

What is wrong with its corresponding matrix shown below?

$$\begin{bmatrix} 2 & -3 & \vdots & 8 \\ 0 & 5 & \vdots & -3 \end{bmatrix}$$

OBJECTIVE

2   Using Matrices to Solve a System of Three Equations

To solve a system of three equations in three variables using matrices, we will write the corresponding matrix in the form

$$\begin{bmatrix} 1 & a & b & \vdots & d \\ 0 & 1 & c & \vdots & e \\ 0 & 0 & 1 & \vdots & f \end{bmatrix}$$

Answer to Concept Check:

matrix should be $\begin{bmatrix} 2 & -3 & \vdots & 8 \\ 1 & 5 & \vdots & -3 \end{bmatrix}$

EXAMPLE 3   Use matrices to solve the system.

$$\begin{cases} x + 2y + z = 2 \\ -2x - y + 2z = 5 \\ x + 3y - 2z = -8 \end{cases}$$

Solution   The corresponding matrix is $\begin{bmatrix} 1 & 2 & 1 & \vdots & 2 \\ -2 & -1 & 2 & \vdots & 5 \\ 1 & 3 & -2 & \vdots & -8 \end{bmatrix}$. Our goal is to write

an equivalent matrix with 1's along the diagonal (see the numbers in red) and 0's below the 1's. The element in row 1, column 1 is already 1. Next we get 0's for each element in the rest of column 1. To do this, first we multiply the elements of row 1 by 2 and add the new elements to row 2. Also, we multiply the elements of row 1 by −1 and add the new elements to the elements of row 3. We *do not change row 1*. Then

$$\begin{bmatrix} 1 & 2 & 1 & \vdots & 2 \\ 2(1)-2 & 2(2)-1 & 2(1)+2 & \vdots & 2(2)+5 \\ -1(1)+1 & -1(2)+3 & -1(1)-2 & \vdots & -1(2)-8 \end{bmatrix}$$ simplifies to $\begin{bmatrix} 1 & 2 & 1 & \vdots & 2 \\ 0 & 3 & 4 & \vdots & 9 \\ 0 & 1 & -3 & \vdots & -10 \end{bmatrix}$

We continue down the diagonal and use elementary row operations to get 1 where the element 3 is now. To do this, we interchange rows 2 and 3.

$$\begin{bmatrix} 1 & 2 & 1 & \vdots & 2 \\ 0 & 3 & 4 & \vdots & 9 \\ 0 & 1 & -3 & \vdots & -10 \end{bmatrix}$$ is equivalent to $\begin{bmatrix} 1 & 2 & 1 & \vdots & 2 \\ 0 & 1 & -3 & \vdots & -10 \\ 0 & 3 & 4 & \vdots & 9 \end{bmatrix}$

Next we want the new row 3, column 2 element to be 0. We multiply the elements of row 2 by −3 and add the result to the elements of row 3.

$$\begin{bmatrix} 1 & 2 & 1 & \vdots & 2 \\ 0 & 1 & -3 & \vdots & -10 \\ -3(0)+0 & -3(1)+3 & -3(-3)+4 & \vdots & -3(-10)+9 \end{bmatrix}$$ simplifies to

$$\begin{bmatrix} 1 & 2 & 1 & \vdots & 2 \\ 0 & 1 & -3 & \vdots & -10 \\ 0 & 0 & 13 & \vdots & 39 \end{bmatrix}$$

Finally, we divide the elements of row 3 by 13 so that the final diagonal element is 1.

$$\begin{bmatrix} 1 & 2 & 1 & \vdots & 2 \\ 0 & 1 & -3 & \vdots & -10 \\ \frac{0}{13} & \frac{0}{13} & \frac{13}{13} & \vdots & \frac{39}{13} \end{bmatrix}$$ simplifies to $\begin{bmatrix} 1 & 2 & 1 & \vdots & 2 \\ 0 & 1 & -3 & \vdots & -10 \\ 0 & 0 & 1 & \vdots & 3 \end{bmatrix}$

This matrix corresponds to the system

$$\begin{cases} x + 2y + z = 2 \\ y - 3z = -10 \\ z = 3 \end{cases}$$

We identify the z-coordinate of the solution as 3. Next, we replace z with 3 in the second equation and solve for y.

$$\begin{aligned} y - 3z &= -10 && \text{Second equation} \\ y - 3(3) &= -10 && \text{Let } z = 3. \\ y &= -1 \end{aligned}$$

To find x, we let $z = 3$ and $y = -1$ in the first equation.

$$x + 2y + z = 2 \quad \text{First equation}$$
$$x + 2(-1) + 3 = 2 \quad \text{Let } z = 3 \text{ and } y = -1.$$
$$x = 1$$

The ordered triple solution is $(1, -1, 3)$. Check to see that it satisfies all three equations in the original system.   □

PRACTICE
3   Use matrices to solve the system.

$$\begin{cases} x + 3y - z = 0 \\ 2x + y + 3z = 5 \\ -x - 2y + 4z = 7 \end{cases}$$

D Exercise Set   MyMathLab®

Solve each system of linear equations using matrices. See Example 1.

1. $\begin{cases} x + y = 1 \\ x - 2y = 4 \end{cases}$

2. $\begin{cases} 2x - y = 8 \\ x + 3y = 11 \end{cases}$

3. $\begin{cases} x + 3y = 2 \\ x + 2y = 0 \end{cases}$

4. $\begin{cases} 4x - y = 5 \\ 3x + 3y = 0 \end{cases}$

Solve each system of linear equations using matrices. See Example 2.

5. $\begin{cases} x - 2y = 4 \\ 2x - 4y = 4 \end{cases}$

6. $\begin{cases} -x + 3y = 6 \\ 3x - 9y = 9 \end{cases}$

7. $\begin{cases} 3x - 3y = 9 \\ 2x - 2y = 6 \end{cases}$

8. $\begin{cases} 9x - 3y = 6 \\ -18x + 6y = -12 \end{cases}$

Solve each system of linear equations using matrices. See Example 3.

9. $\begin{cases} x + y = 3 \\ 2y = 10 \\ 3x + 2y - 4z = 12 \end{cases}$

10. $\begin{cases} 5x = 5 \\ 2x + y = 4 \\ 3x + y - 5z = -15 \end{cases}$

11. $\begin{cases} 2y - z = -7 \\ x + 4y + z = -4 \\ 5x - y + 2z = 13 \end{cases}$

12. $\begin{cases} 4y + 3z = -2 \\ 5x - 4y = 1 \\ -5x + 4y + z = -3 \end{cases}$

MIXED PRACTICE

Solve each system of linear equations using matrices. See Examples 1 through 3.

13. $\begin{cases} x - 4 = 0 \\ x + y = 1 \end{cases}$

14. $\begin{cases} 3y = 6 \\ x + y = 7 \end{cases}$

15. $\begin{cases} x + y + z = 2 \\ 2x - z = 5 \\ 3y + z = 2 \end{cases}$

16. $\begin{cases} x + 2y + z = 5 \\ x - y - z = 3 \\ y + z = 2 \end{cases}$

17. $\begin{cases} 5x - 2y = 27 \\ -3x + 5y = 18 \end{cases}$

18. $\begin{cases} 4x - y = 9 \\ 2x + 3y = -27 \end{cases}$

19. $\begin{cases} 4x - 7y = 7 \\ 12x - 21y = 24 \end{cases}$

20. $\begin{cases} 2x - 5y = 12 \\ -4x + 10y = 20 \end{cases}$

21. $\begin{cases} 4x - y + 2z = 5 \\ 2y + z = 4 \\ 4x + y + 3z = 10 \end{cases}$

22. $\begin{cases} 5y - 7z = 14 \\ 2x + y + 4z = 10 \\ 2x + 6y - 3z = 30 \end{cases}$

23. $\begin{cases} 4x + y + z = 3 \\ -x + y - 2z = -11 \\ x + 2y + 2z = -1 \end{cases}$

24. $\begin{cases} x + y + z = 9 \\ 3x - y + z = -1 \\ -2x + 2y - 3z = -2 \end{cases}$

CONCEPT EXTENSIONS

Solve. See the Concept Check in this section.

25. For the system $\begin{cases} x + z = 7 \\ y + 2z = -6, \\ 3x - y = 0 \end{cases}$ which is the correct corresponding matrix?

a. $\begin{bmatrix} 1 & 1 & \vdots & 7 \\ 1 & 2 & \vdots & -6 \\ 3 & -1 & \vdots & 0 \end{bmatrix}$

b. $\begin{bmatrix} 1 & 0 & 1 & \vdots & 7 \\ 1 & 2 & 0 & \vdots & -6 \\ 3 & -1 & 0 & \vdots & 0 \end{bmatrix}$

c. $\begin{bmatrix} 1 & 0 & 1 & \vdots & 7 \\ 0 & 1 & 2 & \vdots & -6 \\ 3 & -1 & 0 & \vdots & 0 \end{bmatrix}$

Appendix E

Solving Systems of Equations by Determinants

OBJECTIVES

1 Define and Evaluate a 2 × 2 Determinant.

2 Use Cramer's Rule to Solve a System of Two Linear Equations in Two Variables.

3 Define and Evaluate a 3 × 3 Determinant.

4 Use Cramer's Rule to Solve a System of Three Linear Equations in Three Variables.

We have solved systems of two linear equations in two variables in four different ways: graphically, by substitution, by elimination, and by matrices. Now we analyze another method, called **Cramer's rule.**

OBJECTIVE

1 Evaluating 2 × 2 Determinants

Recall that a matrix is a rectangular array of numbers. If a matrix has the same number of rows and columns, it is called a **square matrix.** Examples of square matrices are

$$\begin{bmatrix} 1 & 6 \\ 5 & 2 \end{bmatrix} \qquad \begin{bmatrix} 2 & 4 & 1 \\ 0 & 5 & 2 \\ 3 & 6 & 9 \end{bmatrix}$$

A **determinant** is a real number associated with a square matrix. The determinant of a square matrix is denoted by placing vertical bars about the array of numbers. Thus,

The determinant of the square matrix $\begin{bmatrix} 1 & 6 \\ 5 & 2 \end{bmatrix}$ is $\begin{vmatrix} 1 & 6 \\ 5 & 2 \end{vmatrix}$.

The determinant of the square matrix $\begin{bmatrix} 2 & 4 & 1 \\ 0 & 5 & 2 \\ 3 & 6 & 9 \end{bmatrix}$ is $\begin{vmatrix} 2 & 4 & 1 \\ 0 & 5 & 2 \\ 3 & 6 & 9 \end{vmatrix}$.

We define the determinant of a 2 × 2 matrix first. (Recall that 2 × 2 is read "two by two." It means that the matrix has 2 rows and 2 columns.)

Determinant of a 2 × 2 Matrix

$$\begin{vmatrix} a & b \\ c & d \end{vmatrix} = ad - bc$$

EXAMPLE 1 Evaluate each determinant

a. $\begin{vmatrix} -1 & 2 \\ 3 & -4 \end{vmatrix}$ **b.** $\begin{vmatrix} 2 & 0 \\ 7 & -5 \end{vmatrix}$

Solution First we identify the values of $a, b, c,$ and d. Then we perform the evaluation.

a. Here $a = -1, b = 2, c = 3,$ and $d = -4$.

$$\begin{vmatrix} -1 & 2 \\ 3 & -4 \end{vmatrix} = ad - bc = (-1)(-4) - (2)(3) = -2$$

b. In this example, $a = 2, b = 0, c = 7,$ and $d = -5$.

$$\begin{vmatrix} 2 & 0 \\ 7 & -5 \end{vmatrix} = ad - bc = 2(-5) - (0)(7) = -10$$

OBJECTIVE

2   Using Cramer's Rule to Solve a System of Two Linear Equations

To develop Cramer's rule, we solve the system $\begin{cases} ax + by = h \\ cx + dy = k \end{cases}$ using elimination. First, we eliminate y by multiplying both sides of the first equation by d and both sides of the second equation by $-b$ so that the coefficients of y are opposites. The result is that

$$\begin{cases} d(ax + by) = d \cdot h \\ -b(cx + dy) = -b \cdot k \end{cases} \quad \text{simplifies to} \quad \begin{cases} adx + bdy = hd \\ -bcx - bdy = -kb \end{cases}$$

We now add the two equations and solve for x.

$$\begin{aligned} adx + bdy &= hd \\ \underline{-bcx - bdy} &= \underline{-kb} \\ adx - bcx &= hd - kb \quad \text{Add the equations.} \\ (ad - bc)x &= hd - kb \\ x &= \frac{hd - kb}{ad - bc} \quad \text{Solve for } x. \end{aligned}$$

When we replace x with $\dfrac{hd - kb}{ad - bc}$ in the equation $ax + by = h$ and solve for y, we find that $y = \dfrac{ak - ch}{ad - bc}$.

Notice that the numerator of the value of x is the determinant of

$$\begin{vmatrix} h & b \\ k & d \end{vmatrix} = hd - kb$$

Also, the numerator of the value of y is the determinant of

$$\begin{vmatrix} a & h \\ c & k \end{vmatrix} = ak - hc$$

Finally, the denominators of the values of x and y are the same and are the determinant of

$$\begin{vmatrix} a & b \\ c & d \end{vmatrix} = ad - bc$$

This means that the values of x and y can be written in determinant notation:

$$x = \frac{\begin{vmatrix} h & b \\ k & d \end{vmatrix}}{\begin{vmatrix} a & b \\ c & d \end{vmatrix}} \quad \text{and} \quad y = \frac{\begin{vmatrix} a & h \\ c & k \end{vmatrix}}{\begin{vmatrix} a & b \\ c & d \end{vmatrix}}$$

For convenience, we label the determinants D, D_x, and D_y.

x-coefficients
y-coefficients

$$\begin{vmatrix} a & b \\ c & d \end{vmatrix} = D \qquad \begin{vmatrix} h & b \\ k & d \end{vmatrix} = D_x \qquad \begin{vmatrix} a & h \\ c & k \end{vmatrix} = D_y$$

x-column replaced
by constants

y-column replaced
by constants

These determinant formulas for the coordinates of the solution of a system are known as **Cramer's rule.**

Cramer's Rule for Two Linear Equations in Two Variables

The solution of the system $\begin{cases} ax + by = h \\ cx + dy = k \end{cases}$ is given by

$$x = \frac{\begin{vmatrix} h & b \\ k & d \end{vmatrix}}{\begin{vmatrix} a & b \\ c & d \end{vmatrix}} = \frac{D_x}{D} \qquad y = \frac{\begin{vmatrix} a & h \\ c & k \end{vmatrix}}{\begin{vmatrix} a & b \\ c & d \end{vmatrix}} = \frac{D_y}{D}$$

as long as $D = ad - bc$ is not 0.

When $D = 0$, the system is either inconsistent or the equations are dependent. When this happens, we need to use another method to see which is the case.

EXAMPLE 2 Use Cramer's rule to solve the system

$$\begin{cases} 3x + 4y = -7 \\ x - 2y = -9 \end{cases}$$

Solution First we find D, D_x, and D_y.

$$\begin{array}{ccc} a & b & h \\ \downarrow & \downarrow & \downarrow \end{array}$$

$$\begin{cases} 3x + 4y = -7 \\ x - 2y = -9 \end{cases}$$

$$\begin{array}{ccc} \uparrow & \uparrow & \uparrow \\ c & d & k \end{array}$$

$$D = \begin{vmatrix} a & b \\ c & d \end{vmatrix} = \begin{vmatrix} 3 & 4 \\ 1 & -2 \end{vmatrix} = 3(-2) - 4(1) = -10$$

$$D_x = \begin{vmatrix} h & b \\ k & d \end{vmatrix} = \begin{vmatrix} -7 & 4 \\ -9 & -2 \end{vmatrix} = (-7)(-2) - 4(-9) = 50$$

$$D_y = \begin{vmatrix} a & h \\ c & k \end{vmatrix} = \begin{vmatrix} 3 & -7 \\ 1 & -9 \end{vmatrix} = 3(-9) - (-7)(1) = -20$$

Then $x = \dfrac{D_x}{D} = \dfrac{50}{-10} = -5$ and $y = \dfrac{D_y}{D} = \dfrac{-20}{-10} = 2$.

The ordered pair solution is $(-5, 2)$.

As always, check the solution in both original equations. □

EXAMPLE 3 Use Cramer's rule to solve the system

$$\begin{cases} 5x + y = 5 \\ -7x - 2y = -7 \end{cases}$$

Solution First we find D, D_x, and D_y.

$$D = \begin{vmatrix} 5 & 1 \\ -7 & -2 \end{vmatrix} = 5(-2) - (-7)(1) = -3$$

$$D_x = \begin{vmatrix} 5 & 1 \\ -7 & -2 \end{vmatrix} = 5(-2) - (-7)(1) = -3$$

$$D_y = \begin{vmatrix} 5 & 5 \\ -7 & -7 \end{vmatrix} = 5(-7) - 5(-7) = 0$$

Then

$$x = \frac{D_x}{D} = \frac{-3}{-3} = 1 \qquad y = \frac{D_y}{D} = \frac{0}{-3} = 0$$

The ordered pair solution is $(1, 0)$.

OBJECTIVE
3   Evaluating 3 × 3 Determinants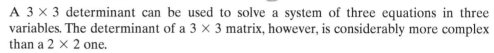

A 3×3 determinant can be used to solve a system of three equations in three variables. The determinant of a 3×3 matrix, however, is considerably more complex than a 2×2 one.

Determinant of a 3 × 3 Matrix

$$\begin{vmatrix} a_1 & b_1 & c_1 \\ a_2 & b_2 & c_2 \\ a_3 & b_3 & c_3 \end{vmatrix} = a_1 \cdot \begin{vmatrix} b_2 & c_2 \\ b_3 & c_3 \end{vmatrix} - a_2 \cdot \begin{vmatrix} b_1 & c_1 \\ b_3 & c_3 \end{vmatrix} + a_3 \cdot \begin{vmatrix} b_1 & c_1 \\ b_2 & c_2 \end{vmatrix}$$

Notice that the determinant of a 3×3 matrix is related to the determinants of three 2×2 matrices. Each determinant of these 2×2 matrices is called a **minor,** and every element of a 3×3 matrix has a minor associated with it. For example, the minor of c_2 is the determinant of the 2×2 matrix found by deleting the row and column containing c_2.

$$\begin{array}{ccc} a_1 & b_1 & c_1 \\ a_2 & b_2 & c_2 \\ a_3 & b_3 & c_3 \end{array} \qquad \text{The minor of } c_2 \text{ is } \begin{vmatrix} a_1 & b_1 \\ a_3 & b_3 \end{vmatrix}$$

Also, the minor of element a_1 is the determinant of the 2×2 matrix that has no row or column containing a_1.

$$\begin{array}{ccc} a_1 & b_1 & c_1 \\ a_2 & b_2 & c_2 \\ a_3 & b_3 & c_3 \end{array} \qquad \text{The minor of } a_1 \text{ is } \begin{vmatrix} b_2 & c_2 \\ b_3 & c_3 \end{vmatrix}$$

So the determinant of a 3×3 matrix can be written as

$$a_1 \cdot (\text{minor of } a_1) - a_2 \cdot (\text{minor of } a_2) + a_3 \cdot (\text{minor of } a_3)$$

Finding the determinant by using minors of elements in the first column is called **expanding** by the minors of the first column. *The value of a determinant can be found by expanding by the minors of any row or column.* The following **array of signs** is helpful in determining whether to add or subtract the product of an element and its minor.

$$\begin{array}{ccc} + & - & + \\ - & + & - \\ + & - & + \end{array}$$

If an element is in a position marked $+$, we add. If marked $-$, we subtract.

EXAMPLE 4 Evaluate by expanding by the minors of the given row or column.

$$\begin{vmatrix} 0 & 5 & 1 \\ 1 & 3 & -1 \\ -2 & 2 & 4 \end{vmatrix}$$

a. First column

b. Second row

Solution

a. The elements of the first column are 0, 1, and −2. The first column of the array of signs is +, −, +.

$$\begin{vmatrix} 0 & 5 & 1 \\ 1 & 3 & -1 \\ -2 & 2 & 4 \end{vmatrix} = 0 \cdot \begin{vmatrix} 3 & -1 \\ 2 & 4 \end{vmatrix} - 1 \cdot \begin{vmatrix} 5 & 1 \\ 2 & 4 \end{vmatrix} + (-2) \cdot \begin{vmatrix} 5 & 1 \\ 3 & -1 \end{vmatrix}$$

$$= 0(12 - (-2)) - 1(20 - 2) + (-2)(-5 - 3)$$

$$= 0 - 18 + 16 = -2$$

b. The elements of the second row are 1, 3, and −1. This time, the signs begin with − and again alternate.

$$\begin{vmatrix} 0 & 5 & 1 \\ 1 & 3 & -1 \\ -2 & 2 & 4 \end{vmatrix} = -1 \cdot \begin{vmatrix} 5 & 1 \\ 2 & 4 \end{vmatrix} + 3 \cdot \begin{vmatrix} 0 & 1 \\ -2 & 4 \end{vmatrix} - (-1) \cdot \begin{vmatrix} 0 & 5 \\ -2 & 2 \end{vmatrix}$$

$$= -1(20 - 2) + 3(0 - (-2)) - (-1)(0 - (-10))$$

$$= -18 + 6 + 10 = -2$$

Notice that the determinant of the 3 × 3 matrix is the same regardless of the row or column you select to expand by.

✓CONCEPT CHECK

Why would expanding by minors of the second row be a good choice for the determinant $\begin{vmatrix} 3 & 4 & -2 \\ 5 & 0 & 0 \\ 6 & -3 & 7 \end{vmatrix}$?

OBJECTIVE

4 **Using Cramer's Rule to Solve a System of Three Linear Equations**

A system of three equations in three variables may be solved with Cramer's rule also. Using the elimination process to solve a system with unknown constants as coefficients leads to the following.

Cramer's Rule for Three Equations in Three Variables

The solution of the system $\begin{cases} a_1x + b_1y + c_1z = k_1 \\ a_2x + b_2y + c_2z = k_2 \\ a_3x + b_3y + c_3z = k_3 \end{cases}$ is given by

$$x = \frac{D_x}{D} \qquad y = \frac{D_y}{D} \qquad \text{and} \qquad z = \frac{D_z}{D}$$

where

$$D = \begin{vmatrix} a_1 & b_1 & c_1 \\ a_2 & b_2 & c_2 \\ a_3 & b_3 & c_3 \end{vmatrix} \qquad D_x = \begin{vmatrix} k_1 & b_1 & c_1 \\ k_2 & b_2 & c_2 \\ k_3 & b_3 & c_3 \end{vmatrix}$$

$$D_y = \begin{vmatrix} a_1 & k_1 & c_1 \\ a_2 & k_2 & c_2 \\ a_3 & k_3 & c_3 \end{vmatrix} \qquad D_z = \begin{vmatrix} a_1 & b_1 & k_1 \\ a_2 & b_2 & k_2 \\ a_3 & b_3 & k_3 \end{vmatrix}$$

as long as D is not 0.

Answer to Concept Check:
Two elements of the second row are 0, which makes calculations easier.

EXAMPLE 5   Use Cramer's rule to solve the system

$$\begin{cases} x - 2y + z = 4 \\ 3x + y - 2z = 3 \\ 5x + 5y + 3z = -8 \end{cases}$$

Solution   First we find $D, D_x, D_y,$ and D_z. Beginning with D, we expand by the minors of the first column.

$$D = \begin{vmatrix} 1 & -2 & 1 \\ 3 & 1 & -2 \\ 5 & 5 & 3 \end{vmatrix} = 1 \cdot \begin{vmatrix} 1 & -2 \\ 5 & 3 \end{vmatrix} - 3 \cdot \begin{vmatrix} -2 & 1 \\ 5 & 3 \end{vmatrix} + 5 \cdot \begin{vmatrix} -2 & 1 \\ 1 & -2 \end{vmatrix}$$

$$= 1(3 - (-10)) - 3(-6 - 5) + 5(4 - 1)$$

$$= 13 + 33 + 15 = 61$$

$$D_x = \begin{vmatrix} 4 & -2 & 1 \\ 3 & 1 & -2 \\ -8 & 5 & 3 \end{vmatrix} = 4 \cdot \begin{vmatrix} 1 & -2 \\ 5 & 3 \end{vmatrix} - 3 \cdot \begin{vmatrix} -2 & 1 \\ 5 & 3 \end{vmatrix} + (-8) \cdot \begin{vmatrix} -2 & 1 \\ 1 & -2 \end{vmatrix}$$

$$= 4(3 - (-10)) - 3(-6 - 5) + (-8)(4 - 1)$$

$$= 52 + 33 - 24 = 61$$

$$D_y = \begin{vmatrix} 1 & 4 & 1 \\ 3 & 3 & -2 \\ 5 & -8 & 3 \end{vmatrix} = 1 \cdot \begin{vmatrix} 3 & -2 \\ -8 & 3 \end{vmatrix} - 3 \cdot \begin{vmatrix} 4 & 1 \\ -8 & 3 \end{vmatrix} + 5 \cdot \begin{vmatrix} 4 & 1 \\ 3 & -2 \end{vmatrix}$$

$$= 1(9 - 16) - 3(12 - (-8)) + 5(-8 - 3)$$

$$= -7 - 60 - 55 = -122$$

$$D_z = \begin{vmatrix} 1 & -2 & 4 \\ 3 & 1 & 3 \\ 5 & 5 & -8 \end{vmatrix} = 1 \cdot \begin{vmatrix} 1 & 3 \\ 5 & -8 \end{vmatrix} - 3 \cdot \begin{vmatrix} -2 & 4 \\ 5 & -8 \end{vmatrix} + 5 \cdot \begin{vmatrix} -2 & 4 \\ 1 & 3 \end{vmatrix}$$

$$= 1(-8 - 15) - 3(16 - 20) + 5(-6 - 4)$$

$$= -23 + 12 - 50 = -61$$

From these determinants, we calculate the solution:

$$x = \frac{D_x}{D} = \frac{61}{61} = 1 \quad y = \frac{D_y}{D} = \frac{-122}{61} = -2 \quad z = \frac{D_z}{D} = \frac{-61}{61} = -1$$

The ordered triple solution is $(1, -2, -1)$. Check this solution by verifying that it satisfies each equation of the system. ☐

E Exercise Set   MyMathLab®

Evaluate. See Example 1.

1. $\begin{vmatrix} 3 & 5 \\ -1 & 7 \end{vmatrix}$

2. $\begin{vmatrix} -5 & 1 \\ 0 & -4 \end{vmatrix}$

3. $\begin{vmatrix} 9 & -2 \\ 4 & -3 \end{vmatrix}$

4. $\begin{vmatrix} 4 & 0 \\ 9 & 8 \end{vmatrix}$

5. $\begin{vmatrix} -2 & 9 \\ 4 & -18 \end{vmatrix}$

6. $\begin{vmatrix} -40 & 8 \\ 70 & -14 \end{vmatrix}$

Use Cramer's rule, if possible, to solve each system of linear equations. See Examples 2 and 3.

7. $\begin{cases} 2y - 4 = 0 \\ x + 2y = 5 \end{cases}$

8. $\begin{cases} 4x - y = 5 \\ 3x - 3 = 0 \end{cases}$

9. $\begin{cases} 3x + y = 1 \\ 2y = 2 - 6x \end{cases}$

10. $\begin{cases} y = 2x - 5 \\ 8x - 4y = 20 \end{cases}$

11. $\begin{cases} 5x - 2y = 27 \\ -3x + 5y = 18 \end{cases}$

12. $\begin{cases} 4x - y = 9 \\ 2x + 3y = -27 \end{cases}$

Evaluate. See Example 4.

13. $\begin{vmatrix} 2 & 1 & 0 \\ 0 & 5 & -3 \\ 4 & 0 & 2 \end{vmatrix}$

14. $\begin{vmatrix} -6 & 4 & 2 \\ 1 & 0 & 5 \\ 0 & 3 & 1 \end{vmatrix}$

15. $\begin{vmatrix} 4 & -6 & 0 \\ -2 & 3 & 0 \\ 4 & -6 & 1 \end{vmatrix}$

16. $\begin{vmatrix} 5 & 2 & 1 \\ 3 & -6 & 0 \\ -2 & 8 & 0 \end{vmatrix}$

17. $\begin{vmatrix} 3 & 6 & -3 \\ -1 & -2 & 3 \\ 4 & -1 & 6 \end{vmatrix}$

18. $\begin{vmatrix} 2 & -2 & 1 \\ 4 & 1 & 3 \\ 3 & 1 & 2 \end{vmatrix}$

Use Cramer's rule, if possible, to solve each system of linear equations. See Example 5.

19. $\begin{cases} 3x \quad\quad + z = -1 \\ -x - 3y + z = 7 \\ \quad\quad 3y + z = 5 \end{cases}$

20. $\begin{cases} \quad\quad 4y - 3z = -2 \\ 8x - 4y \quad\quad = 4 \\ -8x + 4y + z = -2 \end{cases}$

21. $\begin{cases} x + y + z = 8 \\ 2x - y - z = 10 \\ x - 2y + 3z = 22 \end{cases}$

22. $\begin{cases} 5x + y + 3z = 1 \\ x - y - 3z = -7 \\ -x + y \quad\quad = 1 \end{cases}$

MIXED PRACTICE

Evaluate.

23. $\begin{vmatrix} 10 & -1 \\ -4 & 2 \end{vmatrix}$

24. $\begin{vmatrix} -6 & 2 \\ 5 & -1 \end{vmatrix}$

25. $\begin{vmatrix} 1 & 0 & 4 \\ 1 & -1 & 2 \\ 3 & 2 & 1 \end{vmatrix}$

26. $\begin{vmatrix} 0 & 1 & 2 \\ 3 & -1 & 2 \\ 3 & 2 & -2 \end{vmatrix}$

⊙ **27.** $\begin{vmatrix} \frac{3}{4} & \frac{5}{2} \\ -\frac{1}{6} & \frac{7}{3} \end{vmatrix}$

28. $\begin{vmatrix} \frac{5}{7} & \frac{1}{3} \\ \frac{6}{7} & \frac{2}{3} \end{vmatrix}$

29. $\begin{vmatrix} 4 & -2 & 2 \\ 6 & -1 & 3 \\ 2 & 1 & 1 \end{vmatrix}$

30. $\begin{vmatrix} 1 & 5 & 0 \\ 7 & 9 & -4 \\ 3 & 2 & -2 \end{vmatrix}$

31. $\begin{vmatrix} -2 & 5 & 4 \\ 5 & -1 & 3 \\ 4 & 1 & 2 \end{vmatrix}$

32. $\begin{vmatrix} 5 & -2 & 4 \\ -1 & 5 & 3 \\ 1 & 4 & 2 \end{vmatrix}$

Use Cramer's rule, if possible, to solve each system of linear equations.

⊙ **33.** $\begin{cases} 2x - 5y = 4 \\ x + 2y = -7 \end{cases}$

34. $\begin{cases} 3x - y = 2 \\ -5x + 2y = 0 \end{cases}$

35. $\begin{cases} 4x + 2y = 5 \\ 2x + y = -1 \end{cases}$

36. $\begin{cases} 3x + 6y = 15 \\ 2x + 4y = 3 \end{cases}$

37. $\begin{cases} 2x + 2y + z = 1 \\ -x + y + 2z = 3 \\ x + 2y + 4z = 0 \end{cases}$

38. $\begin{cases} 2x - 3y + z = 5 \\ x + y + z = 0 \\ 4x + 2y + 4z = 4 \end{cases}$

39. $\begin{cases} \frac{2}{3}x - \frac{3}{4}y = -1 \\ -\frac{1}{6}x + \frac{3}{4}y = \frac{5}{2} \end{cases}$

40. $\begin{cases} \frac{1}{2}x - \frac{1}{3}y = -3 \\ \frac{1}{8}x + \frac{1}{6}y = 0 \end{cases}$

41. $\begin{cases} 0.7x - 0.2y = -1.6 \\ 0.2x - y = -1.4 \end{cases}$

42. $\begin{cases} -0.7x + 0.6y = 1.3 \\ 0.5x - 0.3y = -0.8 \end{cases}$

43. $\begin{cases} -2x + 4y - 2z = 6 \\ x - 2y + z = -3 \\ 3x - 6y + 3z = -9 \end{cases}$

44. $\begin{cases} -x - y + 3z = 2 \\ 4x + 4y - 12z = -8 \\ -3x - 3y + 9z = 6 \end{cases}$

45. $\begin{cases} x - 2y + z = -5 \\ \quad\quad 3y + 2z = 4 \\ 3x - y \quad\quad = -2 \end{cases}$

46. $\begin{cases} 4x + 5y \quad\quad = 10 \\ \quad\quad 3y + 2z = -6 \\ x + y + z = 3 \end{cases}$

CONCEPT EXTENSIONS

Find the value of x such that each is a true statement.

47. $\begin{vmatrix} 1 & x \\ 2 & 7 \end{vmatrix} = -3$

48. $\begin{vmatrix} 6 & 1 \\ -2 & x \end{vmatrix} = 26$

49. If all the elements in a single row of a square matrix are zero, to what does the determinant evaluate? Explain your answer.

50. If all the elements in a single column of a square matrix are 0, to what does the determinant evaluate? Explain your answer.

51. Suppose you are interested in finding the determinant of a 4×4 matrix. Study the pattern shown in the array of signs for a 3×3 matrix. Use the pattern to expand the array of signs for use with a 4×4 matrix.

52. Why would expanding by minors of the second row be a good choice for the determinant $\begin{vmatrix} 3 & 4 & -2 \\ 5 & 0 & 0 \\ 6 & -3 & 7 \end{vmatrix}$?

Find the value of each determinant. To evaluate a 4×4 determinant, select any row or column and expand by the minors. The array of signs for a 4×4 determinant is the same as for a 3×3 determinant except expanded.

53. $\begin{vmatrix} 5 & 0 & 0 & 0 \\ 0 & 4 & 2 & -1 \\ 1 & 3 & -2 & 0 \\ 0 & -3 & 1 & 2 \end{vmatrix}$

54. $\begin{vmatrix} 1 & 7 & 0 & -1 \\ 1 & 3 & -2 & 0 \\ 1 & 0 & -1 & 2 \\ 0 & -6 & 2 & 4 \end{vmatrix}$

55. $\begin{vmatrix} 4 & 0 & 2 & 5 \\ 0 & 3 & -1 & 1 \\ 0 & 0 & 2 & 0 \\ 0 & 0 & 0 & 1 \end{vmatrix}$

56. $\begin{vmatrix} 2 & 0 & -1 & 4 \\ 6 & 0 & 4 & 1 \\ 2 & 4 & 3 & -1 \\ 4 & 0 & 5 & -4 \end{vmatrix}$

Appendix F

Mean, Median, and Mode

It is sometimes desirable to be able to describe a set of data, or a set of numbers, by a single "middle" number. Three such **measures of central tendency** are the mean, the median, and the mode.

The most common measure of central tendency is the mean (sometimes called the arithmetic mean or the average). The **mean** of a set of data items, denoted by $\bar{x}$, is the sum of the items divided by the number of items.

EXAMPLE 1 Seven students in a psychology class conducted an experiment on mazes. Each student was given a pencil and asked to successfully complete the same maze. The timed results are below.

Student	Ann	Thanh	Carlos	Jesse	Melinda	Ramzi	Dayni
Time (Seconds)	13.2	11.8	10.7	16.2	15.9	13.8	18.5

a. Who completed the maze in the shortest time? Who completed the maze in the longest time?

b. Find the mean.

c. How many students took longer than the mean time? How many students took shorter than the mean time?

Solution

a. Carlos completed the maze in 10.7 seconds, the shortest time. Dayni completed the maze in 18.5 seconds, the longest time.

b. To find the mean, $\bar{x}$, find the sum of the data items and divide by 7, the number of items.

$$\bar{x} = \frac{13.2 + 11.8 + 10.7 + 16.2 + 15.9 + 13.8 + 18.5}{7} = \frac{100.1}{7} = 14.3$$

c. Three students, Jesse, Melinda, and Dayni, had times longer than the mean time. Four students, Ann, Thanh, Carlos, and Ramzi, had times shorter than the mean time. ☐

Two other measures of central tendency are the median and the mode.

The **median** of an ordered set of numbers is the middle number. If the number of items is even, the median is the mean of the two middle numbers. The **mode** of a set of numbers is the number that occurs most often. It is possible for a data set to have no mode or more than one mode.

EXAMPLE 2 Find the median and the mode of the following list of numbers. These numbers were high temperatures for fourteen consecutive days in a city in Montana.

$$76, 80, 85, 86, 89, 87, 82, 77, 76, 79, 82, 89, 89, 92$$

(Continued on next page)

Solution

First, write the numbers in order.

76, 76, 77, 79, 80, 82, 82, 85, 86, 87, 89, 89, 89, 92

two
middle numbers

mode

Since there is an even number of items, the median is the mean of the two middle numbers.

$$\text{median} = \frac{82 + 85}{2} = 83.5$$

The mode is 89, since 89 occurs most often.

F Exercise Set

MyMathLab®

For each of the following data sets, find the mean, the median, and the mode. If necessary, round the mean to one decimal place.

1. 21, 28, 16, 42, 38

2. 42, 35, 36, 40, 50

3. 7.6, 8.2, 8.2, 9.6, 5.7, 9.1

4. 4.9, 7.1, 6.8, 6.8, 5.3, 4.9

5. 0.2, 0.3, 0.5, 0.6, 0.6, 0.9, 0.2, 0.7, 1.1

6. 0.6, 0.6, 0.8, 0.4, 0.5, 0.3, 0.7, 0.8, 0.1

7. 231, 543, 601, 293, 588, 109, 334, 268

8. 451, 356, 478, 776, 892, 500, 467, 780

The eight tallest buildings in the United States are listed below. Use this table for Exercises 9 through 12.

Building	Height (feet)
Willis Tower, Chicago, IL	1454
Empire State, New York, NY	1250
Amoco, Chicago, IL	1136
John Hancock Center, Chicago, IL	1127
First Interstate World Center, Los Angeles, CA	1107
Chrysler, New York, NY	1046
NationsBank Tower, Atlanta, GA	1023
Texas Commerce Tower, Houston, TX	1002

9. Find the mean height for the five tallest buildings.
10. Find the median height for the five tallest buildings.
11. Find the median height for the eight tallest buildings.
12. Find the mean height for the eight tallest buildings.

During an experiment, the following times (in seconds) were recorded: 7.8, 6.9, 7.5, 4.7, 6.9, 7.0.

13. Find the mean. Round to the nearest tenth.
14. Find the median.
15. Find the mode.

In a mathematics class, the following test scores were recorded for a student: 86, 95, 91, 74, 77, 85.

16. Find the mean. Round to the nearest hundredth.
17. Find the median.
18. Find the mode.

The following pulse rates were recorded for a group of fifteen students: 78, 80, 66, 68, 71, 64, 82, 71, 70, 65, 70, 75, 77, 86, 72.

19. Find the mean.
20. Find the median.
21. Find the mode.
22. How many rates were higher than the mean?
23. How many rates were lower than the mean?
24. Have each student in your algebra class take his/her pulse rate. Record the data and find the mean, the median, and the mode.

Find the missing numbers in each list of numbers. (These numbers are not necessarily in numerical order.)

25. __, __, 16, 18, __
   The mode is 21.   The mean is 20.
26. __, __, __, __, 40
   The mode is 35.   The median is 37.   The mean is 38.

Appendix G

Review of Angles, Lines, and Special Triangles

The word **geometry** is formed from the Greek words **geo,** meaning earth, and **metron,** meaning measure. Geometry literally means to measure the earth.

This section contains a review of some basic geometric ideas. It will be assumed that fundamental ideas of geometry such as point, line, ray, and angle are known. In this appendix, the notation $\angle 1$ is read "angle 1" and the notation $m\angle 1$ is read "the measure of angle 1."

We first review types of angles.

Angles

A **right angle** is an angle whose measure is 90°. A right angle can be indicated by a square drawn at the vertex of the angle, as shown below.

An angle whose measure is more than 0° but less than 90° is called an **acute angle.**

An angle whose measure is greater than 90° but less than 180° is called an **obtuse angle.**

An angle whose measure is 180° is called a **straight angle.**

Two angles are said to be **complementary** if the sum of their measures is 90°. Each angle is called the **complement** of the other.

Two angles are said to be **supplementary** if the sum of their measures is 180°. Each angle is called the **supplement** of the other.

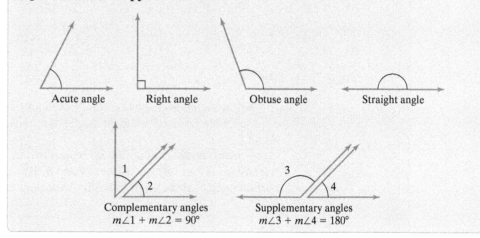

EXAMPLE 1   If an angle measures 28°, find its complement.

Solution   Two angles are complementary if the sum of their measures is 90°. The complement of a 28° angle is an angle whose measure is $90° - 28° = 62°$. To check, notice that $28° + 62° = 90°$. ☐

Plane is an undefined term that we will describe. A plane can be thought of as a flat surface with infinite length and width, but no thickness. A plane is two dimensional.

The arrows in the following diagram indicate that a plane extends indefinitely and has no boundaries.

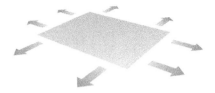

Figures that lie on a plane are called **plane figures.** Lines that lie in the same plane are called **coplanar.**

Lines

Two lines are **parallel** if they lie in the same plane but never meet.
Intersecting lines meet or cross in one point.
Two lines that form right angles when they intersect are said to be **perpendicular.**

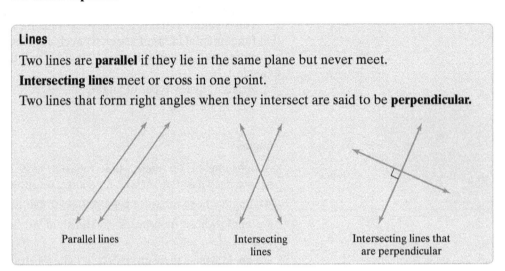

| Parallel lines | Intersecting lines | Intersecting lines that are perpendicular |

Two intersecting lines form **vertical angles.** Angles 1 and 3 are vertical angles. Also, angles 2 and 4 are vertical angles. It can be shown that **vertical angles have equal measures.**

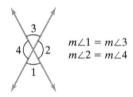

$m\angle 1 = m\angle 3$
$m\angle 2 = m\angle 4$

Adjacent angles have the same vertex and share a side. Angles 1 and 2 are adjacent angles. Other pairs of adjacent angles are angles 2 and 3, angles 3 and 4, and angles 4 and 1.

A **transversal** is a line that intersects two or more lines in the same plane. Line l is a transversal that intersects lines m and n. The eight angles formed are numbered and certain pairs of these angles are given special names.

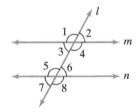

Corresponding angles: $\angle 1$ and $\angle 5$, $\angle 3$ and $\angle 7$, $\angle 2$ and $\angle 6$, and $\angle 4$ and $\angle 8$.
Exterior angles: $\angle 1$, $\angle 2$, $\angle 7$, and $\angle 8$.
Interior angles: $\angle 3$, $\angle 4$, $\angle 5$, and $\angle 6$.
Alternate interior angles: $\angle 3$ and $\angle 6$, $\angle 4$ and $\angle 5$.

These angles and parallel lines are related in the following manner.

Parallel Lines Cut by a Transversal

1. If two parallel lines are cut by a transversal, then
   a. corresponding angles are equal and
   b. alternate interior angles are equal.
2. If corresponding angles formed by two lines and a transversal are equal, then the lines are parallel.
3. If alternate interior angles formed by two lines and a transversal are equal, then the lines are parallel.

EXAMPLE 2 Given that lines m and n are parallel and that the measure of angle 1 is 100°, find the measures of angles 2, 3, and 4.

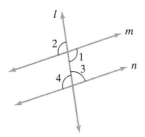

Solution $m\angle 2 = 100°$, since angles 1 and 2 are vertical angles.

$m\angle 4 = 100°$, since angles 1 and 4 are alternate interior angles.

$m\angle 3 = 180° - 100° = 80°$, since angles 4 and 3 are supplementary angles. □

A **polygon** is the union of three or more coplanar line segments that intersect each other only at each end point, with each end point shared by exactly two segments.

A **triangle** is a polygon with three sides. The sum of the measures of the three angles of a triangle is 180°. In the following figure, $m\angle 1 + m\angle 2 + m\angle 3 = 180°$.

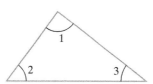

EXAMPLE 3 Find the measure of the third angle of the triangle shown.

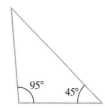

Solution The sum of the measures of the angles of a triangle is 180°. Since one angle measures 45° and the other angle measures 95°, the third angle measures $180° - 45° - 95° = 40°$. □

Two triangles are **congruent** if they have the same size and the same shape. In congruent triangles, the measures of corresponding angles are equal and the lengths of corresponding sides are equal. The following triangles are congruent.

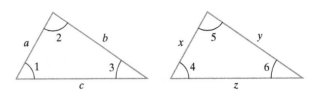

Corresponding angles are equal: $m\angle 1 = m\angle 4, m\angle 2 = m\angle 5$, and $m\angle 3 = m\angle 6$. Also, lengths of corresponding sides are equal: $a = x$, $b = y$, and $c = z$.

Any one of the following may be used to determine whether two triangles are congruent.

Congruent Triangles

1. If the measures of two angles of a triangle equal the measures of two angles of another triangle and the lengths of the sides between each pair of angles are equal, the triangles are congruent.

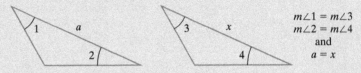

$$m\angle 1 = m\angle 3$$
$$m\angle 2 = m\angle 4$$
and
$$a = x$$

2. If the lengths of the three sides of a triangle equal the lengths of corresponding sides of another triangle, the triangles are congruent.

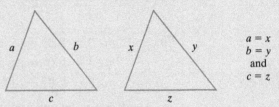

$$a = x$$
$$b = y$$
and
$$c = z$$

3. If the lengths of two sides of a triangle equal the lengths of corresponding sides of another triangle, and the measures of the angles between each pair of sides are equal, the triangles are congruent.

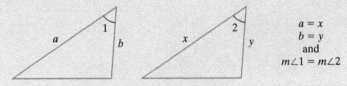

$$a = x$$
$$b = y$$
and
$$m\angle 1 = m\angle 2$$

Two triangles are **similar** if they have the same shape. In similar triangles, the measures of corresponding angles are equal and corresponding sides are in proportion. The following triangles are similar. (All similar triangles drawn in this appendix will be oriented the same.)

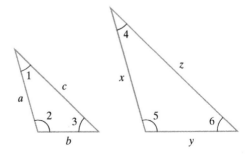

Corresponding angles are equal: $m\angle 1 = m\angle 4$, $m\angle 2 = m\angle 5$, and $m\angle 3 = m\angle 6$.

Also, corresponding sides are proportional: $\dfrac{a}{x} = \dfrac{b}{y} = \dfrac{c}{z}$.

Any one of the following may be used to determine whether two triangles are similar.

> **Similar Triangles**
>
> **1.** If the measures of two angles of a triangle equal the measures of two angles of another triangle, the triangles are similar.
>
>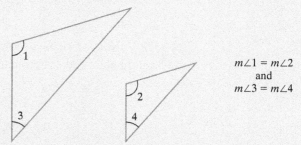
>
> $m\angle 1 = m\angle 2$
> and
> $m\angle 3 = m\angle 4$
>
> **2.** If three sides of one triangle are proportional to three sides of another triangle, the triangles are similar.
>
>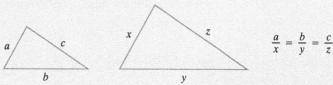
>
> $\dfrac{a}{x} = \dfrac{b}{y} = \dfrac{c}{z}$
>
> **3.** If two sides of a triangle are proportional to two sides of another triangle and the measures of the included angles are equal, the triangles are similar.
>
>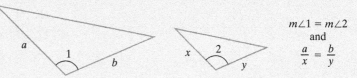
>
> $m\angle 1 = m\angle 2$
> and
> $\dfrac{a}{x} = \dfrac{b}{y}$

EXAMPLE 4   Given that the following triangles are similar, find the missing length x.

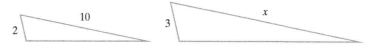

Solution   Since the triangles are similar, corresponding sides are in proportion. Thus, $\dfrac{2}{3} = \dfrac{10}{x}$. To solve this equation for x, we multiply both sides by the LCD, $3x$.

$$3x\left(\frac{2}{3}\right) = 3x\left(\frac{10}{x}\right)$$
$$2x = 30$$
$$x = 15$$

The missing length is 15 units. ☐

A **right triangle** contains a right angle. The side opposite the right angle is called the **hypotenuse,** and the other two sides are called the **legs.** The **Pythagorean theorem** gives a formula that relates the lengths of the three sides of a right triangle.

> **The Pythagorean Theorem**
>
> If a and b are the lengths of the legs of a right triangle, and c is the length of the hypotenuse, then $a^2 + b^2 = c^2$.
>
>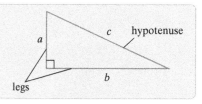

EXAMPLE 5 Find the length of the hypotenuse of a right triangle whose legs have lengths of 3 centimeters and 4 centimeters.

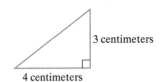

3 centimeters

4 centimeters

Solution Because we have a right triangle, we use the Pythagorean theorem. The legs are 3 centimeters and 4 centimeters, so let $a = 3$ and $b = 4$ in the formula.

$$a^2 + b^2 = c^2$$
$$3^2 + 4^2 = c^2$$
$$9 + 16 = c^2$$
$$25 = c^2$$

Since c represents a length, we assume that c is positive. Thus, if c^2 is 25, c must be 5. The hypotenuse has a length of 5 centimeters. □

G Exercise Set   MyMathLab®

Find the complement of each angle. See Example 1.

1. $19°$ **2.** $65°$

3. $70.8°$ **4.** $45\frac{2}{3}°$

5. $11\frac{1}{4}°$ **6.** $19.6°$

Find the supplement of each angle.

7. $150°$ **8.** $90°$

9. $30.2°$ **10.** $81.9°$

11. $79\frac{1}{2}°$ **12.** $165\frac{8}{9}°$

13. If lines m and n are parallel, find the measures of angles 1 through 7. See Example 2.

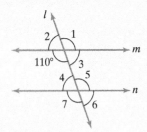

14. If lines m and n are parallel, find the measures of angles 1 through 5. See Example 2.

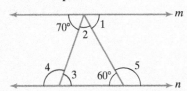

In each of the following, the measures of two angles of a triangle are given. Find the measure of the third angle. See Example 3.

15. $11°, 79°$ **16.** $8°, 102°$

17. $25°, 65°$ **18.** $44°, 19°$

19. $30°, 60°$ **20.** $67°, 23°$

In each of the following, the measure of one angle of a right triangle is given. Find the measures of the other two angles.

21. $45°$ **22.** $60°$

23. $17°$ **24.** $30°$

25. $39\frac{3}{4}°$ **26.** $72.6°$

Given that each of the following pairs of triangles is similar, find the missing lengths. See Example 4.

27.

28.

29.

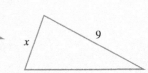

30.

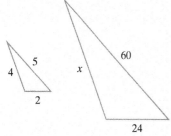
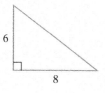

32.

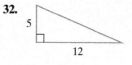

33.

Use the Pythagorean theorem to find the missing lengths in the right triangles. See Example 5.

34.

31.

Contents of Student Resources

Study Skills Builders

Attitude and Study Tips:
1. Have You Decided to Complete This Course Successfully?
2. Tips for Studying for an Exam
3. What to Do the Day of an Exam
4. Are You Satisfied with Your Performance on a Particular Quiz or Exam?
5. How Are You Doing?
6. Are You Preparing for Your Final Exam?

Organizing Your Work:
7. Learning New Terms
8. Are You Organized?
9. Organizing a Notebook
10. How Are Your Homework Assignments Going?

MyMathLab and MathXL:
11. Tips for Turning in Your Homework on Time
12. Tips for Doing Your Homework Online
13. Organizing Your Work
14. Getting Help with Your Homework Assignments
15. Tips for Preparing for an Exam
16. How Well Do You Know the Resources Available to You in MyMathLab?

Additional Help Inside and Outside Your Textbook:
17. How Well Do You Know Your Textbook?
18. Are You Familiar with Your Textbook Supplements?
19. Are You Getting All the Mathematics Help That You Need?

The Bigger Picture—Study Guide Outline

Practice Final Exam

Answers to Selected Exercises

Student Resources

Study Skills Builders

Attitude and Study Tips

Study Skills Builder 1

Have You Decided to Complete This Course Successfully?

Ask yourself if one of your current goals is to complete this course successfully.

If it is not a goal of yours, ask yourself why. One common reason is fear of failure. Amazingly enough, fear of failure alone can be strong enough to keep many of us from doing our best in any endeavor.

Another common reason is that you simply haven't taken the time to think about or write down your goals for this course. To help accomplish this, answer the following questions.

Exercises

1. Write down your goal(s) for this course.

2. Now list steps you will take to make sure your goal(s) in Exercise 1 are accomplished.

3. Rate your commitment to this course with a number between 1 and 5. Use the diagram below to help.

High Commitment		Average Commitment	Not Committed at All	
5	4	3	2	1

4. If you have rated your personal commitment level (from the exercise above) as a 1, 2, or 3, list the reasons why this is so. Then determine whether it is possible to increase your commitment level to a 4 or 5.

Good luck, and don't forget that a positive attitude will make a big difference.

Study Skills Builder 2

Tips for Studying for an Exam

To prepare for an exam, try the following study techniques:

- Start the study process days before your exam.
- Make sure that you are up to date on your assignments.
- If there is a topic that you are unsure of, use one of the many resources that are available to you. For example,

    See your instructor.

    View a lecture video on the topic.

    Visit a learning resource center on campus.

    Read the textbook material and examples on the topic.

- Reread your notes and carefully review the Chapter Highlights at the end of any chapter.
- Work the review exercises at the end of the chapter.
- Find a quiet place to take the Chapter Test found at the end of the chapter. Do not use any resources when taking this sample test. This way, you will have a clear indication of how prepared you are for your exam. Check your answers and use the Chapter Test Prep Videos to make sure that you correct any missed exercises.

Good luck, and keep a positive attitude.

Exercises

Let's see how you did on your last exam.

1. How many days before your last exam did you start studying for that exam?

2. Were you up to date on your assignments at that time or did you need to catch up on assignments?

3. List the most helpful text supplement (if you used one).

4. List the most helpful campus supplement (if you used one).

5. List your process for preparing for a mathematics test.

6. Was this process helpful? In other words, were you satisfied with your performance on your exam?

7. If not, what changes can you make in your process that will make it more helpful to you?

Study Skills Builder 3

What to Do the Day of an Exam

Your first exam may be soon. On the day of an exam, don't forget to try the following:

- Allow yourself plenty of time to arrive.
- Read the directions on the test carefully.
- Read each problem carefully as you take your test. Make sure that you answer the question asked.
- Watch your time and pace yourself so that you may attempt each problem on your test.
- Check your work and answers.
- *Do not turn your test in early.* If you have extra time, spend it double-checking your work.

Good luck!

Exercises

Answer the following questions based on your most recent mathematics exam, whenever that was.

1. How soon before class did you arrive?
2. Did you read the directions on the test carefully?
3. Did you make sure you answered the question asked for each problem on the exam?
4. Were you able to attempt each problem on your exam?
5. If your answer to Exercise 4 is no, list reasons why.
6. Did you have extra time on your exam?
7. If your answer to Exercise 6 is yes, describe how you spent that extra time.

Study Skills Builder 4

Are You Satisfied with Your Performance on a Particular Quiz or Exam?

If not, don't forget to analyze your quiz or exam and look for common errors. Were most of your errors a result of:

- *Carelessness?* Did you turn in your quiz or exam before the allotted time expired? If so, resolve to use any extra time to check your work.
- *Running out of time?* Answer the questions you are sure of first. Then attempt the questions you are unsure of and delay checking your work until all questions have been answered.
- *Not understanding a concept?* If so, review that concept and correct your work so that you make sure you understand it before the next quiz or the final exam.
- *Test conditions?* When studying for a quiz or exam, make sure you place yourself in conditions similar to test conditions. For example, before your next quiz or exam, take a sample test without the aid of your notes or text.

(For a sample test, see your instructor or use the Chapter Test at the end of each chapter.)

Exercises

1. Have you corrected all your previous quizzes and exams?
2. List any errors you have found common to two or more of your graded papers.
3. Is one of your common errors not understanding a concept? If so, are you making sure you understand all the concepts for the next quiz or exam?
4. Is one of your common errors making careless mistakes? If so, are you now taking all the time allotted to check over your work so that you can minimize the number of careless mistakes?
5. Are you satisfied with your grades thus far on quizzes and tests?
6. If your answer to Exercise 5 is no, are there any more suggestions you can make to your instructor or yourself to help? If so, list them here and share these with your instructor.

Study Skills Builder 5

How Are You Doing?

If you haven't done so yet, take a few moments to think about how you are doing in this course. Are you working toward your goal of successfully completing this course? Is your performance on homework, quizzes, and tests satisfactory? If not, you might want to see your instructor to see whether he/she has any suggestions on how you can improve your performance. Reread Section 1.1 for ideas on places to get help with your mathematics course.

Exercises

Answer the following.

1. List any textbook supplements you are using to help you through this course.
2. List any campus resources you are using to help you through this course.
3. Write a short paragraph describing how you are doing in your mathematics course.
4. If improvement is needed, list ways that you can work toward improving your situation as described in Exercise 3.

Study Skills Builder 6

Are You Preparing for Your Final Exam?

To prepare for your final exam, try the following study techniques:

- Review the material that you will be responsible for on your exam. This includes material from your textbook, your notebook, and any handouts from your instructor.
- Review any formulas that you may need to memorize.
- Check to see if your instructor or mathematics department will be conducting a final exam review.
- Check with your instructor to see whether final exams from previous semesters/quarters are available to students for review.

- Use your previously taken exams as a practice final exam. To do so, rewrite the test questions in mixed order on blank sheets of paper. This will help you prepare for exam conditions.
- If you are unsure of a few concepts, see your instructor or visit a learning lab for assistance. Also, view the video segment of any troublesome sections.
- If you need further exercises to work, try the Cumulative Reviews at the end of the chapters.

Once again, good luck! I hope you are enjoying this textbook and your mathematics course.

Organizing Your Work

Study Skills Builder 7

Learning New Terms

Many of the terms used in this text may be new to you. It will be helpful to make a list of new mathematical terms and symbols as you encounter them and to review them frequently. Placing these new terms (including page references) on 3 × 5 index cards might help you later when you're preparing for a quiz.

Exercises

1. Name one way you might place a word and its definition on a 3 × 5 card.
2. How do new terms stand out in this text so that they can be found?

Study Skills Builder 8

Are You Organized?

Have you ever had trouble finding a completed assignment? When it's time to study for a test, are your notes neat and organized? Have you ever had trouble reading your own mathematics handwriting? (Be honest—I have.)

When any of these things happen, it's time to get organized. Here are a few suggestions:

- Write your notes and complete your homework assignments in a notebook with pockets (spiral or ring binder).

- Take class notes in this notebook, and then follow the notes with your completed homework assignment.

- When you receive graded papers or handouts, place them in the notebook pocket so that you will not lose them.

- Mark (possibly with an exclamation point) any note(s) that seem extra important to you.

- Mark (possibly with a question mark) any notes or homework that you are having trouble with.

- See your instructor or a math tutor to help you with the concepts or exercises that you are having trouble understanding.

- If you are having trouble reading your own handwriting, *slow down* and write your mathematics work clearly!

Exercises

1. Have you been completing your assignments on time?
2. Have you been correcting any exercises you may be having difficulty with?
3. If you are having trouble with a mathematical concept or correcting any homework exercises, have you visited your instructor, a tutor, or your campus math lab?
4. Are you taking lecture notes in your mathematics course? (By the way, these notes should include worked-out examples solved by your instructor.)
5. Is your mathematics course material (handouts, graded papers, lecture notes) organized?
6. If your answer to Exercise 5 is no, take a moment to review your course material. List at least two ways that you might organize it better.

Study Skills Builder 9

Organizing a Notebook

It's never too late to get organized. If you need ideas about organizing a notebook for your mathematics course, try some of these:

- Use a spiral or ring binder notebook with pockets and use it for mathematics only.

- Start each page by writing the book's section number you are working on at the top.

- When your instructor is lecturing, take notes. *Always* include any examples your instructor works for you.

- Place your worked-out homework exercises in your notebook immediately after the lecture notes from that section. This way, a section's worth of material is together.

- Homework exercises: Attempt and check all assigned homework.

- Place graded quizzes in the pockets of your notebook or a special section of your binder.

Exercises

Check your notebook organization by answering the following questions.

1. Do you have a spiral or ring binder notebook for your mathematics course only?
2. Have you ever had to flip through several sheets of notes and work in your mathematics notebook to determine what section's work you are in?
3. Are you now writing the textbook's section number at the top of each notebook page?
4. Have you ever lost or had trouble finding a graded quiz or test?
5. Are you now placing all your graded work in a dedicated place in your notebook?
6. Are you attempting all of your homework and placing all of your work in your notebook?
7. Are you checking and correcting your homework in your notebook? If not, why not?
8. Are you writing in your notebook the examples your instructor works for you in class?

Study Skills Builder 10

How Are Your Homework Assignments Going?

It is very important in mathematics to keep up with homework. Why? Many concepts build on each other. Often your understanding of a day's concepts depends on an understanding of the previous day's material.

Remember that completing your homework assignment involves a lot more than attempting a few of the problems assigned.

To complete a homework assignment, remember these four things:

- Attempt all of it.
- Check it.
- Correct it.
- If needed, ask questions about it.

Exercises

Take a moment to review your completed homework assignments. Answer the questions below based on this review.

1. Approximate the fraction of your homework you have attempted.
2. Approximate the fraction of your homework you have checked (if possible).
3. If you are able to check your homework, have you corrected it when errors have been found?
4. When working homework, if you do not understand a concept, what do you do?

MyMathLab and MathXL

Study Skills Builder 11

Tips for Turning in Your Homework on Time

It is very important to keep up with your mathematics homework assignments. Why? Many concepts in mathematics build upon each other.

Remember these four tips to help ensure that your work is completed on time:

- Know the assignments and due dates set by your instructor.
- Do not wait until the last minute to submit your homework.
- Set a goal to submit your homework 6–8 hours before the scheduled due date in case you have unexpected technology trouble.
- Schedule enough time to complete each assignment.

Following these tips will also help you avoid losing points for late or missed assignments.

Exercises

Take a moment to consider your work on your homework assignments to date and answer the following questions:

1. What percentage of your assignments have you turned in on time?
2. Why might it be a good idea to submit your homework 6–8 hours before the scheduled deadline?
3. If you have missed submitting any homework by the due date, list some of the reasons this occurred.
4. What steps do you plan to take in the future to ensure that your homework is submitted on time?

Study Skills Builder 12

Tips for Doing Your Homework Online

Practice is one of the main keys to success in any mathematics course. Did you know that MyMathLab/MathXL provides you with **immediate feedback** for each exercise? If you are incorrect, you are given hints to work the exercise correctly. You have **unlimited practice opportunities** and can rework any exercises you have trouble with until you master them, and submit homework assignments unlimited times before the deadline.

Remember these success tips when doing your homework online:

- Attempt all assigned exercises.
- Write down (neatly) your step-by-step work for each exercise before entering your answer.
- Use the immediate feedback provided by the program to help you check and correct your work for each exercise.
- Rework any exercises you have trouble with until you master them.

- Work through your homework assignment as many times as necessary until you are satisfied.

Exercises

Take a moment to think about your homework assignments to date and answer the following:

1. Have you attempted all assigned exercises?
2. Of the exercises attempted, have you also written out your work before entering your answer so that you can check it?
3. Are you familiar with how to enter answers using the MathXL player so that you avoid answer entry–type errors?
4. List some ways the immediate feedback and practice supports have helped you with your homework. If you have not used these supports, how do you plan to use them with the given success tips on your next assignment?

Study Skills Builder 13

Organizing Your Work

Have you ever used any readily available paper (such as the back of a flyer, another course assignment, Post-it notes, etc.) to work out homework exercises before entering the answer in MathXL? To save time, have you ever entered answers directly into MathXL without working the exercises on paper? When it's time to study, have you ever been unable to find your completed work or read and follow your own mathematics handwriting?

When any of these things happen, it's time to get organized. Here are some suggestions:

- Write your step-by-step work for each homework exercise (neatly) on lined, loose-leaf paper and keep this in a 3-ring binder.
- Refer to your step-by-step work when you receive feedback that your answer is incorrect in MathXL. Double-check against the steps and hints provided by the program and correct your work accordingly.
- Keep your written homework with your class notes for that section.

- Identify any exercises you are having trouble with and ask questions about them.
- Keep all graded quizzes and tests in this binder as well to study later.

If you follow these suggestions, you and your instructor or tutor will be able to follow your steps and correct any mistakes. You will have a written copy of your work to refer to later to ask questions and study for tests.

Exercises

1. Why is it important to write out your step-by-step work to homework exercises and keep a hard copy of all work submitted online?
2. If you have gotten an incorrect answer, are you able to follow your steps and find your error?
3. If you were asked today to review your previous homework assignments and first test, could you find them? If not, list some ways you might organize your work better.

Study Skills Builder 14

Getting Help with Your Homework Assignments

Many helpful resources are available to you through MathXL to help you work through any homework exercises you may have trouble with. It is important for you to know what these resources are and when and how to use them.

Let's review these features, found in the homework exercises:

- **Help Me Solve This**—provides step-by-step help for the exercise you are working. You must work an additional exercise of the same type (without this help) before you can get credit for having worked it correctly.

- **View an Example**—allows you to view a correctly worked exercise similar to the one you are having trouble with. You can go back to your original exercise and work it on your own.

- **E-Book**—allows you to read examples from your text and find similar exercises.

- **Video****—your text author, Elayn Martin-Gay, works an exercise similar to the one you need help with. **Not all exercises have an accompanying video clip.

- **Ask My Instructor**—allows you to email your instructor for help with an exercise.

Exercises

1. How does the "Help Me Solve This" feature work?

2. If the "View an Example" feature is used, is it necessary to work an additional problem before continuing the assignment?

3. When might be a good time to use the "Video" feature? Do all exercises have an accompanying video clip?

4. Which of the features above have you used? List those you found the most helpful to you.

5. If you haven't used the features discussed, list those you plan to try on your next homework assignment.

Study Skills Builder 15

Tips for Preparing for an Exam

Did you know that you can rework your previous homework assignments in MyMathLab and MathXL? This is a great way to prepare for tests. To do this, open a previous homework assignment and click "similar exercise." This will generate new exercises similar to the homework you have submitted. You can then rework the exercises and assignments until you feel confident that you understand them.

To prepare for an exam, follow these tips:

- Review your written work for your previous homework assignments along with your class notes.

- Identify any exercises or topics that you have questions on or have difficulty understanding.

- Rework your previous assignments in MyMathLab and MathXL until you fully understand them and can do them without help.

- Get help for any topics you feel unsure of or for which you have questions.

Exercises

1. Are your current homework assignments up to date and is your written work for them organized in a binder or notebook? If the answer is no, it's time to get organized. For tips on this, see Study Skills Builder 13—Organizing Your Work.

2. How many days in advance of an exam do you usually start studying?

3. List some ways you think that practicing previous homework assignments can help you prepare for your test.

4. List two or three resources you can use to get help for any topics you are unsure of or have questions on.

Good luck!

Study Skills Builder 16

How Well Do You Know the Resources Available to You in MyMathLab?

Many helpful resources are available to you in MyMathLab. Let's take a moment to locate and explore a few of them now. Go into your MyMathLab course and visit the multimedia library, tools for success, and E-book.

Let's see what you found.

Exercises

1. List the resources available to you in the Multimedia Library.

2. List the resources available to you in the Tools for Success folder.

3. Where did you find the English/Spanish Audio Glossary?

4. Can you view videos from the E-book?

5. Did you find any resources you did not know about? If so, which ones?

6. Which resources have you used most often or found most helpful?

Additional Help Inside and Outside Your Textbook

Study Skills Builder 17

How Well Do You Know Your Textbook?

The following questions will help determine whether you are familiar with your textbook. For additional information, see Section 1.1 in this text.

1. What does the ▶ icon mean?
2. What does the ↘ icon mean?
3. What does the △ icon mean?
4. Where can you find a review for each chapter? What answers to this review can be found in the back of your text?

5. Each chapter contains an overview of the chapter along with examples. What is this feature called?

6. Each chapter contains a review of vocabulary. What is this feature called?

7. Practice exercises are contained in this text. What are they and how can they be used?

8. This text contains a student section in the back entitled Student Resources. List the contents of this section and how they might be helpful.

9. What exercise answers are available in this text? Where are they located?

Study Skills Builder 18

Are You Familiar with Your Textbook Supplements?

Below is a review of some of the student supplements available for additional study. Check to see whether you are using the ones most helpful to you.

- Chapter Test Prep Videos. These videos provide video clip solutions to the Chapter Test exercises in this text. You will find this extremely useful when studying for tests or exams.

- Interactive DVD Lecture Series. These are keyed to each section of the text. The material is presented by me, Elayn Martin-Gay, and I have placed a ● by the exercises in the text that I have worked on the video.

- The *Student Solutions Manual.* This contains worked-out solutions to odd-numbered exercises as well as every exercise in the Integrated Reviews, Chapter Reviews, Chapter Tests, and Cumulative Reviews and every Practice exercise.

- Pearson Tutor Center. Mathematics questions may be phoned, faxed, or emailed to this center.

- MyMathLab is a text-specific online course. MathXL is an online homework, tutorial, and assessment system. Take a moment to determine whether these are available to you.

As usual, your instructor is your best source of information.

Exercises

Let's see how you are doing with textbook supplements.

1. Name one way the Lecture Videos can be helpful to you.

2. Name one way the Chapter Test Prep Video can help you prepare for a chapter test.

3. List any textbook supplements that you have found useful.

4. Have you located and visited a learning resource lab located on your campus?

5. List the textbook supplements that are currently housed in your campus's learning resource lab.

Study Skills Builder 19

Are You Getting All the Mathematics Help That You Need?

Remember that, in addition to your instructor, there are many places to get help with your mathematics course. For example:

- This text has an accompanying video lesson by the author for every section. There are also worked-out video solutions by the author to every Chapter Test exercise.

- The back of the book contains answers to odd-numbered exercises.

- A *Student Solutions Manual* is available that contains worked-out solutions to odd-numbered exercises as well as solutions to every exercise in the Integrated Reviews, Chapter Reviews, Chapter Tests, and Cumulative Reviews and every Practice exercise.

- Don't forget to check with your instructor for other local resources available to you, such as a tutor center.

Exercises

1. List items you find helpful in the text and all student supplements to this text.

2. List all the campus help that is available to you for this course.

3. List any help (besides the textbook) from Exercises 1 and 2 above that you are using.

4. List any help (besides the textbook) that you feel you should try.

5. Write a goal for yourself that includes trying everything you listed in Exercise 4 during the next week.

The Bigger Picture—Study Guide Outline

Simplifying Expressions and Solving Equations and Inequalities

I. Simplifying Expressions

A. Real Numbers

1. **Add:** (Sec. 1.5)

$$-1.7 + (-0.21) = -1.91$$

Adding like signs.
Add absolute values. Attach common sign.

$$-7 + 3 = -4$$

Adding different signs.
Subtract absolute values. Attach the sign of the number with the larger absolute value.

2. **Subtract:** Add the first number to the opposite of the second number. (Sec. 1.6)

$$17 - 25 = 17 + (-25) = -8$$

3. **Multiply or divide:** Multiply or divide the two numbers as usual. If the signs are the same, the answer is positive. If the signs are different, the answer is negative. (Sec. 1.7)

$$-10 \cdot 3 = -30, \quad -81 \div (-3) = 27$$

B. Exponents (Secs. 5.1 and 5.5)

$$x^7 \cdot x^5 = x^{12}; \quad (x^7)^5 = x^{35}; \quad \frac{x^7}{x^5} = x^2; \quad x^0 = 1; \quad 8^{-2} = \frac{1}{8^2} = \frac{1}{64}$$

C. Polynomials

1. **Add:** Combine like terms. (Sec. 5.2)

$$(3y^2 + 6y + 7) + (9y^2 - 11y - 15) = 3y^2 + 6y + 7 + 9y^2 - 11y - 15$$
$$= 12y^2 - 5y - 8$$

2. **Subtract:** Change the sign of the terms of the polynomial being subtracted, then add. (Sec. 5.2)

$$(3y^2 + 6y + 7) - (9y^2 - 11y - 15) = 3y^2 + 6y + 7 - 9y^2 + 11y + 15$$
$$= -6y^2 + 17y + 22$$

3. **Multiply:** Multiply each term of one polynomial by each term of the other polynomial. (Secs. 5.3 and 5.4)

$$(x + 5)(2x^2 - 3x + 4) = x(2x^2 - 3x + 4) + 5(2x^2 - 3x + 4)$$
$$= 2x^3 - 3x^2 + 4x + 10x^2 - 15x + 20$$
$$= 2x^3 + 7x^2 - 11x + 20$$

4. **Divide:** (Sec. 5.6)
   a. To divide by a monomial, divide each term of the polynomial by the monomial.

$$\frac{8x^2 + 2x - 6}{2x} = \frac{8x^2}{2x} + \frac{2x}{2x} - \frac{6}{2x} = 4x + 1 - \frac{3}{x}$$

b. To divide by a polynomial other than a monomial, use long division.

$$2x + 5 \overline{\smash{\big)}2x^2 - 7x + 10} \quad x - 6 + \frac{40}{2x + 5}$$

$$\underline{2x^2 + 5x}$$
$$-12x + 10$$
$$\underline{+12x + 30}$$
$$40$$

D. Factoring Polynomials

See the Chapter 6 Integrated Review for steps.

$$3x^4 - 78x^2 + 75 = 3(x^4 - 26x^2 + 25) \quad \text{Factor out GCF—always first step.}$$
$$= 3(x^2 - 25)(x^2 - 1) \quad \text{Factor trinomial.}$$
$$= 3(x + 5)(x - 5)(x + 1)(x - 1) \quad \text{Factor further—each difference of squares.}$$

E. Rational Expressions

1. Simplify: Factor the numerator and denominator. Then divide out factors of 1 by dividing out common factors in the numerator and denominator. (Sec. 7.1)

$$\frac{x^2 - 9}{7x^2 - 21x} = \frac{(x + 3)(x - 3)}{7x(x - 3)} = \frac{x + 3}{7x}$$

2. Multiply: Multiply numerators, then multiply denominators. (Sec. 7.2)

$$\frac{5z}{2z^2 - 9z - 18} \cdot \frac{22z + 33}{10z} = \frac{5 \cdot z}{(2z + 3)(z - 6)} \cdot \frac{11(2z + 3)}{2 \cdot 5 \cdot z} = \frac{11}{2(z - 6)}$$

3. Divide: First fraction times the reciprocal of the second fraction. (Sec. 7.2)

$$\frac{14}{x + 5} \div \frac{x + 1}{2} = \frac{14}{x + 5} \cdot \frac{2}{x + 1} = \frac{28}{(x + 5)(x + 1)}$$

4. Add or subtract: Must have same denominator. If not, find the LCD and write each fraction as an equivalent fraction with the LCD as denominator. (Sec. 7.4)

$$\frac{9}{10} - \frac{x + 1}{x + 5} = \frac{9(x + 5)}{10(x + 5)} - \frac{10(x + 1)}{10(x + 5)}$$

$$= \frac{9x + 45 - 10x - 10}{10(x + 5)} = \frac{-x + 35}{10(x + 5)}$$

F. Radicals

1. Simplify square roots: If possible, factor the radicand so that one factor is a perfect square. Then use the product rule and simplify. (Sec. 10.3)

$$\sqrt{75} = \sqrt{25 \cdot 3} = \sqrt{25} \cdot \sqrt{3} = 5\sqrt{3}$$

2. Add or subtract: Only like radicals (same index and radicand) can be added or subtracted. (Sec. 10.4)

$$8\sqrt{10} - \sqrt{40} + \sqrt{5} = 8\sqrt{10} - 2\sqrt{10} + \sqrt{5} = 6\sqrt{10} + \sqrt{5}$$

3. Multiply or divide: $\sqrt{a} \cdot \sqrt{b} = \sqrt{ab}; \dfrac{\sqrt{a}}{\sqrt{b}} = \sqrt{\dfrac{a}{b}}$. (Sec. 10.4)

$$\sqrt{11} \cdot \sqrt{3} = \sqrt{33}; \frac{\sqrt{140}}{\sqrt{7}} = \sqrt{\frac{140}{7}} = \sqrt{20} = \sqrt{4 \cdot 5} = 2\sqrt{5}$$

4. Rationalizing the denominator: (Sec. 10.5)

a. If denominator is one term,

$$\frac{5}{\sqrt{11}} = \frac{5 \cdot \sqrt{11}}{\sqrt{11} \cdot \sqrt{11}} = \frac{5\sqrt{11}}{11}$$

b. If denominator is two terms, multiply by 1 in the form of $\dfrac{\text{conjugate of denominator}}{\text{conjugate of denominator}}$.

$$\frac{13}{3 + \sqrt{2}} = \frac{13}{3 + \sqrt{2}} \cdot \frac{3 - \sqrt{2}}{3 - \sqrt{2}} = \frac{13(3 - \sqrt{2})}{9 - 2} = \frac{13(3 - \sqrt{2})}{7}$$

II. Solving Equations

A. Linear Equations: (Sec. 2.3)

$$5(x - 2) = \frac{4(2x + 1)}{3}$$

$$3 \cdot 5(x - 2) = \cancel{3} \cdot \frac{4(2x + 1)}{\cancel{3}}$$

$$15x - 30 = 8x + 4$$

$$7x = 34$$

$$x = \frac{34}{7}$$

B. Quadratic and Higher-Degree Equations (Secs. 6.6, 11.1, 11.2, 11.3)

$$2x^2 - 7x = 9$$
$$2x^2 - 7x - 9 = 0$$
$$(2x - 9)(x + 1) = 0$$
$$2x - 9 = 0 \quad \text{or} \quad x + 1 = 0$$
$$x = \frac{9}{2} \quad \text{or} \quad x = -1$$

$$2x^2 + x - 2 = 0$$
$$a = 2, \; b = 1, \; c = -2$$
$$x = \frac{-1 \pm \sqrt{1^2 - 4(2)(-2)}}{2 \cdot 2}$$
$$x = \frac{-1 \pm \sqrt{17}}{4}$$

C. Equations with Rational Expressions (Sec. 7.5)

$$\frac{7}{x - 1} + \frac{3}{x + 1} = \frac{x + 3}{x^2 - 1}$$

$$\cancel{(x - 1)}(x + 1) \cdot \frac{7}{\cancel{x - 1}} + (x - 1)\cancel{(x + 1)} \cdot \frac{3}{\cancel{x + 1}}$$

$$= \cancel{(x - 1)}\cancel{(x + 1)} \cdot \frac{x + 3}{\cancel{(x - 1)}\cancel{(x + 1)}}$$

$$7(x + 1) + 3(x - 1) = x + 3$$
$$7x + 7 + 3x - 3 = x + 3$$
$$9x = -1$$
$$x = -\frac{1}{9}$$

D. Proportions: An equation with two ratios equal. Set cross products equal, then solve. Make sure the proposed solution does not make the denominator 0. (Sec. 7.6)

$$\frac{5}{x} \rightleftharpoons \frac{9}{2x - 3}$$

$$5(2x - 3) = 9 \cdot x \qquad \text{Set cross products equal.}$$

$$10x - 15 = 9x \qquad \text{Multiply.}$$

$$x = 15 \qquad \text{Write equation with variable terms on one side and constants on the other.}$$

E. Absolute Value Equations (Sec. 9.2)

$$|3x - 1| = 8$$

$3x - 1 = 8$ or $3x - 1 = -8$

$3x = 9$ or $3x = -7$

$x = 3$ or $x = -\dfrac{7}{3}$

$$|x - 5| = |x + 1|$$

$x - 5 = x + 1$ or $x - 5 = -(x + 1)$

$\underbrace{-5 = 1}_{\text{No solution}}$ or $x - 5 = -x - 1$

or $2x = 4$

$x = 2$

F. Equations with Radicals (Sec. 10.6)

$$\sqrt{5x + 10} - 2 = x$$
$$\sqrt{5x + 10} = x + 2$$
$$(\sqrt{5x + 10})^2 = (x + 2)^2$$
$$5x + 10 = x^2 + 4x + 4$$
$$0 = x^2 - x - 6$$
$$0 = (x - 3)(x + 2)$$

$x - 3 = 0$ or $x + 2 = 0$

$x = 3$ or $x = -2$

Both solutions check.

G. Exponential Equations (Secs. 12.3, 12.8)

$$9^x = 27^{x+1}$$
$$(3^2)^x = (3^3)^{x+1}$$
$$3^{2x} = 3^{3x+3}$$
$$2x = 3x + 3$$
$$-3 = x$$

$$5^x = 7$$
$$\log 5^x = \log 7$$
$$x \log 5 = \log 7$$
$$x = \dfrac{\log 7}{\log 5}$$

H. Logarithmic Equations (Sec. 12.8)

$$\log 7 + \log(x + 3) = \log 5$$
$$\log 7(x + 3) = \log 5$$
$$7(x + 3) = 5$$
$$7x + 21 = 5$$
$$7x = -16$$
$$x = -\dfrac{16}{7}$$

III. Solving Inequalities
A. Linear Inequalities (Sec. 2.8)

$$-3(x + 2) \geq 6$$
$$-3x - 6 \geq 6$$
$$-3x \geq 12$$
$$\dfrac{-3x}{-3} \leq \dfrac{12}{-3}$$
$$x \leq -4 \quad \text{or} \quad (-\infty, -4]$$

B. Compound Inequalities (Sec. 9.1)

$x \leq 3 \quad and \quad x < -7$

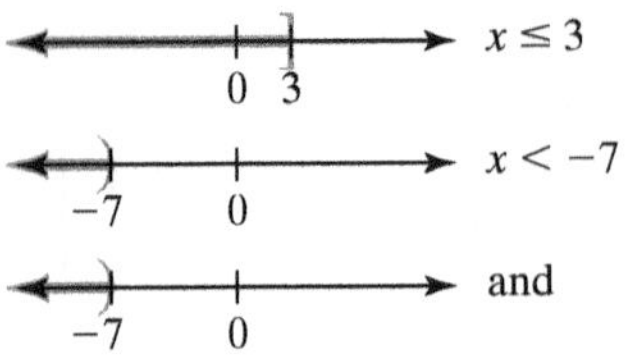

$x \leq 3$

$x < -7$

and

$(-\infty, -7)$

$x \leq 3 \quad or \quad x < -7$

$x \leq 3$

$x < -7$

or

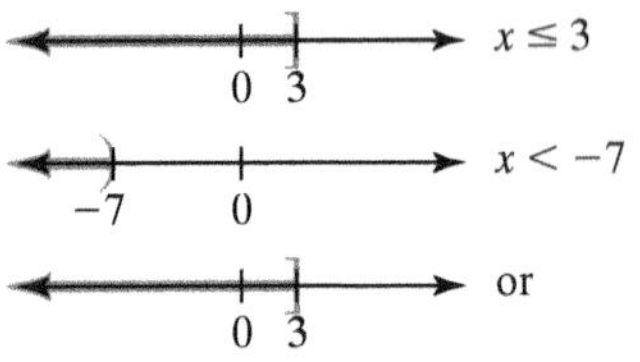

$(-\infty, 3]$

C. Absolute Value Inequalities (Sec. 9.3)

$|x - 5| - 8 < -2$

$|x - 5| < 6$

$-6 < x - 5 < 6$

$-1 < x < 11$

$(-1, 11)$

$|2x + 1| \geq 17$

$2x + 1 \geq 17 \quad or \quad 2x + 1 \leq -17$

$2x \geq 16 \quad or \quad 2x \leq -18$

$x \geq 8 \quad or \quad x \leq -9$

$(-\infty, -9] \cup [8, \infty)$

D. Nonlinear Inequalities (Sec. 11.4)

$x^2 - x < 6$

$x^2 - x - 6 < 0$

$(x - 3)(x + 2) < 0$

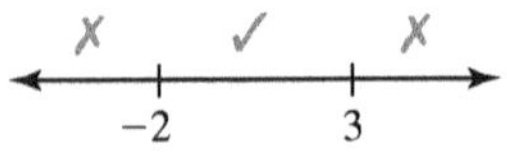

$(-2, 3)$

$\dfrac{x - 5}{x + 1} \geq 0$

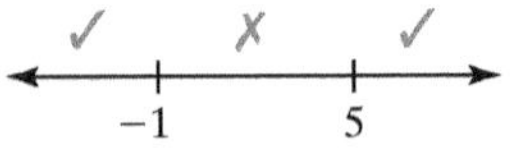

$(-\infty, -1) \cup [5, \infty)$

Evaluate.

1. $6[5 + 2(3 - 8) - 3]$

2. -3^4

3. 4^{-3}

4. $\dfrac{1}{2} - \dfrac{5}{6}$

Perform the indicated operations and simplify if possible.

5. $5x^3 + x^2 + 5x - 2 - (8x^3 - 4x^2 + x - 7)$

6. $(4x - 2)^2$

7. $(3x + 7)(x^2 + 5x + 2)$

Factor.

8. $y^2 - 8y - 48$

9. $9x^3 + 39x^2 + 12x$

10. $180 - 5x^2$

11. $3a^2 + 3ab - 7a - 7b$

12. $8y^3 - 64$

Simplify. Write answer with positive exponents only.

13. $\left(\dfrac{x^2 y^3}{x^3 y^{-4}}\right)^2$

Solve each equation or inequality. Write inequality answers using interval notation.

14. $-4(a + 1) - 3a = -7(2a - 3)$

15. $3x - 5 \geq 7x + 3$

16. $x(x + 6) = 7$

Graph the following.

17. $5x - 7y = 10$

18. $x - 3 = 0$

Find the slope of each line.

19. Through $(6, -5)$ and $(-1, 2)$

20. $-3x + y = 5$

Write equations of the following lines. Write each equation in standard form.

21. Through $(2, -5)$ and $(1, 3)$

22. Through $(-5, -1)$ and parallel to $x = 7$

Solve each system of equations.

23. $\begin{cases} \dfrac{1}{2}x + 2y = -\dfrac{15}{4} \\ 4x = -y \end{cases}$

24. $\begin{cases} 4x - 6y = 7 \\ -2x + 3y = 0 \end{cases}$

25. Divide by long division: $\dfrac{27x^3 - 8}{3x + 2}$

Answer the questions about functions.

26. If $h(x) = x^3 - x$, find

   a. $h(-1)$

   b. $h(0)$

   c. $h(4)$

27. Identify the *x*- and *y*-intercepts. Then find the domain and range of the function graphed.

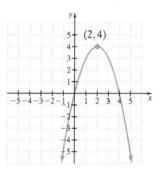

Solve each application.

28. Some states have a single area code for the entire state. Two such states have area codes where one is double the other. If the sum of these integers is 1203, find the two area codes.

29. Two trains leave Los Angeles simultaneously traveling on the same track in opposite directions at speeds of 50 and 64 mph. How long will it take before they are 285 miles apart?

30. Find the amount of a 12% saline solution a lab assistant should add to 80 cc (cubic centimeters) of a 22% saline solution in order to have a 16% solution.

31. Find the domain of the rational function

$$g(x) = \dfrac{9x^2 - 9}{x^2 + 4x + 3}.$$

Perform the indicated operations and simplify if possible.

32. $\dfrac{15x}{2x + 5} - \dfrac{6 - 4x}{2x + 5}$

33. $\dfrac{x^2 - 9}{x^2 - 3x} \div \dfrac{xy + 5x + 3y + 15}{2x + 10}$

34. $\dfrac{5a}{a^2 - a - 6} - \dfrac{2}{a - 3}$

35. $\dfrac{5 - \dfrac{1}{y^2}}{\dfrac{1}{y} + \dfrac{2}{y^2}}$

Solve each equation.

36. $\dfrac{4}{y} - \dfrac{5}{3} = -\dfrac{1}{5}$

37. $\dfrac{5}{y+1} = \dfrac{4}{y+2}$

38. $\dfrac{a}{a-3} = \dfrac{3}{a-3} - \dfrac{3}{2}$

Solve.

39. One number plus five times its reciprocal is equal to six. Find the number.

Simplify. If needed, write answers with positive exponents only.

40. $\sqrt{216}$

41. $\left(\dfrac{1}{125}\right)^{-1/3}$

42. $\left(\dfrac{64c^{4/3}}{a^{-2/3}b^{5/6}}\right)^{1/2}$

Perform the indicated operations and simplify if possible.

43. $\sqrt{125x^3} - 3\sqrt{20x^3}$

44. $(\sqrt{5} + 5)(\sqrt{5} - 5)$

Solve each equation or inequality. Write inequality solutions using interval notation.

45. $|6x - 5| - 3 = -2$

46. $-3 < 2(x - 3) \le 4$

47. $|3x + 1| > 5$

48. $y^2 - 3y = 5$

49. $x = \sqrt{x - 2} + 2$

50. $2x^2 - 7x > 15$

Graph the following.

51. $y > -4x$

52. $g(x) = -|x + 2| - 1$. Also, find the domain and range of this function.

53. $h(x) = x^2 - 4x + 4$. Label the vertex and any intercepts.

54. $f(x) = \begin{cases} -\dfrac{1}{2}x & \text{if } x \le 0 \\ 2x - 3 & \text{if } x > 0 \end{cases}$. Also, find the domain and range of this function.

Write equations of the following lines. Write each equation using function notation.

55. Through $(4, -2)$ and $(6, -3)$

56. Through $(-1, 2)$ and perpendicular to $3x - y = 4$

Find the distance or midpoint.

57. Find the distance between the points $(-6, 3)$ and $(-8, -7)$.

58. Find the midpoint of the line segment whose endpoints are $(-2, -5)$ and $(-6, 12)$.

Rationalize each denominator. Assume that variables represent positive numbers.

59. $\sqrt{\dfrac{9}{y}}$

60. $\dfrac{4 - \sqrt{x}}{4 + 2\sqrt{x}}$

Solve.

61. Suppose that W is inversely proportional to V. If $W = 20$ when $V = 12$, find W when $V = 15$.

62. Given the diagram shown, approximate to the nearest foot how many feet of walking distance a person saves by cutting across the lawn instead of walking on the sidewalk.

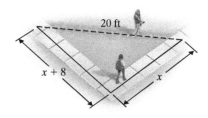

63. A stone is thrown upward from a bridge. The stone's height in feet, $s(t)$, above the water t seconds after the stone is thrown is a function given by the equation

$$s(t) = -16t^2 + 32t + 256$$

a. Find the maximum height of the stone.

b. Find the time it takes the stone to hit the water. Round the answer to two decimal places.

COMPLEX NUMBERS: CHAPTER 10

Perform the indicated operation and simplify. Write the result in the form $a + bi$.

64. $-\sqrt{-8}$

65. $(12 - 6i) - (12 - 3i)$

66. $(4 + 3i)^2$

67. $\dfrac{1 + 4i}{1 - i}$

INVERSE, EXPONENTIAL, AND LOGARITHMIC FUNCTIONS: CHAPTER 12

68. If $g(x) = x - 7$ and $h(x) = x^2 - 6x + 5$, find $(g \circ h)(x)$.

69. Determine whether $f(x) = 6 - 2x$ is a one-to-one function. If it is, find its inverse.

70. Use properties of logarithms to write the expression as a single logarithm.

$$\log_5 x + 3\log_5 x - \log_5(x + 1)$$

Solve. Give exact solutions.

71. $8^{x-1} = \dfrac{1}{64}$

72. $3^{2x+5} = 4$ Give an exact solution and a 4-decimal-place approximation.

73. $\log_8(3x - 2) = 2$

74. $\log_4(x + 1) - \log_4(x - 2) = 3$

75. $\ln\sqrt{e} = x$

76. Graph $y = \left(\dfrac{1}{2}\right)^x + 1$

77. The prairie dog population of the Grand Forks area now stands at 57,000 animals. If the population is growing at a rate of 2.6% annually, how many prairie dogs will there be in that area 5 years from now?

CONIC SECTIONS: CHAPTER 13

Sketch the graph of each equation.

78. $x^2 - y^2 = 36$

79. $16x^2 + 9y^2 = 144$

80. $x^2 + y^2 + 6x = 16$

81. Solve the system: $\begin{cases} x^2 + y^2 = 26 \\ x^2 - 2y^2 = 23 \end{cases}$

SEQUENCES, SERIES, AND THE BINOMIAL THEOREM: CHAPTER 14

82. Find the first five terms of the sequence $a_n = \dfrac{(-1)^n}{n + 4}$.

83. Find the partial sum S_5 of the sequence $a_n = 5(2)^{n-1}$.

84. Find S_∞ of the sequence $\dfrac{3}{2}, -\dfrac{3}{4}, \dfrac{3}{8}, \ldots$

85. Find $\displaystyle\sum_{i=1}^{4} i(i - 2)$

86. Expand: $(2x + y)^5$

Solving Systems of Linear Equations in Three Variables

OBJECTIVE

1 Solve a System of Three Linear Equations in Three Variables.

In this section, the algebraic methods of solving systems of two linear equations in two variables are extended to systems of three linear equations in three variables. We call the equation $3x - y + z = -15$, for example, a **linear equation in three variables** since there are three variables and each variable is raised only to the power 1. A solution of this equation is an **ordered triple (x, y, z)** that makes the equation a true statement. For example, the ordered triple $(2, 0, -21)$ is a solution of $3x - y + z = -15$ since replacing x with 2, y with 0, and z with -21 yields the true statement $3(2) - 0 + (-21) = -15$. The graph of this equation is a plane in three-dimensional space, just as the graph of a linear equation in two variables is a line in two-dimensional space.

Although we will not discuss the techniques for graphing equations in three variables, visualizing the possible patterns of intersecting planes gives us insight into the possible patterns of solutions of a system of three three-variable linear equations. There are four possible patterns.

1. Three planes have a single point in common. This point represents the single solution of the system. This system is **consistent.**

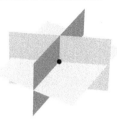

2. Three planes intersect at no point common to all three. This system has no solution. A few ways that this can occur are shown. This system is **inconsistent.**

3. Three planes intersect at all the points of a single line. The system has infinitely many solutions. This system is **consistent.**

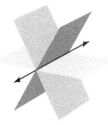

4. Three planes coincide at all points on the plane. The system is consistent, and the equations are **dependent.**

1 Solving a System of Three Linear Equations in Three Variables

Just as with systems of two equations in two variables, we can use the elimination or substitution method to solve a system of three equations in three variables. To use the elimination method, we eliminate a variable and obtain a system of two equations in two variables. Then we use the methods we learned in the previous two sections to solve the system of two equations.

EXAMPLE 1 Solve the system.

$$\begin{cases} 3x - y + z = -15 & \text{Equation (1)} \\ x + 2y - z = 1 & \text{Equation (2)} \\ 2x + 3y - 2z = 0 & \text{Equation (3)} \end{cases}$$

Solution Add equations (1) and (2) to eliminate z.

$$\begin{array}{l} 3x - y + z = -15 \\ \underline{x + 2y - z = 1} \\ 4x + y \phantom{{}-2z} = -14 \quad \text{Equation (4)} \end{array}$$

Next, add two *other* equations and *eliminate z again*. To do so, multiply both sides of equation (1) by 2 and add this resulting equation to equation (3). Then

> **Helpful Hint**
>
> Don't forget to add two other equations besides equations (1) and (2) *and* to **eliminate the same variable.**

$$\begin{cases} 2(3x - y + z) = 2(-15) \\ 2x + 3y - 2z = 0 \end{cases} \quad \text{simplifies to} \quad \begin{cases} 6x - 2y + 2z = -30 \\ \underline{2x + 3y - 2z = 0} \\ 8x + y \phantom{{}-2z} = -30 \quad \text{Equation (5)} \end{cases}$$

Now solve equations (4) and (5) for x and y. To solve by elimination, multiply both sides of equation (4) by -1 and add this resulting equation to equation (5). Then

$$\begin{cases} -1(4x + y) = -1(-14) \\ 8x + y = -30 \end{cases} \quad \text{simplifies to} \quad \begin{cases} -4x - y = 14 \\ \underline{8x + y = -30} \\ 4x \phantom{{}- y} = -16 \quad \text{Add the equations.} \\ x = -4 \quad \text{Solve for } x. \end{cases}$$

Replace x with -4 in equation (4) or (5).

$$\begin{array}{l} 4x + y = -14 \quad \text{Equation (4)} \\ 4(-4) + y = -14 \quad \text{Let } x = -4. \\ y = 2 \quad \text{Solve for } y. \end{array}$$

Finally, replace x with -4 and y with 2 in equation (1), (2), or (3).

$$\begin{array}{l} x + 2y - z = 1 \quad \text{Equation (2)} \\ -4 + 2(2) - z = 1 \quad \text{Let } x = -4 \text{ and } y = 2. \\ -4 + 4 - z = 1 \\ -z = 1 \\ z = -1 \end{array}$$

The solution is $(-4, 2, -1)$. To check, let $x = -4$, $y = 2$, and $z = -1$ in all three original equations of the system.

Equation (1)	*Equation (2)*	*Equation (3)*
$3x - y + z = -15$	$x + 2y - z = 1$	$2x + 3y - 2z = 0$
$3(-4) - 2 + (-1) \stackrel{?}{=} -15$	$-4 + 2(2) - (-1) \stackrel{?}{=} 1$	$2(-4) + 3(2) - 2(-1) \stackrel{?}{=} 0$
$-12 - 2 - 1 \stackrel{?}{=} -15$	$-4 + 4 + 1 \stackrel{?}{=} 1$	$-8 + 6 + 2 \stackrel{?}{=} 0$
$-15 = -15$ True	$1 = 1$ True	$0 = 0$ True

All three statements are true, so the solution is $(-4, 2, -1)$. □

PRACTICE
1 Solve the system. $\begin{cases} 3x + 2y - z = 0 \\ x - y + 5z = 2 \\ 2x + 3y + 3z = 7 \end{cases}$

EXAMPLE 2 Solve the system.

$$\begin{cases} 2x - 4y + 8z = 2 & (1) \\ -x - 3y + z = 11 & (2) \\ x - 2y + 4z = 0 & (3) \end{cases}$$

Solution Add equations (2) and (3) to eliminate x, and the new equation is

$$-5y + 5z = 11 \quad (4)$$

To eliminate x again, multiply both sides of equation (2) by 2 and add the resulting equation to equation (1). Then

$$\begin{cases} 2x - 4y + 8z = 2 \\ 2(-x - 3y + z) = 2(11) \end{cases} \quad \begin{array}{l} \text{simplifies} \\ \text{to} \end{array} \quad \begin{cases} 2x - 4y + 8z = 2 \\ \underline{-2x - 6y + 2z = 22} \\ -10y + 10z = 24 \quad (5) \end{cases}$$

Next, solve for y and z using equations (4) and (5). Multiply both sides of equation (4) by -2 and add the resulting equation to equation (5).

$$\begin{cases} -2(-5y + 5z) = -2(11) \\ -10y + 10z = 24 \end{cases} \quad \begin{array}{l} \text{simplifies} \\ \text{to} \end{array} \quad \begin{cases} 10y - 10z = -22 \\ \underline{-10y + 10z = 24} \\ 0 = 2 \quad \text{False} \end{cases}$$

Since the statement is false, this system is inconsistent and has no solution. The solution set is the empty set $\{\ \}$ or $\varnothing$. □

PRACTICE
2 Solve the system. $\begin{cases} 6x - 3y + 12z = 4 \\ -6x + 4y - 2z = 7 \\ -2x + y - 4z = 3 \end{cases}$

The elimination method is summarized next.

Solving a System of Three Linear Equations by the Elimination Method

Step 1. Write each equation in standard form $Ax + By + Cz = D$.

Step 2. Choose a pair of equations and use the equations to eliminate a variable.

Step 3. Choose any **other** pair of equations and eliminate the **same variable** as in Step 2.

Step 4. Two equations in two variables should be obtained from Step 2 and Step 3. Use methods from Section 4.2 or 4.3 to solve this system for both variables.

Step 5. To solve for the third variable, substitute the values of the variables found in Step 4 into any of the original equations containing the third variable.

Step 6. Check the ordered triple solution in *all three* original equations.

▶ Helpful Hint
Make sure you read closely and follow Step 3.

✓CONCEPT CHECK

In the system

$$\begin{cases} x + y + z = 6 & \text{Equation (1)} \\ 2x - y + z = 3 & \text{Equation (2)} \\ x + 2y + 3z = 14 & \text{Equation (3)} \end{cases}$$

equations (1) and (2) are used to eliminate y. Which action could be used to finish solving best? Why?

a. Use (1) and (2) to eliminate z.   **b.** Use (2) and (3) to eliminate y.

c. Use (1) and (3) to eliminate x.

EXAMPLE 3   Solve the system.

$$\begin{cases} 2x + 4y = 1 & (1) \\ 4x - 4z = -1 & (2) \\ y - 4z = -3 & (3) \end{cases}$$

Solution   Notice that equation (2) has no term containing the variable y. Let us eliminate y using equations (1) and (3). Multiply both sides of equation (3) by -4 and add the resulting equation to equation (1). Then

$$\begin{cases} 2x + 4y = 1 \\ -4(y - 4z) = -4(-3) \end{cases} \quad \text{simplifies to} \quad \begin{cases} 2x + 4y = 1 \\ -4y + 16z = 12 \\ \hline 2x + 16z = 13 \quad (4) \end{cases}$$

Next, solve for z using equations (4) and (2). Multiply both sides of equation (4) by -2 and add the resulting equation to equation (2).

$$\begin{cases} -2(2x + 16z) = -2(13) \\ 4x - 4z = -1 \end{cases} \quad \text{simplifies to} \quad \begin{cases} -4x - 32z = -26 \\ 4x - 4z = -1 \\ \hline -36z = -27 \\ z = \dfrac{3}{4} \end{cases}$$

Replace z with $\dfrac{3}{4}$ in equation (3) and solve for y.

$$y - 4\left(\frac{3}{4}\right) = -3 \quad \text{Let } z = \frac{3}{4} \text{ in equation (3).}$$

$$y - 3 = -3$$

$$y = 0$$

Replace y with 0 in equation (1) and solve for x.

$$2x + 4(0) = 1$$

$$2x = 1$$

$$x = \frac{1}{2}$$

The solution is $\left(\dfrac{1}{2}, 0, \dfrac{3}{4}\right)$. Check to see that this solution satisfies all three equations of the system.   ☐

PRACTICE

3   Solve the system. $$\begin{cases} 3x + 4y = 0 \\ 9x - 4z = 6 \\ -2y + 7z = 1 \end{cases}$$

Answer to Concept Check: **b**

EXAMPLE 4   Solve the system.

$$\begin{cases} x - 5y - 2z = 6 & (1) \\ -2x + 10y + 4z = -12 & (2) \\ \dfrac{1}{2}x - \dfrac{5}{2}y - z = 3 & (3) \end{cases}$$

Solution   Multiply both sides of equation (3) by 2 to eliminate fractions and multiply both sides of equation (2) by $-\dfrac{1}{2}$ so that the coefficient of x is 1. The resulting system is then

$$\begin{cases} x - 5y - 2z = 6 & (1) \\ x - 5y - 2z = 6 & \text{Multiply (2) by } -\dfrac{1}{2}. \\ x - 5y - 2z = 6 & \text{Multiply (3) by 2.} \end{cases}$$

All three equations are identical, and therefore equations (1), (2), and (3) are all equivalent. There are infinitely many solutions of this system. The equations are dependent. The solution set can be written as $\{(x, y, z) \mid x - 5y - 2z = 6\}$.   □

PRACTICE
4   Solve the system.
$$\begin{cases} 2x + y - 3z = 6 \\ x + \dfrac{1}{2}y - \dfrac{3}{2}z = 3 \\ -4x - 2y + 6z = -12 \end{cases}$$

As mentioned earlier, we can also use the substitution method to solve a system of linear equations in three variables.

EXAMPLE 5   Solve the system:

$$\begin{cases} x - 4y - 5z = 35 & (1) \\ x - 3y = 0 & (2) \\ -y + z = -55 & (3) \end{cases}$$

Solution   Notice in equations (2) and (3) that a variable is missing. Also notice that both equations contain the variable y. Let's use the substitution method by solving equation (2) for x and equation (3) for z and substituting the results in equation (1).

$$x - 3y = 0 \qquad (2)$$
$$x = 3y \qquad \text{Solve equation (2) for } x.$$
$$-y + z = -55 \qquad (3)$$
$$z = y - 55 \qquad \text{Solve equation (3) for } z.$$

Now substitute $3y$ for x and $y - 55$ for z in equation (1).

> **Helpful Hint**
> Do not forget to distribute.

$$x - 4y - 5z = 35 \qquad (1)$$
$$3y - 4y - 5(y - 55) = 35 \qquad \text{Let } x = 3y \text{ and } z = y - 55.$$
$$3y - 4y - 5y + 275 = 35 \qquad \text{Use the distributive law and multiply.}$$
$$-6y + 275 = 35 \qquad \text{Combine like terms.}$$
$$-6y = -240 \qquad \text{Subtract 275 from both sides.}$$
$$y = 40 \qquad \text{Solve.}$$

(Continued on next page)

To find x, recall that $x = 3y$ and substitute 40 for y. Then $x = 3y$ becomes $x = 3 \cdot 40 = 120$. To find z, recall that $z = y - 55$ and substitute 40 for y, also. Then $z = y - 55$ becomes $z = 40 - 55 = -15$. The solution is $(120, 40, -15)$.   ☐

PRACTICE
5   Solve the system. $\begin{cases} x + 2y + 4z = 16 \\ x \quad\quad + 2z = -4 \\ \quad\quad y - 3z = 30 \end{cases}$

Vocabulary, Readiness & Video Check

Solve.
1. Choose the equation(s) that has $(-1, 3, 1)$ as a solution.
   a. $x + y + z = 3$ **b.** $-x + y + z = 5$ **c.** $-x + y + 2z = 0$ **d.** $x + 2y - 3z = 2$
2. Choose the equation(s) that has $(2, 1, -4)$ as a solution.
   a. $x + y + z = -1$ **b.** $x - y - z = -3$ **c.** $2x - y + z = -1$ **d.** $-x - 3y - z = -1$
3. Use the result of Exercise 1 to determine whether $(-1, 3, 1)$ is a solution of the system below. Explain your answer.
$$\begin{cases} x + y + z = 3 \\ -x + y + z = 5 \\ x + 2y - 3z = 2 \end{cases}$$
4. Use the result of Exercise 2 to determine whether $(2, 1, -4)$ is a solution of the system below. Explain your answer.
$$\begin{cases} x + y + z = -1 \\ x - y - z = -3 \\ 2x - y + z = -1 \end{cases}$$

Martin-Gay Interactive Videos

See Video 4.4

Watch the section lecture video and answer the following question.

OBJECTIVE
1   5. From ▤ Example 1 and the lecture before, why does Step 3 stress that the same variable be eliminated from two other equations?

4.4 Exercise Set   MyMathLab®

Solve each system. See Examples 1 through 5.

1. $\begin{cases} x - y + z = -4 \\ 3x + 2y - z = 5 \\ -2x + 3y - z = 15 \end{cases}$

2. $\begin{cases} x + y - z = -1 \\ -4x - y + 2z = -7 \\ 2x - 2y - 5z = 7 \end{cases}$

5. $\begin{cases} 2x + 2y + z = 1 \\ -x + y + 2z = 3 \\ x + 2y + 4z = 0 \end{cases}$

6. $\begin{cases} 2x - 3y + z = 5 \\ x + y + z = 0 \\ 4x + 2y + 4z = 4 \end{cases}$

3. $\begin{cases} x + y = 3 \\ 2y = 10 \\ 3x + 2y - 3z = 1 \end{cases}$

4. $\begin{cases} 5x = 5 \\ 2x + y = 4 \\ 3x + y - 4z = -15 \end{cases}$

7. $\begin{cases} x - 2y + z = -5 \\ -3x + 6y - 3z = 15 \\ 2x - 4y + 2z = -10 \end{cases}$

8. $\begin{cases} 3x + y - 2z = 2 \\ -6x - 2y + 4z = -4 \\ 9x + 3y - 6z = 6 \end{cases}$

9. $\begin{cases} 4x - y + 2z = 5 \\ 2y + z = 4 \\ 4x + y + 3z = 10 \end{cases}$

10. $\begin{cases} 5y - 7z = 14 \\ 2x + y + 4z = 10 \\ 2x + 6y - 3z = 30 \end{cases}$

11. $\begin{cases} x + 5z = 0 \\ 5x + y = 0 \\ y - 3z = 0 \end{cases}$

12. $\begin{cases} x - 5y = 0 \\ x - z = 0 \\ -x + 5z = 0 \end{cases}$

13. $\begin{cases} 6x - 5z = 17 \\ 5x - y + 3z = -1 \\ 2x + y = -41 \end{cases}$

14. $\begin{cases} x + 2y = 6 \\ 7x + 3y + z = -33 \\ x - z = 16 \end{cases}$

15. $\begin{cases} x + y + z = 8 \\ 2x - y - z = 10 \\ x - 2y - 3z = 22 \end{cases}$

16. $\begin{cases} 5x + y + 3z = 1 \\ x - y + 3z = -7 \\ -x + y = 1 \end{cases}$

17. $\begin{cases} x + 2y - z = 5 \\ 6x + y + z = 7 \\ 2x + 4y - 2z = 5 \end{cases}$

18. $\begin{cases} 4x - y + 3z = 10 \\ x + y - z = 5 \\ 8x - 2y + 6z = 10 \end{cases}$

▶ **19.** $\begin{cases} 2x - 3y + z = 2 \\ x - 5y + 5z = 3 \\ 3x + y - 3z = 5 \end{cases}$

20. $\begin{cases} 4x + y - z = 8 \\ x - y + 2z = 3 \\ 3x - y + z = 6 \end{cases}$

21. $\begin{cases} -2x - 4y + 6z = -8 \\ x + 2y - 3z = 4 \\ 4x + 8y - 12z = 16 \end{cases}$

22. $\begin{cases} -6x + 12y + 3z = -6 \\ 2x - 4y - z = 2 \\ -x + 2y + \dfrac{z}{2} = -1 \end{cases}$

23. $\begin{cases} 2x + 2y - 3z = 1 \\ y + 2z = -14 \\ 3x - 2y = -1 \end{cases}$

24. $\begin{cases} 7x + 4y = 10 \\ x - 4y + 2z = 6 \\ y - 2z = -1 \end{cases}$

25. $\begin{cases} x + 2y - z = 5 \\ -3x - 2y - 3z = 11 \\ 4x + 4y + 5z = -18 \end{cases}$

26. $\begin{cases} 3x - 3y + z = -1 \\ 3x - y - z = 3 \\ -6x + 4y + 3z = -8 \end{cases}$

27. $\begin{cases} \dfrac{3}{4}x - \dfrac{1}{3}y + \dfrac{1}{2}z = 9 \\ \dfrac{1}{6}x + \dfrac{1}{3}y - \dfrac{1}{2}z = 2 \\ \dfrac{1}{2}x - y + \dfrac{1}{2}z = 2 \end{cases}$

28. $\begin{cases} \dfrac{1}{3}x - \dfrac{1}{4}y + z = -9 \\ \dfrac{1}{2}x - \dfrac{1}{3}y - \dfrac{1}{4}z = -6 \\ x - \dfrac{1}{2}y - z = -8 \end{cases}$

REVIEW AND PREVIEW

Translating *Solve. See Section 2.4.*

29. The sum of two numbers is 45 and one number is twice the other. Find the numbers.

30. The difference of two numbers is 5. Twice the smaller number added to five times the larger number is 53. Find the numbers.

Solve. See Section 2.3.

31. $2(x - 1) - 3x = x - 12$

32. $7(2x - 1) + 4 = 11(3x - 2)$

33. $-y - 5(y + 5) = 3y - 10$

34. $z - 3(z + 7) = 6(2z + 1)$

CONCEPT EXTENSIONS

35. Write a single linear equation in three variables that has $(-1, 2, -4)$ as a solution. (There are many possibilities.) Explain the process you used to write an equation.

36. Write a system of three linear equations in three variables that has $(2, 1, 5)$ as a solution. (There are many possibilities.) Explain the process you used to write an equation.

37. Write a system of linear equations in three variables that has the solution $(-1, 2, -4)$. Explain the process you used to write your system.

38. When solving a system of three equation in three unknowns, explain how to determine that a system has no solution.

39. The fraction $\dfrac{1}{24}$ can be written as the following sum:

$$\frac{1}{24} = \frac{x}{8} + \frac{y}{4} + \frac{z}{3}$$

where the numbers $x, y,$ and z are solutions of

$$\begin{cases} x + y + z = 1 \\ 2x - y + z = 0 \\ -x + 2y + 2z = -1 \end{cases}$$

Solve the system and see that the sum of the fractions is $\dfrac{1}{24}$.

40. The fraction $\dfrac{1}{18}$ can be written as the following sum:

$$\frac{1}{18} = \frac{x}{2} + \frac{y}{3} + \frac{z}{9}$$

where the numbers $x, y,$ and z are solutions of

$$\begin{cases} x + 3y + z = -3 \\ -x + y + 2z = -14 \\ 3x + 2y - z = 12 \end{cases}$$

Solve the system and see that the sum of the fractions is $\dfrac{1}{18}$.

Solving systems involving more than three variables can be accomplished with methods similar to those encountered in this section. Apply what you already know to solve each system of equations in four variables.

41. $\begin{cases} x + y \quad - w = 0 \\ \quad y + 2z + w = 3 \\ x \quad - z \quad = 1 \\ 2x - y \quad - w = -1 \end{cases}$

42. $\begin{cases} 5x + 4y \quad = 29 \\ \quad y + z - w = -2 \\ 5x \quad + z \quad = 23 \\ \quad y - z + w = 4 \end{cases}$

43. $\begin{cases} x + y + z + w = 5 \\ 2x + y + z + w = 6 \\ x + y + z \quad = 2 \\ x + y \quad = 0 \end{cases}$

44. $\begin{cases} 2x \quad - z \quad = -1 \\ \quad y + z + w = 9 \\ \quad y \quad - 2w = -6 \\ x + y \quad = 3 \end{cases}$

45. Write a system of three linear equations in three variables that are dependent equations.

46. What is the solution to the system in Exercise 45?

4.5 Systems of Linear Equations and Problem Solving

OBJECTIVES

1 Solve Problems That Can Be Modeled by a System of Two Linear Equations. ▶

2 Solve Problems with Cost and Revenue Functions. ▶

3 Solve Problems That Can Be Modeled by a System of Three Linear Equations. ▶

OBJECTIVE

1 Solving Problems Modeled by Systems of Two Equations ▶

Thus far, we have solved problems by writing one-variable equations and solving for the variable. Some of these problems can be solved, perhaps more easily, by writing a system of equations, as illustrated in this section.

EXAMPLE 1 **Predicting Equal Consumption of Red Meat and Poultry**

America's consumption of red meat has decreased most years since 2000, while consumption of poultry has increased. The function $y = -0.56x + 113.6$ approximates the annual pounds of red meat consumed per capita, where x is the number of years since 2000. The function $y = 0.76x + 68.57$ approximates the annual pounds of poultry consumed per capita, where x is also the number of years since 2000. If this trend continues, determine the year when the annual consumption of red meat and poultry will be equal. (*Source:* USDA: Economic Research Service)

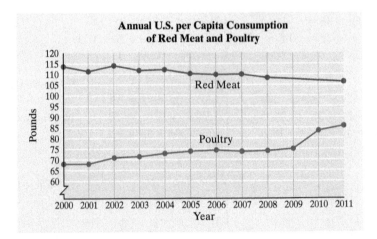

Solution:

1. UNDERSTAND. Read and reread the problem and guess a year. Let's guess the year 2020. This year is 20 years since 2000, so $x = 20$. Now let $x = 20$ in each given function.

Red meat: $y = -0.56x + 113.6 = -0.56(20) + 113.6 = 102.4 \text{ pounds}$

Poultry: $y = 0.76x + 68.57 = 0.76(20) + 68.57 = 83.77 \text{ pounds}$

Since the projected pounds in 2020 for red meat and poultry are not the same, we guessed incorrectly, but we do have a better understanding of the problem. We know that the year will be later than 2020.

2. TRANSLATE. We are already given the system of equations.

3. SOLVE. We want to know the year x in which pounds y are the same, so we solve the system:

$$\begin{cases} y = -0.56x + 113.6 \\ y = 0.76x + 68.57 \end{cases}$$

Since both equations are solved for y, one way to solve is to use the substitution method.

$$y = 0.76x + 68.57 \qquad \text{Second equation}$$

$$-0.56x + 113.6 = 0.76x + 68.57 \qquad \text{Let } y = -0.56x + 113.6$$

$$-1.32x = -45.03$$

$$x = \frac{-45.03}{-1.32} \approx 34.11$$

4. INTERPRET. Since we are only asked to find the year, we need only solve for x.

Check: To check, see whether $x \approx 34.11$ gives approximately the same number of pounds of red meat and poultry.

Red meat: $y = -0.56x + 113.6 = -0.56(34.11) + 113.6 \approx 94.4984 \text{ pounds}$

Poultry: $\quad y = 0.76x + 68.57 = 0.76(34.11) + 68.57 \approx 94.4936 \text{ pounds}$

Since we rounded the number of years, the numbers of pounds do differ slightly. They differ only by 0.0048, so we can assume we solved correctly.

State: The consumption of red meat and poultry will be the same about 34.11 years after 2000, or 2034.11. Thus, in the year 2034, we predict the consumption will be the same. □

PRACTICE

1 Read Example 1. If we use the years 2005, 2006, 2007, and 2008 only to write functions approximating the consumption of red meat and poultry, we have the following:

Red Meat: $y = -0.54x + 110.6$

Poultry: $\quad y = -0.36x + 74.1$

where x is the number of years since 2005 and y is pounds per year consumed.

a. Assuming this trend continues, predict the year when consumption of red meat and poultry will be the same. Round to the nearest year.

b. Does your answer differ from the answer to Example 1? Why or why not?

For Example 1, the equations in the system were given to us. Let's now practice writing our own system of equations that we will use to solve an application.

Many of the applications solved earlier using one-variable equations can also be solved using two equations in **two** variables. We use the same problem-solving steps that have been used throughout this text. The only difference is that two variables are assigned to represent the two unknown quantities and that the stated problem is translated into **two** equations.

Problem-Solving Steps

Step 1. UNDERSTAND the problem. During this step, become comfortable with the problem. Some ways of doing this are to

> Read and reread the problem.
>
> Choose two variables to represent the two unknowns.
>
> Construct a drawing if possible.
>
> Propose a solution and check. Pay careful attention to how you check your proposed solution. This will help when writing equations to model the problem.

Step 2. TRANSLATE the problem into two equations.

Step 3. SOLVE the system of equations.

Step 4. INTERPRET the results: **Check** the proposed solution in the stated problem and **state** your conclusion.

EXAMPLE 2   **Finding Unknown Numbers**

Find two numbers whose sum is 37 and whose difference is 21.

Solution

1. UNDERSTAND. Read and reread the problem. Suppose that one number is 20. If their sum is 37, the other number is 17 because $20 + 17 = 37$. Is their difference 21? No; $20 - 17 = 3$. Our proposed solution is incorrect, but we now have a better understanding of the problem.

Since we are looking for two numbers, we let

x = first number

y = second number

2. TRANSLATE. Since we have assigned two variables to this problem, we translate our problem into two equations.

In words:	two numbers whose sum	is	37
	↓	↓	↓
Translate:	$x + y$	$=$	37

In words:	two numbers whose difference	is	21
	↓	↓	↓
Translate:	$x - y$	$=$	21

3. SOLVE. Now we solve the system

$$\begin{cases} x + y = 37 \\ x - y = 21 \end{cases}$$

Notice that the coefficients of the variable y are opposites. Let's then solve by the addition method and begin by adding the equations.

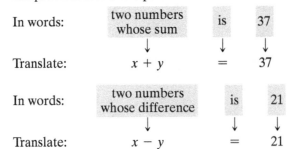

$$\begin{array}{rl} x + y = 37 \\ \underline{x - y = 21} \\ 2x \quad\quad = 58 \end{array} \quad \text{Add the equations.}$$

$$x = \frac{58}{2} = 29 \quad \text{Divide both sides by 2.}$$

Now we let $x = 29$ in the first equation to find y.

$$x + y = 37 \quad \text{First equation}$$
$$29 + y = 37$$
$$y = 8 \quad \text{Subtract 29 from both sides.}$$

4. INTERPRET. The solution of the system is $(29, 8)$.

Check: Notice that the sum of 29 and 8 is $29 + 8 = 37$, the required sum. Their difference is $29 - 8 = 21$, the required difference.

State: The numbers are 29 and 8.   □

PRACTICE

2   Find two numbers whose sum is 30 and whose difference is 6.

EXAMPLE 3   **Finding Unknown Numbers**

A first number is 4 less than a second number. Four times the first number is 6 more than twice the second. Find the numbers.

Solution

1. UNDERSTAND. Read and reread the problem and guess a solution. If a first number is 10 and this is 4 less than a second number, the second number is 14. Four times the first number is $4(10)$, or 40. This is not equal to 6 more than twice the second number, which is $2(14) + 6$ or 34. Although we guessed incorrectly, we now have a better understanding of the problem.

Since we are looking for two numbers, we will let

$$x = \text{first number}$$
$$y = \text{second number}$$

2. TRANSLATE. Since we have assigned two variables to this problem, we will translate the given facts into two equations. For the first statement we have

In words:	the first number	is	4 less than the second number
	↓	↓	↓
Translate:	x	$=$	$y - 4$

Next we translate the second statement into an equation.

In words:	four times the first number	is	6 more than twice the second number
	↓	↓	↓
Translate:	$4x$	$=$	$2y + 6$

3. SOLVE. Here we solve the system

$$\begin{cases} x = y - 4 \\ 4x = 2y + 6 \end{cases}$$

Since the first equation expresses x in terms of y, we will use substitution. We substitute $y - 4$ for x in the second equation and solve for y.

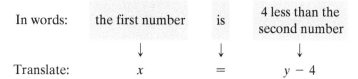

$$4x = 2y + 6 \quad \text{Second equation}$$
$$4(y - 4) = 2y + 6$$
$$4y - 16 = 2y + 6 \quad \text{Let } x = y - 4.$$
$$2y = 22$$
$$y = 11$$

(Continued on next page)

Now we replace y with 11 in the equation $x = y - 4$ and solve for x. Then $x = y - 4$ becomes $x = 11 - 4 = 7$. The ordered pair solution of the system is $(7, 11)$.

4. INTERPRET. Since the solution of the system is $(7, 11)$, then the first number we are looking for is 7 and the second number is 11.

Check: Notice that 7 *is* 4 less than 11, and 4 times 7 *is* 6 more than twice 11. The proposed numbers, 7 and 11, are correct.

State: The numbers are 7 and 11. ☐

PRACTICE

3 A first number is 5 more than a second number. Twice the first number is 2 less than 3 times the second number. Find the numbers.

EXAMPLE 4 **Solving a Problem about Prices**

The Cirque du Soleil show Varekai is performing locally. Matinee admission for 4 adults and 2 children is $374, while admission for 2 adults and 3 children is $285.

a. What is the price of an adult's ticket?

b. What is the price of a child's ticket?

c. Suppose that a special rate of $1000 is offered for groups of 20 persons. Should a group of 4 adults and 16 children use the group rate? Why or why not?

Solution

1. UNDERSTAND. Read and reread the problem and guess a solution. Let's suppose that the price of an adult's ticket is $50 and the price of a child's ticket is $40. To check our proposed solution, let's see if admission for 4 adults and 2 children is $374. Admission for 4 adults is 4($50) or $200 and admission for 2 children is 2($40) or $80. This gives a total admission of $200 + $80 = $280, not the required $374. Again, though, we have accomplished the purpose of this process: We have a better understanding of the problem. To continue, we let

A = the price of an adult's ticket and

C = the price of a child's ticket

2. TRANSLATE. We translate the problem into two equations using both variables.

In words:	admission for 4 adults	and	admission for 2 children	is	$374
	↓	↓	↓	↓	↓
Translate:	$4A$	$+$	$2C$	$=$	374

In words:	admission for 2 adults	and	admission for 3 children	is	$285
	↓	↓	↓	↓	↓
Translate:	$2A$	$+$	$3C$	$=$	285

3. SOLVE. We solve the system.

$$\begin{cases} 4A + 2C = 374 \\ 2A + 3C = 285 \end{cases}$$

Since both equations are written in standard form, we solve by the addition method. First we multiply the second equation by -2 so that when we add the equations, we eliminate the variable A. Then the system

$$\begin{cases} 4A + 2C = 374 \\ -2(2A + 3C) = -2(285) \end{cases} \quad \begin{array}{c} \text{simplifies to} \\ \text{Add the} \\ \text{equations.} \end{array} \quad \begin{cases} 4A + 2C = 374 \\ -4A - 6C = -570 \\ \hline -4C = -196 \\ C = 49 \text{ or } \$49, \text{ the} \\ \text{children's} \\ \text{ticket price.} \end{cases}$$

To find A, we replace C with 49 in the first equation.

$$4A + 2C = 374 \quad \text{First equation}$$
$$4A + 2(49) = 374 \quad \text{Let } C = 49$$
$$4A + 98 = 374$$
$$4A = 276$$
$$A = 69 \text{ or } \$69, \text{ the adult's ticket price}$$

4. INTERPRET.

Check: Notice that 4 adults and 2 children will pay

$4(\$69) + 2(\$49) = \$276 + \$98 = \$374$, the required amount. Also, the price for 2 adults and 3 children is $2(\$69) + 3(\$49) = \$138 + \$147 = \$285$, the required amount.

State: Answer the three original questions.

a. Since $A = 69$, the price of an adult's ticket is $69.

b. Since $C = 49$, the price of a child's ticket is $49.

c. The regular admission price for 4 adults and 16 children is

$$4(\$69) + 16(\$49) = \$276 + \$784$$
$$= \$1060$$

This is $60 more than the special group rate of $1000, so they should request the group rate. □

PRACTICE

4   It is considered a premium game when the Red Sox or the Yankees come to Texas to play the Rangers. Admission for one of these games for three adults and three children under 14 is $75, while admission for two adults and four children is $62. (*Source:* MLB.com, Texas Rangers)

a. What is the price of an adult admission at Ameriquest Park?

b. What is the price of a child's admission?

c. Suppose that a special rate of $200 is offered for groups of 20 persons. Should a group of 5 adults and 15 children use the group rate? Why or why not?

EXAMPLE 5 **Finding the Rate of Speed**

Two cars leave Indianapolis, one traveling east and the other west. After 3 hours, they are 297 miles apart. If one car is traveling 5 mph faster than the other, what is the speed of each?

Solution

1. UNDERSTAND. Read and reread the problem. Let's guess a solution and use the formula $d = rt$ (distance = rate $\cdot$ time) to check. Suppose that one car is traveling at a rate of 55 miles per hour. This means that the other car is traveling at a rate of 50 miles per hour since we are told that one car is traveling 5 mph faster than the other. To find the distance apart after 3 hours, we will first find the distance traveled by each car. One car's distance is rate $\cdot$ time = 55(3) = 165 miles. The other car's distance is rate $\cdot$ time = 50(3) = 150 miles. Since one car is traveling east and the other west, their distance apart is the sum of their distances, or 165 miles + 150 miles = 315 miles. Although this distance apart is not the required distance of 297 miles, we now have a better understanding of the problem.

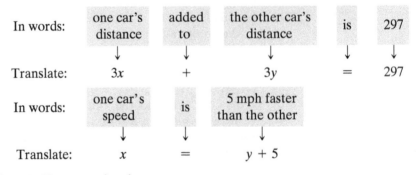

Let's model the problem with a system of equations. We will let

$$x = \text{speed of one car}$$
$$y = \text{speed of the other car}$$

We summarize the information on the following chart. Both cars have traveled 3 hours. Since distance = rate $\cdot$ time, their distances are $3x$ and $3y$ miles, respectively.

	Rate	• Time	= Distance
One Car	x	3	$3x$
Other Car	y	3	$3y$

2. TRANSLATE. We can now translate the stated conditions into two equations.

In words:	one car's distance	added to	the other car's distance	is	297
	↓	↓	↓	↓	↓
Translate:	$3x$	$+$	$3y$	$=$	297

In words:	one car's speed	is	5 mph faster than the other
	↓	↓	↓
Translate:	x	$=$	$y + 5$

3. SOLVE. Here we solve the system

$$\begin{cases} 3x + 3y = 297 \\ x \qquad = y + 5 \end{cases}$$

Again, the substitution method is appropriate. We replace x with $y + 5$ in the first equation and solve for y.

$$3x + 3y = 297 \quad \text{First equation}$$

$$3(\underbrace{y + 5}) + 3y = 297 \quad \text{Let } x = y + 5.$$

$$3y + 15 + 3y = 297$$

$$6y = 282$$

$$y = 47$$

To find x, we replace y with 47 in the equation $x = y + 5$. Then $x = 47 + 5 = 52$. The ordered pair solution of the system is $(52, 47)$.

4. INTERPRET. The solution $(52, 47)$ means that the cars are traveling at 52 mph and 47 mph, respectively.

Check: Notice that one car is traveling 5 mph faster than the other. Also, if one car travels 52 mph for 3 hours, the distance is $3(52) = 156$ miles. The other car traveling for 3 hours at 47 mph travels a distance of $3(47) = 141$ miles. The sum of the distances $156 + 141$ is 297 miles, the required distance.

> ▶ Helpful Hint
>
> Don't forget to attach units if appropriate.

State: The cars are traveling at 52 mph and 47 mph. □

PRACTICE

5 In 2007, the French train TGV V150 became the fastest conventional rail train in the world. It broke the 1990 record of the next fastest conventional rail train, the French TGV Atlantique. Assume the V150 and the Atlantique left the same station in Paris, with one heading west and one heading east. After 2 hours, they were 2150 kilometers apart. If the V150 is 75 kph faster than the Atlantique, what is the speed of each?

EXAMPLE 6 Mixing Solutions

Lynn Pike, a pharmacist, needs 70 liters of a 50% alcohol solution. She has available a 30% alcohol solution and an 80% alcohol solution. How many liters of each solution should she mix to obtain 70 liters of a 50% alcohol solution?

Solution

1. UNDERSTAND. Read and reread the problem. Next, guess the solution. Suppose that we need 20 liters of the 30% solution. Then we need $70 - 20 = 50$ liters of the 80% solution. To see if this gives us 70 liters of a 50% alcohol solution, let's find the amount of pure alcohol in each solution.

number of liters	×	alcohol strength	=	amount of pure alcohol
↓		↓		↓
20 liters	×	0.30	=	6 liters
50 liters	×	0.80	=	40 liters
70 liters	×	0.50	=	35 liters

Since 6 liters + 40 liters = 46 liters and not 35 liters, our guess is incorrect, but we have gained some insight as to how to model and check this problem.

We will let

$$x = \text{amount of 30\% solution, in liters}$$

$$y = \text{amount of 80\% solution, in liters}$$

(Continued on next page)

and use a table to organize the given data.

	Number of Liters	Alcohol Strength	Amount of Pure Alcohol
30% Solution	x	30%	$0.30x$
80% Solution	y	80%	$0.80y$
50% Solution Needed	70	50%	$(0.50)(70)$

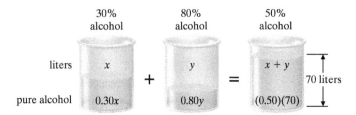

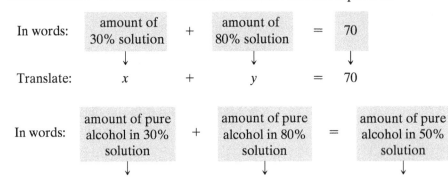

2. TRANSLATE. We translate the stated conditions into two equations.

In words:　$\boxed{\text{amount of 30\% solution}}$ $+$ $\boxed{\text{amount of 80\% solution}}$ $=$ $\boxed{70}$

Translate:　　x　　$+$　　y　　$=$　　70

In words:　$\boxed{\begin{array}{c}\text{amount of pure}\\\text{alcohol in 30\%}\\\text{solution}\end{array}}$ $+$ $\boxed{\begin{array}{c}\text{amount of pure}\\\text{alcohol in 80\%}\\\text{solution}\end{array}}$ $=$ $\boxed{\begin{array}{c}\text{amount of pure}\\\text{alcohol in 50\%}\\\text{solution}\end{array}}$

Translate:　　$0.30x$　$+$　$0.80y$　$=$　$(0.50)(70)$

3. SOLVE. Here we solve the system

$$\begin{cases} x + y = 70 \\ 0.30x + 0.80y = (0.50)(70) \end{cases}$$

To solve this system, we use the elimination method. We multiply both sides of the first equation by -3 and both sides of the second equation by 10. Then

$$\begin{cases} -3(x + y) = -3(70) \\ 10(0.30x + 0.80y) = 10(0.50)(70) \end{cases} \quad \begin{array}{c}\text{simplifies}\\\text{to}\end{array} \quad \begin{cases} -3x - 3y = -210 \\ \underline{3x + 8y = 350} \\ 5y = 140 \\ y = 28 \end{cases}$$

Now we replace y with 28 in the equation $x + y = 70$ and find that $x + 28 = 70$, or $x = 42$.
The ordered pair solution of the system is $(42, 28)$.

4. INTERPRET.

Check: Check the solution in the same way that we checked our guess.

State: The pharmacist needs to mix 42 liters of 30% solution and 28 liters of 80% solution to obtain 70 liters of 50% solution.　□

PRACTICE
6 Keith Robinson is a chemistry teacher who needs 1 liter of a solution of 5% hydrochloric acid to carry out an experiment. If he only has a stock solution of 99% hydrochloric acid, how much water (0% acid) and how much stock solution (99%) of HCL must he mix to get 1 liter of 5% solution? Round answers to the nearest hundredth of a liter.

✓CONCEPT CHECK

Suppose you mix an amount of 25% acid solution with an amount of 60% acid solution. You then calculate the acid strength of the resulting acid mixture. For which of the following results should you suspect an error in your calculation? Why?

a. 14%   **b.** 32%   **c.** 55%

OBJECTIVE

2   **Solving Problems with Cost and Revenue Functions**

Recall that businesses are often computing cost and revenue functions or equations to predict sales, to determine whether prices need to be adjusted, and to see whether the company is making or losing money. Recall also that the value at which revenue equals cost is called the break-even point. When revenue is less than cost, the company is losing money; when revenue is greater than cost, the company is making money.

EXAMPLE 7   **Finding a Break-Even Point**

A manufacturing company recently purchased $3000 worth of new equipment to offer new personalized stationery to its customers. The cost of producing a package of personalized stationery is $3.00, and it is sold for $5.50. Find the number of packages that must be sold for the company to break even.

Solution

1. UNDERSTAND. Read and reread the problem. Notice that the cost to the company will include a one-time cost of $3000 for the equipment and then $3.00 per package produced. The revenue will be $5.50 per package sold.

To model this problem, we will let

$$x = \text{number of packages of personalized stationery}$$
$$C(x) = \text{total cost of producing } x \text{ packages of stationery}$$
$$R(x) = \text{total revenue from selling } x \text{ packages of stationery}$$

2. TRANSLATE. The revenue equation is

In words:	revenue for selling x packages of stationery	=	price per package	·	number of packages
	↓		↓		↓
Translate:	$R(x)$	=	5.5	·	x

The cost equation is

In words:	cost for producing x packages of stationery	=	cost per package	·	number of packages	+	cost for equipment
	↓		↓		↓		↓
Translate:	$C(x)$	=	3	·	x	+	3000

Since the break-even point is when $R(x) = C(x)$, we solve the equation

$$5.5x = 3x + 3000$$

(Continued on next page)

3. SOLVE.

$$5.5x = 3x + 3000$$

$$2.5x = 3000 \qquad \text{Subtract } 3x \text{ from both sides.}$$

$$x = 1200 \qquad \text{Divide both sides by 2.5.}$$

4. INTERPRET.

Check: To see whether the break-even point occurs when 1200 packages are produced and sold, see if revenue equals cost when $x = 1200$. When $x = 1200$, $R(x) = 5.5x = 5.5(1200) = 6600$ and $C(x) = 3x + 3000 = 3(1200) + 3000 = 6600$. Since $R(1200) = C(1200) = 6600$, the break-even point is 1200.

State: The company must sell 1200 packages of stationery to break even. The graph of this system is shown.

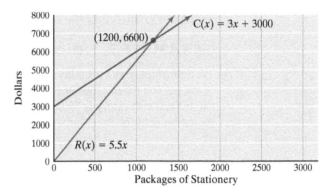

PRACTICE

7 An online-only electronics firm recently purchased $3000 worth of new equipment to create shock-proof packaging for its products. The cost of producing one shock-proof package is $2.50, and the firm charges the customer $4.50 for the packaging. Find the number of packages that must be sold for the company to break even.

OBJECTIVE

3 Solving Problems Modeled by Systems of Three Equations

To introduce problem solving by writing a system of three linear equations in three variables, we solve a problem about triangles.

 EXAMPLE 8 Finding Angle Measures

The measure of the largest angle of a triangle is 80° more than the measure of the smallest angle, and the measure of the remaining angle is 10° more than the measure of the smallest angle. Find the measure of each angle.

Solution

1. UNDERSTAND. Read and reread the problem. Recall that the sum of the measures of the angles of a triangle is 180°. Then guess a solution. If the smallest angle measures 20°, the measure of the largest angle is 80° more, or 20° + 80° = 100°. The measure of the remaining angle is 10° more than the measure of the smallest angle, or 20° + 10° = 30°. The sum of these three angles is 20° + 100° + 30° = 150°, not the required 180°. We now know that the measure of the smallest angle is greater than 20°.

To model this problem, we will let

x = degree measure of the smallest angle

y = degree measure of the largest angle

z = degree measure of the remaining angle

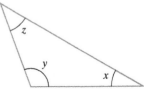

2. TRANSLATE. We translate the given information into three equations.

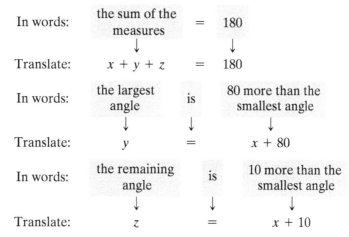

In words: the sum of the measures   =   180

Translate: $x + y + z$ =   180

In words: the largest angle   is   80 more than the smallest angle

Translate: y = $x + 80$

In words: the remaining angle   is   10 more than the smallest angle

Translate: z = $x + 10$

3. SOLVE. We solve the system

$$\begin{cases} x + y + z = 180 \\ y = x + 80 \\ z = x + 10 \end{cases}$$

Since y and z are both expressed in terms of x, we will solve using the substitution method. We substitute $y = x + 80$ and $z = x + 10$ in the first equation. Then

$$x + y + z = 180$$

$$x + (x + 80) + (x + 10) = 180 \quad \text{First equation}$$
$$3x + 90 = 180 \quad \text{Let } y = x + 80 \text{ and } z = x + 10.$$
$$3x = 90$$
$$x = 30$$

Then $y = x + 80 = 30 + 80 = 110$,   and $z = x + 10 = 30 + 10 = 40$.   The ordered triple solution is $(30, 110, 40)$.

4. INTERPRET.

Check: Notice that $30° + 40° + 110° = 180°$. Also, the measure of the largest angle, $110°$, is $80°$ more than the measure of the smallest angle, $30°$. The measure of the remaining angle, $40°$, is $10°$ more than the measure of the smallest angle, $30°$.   ☐

PRACTICE

8   The measure of the largest angle of a triangle is $40°$ more than the measure of the smallest angle, and the measure of the remaining angle is $20°$ more than the measure of the smallest angle. Find the measure of each angle.

Vocabulary, Readiness & Video Check

Martin-Gay Interactive Videos

See Video 4.5

Watch the section lecture video and answer the following questions.

OBJECTIVE
1

1. In ▭ Example 1 and the lecture before, the problem-solving steps for solving applications are mentioned. What is the difference here from when we've used these steps in the past?

OBJECTIVE
2

2. Based on ▭ Example 6, explain the meaning of a break-even point. How do you find the break-even point algebraically?

OBJECTIVE
3

3. In ▭ Example 7, why is the ordered triple not the final stated solution to the application?

4.5 Exercise Set MyMathLab®

Without actually solving each problem, choose each correct solution by deciding which choice satisfies the given conditions.

△ **1.** The length of a rectangle is 3 feet longer than the width. The perimeter is 30 feet. Find the dimensions of the rectangle.
  a. length = 8 feet; width = 5 feet
  b. length = 8 feet; width = 7 feet
  c. length = 9 feet; width = 6 feet

△ **2.** An isosceles triangle, a triangle with two sides of equal length, has a perimeter of 20 inches. Each of the equal sides is one inch longer than the third side. Find the lengths of the three sides.
  a. 6 inches, 6 inches, and 7 inches
  b. 7 inches, 7 inches, and 6 inches
  c. 6 inches, 7 inches, and 8 inches

3. Two computer disks and three notebooks cost $17. However, five computer disks and four notebooks cost $32. Find the price of each.
  a. notebook = $4; computer disk = $3
  b. notebook = $3; computer disk = $4
  c. notebook = $5; computer disk = $2

4. Two music CDs and four music cassette tapes cost a total of $40. However, three music CDs and five cassette tapes cost $55. Find the price of each.
  a. CD = $12; cassette = $4
  b. CD = $15; cassette = $2
  c. CD = $10; cassette = $5

5. Kesha has a total of 100 coins, all of which are either dimes or quarters. The total value of the coins is $13.00. Find the number of each type of coin.
  a. 80 dimes; 20 quarters   **b.** 20 dimes; 44 quarters
  c. 60 dimes; 40 quarters

6. Samuel has 28 gallons of saline solution available in two large containers at his pharmacy. One container holds three times as much as the other container. Find the capacity of each container.
  a. 15 gallons; 5 gallons   **b.** 20 gallons; 8 gallons
  c. 21 gallons; 7 gallons

TRANSLATING

Write a system of equations in x and y describing each situation. Do not solve the system. See Example 2.

7. A smaller number and a larger number add up to 15 and have a difference of 7. (Let *x* be the larger number.)

8. The total of two numbers is 16. The first number plus 2 more than 3 times the second equals 18. (Let *x* be the first number.)

9. Keiko has a total of $6500, which she has invested in two accounts. The larger account is $800 greater than the smaller account. (Let *x* be the amount of money in the larger account.)

10. Dominique has four times as much money in his savings account as in his checking account. The total amount is $2300. (Let *x* be the amount of money in his checking account.)

MIXED PRACTICE

Solve. See Examples 1 through 6. For Exercises 13 and 14, the solutions have been started for you.

⊙ **11.** Two numbers total 83 and have a difference of 17. Find the two numbers.

12. The sum of two numbers is 76 and their difference is 52. Find the two numbers.

13. One number is two more than a second number. Twice the first is 4 less than 3 times the second. Find the numbers.

Start the solution:

1. UNDERSTAND the problem. Since we are looking for two numbers, let

$$x = \text{one number}$$
$$y = \text{second number}$$

2. TRANSLATE. Since we have assigned two variables, we will translate the facts into two equations. (Fill in the blanks.)

First equation:

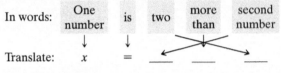

Second equation:

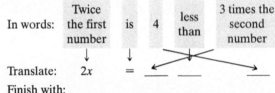

Finish with:

3. SOLVE the system and

4. INTERPRET the results.

14. Three times one number minus a second is 8, and the sum of the numbers is 12. Find the numbers.

Start the solution:

1. UNDERSTAND the problem. Since we are looking for two numbers, let

$$x = \text{one number}$$
$$y = \text{second number}$$

2. TRANSLATE. Since we have assigned two variables, we will translate the facts into two equations. (Fill in the blanks.)

First equation:

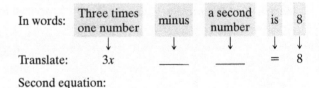

Second equation:

In words: | The sum of the numbers | is | 12 |
Translate: x + ___ ___ 12

Finish with:

3. SOLVE the system and

4. INTERPRET the results.

15. A first number plus twice a second number is 8. Twice the first number, plus the second, totals 25. Find the numbers.

16. One number is 4 more than twice the second number. Their total is 25. Find the numbers.

17. Miguel Cabrera of the Detroit Tigers led Major League Baseball in runs batted in for the 2010 regular season. Alex Rodriguez of the New York Yankees, who came in second to Cabrera, had 1 fewer run batted in for the 2010 regular season. Together, these two players brought home 251 runs during the 2010 regular season. How many runs batted in did each player account for? (*Source:* Major League Baseball)

18. The highest scorer during the WNBA 2010 regular season was Cappie Pondexter of the New York Liberty. Over the season, Pondexter scored 13 more points than the second-highest scorer, Angel McCoughtry of the Atlanta Dream. Together, Pondexter and McCoughtry scored 1445 points during the 2010 regular season. How many points did each player score over the course of the season? (*Source:* Women's National Basketball Association)

▶ 19. Ann Marie Jones has been pricing Amtrak train fares for a group trip to New York. Three adults and four children must pay $159. Two adults and three children must pay $112. Find the price of an adult's ticket and find the price of a child's ticket.

20. Last month, Jerry Papa purchased two DVDs and five CDs at Wall-to-Wall Sound for $65. This month, he bought four DVDs and three CDs for $81. Find the price of each DVD and find the price of each CD.

21. Johnston and Betsy Waring have a jar containing 80 coins, all of which are either quarters or nickels. The total value of the coins is $14.60. How many of each type of coin do they have?

22. Sarah and Keith Robinson purchased 40 stamps, a mixture of 44¢ and 20¢ stamps. Find the number of each type of stamp if they spent $16.40.

23. Norman and Suzanne Scarpulla own 35 shares of McDonald's stock and 69 shares of The Ohio Art Company stock (makers of Etch A Sketch and other toys). On a particular

day in 2011, their stock portfolio consisting of these two stocks was worth $2814. The McDonald's stock was $70 more per share than The Ohio Art Company stock. What was the price of each stock on that day? (*Source:* Yahoo finance)

24. Saralee Rose has investments in Google and Nintendo stock. During a particular day in 2011, Google stock was at $540 per share, and Nintendo stock was at $30 per share. Saralee's portfolio made up of these two stocks was worth $20,610 at that time. If Saralee owns 16 more shares of Google stock than she owns of Nintendo stock, how many shares of each type of stock does she own?

25. Twice last month, Judy Carter rented a car from Enterprise in Fresno, California, and traveled around the Southwest on business. Enterprise rents this car for a daily fee plus an additional charge per mile driven. Judy recalls that her first trip lasted 4 days, she drove 450 miles, and the rental cost her $240.50. On her second business trip, she drove the same model of car a distance of 200 miles in 3 days and paid $146.00 for the rental. Find the daily fee and the mileage charge.

26. Joan Gundersen rented the same car model twice from Hertz, which rents this car model for a daily fee plus an additional charge per mile driven. Joan recalls that the car rented for 5 days and driven for 300 miles cost her $178, while the same model car rented for 4 days and driven for 500 miles cost $197. Find the daily fee and find the mileage charge.

27. Pratap Puri rowed 18 miles down the Delaware River in 2 hours, but the return trip took him $4\frac{1}{2}$ hours. Find the rate Pratap can row in still water and find the rate of the current.

Let x = rate Pratap can row in still water and
$\quad y$ = rate of the current

	d	=	r	·	t
Downstream			$x + y$		
Upstream			$x - y$		

28. The Jonathan Schultz family took a canoe 10 miles down the Allegheny River in $1\frac{1}{4}$ hours. After lunch, it took them 4 hours to return. Find the rate of the current.

Let x = rate the family can row in still water and
$\quad y$ = rate of the current

	d	=	r	·	t
Downstream			$x + y$		
Upstream			$x - y$		

29. Dave and Sandy Hartranft are frequent flyers with Delta Airlines. They often fly from Philadelphia to Chicago, a distance of 780 miles. On one particular trip, they fly into the wind, and the flight takes 2 hours. The return trip, with the wind behind them, only takes $1\frac{1}{2}$ hours. If the wind speed is the same on each trip, find the speed of the wind and find the speed of the plane in still air.

30. With a strong wind behind it, a United Airlines jet flies 2400 miles from Los Angeles to Orlando in $4\frac{3}{4}$ hours. The return trip takes 6 hours because the plane flies into the wind. If the wind speed is the same on each trip, find the speed of the plane in still air and find the wind speed to the nearest tenth of a mile per hour.

31. Kevin Briley began a 114-mile bicycle trip to build up stamina for a triathlete competition. Unfortunately, his bicycle chain broke, so he finished the trip walking. The whole trip took 6 hours. If Kevin walks at a rate of 4 miles per hour and rides at 24 miles per hour, find the amount of time he spent on the bicycle.

32. In Canada, eastbound and westbound trains travel along the same track, with sidings to pull onto to avoid accidents. Two trains are now 150 miles apart, with the westbound train traveling twice as fast as the eastbound train. A warning must be issued to pull one train onto a siding or else the trains will crash in $1\frac{1}{4}$ hours. Find the speed of the eastbound train and the speed of the westbound train.

33. Doreen Schmidt is a chemist with Gemco Pharmaceutical. She needs to prepare 12 liters of a 9% hydrochloric acid solution. Find the amount of a 4% solution and the amount of a 12% solution she should mix to get this solution.

Concentration Rate	Liters of Solution	Liters of Pure Acid
0.04	x	$0.04x$
0.12	y	?
0.09	12	?

34. Elise Everly is preparing 15 liters of a 25% saline solution. Elise has two other saline solutions, with strengths of 40% and 10%. Find the amount of 40% solution and the amount of 10% solution she should mix to get 15 liters of a 25% solution.

Concentration Rate	Liters of Solution	Liters of Pure Salt
0.40	x	$0.40x$
0.10	y	?
0.25	15	?

35. Wayne Osby blends coffee for a local coffee café. He needs to prepare 200 pounds of blended coffee beans selling for $3.95 per pound. He intends to do this by blending together a high-quality bean costing $4.95 per pound and a cheaper bean costing $2.65 per pound. To the nearest pound, find how much high-quality coffee bean and how much cheaper coffee bean he should blend.

36. Macadamia nuts cost an astounding $16.50 per pound, but research by an independent firm says that mixed nuts sell better if macadamias are included. The standard mix costs $9.25 per pound. Find how many pounds of macadamias and how many pounds of the standard mix should be combined to produce 40 pounds that will cost $10 per pound. Find the amounts to the nearest tenth of a pound.

37. Recall that two angles are complementary if the sum of their measures is 90°. Find the measures of two complementary angles if one angle is twice the other.

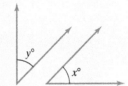

38. Recall that two angles are supplementary if the sum of their measures is 180°. Find the measures of two supplementary angles if one angle is 20° more than four times the other.

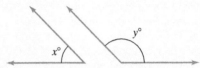

39. Find the measures of two complementary angles if one angle is 10° more than three times the other.

40. Find the measures of two supplementary angles if one angle is 18° more than twice the other.

41. Kathi and Robert Hawn had a pottery stand at the annual Skippack Craft Fair. They sold some of their pottery at the original price of $9.50 each but later decreased the price of each by $2. If they sold all 90 pieces and took in $721, find how many they sold at the original price and how many they sold at the reduced price.

42. A charity fund-raiser consisted of a spaghetti supper where a total of 387 people were fed. They charged $6.80 for adults and half price for children. If they took in $2444.60, find how many adults and how many children attended the supper.

43. The Santa Fe National Historic Trail is approximately 1200 miles between Old Franklin, Missouri, and Santa Fe, New Mexico. Suppose that a group of hikers start from each town and walk the trail toward each other. They meet after a total hiking time of 240 hours. If one group travels $\frac{1}{2}$ mile per hour slower than the other group, find the rate of each group. (*Source:* National Park Service)

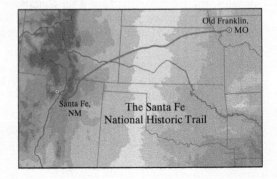

44. California 1 South is a historic highway that stretches 123 miles along the coast from Monterey to Morro Bay. Suppose that two antique cars start driving this highway, one from each town. They meet after 3 hours. Find the rate of each car if one car travels 1 mile per hour faster than the other car. (*Source:* National Geographic)

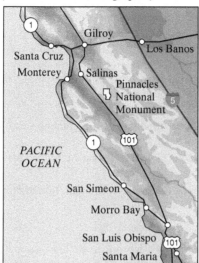

45. A 30% solution of fertilizer is to be mixed with a 60% solution of fertilizer to get 150 gallons of a 50% solution. How many gallons of the 30% solution and 60% solution should be mixed?

46. A 10% acid solution is to be mixed with a 50% acid solution to get 120 ounces of a 20% acid solution. How many ounces of the 10% solution and 50% solution should be mixed?

47. Traffic signs are regulated by the *Manual on Uniform Traffic Control Devices* (MUTCD). According to this manual, if the sign below is placed on a freeway, its perimeter must be 144 inches. Also, its length is 12 inches longer than its width. Find the dimensions of this sign.

48. According to the MUTCD (see Exercise 47), this sign must have a perimeter of 60 inches. Also, its length must be 6 inches longer than its width. Find the dimensions of this sign.

49. In the United States, the percent of adult blogging has changed within the various age ranges. From 2007 to 2009, the function $y = -4.5x + 24$ can be used to estimate the percent of adults under 30 who blogged, and the function $y = 2x + 7$ can be used to estimate the percent of adults over 30 who blogged. For both functions, x is the number of years after 2007. (*Source:* Pew Internet & American Life Project)

  a. If this trend continued, estimate the year in which the percent of adults under 30 and the percent of adults over 30 who blogged was the same.

  b. Use these equations to predict the percent of adults under 30 who blog and the percent of adults over 30 who blog for the current year.

50. The rate of fatalities per 100 million vehicle-miles has been decreasing for both automobiles and light trucks (pickups, sport-utility vehicles, and minivans). For the years 2001 through 2009, the function $y = -0.06x + 1.7$ can be used to estimate the rate of fatalities per 100 million vehicle-miles for automobiles during this period, and the function $y = -0.08x + 2.1$ can be used to estimate the rate of fatalities per 100 million vehicle-miles for light trucks during this period. For both functions, x is the number of years since 2000. (*Source:* Bureau of Statistics, U.S. Department of Transportation)

  a. If this trend continues, predict the year in which the fatality rate for automobiles equals the fatality rate for light trucks.

  b. Use these equations to predict the fatality rate per million vehicle-miles for automobiles and light trucks for the current year.

51. The annual U.S. per capita consumption of cheddar cheese has remained about the same since the millennium, while the consumption of mozzarella cheese has increased. For the years 2000–2010, the function $y = 0.06x + 9.7$ approximates the annual U.S. per capita consumption of cheddar cheese in pounds, and the function $y = 0.21x + 9.3$ approximates the annual U.S. per capita consumption of mozzarella cheese in pounds. For both functions, x is the number of years after 2000.

  a. Explain how the given function verifies that the consumption of cheddar cheese has remained the same, while the given function verifies that the consumption of mozzarella cheese has increased.

  b. Based on this information, determine the year in which the pounds of cheddar cheese consumed equaled the pounds of mozzarella cheese consumed. (*Source:* Based on data from the U.S. Department of Agriculture)

52. Two of the major job categories defined by the U.S. Department of Labor are manufacturing jobs and jobs in the service sector. Jobs in the manufacturing sector have decreased nearly every year since the 1960s. During the same time period, service sector jobs have been steadily increasing. For the years from 1988 through 2009, the function $y = -0.225x + 16.1$ approximates the percent of jobs in the U.S. economy that are manufacturing jobs, while the function $y = 0.45x + 21.7$ approximates the percent of jobs that are service sector jobs. (*Source:* Based on data from the U.S. Department of Labor)

a. Explain how the decrease in manufacturing jobs can be verified by the given function, and the increase of service sector jobs can be verified by the given function.

b. Based on this information, determine the year when the percent of manufacturing jobs and the percent of service sector jobs were the same.

△ **53.** In the figure, line *l* and line *m* are parallel lines cut by transversal *t*. Find the values of *x* and *y*.

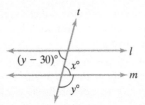

△ **54.** Find the values of *x* and *y* in the following isosceles triangle.

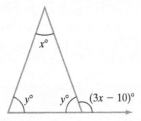

Given the cost function $C(x)$ and the revenue function $R(x)$, find the number of units x that must be sold to break even. See Example 7.

55. $C(x) = 30x + 10,000$ $R(x) = 46x$

56. $C(x) = 12x + 15,000$ $R(x) = 32x$

57. $C(x) = 1.2x + 1500$ $R(x) = 1.7x$

58. $C(x) = 0.8x + 900$ $R(x) = 2x$

59. $C(x) = 75x + 160,000$ $R(x) = 200x$

60. $C(x) = 105x + 70,000$ $R(x) = 245x$

▶ 61. The planning department of Abstract Office Supplies has been asked to determine whether the company should introduce a new computer desk next year. The department estimates that $6000 of new manufacturing equipment will need to be purchased and that the cost of constructing each desk

will be $200. The department also estimates that the revenue from each desk will be $450.

a. Determine the revenue function $R(x)$ from the sale of *x* desks.

b. Determine the cost function $C(x)$ for manufacturing *x* desks.

c. Find the break-even point.

62. Baskets, Inc., is planning to introduce a new woven basket. The company estimates that $500 worth of new equipment will be needed to manufacture this new type of basket and that it will cost $15 per basket to manufacture. The company also estimates that the revenue from each basket will be $31.

a. Determine the revenue function $R(x)$ from the sale of *x* baskets.

b. Determine the cost function $C(x)$ for manufacturing *x* baskets.

c. Find the break-even point. Round up to the nearest whole basket.

Solve. See Example 8.

63. Rabbits in a lab are to be kept on a strict daily diet that includes 30 grams of protein, 16 grams of fat, and 24 grams of carbohydrates. The scientist has only three food mixes available with the following grams of nutrients per unit.

	Protein	*Fat*	*Carbohydrate*
Mix A	4	6	3
Mix B	6	1	2
Mix C	4	1	12

Find how many units of each mix are needed daily to meet each rabbit's dietary need.

64. Gerry Gundersen mixes different solutions with concentrations of 25%, 40%, and 50% to get 200 liters of a 32% solution. If he uses twice as much of the 25% solution as of the 40% solution, find how many liters of each kind he uses.

65. The perimeter of a quadrilateral (four-sided polygon) is 29 inches. The longest side is twice as long as the shortest side. The other two sides are equally long and are 2 inches longer than the shortest side. Find the lengths of all four sides.

66. The measure of the largest angle of a triangle is 90° more than the measure of the smallest angle, and the measure of the remaining angle is 30° more than the measure of the smallest angle. Find the measure of each angle.

67. The sum of three numbers is 40. The first number is five more than the second number. It is also twice the third. Find the numbers.

68. The sum of the digits of a three-digit number is 15. The tens-place digit is twice the hundreds-place digit, and the ones-place digit is 1 less than the hundreds-place digit. Find the three-digit number.

69. During the 2010–2011 regular NBA season, the top-scoring player was Kevin Durant of the Oklahoma City Thunder. Durant scored a total of 2161 points during the regular season. The number of free throws (each worth one point) he made was 14 more than four times the number of three-point field goals he made. The number of two-point field goals that Durant made was 28 less than the number of free throws he made. How many free throws, two-point field goals, and three-point field goals did Kevin Durant make during the 2010–2011 NBA season? (*Source*: National Basketball Association)

70. For 2010, the WNBA's top scorer was Diana Taurasi of the Phoenix Mercury. She scored a total of 745 points during the regular season. The number of two-point field goals Taurasi made was 36 fewer than two times the number of three-point field goals she made. The number of free throws (each worth one point) she made was 61 more than the number of two-point field goals she made. Find how many free throws, two-point field goals, and three-point field goals Diana Taurasi made during the 2010 regular season. (*Source*: Women's National Basketball Association)

71. Find the values of $x, y,$ and z in the following triangle.

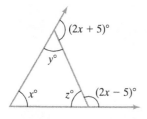

72. The sum of the measures of the angles of a quadrilateral is $360°$. Find the values of $x, y,$ and z in the following quadrilateral.

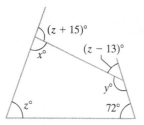

REVIEW AND PREVIEW

Solve each linear inequality. Write your solution in interval notation. See Section 2.8.

73. $-3x < -9$

74. $2x - 7 \leq 5x + 11$

75. $4(2x - 1) \geq 0$

76. $\frac{2}{3}x < \frac{1}{3}$

CONCEPT EXTENSIONS

Solve. See the Concept Check in this section.

77. Suppose you mix an amount of candy costing $0.49 a pound with candy costing $0.65 a pound. Which of the following costs per pound could result?

a. $0.58   **b.** $0.72   **c.** $0.29

78. Suppose you mix a 50% acid solution with pure acid (100%). Which of the following acid strengths are possible for the resulting acid mixture?

a. 25%   **b.** 150%   **c.** 62%   **d.** 90%

79. Dale and Sharon Mahnke have decided to fence off a garden plot behind their house, using their house as the "fence" along one side of the garden. The length (which runs parallel to the house) is 3 feet less than twice the width. Find the dimensions if 33 feet of fencing is used along the three sides requiring it.

80. Judy McElroy plans to erect 152 feet of fencing around her rectangular horse pasture. A river bank serves as one side length of the rectangle. If each width is 4 feet longer than half the length, find the dimensions.

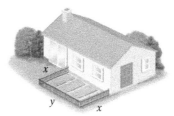

81. Find the values of $a, b,$ and c such that the equation $y = ax^2 + bx + c$ has ordered pair solutions $(1, 6), (-1, -2),$ and $(0, -1)$. To do so, substitute each ordered pair solution into the equation. Each time, the result is an equation in three unknowns: $a, b,$ and c. Then solve the resulting system of three linear equations in three unknowns, $a, b,$ and c.

82. Find the values of $a, b,$ and c such that the equation $y = ax^2 + bx + c$ has ordered pair solutions $(1, 2), (2, 3),$ and $(-1, 6)$. (*Hint:* See Exercise 81.)

83. Data (x, y) for the total number (in thousands) of college-bound students who took the ACT assessment in the year x are approximately $(3, 927), (11, 1179),$ and $(19, 1495),$ where $x = 3$ represents 1993 and $x = 11$ represents 2001. Find the values $a, b,$ and c such that the equation $y = ax^2 + bx + c$ models these data. According to your model, how many students will take the ACT in 2015? (*Source:* ACT, Inc.)

84. Monthly normal rainfall data (x, y) for Portland, Oregon, are $(4, 2.47), (7, 0.58), (8, 1.07),$ where x represents time in months (with $x = 1$ representing January) and y represents rainfall in inches. Find the values of $a, b,$ and c rounded to 2 decimal places such that the equation $y = ax^2 + bx + c$ models this data. According to your model, how much rain should Portland expect during September? (*Source:* National Climatic Data Center)

The function $f(x) = -8.6x + 275$ represents the U.S. average number of monthly calls (sent or received) per wireless subscriber and the function $f(x) = 204.9x - 1217$ represents the average number of text messages (sent or received) per wireless subscriber. For both functions, x is the number of years since 2000, and these functions are good for the years 2006–2010.

85. Solve the system formed by these functions. Round each coordinate to the nearest whole number.

86. Use your answer to Exercise 85 to predict the year in which the monthly calls and text messages are/were the same.

Answers to Selected Exercises

CHAPTER 1 REVIEW OF REAL NUMBERS

Section 1.2
Practice Exercises

1. a. $<$ **b.** $>$ **c.** $<$ **2. a.** True **b.** False **c.** True **d.** True **3. a.** $3 < 8$ **b.** $15 \geq 9$ **c.** $6 \neq 7$ **4.** -10 **5. a.** 25
b. 25 **c.** $25, -15, -99$ **d.** $25, \frac{7}{3}, -15, -\frac{3}{4}, -3.7, 8.8, -99$ **e.** $\sqrt{5}$ **f.** $25, \frac{7}{3}, -15, -\frac{3}{4}, \sqrt{5}, -3.7, 8.8, -99$ **6. a.** $<$ **b.** $>$ **c.** $=$
7. a. 8 **b.** 9 **c.** 2.5 **d.** $\frac{5}{11}$ **e.** $\sqrt{3}$ **8. a.** $=$ **b.** $>$ **c.** $<$ **d.** $>$ **e.** $<$

Vocabulary, Readiness & Video Check 1.2

1. whole **3.** inequality **5.** real **7.** irrational **9.** To form a true statement: $0 < 7$. **11.** 0 belongs to the whole numbers, the integers, the rational numbers, and the real numbers; because 0 is a rational number, it cannot also be an irrational number

Exercise Set 1.2

1. $>$ **3.** $=$ **5.** $<$ **7.** $<$ **9.** $32 < 212$ **11.** $30 \leq 45$ **13.** true **15.** false **17.** false **19.** true **21.** false **23.** $8 < 12$
25. $5 \geq 4$ **27.** $15 \neq -2$ **29.** $14,494; -282$ **31.** $-28,000$ **33.** $350; -126$ **35.** whole, integers, rational, real **37.** integers, rational, real
39. natural, whole, integers, rational, real **41.** rational, real **43.** irrational, real **45.** false **47.** true **49.** true **51.** true **53.** false
55. $>$ **57.** $>$ **59.** $<$ **61.** $<$ **63.** $>$ **65.** $=$ **67.** $<$ **69.** $<$ **71.** 2009 **73.** 2009, 2010 **75.** 280 million $<$ 281 million
77. 49 million $>$ 16 million **79.** 38 million pounds less, or -38 million **81.** $-0.04 > -26.7$ **83.** sun **85.** sun **87.** $20 \leq 25$ **89.** $6 > 0$
91. $-12 < -10$ **93.** answers may vary

Section 1.3
Practice Exercises

1. a. $2 \cdot 2 \cdot 3 \cdot 3$ **b.** $2 \cdot 2 \cdot 2 \cdot 5 \cdot 5$ **2. a.** $\frac{7}{8}$ **b.** $\frac{16}{3}$ **c.** $\frac{7}{25}$ **3.** $\frac{7}{24}$ **4. a.** $\frac{27}{16}$ **b.** $\frac{1}{36}$ **c.** $\frac{5}{2}$ **5. a.** 1 **b.** $\frac{6}{5}$ **c.** $\frac{4}{5}$ **d.** $\frac{1}{2}$
6. $\frac{14}{21}$ **7. a.** $\frac{46}{77}$ **b.** $\frac{1}{14}$ **c.** $\frac{1}{2}$ **8.** $22\frac{11}{15}$ **9.** $40\frac{5}{6}$

Vocabulary, Readiness & Video Check 1.3

1. fraction **3.** product **5.** factors, product **7.** equivalent **9.** The division operation changes to multiplication and the second fraction $\frac{1}{20}$
changes to its reciprocal $\frac{20}{1}$. **11.** The number $4\frac{7}{6}$ is not in proper mixed number form as the fraction part, $\frac{7}{6}$, should not be an improper fraction.

Exercise Set 1.3

1. $\frac{3}{8}$ **3.** $\frac{5}{7}$ **5.** $3 \cdot 11$ **7.** $2 \cdot 7 \cdot 7$ **9.** $2 \cdot 2 \cdot 5$ **11.** $3 \cdot 5 \cdot 5$ **13.** $3 \cdot 3 \cdot 5$ **15.** $\frac{1}{2}$ **17.** $\frac{2}{3}$ **19.** $\frac{3}{7}$ **21.** $\frac{3}{5}$ **23.** $\frac{30}{61}$ **25.** $\frac{3}{8}$
27. $\frac{1}{2}$ **29.** $\frac{6}{7}$ **31.** 15 **33.** $\frac{1}{6}$ **35.** $\frac{25}{27}$ **37.** $\frac{11}{20}$ sq mi **39.** $\frac{7}{36}$ sq ft **41.** $\frac{3}{5}$ **43.** 1 **45.** $\frac{1}{3}$ **47.** $\frac{9}{35}$ **49.** $\frac{21}{30}$ **51.** $\frac{4}{18}$
53. $\frac{16}{20}$ **55.** $\frac{23}{21}$ **57.** $\frac{11}{60}$ **59.** $\frac{5}{66}$ **61.** $\frac{7}{5}$ **63.** $\frac{1}{5}$ **65.** $\frac{3}{8}$ **67.** $\frac{1}{9}$ **69.** $18\frac{20}{27}$ **71.** $2\frac{28}{29}$ **73.** $48\frac{1}{15}$ **75.** $7\frac{1}{12}$ **77.** $\frac{5}{7}$
79. $\frac{65}{21}$ **81.** $\frac{2}{5}$ **83.** $\frac{10}{9}$ **85.** $\frac{17}{3}$ **87.** 37 **89.** $\frac{5}{66}$ **91.** $\frac{1}{5}$ **93.** $5\frac{1}{6}$ **95.** $\frac{17}{18}$ **97.** $55\frac{1}{4}$ ft **99.** answers may vary
101. $3\frac{3}{8}$ mi **103.** $\frac{21}{100}$ **105.** multiplexes **107.** incorrect; $\frac{12}{24} = \frac{2 \cdot 2 \cdot 3}{2 \cdot 2 \cdot 2 \cdot 3} = \frac{1}{2}$ **109.** incorrect; $\frac{2}{7} + \frac{9}{7} = \frac{11}{7}$

Section 1.4
Practice Exercises

1. a. 1 **b.** 25 **c.** $\frac{1}{100}$ **d.** 9 **e.** $\frac{8}{125}$ **2. a.** 33 **b.** 11 **c.** $\frac{32}{9}$ or $3\frac{5}{9}$ **d.** 36 **e.** $\frac{3}{16}$ **3.** $\frac{31}{11}$ **4.** 4 **5.** $\frac{9}{22}$ **6. a.** 9
b. $\frac{8}{15}$ **c.** $\frac{19}{10}$ **d.** 33 **7.** No **8. a.** $6x$ **b.** $x - 8$ **c.** $x \cdot 9$ or $9x$ **d.** $2x + 3$ **e.** $7 + x$ **9. a.** $x + 7 = 13$ **b.** $x - 2 = 11$
c. $2x + 9 \neq 25$ **d.** $5(11) \geq x$

Graphing Calculator Explorations 1.4
1. 625 **3.** 59,049 **5.** 30 **7.** 9857 **9.** 2376

Vocabulary, Readiness & Video Check 1.4
1. base; exponent **3.** variable **5.** equation **7.** solving **9.** The replacement value for z is not used because it's not needed–there is no variable z in the given algebraic expression. **11.** We translate phrases to mathematical expressions and sentences to mathematical equations.

Exercise Set 1.4

1. 243   **3.** 27   **5.** 1   **7.** 5   **9.** 49   **11.** $\frac{16}{81}$ **13.** $\frac{1}{125}$ **15.** 1.44   **17.** 0.000064   **19.** 17   **21.** 20   **23.** 10   **25.** 21

27. 45   **29.** 0   **31.** 30   **33.** 2   **35.** $\frac{7}{18}$ **37.** $\frac{27}{10}$ **39.** $\frac{7}{5}$ **41.** 32   **43.** $\frac{23}{27}$ **45. a.** 64   **b.** 43   **c.** 19   **d.** 22   **47.** 9

49. 1   **51.** 1   **53.** 11   **55.** 8   **57.** 45   **59.** 27   **61.** 132   **63.** $\frac{37}{18}$ **65.** 16; 64; 144; 256   **67.** yes   **69.** no   **71.** no   **73.** yes

75. no   **77.** $x + 15$ **79.** $x - 5$ **81.** $\frac{x}{4}$ **83.** $3x + 22$ **85.** $1 + 2 = 9 \div 3$ **87.** $3 \neq 4 \div 2$ **89.** $5 + x = 20$ **91.** $7.6x = 17$

93. $13 - 3x = 13$ **95.** multiply   **97.** subtract   **99.** no; answers may vary   **101.** 14 in., 12 sq in.   **103.** 14 in., 9.01 sq in.   **105.** Rectangles with the same perimeter can have different areas.   **107.** $(20 - 4) \cdot 4 \div 2$ **109. a.** expression   **b.** equation   **c.** equation   **d.** expression   **e.** expression   **111.** answers may vary   **113.** answers may vary, for example, $-2(5) - 1$ **115.** 12,000 sq ft   **117.** 51 mph

Section 1.5
Practice Exercises

1.   **2.**   **3. a.** -13 **b.** -32 **4.**

5. a. -3 **b.** 1   **c.** -0.2 **6. a.** -1 **b.** -6 **c.** 0.5   **d.** $\frac{1}{70}$ **7. a.** -6 **b.** -6 **8.** 4°F   **9. a.** $\frac{5}{9}$ **b.** -8 **c.** -6.2

d. 3   **10. a.** -15 **b.** $\frac{3}{5}$ **c.** $5y$ **d.** 8

Vocabulary, Readiness & Video Check 1.5

1. opposites   **3.** n **5.** absolute values   **7.** Negative temperatures; the high temperature for the day was -6°F

Exercise Set 1.5

1. 9   **3.** -14 **5.** 1   **7.** -12 **9.** -5 **11.** -12 **13.** -4 **15.** 7   **17.** -2 **19.** 0   **21.** -19 **23.** 31   **25.** -47

27. -2.1 **29.** -8 **31.** 38   **33.** -13.1 **35.** $\frac{2}{8} = \frac{1}{4}$ **37.** $-\frac{3}{16}$ **39.** $-\frac{13}{10}$ **41.** -8 **43.** -59 **45.** -9 **47.** 5   **49.** 11

51. -18 **53.** 19   **55.** -0.7 **57.** $-6°$ **59.** 146 ft   **61.** $-\$6.9$ million   **63.** -16 **65.** -6 **67.** 2   **69.** 0   **71.** -6 **73.** -2

75. 0   **77.** $-\frac{2}{3}$ **79.** yes   **81.** no   **83.** July   **85.** October   **87.** 4.7°F   **89.** -3 **91.** -22 **93.** negative   **95.** positive   **97.** true

99. false   **101.** answers may vary   **103.** answers may vary

Section 1.6
Practice Exercises

1. a. -13 **b.** -7 **c.** 12   **d.** -2 **2. a.** 10.9   **b.** $-\frac{1}{2}$ **c.** $-\frac{19}{20}$ **3.** -7 **4. a.** -6 **b.** 6.1   **5. a.** -20 **b.** 13   **6. a.** 2

b. 13   **7.** $\$357$ **8. a.** 28°   **b.** 137°

Vocabulary, Readiness & Video Check 1.6

1. $7 - x$ **3.** $x - 7$ **5.** $7 - x$ **7.** $-10 - (-14)$; d   **9.** addition; opposite   **11.** There's a minus sign in the numerator and the replacement value is negative (notice parentheses are used around the replacement value), and it's always good to be careful when working with negative signs.   **13.** In Example 9, you have two supplementary angles and know the measure of one of them. From the definition, you know that two supplementary angles must sum to 180°. Therefore you can subtract the known angle measure from 180° to get the measure of the other angle.

Exercise Set 1.6

1. -10 **3.** -5 **5.** 19   **7.** $\frac{1}{6}$ **9.** 2   **11.** -11 **13.** 11   **15.** 5   **17.** 37   **19.** -6.4 **21.** -71 **23.** 0   **25.** 4.1

27. $\frac{2}{11}$ **29.** $-\frac{11}{12}$ **31.** 8.92   **33.** 13   **35.** -5 **37.** -1 **39.** -23 **41.** -26 **43.** -24 **45.** 3   **47.** -45 **49.** -4

51. 13   **53.** 6   **55.** 9   **57.** -9 **59.** -7 **61.** $\frac{7}{5}$ **63.** 21   **65.** $\frac{1}{4}$ **67.** 100°F   **69.** 265°F   **71.** 35,653 ft   **73.** -308 ft

75. 19,852 ft   **77.** 130°   **79.** 30°   **81.** no   **83.** no   **85.** yes   **87.** $-5 + x$ **89.** $-20 - x$ **91.** $-4.4°$; 2.6°; 12°; 23.5°; 15.3°   **93.** May   **95.** answers may vary   **97.** 16   **99.** -20 **101.** true; answers may vary   **103.** false; answers may vary   **105.** negative, $-30,387$

Integrated Review

1. negative   **2.** negative   **3.** positive   **4.** 0   **5.** positive   **6.** 0   **7.** positive   **8.** positive   **9.** $-\frac{1}{7}; \frac{1}{7}$ **10.** $\frac{12}{5}; \frac{12}{5}$ **11.** 3; 3

12. $-\frac{9}{11}; \frac{9}{11}$ **13.** -42 **14.** 10   **15.** 2   **16.** -18 **17.** -7 **18.** -39 **19.** -2 **20.** -9 **21.** -3.4 **22.** -9.8 **23.** $-\frac{25}{28}$

24. $-\frac{5}{24}$ **25.** -4 **26.** -24 **27.** 6   **28.** 20   **29.** 6   **30.** 61   **31.** -6 **32.** -16 **33.** -19 **34.** -13 **35.** -4 **36.** -1

37. $\frac{13}{20}$ **38.** $-\frac{29}{40}$ **39.** 4   **40.** 9   **41.** -1 **42.** -3 **43.** 8   **44.** 10   **45.** 47   **46.** $\frac{2}{3}$

Section 1.7
Practice Exercises

1. a. -40 **b.** 12 **c.** -54 **2. a.** -30 **b.** 24 **c.** 0 **d.** 26 **3. a.** -0.046 **b.** $-\dfrac{4}{15}$ **c.** 14 **4. a.** 36 **b.** -36 **c.** -64

d. -64 **5. a.** $\dfrac{3}{8}$ **b.** $\dfrac{1}{15}$ **c.** $-\dfrac{7}{2}$ **d.** $-\dfrac{1}{5}$ **6. a.** -8 **b.** -4 **c.** 5 **7. a.** 3 **b.** -16 **c.** $-\dfrac{6}{5}$ **d.** $-\dfrac{1}{18}$ **8. a.** 0

b. undefined **c.** undefined **9. a.** $-\dfrac{84}{5}$ **b.** 11 **10. a.** -9 **b.** 33 **c.** $\dfrac{5}{3}$ **11.** -52

Graphing Calculator Explorations 1.7
1. 38 **3.** -441 **5.** $163.\overline{3}$ **7.** 54,499 **9.** 15,625

Vocabulary, Readiness & Video Check 1.7
1. 0; 0 **3.** positive **5.** negative **7.** positive **9.** The parentheses, or lack of them, determine the base of the expression. In Example 6, $(-2)^4$, the base is -2 and all of -2 is raised to 4. In Example 7, -2^4, the base is 2 and only 2 is raised to 4. **11.** Yes; because division of real numbers is defined in terms of multiplication. **13.** The football team lost 4 yards on each play and a loss of yardage is represented by a negative number.

Exercise Set 1.7

1. -24 **3.** -2 **5.** 50 **7.** -12 **9.** 0 **11.** -18 **13.** $\dfrac{3}{10}$ **15.** $\dfrac{2}{3}$ **17.** -7 **19.** 0.14 **21.** -800 **23.** -28 **25.** 25

27. $-\dfrac{8}{27}$ **29.** -121 **31.** $-\dfrac{1}{4}$ **33.** -30 **35.** 23 **37.** -7 **39.** true **41.** false **43.** 16 **45.** -1 **47.** 25 **49.** -49

51. $\dfrac{1}{9}$ **53.** $\dfrac{3}{2}$ **55.** $-\dfrac{1}{14}$ **57.** $-\dfrac{11}{3}$ **59.** $\dfrac{1}{0.2}$ **61.** -6.3 **63.** -9 **65.** 4 **67.** -4 **69.** 0 **71.** -5 **73.** undefined

75. 3 **77.** -15 **79.** $-\dfrac{18}{7}$ **81.** $\dfrac{20}{27}$ **83.** -1 **85.** $-\dfrac{9}{2}$ **87.** -4 **89.** 16 **91.** -3 **93.** $-\dfrac{16}{7}$ **95.** 2 **97.** $\dfrac{6}{5}$ **99.** -5

101. $\dfrac{3}{2}$ **103.** -21 **105.** 41 **107.** -134 **109.** 3 **111.** 0 **113.** $-71 \cdot x$ or $-71x$ **115.** $-16 - x$ **117.** $-29 + x$ **119.** $\dfrac{x}{-33}$

or $x \div (-33)$ **121.** $3 \cdot (-4) = -12$; a loss of 12 yd **123.** $5(-20) = -100$; a depth of 100 ft **125.** yes **127.** no **129.** yes **131.** $-162°F$

133. answers may vary **135.** $1, -1$ **137.** positive **139.** not possible **141.** negative **143.** $-2 + \dfrac{-15}{3}; -7$ **145.** $2[-5 + (-3)]; -16$

Section 1.8
Practice Exercises
1. a. $8 \cdot x$ **b.** $17 + x$ **2. a.** $2 + (9 + 7)$ **b.** $(-4 \cdot 2) \cdot 7$ **3. a.** $x + 14$ **b.** $-30x$ **4. a.** $5x - 5y$ **b.** $-24 - 12t$
c. $6x - 8y - 2z$ **d.** $-3 + y$ **e.** $-x + 7 - 2s$ **f.** $x + 11$ **5. a.** $5(w + 3)$ **b.** $9(w + z)$ **6. a.** commutative property of
multiplication **b.** associative property of addition **c.** identity element for addition **d.** multiplicative inverse property **e.** commutative
property of addition **f.** additive inverse property **g.** commutative and associative properties of multiplication

Vocabulary, Readiness & Video Check 1.8
1. commutative property of addition **3.** distributive property **5.** associative property of addition **7.** opposites or additive inverses
9. 2 is outside the parentheses, so the point is made that you should only distribute the -9 to the terms within the parentheses and not also to the 2.

Exercise Set 1.8
1. $16 + x$ **3.** $y \cdot (-4)$ **5.** yx **7.** $13 + 2x$ **9.** $x \cdot (yz)$ **11.** $(2 + a) + b$ **13.** $(4a) \cdot b$ **15.** $a + (b + c)$ **17.** $17 + b$
19. $24y$ **21.** y **23.** $26 + a$ **25.** $-72x$ **27.** s **29.** $2 + x$ **31.** $4x + 4y$ **33.** $9x - 54$ **35.** $6x + 10$ **37.** $28x - 21$
39. $18 + 3x$ **41.** $-2y + 2z$ **43.** $-21y - 35$ **45.** $5x + 20m + 10$ **47.** $-4 + 8m - 4n$ **49.** $-5x - 2$ **51.** $-r + 3 + 7p$
53. $3x + 4$ **55.** $-x + 3y$ **57.** $6r + 8$ **59.** $-36x - 70$ **61.** $-16x - 25$ **63.** $4(1 + y)$ **65.** $11(x + y)$ **67.** $-1(5 + x)$
69. $30(a + b)$ **71.** commutative property of multiplication **73.** associative property of addition **75.** distributive property
77. associative property of multiplication **79.** identity element of addition **81.** distributive property **83.** commutative and associative

properties of multiplication **85.** $-8; \dfrac{1}{8}$ **87.** $-x; \dfrac{1}{x}$ **89.** $2x; -2x$ **91.** false **93.** no **95.** yes **97.** yes **99.** no

101. a. commutative property of addition **b.** commutative property of addition **c.** associative property of addition **103.** answers may vary
105. answers may vary

Chapter 1 Vocabulary Check
1. inequality symbols **2.** equation **3.** absolute value **4.** variable **5.** opposites **6.** numerator **7.** solution **8.** reciprocals
9. base; exponent **10.** denominator **11.** grouping symbols **12.** set

Chapter 1 Review
1. $<$ **3.** $>$ **5.** $<$ **7.** $=$ **9.** $>$ **11.** $4 \geq -3$ **13.** $0.03 < 0.3$ **15. a.** $1, 3$ **b.** $0, 1, 3$ **c.** $-6, 0, 1, 3$

d. $-6, 0, 1, 1\dfrac{1}{2}, 3, 9.62$ **e.** π **f.** $-6, 0, 1, 1\dfrac{1}{2}, 3, \pi, 9.62$ **17.** Friday **19.** $2 \cdot 2 \cdot 3 \cdot 3$ **21.** $\dfrac{12}{25}$ **23.** $\dfrac{13}{10}$ **25.** $9\dfrac{3}{8}$ **27.** 15

29. $\dfrac{7}{12}$ **31.** $A = 1\dfrac{1}{6}$ sq m; $P = 4\dfrac{5}{12}$ m **33.** $14\dfrac{1}{8}$ lb **35.** $18\dfrac{7}{16}$ lb **37.** Baby E **39.** c **41.** $\dfrac{4}{49}$ **43.** 37 **45.** $\dfrac{18}{7}$

47. $20 - 12 = 2 \cdot 4$ **49.** 18 **51.** 5 **53.** $63°$ **55.** yes **57.** 9 **59.** -2 **61.** -11 **63.** $-\dfrac{3}{16}$ **65.** -13.9 **67.** -14

69. 5   **71.** -19 **73.** a   **75.** \$51   **77.** $-\dfrac{1}{6}$ **79.** -48 **81.** 3   **83.** undefined   **85.** undefined   **87.** -12 **89.** 9

91. $-7 \cdot x$ or $-7x$ **93.** $-20 - x$ **95.** commutative property of addition   **97.** distributive property   **99.** associative property of addition
101. distributive property   **103.** multiplicative inverse property   **105.** $5y - 10$ **107.** $-7 + x - 4z$ **109.** $-12z - 27$ **111.** $<$

113. -15.3 **115.** -80 **117.** $-\dfrac{1}{4}$ **119.** 16   **121.** -5 **123.** $-\dfrac{5}{6}$ **125.** $1\dfrac{3}{8}$ ft

Chapter 1 Test

1. $|-7| > 5$ **2.** $9 + 5 \geq 4$ **3.** -5 **4.** -11 **5.** -3 **6.** -39 **7.** 12   **8.** -2 **9.** undefined   **10.** -8 **11.** $-\dfrac{1}{3}$ **12.** $4\dfrac{5}{8}$

13. 1.275   **14.** -32 **15.** -48 **16.** 3   **17.** 0   **18.** $>$ **19.** $>$ **20.** $<$ **21.** $=$ **22.** $2221 < 10{,}993$ **23. a.** $1, 7$ **b.** $0, 1, 7$

c. $-5, -1, 0, 1, 7$ **d.** $-5, -1, 0, \dfrac{1}{4}, 1, 7, 11.6$ **e.** $\sqrt{7}, 3\pi$ **f.** $-5, -1, 0, \dfrac{1}{4}, 1, 7, 11.6, \sqrt{7}, 3\pi$ **24.** 40   **25.** 12   **26.** 22   **27.** -1
28. associative property of addition   **29.** commutative property of multiplication   **30.** distributive property   **31.** multiplicative inverse property
32. 9   **33.** -3 **34.** second down   **35.** yes   **36.** $17°$ **37.** \$650 million   **38.** \$420

CHAPTER 2 EQUATIONS, INEQUALITIES, AND PROBLEM SOLVING

Section 2.1
Practice Exercises

1. a. 1   **b.** -7 **c.** $-\dfrac{1}{5}$ **d.** 43   **e.** -1 **2. a.** like terms   **b.** unlike terms   **c.** like terms   **d.** like terms   **3. a.** $8y$ **b.** $5x^2$

c. $5x + 5x^2$ **d.** $21y^2$ **4. a.** $11y - 5$ **b.** $5x - 6$ **c.** $-\dfrac{1}{4}t$ **d.** $12.2y + 13$ **e.** $5z - 3z^4$ **5. a.** $6x - 21$ **b.** $-5x + 2.5z + 25$

c. $-2x + y - z + 2$ **6. a.** $36x + 10$ **b.** $-11x + 1$ **c.** $-30x - 17$ **7.** $-5x + 4$ **8. a.** $2x + 3$ **b.** $x - 1$ **c.** $2x + 10$ **d.** $\dfrac{13}{2}x$

Vocabulary, Readiness & Video Check 2.1
1. expression; term   **3.** numerical coefficient   **5.** numerical coefficient   **7.** Although these terms have exactly the same variables, the exponents
on each are not exactly the same—the exponents on x differ in each term.   **9.** -1

Exercise Set 2.1
1. -7 **3.** 1   **5.** 17   **7.** like   **9.** unlike   **11.** like   **13.** $15y$ **15.** $13w$ **17.** $-7b - 9$ **19.** $-m - 6$ **21.** -8 **23.** $7.2x - 5.2$
25. $4x - 3$ **27.** $5x^2$ **29.** $1.3x + 3.5$ **31.** $5y - 20$ **33.** $-2x - 4$ **35.** $7d - 11$ **37.** $-10x + 15y - 30$ **39.** $-3x + 2y - 1$
41. $2x + 14$ **43.** $10x - 3$ **45.** $-4x - 9$ **47.** $-4m - 3$ **49.** $k - 6$ **51.** $-15x + 18$ **53.** 16   **55.** $x + 5$ **57.** $x + 2$

59. $2k + 10$ **61.** $-3x + 5$ **63.** -11 **65.** $3y + \dfrac{5}{6}$ **67.** $-22 + 24x$ **69.** $0.9m + 1$ **71.** $10 - 6x - 9y$ **73.** $-x - 38$ **75.** $5x - 7$

77. $2x - 4$ **79.** $2x + 7$ **81.** $\dfrac{3}{4}x + 12$ **83.** $-2 + 12x$ **85.** $8(x + 6)$ or $8x + 48$ **87.** $x - 10$ **89.** $7x - 7$ **91.** 2   **93.** -23

95. -25 **97.** $(18x - 2)$ ft   **99.** balanced   **101.** balanced   **103.** answers may vary   **105.** $(15x + 23)$ in.   **107.** answers may vary
109. $5b^2c^3 + b^3c^2$ **111.** $5x^2 + 9x$ **113.** $-7x^2y$

Section 2.2
Practice Exercises
1. -8 **2.** -1.8 **3.** -10 **4.** 18   **5.** 20   **6.** -12 **7.** 65   **8.** -3 **9. a.** 7   **b.** $9 - x$ **c.** $(9 - x)$ ft   **10.** $3x + 6$

Vocabulary, Readiness & Video Check 2.2
1. equation; expression   **3.** solution   **5.** addition   **7.** multiplication   **9.** true   **11.** both sides   **13.** addition property; multiplication
property; answers may vary

Exercise Set 2.2
1. 3   **3.** -2 **5.** -14 **7.** 0.5   **9.** -3 **11.** -0.7 **13.** 3   **15.** 11   **17.** 0   **19.** -3 **21.** 16   **23.** -4 **25.** 0   **27.** 12
29. 10   **31.** -12 **33.** 3   **35.** -2 **37.** 0   **39.** answers may vary   **41.** 10   **43.** -20 **45.** 0   **47.** -5 **49.** 0

51. $-\dfrac{3}{2}$ **53.** -21 **55.** $\dfrac{11}{2}$ **57.** 1   **59.** $-\dfrac{1}{4}$ **61.** 12   **63.** -30 **65.** $\dfrac{9}{10}$ **67.** -30 **69.** 2   **71.** -2 **73.** 23
75. $20 - p$ **77.** $(10 - x)$ ft   **79.** $(180 - x)°$ **81.** $(n + 284)$ votes   **83.** $(m - 60)$ ft   **85.** $(n - 28{,}000)$ students   **87.** $7x$ sq mi
89. $2x + 2$ **91.** $2x + 2$ **93.** $5x + 20$ **95.** $7x - 12$ **97.** 1   **99.** $>$ **101.** $=$ **103.** $(173 - 3x)°$ **105.** answers may vary

107. 4   **109.** answers may vary   **111.** answers may vary   **113.** -48 **115.** $\dfrac{700}{3}$ mg   **117.** solution   **119.** -2.95 **121.** 0.02

Section 2.3
Practice Exercises

1. 3   **2.** $\dfrac{21}{13}$ **3.** -15 **4.** 3   **5.** 0   **6.** no solution   **7.** all real numbers

Graphing Calculator Explorations 2.3
1. solution   **3.** not a solution   **5.** solution

Vocabulary, Readiness & Video Check 2.3
1. equation   **3.** expression   **5.** expression   **7.** equation   **9.** 3; distributive property, addition property of equality, multiplication property of equality   **11.** The number of decimal places in each number helps you determine what power of 10 you can multiply through by so you are no longer dealing with decimals.

Exercise Set 2.3
1. -6 **3.** 3   **5.** 1   **7.** $\frac{3}{2}$ **9.** 0   **11.** -1 **13.** 4   **15.** -4 **17.** -3 **19.** 2   **21.** 50   **23.** 1   **25.** $\frac{7}{3}$ **27.** 0.2

29. all real numbers   **31.** no solution   **33.** no solution   **35.** all real numbers   **37.** 18   **39.** $\frac{19}{9}$ **41.** $\frac{14}{3}$ **43.** 13   **45.** 4

47. all real numbers   **49.** $-\frac{3}{5}$ **51.** -5 **53.** 10   **55.** no solution   **57.** 3   **59.** -17 **61.** -4 **63.** 3   **65.** all real numbers

67. $-8 - x$ **69.** $-3 + 2x$ **71.** $9(x + 20)$ **73.** $(6x - 8)$ m   **75. a.** all real numbers   **b.** answers may vary   **c.** answers may vary   **77.** A   **79.** B   **81.** C   **83.** answers may vary   **85. a.** $x + x + x + 2x + 2x = 28$ **b.** $x = 4$ **c.** $x = 4$ cm; $2x = 8$ cm   **87.** answers may vary   **89.** 15.3   **91.** -0.2 **93.** $-\frac{7}{8}$ **95.** no solution

Integrated Review
1. 6   **2.** -17 **3.** 12   **4.** -26 **5.** -3 **6.** -1 **7.** $\frac{27}{2}$ **8.** $\frac{25}{2}$ **9.** 8   **10.** -64 **11.** 2   **12.** -3 **13.** no solution

14. no solution   **15.** -2 **16.** -2 **17.** $-\frac{5}{6}$ **18.** $\frac{1}{6}$ **19.** 1   **20.** 6   **21.** 4   **22.** 1   **23.** $\frac{9}{5}$ **24.** $-\frac{6}{5}$ **25.** all real numbers

26. all real numbers   **27.** 0   **28.** -1.6 **29.** $\frac{4}{19}$ **30.** $-\frac{5}{19}$ **31.** $\frac{7}{2}$ **32.** $-\frac{1}{4}$ **33.** 2   **34.** 2   **35.** no solution   **36.** no solution

37. $\frac{7}{6}$ **38.** $\frac{1}{15}$

Section 2.4
Practice Exercises
1. 9   **2.** 2   **3.** 9 in. and 36 in.   **4.** 29 Republican and 20 Democratic governors   **5.** $25°, 75°, 80°$ **6.** $46, 48, 50$

Vocabulary, Readiness & Video Check 2.4
1. $2x; 2x - 31$ **3.** $x + 5; 2(x + 5)$ **5.** $20 - y; \frac{20 - y}{3}$ or $(20 - y) \div 3$ **7.** in the statement of the application   **9.** That the 3 angle measures are consecutive even integers and that they sum to 180°.

Exercise Set 2.4
1. $6x + 1 = 5x; -1$ **3.** $3x - 6 = 2x + 8; 14$ **5.** $2(x - 8) = 3(x + 3); -25$ **7.** $2(-2 + x) = x - \frac{1}{2}; \frac{7}{2}$ **9.** 3 in.; 6 in.; 16 in.

11. 1st piece: 5 in.; 2nd piece: 10 in.; 3rd piece: 25 in.   **13.** 7837 screens; 31,710; In 2010, 7837 screens were 3D.   **15.** 1st angle: 37.5°; 2nd angle: 37.5°; 3rd angle: 105°   **17.** $3x + 3$ **19.** $x + 2; x + 4; 2x + 4$ **21.** $x + 1; x + 2; x + 3; 4x + 6$ **23.** $x + 2; x + 4; 2x + 6$

25. 234, 235   **27.** Belgium: 32; France: 33; Spain: 34   **29.** Sahara: 3,500,000 sq mi; Gobi: 500,000 sq mi   **31.** 5 ft, 12 ft   **33.** $\frac{5}{4}$

35. Botswana: 32,000,000 carats; Angola: 8,000,000 carats   **37.** $58°, 60°, 62°$ **39.** South Korea: 14; Russia: 15; Austria: 16   **41.** -16 **43.** $43°, 137°$

45. 1   **47.** $\frac{3}{2}$ **49.** Maglev: 361 mph; TGV: 357.2 mph   **51.** $\frac{5}{2}$ **53.** California: 58; Montana: 56   **55.** 111°   **57.** 1st piece: 3 ft; 2nd piece: 12 ft; 3rd piece: 15 ft   **59.** Eagles: *Their Greatest Hits, 1971–1975*   **61.** *Thriller*: $27 million; *The Wall*: $23 million   **63.** answers may vary   **65.** 34   **67.** 225π **69.** 15 ft by 24 ft   **71.** 5400 chirps per hour; 129,600 chirps per day; 47,304,000 chirps per year   **73.** answers may vary   **75.** answers may vary   **77.** c

Section 2.5
Practice Exercises
1. 116 sec or 1 min 56 sec   **2.** 9 ft   **3.** 46.4°F   **4.** length: 28 in.; width: 5 in.   **5.** $r = \frac{I}{Pt}$ **6.** $s = \frac{H - 10a}{5a}$ **7.** $d = \frac{N - F}{n - 1}$

8. $B = \frac{2A - ab}{a}$

Vocabulary, Readiness & Video Check 2.5
1. relationships   **3.** To show that the process of solving this equation for x—dividing both sides by 5, the coefficient of x—is the same process used to solve a formula for a specific variable. Treat whatever is multiplied by that specific variable as the coefficient—the coefficient is all the factors except that specific variable.

Exercise Set 2.5
1. $h = 3$ **3.** $h = 3$ **5.** $h = 20$ **7.** $c = 12$ **9.** $r \approx 2.5$ **11.** $T = 3$ **13.** $h \approx 15$ **15.** $h = \frac{f}{5g}$ **17.** $w = \frac{V}{lh}$ **19.** $y = 7 - 3x$

21. $R = \frac{A - P}{PT}$ **23.** $A = \frac{3V}{h}$ **25.** $a = P - b - c$ **27.** $h = \frac{S - 2\pi r^2}{2\pi r}$ **29.** 120 ft   **31. a.** area: 103.5 sq ft; perimeter: 41 ft

b. baseboard: perimeter; carpet: area   **33. a.** area: 480 sq in.; perimeter: 120 in.   **b.** frame: perimeter; glass: area   **35.** −10°C   **37.** length: 78 ft; width: 52 ft   **39.** 18 ft, 36 ft, 48 ft   **41.** 55.2 mph   **43.** 96 piranhas   **45.** 61.5°F   **47.** 60 chirps per minute   **49.** increases   **51.** 2 bags   **53.** one 16-in. pizza   **55.** $x = 6$ m, $2.5x = 15$ m   **57.** 22 hr   **59.** 13 in.   **61.** 2.25 hr   **63.** 12,090 ft   **65.** 50°C   **67.** 332.6°F   **69.** 449 cu in.   **71.** 0.32   **73.** 2.00 or 2   **75.** 17%   **77.** 720%   **79.** multiplies the volume by 8; answers may vary   **81.** $53\frac{1}{3}$

83. $V = G(N - R)$ **85.** 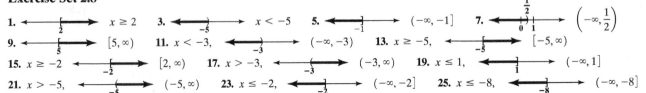   **87.** 500 sec or $8\frac{1}{3}$ min   **89.** 608.33 ft   **91.** 4.42 min   **93.** $35\frac{11}{17}$ mph

Section 2.6
Practice Exercises
1. 62.5%   **2.** 360   **3. a.** 42%   **b.** 98%   **c.** 79.3 million dogs   **4.** discount: $408; new price: $72   **5.** 42.6%   **6.** 3554 screens   **7.** 2 liters of 5% eyewash; 4 liters of 2% eyewash

Vocabulary, Readiness & Video Check 2.6
1. no   **3.** yes   **5. a.** equals; =   **b.** multiplication; ·   **c.** Drop the percent symbol and move the decimal point two places to the left.   **7.** You must first find the actual amount of increase in price by subtracting the original price from the new price.

Exercise Set 2.6
1. 11.2   **3.** 55%   **5.** 180   **7.** 4%   **9.** 9990   **11.** discount: $1480; new price: $17,020   **13.** $46.58   **15.** 9.8%   **17.** 30%   **19.** $104   **21.** $42,500   **23.** 2 gal   **25.** 7 lb   **27.** 4.6   **29.** 50   **31.** 30%   **33.** 23%   **35.** 90,405   **37.** 59%; 5%; 26%; 2%; 99% due to rounding   **39.** decrease: $64; sale price: $192   **41.** 27.2%   **43.** 239 million   **45.** 300%   **47.** 400 oz   **49.** 66.7%   **51.** 120 employees   **53.** 361 college students   **55.** 400 oz   **57.** 854 thousand Scoville units   **59.** >   **61.** =   **63.** >   **65.** no; answers may vary   **67.** no; answers may vary   **69.** 9.6%   **71.** 26.9%; yes   **73.** 17.1%

Section 2.7
Practice Exercises
1. 2.2 hr   **2.** eastbound: 62 mph; westbound: 52 mph   **3.** 106 $5 bills; 59 $20 bills   **4.** $18,000 at 11.5%; $12,000 at 6%

Vocabulary, Readiness & Video Check 2.7
1.

	r	·	t	=	d
bus	55		x		$55x$
car	50		$x + 3$		$50(x + 3)$

; $55x = 50(x + 3)$

3.

	P	·	R	·	T	=	I
	x		0.06		1		$0.06x$
	$36,000 - x$		0.04		1		$0.04(36,000 - x)$

; $0.06x = 0.04(36,000 - x)$

Exercise Set 2.7
1. $666\frac{2}{3}$ mi   **3.** 55 mph   **5.** $0.10\, y$ **7.** $0.05(x + 7)$ **9.** $20(4y)$ or $80y$ **11.** $50(35 - x)$ **13.** 12 $10 bills; 32 $5 bills   **15.** $11,500 at 8%; $13,500 at 9%   **17.** $7000 at 11% profit; $3000 at 4% loss   **19.** 187 adult tickets; 313 child tickets   **21.** 2 hr   **23.** $30,000 at 8%; $24,000 at 10%   **25.** 2 hr $37\frac{1}{2}$ min   **27.** 36 mph; 46 mph   **29.** 483 dimes; 161 nickels   **31.** 4 hr   **33.** 2.5 hr   **35.** $4500   **37.** 2.2 mph; 3.3 mph   **39.** 27.5 mi   **41.** −4   **43.** $\frac{9}{16}$ **45.** −4   **47.** 25 $100 bills; 71 $50 bills; 175 $20 bills   **49.** 25 skateboards   **51.** 800 books   **53.** answers may vary

Section 2.8
Practice Exercises
1. $(-\infty, 5)$ **2.** $[-5, \infty)$ **3.** $(-\infty, 3]$ **4.** $(-3, \infty)$ **5.** $[7, \infty)$ **6.** $(-\infty, -7]$ **7.** $\left(-\infty, \frac{9}{4}\right)$ **8.** $[0, \infty)$ **9.** $[-3, 1)$ **10.** $(-2, 2]$ **11.** $\left(-\frac{16}{3}, \frac{4}{3}\right)$ **12.** all numbers less than 10

13. Kasonga can afford at most 3 classes.

Vocabulary, Readiness & Video Check 2.8
1. expression   **3.** inequality   **5.** −5   **7.** The graph of Example 1 is shaded from −∞ to and including −1, as indicated by a bracket. To write interval notation, you write down what is shaded for the inequality from left to right. A parenthesis is always used with −∞, so from the graph, the interval notation is $(-\infty, -1]$.   **9.** You would divide the left, middle, and right by −3 instead of 3, which would reverse the directions of both inequality symbols.

Exercise Set 2.8
1. $x \geq 2$ **3.** $x < -5$ **5.** $(-\infty, -1]$ **7.** $\left(-\infty, \frac{1}{2}\right)$ **9.** $[5, \infty)$ **11.** $x < -3$, $(-\infty, -3)$ **13.** $x \geq -5$, $[-5, \infty)$ **15.** $x \geq -2$ $[2, \infty)$ **17.** $x > -3$, $(-3, \infty)$ **19.** $x \leq 1$, $(-\infty, 1]$ **21.** $x > -5$, $(-5, \infty)$ **23.** $x \leq -2$, $(-\infty, -2]$ **25.** $x \leq -8$, $(-\infty, -8]$

27. $x > 4$, ⟶ $(4, \infty)$ **29.** $x \geq 20$, ⟶ $[20, \infty)$ **31.** $x > 16$, ⟶ $(16, \infty)$

33. $x > -3$, ⟶ $(-3, \infty)$ **35.** $x \leq -\dfrac{2}{3}$, ⟶ $\left(-\infty, -\dfrac{2}{3}\right]$ **37.** $x > \dfrac{8}{3}$, ⟶ $\left(\dfrac{8}{3}, \infty\right)$

39. $x > -13$, ⟶ $(-13, \infty)$ **41.** $x < 0$, ⟶ $(-\infty, 0)$ **43.** $x \leq 0$, ⟶ $(-\infty, 0]$

45. $x > 3$, ⟶ $(3, \infty)$ **47.** $x > \dfrac{8}{3}$ ⟶ $\left(\dfrac{8}{3}, \infty\right)$ **49.** ⟶ $(-1, 3)$ **51.** ⟶ $[0, 2)$

53. ⟶ $(-1, 2)$ **55.** ⟶ $[4, 5]$ **57.** ⟶ $(1, 5]$ **59.** ⟶ $(1, 4)$

61. ⟶ $\left(0, \dfrac{14}{3}\right]$ **63.** all numbers greater than -10 **65.** 35 cm   **67.** at least 193   **69.** 86 people   **71.** at least 35 min

73. $-3 < x < 3$ **75.** 8   **77.** 1   **79.** $\dfrac{16}{49}$ **81.** $>$ **83.** $\geq$ **85.** when multiplying or dividing by a negative number

87. final exam score ≥ 78.5 **89.** answers may vary   **91.** answers may vary   **93.** $0.924 \leq d \leq 0.987$ **95.** ⟶ $(1, \infty)$

97. ⟶ $\left(-\infty, \dfrac{5}{8}\right)$

Chapter 2 Vocabulary Check
1. like terms   **2.** unlike terms   **3.** linear equation in one variable   **4.** linear inequality in one variable   **5.** compound inequalities   **6.** formula   **7.** numerical coefficient   **8.** equivalent equations   **9.** all real numbers   **10.** no solution   **11.** the same   **12.** reversed

Chapter 2 Review
1. $6x$ **3.** $4x - 2$ **5.** $3n - 18$ **7.** $-6x + 7$ **9.** $3x - 7$ **11.** 4   **13.** 6   **15.** 0   **17.** -23 **19.** $5; 5$ **21.** b   **23.** b   **25.** -12

27. 0   **29.** 0.75   **31.** -6 **33.** -1 **35.** $-\dfrac{1}{5}$ **37.** $3x + 3$ **39.** -4 **41.** 2   **43.** no solution   **45.** $\dfrac{3}{4}$ **47.** 20   **49.** $\dfrac{23}{7}$

51. 102   **53.** 6665.5 in.   **55.** Kellogg: 35 plants; Keebler: 18 plants   **57.** 3   **59.** $w = 9$ **61.** $m = \dfrac{y - b}{x}$ **63.** $x = \dfrac{2y - 7}{5}$ **65.** $\pi = \dfrac{C}{D}$

67. 15 m   **69.** 1 hr 20 min   **71.** 20%   **73.** 110   **75.** mark-up: \$209; new price: \$2109   **77.** 40% solution: 10 gal; 10% solution: 20 gal   **79.** 18%   **81.** 966 customers   **83.** 32%   **85.** 50 km   **87.** 80 nickels   **89.** $(0, \infty)$ ⟶   **91.** $[0.5, 1.5)$ ⟶

93. $(-\infty, -4)$ ⟶   **95.** $(-\infty, 4]$ ⟶   **97.** $\left(-\dfrac{1}{2}, \dfrac{3}{4}\right)$ ⟶   **99.** $\left(-\infty, \dfrac{19}{3}\right]$ ⟶

101. \$2500   **103.** 4   **105.** $-\dfrac{3}{2}$ **107.** all real numbers   **109.** -13 **111.** $h = \dfrac{3V}{A}$ **113.** 160   **115.** $(9, \infty)$ ⟶

117. $(-\infty, 0]$ ⟶

Chapter 2 Test
1. $y - 10$ **2.** $5.9x + 1.2$ **3.** $-2x + 10$ **4.** $10y + 1$ **5.** -5 **6.** 8   **7.** $\dfrac{7}{10}$ **8.** 0   **9.** 27   **10.** 3   **11.** 0.25   **12.** $\dfrac{25}{7}$

13. no solution   **14.** $x = 6$ **15.** $h = \dfrac{V}{\pi r^2}$ **16.** $y = \dfrac{3x - 10}{4}$ **17.** $(-\infty, -2]$ ⟶   **18.** $(-\infty, 4)$ ⟶

19. $\left(-1, \dfrac{7}{3}\right)$ ⟶   **20.** $\left(\dfrac{2}{5}, \infty\right)$ ⟶   **21.** 21   **22.** 62 ft by 64 ft   **23.** 401, 802   **24.** \$8500 at 10%; \$17,000 at 12%

25. $2\dfrac{1}{2}$ hr   **26.** 552   **27.** 40%   **28.** 16%

Chapter 2 Cumulative Review
1. a. $11, 112$ **b.** $0, 11, 112$ **c.** $-3, -2, 0, 11, 112$ **d.** $-3, -2, -1.5, 0, \dfrac{1}{4}, 11, 112$ **e.** $\sqrt{2}$ **f.** all numbers in the given set; Sec. 1.2, Ex. 5

3. a. 4   **b.** 5   **c.** 0   **d.** $\dfrac{1}{2}$ **e.** 5.6; Sec. 1.2, Ex. 7   **5. a.** $2 \cdot 2 \cdot 2 \cdot 5$ **b.** $3 \cdot 3 \cdot 7$; Sec. 1.3, Ex. 1   **7.** $\dfrac{8}{20}$; Sec. 1.3, Ex. 6   **9.** 66; Sec. 1.4, Ex. 4

11. 2 is a solution; Sec. 1.4, Ex. 7   **13.** -3; Sec. 1.5, Ex. 2   **15.** 2; Sec. 1.5, Ex. 4   **17. a.** 10   **b.** $\dfrac{1}{2}$ **c.** $2x$ **d.** -6; Sec. 1.5, Ex. 10

19. a. 9.9   **b.** $-\dfrac{4}{5}$ **c.** $\dfrac{2}{15}$; Sec. 1.6, Ex. 2   **21. a.** $52°$ **b.** $118°$; Sec. 1.6, Ex. 8   **23. a.** -0.06 **b.** $-\dfrac{7}{15}$ **c.** 16; Sec. 1.7, Ex. 3

25. a. 6   **b.** -12 **c.** $-\dfrac{8}{15}$ **d.** $-\dfrac{1}{6}$; Sec. 1.7, Ex. 7   **27. a.** $5 + x$ **b.** $x \cdot 3$; Sec. 1.8, Ex. 1   **29. a.** $8(2 + x)$ **b.** $7(s + t)$; Sec. 1.8, Ex. 5

31. $-2x - 1$; Sec. 2.1, Ex. 7   **33.** -1.6; Sec. 2.2, Ex. 2   **35.** 8; Sec. 2.2, Ex. 4   **37.** 140; Sec. 2.2, Ex. 7   **39.** 2; Sec. 2.3, Ex. 1   **41.** 10; Sec. 2.4, Ex. 2

43. $\dfrac{V}{wh} = l$; Sec. 2.5, Ex. 5   **45.** $(-\infty, -10]$ ⟶ ; Sec. 2.8, Ex. 2

CHAPTER 3 GRAPHING

Section 3.1
Practice Exercises

1. a. Africa/Middle East region, 145 million Internet users   **b.** 640 million more Internet users   **2. a.** 70 beats per minute   **b.** 60 beats per minute
c. 5 minutes after lighting   **3.**
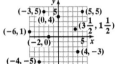
4. a. (2004, 65), (2005, 67), (2006, 96), (2007, 86), (2008, 79), (2009, 79), (2010, 72)

b.
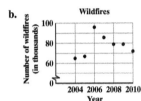

5. a. yes   **b.** yes   **c.** no   **6. a.** $(0, -8)$ **b.** $(6, 4)$ **c.** $(-3, -14)$

7.

	x	y
a.	-2	8
b.	3	-12
c.	0	0

8.

	x	y
a.	-10	-4
b.	0	-2
c.	10	0

9.

x	0	1	2	3	4
y	12,000	10,200	8400	6600	4800

Vocabulary, Readiness & Video Check 3.1

1. x-axis; y-axis   **3.** quadrants; four   **5.** one   **7.** horizontal: top tourist countries; vertical: number of arrivals (in millions) to these countries
9. Data occurring in pairs of numbers can be written as ordered pairs, called paired data, and then graphed on a coordinate system.   **11.** a linear equation in one variable

Exercise Set 3.1

1. France   **3.** France, U.S., Spain, Italy, and China   **5.** 43 million   **7.** 71,000   **9.** 2011; 103,000   **11.** 15.9   **13.** from 1998 to 2000

15. 2014   **17.**

$(1, 5)$ and $(3.7, 2.2)$ are in quadrant I, $\left(-1, 4\frac{1}{2}\right)$ is in quadrant II, $(-5, -2)$ is in quadrant III, $(2, -4)$ and $\left(\frac{1}{2}, -3\right)$
are in quadrant IV, $(-3, 0)$ lies on the x-axis, $(0, -1)$ lies on the y-axis   **19.** $(0, 0)$ **21.** $(3, 2)$
23. $(-2, -2)$ **25.** $(2, -1)$ **27.** $(0, -3)$ **29.** $(1, 3)$ **31.** $(-3, -1)$

33. a. (2006, 25.5), (2007, 26.3), (2008, 27.7), (2009, 29.4), (2010, 31.8)   **b.** In the year 2010, the worldwide box office was $31.8 billion.
c.
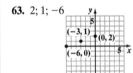
d. The worldwide box office increased every year.   **35. a.** (0.50, 10), (0.75, 12), (1.00, 15), (1.25, 16), (1.50, 18),
(1.50, 19), (1.75, 19), (2.00, 20)   **b.** When Minh studied 1.25 hours, her quiz score was 16.   **c.**

d. answers may very

37. a. (2313, 2), (2085, 1), (2711, 21), (2869, 39), (2920, 42), (4038, 99), (1783, 0), (2493, 9)   **b.**
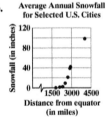
c. The farther from the equator,
the more snowfall.   **39.** yes; no; yes   **41.** yes; yes   **43.** no; yes; yes

45. $(-4, -2)$, $(4, 0)$ **47.** $(-8, -5)$, $(16, 1)$ **49.** 0; 7; $-\frac{2}{7}$ **51.** 2; 2; 5

53. 0; -3; 2   **55.** 2; 6; 3   **57.** -12; 5; -6 **59.** $\frac{5}{7}$; $\frac{5}{2}$; -1 **61.** 0; -5; -2

63. 2; 1; -6 **65. a.** 13,000; 21,000; 29,000   **b.** 45 desks   **67. a.** 5.52; 6.00; 6.48   **b.** year 9; 2009   **c.** 2016
d. In 2005, the average cinema admission price was $6.48.   **69.** In 2010, there were 3755 Walmart stores in the U.S.
71. year 8: 100 stores; year 9: 105 stores; year 10: 100 stores   **73.** The y-values are all 0.   **75.** $y = 5 - x$
77. $y = -\frac{1}{2}x + \frac{5}{4}$ **79.** $y = -2x$ **81.** $y = \frac{1}{3}x - 2$ **83.** false   **85.** true   **87.** negative; negative

89. positive; negative   **91.** 0; 0   **93.** *y*   **95.** no; answers may vary   **97.** answers may vary   **99.** $(4, -7)$ **101.** 26 units   **103. a.** $(-2, 6)$
b. 28 units   **c.** 45 sq units

Section 3.2
Practice Exercises

1. a. yes   **b.** no   **c.** yes   **d.** yes   **2.** 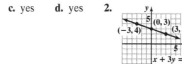   **3.** 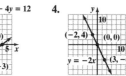   **4.** 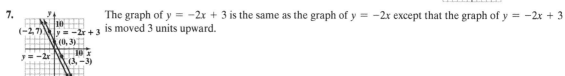   **5.**

6. 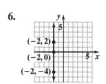   **7.** 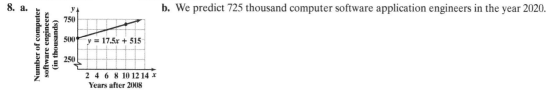   The graph of $y = -2x + 3$ is the same as the graph of $y = -2x$ except that the graph of $y = -2x + 3$ is moved 3 units upward.

8. a. 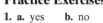   **b.** We predict 725 thousand computer software application engineers in the year 2020.

Graphing Calculator Explorations 3.2

1. **3.** **5.**

Vocabulary, Readiness & Video Check 3.2

1. In the definition, *x* and *y* both have an understood power of 1. Example 3 shows an equation where *y* has a power of 2, so it is not a linear equation in two variables.   **3.** An infinite number of points make up the line and each point corresponds to an ordered pair that is a solution of the linear equation in two variables.

Exercise Set 3.2

1. yes   **3.** yes   **5.** no   **7.** yes   **9.**

x	*y*
6	0
4	-2
5	-1

11.

x	*y*
1	-4
0	0
-1	4

13.

x	*y*
0	0
6	2
-3	-1

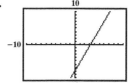

15.

x	*y*
0	3
1	-1
2	-5

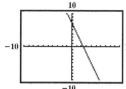

17. 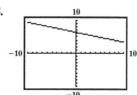   **19.**   **21.**   **23.**   **25.**

25.   **27.**   **29.**   **31.**   **33.** 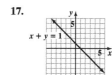   **35.**

37.
39.
41.
43.
45.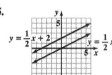

47. c   **49.** d   **51. a.** $(8, 31)$ **b.** In 2008, there were 31 million joggers.   **c.** 40 million joggers   **53. a.** $(8, 207.6)$ **b.** In 2008, there were 207.6 million people with driver's licenses.   **c.** 225.2 million   **55.** $(4, -1)$ **57.** $3; -3$ **59.** $0; 0$ **61.** $y = x + 5$

63. $2x + 3y = 6$ **65.** $x + y = 12; y = 9$ cm   **67.** answers may vary   **69.** $0; 1; 1; 4; 4$

Section 3.3
Practice Exercises

1. x-intercept: $(-4, 0)$
  y-intercept: $(0, -6)$
2. x-intercepts: $(-2, 0), (2, 0)$
  y-intercept: $(0, -3)$
3. x-intercept: $(0, 0)$
  y-intercept: $(0, 0)$
4. x-intercept: none
  y-intercept: $(0, 3)$
5. x-intercepts: $(-1, 0), (5, 0)$
  y-intercepts: $(0, 2), (0, -2)$

6.
7.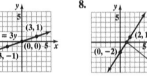
8.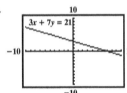
9.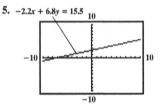
10.

Graphing Calculator Explorations 3.3

1.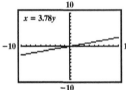
3.
5. $-2.2x + 6.8y = 15.5$

Vocabulary, Readiness & Video Check 3.3

1. linear   **3.** horizontal   **5.** y-intercept   **7.** $y; x$ **9.** Because x-intercepts lie on the x-axis; because y-intercepts lie on the y-axis.
11. For a horizontal line, the coefficient of x will be 0 and the coefficient of y will be 1; for a vertical line, the coefficient of y will be 0 and the coefficient of x will be 1.

Exercise Set 3.3

1. $(-1, 0); (0, 1)$ **3.** $(-2, 0); (2, 0); (0, -2)$ **5.** $(-2, 0); (1, 0); (3, 0); (0, 3)$ **7.** $(-1, 0); (1, 0); (0, 1); (0, -2)$ **9.** infinite   **11.** 0
13.
15.
17.
19.
21.
23.

25.
27.
29.
31.
33.
35.

37.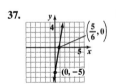
39.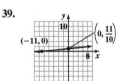
41.
43.
45.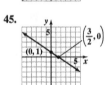
47.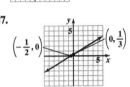

49. C **51.** E **53.** B **55.** $\dfrac{3}{2}$ **57.** 6 **59.** $-\dfrac{6}{5}$ **61.** false **63.** true **65.** $(0, 200)$; no chairs and 200 desks are manufactured,
67. 300 chairs **69. a.** $(62, 0)$ **b.** 62 years after 2002, 0 people will attend the movies at the theater. **c.** answers may very **71.** $x = 1$
73. answers may vary **75.** answers may vary

Section 3.4
Practice Exercises

1. -1 **2.** $\dfrac{1}{3}$ **3.** $m = \dfrac{2}{3}$; y-intercept: $(0, -2)$ **4.** $m = 6$; y-intercept: $(0, -5)$ **5.** $m = -\dfrac{5}{2}$; y-intercept: $(0, 4)$ **6.** $m = 0$

7. slope is undefined **8. a.** perpendicular **b.** neither **c.** parallel **9.** 25% **10.** $m = \dfrac{0.75 \text{ dollar}}{1 \text{ pound}}$; The Wash-n-Fold charges $0.75 per pound of laundry.

Graphing Calculator Explorations 3.4

1.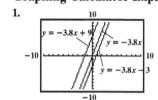

3.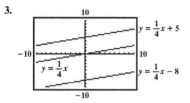

Vocabulary, Readiness & Video Check 3.4

1. slope **3.** 0 **5.** positive **7.** $y; x$ **9.** solve the equation for y; the slope is the coefficient of x. **11.** slope-intercept form; this form makes the slope easy to see, and you need to compare slopes to determine if two lines are parallel or perpendicular.

Exercise Set 3.4

1. -1 **3.** undefined **5.** $-\dfrac{2}{3}$ **7.** 0 **9.** $m = -\dfrac{4}{3}$ **11.** undefined slope **13.** $m = \dfrac{5}{2}$ **15.** negative **17.** undefined **19.** upward
21. horizontal **23.** line 1 **25.** line 2 **27.** D **29.** B **31.** E **33.** undefined slope **35.** $m = 0$ **37.** undefined slope

39. $m = 0$ **41.** $m = 5$ **43.** $m = -0.3$ **45.** $m = -2$ **47.** $m = \dfrac{2}{3}$ **49.** undefined slope **51.** $m = \dfrac{1}{2}$ **53.** $m = 0$ **55.** $m = -\dfrac{3}{4}$

57. $m = 4$ **59. a.** 1 **b.** -1 **61. a.** $\dfrac{9}{11}$ **b.** $-\dfrac{11}{9}$ **63.** neither **65.** neither **67.** parallel **69.** perpendicular **71.** $\dfrac{3}{5}$ **73.** 12.5%

75. 40% **77.** 37%; 35% **79.** $m = \dfrac{1}{1}$ or 1; Every 1 year, there are 1 million more U.S. households with televisions. **81.** $m = 0.47$; It costs $0.47
per 1 mile to own and operate a compact car. **83.** $y = 2x - 14$ **85.** $y = -6x - 11$ **87.** $m = \dfrac{1}{2}$ **89.** answers may vary **91.** 2005 to 2006
93. 2000; 28.5 mi per gallon **95.** from 2008 to 2009 **97.** $x = 6$ **99. a.** $(2007, 2207)$; $(2010, 2333)$ **b.** 42 **c.** For the years 2007 through 2010,
the number of heart transplants increased at a rate of 42 per year. **101.** The slope through $(-3, 0)$ and $(1, 1)$ is $\dfrac{1}{4}$. The slope through $(-3, 0)$ and $(-4, 4)$
is -4. The product of the slopes is -1, so the sides are perpendicular. **103.** -0.25 **105.** 0.875 **107.** The line becomes steeper.

Integrated Review

1. $m = 2$ **2.** $m = 0$ **3.** $m = -\dfrac{2}{3}$ **4.** undefined slope **5.** **6.** $x + y = 3$ **7.**

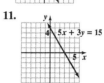 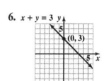

8. **9.** **10.** **11.** **12.**

13. parallel **14.** neither **15. a.** $(0, 587)$ **b.** In 2000, there were 587 thousand bridges on public roads. **c.** 1.7 **d.** For the years 2000
through 2009, the number of bridges on public roads increased at a rate of 1.7 thousand per year. **16. a.** $(9, 26.6)$ **b.** In 2009, the revenue for
online advertising was $26.6 billion.

Section 3.5
Practice Exercises

1. **2.** **3.** $y = \frac{1}{2}x + 7$ **4.** $4x - y = 5$ **5.** $5x + 4y = 19$ **6.** $x = 3$ **7.** $y = 3$

8. a. $y = -1500x + 195{,}000$ **b.** $105{,}000

Graphing Calculator Explorations 3.5

1. 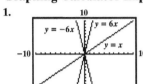 **3.** 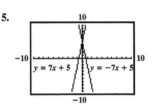 **5.**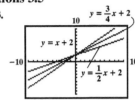

Vocabulary, Readiness & Video Check 3.5

1. slope-intercept; m; b **3.** y-intercept; fraction **5.** Write the equation with x- and y- terms on one side of the equal sign and a constant on the other side. **7.** Example 6: $y = -3$; Example 7: $x = -2$

Exercise Set 3.5

1. **3.** **5.** **7.** **9.** **11.**

13. $y = 5x + 3$ **15.** $y = -4x - \frac{1}{6}$ **17.** $y = \frac{2}{3}x$ **19.** $y = -8$ **21.** $y = -\frac{1}{5}x + \frac{1}{9}$ **23.** $-6x + y = -10$ **25.** $8x + y = -13$

27. $3x - 2y = 27$ **29.** $x + 2y = -3$ **31.** $2x - y = 4$ **33.** $8x - y = -11$ **35.** $4x - 3y = -1$ **37.** $8x + 13y = 0$ **39.** $x = 0$

41. $y = 3$ **43.** $x = -\frac{7}{3}$ **45.** $y = 2$ **47.** $y = 5$ **49.** $x = 6$ **51.** $y = -\frac{1}{2}x + \frac{5}{3}$ **53.** $y = -x + 17$ **55.** $x = -\frac{3}{4}$

57. $y = x + 16$ **59.** $y = -5x + 7$ **61.** $y = 7$ **63.** $y = \frac{3}{2}x$ **65.** $y = -3$ **67.** $y = -\frac{4}{7}x - \frac{18}{7}$ **69. a.** $s = 32t$ **b.** 128 ft/sec

71. a. $y = -33x + 356$ **b.** 92 thousand gasoline-electric hybrids **73. a.** $y = 0.6x + 85$ **b.** 93.4 persons per sq mi **75. a.** $y = -1.75x + 60$
b. 32 million **77. a.** $S = -1000p + 13{,}000$ **b.** 9500 Fun Noodles **79.** -1 **81.** 5 **83.** no **85.** yes **87.** point-slope
89. slope-intercept **91.** horizontal **93.** answers may vary **95. a.** $3x - y = -5$ **b.** $x + 3y = 5$ **97. a.** $3x + 2y = -1$
b. $2x - 3y = 21$

Section 3.6
Practice Exercises

1. Domain: $\{0, 1, 5\}$; Range: $\{-2, 0, 3, 4\}$ **2. a.** function **b.** not a function **3. a.** not a function **b.** function **4. a.** function
b. function **c.** function **d.** not a function **5. a.** function **b.** function **c.** function **d.** not a function **6. a.** 69°F **b.** February
c. yes **7. a.** $h(2) = 9$; $(2, 9)$ **b.** $h(-5) = 30$; $(-5, 30)$ **c.** $h(0) = 5$; $(0, 5)$ **8. a.** domain: $(-\infty, \infty)$ **b.** domain: $(-\infty, 0) \cup (0, \infty)$
9. a. domain: $[-4, 6]$; range: $[-2, 3]$ **b.** domain: $(-\infty, \infty)$; range: $(-\infty, 3]$

Vocabulary, Readiness & Video Check 3.6

1. relation **3.** range **5.** vertical **7.** A relation is a set of ordered pairs and an equation in two variables defines a set of ordered pairs.
Therefore, an equation in two variables can also define a relation. **9.** A vertical line represents one x-value paired with many y-values. A function
only allows an x-value paired with exactly one y-value, so if a vertical line intersects a graph more than once, there's an x-value paired with more than
one y-value, and we don't have a function.

Exercise Set 3.6

1. $\{-7, 0, 2, 10\}$; $\{-7, 0, 4, 10\}$ **3.** $\{0, 1, 5\}$; $\{-2\}$ **5.** yes **7.** no **9.** no **11.** yes **13.** yes **15.** no **17.** yes **19.** yes
21. yes **23.** no **25.** no **27.** 9:30 p.m. **29.** January 1 and December 1 **31.** yes; it passes the vertical line test **33.** $4.25 per hour
35. 2009 **37.** yes; answers may vary **39.** $1.50 **41.** more than 1 ounce and less than or equal to 2 ounces **43.** yes; answers may vary

45. $-9, -5, 1$ **47.** $6, 2, 11$ **49.** $-6, 0, 9$ **51.** $2, 0, 3$ **53.** $5, 0, -20$ **55.** $5, 3, 35$ **57.** $(3, 6)$ **59.** $\left(0, -\frac{1}{2}\right)$ **61.** $(-2, 9)$

63. $(-\infty, \infty)$ **65.** all real number except -5 or $(-\infty, -5) \cup (-5, \infty)$ **67.** $(-\infty, \infty)$ **69.** domain: $(-\infty, \infty)$; range: $[-4, \infty)$ **71.** domain:
$(-\infty, \infty)$; range: $(-\infty, \infty)$ **73.** domain: $(-\infty, \infty)$; range: $\{2\}$ **75.** -1 **77.** -1 **79.** $-1, 5$ **81.** $(-2, 1)$ **83.** $(-3, -1)$
85. $f(-5) = 12$ **87.** $(3, -4)$ **89.** $f(5) = 0$ **91. a.** 166.38 cm **b.** 148.25 cm **93.** answers may vary **95.** $f(x) = x + 7$
97. a. 11 **b.** $2a + 7$ **99. a.** 16 **b.** $a^2 + 7$

Chapter 3 Vocabulary Check

1. solution **2.** y-axis **3.** linear **4.** x-intercept **5.** standard **6.** y-intercept **7.** slope-intercept **8.** point-slope **9.** y
10. x-axis **11.** x **12.** slope **13.** function **14.** domain **15.** range **16.** relation

Chapter 3 Review

1. 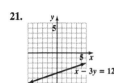 **3.** **5.** **7. a.** $(5.00, 50), (8.50, 100), (20.00, 250), (27.00, 500)$ **b.**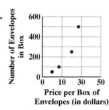

9. no; yes **11.** yes; yes **13.** $(7, 44)$ **15.** $(-3, 0); (1, 3); (9, 9)$ 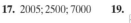 **17.** $2005; 2500; 7000$ **19.**

21. **23.** **25.** **27.** $(4, 0), (0, -2)$ **29.** $(-2, 0), (2, 0), (0, 2), (0, -2)$

31. **33.** **35.** **37.** **39.** $m = -\dfrac{3}{4}$ **41.** d **43.** c **45.** $\dfrac{3}{4}$ **47.** 4

49. 3 **51.** 0 **53.** perpendicular **55.** neither **57.** $m = 44$; Every 1 year, 44 thousand (44,000) more students graduate with an associate's

degree. **59.** $m = -3; (0, 7)$ **61.** $m = 0; (0, 2)$ **63.** **65.** **67.** $y = -5x + \dfrac{1}{2}$ **69.** c

71. b **73.** $(0, 1859)$ **75.** $3x + y = -5$ **77.** $y = -3$ **79.** $6x + y = 11$ **81.** $x + y = 6$ **83.** $x = 5$ **85.** $x = 6$ **87.** no
89. yes **91.** no **93.** no **95. a.** 6 **b.** 10 **c.** 5 **97. a.** 45 **b.** -35 **c.** 0 **99.** $(-\infty, \infty)$ **101.** domain: $[-3, 5]$ range: $[-4, 2]$
103. domain: $\{3\}$; range: $(-\infty, \infty)$ **105.** 7; -1; -3 **107.** $(3, 0); (0, -2)$ **109.** **111.** **113.**
115. $m = -1$ **117.** $m = 2$ **119.** $m = \dfrac{2}{3}; (0, -5)$ **121.** $5x + y = 8$
123. $4x + y = -3$ **125.** $y = 238x + 2134$

Chapter 3 Test

1. **2.** **3.** **4.** **5.**

6. $\dfrac{2}{5}$ **7.** 0 **8.** -1 **9.** 3 **10.** undefined **11.** $m = \dfrac{7}{3}; \left(0, -\dfrac{2}{3}\right)$ **12.** neither **13.** $x + 4y = 10$ **14.** $7x + 6y = 0$
15. $8x + y = 11$ **16.** $x = -5$ **17.** $x - 8y = -96$ **18.** yes **19.** no **20. a.** 0 **b.** 0 **c.** 60 **21.** all real numbers except -1 or
$(-\infty, -1) \cup (-1, \infty)$ **22. a.** x-intercepts: $(0, 0), (4, 0)$; y-intercept: $(0, 0)$ **b.** domain: $(-\infty, \infty)$; range: $(-\infty, 4]$ **23. a.** x-intercept: $(2, 0)$;
y-intercept; $(0, -2)$ **b.** domain: $(-\infty, \infty)$; range: $(-\infty, \infty)$ **24.** $(7, 20)$ **25.** 210 liters **26.** 490 liters **27.** July **28.** 63°F **29.** January,
February, March, November, December **30. a.** $(2003, 66.0); (2004, 65.4); (2005, 65.4); (2006, 65.6); (2007, 64.9); (2008, 63.7); (2009, 62.1)$
b. 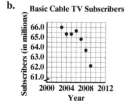 **31. a.** $m = -8$; Every 1 year, 8 million fewer movie tickets are sold. **b.** $(0, 1380), (5, 1340)$ **c.** $y = -8x + 1380$
d. In 2015, we predict that 1300 million movie tickets will be sold in the U.S. and Canada.

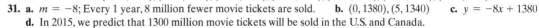

Chapter 3 Cumulative Review

1. a. < **b.** > **c.** >; Sec. 1.2, Ex. 1 **3.** $\frac{2}{39}$; Sec. 1.3, Ex. 3 **5.** $\frac{8}{3}$; Sec. 1.4, Ex. 3 **7. a.** -19 **b.** 30 **c.** -0.5 **d.** $-\frac{4}{5}$ **e.** 6.7

f. $\frac{1}{40}$; Sec. 1.5, Ex. 6 **9. a.** -6; **b.** 6.3; Sec. 1.6, Ex. 4 **11. a.** -6 **b.** 0 **c.** $\frac{3}{4}$; Sec. 1.7, Ex. 10 **13. a.** $22 + x$ **b.** $-21x$; Sec. 1.8, Ex. 3

15. a. -3 **b.** 22 **c.** 1 **d.** -1 **e.** $\frac{1}{7}$; Sec. 2.1, Ex. 1 **17.** 17; Sec. 2.2, Ex. 1 **19.** 6; Sec. 2.2, Ex. 5 **21.** $3x + 3$; Sec. 2.2, Ex. 10

23. 0; Sec. 2.3, Ex. 4 **25.** 242 Republicans, 193 Democrats; Sec. 2.4, Ex. 4 **27.** 40 ft; Sec. 2.5, Ex. 2 **29.** $\frac{y - b}{m} = x$; Sec. 2.5, Ex. 6

31. 40% solution: 8 liters; 70% solution: 4 liters; Sec. 2.6, Ex. 7 **33.** 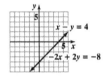 $[-1, \infty)$; Sec. 2.8, Ex. 1 **35.** $[1, 4)$; Sec. 2.8, Ex. 10

37. a. solution **b.** not a solution **c.** solution; Sec. 3.1, Ex. 5 **39. a.** yes **b.** yes **c.** no **d.** yes; Sec. 3.2, Ex. 1 **41.** 0; Sec. 3.4, Ex. 6

43. $y = \frac{1}{4}x - 3$; Sec. 3.5, Ex. 3

CHAPTER 4 SOLVING SYSTEMS OF LINEAR EQUATIONS

Section 4.1
Practice Exercises

1. no **2.** yes **3.** $(8, 5)$ **4.** $(-3, -5)$ **5.** no solution; inconsistent system; $\{\ \}$ or $\varnothing$

6. infinite number of solutions; consistent system, $\{(x, y)\,|\,3x + 4y = 12\}$ or $\{(x, y)\,|\,9x + 12y = 36\}$ **7.** one solution **8.** no solution

Graphing Calculator Explorations 4.1
1. $(0.37, 0.23)$ **3.** $(0.03, -1.89)$

Vocabulary, Readiness & Video Check 4.1
1. dependent **3.** consistent **5.** inconsistent **7.** The ordered pair must satisfy all equations of the system in order to be a solution of the system, so we must check that the ordered pair is a solution of both equations. **9.** Writing the equations of a system in slope-intercept form lets you see their slope and y-intercept. Different slopes mean one solution; same slope with different y-intercepts means no solution; same slope with same y-intercept means infinite number of solutions.

Exercise Set 4.1
1. one solution, $(-1, 3)$ **3.** infinite number of solutions **5. a.** no **b.** yes **7. a.** yes **b.** no **9. a.** yes **b.** yes **11. a.** no **b.** no

13. **15.** 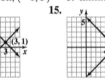 **17.** **19.** **21.** **23.**

25. no solution **27.** **29.** **31.** no solution; $\{\ \}$ or $\varnothing$ 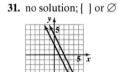 **33.** infinite number of solutions;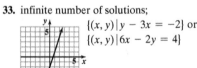
$\{(x, y)\,|\,y - 3x = -2\}$ or
$\{(x, y)\,|\,6x - 2y = 4\}$

35. **37.** **39.** **41.** infinite number of solutions;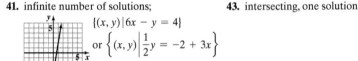
$\{(x, y)\,|\,6x - y = 4\}$
or $\left\{(x, y)\,\middle|\,\frac{1}{2}y = -2 + 3x\right\}$ **43.** intersecting, one solution

45. parallel; no solution **47.** identical lines; infinite number of solutions **49.** intersecting; one solution **51.** intersecting; one solution

53. identical lines; infinite number of solutions **55.** parallel; no solution **57.** 2 **59.** $-\frac{2}{5}$ **61.** 2

63. answers may vary; possible answer   **65.** answers may vary; possible answer   **67.** answers may vary   **69.** 1988–1989; 2001–2002

71. 2003, 2004, 2005, 2006, 2007   **73.** answers may vary   **75. a.** $(4, 9)$ **b.**   **c.** yes   **77.** answers may vary

Section 4.2
Practice Exercises

1. $(8, 7)$ **2.** $(-3, -6)$ **3.** $\left(4, \dfrac{2}{3}\right)$ **4.** $(-3, 2)$ **5.** infinite number of solutions; $\left\{(x, y)\,\middle|\,\dfrac{1}{4}x - y = 2\right\}$ or $\{(x, y)\,|\,x = 4y + 8\}$
6. no solution; $\{\ \}$ or $\varnothing$

Vocabulary, Readiness & Video Check 4.2
1. $(1, 4)$ **3.** infinite number of solutions   **5.** $(0, 0)$ **7.** You solved one equation for a variable. Now be sure to substitute this expression for the variable into the *other* equation.

Exercise Set 4.2

1. $(2, 1)$ **3.** $(-3, 9)$ **5.** $(2, 7)$ **7.** $\left(-\dfrac{1}{5}, \dfrac{43}{5}\right)$ **9.** $(2, -1)$ **11.** $(-2, 4)$ **13.** $(4, 2)$ **15.** $(-2, -1)$ **17.** no solution; $\{\ \}$ or $\varnothing$

19. $(3, -1)$ **21.** $(3, 5)$ **23.** $\left(\dfrac{2}{3}, -\dfrac{1}{3}\right)$ **25.** $(-1, -4)$ **27.** $(-6, 2)$ **29.** $(2, 1)$ **31.** no solution; $\{\ \}$ or $\varnothing$ **33.** infinite number of

solutions; $\left\{(x, y)\,\middle|\,\dfrac{1}{3}x - y = 2\right\}$ or $\{(x, y)\,|\,x - 3y = 6\}$ **35.** $\left(\dfrac{1}{2}, 2\right)$ **37.** $(1, -3)$ **39.** $-6x - 4y = -12$ **41.** $-12x + 3y = 9$ **43.** $5n$

45. $-15b$ **47.** answers may vary   **49.** no; answers may vary   **51.** **c;** answers may vary   **53. a.** $(13, 492)$ **b.** In $1970 + 13 = 1983$, the number of men and women receiving bachelor's degrees was the same.   **c.** answers may vary   **55.** $(-2.6, 1.3)$
57. $(3.28, 2.11)$

Section 4.3
Practice Exercises
1. $(5, 3)$ **2.** $(3, -4)$ **3.** no solution; $\{\ \}$ or $\varnothing$ **4.** infinite number of solutions; $\{(x, y)\,|\,4x - 3y = 5\}$ or $\{(x, y)\,|\,-8x + 6y = -10\}$
5. $(2, 2)$ **6.** $\left(-\dfrac{8}{5}, \dfrac{6}{5}\right)$

Vocabulary, Readiness & Video Check 4.3
1. false   **3.** true   **5.** The multiplication property of equality; be sure to multiply *both* sides of the equation by the number chosen.

Exercise Set 4.3
1. $(1, 2)$ **3.** $(2, -3)$ **5.** $(-2, -5)$ **7.** $(5, -2)$ **9.** $(-7, 5)$ **11.** $(6, 0)$ **13.** no solution; $\{\ \}$ or $\varnothing$ **15.** infinite number of solutions;

$\{(x, y)\,|\,-x + 5y = -1\}$ or $\{(x, y)\,|\,3x - 15y = 3\}$ **17.** $\left(2, -\dfrac{1}{2}\right)$ **19.** $(-2, 0)$ **21.** $(1, -1)$ **23.** no solution; $\{\ \}$ or $\varnothing$ **25.** $\left(\dfrac{12}{11}, -\dfrac{4}{11}\right)$

27. $\left(\dfrac{3}{2}, 3\right)$ **29.** infinite number of solutions; $\left\{(x, y)\,\middle|\,\dfrac{10}{3}x + 4y = -4\right\}$ or $\{(x, y)\,|\,5x + 6y = -6\}$ **31.** $(1, 6)$ **33.** $\left(-\dfrac{1}{2}, -2\right)$ **35.** infinite

number of solutions; $\left\{(x, y)\,\middle|\,\dfrac{x}{3} - y = 2\right\}$ or $\left\{(x, y)\,\middle|\,-\dfrac{x}{2} + \dfrac{3y}{2} = -3\right\}$ **37.** $\left(-\dfrac{2}{3}, \dfrac{2}{5}\right)$ **39.** $(2, 4)$ **41.** $(-0.5, 2.5)$ **43.** $(2, 5)$

45. $(-3, 2)$ **47.** $(0, 3)$ **49.** $(5, 7)$ **51.** $\left(\dfrac{1}{3}, 1\right)$ **53.** infinite number of solutions; $\left\{(x, y)\,\middle|\,\dfrac{x + 2}{2} = \dfrac{y + 11}{3}\right\}$ or $\left\{(x, y)\,\middle|\,\dfrac{x}{2} = \left(\dfrac{2y + 16}{6}\right)\right\}$
55. $(-8.9, 10.6)$ **57.** $2x + 6 = x - 3$ **59.** $20 - 3x = 2$ **61.** $4(n + 6) = 2n$ **63.** $2; 6x - 2y = -24$ **65.** **b;** answers may vary
67. answers may vary   **69. a.** $b = 15$ **b.** any real number except 15   **71.** $(-4.2, 9.6)$ **73. a.** $(7, 22)$ **b.** In 2015 $(2008 + 7)$, the percent of workers age 25–34 and the percent of workers age 55 and older will be the same.   **c.** 22% of the workforce for each of these age groups.

Integrated Review
1. $(2, 5)$ **2.** $(4, 2)$ **3.** $(5, -2)$ **4.** $(6, -14)$ **5.** $(-3, 2)$ **6.** $(-4, 3)$ **7.** $(0, 3)$ **8.** $(-2, 4)$ **9.** $(5, 7)$ **10.** $(-3, -23)$
11. $\left(\dfrac{1}{3}, 1\right)$ **12.** $\left(-\dfrac{1}{4}, 2\right)$ **13.** no solution; $\{\ \}$ or $\varnothing$ **14.** infinite number of solutions; $\{(x, y)\,|\,-x + 2y = 3\}$ or $\{(x, y)\,|\,3x - 6y = -9\}$
15. $(0.5, 3.5)$ **16.** $(-0.75, 1.25)$ **17.** infinite number of solutions; $\{(x, y)\,|\,x = 3y - 7\}$ or $\{(x, y)\,|\,2x - 6y = -14\}$ **18.** no solution; $\{\ \}$ or $\varnothing$
19. $(7, -3)$ **20.** $(-1, -3)$ **21.** answers may vary   **22.** answers may vary

Section 4.4
Practice Exercises

1. $(-1, 2, 1)$ **2.** $\{\ \}$ or $\varnothing$ **3.** $\left(\frac{2}{3}, -\frac{1}{2}, 0\right)$ **4.** $\{(x, y, z) \mid 2x + y - 3z = 6\}$ **5.** $(6, 15, -5)$

Vocabulary, Readiness & Video Check 4.4

1. a, b, d   **3.** yes; answers may vary   **5.** Once we have one equation in two variables, we need to get another equation in the *same* two variables, giving us a system of two equations in two variables. We solve this new system to find the value of two variables. We then substitute these values into an original equation to find the value of the third.

Exercise Set 4.4

1. $(-1, 5, 2)$ **3.** $(-2, 5, 1)$ **5.** $(-2, 3, -1)$ **7.** $\{(x, y, z) \mid x - 2y + z = -5\}$ **9.** $\varnothing$ **11.** $(0, 0, 0)$ **13.** $(-3, -35, -7)$
15. $(6, 22, -20)$ **17.** $\varnothing$ **19.** $(3, 2, 2)$ **21.** $\{(x, y, z) \mid x + 2y - 3z = 4\}$ **23.** $(-3, -4, -5)$ **25.** $\left(0, \frac{1}{2}, -4\right)$ **27.** $(12, 6, 4)$
29. 15 and 30   **31.** 5   **33.** $-\frac{5}{3}$ **35.** answers may vary   **37.** answers may vary   **39.** $(1, 1, -1)$ **41.** $(1, 1, 0, 2)$ **43.** $(1, -1, 2, 3)$
45. answers may vary

Section 4.5
Practice Exercises

1. a. 2208   **b.** yes; answers may vary   **2.** 18, 12   **3.** 17 and 12   **4. a.** Adult: \$19   **b.** Child: \$6   **c.** No, the regular rates are less than the group rate   **5.** Atlantique: 500 kph; V150: 575 kph   **6.** 0.95 liter of water; 0.05 liter of 99% HCL   **7.** 1500 packages   **8.** 40°, 60°, 80°

Vocabulary, Readiness & Video Check 4.5

1. Up to now we've been choosing one variable/unknown and translating to one equation. To solve by a system of equations, we'll choose two variables to represent two unknowns and translate to two equations.   **3.** The ordered triple still needs to be interpreted in the context of the application. Each value actually represents the angle measure of a triangle, in degrees.

Exercise Set 4.5

1. c   **3.** b   **5.** a   **7.** $\begin{cases} x + y = 15 \\ x - y = 7 \end{cases}$ **9.** $\begin{cases} x + y = 6500 \\ x = y + 800 \end{cases}$ **11.** 33 and 50   **13.** 10 and 8   **15.** 14 and -3 **17.** Cabrera: 126; Rodriguez: 125
19. child's ticket: \$18; adult's ticket: \$29   **21.** quarters: 53; nickels: 27   **23.** McDonald's: \$73.50; The Ohio Art Company: \$3.50   **25.** daily fee: \$32;
mileage charge: \$0.25 per mi   **27.** distance downstream = distance upstream = 18 mi; time downstream: 2 hr; time upstream: $4\frac{1}{2}$ hr; still water: 6.5 mph;
current: 2.5 mph   **29.** still air: 455 mph; wind: 65 mph   **31.** $4\frac{1}{2}$ hr   **33.** 12% solution: $7\frac{1}{2}$ liters; 4% solution: $4\frac{1}{2}$ liters   **35.** \$4.95 beans: 113 lb;
\$2.65 beans: 87 lb   **37.** 60°, 30°   **39.** 20°, 70°   **41.** number sold at \$9.50: 23; number sold at \$7.50: 67   **43.** $2\frac{1}{4}$ mph and $2\frac{3}{4}$ mph
45. 30%: 50 gal; 60%: 100 gal   **47.** length: 42 in.; width: 30 in.   **49. a.** 2010   **b.** answers may vary   **51. a.** answers may vary   **b.** 2003
53. $x = 75; y = 105$ **55.** 625 units   **57.** 3000 units   **59.** 1280 units   **61. a.** $R(x) = 450x$ **b.** $C(x) = 200x + 6000$ **c.** 24 desks
63. 2 units of Mix A; 3 units of Mix B; 1 unit of Mix C   **65.** 5 in.; 7 in.; 7 in.; 10 in.   **67.** 18, 13, and 9   **69.** free throws: 594; 2-pt field goals: 566;
3-pt fields goals: 145   **71.** $x = 60; y = 55; z = 65$ **73.** $(3, \infty)$ **75.** $\left[\frac{1}{2}, \infty\right)$ **77.** a   **79.** width: 9 ft; length: 15 ft   **81.** $a = 3, b = 4, c = -1$
83. $a = 0.5, b = 24.5, c = 849; 2015: 1774$ thousand students   **85.** $(7, 215)$

Chapter 4 Vocabulary Check

1. dependent   **2.** system of linear equations   **3.** consistent   **4.** solution   **5.** addition; substitution   **6.** inconsistent   **7.** independent

Chapter 4 Review

1. a. no   **b.** yes   **c.** no   **3. a.** no   **b.** no   **c.** yes   **5.**   **7.**   **9.**

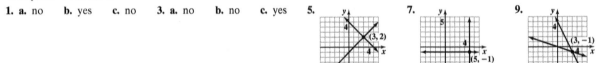

11. no solution; $\{\ \}$ or $\varnothing$

13. $(-1, 4)$ **15.** $(3, -2)$ **17.** infinite number of solutions; $\{(x, y) \mid 4y = 2x + 6\}$ or $\{(x, y) \mid x - 2y = -3\}$
19. no solution; $\{\ \}$ or $\varnothing$ **21.** $(-6, 2)$ **23.** $(3, 7)$

25. infinite number of solutions; $\{(x, y) \mid 2x - 6y = -1\}$ or $\left\{(x, y) \mid -x + 3y = \frac{1}{2}\right\}$ **27.** $(8, -6)$ **29.** $(2, 0, 2)$ **31.** $\left(-\frac{1}{2}, \frac{3}{4}, 1\right)$ **33.** $\varnothing$

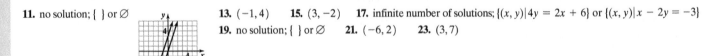

35. $(1, 1, -2)$ **37.** -6 and 22   **39.** current of river: 3.2 mph; speed in still water: 21.1 mph   **41.** egg: \$0.40; strip of bacon: \$0.65
43. 17 pennies; 20 nickels; 16 dimes   **45.** two sides: 22 cm each; third side: 29 cm

47.   **49.** $(3, 2)$ **51.** $\left(1\frac{1}{2}, -3\right)$ **53.** infinite number of solutions; $\{(x, y) | 3x - y = 4\}$ or $\{(x, y) | 4y = 12x - 16\}$ **55.** $(-5, 2)$

57. $(-1, 3, 5)$ **59.** 4 and 8   **61.** 24 nickels and 41 dimes   **63.** 28 units, 42 units, 56 units

Chapter 4 Test

1. false   **2.** false   **3.** true   **4.** false   **5.** no   **6.** yes

7. $(-4, 2)$ **8.** $(-4, 1)$ **9.** $\left(\frac{1}{2}, -2\right)$ **10.** $(4, -2)$ **11.** no solution; $\{\ \}$ or $\varnothing$ **12.** $(4, -5)$ **13.** $(7, 2)$

14. $(5, -2)$ **15.** 78, 46   **16.** 120 cc   **17.** Texas: 248 thousand; Missouri: 108 thousand

18. 3 mph; 6 mph   **19.** $(-1, -2, 4)$ **20.** $\varnothing$ **21.** $23°, 45°, 112°$

Chapter 4 Cumulative Review

1. a. $<$ **b.** $=$ **c.** $>$; Sec. 1.2, Ex. 6   **3. a.** commutative property of multiplication   **b.** associative property of addition   **c.** identity element for addition   **d.** commutative property of multiplication   **e.** multiplicative inverse property   **f.** additive inverse property   **g.** commutative and associative properties of multiplication; Sec. 1.8, Ex. 6   **5.** $-2x - 1$; Sec. 2.1, Ex. 7   **7.** 8; Sec. 2.2, Ex. 4

9. 6; Sec. 2.2, Ex. 5   **11.** 12; Sec. 2.3, Ex. 3   **13.** 10; Sec. 2.4, Ex. 2   **15.** $x = \dfrac{y - b}{m}$; Sec. 2.5, Ex. 6   **17.** $[2, \infty)$; Sec. 2.8, Ex. 3

19. ; Sec. 3.3, Ex. 7   **21.** $-\dfrac{8}{3}$; Sec. 3.4, Ex. 1   **23.** slope: $\dfrac{3}{4}$; y-intercept: $(0, 6)$; Sec. 3.4, Ex. 3   **25.** slope: $\dfrac{3}{4}$; y-intercept: $(0, -1)$; Sec. 3.4, Ex. 5   **27.** $y = -2x + 3$; $2x + y = 3$; Sec. 3.5, Ex. 4   **29.** $x = -1$; Sec. 3.5, Ex. 6   **31.** domain: $\{-1, 0, 3\}$; range: $\{-2, 0, 2, 3\}$; Sec. 3.6, Ex. 1   **33. a.** function   **b.** not a function; Sec. 3.6, Ex. 2   **35.** one solution; Sec. 4.1, Ex. 8   **37.** $\left(6, \dfrac{1}{2}\right)$; Sec. 4.2, Ex. 3   **39.** $(6, 1)$; Sec. 4.3, Ex. 1   **41.** $(-4, 2, -1)$; Sec. 4.4, Ex. 1   **43.** 7 and 11; Sec. 4.5, Ex. 3

CHAPTER 5 EXPONENTS AND POLYNOMIALS

Section 5.1
Practice Exercises

1. a. 27   **b.** 4   **c.** 64   **d.** -64 **e.** $\dfrac{27}{64}$ **f.** 0.0081   **g.** 75   **2. a.** 243   **b.** $\dfrac{3}{8}$ **3. a.** 3^{10} **b.** y^5 **c.** z^5 **d.** x^{11} **e.** $(-2)^8$ **f.** $b^3 \cdot t^5$ **4.** $15y^7$ **5. a.** $y^{12}z^4$ **b.** $-7m^5n^{14}$ **6. a.** z^{21} **b.** 4^{18} **c.** $(-2)^{15}$ **7. a.** p^5r^5 **b.** $36b^2$ **c.** $\dfrac{1}{64}x^6y^3$ **d.** $81a^{12}b^{16}c^4$ **8. a.** $\dfrac{x^5}{y^{10}}$ **b.** $\dfrac{32a^{20}}{b^{15}}$ **9. a.** z^4 **b.** 25   **c.** 64   **d.** $\dfrac{q^5}{t^2}$ **e.** $6x^2y^2$ **10. a.** -1 **b.** 1   **c.** 1   **d.** 1   **e.** 1   **f.** 7   **11. a.** $\dfrac{z^2}{144}$ **b.** $64x^{18}$ **c.** y^{13} **12. a.** 63   **b.** 2   **c.** $\dfrac{x^6}{9y^8}$ **d.** $-z^{30}$

Vocabulary, Readiness & Video Check 5.1

1. exponent   **3.** add   **5.** 1   **7.** Example 4 can be written as $-4^2 = -1 \cdot 4^2$, which is similar to Example 7, $4 \cdot 3^2$, and shows why the negative sign should not be considered part of the base when there are no parentheses.   **9.** Be careful not to confuse the power rule with the product rule. The power rule involves a power raised to a power (exponents are multiplied), and the product rule involves a product (exponents are added).   **11.** the quotient rule

Exercise Set 5.1

1. exponent: 2; base: 3   **3.** exponent: 2; base: 4   **5.** exponent: 2; base: x **7.** 49   **9.** -5 **11.** -16 **13.** 16   **15.** 0.00001   **17.** $\dfrac{1}{81}$

19. 224   **21.** -250 **23.** 4   **25.** 135   **27.** 150   **29.** $\dfrac{32}{5}$ **31.** x^7 **33.** $(-3)^{12}$ **35.** $15y^5$ **37.** $x^{19}y^6$ **39.** $-72m^3n^8$ **41.** $-24z^{20}$

43. $20x^5$ sq ft   **45.** x^{36} **47.** p^8q^8 **49.** $8a^{15}$ **51.** $x^{10}y^{15}$ **53.** $49a^4b^{10}c^2$ **55.** $\dfrac{r^9}{s^9}$ **57.** $\dfrac{m^5p^5}{n^5}$ **59.** $\dfrac{4x^2z^2}{y^{10}}$ **61.** $64z^{10}$ sq dm

63. $27y^{12}$ cu ft   **65.** x^2 **67.** -64 **69.** p^6q^5 **71.** $\dfrac{y^3}{2}$ **73.** 1   **75.** 1   **77.** -7 **79.** 2   **81.** -81 **83.** $\dfrac{1}{64}$ **85.** b^6 **87.** a^9

89. $-16x^7$ **91.** $a^{11}b^{20}$ **93.** $26m^9n^7$ **95.** z^{40} **97.** $64a^3b^3$ **99.** $36x^2y^2z^6$ **101.** $3x$ **103.** $81x^2y^2$ **105.** 9   **107.** $\dfrac{y^{15}}{8x^{12}}$ **109.** $2x^2y$

111. 2   **113.** $\dfrac{x^{18}}{4y^{22}}$ **115.** $-b^5$ **117.** $2y - 10$ **119.** $-x - 4$ **121.** $-x + 5$ **123.** c   **125.** e   **127.** answers may vary

129. answers may vary   **131.** 343 cu m   **133.** volume   **135.** answers may vary   **137.** answers may vary   **139.** x^{9a} **141.** a^{5b} **143.** x^{5a}

145. \$1045.85

Section 5.2
Practice Exercises
1. a. degree 3 **b.** degree 2 **c.** degree 1 **d.** degree 8 **e.** degree 0 **2. a.** trinomial, degree 2 **b.** binomial, degree 1 **c.** none of these, degree 3 **3.**

Term	Numerical Coefficient	Degree of Term
$-3x^3y^2$	-3	5
$4xy^2$	4	3
$-y^2$	-1	2
$3x$	3	1
-2	-2	0

4. a. 4 **b.** -21 **5.** 114 ft; 66 ft **6. a.** $-2y$ **b.** $z + 5z^3$ **c.** $14x^3$ **d.** $4a^2 - 12$ **e.** $\frac{1}{3}x^4 + \frac{11}{24}x^3 - x^2$
7. $-3x^2 + 5xy + 5y^2$ **8.** $x^2 + 2x + 4 + 5x + 3x^2; 4x^2 + 7x + 4$
9. a. $5y^2 - 3y + 2x - 9$ **b.** $-8a^2b - 3ab^2$
10. $7x^3 - 6x + 7$ **11.** $2x^3 - 4x^2 + 4x - 6$
12. $7x - 11$ **13. a.** $-5a^2 - ab + 6b^2$
b. $3x^2y^2 - 10xy - 4xy^2 + 5 - 6y^2$

Graphing Calculator Explorations 5.2
1. $x^3 - 4x^2 + 7x - 8$ **3.** $-2.1x^2 - 3.2x - 1.7$ **5.** $7.69x^2 - 1.26x + 5.3$

Vocabulary, Readiness & Video Check 5.2
1. binomial **3.** trinomial **5.** constant **7.** The degree of the polynomial is the greatest degree of any of its terms, so we need to find the degree of each term first. **9.** simplifying it

Exercise Set 5.2
1. 1; binomial **3.** 3; none of these **5.** 6; trinomial **7.** 8; binomial **9.** 3 **11.** 2 **13.** 57 **15.** 499 **17.** 1 **19.** $-\dfrac{11}{16}$ **21.** 1134 ft

23. 1006 ft **25.** 164 thousand **27.** $23x^2$ **29.** $12x^2 - y$ **31.** $7s$ **33.** $-1.1y^2 + 4.8$ **35.** $-\dfrac{7}{12}x^3 + \dfrac{7}{5}x^2 + 6$ **37.** $5a^2 - 9ab + 16b^2$

39. $-3x^2 + 10$ **41.** $-x^2 + 14$ **43.** $-2x + 9$ **45.** $2x^2 + 7x - 16$ **47.** $8t^2 - 4$ **49.** $-2z^2 - 16z + 6$ **51.** $2x^3 - 2x^2 + 7x + 2$
53. $-y^2 - 3y - 1$ **55.** $2x^2 + 11x$ **57.** $-16x^4 + 8x + 9$ **59.** $7x^2 + 14x + 18$ **61.** $3x - 3$ **63.** $7x^2 - 4x + 2$ **65.** $62x^2 + 5$
67. $7x^2 - 2x + 2$ **69.** $12x + 2$ **71.** $4y^2 + 12y + 19$ **73.** $4x^2 + 7x + x^2 + 5x; 5x^2 + 12x$ **75.** $-2a - b + 1$ **77.** $3x^2 + 5$
79. $6x^2 - 2xy + 19y^2$ **81.** $8r^2s + 16rs - 8 + 7r^2s^2$ **83.** $-5.42x^2 + 7.75x - 19.61$ **85.** $3.7y^4 - 0.7y^3 + 2.2y - 4$ **87.** $6x^2$
89. $-12x^8$ **91.** $200x^3y^2$ **93.** $18x + 44$ **95.** $(x^2 + 7x + 4)$ ft **97.** $(3y^2 + 4y + 11)$ m **99.** 7.33 million **101.** answers may vary
103. answers may vary **105.** b **107.** e **109. a.** $4z$ **b.** $3z^2$ **c.** $-4z$ **d.** $3z^2$; answers may vary **111. a.** m^3 **b.** $3m$ **c.** $-m^3$
d. $-3m$; answers may vary **113.** $3x^{2a} + 2x^a + 0.7$ **115.** $4x^{2y} + 2x^y - 11$ **117.** $4x^2 - 3x + 6$ **119.** $-x^2 - 6x + 10$ **121.** $3x^2 - 12x + 13$
123. a. $2a - 3$ **b.** $-2x - 3$ **c.** $2x + 2h - 3$ **125. a.** $4a$ **b.** $-4x$ **c.** $4x + 4h$ **127.** 2; 2 **129.** 4; 3; 3; 4 **131.** $2x^2 + 4xy$

Section 5.3
Practice Exercises
1. $10y^2$ **2.** $-2z^8$ **3.** $\dfrac{7}{72}b^9$ **4. a.** $27x^6 + 33x$ **b.** $-12x^5 + 54x^4 - 12x^3$ **5.** $10x^2 + 11x - 6$ **6.** $25x^2 - 30xy + 9y^2$
7. $2y^3 + 5y^2 - 7y + 20$ **8.** $s^3 + 6s^2t + 12st^2 + 8t^3$ **9.** $5x^3 - 23x^2 + 17x - 20$ **10.** $x^5 - 2x^4 + 2x^3 - 3x^2 + 2$
11. $5x^4 - 3x^3 + 11x^2 + 8x - 6$

Vocabulary, Readiness & Video Check 5.3
1. distributive **3.** $(5y - 1)(5y - 1)$ **5.** No. The monomials are unlike terms. **7.** Yes. The parentheses have been removed for the vertical format, but every term in the first polynomial is still distributed to every term in the second polynomial.

Exercise Set 5.3
1. $-28n^{10}$ **3.** $-12.4x^{12}$ **5.** $-\dfrac{2}{15}y^3$ **7.** $-24x^8$ **9.** $6x^2 + 15x$ **11.** $-2a^2 - 8a$ **13.** $6x^3 - 9x^2 + 12x$ **15.** $-6a^4 + 4a^3 - 6a^2$

17. $-4x^3y + 7x^2y^2 - xy^3 - 3y^4$ **19.** $4x^4 - 3x^3 + \dfrac{1}{2}x^2$ **21.** $x^2 + 7x + 12$ **23.** $a^2 + 5a - 14$ **25.** $x^2 + \dfrac{1}{3}x - \dfrac{2}{9}$ **27.** $12x^4 + 25x^2 + 7$

29. $4y^2 - 16y + 16$ **31.** $12x^2 - 29x + 15$ **33.** $9x^4 + 6x^2 + 1$ **35. a.** $-4y^4$ **b.** $3y^2$ **c.** answers may vary **37.** $x^3 - 5x^2 + 13x - 14$
39. $x^4 + 5x^3 - 3x^2 - 11x + 20$ **41.** $10a^3 - 27a^2 + 26a - 12$ **43.** $x^3 + 6x^2 + 12x + 8$ **45.** $8y^3 - 36y^2 + 54y - 27$
47. $12x^2 - 64x - 11$ **49.** $10x^3 + 22x^2 - x - 1$ **51.** $2x^4 + 3x^3 - 58x^2 + 4x + 63$ **53.** $8.4y^7$ **55.** $-3x^3 - 6x^2 + 24x$
57. $2x^2 + 39x + 19$ **59.** $x^2 - \dfrac{2}{7}x - \dfrac{3}{49}$ **61.** $9y^2 + 30y + 25$ **63.** $a^3 - 2a^2 - 18a + 24$ **65.** $8x^3 - 60x^2 + 150x - 125$
67. $32x^3 + 48x^2 - 6x - 20$ **69.** $6x^4 - 8x^3 - 7x^2 + 22x - 12$ **71.** $(4x^2 - 25)$ sq yd **73.** $(6x^2 - 4x)$ sq in.
75. $5a + 15a = 20a; 5a - 15a = -10a; 5a \cdot 15a = 75a^2; \dfrac{5a}{15a} = \dfrac{1}{3}$ **77.** $-3y^5 + 9y^4$, cannot be simplified; $-3y^5 - 9y^4$, cannot be simplified;
$-3y^5 \cdot 9y^4 = -27y^9; \dfrac{-3y^5}{9y^4} = -\dfrac{y}{3}$ **79. a.** $6x + 12$ **b.** $9x^2 + 36x + 35$; answers may vary **81.** $13x - 7$ **83.** $30x^2 - 28x + 6$
85. $-7x + 5$ **87.** $x^2 + 3x$ **89.** $x^2 + 5x + 6$ **91.** $11a$ **93.** $25x^2 + 4y^2$ **95. a.** $a^2 - b^2$ **b.** $4x^2 - 9y^2$ **c.** $16x^2 - 49$
d. answers may vary **97.** $(x^2 + 6x + 5)$ sq units

Section 5.4
Practice Exercises
1. $x^2 - 3x - 10$ **2.** $4x^2 - 13x + 9$ **3.** $9x^2 + 42x - 15$ **4.** $16x^2 - 8x + 1$ **5. a.** $b^2 + 6b + 9$ **b.** $x^2 - 2xy + y^2$
c. $9y^2 + 12y + 4$ **d.** $a^4 - 10a^2b + 25b^2$ **6. a.** $3x^2 - 75$ **b.** $16b^2 - 9$ **c.** $x^2 - \dfrac{4}{9}$ **d.** $25s^2 - t^2$ **e.** $4y^2 - 9z^4$
7. a. $4x^2 - 21x - 18$ **b.** $49b^2 - 28b + 4$ **c.** $x^2 - 0.16$ **d.** $3x^6 - \dfrac{9}{7}x^4 + \dfrac{2}{7}x^2 - \dfrac{6}{49}$ **e.** $x^3 + 6x^2 + 3x - 2$

Vocabulary, Readiness & Video Check 5.4
1. false   **3.** false   **5.** a binomial times a binomial   **7.** Multiplying gives you four terms, and the two like terms will always subtract out.

Exercise Set 5.4
1. $x^2 + 7x + 12$ **3.** $x^2 + 5x - 50$ **5.** $5x^2 + 4x - 12$ **7.** $20y^2 - 125y + 30$ **9.** $6x^2 + 13x - 5$ **11.** $x^2 + \dfrac{1}{3}x - \dfrac{2}{9}$ **13.** $x^2 + 4x + 4$
15. $4x^2 - 4x + 1$ **17.** $9a^2 - 30a + 25$ **19.** $25x^2 + 90x + 81$ **21.** $a^2 - 49$ **23.** $9x^2 - 1$ **25.** $9x^2 - \dfrac{1}{4}$ **27.** $81x^2 - y^2$
29. $4x^2 - 0.01$ **31.** $a^2 + 9a + 20$ **33.** $a^2 + 14a + 49$ **35.** $12a^2 - a - 1$ **37.** $x^2 - 4$ **39.** $9a^2 + 6a + 1$ **41.** $4x^3 - x^2y^4 + 4xy - y^5$
43. $x^3 - 3x^2 - 17x + 3$ **45.** $4a^2 - 12a + 9$ **47.** $25x^2 - 36z^2$ **49.** $x^{10} - 8x^5 + 15$ **51.** $x^2 - 0.64$ **53.** $a^7 - 3a^3 + 11a^4 - 33$
55. $3x^2 - 12x + 12$ **57.** $6b^2 - b - 35$ **59.** $49p^2 - 64$ **61.** $\dfrac{1}{9}a^4 - 49$ **63.** $15x^4 - 5x^3 + 10x^2$ **65.** $4r^2 - 9s^2$
67. $9x^2 - 42xy + 49y^2$ **69.** $16x^2 - 25$ **71.** $64x^2 + 64x + 16$ **73.** $a^2 - \dfrac{1}{4}y^2$ **75.** $\dfrac{1}{25}x^2 - y^2$ **77.** $3a^3 + 2a^2 + 1$
79. $(2x + 1)(2x + 1)$ sq ft or $(4x^2 + 4x + 1)$ sq ft   **81.** $\dfrac{5b^5}{7}$ **83.** $-2a^{10}b^5$ **85.** $\dfrac{2y^8}{3}$ **87.** $\dfrac{1}{3}$ **89.** 1   **91.** c   **93.** d   **95.** 2; 2
97. $(x^4 - 3x^2 + 1)$ sq m   **99.** $(24x^2 - 32x + 8)$ sq m   **101.** $(x^2 + 10x + 25)$ sq units   **103.** answers may vary   **105.** answers may vary
107. answers may vary   **109.** $x^2 + 2xy + y^2 - 9$ **111.** $a^2 - 6a + 9 - b^2$

Integrated Review
1. $35x^5$ **2.** $32y^9$ **3.** -16 **4.** 16   **5.** $2x^2 - 9x - 5$ **6.** $3x^2 + 13x - 10$ **7.** $3x - 4$ **8.** $4x + 3$ **9.** $7x^6y^2$ **10.** $\dfrac{10b^6}{7}$
11. $144m^{14}n^{12}$ **12.** $64y^{27}z^{30}$ **13.** $48y^2 - 27$ **14.** $98x^2 - 2$ **15.** $x^{63}y^{45}$ **16.** $27x^{27}$ **17.** $2x^2 - 2x - 6$ **18.** $6x^2 + 13x - 11$
19. $2.5y^2 - 6y - 0.2$ **20.** $8.4x^2 - 6.8x - 5.7$ **21.** $x^2 + 8xy + 16y^2$ **22.** $y^2 - 18yz + 81z^2$ **23.** $2x + 8y$ **24.** $2y - 18z$
25. $7x^2 - 10xy + 4y^2$ **26.** $-a^2 - 3ab + 6b^2$ **27.** $x^3 + 2x^2 - 16x + 3$ **28.** $x^3 - 2x^2 - 5x - 2$ **29.** $6x^5 + 20x^3 - 21x^2 - 70$
30. $20x^7 + 25x^3 - 4x^4 - 5$ **31.** $2x^3 - 19x^2 + 44x - 7$ **32.** $5x^3 + 9x^2 - 17x + 3$ **33.** cannot simplify   **34.** $25x^3y^3$ **35.** $125x^9$
36. $\dfrac{x^3}{y^3}$ **37.** $2x$ **38.** x^2

Section 5.5
Practice Exercises
1. a. $\dfrac{1}{125}$ **b.** $\dfrac{3}{y^4}$ **c.** $\dfrac{5}{6}$ **d.** $\dfrac{1}{25}$ **e.** $\dfrac{1}{x^5}$ **2. a.** s^5 **b.** 8   **c.** $\dfrac{y^5}{x^7}$ **d.** $\dfrac{9}{64}$ **3. a.** $\dfrac{1}{x^5}$ **b.** $5y^7$ **c.** z^5 **d.** $\dfrac{81}{25}$ **4. a.** $\dfrac{b^{15}}{a^{20}}$
b. x^{10} **c.** $\dfrac{q^2}{25p^{16}}$ **d.** $\dfrac{6y^2}{x^7}$ **e.** $-27x^6y^9$ **5. a.** 7×10^{-6} **b.** 2.07×10^7 **c.** 4.3×10^{-3} **d.** 8.12×10^8 **6. a.** 0.000367
b. 8,954,000   **c.** 0.00002009   **d.** 4054   **7. a.** 4000   **b.** 20,000,000,000

Graphing Calculator Explorations 5.5
1. 5.31 EE 3   **3.** 6.6 EE -9 **5.** 1.5×10^{13} **7.** 8.15×10^{19}

Vocabulary, Readiness & Video Check 5.5
1. $\dfrac{1}{x^3}$ **3.** scientific notation   **5.** A negative exponent has nothing to do with the sign of the simplified result.   **7.** When you move the decimal point to the left, the sign of the exponent will be positive; when you move the decimal point to the right, the sign of the exponent will be negative.
9. the quotient rule

Exercise Set 5.5
1. $\dfrac{1}{64}$ **3.** $\dfrac{1}{81}$ **5.** $\dfrac{7}{x^3}$ **7.** 32   **9.** -64 **11.** $\dfrac{8}{15}$ **13.** p^3 **15.** $\dfrac{q^4}{p^5}$ **17.** $\dfrac{1}{x^3}$ **19.** z^3 **21.** $\dfrac{4}{9}$ **23.** $-p^4$ **25.** -2 **27.** x^4
29. p^4 **31.** m^{11} **33.** r^6 **35.** $\dfrac{1}{x^{15}y^9}$ **37.** $\dfrac{1}{x^4}$ **39.** $\dfrac{1}{a^2}$ **41.** $4k^3$ **43.** $3m$ **45.** $-\dfrac{4a^5}{b}$ **47.** $-\dfrac{6x^2}{y^3}$ **49.** $\dfrac{a^{30}}{b^{12}}$ **51.** $\dfrac{1}{x^{10}y^6}$
53. $\dfrac{z^2}{4}$ **55.** $\dfrac{1}{32x^5}$ **57.** $\dfrac{49a^4}{b^6}$ **59.** $a^{24}b^8$ **61.** x^9y^{19} **63.** $-\dfrac{y^8}{8x^2}$ **65.** $-\dfrac{6x}{7y^2}$ **67.** $\dfrac{25b^{33}}{a^{16}}$ **69.** 7.8×10^4 **71.** 1.67×10^{-6}
73. 6.35×10^{-3} **75.** 1.16×10^6 **77.** 2×10^9 **79.** 2.4×10^3 **81.** 0.0000000008673   **83.** 0.033   **85.** 20,320   **87.** 700,000,000
89. 9,460,000,000,000   **91.** 1.84×10^{11} **93.** 155,000,000,000   **95.** 35,000   **97.** 0.000036   **99.** 0.0000000000000000028   **101.** 0.0000005
103. 200,000   **105.** $\dfrac{5x^3}{3}$ **107.** $\dfrac{5z^3y^2}{7}$ **109.** $5y - 6 + \dfrac{5}{y}$ **111.** $\dfrac{27}{x^6z^3}$ cu in.   **113.** $9a^{13}$ **115.** -5 **117.** answers may vary
119. a. 1.3×10^1 **b.** 4.4×10^7 **c.** 6.1×10^{-2} **121.** answers may vary   **123.** a^m **125.** $27y^{6z}$ **127.** -394.5 **129.** 1.3 sec

Section 5.6
Practice Exercises

1. $2t + 1$ **2.** $4x^4 + 5x - \dfrac{3}{x}$ **3.** $3x^3y^3 - 2 + \dfrac{1}{5x}$ **4.** $x + 3$ **5.** $2x + 3 + \dfrac{-10}{2x + 1}$ or $2x + 3 - \dfrac{10}{2x + 1}$ **6.** $3x^2 - 2x + 5 + \dfrac{-13}{3x + 2}$ or

$3x^2 - 2x + 5 - \dfrac{13}{3x - 2}$ **7.** $3x^2 - 2x - 9 + \dfrac{5x + 22}{x^2 + 2}$ **8.** $x^2 - 3x + 9$

Vocabulary, Readiness & Video Check 5.6
1. dividend, quotient, divisor   **3.** a^2 **5.** y **7.** the common denominator

Exercise Set 5.6

1. $12x^3 + 3x$ **3.** $4x^3 - 6x^2 + x + 1$ **5.** $5p^2 + 6p$ **7.** $-\dfrac{3}{2x} + 3$ **9.** $-3x^2 + x - \dfrac{4}{x^3}$ **11.** $-1 + \dfrac{3}{2x} - \dfrac{7}{4x^4}$ **13.** $x + 1$ **15.** $2x + 3$

17. $2x + 1 + \dfrac{7}{x - 4}$ **19.** $3a^2 - 3a + 1 + \dfrac{2}{3a + 2}$ **21.** $4x + 3 - \dfrac{2}{2x + 1}$ **23.** $2x^2 + 6x - 5 - \dfrac{2}{x - 2}$ **25.** $x + 6$ **27.** $x^2 + 3x + 9$

29. $-3x + 6 - \dfrac{11}{x + 2}$ **31.** $2b - 1 - \dfrac{6}{2b - 1}$ **33.** $ab - b^2$ **35.** $4x + 9$ **37.** $x + 4xy - \dfrac{y}{2}$ **39.** $2b^2 + b + 2 - \dfrac{12}{b + 4}$

41. $5x - 2 + \dfrac{2}{x + 6}$ **43.** $x^2 - \dfrac{12x}{5} - 1$ **45.** $6x - 1 - \dfrac{1}{x + 3}$ **47.** $6x - 1$ **49.** $-x^3 + 3x^2 - \dfrac{4}{x}$ **51.** $x^2 + 3x + 9$

53. $y^2 + 5y + 10 + \dfrac{24}{y - 2}$ **55.** $-6x - 12 - \dfrac{19}{x - 2}$ **57.** $x^3 - x^2 + x$ **59.** $2a^3 + 2a$ **61.** $2x^3 + 14x^2 - 10x$ **63.** $-3x^2y^3 - 21x^3y^2 - 24xy$

65. $9a^2b^3c + 36ab^2c - 72ab$ **67.** $(3x^3 + x - 4)$ ft   **69.** c   **71.** answers may vary   **73.** $(2x + 5)$ m   **75.** $9x^{7a} - 6x^{5a} + 7x^{2a} - 1$

Section 5.7
Practice Exercises

1. $4x^2 + x + 7 + \dfrac{12}{x - 1}$ **2.** $x^3 - 5x + 21 - \dfrac{51}{x + 3}$ **3. a.** -4 **b.** -4 **4.** 15

Vocabulary, Readiness & Video Check 5.7
1. The last number n is the remainder and the other numbers are the coefficients of the variables in the quotient; the degree of the quotient is one less than the degree of the dividend

Exercise Set 5.7

1. $x + 8$ **3.** $x - 1$ **5.** $x^2 - 5x - 23 - \dfrac{41}{x - 2}$ **7.** $4x + 8 + \dfrac{7}{x - 2}$ **9.** 3 **11.** 73 **13.** -8 **15.** $x^2 + \dfrac{2}{x - 3}$ **17.** $6x + 7 + \dfrac{1}{x + 1}$

19. $2x^3 - 3x^2 + x - 4$ **21.** $3x - 9 + \dfrac{12}{x + 3}$ **23.** $3x^2 - \dfrac{9}{2}x + \dfrac{7}{4} + \dfrac{47}{8(x - \frac{1}{2})}$ **25.** $3x^2 + 3x - 3$ **27.** $3x^2 + 4x - 8 + \dfrac{20}{x + 1}$

29. $x^2 + x + 1$ **31.** $x - 6$ **33.** 1 **35.** -133 **37.** 3 **39.** $-\dfrac{187}{81}$ **41.** $\dfrac{95}{32}$ **43.** answers may vary   **45.** $-\dfrac{5}{6}$ **47.** 54 **49.** 8

51. -32 **53.** 48 **55.** 25 **57.** -2 **59.** yes   **61.** no   **63.** $(x^3 - 5x^2 + 2x - 1)$ cm   **65.** $x^3 + \dfrac{5}{3}x^2 + \dfrac{5}{3}x + \dfrac{8}{3} + \dfrac{8}{3(x - 1)}$

67. $(x + 3)(x^2 + 4) = x^3 + 3x^2 + 4x + 12$ **69.** 0 **71.** $x^3 + 2x^2 + 7x + 28$

Chapter 5 Vocabulary Check
1. term   **2.** FOIL   **3.** trinomial   **4.** degree of a polynomial   **5.** binomial   **6.** coefficient   **7.** degree of a term   **8.** monomial
9. polynomials   **10.** distributive

Chapter 5 Review
1. base: 7; exponent: 9   **3.** base: 5; exponent: 4   **5.** 512 **7.** -36 **9.** 1 **11.** y^9 **13.** $-6x^{11}$ **15.** x^8 **17.** $81y^{24}$ **19.** x^5

21. a^4b^3 **23.** $\dfrac{x^3y^4}{4}$ **25.** $40a^{19}$ **27.** 3 **29.** b   **31.** 7 **33.** 8 **35.** 5 **37.** 5 **39.** 4000 ft; 3984 ft; 3856 ft; 3600 ft   **41.** $15a^2 + 4a$

43. $-6a^2b - 3b^2 - q^2$ **45.** $8x^2 + 3x + 6$ **47.** $-7y^2 - 1$ **49.** $4x - 13y$ **51.** 290 **53.** $(6x^2y - 12x + 12)$ cm   **55.** $8a + 28$

57. $-7x^3 - 35x$ **59.** $-6a^4 + 8a^2 - 2a$ **61.** $2x^2 - 12x - 14$ **63.** $x^2 - 18x + 81$ **65.** $4a^2 + 27a - 7$ **67.** $25x^2 + 20x + 4$

69. $x^4 + 7x^3 + 4x^2 + 23x - 35$ **71.** $x^4 + 4x^3 + 4x^2 - 16$ **73.** $x^3 + 21x^2 + 147x + 343$ **75.** $x^2 + 14x + 49$ **77.** $9x^2 - 42x + 49$

79. $25x^2 - 90x + 81$ **81.** $49x^2 - 16$ **83.** $4x^2 - 36$ **85.** $(9x^2 - 6x + 1)$ sq m   **87.** $\dfrac{1}{49}$ **89.** $\dfrac{2}{x^4}$ **91.** 125 **93.** $\dfrac{17}{16}$ **95.** x^8

97. r **99.** c^4 **101.** $\dfrac{1}{x^6y^{13}}$ **103.** a^{11m} **105.** $27x^3y^{6z}$ **107.** 2.7×10^{-4} **109.** 8.08×10^7 **111.** 9.1×10^7 **113.** $867,000$

115. 0.00086 **117.** $1,431,280,000,000,000$ **119.** 0.016 **121.** $\dfrac{1}{7} + \dfrac{3}{x} + \dfrac{7}{x^2}$ **123.** $a + 1 + \dfrac{6}{a - 2}$ **125.** $a^2 + 3a + 8 + \dfrac{22}{a - 2}$

127. $2x^3 - x^2 + 2 - \dfrac{1}{2x - 1}$ **129.** $\left(5x - 1 + \dfrac{20}{x^2}\right)$ ft   **131.** $3x^2 + 6x + 24 + \dfrac{44}{x - 2}$ **133.** $x^4 - x^3 + x^2 - x + 1 - \dfrac{2}{x + 1}$

135. $3x^3 + 13x^2 + 51x + 204 + \dfrac{814}{x - 4}$ **137.** 3043 **139.** $-\dfrac{1}{8}$ **141.** $\dfrac{2x^6}{3}$ **143.** $\dfrac{x^{16}}{16y^{12}}$ **145.** $11x - 5$ **147.** $5y^2 - 3y - 1$

149. $28x^3 + 12x$ **151.** $x^3 + x^2 - 18x + 18$ **153.** $25x^2 + 40x + 16$ **155.** $4a - 1 + \dfrac{2}{a^2} - \dfrac{5}{2a^3}$ **157.** $2x^2 + 7x + 5 + \dfrac{19}{2x - 3}$

Chapter 5 Test

1. 32   **2.** 81   **3.** -81 **4.** $\dfrac{1}{64}$ **5.** $-15x^{11}$ **6.** y^5 **7.** $\dfrac{1}{r^5}$ **8.** $\dfrac{y^{14}}{x^2}$ **9.** $\dfrac{1}{6xy^8}$ **10.** 5.63×10^5 **11.** 8.63×10^{-5} **12.** 0.0015

13. $62{,}300$ **14.** 0.036 **15. a.** $4,3;7,3;1,4;-2,0$ **b.** 4   **16.** $-2x^2 + 12xy + 11$ **17.** $16x^3 + 7x^2 - 3x - 13$ **18.** $-3x^3 + 5x^2 + 4x + 5$

19. $x^3 + 8x^2 + 3x - 5$ **20.** $3x^3 + 22x^2 + 41x + 14$ **21.** $6x^4 - 9x^3 + 21x^2$ **22.** $3x^2 + 16x - 35$ **23.** $9x^2 - \dfrac{1}{25}$ **24.** $16x^2 - 16x + 4$

25. $64x^2 + 48x + 9$ **26.** $x^4 - 81b^2$ **27.** 1001 ft; 985 ft; 857 ft; 601 ft   **28.** $(4x^2 - 9)$ sq in.   **29.** $\dfrac{x}{2y} + 3 - \dfrac{7}{8y}$ **30.** $x + 2$

31. $9x^2 - 6x + 4 - \dfrac{16}{3x + 2}$ **32. a.** 960 ft   **b.** 953.44 ft   **33.** $4x^3 - 15x^2 + 45x - 136 + \dfrac{407}{x + 3}$ **34.** 91

Chapter 5 Cumulative Review

1. a. true   **b.** true   **c.** false   **d.** true; Sec. 1.2, Ex. 2   **3. a.** $\dfrac{64}{25}$ **b.** $\dfrac{1}{20}$ **c.** $\dfrac{5}{4}$; Sec. 1.3, Ex. 4   **5. a.** 9   **b.** 125   **c.** 16   **d.** 7

e. $\dfrac{9}{49}$; Sec. 1.4, Ex. 1   **7. a.** -10 **b.** -21 **c.** -12; Sec. 1.5, Ex. 3   **9.** -12; Sec. 1.6, Ex. 3   **11. a.** $\dfrac{1}{22}$ **b.** $\dfrac{16}{3}$ **c.** $-\dfrac{1}{10}$ **d.** $-\dfrac{13}{9}$; Sec. 1.7, Ex. 5

13. a. $(5 + 4) + 6$ **b.** $-1 \cdot (2 \cdot 5)$; Sec. 1.8, Ex. 2   **15. a.** $22 + x$ **b.** $-21x$; Sec. 1.8, Ex. 3   **17. a.** $15x + 10$ **b.** $-2y - 0.6z + 2$

c. $-9x - y + 2z - 6$; Sec. 2.1, Ex. 5   **19.** 17; Sec. 2.2, Ex. 1   **21.** 6; Sec. 2.2, Ex. 5   **23.** -10; Sec. 2.4, Ex. 1   **25.** 10; Sec. 2.4, Ex. 2

27. width: 4 ft; length: 10 ft; Sec. 2.5, Ex. 4   **29.** $\dfrac{5F - 160}{9} = C$; Sec. 2.5, Ex. 8   **31.** [graph]; Sec. 2.8, Ex. 9   **33. a.** $(0, 12)$ **b.** $(2, 6)$

c. $(-1, 15)$; Sec. 3.1, Ex. 6   **35.** [graph]; Sec. 3.2, Ex. 2   **37.** [graph]; Sec. 3.3, Ex. 9   **39.** undefined slope; Sec. 3.4, Ex. 7

41. $9x^2 - 6x - 1$ (Sec. 5.2, Ex. 11)   **43.** $-6x^7$; Sec. 5.1, Ex. 4   **45.** $12x^3 - 12x^2 - 9x + 2$; Sec. 5.2, Ex. 10   **47.** $4x^2 - 4xy + y^2$; Sec. 5.3, Ex. 6

49. $3m + 1$; Sec. 5.6, Ex. 1

CHAPTER 6 FACTORING POLYNOMIALS

Section 6.1
Practice Exercises

1. a. 6   **b.** 1   **c.** 4   **2. a.** y^4 **b.** x **3. a.** $5y^2$ **b.** x^2 **c.** a^2b^2 **4. a.** $4(t + 3)$ **b.** $y^4(y^4 + 1)$ **5.** $8b^2(-b^4 + 2b^2 - 1)$ or

$-8b^2(b^4 - 2b^2 + 1)$ **6.** $5x(x^3 - 4)$ **7.** $\dfrac{1}{9}z^3(5z^2 + z - 2)$ **8.** $4ab^3(2ab - 5a^2 + 3)$ **9.** $(y - 2)(8 + x)$ **10.** $(p + q)(7xy^3 - 1)$

11. $(x + 3)(y + 4)$ **12.** $(5x - 3)(8x^2 + 3)$ **13.** $(2x + 3y)(y - 1)$ **14.** $(7a + 5)(a^2 + 1)$ **15.** $(y - 3)(4x - 5)$ **16.** cannot be factored by grouping   **17.** $3(x - a)(y - 2a)$

Vocabulary, Readiness & Video Check 6.1

1. factors   **3.** least   **5.** false   **7.** The GCF of a list of numbers is the largest number that is a factor of all numbers in the list.   **9.** When factoring out a GCF, the number of terms in the other factor should have the same number of terms as your original polynomial.

Exercise Set 6.1

1. 4   **3.** 6   **5.** 1   **7.** y^2 **9.** z^7 **11.** xy^2 **13.** 7   **15.** $4y^3$ **17.** $5x^2$ **19.** $3x^3$ **21.** $9x^2y$ **23.** $10a^6b$ **25.** $3(a + 2)$

27. $15(2x - 1)$ **29.** $x^2(x + 5)$ **31.** $2y^3(3y + 1)$ **33.** $4(x - 2y + 1)$ **35.** $3x(2x^2 - 3x + 4)$ **37.** $a^2b^2(a^5b^4 - a + b^3 - 1)$

39. $4(2x^5 + 4x^4 - 5x^3 + 3)$ **41.** $\dfrac{1}{3}x(x^3 + 2x^2 - 4x^4 + 1)$ **43.** $(x^2 + 2)(y + 3)$ **45.** $(y + 4)(z - 3)$ **47.** $(z^2 - 6)(r + 1)$

49. $-2(x + 7)$ **51.** $-x^5(2 - x^2)$ **53.** $-3a^2(2a^2 - 3a + 1)$ **55.** $(x + 2)(x^2 + 5)$ **57.** $(x + 3)(5 + y)$ **59.** $(3x - 2)(2x^2 + 5)$

61. $(5m^2 + 6n)(m + 1)$ **63.** $(y - 4)(2 + x)$ **65.** $(2x - 1)(x^2 + 4)$ **67.** not factorable by grouping   **69.** $(x - 2y)(4x - 3)$

71. $(5q - 4p)(q - 1)$ **73.** $x(x^2 + 1)(2x + 5)$ **75.** $2(2y - 7)(3x^2 - 1)$ **77.** $2x(16y - 9x)$ **79.** $(x + 2)(y - 3)$ **81.** $7xy(2x^2 + x - 1)$

83. $(4x - 1)(7x^2 + 3)$ **85.** $-8x^8y^5(5y + 2x)$ **87.** $3(2a + 3b^2)(a + b)$ **89.** $x^2 + 7x + 10$ **91.** $b^2 - 3b - 4$ **93.** $2, 6$ **95.** $-1, -8$

97. $-2, 5$ **99.** b   **101.** factored   **103.** not factored   **105.** answers may vary   **107.** answers may vary   **109. a.** 1200 million

b. 1120 million   **c.** $-20(x^2 - 15x - 6)$ **111.** $12x^3 - 2x; 2x(6x^2 - 1)$ **113.** $(n^3 - 6)$units   **115.** $(x^n + 2)(x^n + 3)$

117. $(3x^n - 5)(x^n + 7)$

Section 6.2
Practice Exercises

1. $(x + 2)(x + 3)$ **2.** $(x - 10)(x - 7)$ **3.** $(x + 7)(x - 2)$ **4.** $(p - 9)(p + 7)$ **5.** prime polynomial   **6.** $(x + 3y)(x + 4y)$

7. $(x^2 + 12)(x^2 + 1)$ **8.** $(x - 6)(x - 8)$ **9.** $4(x - 3)(x - 3)$ **10.** $3y^2(y - 7)(y + 1)$

Vocabulary, Readiness & Video Check 6.2

1. true   **3.** false   **5.** $+5$ **7.** -3 **9.** $+2$ **11.** 15 is positive, so its factors would have to either be both positive or both negative. Since the factors need to sum to -8, both factors must be negative.

Exercise Set 6.2

1. $(x+6)(x+1)$ **3.** $(y-9)(y-1)$ **5.** $(x-3)(x-3)$ or $(x-3)^2$ **7.** $(x-6)(x+3)$ **9.** $(x+10)(x-7)$ **11.** prime
13. $(x+5y)(x+3y)$ **15.** $(a^2-5)(a^2+3)$ **17.** $(m+13)(m+1)$ **19.** $(t-2)(t+12)$ **21.** $(a-2b)(a-8b)$ **23.** $2(z+8)(z+2)$
25. $2x(x-5)(x-4)$ **27.** $(x-4y)(x+y)$ **29.** $(x+12)(x+3)$ **31.** $(x-2)(x+1)$ **33.** $(r-12)(r-4)$ **35.** $(x+2y)(x-y)$
37. $3(x+5)(x-2)$ **39.** $3(x-18)(x-2)$ **41.** $(x-24)(x+6)$ **43.** prime   **45.** $(x-5)(x-3)$ **47.** $6x(x+4)(x+5)$
49. $4y(x^2+x-3)$ **51.** $(x-7)(x+3)$ **53.** $(x+5y)(x+2y)$ **55.** $2(t+8)(t+4)$ **57.** $x(x-6)(x+4)$ **59.** $2t^3(t-4)(t-3)$
61. $5xy(x-8y)(x+3y)$ **63.** $3(m-9)(m-6)$ **65.** $-1(x-11)(x-1)$ **67.** $\frac{1}{2}(y-11)(y+2)$ **69.** $x(xy-4)(xy+5)$
71. $2x^2+11x+5$ **73.** $15y^2-17y+4$ **75.** $9a^2+23ab-12b^2$ **77.** $x^2+5x-24$ **79.** answers may vary
81. $2x^2+28x+66; 2(x+3)(x+11)$ **83.** $-16(t-5)(t+1)$ **85.** $\left(x+\frac{1}{4}\right)\left(x+\frac{1}{4}\right)$ or $\left(x+\frac{1}{4}\right)^2$ **87.** $(x+1)(z-10)(z+7)$
89. $(x^n+10)(x^n-2)$ **91.** $5; 8; 9$ **93.** $3; 4$ **95.** $8; 16$ **97.** $6; 26$

Section 6.3
Practice Exercises

1. $(2x+5)(x+3)$ **2.** $(5x-4)(3x-2)$ **3.** $(4x-1)(x+3)$ **4.** $(7x-y)(3x+2y)$ **5.** $(2x^2-7)(x^2+1)$ **6.** $x(3x+2)(x+5)$
7. $-1(4x-3)(2x+1)$ **8.** $(x+7)^2$ **9.** $(2x+9y)(2x+y)$ **10.** $(6n^2-1)^2$ **11.** $3x(2x-7)^2$

Vocabulary, Readiness & Video Check 6.3

1. perfect square trinomial   **3.** perfect square trinomial   **5.** d   **7.** Consider the factors of the first and last terms and the signs of the trinomial. Continue to check by multiplying until you get the middle term of the trinomial.   **9.** The first and last terms are squares, a^2 and b^2, and the middle term is $2 \cdot a \cdot b$ or $-2 \cdot a \cdot b$.

Exercise Set 6.3

1. $x+4$ **3.** $10x-1$ **5.** $5x-2$ **7.** $(2x+3)(x+5)$ **9.** $(y-1)(8y-9)$ **11.** $(2x+1)(x-5)$ **13.** $(4r-1)(5r+8)$
15. $(10x+1)(x+3)$ **17.** prime   **19.** $(3x-5y)(2x-y)$ **21.** $(3m-5)(5m+3)$ **23.** $x(3x+2)(4x+1)$ **25.** $3(7b+5)(b-3)$
27. $(3z+4)(4z-3)$ **29.** $2y^2(3x-10)(x+3)$ **31.** $(2x-7)(2x+3)$ **33.** $-1(x-6)(x+4)$ **35.** $x(4x+3)(x-3)$
37. $(4x-9)(6x-1)$ **39.** $(x+11)^2$ **41.** $(x-8)^2$ **43.** $(4a-3)^2$ **45.** $(x^2+2)^2$ **47.** $2(n-7)^2$ **49.** $(4y+5)^2$
51. $(2x+11)(x-9)$ **53.** $(8x+3)(3x+4)$ **55.** $(3a+b)(a+3b)$ **57.** $(x-4)(x-5)$ **59.** $(p+6q)^2$ **61.** $(xy-5)^2$
63. $b(8a-3)(5a+3)$ **65.** $2x(3x+2)(5x+3)$ **67.** $2y(3y+5)(y-3)$ **69.** $5x^2(2x-y)(x+3y)$ **71.** $-1(2x-5)(7x-2)$
73. $p^2(4p-5)^2$ **75.** $(3x-2)(x+1)$ **77.** $(4x+9y)(2x-3y)$ **79.** prime   **81.** $(3x-4y)^2$ **83.** $(6x-7)(3x+2)$
85. $(7t+1)(t-4)$ **87.** $(7p+1)(7p-2)$ **89.** $m(m+9)^2$ **91.** prime   **93.** $a(6a^2+b^2)(a^2+6b^2)$ **95.** x^2-4 **97.** a^3+27
99. $25-34$ **101.** answers may vary   **103.** no   **105.** answers may vary   **107.** $4x^2+21x+5; (4x+1)(x+5)$ **109.** $\left(2x+\frac{1}{2}\right)^2$
111. $(y-1)^2(4x^2+10x+25)$ **113.** 8   **115.** $a^2+2ab+b^2$ **117.** $2; 14$ **119.** 2   **121.** $-3xy^2(4x-5)(x+1)$
123. $(y-1)^2(2x+5)^2$ **125.** $(3x^n+2)(x^n+5)$ **127.** answers may vary

Section 6.4
Practice Exercises

1. $(5x+1)(x+12)$ **2.** $(4x-5)(3x-1)$ **3.** $2(5x+1)(3x-2)$ **4.** $5m^2(8m-7)(m+1)$ **5.** $(4x+3)^2$

Vocabulary, Readiness & Video Check 6.4

1. a   **3.** b   **5.** This gives us a four-term polynomial, which may be factored by grouping.

Exercise Set 6.4

1. $(x+3)(x+2)$ **3.** $(y+8)(y-2)$ **5.** $(8x-5)(x-3)$ **7.** $(5x^2-3)(x^2+5)$ **9. a.** $9, 2$ **b.** $9x+2x$ **c.** $(3x+1)(2x+3)$
11. a. $-20, -3$ **b.** $-20x-3x$ **c.** $(3x-4)(5x-1)$ **13.** $(3y+2)(7y+1)$ **15.** $(7x-11)(x+1)$ **17.** $(5x-2)(2x-1)$
19. $(2x-5)(x-1)$ **21.** $(2x+3)^2$ **23.** $(2x+3)(2x-7)$ **25.** $(5x-4)(2x-3)$ **27.** $x(2x+3)(x+5)$
29. $2(8y-9)(y-1)$ **31.** $(2x-3)(3x-2)$ **33.** $3(3a+2)(6a-5)$ **35.** $a(4a+1)(5a+8)$ **37.** $3x(4x+3)(x-3)$
39. $y(3x+y)(x+y)$ **41.** prime   **43.** $5(x+5y)^2$ **45.** $6(a+b)(4a-5b)$ **47.** $p^2(15p+q)(p+2q)$ **49.** $2(9a^2-2)^2$
51. $(7+x)(5+x)$ or $(x+7)(x+5)$ **53.** $(6-5x)(1-x)$ or $(5x-6)(x-1)$ **55.** x^2-4 **57.** $y^2+8y+16$ **59.** $81z^2-25$
61. x^3-27 **63.** $10x^2+45x+45; 5(2x+3)(x+3)$ **65.** $(x^n+2)(x^n+3)$ **67.** $(3x^n-5)(x^n+7)$ **69.** answers may vary

Section 6.5
Practice Exercises

1. $(x+9)(x-9)$ **2. a.** $(3x-1)(3x+1)$ **b.** $(6a-7b)(6a+7b)$ **c.** $\left(p+\frac{5}{6}\right)\left(p-\frac{5}{6}\right)$ **3.** $(p^2-q^5)(p^2+q^5)$
4. a. $(z^2+9)(z+3)(z-3)$ **b.** prime polynomial   **5.** $y(6y+5)(6y-5)$ **6.** $5(4y^2+1)(2y+1)(2y-1)$
7. $-1(3x+10)(3x-10)$ or $(10+3x)(10-3x)$ **8.** $(x+4)(x^2-4x+16)$ **9.** $(x-5)(x^2+5x+25)$ **10.** $(3y+1)(9y^2-3y+1)$
11. $4(2x-5y)(4x^2+10xy+25y^2)$

Graphing Calculator Explorations 6.5

	$x^2 - 2x + 1$	$x^2 - 2x - 1$	$(x - 1)^2$
$x = 5$	16	14	16
$x = -3$	16	14	16
$x = 2.7$	2.89	0.89	2.89
$x = -12.1$	171.61	169.61	171.61
$x = 0$	1	-1	1

Vocabulary, Readiness & Video Check 6.5

1. difference of two cubes   **3.** sum of two cubes   **5.** $(7x)^2$ **7.** $(2y)^3$ **9.** In order to recognize the binomial as a difference of squares and also to identify the terms to use in the special factoring formula.   **11.** First rewrite the original binomial with terms writtten as cubes. Answers will then vary depending on your interpretation.

Exercise Set 6.5

1. $(x + 2)(x - 2)$ **3.** $(9p + 1)(9p - 1)$ **5.** $(5y - 3)(5y + 3)$ **7.** $(11m + 10n)(11m - 10n)$ **9.** $(xy - 1)(xy + 1)$

11. $\left(x - \dfrac{1}{2}\right)\left(x + \dfrac{1}{2}\right)$ **13.** $-1(2r + 1)(2r - 1)$ **15.** prime   **17.** $(-6 + x)(6 + x)$ or $-1(6 + x)(6 - x)$ **19.** $(m^2 + 1)(m + 1)(m - 1)$

21. $(m^2 + n^9)(m^2 - n^9)$ **23.** $(x + 5)(x^2 - 5x + 25)$ **25.** $(2a - 1)(4a^2 + 2a + 1)$ **27.** $(m + 3n)(m^2 - 3mn + 9n^2)$

29. $5(k + 2)(k^2 - 2k + 4)$ **31.** $(xy - 4)(x^2y^2 + 4xy + 16)$ **33.** $2(5r - 4t)(25r^2 + 20rt + 16t^2)$ **35.** $(r + 8)(r - 8)$

37. $(x + 13y)(x - 13y)$ **39.** $(3 - t)(9 + 3t + t^2)$ **41.** $2(3r + 2)(3r - 2)$ **43.** $x(3y + 2)(3y - 2)$ **45.** $8(m + 2)(m^2 - 2m + 4)$

47. $xy(y - 3z)(y + 3z)$ **49.** $4(3x - 4y)(3x + 4y)$ **51.** $9(4 - 3x)(4 + 3x)$ **53.** $(xy - z^2)(x^2y^2 + xyz^2 + z^4)$ **55.** $\left(7 - \dfrac{3}{5}m\right)\left(7 + \dfrac{3}{5}m\right)$

57. $(t + 7)(t^2 - 7t + 49)$ **59.** $n(n^2 + 49)$ **61.** $x^2(x^2 + 9)(x + 3)(x - 3)$ **63.** $pq(8p + 9q)(8p - 9q)$ **65.** $xy^2(27xy + 1)$

67. $a(5a - 4b)(25a^2 + 20ab + 16b^2)$ **69.** $16x^2(x + 2)(x - 2)$ **71.** 6   **73.** -2 **75.** $\dfrac{1}{5}$ **77.** $(x + 2 + y)(x + 2 - y)$

79. $(a + 4)(a - 4)(b - 4)$ **81.** $(x + 3 + 2y)(x + 3 - 2y)$ **83.** $(x^n + 10)(x^n - 10)$ **85.** $(x + 6)$ **87.** answers may vary
89. a. 2560 ft   **b.** 1920 ft   **c.** 13 sec   **d.** $16(13 - t)(13 + t)$ **91. a.** 1456 ft   **b.** 816 ft   **c.** 10 sec   **d.** $16(10 + t)(10 - t)$

Integrated Review
Practice Exercises

1. $(3x - 1)(2x - 3)$ **2.** $(3x + 1)(x - 2)(x + 2)$ **3.** $3(3x - y)(3x + y)$ **4.** $(2a + b)(4a^2 - 2ab + b^2)$ **5.** $6xy^2(5x + 2)(2x - 3)$

Exercise Set

1. $(x + y)^2$ **2.** $(x - y)^2$ **3.** $(a + 12)(a - 1)$ **4.** $(a - 10)(a - 1)$ **5.** $(a + 2)(a - 3)$ **6.** $(a - 1)^2$ **7.** $(x + 1)^2$
8. $(x + 2)(x - 1)$ **9.** $(x + 1)(x + 3)$ **10.** $(x + 3)(x - 2)$ **11.** $(x + 3)(x + 4)$ **12.** $(x + 4)(x - 3)$ **13.** $(x + 4)(x - 1)$
14. $(x - 5)(x - 2)$ **15.** $(x + 5)(x - 3)$ **16.** $(x + 6)(x + 5)$ **17.** $(x - 6)(x + 5)$ **18.** $(x + 8)(x + 3)$ **19.** $2(x + 7)(x - 7)$
20. $3(x + 5)(x - 5)$ **21.** $(x + 3)(x + y)$ **22.** $(y - 7)(3 + x)$ **23.** $(x + 8)(x - 2)$ **24.** $(x - 7)(x + 4)$ **25.** $4x(x + 7)(x - 2)$
26. $6x(x - 5)(x + 4)$ **27.** $2(3x + 4)(2x + 3)$ **28.** $(2a - b)(4a + 5b)$ **29.** $(2a + b)(2a - b)$ **30.** $(4 - 3x)(7 + 2x)$
31. $(5 - 2x)(4 + x)$ **32.** prime   **33.** prime   **34.** $(3y + 5)(2y - 3)$ **35.** $(4x - 5)(x + 1)$ **36.** $y(x + y)(x - y)$ **37.** $4(t^2 + 9)$
38. $(x + 1)(x + y)$ **39.** $(x + 1)(a + 2)$ **40.** $9x(2x^2 - 7x + 1)$ **41.** $4a(3a^2 - 6a + 1)$ **42.** $(x + 16)(x - 2)$ **43.** prime
44. $(4a - 7b)^2$ **45.** $(5p - 7q)^2$ **46.** $(7x + 3y)(x + 3y)$ **47.** $(5 - 2y)(25 + 10y + 4y^2)$ **48.** $(4x + 3)(16x^2 - 12x + 9)$
49. $-(x - 5)(x + 6)$ **50.** $-(x - 2)(x - 4)$ **51.** $(7 - x)(2 + x)$ **52.** $(3 + x)(1 - x)$ **53.** $3x^2y(x + 6)(x - 4)$ **54.** $2xy(x + 5y)(x - y)$
55. $5xy^2(x - 7y)(x - y)$ **56.** $4x^2y(x - 5)(x + 3)$ **57.** $3xy(4x^2 + 81)$ **58.** $2xy^2(3x^2 + 4)$ **59.** $(2 + x)(2 - x)$ **60.** $(3 + y)(3 - y)$
61. $(s + 4)(3r - 1)$ **62.** $(x - 2)(x^2 + 3)$ **63.** $(4x - 3)(x - 2y)$ **64.** $(2x - y)(2x + 7z)$ **65.** $6(x + 2y)(x + y)$
66. $2(x + 4y)(6x - y)$ **67.** $(x + 3)(y + 2)(y - 2)$ **68.** $(y + 3)(y - 3)(x^2 + 3)$ **69.** $(5 + x)(x + y)$ **70.** $(x - y)(7 + y)$
71. $(7t - 1)(2t - 1)$ **72.** prime   **73.** $(3x + 5)(x - 1)$ **74.** $(7x - 2)(x + 3)$ **75.** $(x + 12y)(x - 3y)$ **76.** $(3x - 2y)(x + 4y)$
77. $(1 - 10ab)(1 + 2ab)$ **78.** $(1 + 5ab)(1 - 12ab)$ **79.** $(3 + x)(3 - x)(1 + x)(1 - x)$ **80.** $(3 + x)(3 - x)(2 + x)(2 - x)$
81. $(x + 4)(x - 4)(x^2 + 2)$ **82.** $(x + 5)(x - 5)(x^2 + 3)$ **83.** $(x - 15)(x - 8)$ **84.** $(y + 16)(y + 6)$ **85.** $2x(3x - 2)(x - 4)$
86. $2y(3y + 5)(y - 3)$ **87.** $(3x - 5y)(9x^2 + 15xy + 25y^2)$ **88.** $(6y - z)(36y^2 + 6yz + z^2)$ **89.** $(xy + 2z)(x^2y^2 - 2xyz + 4z^2)$
90. $(3ab + 2)(9a^2b^2 - 6ab + 4)$ **91.** $2xy(1 + 6x)(1 - 6x)$ **92.** $2x(x + 3)(x - 3)$ **93.** $(x + 2)(x - 2)(x + 6)$
94. $(x - 2)(x + 6)(x - 6)$ **95.** $2a^2(3a + 5)$ **96.** $2n(2n - 3)$ **97.** $(a^2 + 2)(a + 2)$ **98.** $(a - b)(1 + x)$ **99.** $(x + 2)(x - 2)(x + 7)$
100. $(a + 3)(a - 3)(a + 5)$ **101.** $(x - y + z)(x - y - z)$ **102.** $(x + 2y + 3)(x + 2y - 3)$ **103.** $(9 + 5x + 1)(9 - 5x - 1)$
104. $(b + 4a + c)(b - 4a - c)$ **105.** answers may vary   **106.** yes; $9(x^2 + 9y^2)$ **107.** a, c   **108.** b, c

Section 6.6
Practice Exercises

1. $-4, 5$ **2.** $-\dfrac{3}{4}, 12$ **3.** $0, \dfrac{6}{7}$ **4.** $-4, 12$ **5.** $\dfrac{4}{3}$ **6.** $-3, \dfrac{2}{3}$ **7.** $-6, 4$ **8.** $-3, 0, 3$ **9.** $\dfrac{2}{3}, \dfrac{3}{2}, 5$ **10.** $-3, 0, 2$
11. The x-intercepts are $(2, 0)$ and $(4, 0)$.

Graphing Calculator Explorations 6.6

1. $-0.9, 2.2$ **3.** no real solution   **5.** $-1.8, 2.8$

Vocabulary, Readiness & Video Check 6.6

1. quadratic **3.** $3, -5$ **5.** One side of the equation must be a factored polynomial and the other side must be zero. **7.** To find the x-intercepts of any graph in two variables, we let $y = 0$. Doing this with our quadratic equation gives us an equation $= 0$, which we can solve by factoring.

Exercise Set 6.6

1. $6, 7$ **3.** $2, -1$ **5.** $-9, -17$ **7.** $0, -6$ **9.** $0, 8$ **11.** $-\dfrac{3}{2}, \dfrac{5}{4}$ **13.** $\dfrac{7}{2}, -\dfrac{2}{7}$ **15.** $\dfrac{1}{2}, -\dfrac{1}{3}$ **17.** $-0.2, -1.5$ **19.** $9, 4$ **21.** $-4, 2$

23. $0, 7$ **25.** $8, -4$ **27.** $4, -4$ **29.** $-3, 12$ **31.** $\dfrac{7}{3}, -2$ **33.** $-5, 5$ **35.** $-2, \dfrac{1}{6}$ **37.** $0, 4, 8$ **39.** $\dfrac{3}{4}$ **41.** $-\dfrac{1}{2}, 0, \dfrac{1}{2}$ **43.** $-\dfrac{3}{8}, 0, \dfrac{1}{2}$

45. $-3, 2$ **47.** $-20, 0$ **49.** $\dfrac{17}{2}$ **51.** $-\dfrac{1}{2}, \dfrac{1}{2}$ **53.** $-\dfrac{3}{2}, -\dfrac{1}{2}, 3$ **55.** $-5, 3$ **57.** $-\dfrac{5}{6}, \dfrac{6}{5}$ **59.** $2, -\dfrac{4}{5}$ **61.** $-\dfrac{4}{3}, 5$ **63.** $-4, 3$

65. $\dfrac{8}{3}, -9, 0$ **67.** -7 **69.** $0, \dfrac{3}{2}$ **71.** $0, 1, -1$ **73.** $-6, \dfrac{4}{3}$ **75.** $\dfrac{6}{7}, 1$ **77.** $\left(-\dfrac{4}{3}, 0\right), (1, 0)$ **79.** $(-2, 0), (5, 0)$ **81.** $(-6, 0), \left(\dfrac{1}{2}, 0\right)$

83. e **85.** b **87.** c **89.** $\dfrac{47}{45}$ **91.** $\dfrac{17}{60}$ **93.** $\dfrac{15}{8}$ **95.** $\dfrac{7}{10}$ **97.** didn't write equation in standard form; should be $x = 4$ or $x = -2$

99. answers may vary; for example $(x - 6)(x + 1) = 0$ **101.** answers may vary; for example, $x^2 - 12x + 35 = 0$ **103. a.** $300; 304; 276; 216;$ $124; 0; -156$ **b.** 5 sec **c.** 304 ft **d.**

$y = -16x^2 + 20x + 300$

105. $0, \dfrac{1}{2}$ **107.** $0, -15$

Section 6.7
Practice Exercises

1. 2 sec **2.** There are two numbers. They are -4 and 12. **3.** base: 35 ft; height: 12 ft **4.** 7 and 8 or -6 and -5 **5.** leg: 8 units; leg: 15 units; hypotenuse: 17 units

Vocabulary, Readiness & Video Check 6.7

1. In applications, the context of the problem needs to be considered. Each exercise resulted in both a positive and a negative solution, and a negative solution is not appropriate for any of the problems.

Exercise Set 6.7

1. width $= x$; length $= x + 4$ **3.** x and $x + 2$ if x is an odd integer **5.** base $= x$; height $= 4x + 1$ **7.** 11 units **9.** 15 cm, 13 cm, 70 cm, 22 cm **11.** base $= 16$ mi; height $= 6$ mi **13.** 5 sec **15.** width $= 5$ cm; length $= 6$ cm **17.** 54 diagonals **19.** 10 sides **21.** -12 or 11 **23.** 14, 15 **25.** 13 feet **27.** 5 in. **29.** 12 mm, 16 mm, 20 mm **31.** 10 km **33.** 36 ft **35.** 9.5 sec **37.** 20% **39.** length: 15 mi; width: 8 mi

41. 105 units **43.** 2 million **45.** 1.9 million **47.** 2003 **49.** answers may vary **51.** $\dfrac{4}{7}$ **53.** $\dfrac{3}{2}$ **55.** $\dfrac{1}{3}$

57. slow boat: 8 mph; fast boat: 15 mph **59.** 13 and 7 **61.** width: 29 m; length: 35 m **63.** answers may vary

Chapter 6 Vocabulary Check

1. quadratic equation **2.** factoring **3.** greatest common factor **4.** perfect square trinomial **5.** difference of two squares **6.** difference of two cubes **7.** sum of two cubes **8.** 0 **9.** hypotenuse **10.** leg **11.** hypotenuse

Chapter 6 Review

1. $2x - 5$ **3.** $4x(5x + 3)$ **5.** $(2x + 3)(3x - 5)$ **7.** $(x - 1)(3x + 2)$ **9.** $(2a + b)(5a + 7b)$ **11.** $(x + 4)(x + 2)$ **13.** prime **15.** $(x + 6y)(x - 2y)$ **17.** $2(3 - x)(12 + x)$ **19.** $10a(a - 1)(a - 10)$ **21.** $-48, 2$ **23.** $(2x + 1)(x + 6)$ **25.** $(3x + 4y)(2x - y)$ **27.** $5y(2y - 3)(y + 4)$ **29.** $2(3x - 5)^2$ **31.** $(2x + 3)(2x - 3)$ **33.** prime **35.** $(2x + 3)(4x^2 - 6x + 9)$ **37.** $2(3 - xy)(9 + 3xy + x^2y^2)$ **39.** $(4x^2 + 1)(2x + 1)(2x - 1)$ **41.** $-6, 2$ **43.** $-\dfrac{1}{5}, -3$ **45.** $-4, 6$ **47.** $2, 8$ **49.** $-\dfrac{2}{7}, \dfrac{3}{8}$ **51.** $-\dfrac{2}{5}$ **53.** 3 **55.** $0, -\dfrac{7}{4}, 3$

57. c **59.** 9 units **61.** width: 20 in.; length: 25 in. **63.** 19 and 20 **65. a.** 17.5 sec and 10 sec; The rocket reaches a height of 2800 ft on its way up and on its way back down. **b.** 27.5 sec **67.** $7(x - 9)$ **69.** $\left(m + \dfrac{2}{5}\right)\left(m - \dfrac{2}{5}\right)$ **71.** $(y + 2)(x - 1)$ **73.** $3x(x - 9)(x - 1)$

75. $2(x + 3)(x - 3)$ **77.** $5(x + 2)^2$ **79.** $2xy(2x - 3y)$ **81.** $3(8x^2 - x - 6)$ **83.** $(x + 3)(x + 2)(x - 2)$

85. $5x^2 - 9x - 2; (5x + 1)(x - 2)$ **87.** $-\dfrac{7}{2}, 4$ **89.** $0, -7, -4$ **91.** $0, 16$ **93.** length: 6 in.; width: 2 in. **95.** $28x^2 - \pi x^2; x^2(28 - \pi)$

Chapter 6 Test

1. $(x + 7)(x + 4)$ **2.** $(7 - m)(7 + m)$ **3.** $(y + 11)^2$ **4.** $(a + 3)(4 - y)$ **5.** prime **6.** $(y - 12)(y + 4)$ **7.** prime **8.** $3x(3x + 1)(x + 4)$ **9.** $(3a - 7)(a + b)$ **10.** $(3x - 2)(x - 1)$ **11.** $(x + 12y)(x + 2y)$ **12.** $5(6 + x)(6 - x)$ **13.** $(6t + 5)(t - 1)$ **14.** $(y + 2)(y - 2)(x - 7)$ **15.** $x(1 + x^2)(1 + x)(1 - x)$ **16.** $-xy(y^2 + x^2)$ **17.** $(4x - 1)(16x^2 + 4x + 1)$

18. $8(y - 2)(y^2 + 2y + 4)$ **19.** $-9, 3$ **20.** $-7, 2$ **21.** $-7, 1$ **22.** $0, \dfrac{3}{2}, -\dfrac{4}{3}$ **23.** $0, 3, -3$ **24.** $-3, 5$ **25.** $0, \dfrac{5}{2}$ **26.** 17 ft
27. 8 and 9   **28.** 7 sec   **29.** hypotenuse: 25 cm; legs: 15 cm, 20 cm

Chapter 6 Cumulative Review

1. a. $9 \le 11$ **b.** $8 > 1$ **c.** $3 \ne 4$; Sec. 1.2, Ex. 3   **3. a.** $\dfrac{6}{7}$ **b.** $\dfrac{11}{27}$ **c.** $\dfrac{22}{5}$; Sec. 1.3, Ex. 2   **5.** $\dfrac{14}{3}$; Sec. 1.4, Ex. 5   **7. a.** -12
b. -1; Sec. 1.5, Ex. 7   **9. a.** -32 **b.** -14 **c.** 90; Sec. 1.7, Ex. 1   **11. a.** $4x$ **b.** $11y^2$ **c.** $8x^2 - x$ **d.** $5n^2$; Sec. 2.1, Ex. 3
13. 140; Sec. 2.2, Ex. 7   **15.** -11; Sec. 2.2, Ex. 6   **17.** $\dfrac{16}{3}$; Sec. 2.3, Ex. 2   **19.** shorter: 12 in.; longer: 36 in.; Sec. 2.4, Ex. 3

21. 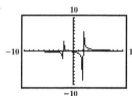 ; Sec. 3.2, Ex. 5   **23.** $m = \dfrac{3}{4}$; y-intercept: $(0, -1)$; Sec. 3.4, Ex. 5   **25. a.** 250   **b.** 1; Sec. 5.1, Ex. 2   **27. a.** 2   **b.** 5
c. 1   **d.** 6   **e.** 0; Sec. 5.2, Ex. 1   **29.** $9x^2 - 6x - 1$; Sec. 5.2, Ex. 11   **31.** $6x^2 - 11x - 10$; Sec. 5.3, Ex. 5
33. $9y^2 + 6y + 1$; Sec. 5.4, Ex. 4   **35. a.** $\dfrac{1}{9}$ **b.** $\dfrac{2}{x^3}$ **c.** $\dfrac{3}{4}$ **d.** $\dfrac{1}{16}$ **e.** $\dfrac{1}{y^4}$ (Sec. 5.5, Ex. 1)
37. a. 3.67×10^8 **b.** 3.0×10^{-6} **c.** 2.052×10^{10} **d.** 8.5×10^{-4}; Sec. 5.5, Ex. 5   **39.** $x + 4$; Sec. 5.6, Ex. 4
41. a. x^3 **b.** y; Sec. 6.1, Ex. 2   **43.** $(x + 3)(x + 4)$; Sec. 6.2, Ex. 1   **45.** $(4x - 1)(2x - 5)$; Sec. 6.3, Ex. 2   **47.** $(5a + 3b)(5a - 3b)$;
Sec. 6.5, Ex. 2b   **49.** $3, -1$; Sec. 6.6, Ex. 1

CHAPTER 7 RATIONAL EXPRESSIONS

Section 7.1
Practice Exercises

1. a. $\{x \mid x \text{ is a real number}\}$ **b.** $\{x \mid x \text{ is a real number and } x \ne -3\}$ **c.** $\{x \mid x \text{ is a real number and } x \ne 2, x \ne 3\}$ **2. a.** $\dfrac{1}{2z - 1}$ **b.** $\dfrac{5x + 3}{6x - 5}$
3. a. 1   **b.** -1 **4.** $-\dfrac{5(2 + x)}{x + 3}$ **5. a.** $x^2 - 4x + 16$ **b.** $\dfrac{5}{z - 3}$ **6.** $\dfrac{-(x + 3)}{6x - 11}; \dfrac{-x - 3}{6x - 11}; \dfrac{x + 3}{-(6x - 11)}; \dfrac{x + 3}{-6x + 11}; \dfrac{x + 3}{11 - 6x}$
7. a. $7.20   **b.** $3.60

Graphing Calculator Explorations 7.1

1. $\{x \mid x \text{ is a real number and } x \ne -2, x \ne 2\}$ **3.** $\left\{ x \mid x \text{ is a real number and } x \ne -4, x \ne \dfrac{1}{2}\right\}$

Vocabulary, Readiness & Video Check 7.1

1. rational   **3.** domain   **5.** 1   **7.** $\dfrac{-a}{b}; \dfrac{a}{-b}$ **9.** Rational expressions are fractions and are therefore undefined if the denominator
is zero; the domain of a rational function is all real numbers except those that make the denominator of the related rational expression equal to 0.
11. You would need to write parentheses around the numerator or denominator if it had more than one term because the negative sign needs to
apply to the entire numerator or denominator.

Exercise Set 7.1

1. $\{x \mid x \text{ is a real number}\}$ **3.** $\{t \mid t \text{ is a real number and } t \ne 0\}$ **5.** $\{x \mid x \text{ is a real number and } x \ne 7\}$ **7.** $\left\{ x \mid x \text{ is a real number and } x \ne \dfrac{1}{3}\right\}$
9. $\{x \mid x \text{ is a real number and } x \ne -2, x \ne 0, x \ne 1\}$ **11.** $\{x \mid x \text{ is a real number and } x \ne 2, x \ne -2\}$ **13.** $\dfrac{-(x - 10)}{x + 8}; \dfrac{-x + 10}{x + 8}; \dfrac{x - 10}{-(x + 8)}; \dfrac{x - 10}{-x - 8}$
15. $\dfrac{-(5y - 3)}{y - 12}; \dfrac{-5y + 3}{y - 12}; \dfrac{5y - 3}{-(y - 12)}; \dfrac{5y - 3}{-y + 12}$ **17.** 1   **19.** -1 **21.** $\dfrac{1}{4(x + 2)}$ **23.** -5 **25.** $\dfrac{7}{x}$ **27.** $\dfrac{1}{x - 9}$ **29.** $5x + 1$
31. $\dfrac{x^2}{x - 2}$ **33.** $\dfrac{x + 2}{2}$ **35.** $-(x + 2)$ or $-x - 2$ **37.** $\dfrac{11x}{6}$ **39.** $x + y$ **41.** $x^2 - 2x + 4$ **43.** $-x^2 - x - 1$ **45.** $\dfrac{2y + 5}{3y + 4}$
47. $\dfrac{x - 2}{2x^2 + 1}$ **49.** $\dfrac{1}{3x + 5}$ **51.** correct   **53.** correct   **55.** $\dfrac{10}{3}, -8, -\dfrac{7}{3}$ **57.** $-\dfrac{17}{48}, \dfrac{2}{7}, -\dfrac{3}{8}$ **59. a.** $200 million   **b.** $500 million
c. $300 million   **d.** $\{x \mid x \text{ is a real number}\}$ **61.** 400 mg   **63.** $C = 78.125$; medium   **65.** 59.6%   **67.** $\dfrac{3}{11}$ **69.** $\dfrac{4}{3}$ **71.** $\dfrac{117}{40}$
73. correct   **75.** incorrect; $\dfrac{1 + 2}{1 + 3} = \dfrac{3}{4}$ **77.** no   **79.** yes; 1   **81.** yes; -1 **83.** no; answers may vary   **85.** answers may vary

87. $0, \dfrac{20}{9}, \dfrac{60}{7}, 20, \dfrac{140}{3}, 180, 380, 1980;$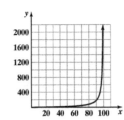

89.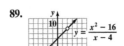

91.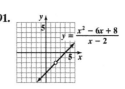

Section 7.2

Practice Exercises

1. a. $\dfrac{12a}{5b^2}$ **b.** $-\dfrac{2q}{3}$ **2.** $\dfrac{3}{x+1}$ **3.** $-\dfrac{3x-5}{2x(x+2)}$ **4.** $\dfrac{b^2}{8a^2}$ **5.** $\dfrac{3(x-5)}{4}$ **6.** $\dfrac{2}{x(x-3)}$ **7.** 1 **8. a.** $\dfrac{(y+9)^2}{16x^2}$ **b.** $\dfrac{1}{4x}$

c. $-\dfrac{7(x-2)}{x+4}$ **9.** 2 sq ft **10.** 504 sq in. **11.** 549,000 sq ft **12.** 70.0 miles per hour

Vocabulary, Readiness & Video Check 7.2

1. reciprocals **3.** $\dfrac{a\cdot d}{b\cdot c}$ or $\dfrac{ad}{bc}$ **5.** $\dfrac{6}{7}$ **7.** fractions; reciprocal **9.** The units in the unit fraction consist of $\dfrac{\text{units converting to}}{\text{original units}}$.

Exercise Set 7.2

1. $\dfrac{21}{4y}$ **3.** x^4 **5.** $-\dfrac{b^2}{6}$ **7.** $\dfrac{x^2}{10}$ **9.** $\dfrac{1}{3}$ **11.** $\dfrac{m+n}{m-n}$ **13.** $\dfrac{x+5}{x}$ **15.** $\dfrac{(x+2)(x-3)}{(x-4)(x+4)}$ **17.** $\dfrac{2x^4}{3}$ **19.** $\dfrac{12}{y^6}$ **21.** $x(x+4)$

23. $\dfrac{3(x+1)}{x^3(x-1)}$ **25.** $m^2 - n^2$ **27.** $-\dfrac{x+2}{x-3}$ **29.** $\dfrac{x+2}{x-3}$ **31.** $\dfrac{5}{6}$ **33.** $\dfrac{3x}{8}$ **35.** $\dfrac{3}{2}$ **37.** $\dfrac{3x+4y}{2(x+2y)}$ **39.** $\dfrac{2(x+2)}{x-2}$

41. $-\dfrac{y(x+2)}{4}$ **43.** $\dfrac{(a+5)(a+3)}{(a+2)(a+1)}$ **45.** $\dfrac{5}{x}$ **47.** $\dfrac{2(n-8)}{3n-1}$ **49.** $4x^3(x-3)$ **51.** $\dfrac{(a+b)^2}{a-b}$ **53.** $\dfrac{3x+5}{x^2+4}$ **55.** $\dfrac{4}{x-2}$

57. $\dfrac{a-b}{6(a^2+ab+b^2)}$ **59.** 1440 **61.** 5 **63.** 81 **65.** 73 **67.** 56.7 **69.** 1,201,500 sq ft **71.** 244.9 miles/hour **73.** 1

75. $-\dfrac{10}{9}$ **77.** $-\dfrac{1}{5}$ **79.** **81.** true **83.** false; $\dfrac{x^2+3x}{20}$ **85.** $\dfrac{2}{9(x-5)}$ sq ft **87.** $\dfrac{x}{2}$ **89.** $\dfrac{5a(2a+b)(3a-2b)}{b^2(a-b)(a+2b)}$

91. answers may vary

Section 7.3

Practice Exercises

1. $\dfrac{2a}{b}$ **2.** 1 **3.** $4x-5$ **4. a.** 42 **b.** $45y^3$ **5. a.** $(y-5)(y-4)$ **b.** $a(a+2)$ **6.** $3(2x-1)^2$ **7.** $(x+4)(x-4)(x+1)$

8. $3-x$ or $x-3$ **9. a.** $\dfrac{21x^2y}{35xy^2}$ **b.** $\dfrac{18x}{8x+14}$ **10.** $\dfrac{3x-6}{(x-2)(x+3)(x-5)}$

Vocabulary, Readiness & Video Check 7.3

1. $\dfrac{9}{11}$ **3.** $\dfrac{a+c}{b}$ **5.** $\dfrac{5-(6+x)}{x}$ **7.** We factor denominators into the smallest factors—including coefficients—so we can determine the most number of times each unique factor occurs in any one denominator for the LCD.

Exercise Set 7.3

1. $\dfrac{a+9}{13}$ **3.** $\dfrac{3m}{n}$ **5.** 4 **7.** $\dfrac{y+10}{3+y}$ **9.** $5x+3$ **11.** $\dfrac{4}{a+5}$ **13.** $\dfrac{1}{x-6}$ **15.** $\dfrac{5x+7}{x-3}$ **17.** $x+5$ **19.** 3 **21.** $4x^3$

23. $8x(x+2)$ **25.** $(x+3)(x-2)$ **27.** $3(x+6)$ **29.** $5(x-6)^2$ **31.** $6(x+1)^2$ **33.** $x-8$ or $8-x$ **35.** $(x-1)(x+4)(x+3)$

37. $(3x+1)(x+1)(x-1)(2x+1)$ **39.** $2x^2(x+4)(x-4)$ **41.** $\dfrac{6x}{4x^2}$ **43.** $\dfrac{24b^2}{12ab^2}$ **45.** $\dfrac{9y}{2y(x+3)}$ **47.** $\dfrac{9ab+2b}{5b(a+2)}$

49. $\dfrac{x^2+x}{x(x+4)(x+2)(x+1)}$ **51.** $\dfrac{18y-2}{30x^2-60}$ **53.** $2x$ **55.** $\dfrac{x+3}{2x-1}$ **57.** $x+1$ **59.** $\dfrac{1}{x^2-8}$ **61.** $\dfrac{6(4x+1)}{x(2x+1)}$ **63.** $\dfrac{29}{21}$ **65.** $-\dfrac{7}{12}$

67. $\dfrac{7}{30}$ **69.** d **71.** answers may vary **73.** c **75.** b **77.** $-\dfrac{5}{x-2}$ **79.** $\dfrac{7+x}{x-2}$ **81.** $\dfrac{20}{x-2}m$ **83.** answers may vary

85. 95,304 Earth days **87.** answers may vary **89.** answers may vary

Section 7.4
Practice Exercises

1. a. 0   **b.** $\dfrac{21a + 10}{24a^2}$ **2.** $\dfrac{6}{x - 5}$ **3.** $\dfrac{13y + 3}{5y(y + 1)}$ **4.** $\dfrac{13}{x - 5}$ **5.** $\dfrac{3b + 6}{b + 3}$ or $\dfrac{3(b + 2)}{b + 3}$ **6.** $\dfrac{10 - 3x^2}{2x(2x + 3)}$ **7.** $\dfrac{x(5x + 6)}{(x + 4)(x + 3)(x - 3)}$

Vocabulary, Readiness & Video Check 7.4
1. d   **3.** a   **5.** The problem adds two rational expressions with denominators that are opposites of each other. Recognizing this special case can save you time and effort. If you recognize that one denominator is −1 times the other denominator, you may save time.

Exercise Set 7.4
1. $\dfrac{5}{x}$ **3.** $\dfrac{75a - 6b^2}{5b}$ **5.** $\dfrac{6x + 5}{2x^2}$ **7.** $\dfrac{11}{x + 1}$ **9.** $\dfrac{x - 6}{(x - 2)(x + 2)}$ **11.** $\dfrac{35x - 6}{4x(x - 2)}$ **13.** $-\dfrac{2}{x - 3}$ **15.** 0   **17.** $-\dfrac{1}{x^2 - 1}$

19. $\dfrac{5 + 2x}{x}$ **21.** $\dfrac{6x - 7}{x - 2}$ **23.** $-\dfrac{y + 4}{y + 3}$ **25.** $\dfrac{-5x + 14}{4x}$ or $-\dfrac{5x - 14}{4x}$ **27.** 2   **29.** $\dfrac{9x^4 - 4x^2}{21}$ **31.** $\dfrac{x + 2}{(x + 3)^2}$ **33.** $\dfrac{9b - 4}{5b(b - 1)}$

35. $\dfrac{2 + m}{m}$ **37.** $\dfrac{x^2 + 3x}{(x - 7)(x - 2)}$ or $\dfrac{x(x + 3)}{(x - 7)(x - 2)}$ **39.** $\dfrac{10}{1 - 2x}$ **41.** $\dfrac{15x - 1}{(x + 1)^2(x - 1)}$ **43.** $\dfrac{x^2 - 3x - 2}{(x - 1)^2(x + 1)}$ **45.** $\dfrac{a + 2}{2(a + 3)}$

47. $\dfrac{y(2y + 1)}{(2y + 3)^2}$ **49.** $\dfrac{x - 10}{2(x - 2)}$ **51.** $\dfrac{2x + 21}{(x + 3)^2}$ **53.** $\dfrac{-5x + 23}{(x - 2)(x - 3)}$ **55.** $\dfrac{7}{2(m - 10)}$ **57.** $\dfrac{2x^2 - 2x - 46}{(x + 1)(x - 6)(x - 5)}$ or $\dfrac{2(x^2 - x - 23)}{(x + 1)(x - 6)(x - 5)}$

59. $\dfrac{n + 4}{4n(n - 1)(n - 2)}$ **61.** 10   **63.** 2   **65.** $\dfrac{25a}{9(a - 2)}$ **67.** $\dfrac{x + 4}{(x - 2)(x - 1)}$ **69.** $x = \dfrac{2}{3}$ **71.** $x = -\dfrac{1}{2}, x = 1$ **73.** $x = -\dfrac{15}{2}$

75. $\dfrac{6x^2 - 5x - 3}{x(x + 1)(x - 1)}$ **77.** $\dfrac{4x^2 - 15x + 6}{(x - 2)^2(x + 2)(x - 3)}$ **79.** $\dfrac{-2x^2 + 14x + 55}{(x + 2)(x + 7)(x + 3)}$ **81.** $\dfrac{2x - 16}{(x + 4)(x - 4)}$ in.   **83.** $\dfrac{P - G}{P}$ **85.** answers may vary

87. $\left(\dfrac{90x - 40}{x}\right)^\circ$ **89.** answers may vary

Section 7.5
Practice Exercises

1. −2   **2.** 13   **3.** −1, 7   **4.** $-\dfrac{19}{2}$ **5.** 3   **6.** −8   **7.** $b = \dfrac{ax}{a - x}$

Graphing Calculator Explorations 7.5
1.   **3.**

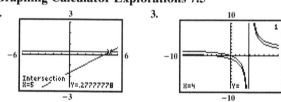

Vocabulary, Readiness & Video Check 7.5
1. c   **3.** b   **5.** a   **7.** These equations are solved in very different ways, so you need to determine the next correct move to make. For a linear equation, you first "move" variable terms on one side and numbers on the other; for a quadratic equation, you first set the equation equal to 0. **9.** the steps for solving an equation containing rational expressions; as if it's the only variable in the equation

Exercise Set 7.5
1. 30   **3.** 0   **5.** −2   **7.** −5, 2   **9.** 5   **11.** 3   **13.** 1   **15.** 5   **17.** no solution   **19.** 4   **21.** −8   **23.** 6, −4   **25.** 1

27. 3, −4   **29.** −3   **31.** 0   **33.** −2   **35.** 8, −2   **37.** no solution   **39.** 3   **41.** −11, 1   **43.** $I = \dfrac{E}{R}$ **45.** $B = \dfrac{2U - TE}{T}$

47. $w = \dfrac{Bh^2}{705}$ **49.** $G = \dfrac{V}{N - R}$ **51.** $r = \dfrac{C}{2\pi}$ **53.** $x = \dfrac{3y}{3 + y}$ **55.** $\dfrac{1}{x}$ **57.** $\dfrac{1}{x} + \dfrac{1}{2}$ **59.** $\dfrac{1}{3}$ **61.** $(2, 0), (0, -2)$

63. $(-4, 0), (-2, 0), (3, 0), (0, 4)$ **65.** answers may vary   **67.** $\dfrac{5x + 9}{9x}$ **69.** no solution   **71.** $100°, 80°$ **73.** $22.5°, 67.5°$ **75.** $\dfrac{17}{4}$

Integrated Review
1. expression; $\dfrac{3 + 2x}{3x}$ **2.** expression; $\dfrac{18 + 5a}{6a}$ **3.** equation; 3   **4.** equation; 18   **5.** expression; $\dfrac{x + 1}{x(x - 1)}$ **6.** expression; $\dfrac{3(x + 1)}{x(x - 3)}$

7. equation; no solution   **8.** equation; 1   **9.** expression; 10   **10.** expression; $\dfrac{z}{3(9z - 5)}$ **11.** expression; $\dfrac{5x + 7}{x - 3}$ **12.** expression; $\dfrac{7p + 5}{2p + 7}$

13. equation; 23   **14.** equation; 5   **15.** expression; $\dfrac{25a}{9(a - 2)}$ **16.** expression; $\dfrac{4x + 5}{(x + 1)(x - 1)}$ **17.** expression; $\dfrac{3x^2 + 5x + 3}{(3x - 1)^2}$

18. expression; $\dfrac{2x^2 - 3x - 1}{(2x - 5)^2}$ **19.** expression; $\dfrac{4x - 37}{5x}$ **20.** expression; $\dfrac{29x - 23}{3x}$ **21.** equation; $\dfrac{8}{5}$ **22.** equation; $-\dfrac{7}{3}$

23. answers may vary   **24.** answers may vary

Section 7.6
Practice Exercises

1. 99   **2.** $\dfrac{13}{3}$ **3.** $9.03   **4.** 6   **5.** 15   **6.** $1\dfrac{5}{7}$ hr   **7.** bus: 45 mph; car: 60 mph

Vocabulary, Readiness & Video Check 7.6

1. c   **3.** $\dfrac{1}{x}; \dfrac{1}{x} - 3$ **5.** $z + 5; \dfrac{1}{z + 5}$ **7.** $2y; \dfrac{11}{2y}$ **9.** No. Proportions are actually equations containing rational expressions, so they can also

be solved by using the steps to solve those equations.   **11.** divided by, quotient   **13.** $\dfrac{325}{x + 7} = \dfrac{290}{x}$

Exercise Set 7.6

1. 4   **3.** $\dfrac{50}{9}$ **5.** -3 **7.** $\dfrac{14}{9}$ **9.** 123 lb   **11.** 165 cal   **13.** $y = 21.25$ **15.** $y = 5\dfrac{5}{7}$ ft   **17.** 2   **19.** -3 **21.** $2\dfrac{2}{9}$ hr

23. $1\dfrac{1}{2}$ min   **25.** trip to park rate: r; to park time: $\dfrac{12}{r}$; return trip rate: r; return time: $\dfrac{18}{r} = \dfrac{12}{r} + 1; r = 6$ mph   **27.** 1st portion: 10 mph; cooldown: 8 mph

29. 360 sq ft   **31.** 2   **33.** $108.00   **35.** 20 mph   **37.** $y = 37\dfrac{1}{2}$ ft   **39.** 41 mph; 51 mph   **41.** 5   **43.** 217 mph   **45.** 9 gal   **47.** 8 mph

49. 2.2 mph; 3.3 mph   **51.** 3 hr   **53.** $26\dfrac{2}{3}$ ft   **55.** 216 nuts   **57.** $666\dfrac{2}{3}$ mi   **59.** 20 hr   **61.** car: 70 mph; motorcycle: 60 mph   **63.** $5\dfrac{1}{4}$ hr

65. 8   **67.** first car: 64 mph; second car: 50 mph   **69.** 510 mph   **71.** $x = 5$ **73.** $x = 13.5$ **75.** $-\dfrac{4}{3}$; downward   **77.** $\dfrac{11}{4}$; upward

79. undefined slope; vertical   **81.** 40,200 megawatts   **83.** 22,510,000 people   **85.** yes   **87.** first pump: 28 min; second pump: 84 min

89. none; answers may vary   **91.** answers may vary   **93.** $R = \dfrac{D}{T}$

Section 7.7
Practice Exercises

1. a. $\dfrac{1}{12m}$ **b.** $\dfrac{8x(x + 4)}{3(x - 4)}$ **c.** $\dfrac{b^2}{a^2}$ **2. a.** $\dfrac{8x(x + 4)}{3(x - 4)}$ **b.** $\dfrac{b^2}{a^2}$ **3.** $\dfrac{y(3xy + 1)}{x^2(1 + xy)}$ **4.** $\dfrac{1 - 6x}{15 + 6x}$

Vocabulary, Readiness & Video Check 7.7

1. $\dfrac{7}{1 + z}$ **3.** $\dfrac{1}{x^2}$ **5.** $\dfrac{2}{x}$ **7.** $\dfrac{1}{9y}$ **9.** a single fraction in the numerator and in the denominator   **11.** Since a negative exponent moves its
base from a numerator to a denominator of the expression only, a rational expression containing negative exponents can become a complex fraction
when rewritten with positive exponents.

Exercise Set 7.7

1. 4   **3.** $\dfrac{7}{13}$ **5.** $\dfrac{4}{x}$ **7.** $\dfrac{9(x - 2)}{9x^2 + 4}$ **9.** $2x + y$ **11.** $\dfrac{2(x + 1)}{2x - 1}$ **13.** $\dfrac{2x + 3}{4 - 9x}$ **15.** $\dfrac{1}{x^2 - 2x + 4}$ **17.** $\dfrac{x}{5(x - 2)}$ **19.** $\dfrac{x - 2}{2x - 1}$

21. $\dfrac{x}{2 - 3x}$ **23.** $-\dfrac{y}{x + y}$ **25.** $-\dfrac{2x^3}{y(x - y)}$ **27.** $\dfrac{2x + 1}{y}$ **29.** $\dfrac{x - 3}{9}$ **31.** $\dfrac{1}{x + 2}$ **33.** 2   **35.** $\dfrac{xy^2}{x^2 + y^2}$ **37.** $\dfrac{2b^2 + 3a}{b(b - a)}$

39. $\dfrac{x}{(x + 1)(x - 1)}$ **41.** $\dfrac{1 + a}{1 - a}$ **43.** $\dfrac{x(x + 6y)}{2y}$ **45.** $\dfrac{5a}{2(a + 2)}$ **47.** $xy(5y + 2x)$ **49.** $\dfrac{xy}{2x + 5y}$ **51.** $\dfrac{x^2y^2}{4}$ **53.** $-9x^3y^4$

55. -9 **57.** a and c   **59.** $\dfrac{770a}{770 - s}$ **61.** a, b   **63.** answers may vary   **65.** $\dfrac{1 + x}{2 + x}$ **67.** $x(x + 1)$ **69.** $\dfrac{x - 3y}{x + 3y}$ **71.** $3a^2 + 4a + 4$

73. a. $\dfrac{1}{a + h}$ **b.** $\dfrac{1}{a}$ **c.** $\dfrac{\dfrac{1}{a + h} - \dfrac{1}{a}}{h}$ **d.** $-\dfrac{1}{a(a + h)}$ **75. a.** $\dfrac{3}{a + h + 1}$ **b.** $\dfrac{3}{a + 1}$ **c.** $\dfrac{\dfrac{3}{a + h + 1} - \dfrac{3}{a + 1}}{h}$ **d.** $-\dfrac{3}{(a + h + 1)(a + 1)}$

Chapter 7 Vocabulary Check

1. rational expression   **2.** complex fraction   **3.** $\dfrac{-a}{b}; \dfrac{a}{-b}$ **4.** denominator   **5.** simplifying   **6.** reciprocals   **7.** least common denominator

8. ratio   **9.** proportion   **10.** cross products   **11.** domain

Chapter 7 Review

1. $\{x \mid x \text{ is a real number}\}$ **3.** $\{x \mid x \text{ is a real number and } x \neq 5\}$ **5.** $\{x \mid x \text{ is a real number and } x \neq 0, x \neq -8\}$ **7.** -1 **9.** $\dfrac{1}{x - 7}$

11. $\dfrac{x + a}{x - c}$ **13.** $-\dfrac{1}{x^2 + 4x + 16}$ **15.** $119   **17.** $\dfrac{3x^2}{y}$ **19.** $\dfrac{x - 3}{x + 2}$ **21.** $\dfrac{x + 3}{x - 4}$ **23.** $(x - 6)(x - 3)$ **25.** $\dfrac{1}{2}$ **27.** $-\dfrac{2(2x + 3)}{y - 2}$

29. $\dfrac{1}{x + 2}$ **31.** $\dfrac{2x - 10}{3x^2}$ **33.** $14x$ **35.** $\dfrac{10x^2y}{14x^3y}$ **37.** $\dfrac{x^2 - 3x - 10}{(x + 2)(x - 5)(x + 9)}$ **39.** $\dfrac{4y - 30x^2}{5x^2y}$ **41.** $\dfrac{-2x - 2}{x + 3}$ **43.** $\dfrac{x - 4}{3x}$

45. $\dfrac{x^2 + 2x + 4}{4x}; \dfrac{x + 2}{32}$ **47.** 30   **49.** no solution   **51.** $\dfrac{9}{7}$ **53.** $b = \dfrac{4A}{5x^2}$ **55.** $x = 6$ **57.** $x = 9$ **59.** 675 parts   **61.** 3

63. fast car speed: 30 mph; slow car speed: 20 mph   **65.** $17\dfrac{1}{2}$ hr   **67.** $x = 15$ **69.** $-\dfrac{7}{18y}$ **71.** $\dfrac{3y - 1}{2y - 1}$ **73.** $-\dfrac{x^2 + 9}{6x}$ **75.** $\dfrac{xy + 1}{x}$

77. $\dfrac{1}{2x}$ **79.** $\dfrac{x - 4}{x + 4}$ **81.** $\dfrac{1}{x - 6}$ **83.** $\dfrac{2}{(x + 3)(x - 2)}$ **85.** $\dfrac{1}{2}$ **87.** 1   **89.** $x = 6$ **91.** $\dfrac{3}{10}$ **93.** $\dfrac{1}{y^2 - 1}$

Chapter 7 Test

1. $\{x \mid x \text{ is a real number}, x \neq -1, x \neq -3\}$ **2. a.** \$115   **b.** \$103   **3.** $\dfrac{3}{5}$ **4.** $\dfrac{1}{x + 6}$ **5.** $\dfrac{1}{x^2 - 3x + 9}$ **6.** $\dfrac{2m(m + 2)}{m - 2}$ **7.** $\dfrac{a + 2}{a + 5}$

8. $-\dfrac{1}{x + y}$ **9.** 15   **10.** $\dfrac{y - 2}{4}$ **11.** $\dfrac{19x - 6}{2x + 5}$ **12.** $\dfrac{3a - 4}{(a - 3)(a + 2)}$ **13.** $\dfrac{3}{x - 1}$ **14.** $\dfrac{2(x + 5)}{x(y + 5)}$ **15.** $\dfrac{x^2 + 2x + 35}{(x + 9)(x + 2)(x - 5)}$

16. $\dfrac{30}{11}$ **17.** -6 **18.** no solution   **19.** $-2, 5$ **20.** no solution   **21.** $\dfrac{xz}{2y}$ **22.** $\dfrac{5y^2 - 1}{y + 2}$ **23.** $b - a$ **24.** 18 bulbs   **25.** 5 or 1

26. 30 mph   **27.** $6\dfrac{2}{3}$ hr   **28.** $x = 12$

Chapter 7 Cumulative Review

1. a. $\dfrac{15}{x} = 4$ **b.** $12 - 3 = x$ **c.** $4x + 17 \neq 21$ **d.** $3x < 48$; Sec. 1.4, Ex. 9   **3.** amount at 7%: \$12,500; amount at 9%: \$7500; Sec. 2.7, Ex. 4

5. ; Sec. 3.3, Ex. 6   **7. a.** 4^7 **b.** x^{10} **c.** y^4 **d.** y^{12} **e.** $(-5)^{15}$ **f.** $a^2 b^2$; Sec. 5.1, Ex. 3   **9.** $12z + 16$; Sec. 5.2, Ex. 12

11. $27a^3 + 27a^2 b + 9ab^2 + b^3$; Sec. 5.3, Ex. 8   **13. a.** $t^2 + 4t + 4$ **b.** $p^2 - 2pq + q^2$ **c.** $4x^2 + 20x + 25$ **d.** $x^4 - 14x^2 y + 49y^2$; Sec. 5.4, Ex. 5

15. a. x^3 **b.** 81   **c.** $\dfrac{q^9}{p^4}$ **d.** $\dfrac{32}{125}$; Sec. 5.5, Ex. 2   **17.** $4x^2 - 4x + 6 + \dfrac{-11}{2x + 3}$; Sec. 5.6, Ex. 6   **19. a.** 4   **b.** 1   **c.** 3; Sec. 6.1, Ex. 1

21. $-3a(3a^4 - 6a + 1)$; Sec. 6.1, Ex. 5   **23.** $3(m + 2)(m - 10)$; Sec. 6.2, Ex. 9   **25.** $(3x + 2)(x + 3)$; Sec. 6.3, Ex. 1   **27.** $(x + 6)^2$; Sec. 6.3, Ex. 8
29. prime polynomial; Sec. 6.5, Ex. 4b   **31.** $(x + 2)(x^2 - 2x + 4)$; Sec. 6.5, Ex. 8   **33.** $(2x + 3)(x + 1)(x - 1)$; Ch. 6 Int. Rev., Ex. 2

35. $3(2m + n)(2m - n)$; Ch. 6 Int. Rev., Ex. 3   **37.** $-\dfrac{1}{2}, 4$; Sec. 6.6, Ex. 6   **39.** $(1, 0), (4, 0)$; Sec. 6.6, Ex. 11   **41.** base: 6 m; height: 10 m; Sec. 6.7, Ex. 3

43. $-\dfrac{2(3 + x)}{x + 1}$; Sec. 7.1, Ex. 4   **45.** $\dfrac{2}{x(x + 1)}$; Sec. 7.2, Ex. 6   **47.** $\dfrac{1 + 2x}{2(2 - x)}$; Sec. 7.7, Ex. 4

CHAPTER 8 MORE ON FUNCTIONS AND GRAPHS

Section 8.1
Practice Exercises

1. 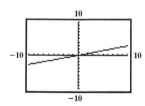   **2.** 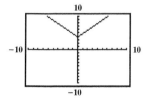   **3.** $f(x) = -4x - 3$ **4.** $f(x) = -\dfrac{2}{3}x + \dfrac{4}{3}$ **5.** $f(x) = -2$ **6.** $3x + 4y = 12$

7. $f(x) = \dfrac{4}{3}x - \dfrac{41}{3}$

Graphing Calculator Explorations 8.1

1. $y = \dfrac{x}{3.5}$ 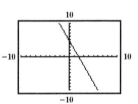   **3.** $y = -\dfrac{5.78}{2.31}x + \dfrac{10.98}{2.31}$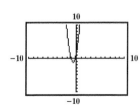

5. $y = |x| + 3.78$ **7.** $y = 5.6x^2 + 7.7x + 1.5$

Vocabulary, Readiness & Video Check 8.1

1. linear   **3.** $m = -4$, y-intercept: $(0, 12)$ **5.** $m = 5$, y-intercept: $(0, 0)$ **7.** parallel   **9.** neither   **11.** $f(x) = mx + b$,
or slope-intercept form   **13.** if one of the two points given is the y-intercept

Exercise Set 8.1

1. $f(x) = -2x$

3. 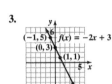 $f(x) = -2x + 3$

5. 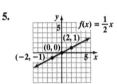 $f(x) = \frac{1}{2}x$

7. 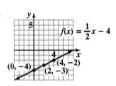 $f(x) = \frac{1}{2}x - 4$

9. C **11.** D **13.** $f(x) = -x + 1$

15. $f(x) = 2x + \frac{3}{4}$ **17.** $f(x) = \frac{2}{7}x$ **19.** $f(x) = 3x - 1$ **21.** $f(x) = -2x - 1$ **23.** $f(x) = \frac{1}{2}x + 5$ **25.** $f(x) = -\frac{9}{10}x - \frac{27}{10}$

27. $f(x) = 3x - 6$ **29.** $f(x) = -2x + 1$ **31.** $f(x) = -\frac{1}{2}x - 5$ **33.** $f(x) = \frac{1}{3}x - 7$ **35.** $f(x) = -\frac{3}{8}x + \frac{5}{8}$ **37.** $f(x) = -4$

39. $f(x) = 5$ **41.** $f(x) = 4x - 4$ **43.** $f(x) = -3x + 1$ **45.** $f(x) = -\frac{3}{2}x - 6$ **47.** $2x - y = -7$ **49.** $f(x) = -x + 7$

51. $f(x) = -\frac{1}{2}x + 11$ **53.** $2x + 7y = -42$ **55.** $4x + 3y = -20$ **57.** $f(x) = -10$ **59.** $x + 2y = 2$ **61.** $f(x) = 12$

63. $8x - y = 47$ **65.** $x = 5$ **67.** $f(x) = -\frac{3}{8}x - \frac{29}{4}$ **69.** 28.4; In 2009, about 28.4% of students took at least one online course. **71.** 54.22;

In 2016, we predict that 54.22% of students will take at least one online course. **73.** answers may vary **75.** $f(x) = -2x + 3$ **77.** $f(x) = \frac{2}{3}x + \frac{7}{3}$

79. a. $y = 32x$ **b.** 128 ft per sec **81. a.** $y = -250x + 3500$ **b.** 1625 Frisbees **83. a.** $y = 58.1x + 2619$ **b.** 2851.4 thousand
85. a. $y = -4820x + 297,000$ **b.** \$258,440 **87.** $-4x + y = 4$ **89.** $2x + y = -23$ **91.** $3x - 2y = -13$ **93.** answers may vary

Section 8.2
Practice Exercises
1. a. -3 **b.** -2 **c.** 3 **d.** 1 **e.** -1 and 3 **f.** -3 **2.** 17 million or 17,000,000 students **3.** 5.8 million or 5,800,000 students

4. a. 11 **b.** $\frac{1}{4}$ **c.** -8 **d.** not a real number **e.** 10 **5.** 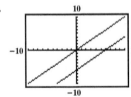 $f(x) = 2x^2$ **6.** 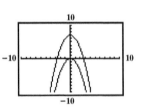 $f(x) = -|x|$ **7.** $f(x) = \sqrt{x} + 1$

Graphing Calculator Explorations 8.2
1. 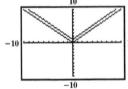 **3.**   **5.**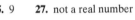

Vocabulary, Readiness & Video Check 8.2
1. V-shaped **3.** $(-2, 1.7)$ **5.** Using function notation, the replacement value for x and the resulting $f(x)$ or y-value corresponds to an ordered pair (x, y) solution to the function **7.** not; shape

Exercise Set 8.2
1. 0 **3.** -4 **5.** 3 **7.** $(1, -10)$ **9.** $(4, 56)$ **11.** $f(-1) = -2$ **13.** $g(2) = 0$ **15.** $-4, 0$ **17.** 3 **19.** 7 **21.** $-\frac{2}{3}$ **23.** 8

25. 9 **27.** not a real number **29.** $f(x) = x^2 + 3$ **31.** $h(x) = |x| - 2$ **33.** $g(x) = 2x^2$ **35.** $f(x) = 5x - 1$

37. $f(x) = \sqrt{x} + 1$ **39.** $g(x) = -2|x|$ **41.** $h(x) = \sqrt{x} + 2$ **43. a.** answers may vary; between 5 and 6 million **b.** 5.25 million
or 5,250,000 students **45.** \$15.54 billion **47.** 25π sq cm
49. 2744 cu in. **51.** 166.38 cm **53.** 163.2 mg

55. infinite number **57.** -5 **59.** $-\frac{1}{10}$

61. b **63.** c **65.** 1997 **67.** answers may vary

69. $y = x^2 - 4x + 7$ **71.** 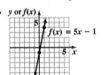 $f(x) = |x|$

Integrated Review

1. $m = 3$; $(0, -5)$ **2.** $m = \frac{5}{2}$; $\left(0, -\frac{7}{2}\right)$ **3.** parallel   **4.** perpendicular   **5.** $f(x) = -x + 7$ **6.** $f(x) = -\frac{3}{8}x - \frac{29}{4}$ **7.** $f(x) = 3x - 2$

8. $f(x) = -\frac{5}{4}x + 4$ **9.** $f(x) = \frac{1}{4}x - \frac{7}{2}$ **10.** $f(x) = -\frac{5}{2}x - \frac{5}{2}$

11. linear   **12.** linear   **13.** not linear   **14.** not linear   **15.** not linear   **16.** not linear

17. not linear   **18.** not linear   **19.** linear   **20.** linear   **21.** not linear   **22.** not linear

23. linear   **24.** linear   **25.** linear   **26.** linear

Section 8.3
Practice Exercises

1. $f(4) = 5$; $f(-2) = 6$; $f(0) = -2$; $(4, 5), (-2, 6), (0, -2)$ **2.**   **3.** 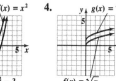   **4.**   **5.**

6. 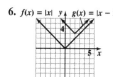   **7.**

Vocabulary, Readiness & Video Check 8.3

1. C   **3.** D   **5.** Although $f(x) = x + 3$ isn't defined for $x = -1$, we need to clearly indicate the point where this piece of the graph ends. Therefore, we find this point and graph it as an open circle.   **7.** x-axis

Exercise Set 8.3

1.   **3.**   **5.**   **7.**   **9.** domain: $(-\infty, \infty)$; range: $[0, \infty)$

11. domain: $(-\infty, \infty)$; range: $(-\infty, 5)$ **13.** domain: $(-\infty, \infty)$; range: $(-\infty, 6]$ **15.** domain: $(-\infty, 0] \cup [1, \infty)$; range: $\{-4, -2\}$

17.   **19.**   **21.**   **23.**   **25.**   **27.**

29.   **31.**   **33.**   **35.**   **37.**   **39.**

41.   **43.**   **45.**   **47.**   **49.** A   **51.** D   **53.** answers may vary

55.   **57.** domain: $[2, \infty)$; range: $[3, \infty)$ **59.** domain: $(-\infty, \infty)$; range: $(-\infty, 3]$ **61.** $[20, \infty)$ **63.** $(-\infty, \infty)$ **65.** $[-103, \infty)$

67.   domain: $(-\infty, \infty)$; range: $[0, \infty)$ **69.**   domain: $(-\infty, \infty)$; range: $(-\infty, 0] \cup (2, \infty)$

Section 8.4
Practice Exercises
1. $k = \frac{4}{3}; y = \frac{4}{3}x$ **2.** $18\frac{3}{4}$ in.   **3.** $k = 45; b = \frac{45}{a}$ **4.** $653\frac{1}{3}$ kilopascals   **5.** $A = kpa$ **6.** $k = 4; y = \frac{4}{x^3}$ **7.** $k = 81; y = \frac{81z}{x^3}$

Vocabulary, Readiness & Video Check 8.4
1. direct   **3.** joint   **5.** inverse   **7.** direct   **9.** linear; slope   **11.** $y = ka^2b^5$

Exercise Set 8.4
1. $k = \frac{1}{5}; y = \frac{1}{5}x$ **3.** $k = \frac{3}{2}; y = \frac{3}{2}x$ **5.** $k = 14; y = 14x$ **7.** $k = 0.25; y = 0.25x$ **9.** 4.05 lb   **11.** 187,239 tons   **13.** $k = 30; y = \frac{30}{x}$

15. $k = 700; y = \frac{700}{x}$ **17.** $k = 2; y = \frac{2}{x}$ **19.** $k = 0.14; y = \frac{0.14}{x}$ **21.** 54 mph   **23.** 72 amps   **25.** divided by 4   **27.** $x = kyz$

29. $r = kst^3$ **31.** $k = \frac{1}{3}; y = \frac{1}{3}x^3$ **33.** $k = 0.2; y = 0.2\sqrt{x}$ **35.** $k = 1.3; y = \frac{1.3}{x^2}$ **37.** $k = 3; y = 3xz^3$ **39.** 22.5 tons   **41.** 15π cu in.

43. 8 ft   **45.** $y = kx$ **47.** $a = \frac{k}{b}$ **49.** $y = kxz$ **51.** $y = \frac{k}{x^3}$ **53.** $y = \frac{kx}{p^2}$ **55.** $C = 8\pi$ in.; $A = 16\pi$ sq in.

57. $C = 18\pi$ cm; $A = 81\pi$ sq cm   **59.** 1.2   **61.** -7 **63.** $-\frac{1}{2}$ **65.** $\frac{8}{27}$ **67.** a   **69.** c   **71.** multiplied by 8   **73.** multiplied by 2

75. 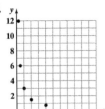   **77.**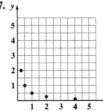

Chapter 8 Vocabulary Check
1. Parallel   **2.** Slope-intercept   **3.** function   **4.** slope   **5.** perpendicular   **6.** linear function   **7.** directly   **8.** inversely   **9.** jointly

Chapter 8 Review
1.   **3.**   **5.** C   **7.** B   **9.** $m = \frac{2}{5}$; y-intercept $\left(0, -\frac{4}{3}\right)$ **11.** $2x - y = 12$ **13.** $11x + y = -52$

15. $y = -5$ **17.** $f(x) = -1$ **19.** $f(x) = -x - 2$ **21.** $f(x) = -\frac{3}{2}x - 8$

23. $f(x) = -\frac{3}{2}x - 1$ **25. a.** $y = 12,000x + 126,000$ **b.** \$342,000   **27.** 0   **29.** $-2, 4$

31. linear   **33.** not linear   **35.** linear 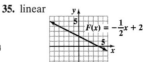   **37.** linear $y = -1.36x$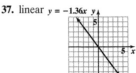

39. not linear **41.** **43.** **45.** **47.** 9 **49.** 3.125 cu ft **51.** $f(x) = \dfrac{9}{2}$

53. $f(x) = -5x - 7$ **55.** $f(x) = -\dfrac{4}{5}x + 3$ **57.** **59.**

Chapter 8 Test

1. 3 **2.** -5 **3.** $2, -2$ **4.** 0 **5.** **6.** **7.** $y = -8$ **8.** $3x + y = 11$ **9.** $5x - y = 2$

10. $f(x) = -\dfrac{1}{2}x$ **11.** $f(x) = -\dfrac{1}{3}x + \dfrac{5}{3}$ **12.** $f(x) = -\dfrac{1}{2}x - \dfrac{1}{2}$ **13.** neither **14.** domain: $(-\infty, \infty)$; range: $\{5\}$; function
15. domain: $\{-2\}$; range: $(-\infty, \infty)$; not a function **16.** domain: $(-\infty, \infty)$; range: $[0, \infty)$; function **17.** domain: $(-\infty, \infty)$; range: $(-\infty, \infty)$;
function **18. a.** 81 games **b.** 79 games **c.** \$231 million **d.** 0.096; Every million dollars spent on payroll increases winnings by 0.096 game.
19. domain: $(-\infty, \infty)$; range: $(-3, \infty)$ **20.** **21.** domain: $(-\infty, \infty)$; range: $(-\infty, -1]$ **22.**

23. 16 **24.** 9 **25.** 256 ft

Chapter 8 Cumulative Review

1. 66; Sec. 1.4, Ex. 4 **3. a.** $\dfrac{1}{2}$ **b.** 19; Sec. 1.6, Ex. 6 **5.** -11; Sec. 2.2, Ex. 6 **7.** $\dfrac{16}{3}$; Sec. 2.3, Ex. 2 **9.** $x = \dfrac{y - b}{m}$; Sec. 2.5, Ex. 6

11. $(-\infty, 4]$; Sec. 2.8, Ex. 5 **13.** 0; Sec. 3.4, Ex. 6 **15. a.** $1; (2, 1)$ **b.** $1; (-2, 1)$ **c.** $-3; (0, -3)$; Sec. 3.6, Ex. 7 **17.** $(4, 2)$; Sec. 4.2, Ex. 1

19. $\left(-\dfrac{15}{7}, -\dfrac{5}{7}\right)$; Sec. 4.3, Ex. 6 **21.** $x + 4$; Sec. 5.6, Ex. 4 **23. a.** $6(t + 3)$ **b.** $y^5(1 - y^2)$; Sec. 6.1, Ex. 4 **25.** $(x - 2)(x + 6)$; Sec. 6.2, Ex. 3

27. $(2x - 3y)(5x + y)$; Sec. 6.3, Ex. 4 **29.** $(x + 2)(x^2 - 2x + 4)$; Sec. 6.5, Ex. 8 **31.** $11, -2$; Sec. 6.6, Ex. 4 **33. a.** $\dfrac{1}{5x - 1}$

b. $\dfrac{9x + 4}{8x - 7}$; Sec. 7.1, Ex. 2 **35.** $-\dfrac{3(x + 1)}{5x(2x - 3)}$; Sec. 7.2, Ex. 3 **37.** $3x - 5$; Sec. 7.3, Ex. 3 **39.** $-3, -2$; Sec. 7.5, Ex. 3

41. $f(x) = \dfrac{5}{8}x - \dfrac{5}{2}$; Sec. 8.1, Ex. 4

CHAPTER 9 INEQUALITIES AND ABSOLUTE VALUE

Section 9.1
Practice Exercises

1. $\{1, 3\}$ **2.** $(-\infty, 2)$ **3.** $\{\ \}$ or $\varnothing$ **4.** $(-4, 2)$ **5.** $[-6, 8]$ **6.** $\{1, 2, 3, 4, 5, 6, 7, 9\}$ **7.** $\left(-\infty, \dfrac{3}{8}\right] \cup [3, \infty)$ **8.** $(-\infty, \infty)$

Vocabulary, Readiness & Video Check 9.1
1. compound **3.** or **5.** $\cup$ **7.** and **9.** or

Exercise Set 9.1
1. $\{2, 3, 4, 5, 6, 7\}$ **3.** $\{4, 6\}$ **5.** $\{\ldots, -2, -1, 0, 1, \ldots\}$ **7.** $\{5, 7\}$ **9.** $\{x \mid x \text{ is an odd integer or } x = 2 \text{ or } x = 4\}$ **11.** $\{2, 4\}$
13. $(-3, 1)$ **15.** $\varnothing$ **17.** $(-\infty, -1)$ **19.** $[6, \infty)$ **21.** $(-\infty, -3]$ **23.** $(4, 10)$

25. $(11, 17)$ **27.** $[1, 4]$ **29.** $\left[-3, \frac{3}{2}\right]$ **31.** $\left[-\frac{7}{3}, 7\right]$ **33.** $(-\infty, 5)$ **35.** $(-\infty, -4] \cup [1, \infty)$

37. $(-\infty, \infty)$ **39.** $[2, \infty)$ **41.** $(-\infty, -4) \cup (-2, \infty)$ **43.** $(-\infty, \infty)$ **45.** $\left(-\frac{1}{2}, \frac{2}{3}\right)$ **47.** $(-\infty, \infty)$ **49.** $\left[\frac{3}{2}, 6\right]$ **51.** $\left(\frac{5}{4}, \frac{11}{4}\right)$

53. $\varnothing$ **55.** $\left(-\infty, -\frac{56}{5}\right) \cup \left(\frac{5}{3}, \infty\right)$ **57.** $\left(-5, \frac{5}{2}\right)$ **59.** $\left(0, \frac{14}{3}\right]$ **61.** $(-\infty, -3]$ **63.** $(-\infty, 1] \cup \left(\frac{29}{7}, \infty\right)$ **65.** $\varnothing$ **67.** $\left[-\frac{1}{2}, \frac{3}{2}\right)$

69. $\left(-\frac{4}{3}, \frac{7}{3}\right)$ **71.** $(6, 12)$ **73.** -12 **75.** -4 **77.** $-7, 7$ **79.** 0 **81.** $2004, 2005$ **83.** answers may vary **85.** $(6, \infty)$ **87.** $[3, 7]$

89. $(-\infty, -1)$ **91.** $-20.2° \le F \le 95°$ **93.** $67 \le$ final score ≤ 94

Section 9.2
Practice Exercises
1. $-3, 3$ **2.** $-1, 4$ **3.** $-80, 70$ **4.** $-2, 2$ **5.** 0 **6.** $\{\ \}$ or $\varnothing$ **7.** $\{\ \}$ or $\varnothing$ **8.** $-\frac{3}{5}, 5$ **9.** 5

Vocabulary, Readiness & Video Check 9.2
1. C **3.** B **5.** D

Exercise Set 9.2
1. $-7, 7$ **3.** $4.2, -4.2$ **5.** $7, -2$ **7.** $8, 4$ **9.** $5, -5$ **11.** $3, -3$ **13.** 0 **15.** $\varnothing$ **17.** $\frac{1}{5}$ **19.** $9, -\frac{1}{2}$ **21.** $-\frac{5}{2}$ **23.** $4, -4$

25. 0 **27.** $\varnothing$ **29.** $0, \frac{14}{3}$ **31.** $2, -2$ **33.** $\varnothing$ **35.** $7, -1$ **37.** $\varnothing$ **39.** $\varnothing$ **41.** $-\frac{1}{8}$ **43.** $\frac{1}{2}, -\frac{5}{6}$ **45.** $2, -\frac{12}{5}$ **47.** $3, -2$

49. $-8, \frac{2}{3}$ **51.** $\varnothing$ **53.** 4 **55.** $13, -8$ **57.** $3, -3$ **59.** $8, -7$ **61.** $2, 3$ **63.** $2, -\frac{10}{3}$ **65.** $\frac{3}{2}$ **67.** $\varnothing$ **69.** 31% **71.** $32.4°$

73. answers may vary **75.** answers may vary **77.** $\varnothing$ **79.** $|x| = 5$ **81.** answers may vary **83.** $|x - 1| = 5$ **85.** answers may vary

87. $|x| = 6$ **89.** $|x - 2| = |3x - 4|$

Section 9.3
Practice Exercises
1. $(-5, 5)$ **2.** $(-4, 2)$ **3.** $\left[-\frac{2}{3}, 2\right]$ **4.** $\{\ \}$ or $\varnothing$ **5.** $\{2\}$

6. $(-\infty, -10] \cup [2, \infty)$ **7.** $(-\infty, \infty)$ **8.** $(-\infty, 0) \cup (12, \infty)$

Vocabulary, Readiness & Video Check 9.3
1. D **3.** C **5.** A **7.** The solution set involves "or" and "or" means "union."

Exercise Set 9.3
1. $[-4, 4]$ **3.** $(1, 5)$ **5.** $(-5, -1)$ **7.** $[-10, 3]$

9. $[-5, 5]$ **11.** $\varnothing$ **13.** $[0, 12]$ **15.** $(-\infty, -3) \cup (3, \infty)$

17. $(-\infty, -24] \cup [4, \infty)$ **19.** $(-\infty, -4) \cup (4, \infty)$ **21.** $(-\infty, \infty)$

23. $\left(-\infty, \frac{2}{3}\right) \cup (2, \infty)$ **25.** $\{0\}$ **27.** $\left(-\infty, -\frac{3}{8}\right) \cup \left(-\frac{3}{8}, \infty\right)$ **29.** $[-2, 2]$

31. $(-\infty, -1) \cup (1, \infty)$ **33.** $(-5, 11)$ **35.** $(-\infty, 4) \cup (6, \infty)$ **37.** $\varnothing$

39. $(-\infty, \infty)$ **41.** $[-2, 9]$ **43.** $(-\infty, -11] \cup [1, \infty)$ **45.** $(-\infty, 0) \cup (0, \infty)$

47. $(-\infty, \infty)$ **49.** $\left[-\frac{1}{2}, 1\right]$ **51.** $(-\infty, -3) \cup (0, \infty)$ **53.** $\varnothing$

55. $\left\{\frac{3}{8}\right\}$ **57.** $\left(-\frac{2}{3}, 0\right)$ **59.** $(-\infty, -12) \cup (0, \infty)$ **61.** $[-1, 8]$

63. $\left[-\frac{23}{8}, \frac{17}{8}\right]$ **65.** $(-2, 5)$ **67.** $5, -2$ **69.** $(-\infty, -7] \cup [17, \infty)$ **71.** $-\frac{9}{4}$ **73.** $(-2, 1)$ **75.** $2, \frac{4}{3}$ **77.** $\varnothing$

79. $\frac{19}{2}, -\frac{17}{2}$ **81.** $\left(-\infty, -\frac{25}{3}\right) \cup \left(\frac{35}{3}, \infty\right)$ **83.** 55 million, 97 million, 138 million **85.** -1.5 **87.** 0 **89.** $|x| < 7$ **91.** $|x| \le 5$

93. answers may vary **95.** $3.45 < x < 3.55$

Integrated Review
1. $(-5, 7)$ **2.** $(-\infty, \infty)$ **3.** $1, \frac{1}{2}$ **4.** $(-3, 2)$ **5.** $(-\infty, -1] \cup [1, \infty)$ **6.** $-18, -\frac{4}{3}$

7. $\left[-\frac{2}{3}, 4\right]$ **8.** $\varnothing$ **9.** $(-\infty, 1]$ **10.** $(-\infty, 0]$ **11.** $[0, 6]$ **12.** $-\frac{3}{2}, 1$ **13.** B **14.** E

15. A **16.** C **17.** D

Section 9.4
Practice Exercises

1.   **2.**   **3.**   **4.**   **5.**   **6.**

7.   **8.**

Vocabulary, Readiness & Video Check 9.4

1. linear inequality in two variables   **3.** false   **5.** true   **7.** yes   **9.** yes   **11.** We find the boundary line equation by replacing the inequality symbol with =. The points on this line are solutions (line is solid) if the inequality is ≥ or ≤; they are not solutions (line is dashed) if the inequality is > or <.

Exercise Set 9.4

1. no; yes   **3.** no; no   **5.** no; yes   **7.** 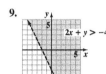   **9.**   **11.**   **13.**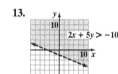

15. 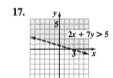   **17.**   **19.** 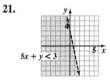   **21.** 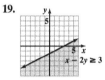   **23.**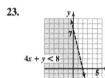

25. 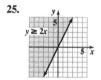   **27.**   **29.**   **31.** 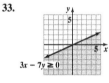   **33.**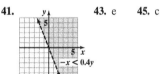

35.   **37.**   **39.** 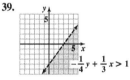   **41.**   **43.** e   **45.** c   **47.** f

49.   **51.** 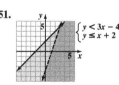   **53.** 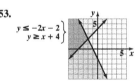   **55.** 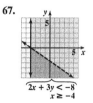   **57.**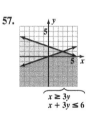

59.   **61.** 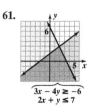   **63.**   **65.** 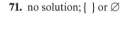   **67.**

69. 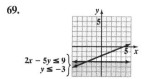   **71.** no solution; { } or ∅   **73.** 25   **75.** −2   **77.** yes   **79.** yes   **81.** $x + y \geq 13$

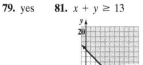

83. answers may vary   **85.**   **87.** answers may vary   **89. a.** $30x + 0.15y \leq 500$ **b.**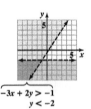

c. answers may vary   **91.** C   **93.** D   **95.** 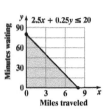   **97.** answers may vary

Chapter 9 Vocabulary Check

1. compound inequality   **2.** intersection   **3.** union   **4.** absolute value   **5.** solution   **6.** system of linear inequalities

Chapter 9 Review

1. $\left(\frac{1}{8}, 2\right)$ **3.** $\left(\frac{7}{8}, \frac{27}{20}\right]$ **5.** $\left(\frac{11}{3}, \infty\right)$ **7.** $5, 11$ **9.** $-1, \frac{11}{3}$ **11.** $-\frac{1}{6}$ **13.** $\varnothing$ **15.** $5, -\frac{1}{3}$ **17.** $7, -\frac{8}{5}$ **19.** ⟵———⟶ $-\frac{8}{5}$ 2 $\left(-\frac{8}{5}, 2\right)$

21. ⟵———⟶ -3 3 $(-\infty, -3) \cup (3, \infty)$ **23.** ⟵——⟶ 0 $\varnothing$ **25.** ⟵———⟶ $-\frac{22}{15}$ $\frac{6}{5}$ $\left(-\infty, -\frac{22}{15}\right] \cup \left[\frac{6}{5}, \infty\right)$

27. ⟵———⟶ -27 -9 $(-\infty, -27) \cup (-9, \infty)$ **29.** $3x - 4y \leq 0$ **31.** $x + 6y < 6$ **33.** $y \geq -7$

35. $y \geq 2x - 3$ $y \leq -2x + 1$ **37.** $x + 2y > 0$ $x - y \leq 6$ **39.** $3x - 2y \leq 4$ $2x + y \geq 5$ **41.** $\left[-\frac{4}{3}, \frac{7}{6}\right]$ **43.** $(5, \infty)$ **45.** $\varnothing$ **47.** $(-\infty, \infty)$

49. $-x \leq y$ **51.** $-3x + 2y > -1$ $y < -2$

Chapter 9 Test

1. $1, \frac{2}{3}$ **2.** $\varnothing$ **3.** $\frac{3}{2}$ **4.** $\left(\frac{3}{2}, 5\right]$ **5.** $(-\infty, -2) \cup \left(\frac{4}{3}, \infty\right)$ **6.** $(3, 7)$ **7.** $(-\infty, -5]$ **8.** $(-\infty, -2]$ **9.** $[-3, -1)$ **10.** $(-\infty, \infty)$

11. $3, -\frac{1}{5}$ **12.** $(-\infty, \infty)$ **13.** $\left[1, \frac{11}{2}\right)$ **14.** $y > -4x$ **15.** $2x - 3y > -6$ **16.** $y + 2x \leq 4$ $y \geq 2$ **17.** $2y - x \geq 1$ $x + y \geq -4$

Chapter 9 Cumulative Review

1. a. $\frac{1}{2}$ **b.** 19; Sec. 1.6, Ex. 6   **3. a.** $-\frac{39}{5}$ **b.** 2; Sec. 1.7, Ex. 9   **5. a.** $5x + 7$ **b.** $-4a - 1$ **c.** $4y - 3y^2$ **d.** $7.3x - 6$

e. $\frac{1}{2}b$; Sec. 2.1, Ex. 4   **7.** -3; Sec. 2.2, Ex. 3   **9.**

x	y
-1	-3
0	0
-3	-9

; Sec. 3.1, Ex. 7   **11. a.** x-int: $(-3, 0)$; y-int: $(0, 2)$ **b.** x-int: $(-4, 0), (-1, 0)$; y-int: $(0, 1)$

c. *x*-int and *y*-int: $(0,0)$ **d.** *x*-int: $(2,0)$; *y*-int: none   **e.** *x*-int: $(-1,0)$, $(3,0)$; *y*-int: $(0,-1)$, $(0,2)$; Sec. 3.3, Ex. 1–5   **13.** parallel; Sec. 3.4, Ex. 8a

15. $y = \dfrac{1}{4}x - 3$; Sec. 3.5, Ex. 3   **17.** $y = -3$; Sec. 3.5, Ex. 7   **19.** a, b, c; Sec. 3.6, Ex. 5   **21.** solution; Sec. 4.1, Ex. 1

23. $12x^3 - 12x^2 - 9x + 2$; Sec. 5.2, Ex. 10   **25.** $(x + 6y)(x + y)$; Sec. 6.2, Ex. 6   **27.** $\dfrac{3y^9}{160}$; Sec. 7.2, Ex. 4   **29.** 1; Sec. 7.3, Ex. 2

31. $\dfrac{x(3x - 1)}{(x + 1)^2(x - 1)}$; Sec. 7.4, Ex. 7   **33.** -5; Sec. 7.5, Ex. 1   **35.** no solution; $\{\ \}$ or $\varnothing$; Sec. 4.1, Ex. 5   **37.** $(-2, 0)$; Sec. 4.2, Ex. 4

39. $\{(x, y)\,|\,3x - 2y = 2\}$ or $\{(x, y)\,|\,-9x + 6y = -6\}$; Sec. 4.3, Ex. 4   **41.**   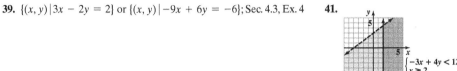   ; Sec. 9.4, Ex. 8   **43. a.** x^{11} **b.** $\dfrac{t^4}{16}$

c. $81y^{10}$; Sec. 5.1, Ex. 11   **45.** $-6, -\dfrac{3}{2}, \dfrac{1}{5}$; Sec. 6.6, Ex. 9   **47.** 63; Sec. 7.6, Ex. 1

CHAPTER 10 RATIONAL EXPONENTS, RADICALS, AND COMPLEX NUMBERS

Section 10.1
Practice Exercises

1. a. 7   **b.** 0   **c.** $\dfrac{4}{9}$ **d.** 0.8   **e.** z^4 **f.** $4b^2$ **g.** -6 **h.** not a real number   **2.** 6.708   **3. a.** -1 **b.** 3   **c.** $\dfrac{3}{4}$ **d.** x^4 **e.** $-2x$

4. a. 10   **b.** -1 **c.** -9 **d.** not a real number   **e.** $3x^3$ **5. a.** 4   **b.** $|x^7|$ **c.** $|x + 7|$ **d.** -7 **e.** $3x - 5$
f. $7|x|$ **g.** $|x + 8|$ **6. a.** 4   **b.** 2   **c.** 2   **d.** $\sqrt[3]{-9}$ **7.**   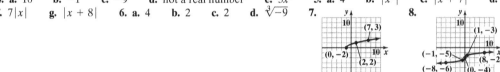   **8.**

Vocabulary, Readiness & Video Check 10.1

1. index; radical sign; radicand   **3.** is not   **5.** $[0, \infty)$ **7.** $(16, 4)$ **9.** Divide the index into each exponent in the radicand.   **11.** The square root of a negative number is not a real number, but the cube root of a negative number is a real number.   **13.** For odd roots, there's only one root/answer whether the radicand is positive or negative, so absolute value bars aren't needed.

Exercise Set 10.1

1. 10   **3.** $\dfrac{1}{2}$ **5.** 0.01   **7.** -6 **9.** x^5 **11.** $4y^3$ **13.** 2.646   **15.** 6.164   **17.** 14.142   **19.** 4   **21.** $\dfrac{1}{2}$ **23.** -1 **25.** x^4

27. $-3x^3$ **29.** -2 **31.** not a real number   **33.** -2 **35.** x^4 **37.** $2x^2$ **39.** $9x^2$ **41.** $4x^2$ **43.** 8   **45.** -8 **47.** $2|x|$

49. x **51.** $|x - 5|$ **53.** $|x + 2|$ **55.** -11 **57.** $2x$ **59.** y^6 **61.** $5ab^{10}$ **63.** $-3x^4y^3$ **65.** a^4b **67.** $-2x^2y$ **69.** $\dfrac{5}{7}$

71. $\dfrac{x^{10}}{2y}$ **73.** $-\dfrac{z^7}{3x}$ **75.** $\dfrac{x}{2}$ **77.** $\sqrt{3}$ **79.** -1 **81.** -3 **83.** $\sqrt{7}$

85. $[0, \infty)$;   **87.** $[3, \infty)$; 0, 1, 2, 3   **89.** $(-\infty, \infty)$;   **91.** $(-\infty, \infty)$; 0, 1, -1, 2, -2

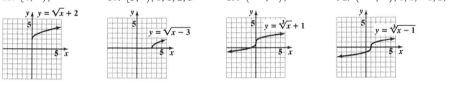

93. $-32x^{15}y^{10}$ **95.** $-60x^7y^{10}z^5$ **97.** $\dfrac{x^9y^5}{2}$ **99.** not a real number   **101.** not a real number   **103.** d   **105.** d   **107.** b   **109.** b

111. answers may vary   **113.** 1.69 sq m   **115.** 11,181 m per sec   **117.** answers may vary   **119.**

121.

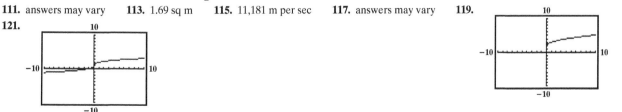

Section 10.2
Practice Exercises
1. a. 6 **b.** 10 **c.** $\sqrt[3]{x}$ **d.** 1 **e.** -8 **f.** $5x^3$ **g.** $3\sqrt[4]{x}$ **2. a.** 64 **b.** -1 **c.** -27 **d.** $\dfrac{1}{125}$ **e.** $\sqrt[9]{(3x+2)^5}$

3. a. $\dfrac{1}{27}$ **b.** $\dfrac{1}{16}$ **4. a.** $y^{10/3}$ **b.** $x^{17/20}$ **c.** $\dfrac{1}{9}$ **d.** $b^{2/9}$ **e.** $\dfrac{81}{x^3y^{11/3}}$ **5. a.** $x^{14/15} - x^{13/5}$ **b.** $x + 4x^{1/2} - 12$ **6.** $x^{-1/5}(2 - 7x)$

7. a. $\sqrt[9]{x}$ **b.** $\sqrt{6}$ **c.** $\sqrt[4]{a^2b}$ **8. a.** $\sqrt[12]{x^7}$ **b.** $\sqrt[15]{y^2}$ **c.** $\sqrt[6]{675}$

Vocabulary, Readiness & Video Check 10.2
1. true **3.** true **5.** multiply, c **7.** $-\sqrt[5]{3x}$ **9.** denominator; positive **11.** Write the radical using an equivalent fractional exponent form, simplify the fraction, then write as a radical again.

Exercise Set 10.2
1. 7 **3.** 3 **5.** $\dfrac{1}{2}$ **7.** 13 **9.** $2\sqrt[3]{m}$ **11.** $3x^2$ **13.** -3 **15.** -2 **17.** 8 **19.** 16 **21.** not a real number **23.** $\sqrt[5]{(2x)^3}$

25. $\sqrt[9]{(7x+2)^2}$ **27.** $\dfrac{64}{27}$ **29.** $\dfrac{1}{16}$ **31.** $\dfrac{1}{16}$ **33.** not a real number **35.** $\dfrac{1}{x^{1/4}}$ **37.** $a^{2/3}$ **39.** $\dfrac{5x^{3/4}}{7}$ **41.** $a^{7/3}$ **43.** x **45.** $3^{5/8}$

47. $y^{1/6}$ **49.** $8u^3$ **51.** $-b$ **53.** $\dfrac{1}{x^2}$ **55.** $27x^{2/3}$ **57.** $\dfrac{y}{z^{1/6}}$ **59.** $\dfrac{1}{x^{7/4}}$ **61.** $y - y^{7/6}$ **63.** $x^{5/3} - 2x^{2/3}$ **65.** $4x^{2/3} - 9$

67. $x^{8/3}(1 + x^{2/3})$ **69.** $x^{1/5}(x^{1/5} - 3)$ **71.** $x^{-1/3}(5 + x)$ **73.** $\sqrt{x}$ **75.** $\sqrt[3]{2}$ **77.** $2\sqrt{x}$ **79.** $\sqrt{xy}$ **81.** $\sqrt[3]{a^2b}$ **83.** $\sqrt{x+3}$

85. $\sqrt[15]{y^{11}}$ **87.** $\sqrt[12]{b^5}$ **89.** $\sqrt[24]{x^{23}}$ **91.** $\sqrt{a}$ **93.** $\sqrt[6]{432}$ **95.** $\sqrt[15]{343y^5}$ **97.** $\sqrt[6]{125r^3s^2}$ **99.** $25 \cdot 3$ **101.** $16 \cdot 3$ or $4 \cdot 12$

103. $8 \cdot 2$ **105.** $27 \cdot 2$ **107.** A **109.** C **111.** B **113.** 1509 calories **115.** 302.0 million **117.** answers may vary **119.** $a^{1/3}$

121. $x^{1/5}$ **123.** 1.6818 **125.** 5.6645 **127.** $\dfrac{t^{1/2}}{u^{1/2}}$

Section 10.3
Practice Exercises
1. a. $\sqrt{35}$ **b.** $\sqrt{13z}$ **c.** 5 **d.** $\sqrt[3]{15x^2y}$ **e.** $\sqrt{\dfrac{5t}{2m}}$ **2. a.** $\dfrac{6}{7}$ **b.** $\dfrac{\sqrt{z}}{4}$ **c.** $\dfrac{5}{2}$ **d.** $\dfrac{\sqrt[4]{5}}{3x^2}$ **3. a.** $7\sqrt{2}$ **b.** $3\sqrt[3]{2}$

c. $\sqrt{35}$ **d.** $3\sqrt[4]{3}$ **4. a.** $6z^3\sqrt{z}$ **b.** $2pq^2\sqrt[3]{4pq}$ **c.** $2x^3\sqrt[4]{x^3}$ **5. a.** 4 **b.** $\dfrac{7}{3}\sqrt{z}$ **c.** $10xy^2\sqrt[3]{x^2}$ **d.** $6x^2y\sqrt[5]{2y}$

6. $\sqrt{17}$ units ≈ 4.123 units **7.** $\left(\dfrac{13}{2}, -4\right)$

Vocabulary, Readiness & Video Check 10.3
1. midpoint; point **3.** distance **5.** the indexes must be the same **7.** The power must be 1. Any even power is a perfect square and will leave no factor in the radicand; any higher odd power can have an even power factored from it, leaving one factor remaining in the radicand. **9.** average; average

Exercise Set 10.3
1. $\sqrt{14}$ **3.** 2 **5.** $\sqrt[3]{36}$ **7.** $\sqrt{6x}$ **9.** $\sqrt{\dfrac{14}{xy}}$ **11.** $\sqrt[4]{20x^3}$ **13.** $\dfrac{\sqrt{6}}{7}$ **15.** $\dfrac{\sqrt{2}}{7}$ **17.** $\dfrac{\sqrt[4]{x^3}}{2}$ **19.** $\dfrac{\sqrt[3]{4}}{3}$ **21.** $\dfrac{\sqrt[4]{8}}{x^2}$

23. $\dfrac{\sqrt[3]{2x}}{3y^4\sqrt[3]{3}}$ **25.** $\dfrac{x\sqrt{y}}{10}$ **27.** $\dfrac{x\sqrt{5}}{2y}$ **29.** $-\dfrac{z^2\sqrt[3]{z}}{3x}$ **31.** $4\sqrt{2}$ **33.** $4\sqrt[3]{3}$ **35.** $25\sqrt{3}$ **37.** $2\sqrt{6}$ **39.** $10x^2\sqrt{x}$ **41.** $2y^2\sqrt[3]{2y}$

43. $a^2b\sqrt[4]{b^3}$ **45.** $y^2\sqrt{y}$ **47.** $5ab\sqrt{b}$ **49.** $-2x^2\sqrt[5]{y}$ **51.** $x^4\sqrt[3]{50x^2}$ **53.** $-4a^4b^3\sqrt{2b}$ **55.** $3x^3y^4\sqrt{xy}$ **57.** $5r^3s^4$

59. $2x^3y\sqrt[4]{2y}$ **61.** $\sqrt{2}$ **63.** 2 **65.** 10 **67.** x^2y **69.** $24m^2$ **71.** $\dfrac{15x\sqrt{2x}}{2}$ or $\dfrac{15x}{2}\sqrt{2x}$ **73.** $2a^2\sqrt[4]{2}$ **75.** $2xy^2\sqrt[5]{x^2}$ **77.** 5 units

79. $\sqrt{41}$ units ≈ 6.403 units **81.** $\sqrt{10}$ units ≈ 3.162 units **83.** $\sqrt{5}$ units ≈ 2.236 units **85.** $\sqrt{192.58}$ units ≈ 13.877 units **87.** $(4, -2)$

89. $\left(-5, \dfrac{5}{2}\right)$ **91.** $(3, 0)$ **93.** $\left(-\dfrac{1}{2}, \dfrac{1}{2}\right)$ **95.** $\left(\sqrt{2}, \dfrac{\sqrt{5}}{2}\right)$ **97.** $(6.2, -6.65)$ **99.** $14x$ **101.** $2x^2 - 7x - 15$ **103.** y^2

105. $-3x - 15$ **107.** $x^2 - 8x + 16$ **109.** true **111.** false **113.** true **115.** $\dfrac{\sqrt[3]{64}}{\sqrt{64}} = \dfrac{4}{8} = \dfrac{1}{2}$ **117.** x^7 **119.** a^3bc^5 **121.** $z^{10}\sqrt[3]{z^2}$

123. $q^2r^5s\sqrt[3]{q^3r^5}$ **125.** 1.6 m **127. a.** 20π sq cm **b.** 211.57 sq ft

Section 10.4
Practice Exercises
1. a. $8\sqrt{17}$ **b.** $-5\sqrt[3]{5z}$ **c.** $3\sqrt{2} + 5\sqrt[3]{2}$ **2. a.** $11\sqrt{6}$ **b.** $-9\sqrt[3]{3}$ **c.** $-2\sqrt{3x}$ **d.** $2\sqrt{10} + 2\sqrt[3]{5}$ **e.** $4x\sqrt[3]{3x}$

3. a. $\dfrac{5\sqrt{7}}{12}$ **b.** $\dfrac{13\sqrt[3]{6y}}{4}$ **4. a.** $2\sqrt{5} + 5\sqrt{3}$ **b.** $2\sqrt{3} + 2\sqrt{2} - \sqrt{30} - 2\sqrt{5}$ **c.** $6z + \sqrt{z} - 12$ **d.** $-6\sqrt{6} + 15$

e. $5x - 9$ **f.** $6\sqrt{x+2} + x + 11$

Vocabulary, Readiness & Video Check 10.4

1. Unlike   **3.** Like   **5.** $6\sqrt{3}$ **7.** $7\sqrt{x}$ **9.** $8\sqrt[3]{x}$ **11.** Sometimes you can't see that there are like radicals until you simplify, so you may incorrectly think you cannot add or subtract if you don't simplify first.

Exercise Set 10.4

1. $-2\sqrt{2}$ **3.** $10x\sqrt{2x}$ **5.** $17\sqrt{2} - 15\sqrt{5}$ **7.** $-\sqrt[3]{2x}$ **9.** $5b\sqrt{b}$ **11.** $\dfrac{31\sqrt{2}}{15}$ **13.** $\dfrac{\sqrt[3]{11}}{3}$ **15.** $\dfrac{5\sqrt{5x}}{9}$ **17.** $14 + \sqrt{3}$

19. $7 - 3y$ **21.** $6\sqrt{3} - 6\sqrt{2}$ **23.** $-23\sqrt[3]{5}$ **25.** $2a^3b\sqrt{ab}$ **27.** $20y\sqrt{2y}$ **29.** $2y\sqrt[3]{2x}$ **31.** $6\sqrt[3]{11} - 4\sqrt{11}$ **33.** $3x\sqrt[4]{x^3}$

35. $\dfrac{2\sqrt{3}}{3}$ **37.** $\dfrac{5x\sqrt[3]{x}}{7}$ **39.** $\dfrac{5\sqrt{7}}{2x}$ **41.** $\dfrac{\sqrt[3]{2}}{6}$ **43.** $\dfrac{14x\sqrt[3]{2x}}{9}$ **45.** $15\sqrt{3}$ in.   **47.** $\sqrt{35} + \sqrt{21}$ **49.** $7 - 2\sqrt{10}$ **51.** $3\sqrt{x} - x\sqrt{3}$

53. $6x - 13\sqrt{x} - 5$ **55.** $\sqrt[3]{a^2} + \sqrt[3]{a} - 20$ **57.** $6\sqrt{2} - 12$ **59.** $2 + 2x\sqrt{3}$ **61.** $-16 - \sqrt{35}$ **63.** $x - y^2$ **65.** $3 + 2x\sqrt{3} + x^2$

67. $23x - 5x\sqrt{15}$ **69.** $2\sqrt[3]{2} - \sqrt[3]{4}$ **71.** $x + 1$ **73.** $x + 24 + 10\sqrt{x - 1}$ **75.** $2x + 6 - 2\sqrt{2x + 5}$ **77.** $x - 7$ **79.** $\dfrac{7}{x + y}$

81. $2a - 3$ **83.** $\dfrac{-2 + \sqrt{3}}{3}$ **85.** $22\sqrt{5}$ ft; 150 sq ft   **87. a.** $2\sqrt{3}$ **b.** 3   **c.** answers may vary   **89.** $2\sqrt{6} - 2\sqrt{2} - 2\sqrt{3} + 6$

91. answers may vary

Section 10.5
Practice Exercises

1. a. $\dfrac{5\sqrt{3}}{3}$ **b.** $\dfrac{15\sqrt{x}}{2x}$ **c.** $\dfrac{\sqrt[3]{6}}{3}$ **2.** $\dfrac{\sqrt{15yz}}{5y}$ **3.** $\dfrac{\sqrt[3]{z^2x^2}}{3x^2}$ **4. a.** $\dfrac{5(3\sqrt{5} - 2)}{41}$ **b.** $\dfrac{\sqrt{6} + 5\sqrt{3} + \sqrt{10} + 5\sqrt{5}}{-2}$ **c.** $\dfrac{6x - 3\sqrt{xy}}{4x - y}$

5. $\dfrac{2}{\sqrt{10}}$ **6.** $\dfrac{5b}{\sqrt[3]{50ab^2}}$ **7.** $\dfrac{x - 9}{4(\sqrt{x} + 3)}$

Vocabulary, Readiness & Video Check 10.5

1. conjugate   **3.** rationalizing the numerator   **5.** To write an equivalent expression without a radical in the denominator.   **7.** No, except for the fact you're working with numerators, the process is the same.

Exercise Set 10.5

1. $\dfrac{\sqrt{14}}{7}$ **3.** $\dfrac{\sqrt{5}}{5}$ **5.** $\dfrac{2\sqrt{x}}{x}$ **7.** $\dfrac{4\sqrt[3]{9}}{3}$ **9.** $\dfrac{3\sqrt{2x}}{4x}$ **11.** $\dfrac{3\sqrt[3]{2x}}{2x}$ **13.** $\dfrac{3\sqrt{3a}}{a}$ **15.** $\dfrac{3\sqrt[3]{4}}{2}$ **17.** $\dfrac{2\sqrt{21}}{7}$ **19.** $\dfrac{\sqrt{10xy}}{5y}$ **21.** $\dfrac{\sqrt[3]{75}}{5}$

23. $\dfrac{\sqrt{6x}}{10}$ **25.** $\dfrac{\sqrt{3z}}{6z}$ **27.** $\dfrac{\sqrt[3]{6xy^2}}{3x}$ **29.** $\dfrac{3\sqrt[4]{2}}{2}$ **31.** $\dfrac{2\sqrt[4]{9x}}{3x^2}$ **33.** $\dfrac{5\sqrt[5]{4ab^4}}{2ab^3}$ **35.** $\sqrt{2} - x$ **37.** $5 + \sqrt{a}$ **39.** $-7\sqrt{5} - 8\sqrt{x}$

41. $-2(2 + \sqrt{7})$ **43.** $\dfrac{7(3 + \sqrt{x})}{9 - x}$ **45.** $-5 + 2\sqrt{6}$ **47.** $\dfrac{2a + 2\sqrt{a} + \sqrt{ab} + \sqrt{b}}{4a - b}$ **49.** $-\dfrac{8(1 - \sqrt{10})}{9}$ **51.** $\dfrac{x - \sqrt{xy}}{x - y}$

53. $\dfrac{5 + 3\sqrt{2}}{7}$ **55.** $\dfrac{5}{\sqrt{15}}$ **57.** $\dfrac{6}{\sqrt{10}}$ **59.** $\dfrac{2x}{7\sqrt{x}}$ **61.** $\dfrac{5y}{\sqrt[3]{100xy}}$ **63.** $\dfrac{2}{\sqrt{10}}$ **65.** $\dfrac{2x}{11\sqrt{2x}}$ **67.** $\dfrac{7}{2\sqrt[3]{49}}$ **69.** $\dfrac{3x^2}{10\sqrt[3]{9x}}$ **71.** $\dfrac{6x^2y^3}{\sqrt{6z}}$

73. $\dfrac{-7}{12 + 6\sqrt{11}}$ **75.** $\dfrac{3}{10 + 5\sqrt{7}}$ **77.** $\dfrac{x - 9}{x - 3\sqrt{x}}$ **79.** $\dfrac{1}{3 + 2\sqrt{2}}$ **81.** $\dfrac{x - 1}{x - 2\sqrt{x} + 1}$ **83.** 5   **85.** $-\dfrac{1}{2}, 6$ **87.** 2, 6   **89.** $r = \dfrac{\sqrt{A\pi}}{2\pi}$

91. a. $\dfrac{y\sqrt{15xy}}{6x^2}$ **b.** $\dfrac{y\sqrt{15xy}}{6x^2}$ **c.** answers may vary   **93.** $\sqrt[3]{25}$ **95.** answers may vary   **97.** answers may vary

Integrated Review

1. 9   **2.** -2 **3.** $\dfrac{1}{2}$ **4.** x^3 **5.** y^3 **6.** $2y^5$ **7.** $-2y$ **8.** $3b^3$ **9.** 6   **10.** $\sqrt[3]{3y}$ **11.** $\dfrac{1}{16}$ **12.** $\sqrt[5]{(x + 1)^3}$ **13.** y

14. $16x^{1/2}$ **15.** $x^{5/4}$ **16.** $4^{11/15}$ **17.** $2x^2$ **18.** $\sqrt[4]{a^3b^2}$ **19.** $\sqrt[4]{x^3}$ **20.** $\sqrt[6]{500}$ **21.** $2\sqrt{10}$ **22.** $2xy^2\sqrt[4]{x^3y^2}$ **23.** $3x\sqrt[3]{2x}$

24. $-2b^2\sqrt[3]{2}$ **25.** $\sqrt{5x}$ **26.** $4x$ **27.** $7y^2\sqrt{y}$ **28.** $2a^2\sqrt[4]{3}$ **29.** $2\sqrt{5} - 5\sqrt{3} + 5\sqrt{7}$ **30.** $y\sqrt[3]{2y}$ **31.** $\sqrt{15} - \sqrt{6}$ **32.** $10 + 2\sqrt{21}$

33. $4x^2 - 5$ **34.** $x + 2 - 2\sqrt{x + 1}$ **35.** $\dfrac{\sqrt{21}}{3}$ **36.** $\dfrac{5\sqrt[3]{4x}}{2x}$ **37.** $\dfrac{13 - 3\sqrt{21}}{5}$ **38.** $\dfrac{7}{\sqrt{21}}$ **39.** $\dfrac{3y}{\sqrt[3]{33y^2}}$ **40.** $\dfrac{x - 4}{x + 2\sqrt{x}}$

Section 10.6
Practice Exercises

1. 18   **2.** $\dfrac{1}{4}, \dfrac{3}{4}$ **3.** 10   **4.** 9   **5.** $\dfrac{3}{25}$ **6.** $6\sqrt{3}$ meters   **7.** $\sqrt{193}$ in. ≈ 13.89 in.

Graphing Calculator Explorations 10.6

1. 3.19   **3.** $\varnothing$ **5.** 3.23

Vocabulary, Readiness & Video Check 10.6

1. extraneous solution   **3.** $x^2 - 10x + 25$ **5.** Applying the power rule can result in an equation with more solutions than the original equation, so you need to check all proposed solutions in the original equation.   **7.** Our answer is either a positive square root of a value or a negative square root of a value. We're looking for a length, which must be positive, so our answer must be the positive square root.

Exercise Set 10.6

1. 8   **3.** 7   **5.** ∅   **7.** 7   **9.** 6   **11.** $-\dfrac{9}{2}$ **13.** 29   **15.** 4   **17.** -4 **19.** ∅   **21.** 7   **23.** 9   **25.** 50   **27.** ∅

29. $\dfrac{15}{4}$ **31.** 13   **33.** 5   **35.** -12 **37.** 9   **39.** -3 **41.** 1   **43.** 1   **45.** $\dfrac{1}{2}$ **47.** 0, 4   **49.** $\dfrac{37}{4}$ **51.** $3\sqrt{5}$ ft

53. $2\sqrt{10}$ m   **55.** $2\sqrt{131}$ m ≈ 22.9 m   **57.** $\sqrt{100.84}$ mm ≈ 10.0 mm   **59.** 17 ft   **61.** 13 ft   **63.** 14,657,415 sq mi   **65.** 100 ft

67. 100   **69.** $\dfrac{\pi}{2}$ sec ≈ 1.57 sec   **71.** 12.97 ft   **73.** answers may vary   **75.** $15\sqrt{3}$ sq mi ≈ 25.98 sq mi   **77.** answers may vary

79. 0.51 km   **81.** function   **83.** function   **85.** not a function   **87.** $\dfrac{x}{4x+3}$ **89.** $-\dfrac{4z+2}{3z}$

91. $\sqrt{5x-1}+4=7$
$\sqrt{5x-1}=3$
$(\sqrt{5x-1})^2=3^2$
$5x-1=9$
$5x=10$
$x=2$

93. 1   **95. a.–b.** answers may vary   **97.** $-1, 0, 8, 9$ **99.** $-1, 4$

Section 10.7
Practice Exercises

1. a. $2i$ **b.** $i\sqrt{7}$ **c.** $-3i\sqrt{2}$ **2. a.** $-\sqrt{30}$ **b.** -3 **c.** $25i$ **d.** $3i$ **3. a.** $-1-4i$ **b.** $-3+5i$ **c.** $3-2i$ **4. a.** $20+0i$

b. $-5+10i$ **c.** $15+16i$ **d.** $8-6i$ **e.** $85+0i$ **5. a.** $\dfrac{11}{10}-\dfrac{7i}{10}$ **b.** $0-\dfrac{5i}{2}$ **6. a.** i **b.** 1   **c.** -1 **d.** 1

Vocabulary, Readiness & Video Check 10.7

1. complex   **3.** -1 **5.** real   **7.** The product rule for radicals; you need to first simplify each separate radical and have nonnegative radicands before applying the product rule.   **9.** the fact that $i^2=-1$ **11.** $i, i^2=-1, i^3=-i, i^4=1$

Exercise Set 10.7

1. $9i$ **3.** $i\sqrt{7}$ **5.** -4 **7.** $8i$ **9.** $2i\sqrt{6}$ **11.** $-6i$ **13.** $24i\sqrt{7}$ **15.** $-3\sqrt{6}+0i$ **17.** $-\sqrt{14}$ **19.** $-5\sqrt{2}$ **21.** $4i$ **23.** $i\sqrt{3}$
25. $2\sqrt{2}$ **27.** $6-4i$ **29.** $-2+6i$ **31.** $-2-4i$ **33.** $-40+0i$ **35.** $18+12i$ **37.** $7+0i$ **39.** $12-16i$ **41.** $0-4i$
43. $\dfrac{28}{25}-\dfrac{21}{25}i$ **45.** $4+i$ **47.** $\dfrac{17}{13}+\dfrac{7}{13}i$ **49.** $63+0i$ **51.** $2-i$ **53.** $27+3i$ **55.** $-\dfrac{5}{2}-2i$ **57.** $18+13i$ **59.** $20+0i$

61. $10+0i$ **63.** $2+0i$ **65.** $-5+\dfrac{16}{3}i$ **67.** $17+144i$ **69.** $\dfrac{3}{5}-\dfrac{1}{5}i$ **71.** $5-10i$ **73.** $\dfrac{1}{5}-\dfrac{8}{5}i$ **75.** $8-i$ **77.** $7+0i$

79. $12-16i$ **81.** 1   **83.** i **85.** $-i$ **87.** -1 **89.** -64 **91.** $-243i$ **93.** $40°$ **95.** $x^2-5x-2-\dfrac{6}{x-1}$ **97.** 5 people

99. 14 people   **101.** 16.7%   **103.** $-1-i$ **105.** $0+0i$ **107.** $2+3i$ **109.** $2+i\sqrt{2}$ **111.** $\dfrac{1}{2}-\dfrac{\sqrt{3}}{2}i$ **113.** answers may vary

115. $6-3i\sqrt{3}$ **117.** yes

Chapter 10 Vocabulary Check

1. conjugate   **2.** principal square root   **3.** rationalizing   **4.** imaginary unit   **5.** cube root   **6.** index; radicand   **7.** like radicals
8. complex number   **9.** distance   **10.** midpoint

Chapter 10 Review

1. 9   **3.** -2 **5.** $-\dfrac{1}{7}$ **7.** -6 **9.** $-a^2b^3$ **11.** $2ab^2$ **13.** $\dfrac{x^6}{6y}$ **15.** $|-x|$ **17.** -27 **19.** $-x$ **21.** $2|2y+z|$ **23.** y **25. a.** 3, 6

b. $[0, \infty)$ **c.**

$f(x)=\sqrt{x}+3$

27. $\dfrac{1}{3}$ **29.** $-\dfrac{1}{3}$ **31.** -27 **33.** not a real number   **35.** $\dfrac{9}{4}$ **37.** $x^{2/3}$ **39.** $\sqrt[5]{y^4}$ **41.** $\dfrac{1}{\sqrt[3]{x+2}}$

43. $a^{13/6}$ **45.** $\dfrac{1}{a^{9/2}}$ **47.** a^4b^6 **49.** $\dfrac{b^{5/6}}{49a^{1/4}c^{5/3}}$ **51.** 4.472   **53.** 5.191   **55.** -26.246 **57.** $\sqrt[6]{1372}$

59. $2\sqrt{6}$ **61.** $2x$ **63.** $2\sqrt{15}$ **65.** $3\sqrt[3]{6}$ **67.** $6x^3\sqrt{x}$ **69.** $\dfrac{p^8\sqrt{p}}{11}$ **71.** $\dfrac{y\sqrt[4]{xy^2}}{3}$

73. $\dfrac{5}{\sqrt{\pi}}$ m or $\dfrac{5\sqrt{\pi}}{\pi}$ m   **75.** $\sqrt{197}$ units ≈ 14.036 units   **77.** $\sqrt{73}$ units ≈ 8.544 units   **79.** $2\sqrt{11}$ units ≈ 6.633 units   **81.** $(-5, 5)$

83. $\left(-\dfrac{11}{2}, -2\right)$ **85.** $\left(\dfrac{1}{4}, -\dfrac{2}{7}\right)$ **87.** $-2\sqrt{5}$ **89.** $9\sqrt[3]{2}$ **91.** $\dfrac{15+2\sqrt{3}}{6}$ **93.** $17\sqrt{2}-15\sqrt{5}$ **95.** 6   **97.** $-8\sqrt{5}$

99. $a-9$ **101.** $\sqrt[3]{25x^2}-81$ **103.** $\dfrac{3\sqrt{7}}{7}$ **105.** $\dfrac{5\sqrt[3]{2}}{2}$ **107.** $\dfrac{x^2y^2\sqrt[3]{15yz}}{z}$ **109.** $\dfrac{3\sqrt{y}+6}{y-4}$ **111.** $\dfrac{11}{3\sqrt{11}}$ **113.** $\dfrac{3}{7\sqrt[3]{3}}$ **115.** $\dfrac{xy}{\sqrt[3]{10x^2yz}}$

117. 32   **119.** 35   **121.** 9   **123.** $3\sqrt{2}$ cm   **125.** 51.2 ft   **127.** $0 + 2i\sqrt{2}$ **129.** $0 + 6i$ **131.** $15 - 4i$ **133.** -64

135. $-12 - 18i$ **137.** $-5 - 12i$ **139.** $\dfrac{3}{2} - i$ **141.** x **143.** -10 **145.** $\dfrac{y^5}{2x^3}$ **147.** $\dfrac{1}{8}$ **149.** $\dfrac{1}{x^{13/2}}$ **151.** $\dfrac{n\sqrt{3n}}{11m^5}$

153. $4x - 20\sqrt{x} + 25$ **155.** $(4, 16)$ **157.** $\dfrac{2\sqrt{x} - 6}{x - 9}$ **159.** 5

Chapter 10 Test

1. $6\sqrt{6}$ **2.** $-x^{16}$ **3.** $\dfrac{1}{5}$ **4.** 5   **5.** $\dfrac{4x^2}{9}$ **6.** $-a^6b^3$ **7.** $\dfrac{8a^{1/3}c^{2/3}}{b^{5/12}}$ **8.** $a^{7/12} - a^{7/3}$ **9.** $|4xy|$ or $4|xy|$ **10.** -27 **11.** $\dfrac{3\sqrt{y}}{y}$

12. $\dfrac{8 - 6\sqrt{x} + x}{8 - 2x}$ **13.** $\dfrac{\sqrt[3]{b^2}}{b}$ **14.** $\dfrac{6 - x^2}{8(\sqrt{6} - x)}$ **15.** $-x\sqrt{5x}$ **16.** $4\sqrt{3} - \sqrt{6}$ **17.** $x + 2\sqrt{x} + 1$ **18.** $\sqrt{6} - 4\sqrt{3} + \sqrt{2} - 4$

19. -20 **20.** 23.685   **21.** 0.019   **22.** 2,3   **23.** $\varnothing$ **24.** 6   **25.** $0 + i\sqrt{2}$ **26.** $0 - 2i\sqrt{2}$ **27.** $0 - 3i$ **28.** $40 + 0i$ **29.** $7 + 24i$

30. $-\dfrac{3}{2} + \dfrac{5}{2}i$ **31.** $\dfrac{5\sqrt{2}}{2}$ **32.** $[-2, \infty)$; 0, 1, 2, 3;   **33.** $2\sqrt{26}$ units   **34.** $\sqrt{95}$ units   **35.** $\left(-4, \dfrac{7}{2}\right)$ **36.** $\left(-\dfrac{1}{2}, \dfrac{3}{10}\right)$

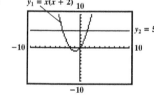

37. 27 mph   **38.** 360 ft

Chapter 10 Cumulative Review

1. a. -12 **b.** -3; Sec. 1.6, Ex. 5   **3.** 12; Sec. 2.3, Ex. 3   **5.** 12 in., 36 in.; Sec. 2.4, Ex. 3   **7.** one; Sec. 4.1, Ex. 8   **9.** $\left(6, \dfrac{1}{2}\right)$; Sec. 4.2, Ex. 3

11. no solution; $\{\ \}$ or $\varnothing$; Sec. 4.3, Ex. 3   **13.** 30% solution: 42 L; 80% solution: 28 L; Sec. 4.5, Ex. 6   **15. a.** -4 **b.** 11; Sec. 5.2, Ex. 4

17. $3m + 1$; Sec. 5.6, Ex. 1   **19.** $2x^2 + 5x + 2 + \dfrac{7}{x - 3}$; Sec. 5.7, Ex. 1   **21.** $(t - 8)(t - 5)$; Sec. 6.2, Ex. 8   **23. a.** $x^2 - 2x + 4$

b. $\dfrac{2}{y - 5}$; Sec. 7.1, Ex. 5   **25.** 4; Sec. 9.2, Ex. 9   **27.** $3x - 5$; Sec. 7.3, Ex. 3   **29.** $\dfrac{2m + 1}{m + 1}$; Sec. 7.4, Ex. 5   **31. a.** $\dfrac{x(x - 2)}{2(x + 2)}$

b. $\dfrac{x^2}{y^2}$; Sec. 7.7, Ex. 2   **33.** $\left[-2, \dfrac{8}{5}\right]$; Sec. 9.3, Ex. 3   **35.** 15 yd; Sec. 7.6, Ex. 4   **37. a.** 1   **b.** -4 **c.** $\dfrac{2}{5}$ **d.** x^2 **e.** $-3x^3$; Sec. 10.1, Ex. 3

39. a. $\dfrac{1}{8}$ **b.** $\dfrac{1}{9}$; Sec. 10.2, Ex. 3   **41.** $\dfrac{x - 4}{5(\sqrt{x} - 2)}$; Sec. 10.5, Ex. 7   **43.** constant of variation: 15, $u = \dfrac{15}{w}$; Sec. 8.4, Ex. 3

CHAPTER 11 QUADRATIC EQUATIONS AND FUNCTIONS

Section 11.1
Practice Exercises

1. $-4\sqrt{2}, 4\sqrt{2}$ **2.** $-\sqrt{10}, \sqrt{10}$ **3.** $-3 - 2\sqrt{5}, -3 + 2\sqrt{5}$ **4.** $\dfrac{2 + 3i}{5}, \dfrac{2 - 3i}{5}$ or $\dfrac{2}{5} \pm \dfrac{3}{5}i$ **5.** $-2 - \sqrt{7}, -2 + \sqrt{7}$

6. $\dfrac{3 - \sqrt{5}}{2}, \dfrac{3 + \sqrt{5}}{2}$ **7.** $\dfrac{6 - \sqrt{33}}{3}, \dfrac{6 + \sqrt{33}}{3}$ **8.** $\dfrac{5 - i\sqrt{31}}{4}, \dfrac{5 + i\sqrt{31}}{4}$ or $\dfrac{5}{4} \pm \dfrac{\sqrt{31}}{4}i$ **9.** 6%

Graphing Calculator Explorations 11.1

1. $-1.27, 6.27$ **3.** $-1.10, 0.90$ **5.** no real solutions

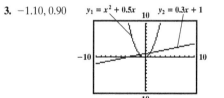
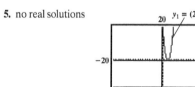

Vocabulary, Readiness & Video Check 11.1

1. $\pm\sqrt{b}$ **3.** completing the square   **5.** 9   **7.** We need a quantity squared by itself on one side of the equation. The only quantity squared is x, so we need to divide both sides by 2 before applying the square root property.   **9.** We're looking for an interest rate so a negative value does not make sense.

Exercise Set 11.1

1. $-4, 4$ **3.** $-\sqrt{7}, \sqrt{7}$ **5.** $-3\sqrt{2}, 3\sqrt{2}$ **7.** $-\sqrt{10}, \sqrt{10}$ **9.** $-8, -2$ **11.** $6 - 3\sqrt{2}, 6 + 3\sqrt{2}$ **13.** $\dfrac{3 - 2\sqrt{2}}{2}, \dfrac{3 + 2\sqrt{2}}{2}$

15. $-3i, 3i$ **17.** $-\sqrt{6}, \sqrt{6}$ **19.** $-2i\sqrt{2}, 2i\sqrt{2}$ **21.** $\dfrac{1 - 4i}{3}, \dfrac{1 + 4i}{3}$ or $\dfrac{1}{3} \pm \dfrac{4}{3}i$ **23.** $-7 - \sqrt{5}, -7 + \sqrt{5}$ **25.** $-3 - 2i\sqrt{2}, -3 + 2i\sqrt{2}$

27. $x^2 + 16x + 64 = (x + 8)^2$ **29.** $z^2 - 12z + 36 = (z - 6)^2$ **31.** $p^2 + 9p + \dfrac{81}{4} = \left(p + \dfrac{9}{2}\right)^2$ **33.** $x^2 + x + \dfrac{1}{4} = \left(x + \dfrac{1}{2}\right)^2$

35. $-5, -3$ **37.** $-3 - \sqrt{7}, -3 + \sqrt{7}$ **39.** $\dfrac{-1 - \sqrt{5}}{2}, \dfrac{-1 + \sqrt{5}}{2}$ **41.** $-1 - \sqrt{6}, -1 + \sqrt{6}$ **43.** $\dfrac{-1 - \sqrt{29}}{2}, \dfrac{-1 + \sqrt{29}}{2}$

45. $\dfrac{6 - \sqrt{30}}{3}, \dfrac{6 + \sqrt{30}}{3}$ **47.** $\dfrac{3 - \sqrt{11}}{2}, \dfrac{3 + \sqrt{11}}{2}$ **49.** $-4, \dfrac{1}{2}$ **51.** $-4 - \sqrt{15}, -4 + \sqrt{15}$ **53.** $\dfrac{-3 - \sqrt{21}}{3}, \dfrac{-3 + \sqrt{21}}{3}$

55. $-1, \dfrac{5}{2}$ **57.** $-1 - i, -1 + i$ **59.** $3 - \sqrt{17}, 3 + \sqrt{17}$ **61.** $-2 - i\sqrt{2}, -2 + i\sqrt{2}$ **63.** $\dfrac{-15 - 7\sqrt{5}}{10}, \dfrac{-15 + 7\sqrt{5}}{10}$

65. $\dfrac{1 - i\sqrt{47}}{4}, \dfrac{1 + i\sqrt{47}}{4}$ or $\dfrac{1}{4} \pm \dfrac{\sqrt{47}}{4}i$ **67.** $-5 - i\sqrt{3}, -5 + i\sqrt{3}$ **69.** $-4, 1$ **71.** $\dfrac{2 - i\sqrt{2}}{2}, \dfrac{2 + i\sqrt{2}}{2}$ or $1 \pm \dfrac{\sqrt{2}}{2}i$

73. $\dfrac{-3 - \sqrt{69}}{6}, \dfrac{-3 + \sqrt{69}}{6}$ **75.** 20%   **77.** 4%   **79.** 9.63 sec   **81.** 8.29 sec   **83.** 15 ft by 15 ft   **85.** $10\sqrt{2}$ cm   **87.** -1

89. $3 + 2\sqrt{5}$ **91.** $\dfrac{1 - 3\sqrt{2}}{2}$ **93.** $2\sqrt{6}$ **95.** 5   **97.** complex, but not real numbers   **99.** real numbers   **101.** complex, but not real numbers   **103.** $-8x, 8x$ **105.** $-5z, 5z$ **107.** answers may vary   **109.** compound; answers may vary   **111.** 6 thousand scissors

Section 11.2
Practice Exercises

1. $2, -\dfrac{1}{3}$ **2.** $\dfrac{4 - \sqrt{22}}{3}, \dfrac{4 + \sqrt{22}}{3}$ **3.** $1 - \sqrt{17}, 1 + \sqrt{17}$ **4.** $\dfrac{-1 - i\sqrt{15}}{4}, \dfrac{-1 + i\sqrt{15}}{4}$ or $-\dfrac{1}{4} \pm \dfrac{\sqrt{15}}{4}i$ **5. a.** one real solution
b. two real solutions   **c.** two complex, but not real solutions   **6.** 6 ft   **7.** 2.4 sec

Vocabulary, Readiness & Video Check 11.2

1. $x = \dfrac{-b \pm \sqrt{b^2 - 4ac}}{2a}$ **3.** $-5; -7$ **5.** $1; 0$ **7. a.** Yes, in order to make sure we have correct values for $a, b,$ and c.   **b.** No; clearing
fractions makes the work less tedious, but it's not a necessary step.   **9.** With applications, we need to make sure we answer the question(s) asked.
Here we're asked how much distance is saved, so once the dimensions of the triangle are known, further calculations are needed to answer this question
and solve the problem.

Exercise Set 11.2

1. $-6, 1$ **3.** $-\dfrac{3}{5}, 1$ **5.** 3   **7.** $\dfrac{-7 - \sqrt{33}}{2}, \dfrac{-7 + \sqrt{33}}{2}$ **9.** $\dfrac{1 - \sqrt{57}}{8}, \dfrac{1 + \sqrt{57}}{8}$ **11.** $\dfrac{7 - \sqrt{85}}{6}, \dfrac{7 + \sqrt{85}}{6}$ **13.** $1 - \sqrt{3}, 1 + \sqrt{3}$

15. $-\dfrac{3}{2}, 1$ **17.** $\dfrac{3 - \sqrt{11}}{2}, \dfrac{3 + \sqrt{11}}{2}$ **19.** $\dfrac{-5 - \sqrt{17}}{2}, \dfrac{-5 + \sqrt{17}}{2}$ **21.** $\dfrac{5}{2}, 1$ **23.** $-3 - 2i, -3 + 2i$ **25.** $-2 - \sqrt{11}, -2 + \sqrt{11}$

27. $\dfrac{3 - i\sqrt{87}}{8}, \dfrac{3 + i\sqrt{87}}{8}$ or $\dfrac{3}{8} \pm \dfrac{\sqrt{87}}{8}i$ **29.** $\dfrac{3 - \sqrt{29}}{2}, \dfrac{3 + \sqrt{29}}{2}$ **31.** $\dfrac{-5 - i\sqrt{5}}{10}, \dfrac{-5 + i\sqrt{5}}{10}$ or $-\dfrac{1}{2} \pm \dfrac{\sqrt{5}}{10}i$ **33.** $\dfrac{-1 - \sqrt{19}}{6}, \dfrac{-1 + \sqrt{19}}{6}$

35. $\dfrac{-1 - i\sqrt{23}}{4}, \dfrac{-1 + i\sqrt{23}}{4}$ or $-\dfrac{1}{4} \pm \dfrac{\sqrt{23}}{4}i$ **37.** 1   **39.** $3 - \sqrt{5}, 3 + \sqrt{5}$ **41.** two real solutions   **43.** one real solution

45. two real solutions   **47.** two complex but not real solutions   **49.** two real solutions   **51.** 14 ft   **53.** $(2 + 2\sqrt{2})$ cm, $(2 + 2\sqrt{2})$ cm,
$(4 + 2\sqrt{2})$ cm   **55.** width: $(-5 + 5\sqrt{17})$ ft; length: $(5 + 5\sqrt{17})$ ft   **57. a.** $50\sqrt{2}$ m   **b.** 5000 sq m   **59.** 37.4 ft by 38.5 ft

61. base, $(2 + 2\sqrt{43})$ cm; height, $(-1 + \sqrt{43})$ cm   **63.** 8.9 sec   **65.** 2.8 sec   **67.** $\dfrac{11}{5}$ **69.** 15   **71.** $(x^2 + 5)(x + 2)(x - 2)$

73. $(z + 3)(z - 3)(z + 2)(z - 2)$ **75.** b   **77.** answers may vary   **79.** 0.6, 2.4   **81.** Sunday to Monday   **83.** Wednesday   **85.** 32; yes

87. a. 20,568 students   **b.** 2015   **89. a.** 9076 thousand barrels per day   **b.** 2007   **c.** 2012   **91.** answers may vary   **93.** $\dfrac{\sqrt{3}}{3}$

95. $\dfrac{-\sqrt{2} - i\sqrt{2}}{2}, \dfrac{-\sqrt{2} + i\sqrt{2}}{2}$ or $-\dfrac{\sqrt{2}}{2} \pm \dfrac{\sqrt{2}}{2}i$ **97.** $\dfrac{\sqrt{3} - \sqrt{11}}{4}, \dfrac{\sqrt{3} + \sqrt{11}}{4}$

99. 8.9 sec: 2.8 sec: **101.** two real solutions

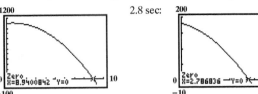

Section 11.3
Practice Exercises

1. 8   **2.** $\dfrac{5 \pm \sqrt{137}}{8}$ **3.** $4, -4, 3i, -3i$ **4.** $1, -3$ **5.** $1, 64$ **6.** Katy: $\dfrac{7 + \sqrt{65}}{2} \approx 7.5$ hr; Steve: $\dfrac{9 + \sqrt{65}}{2} \approx 8.5$ hr

7. to Shanghai: 40 km/hr; to Ningbo: 90 km/hr

Vocabulary, Readiness & Video Check 11.3

1. The values we get for the substituted variable are *not* our final answers. Remember to always substitute back to the original variable and solve
for it if necessary.

Exercise Set 11.3

1. 2 **3.** 16 **5.** 1, 4 **7.** $3 - \sqrt{7}, 3 + \sqrt{7}$ **9.** $\dfrac{3 - \sqrt{57}}{4}, \dfrac{3 + \sqrt{57}}{4}$ **11.** $\dfrac{1 - \sqrt{29}}{2}, \dfrac{1 + \sqrt{29}}{2}$ **13.** $-2, 2, -2i, 2i$

15. $-\dfrac{1}{2}, \dfrac{1}{2}, -i\sqrt{3}, i\sqrt{3}$ **17.** $-3, 3, -2, 2$ **19.** $125, -8$ **21.** $-\dfrac{4}{5}, 0$ **23.** $-\dfrac{1}{8}, 27$ **25.** $-\dfrac{2}{3}, \dfrac{4}{3}$ **27.** $-\dfrac{1}{125}, \dfrac{1}{8}$ **29.** $-\sqrt{2}, \sqrt{2}, -\sqrt{3}, \sqrt{3}$

31. $\dfrac{-9 - \sqrt{201}}{6}, \dfrac{-9 + \sqrt{201}}{6}$ **33.** 2, 3 **35.** 3 **37.** 27, 125 **39.** $1, -3i, 3i$ **41.** $\dfrac{1}{8}, -8$ **43.** $-\dfrac{1}{2}, \dfrac{1}{3}$ **45.** 4 **47.** -3

49. $-\sqrt{5}, \sqrt{5}, -2i, 2i$ **51.** $-3, \dfrac{3 - 3i\sqrt{3}}{2}, \dfrac{3 + 3i\sqrt{3}}{2}$ or $-3, \dfrac{3}{2} \pm \dfrac{3\sqrt{3}}{2}i$ **53.** 6, 12 **55.** $-\dfrac{1}{3}, \dfrac{1}{3}, -\dfrac{i\sqrt{6}}{3}, \dfrac{i\sqrt{6}}{3}$ **57.** 5 **59.** 55 mph: 66 mph

61. 5 mph, then 4 mph **63.** inlet pipe: 15.5 hr; hose: 16.5 hr **65.** 8.5 hr **67.** 12 or -8 **69. a.** $(x - 6)$ in. **b.** $300 = (x - 6) \cdot (x - 6) \cdot 3$
c. 16 in. by 16 in. **71.** 22 feet **73.** $(-\infty, 3]$ **75.** $(-5, \infty)$ **77.** domain: $(-\infty, \infty)$; range: $(-\infty, \infty)$; function **79.** domain: $(-\infty, \infty)$;

range: $[-1, \infty)$; function **81.** $1, -3i, 3i$ **83.** $-\dfrac{1}{2}, \dfrac{1}{3}$ **85.** $-3, \dfrac{3 - 3i\sqrt{3}}{2}, \dfrac{3 + 3i\sqrt{3}}{2}$ or $-3, \dfrac{3}{2} \pm \dfrac{3\sqrt{3}}{2}i$ **87.** answers may vary

89. a. 11.615 m/sec **b.** 11.612 m/sec **c.** 25.925 mph

Integrated Review

1. $-\sqrt{10}, \sqrt{10}$ **2.** $-\sqrt{14}, \sqrt{14}$ **3.** $1 - 2\sqrt{2}, 1 + 2\sqrt{2}$ **4.** $-5 - 2\sqrt{3}, -5 + 2\sqrt{3}$ **5.** $-1 - \sqrt{13}, -1 + \sqrt{13}$ **6.** 1, 11

7. $\dfrac{-3 - \sqrt{69}}{6}, \dfrac{-3 + \sqrt{69}}{6}$ **8.** $\dfrac{-2 - \sqrt{5}}{4}, \dfrac{-2 + \sqrt{5}}{4}$ **9.** $\dfrac{2 - \sqrt{2}}{2}, \dfrac{2 + \sqrt{2}}{2}$ **10.** $-3 - \sqrt{5}, -3 + \sqrt{5}$ **11.** $-2 - i\sqrt{3}, -2 + i\sqrt{3}$

12. $\dfrac{-1 - i\sqrt{11}}{2}, \dfrac{-1 + i\sqrt{11}}{2}$ or $-\dfrac{1}{12} \pm \dfrac{\sqrt{11}}{2}i$ **13.** $\dfrac{-3 - i\sqrt{15}}{2}, \dfrac{-3 + i\sqrt{15}}{2}$ or $-\dfrac{3}{2} \pm \dfrac{\sqrt{15}}{2}i$ **14.** $-3i, 3i$ **15.** $-17, 0$

16. $\dfrac{1 - \sqrt{13}}{4}, \dfrac{1 + \sqrt{13}}{4}$ **17.** $2 - 3\sqrt{3}, 2 + 3\sqrt{3}$ **18.** $2 - \sqrt{3}, 2 + \sqrt{3}$ **19.** $-2, \dfrac{4}{3}$ **20.** $\dfrac{-5 - \sqrt{17}}{4}, \dfrac{-5 + \sqrt{17}}{4}$

21. $1 - \sqrt{6}, 1 + \sqrt{6}$ **22.** $-\sqrt{31}, \sqrt{31}$ **23.** $-\sqrt{11}, \sqrt{11}$ **24.** $-i\sqrt{11}, i\sqrt{11}$ **25.** $-11, 6$ **26.** $\dfrac{-3 - \sqrt{19}}{5}, \dfrac{-3 + \sqrt{19}}{5}$

27. $\dfrac{-3 - \sqrt{17}}{4}, \dfrac{-3 + \sqrt{17}}{4}$ **28.** 4 **29.** $\dfrac{-1 - \sqrt{17}}{8}, \dfrac{-1 + \sqrt{17}}{8}$ **30.** $10\sqrt{2}\,\text{ft} \approx 14.1\,\text{ft}$ **31.** Jack: 9.1 hr; Lucy: 7.1 hr

32. 5 mph during the first part, then 6 mph

Section 11.4
Practice Exercises

1. $(-\infty, -3) \cup (4, \infty)$ **2.** $[0, 8]$ **3.** $(-\infty, -3] \cup [-1, 2]$ **4.** $(-4, 5]$ **5.** $(-\infty, -3) \cup \left(-\dfrac{8}{5}, \infty\right)$

Vocabulary, Readiness & Video Check 11.4

1. $[-7, 3)$ **3.** $(-\infty, 0]$ **5.** $(-\infty, -12) \cup [-10, \infty)$ **7.** We use the solutions to the related equation to divide the number line into regions that either entirely are or entirely are not solution regions; the solutions to the related equation are solutions to the inequality only if the inequality symbol is $\leq$ or $\geq$.

Exercise Set 11.4

1. $(-\infty, -5) \cup (-1, \infty)$ **3.** $[-4, 3]$ **5.** $[2, 5]$ **7.** $\left(-5, -\dfrac{1}{3}\right)$ **9.** $(2, 4) \cup (6, \infty)$ **11.** $(-\infty, -4] \cup [0, 1]$

13. $(-\infty, -3) \cup (-2, 2) \cup (3, \infty)$ **15.** $(-7, 2)$ **17.** $(-1, \infty)$ **19.** $(-\infty, -1] \cup (4, \infty)$ **21.** $(-\infty, 2) \cup \left(\dfrac{11}{4}, \infty\right)$ **23.** $(0, 2] \cup [3, \infty)$

25. $(-\infty, 3)$ **27.** $\left[-\dfrac{5}{4}, \dfrac{3}{2}\right]$ **29.** $(-\infty, 0) \cup (1, \infty)$ **31.** $(-\infty, -4] \cup [4, 6]$ **33.** $\left(-\infty, -\dfrac{2}{3}\right] \cup \left[\dfrac{3}{2}, \infty\right)$ **35.** $\left(-4, -\dfrac{3}{2}\right) \cup \left(\dfrac{3}{2}, \infty\right)$

37. $(-\infty, -5] \cup [-1, 1] \cup [5, \infty)$ **39.** $\left(-\infty, -\dfrac{5}{3}\right) \cup \left(\dfrac{7}{2}, \infty\right)$ **41.** $(0, 10)$ **43.** $(-\infty, -4) \cup [5, \infty)$ **45.** $(-\infty, -6] \cup (-1, 0] \cup (7, \infty)$

47. $(-\infty, 1) \cup (2, \infty)$ **49.** $(-\infty, -8] \cup (-4, \infty)$ **51.** $(-\infty, 0] \cup \left(5, \dfrac{11}{2}\right]$ **53.** $(0, \infty)$ **55.** 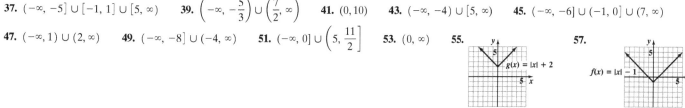 **57.**

$g(x) = |x| + 2$ $f(x) = |x| - 1$

59. 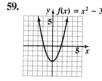 $f(x) = x^2 - 3$ **61.** $h(x) = x^2 + 1$ **63.** answers may vary **65.** $(-\infty, -1) \cup (0, 1)$, or any number less than -1 or between 0 and 1
67. x is between 2 and 11 **69.** 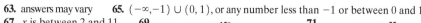 **71.**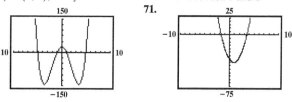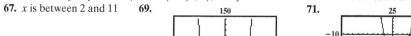

Section 11.5
Practice Exercises

1. $f(x) = x^2$ $g(x) = x^2 - 4$ $(0, -4)$ $(0, 0)$

2. a. 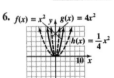 $(0, -5)$

b. $(0, 3)$

3. 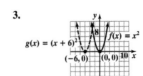 $g(x) = (x + 6)^2$ $f(x) = x^2$ $(-6, 0)$ $(0, 0)$

4. a. $(-4, 0)$

b. $(7, 0)$

5. 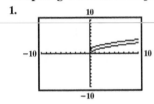 $(-2, 2)$

6. 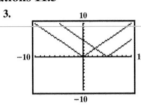 $f(x) = x^2$ $g(x) = 4x^2$ $h(x) = \frac{1}{4}x^2$

7. 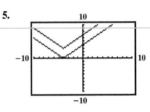 $(0, 0)$ $(2, -2)$ $(-2, -2)$ $(-4, -8)$ $(4, -8)$

8. $(4, -3)$ $x = 4$

Graphing Calculator Explorations 11.5

1.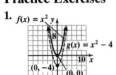

3.

5.

Vocabulary, Readiness & Video Check 11.5

1. quadratic   **3.** upward   **5.** lowest   **7.** $(0, 0)$ **9.** $(2, 0)$ **11.** $(0, 3)$ **13.** $(-1, 5)$ **15.** Graphs of the form $f(x) = x^2 + k$ shift up or down the y-axis k units from $y = x^2$; the y-intercept.   **17.** The vertex, (h, k), and the axis of symmetry, $x = h$; the basic shape of $y = x^2$ does not change.   **19.** the coordinates of the vertex, whether the graph opens upward or downward, whether the graph is narrower or wider than $y = x^2$, and the graph's axis of symmetry

Exercise Set 11.5

1. $V(0, -1)$ $x = 0$

3. $V(0, 5)$ $x = 0$

5. $V(0, 7)$ $x = 0$

7. $V(5, 0)$ $x = 5$

9. $V(-2, 0)$ $x = -2$

11. 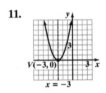 $V(-3, 0)$ $x = -3$

13. $V(2, 5)$ $x = 2$

15. $V(-1, 4)$ $x = -1$

17. 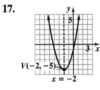 $V(-2, -5)$ $x = -2$

19. $V(0, 0)$ $x = 0$

21. $V(0, 0)$ $x = 0$

23. $V(0, 0)$ $x = 0$

25. $V(1, 3)$ $x = 1$

27. $V(-3, 1)$ $x = -3$

29. $V(6, -3)$ $x = 6$

31. $x = 2$ $V(2, 0)$ $y = -(x - 2)^2$

33. $x = 0$ $V(0, 4)$ $y = -x^2 + 4$

35. 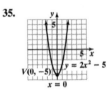 $V(0, -5)$ $y = 2x^2 - 5$ $x = 0$

37. $y = (x - 6)^2 + 4$ $V(6, 4)$ $x = 6$

39. 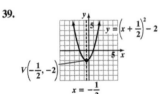 $y = \left(x + \frac{1}{2}\right)^2 - 2$ $V\left(-\frac{1}{2}, -2\right)$ $x = -\frac{1}{2}$

41. 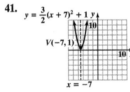 $y = \frac{3}{2}(x + 7)^2 + 1$ $V(-7, 1)$ $x = -7$

43. 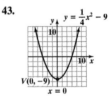 $y = \frac{1}{4}x^2 - 9$ $V(0, -9)$ $x = 0$

45. 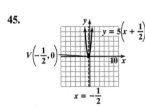 $y = 5\left(x + \frac{1}{2}\right)^2$ $V\left(-\frac{1}{2}, 0\right)$ $x = -\frac{1}{2}$

47. 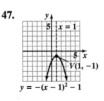 $x = 1$ $V(1, -1)$ $y = -(x - 1)^2 - 1$

49. 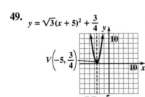 $y = \sqrt{3}(x + 5)^2 + \frac{3}{4}$ $V\left(-5, \frac{3}{4}\right)$ $x = -5$

51. 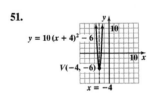 $y = 10(x + 4)^2 - 6$ $V(-4, -6)$ $x = -4$

53.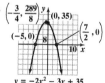
$y = -2(x - 4)^2 + 5$

55. $x^2 + 8x + 16$ **57.** $z^2 - 16z + 64$ **59.** $y^2 + y + \dfrac{1}{4}$ **61.** $-6, 2$ **63.** $-5 - \sqrt{26}, -5 + \sqrt{26}$

65. $4 - 3\sqrt{2}, 4 + 3\sqrt{2}$ **67.** c **69.** $f(x) = 5(x - 2)^2 + 3$ **71.** $f(x) = 5(x + 3)^2 + 6$

73.   **75.**   **77.**   **79. a.** 119,141 million **b.** 284,953 million

Section 11.6
Practice Exercises

1.   **2.** $\left(-\dfrac{1}{2}, 2\right)$ **3.**   **4.** $(1, -4)$ **5.** Maximum height 9 feet in $\dfrac{3}{4}$ second

Vocabulary, Readiness & Video Check 11.6
1. (h, k) **3.** We can immediately identify the vertex (h, k), whether the parabola opens upward or downward, and know its axis of symmetry; completing the square. **5.** the vertex

Exercise Set 11.6

1. $0; 1$ **3.** $2; 1$ **5.** $1; 1$ **7.** down **9.** up **11.** $(-4, -9)$ **13.** $(5, 30)$ **15.** $(1, -2)$ **17.** $\left(\dfrac{1}{2}, \dfrac{5}{4}\right)$ **19.** D **21.** B

23.   **25.**   **27.**   **29.**   **31.**

33.   **35.** 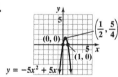 **37.**   **39.**   **41.**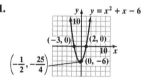

43.   **45.**   **47.** 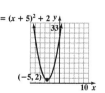 **49.** 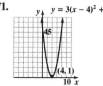 **51.**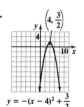

53. $\left(-\dfrac{3}{4}, \dfrac{289}{8}\right)$ **55.** 144 ft **57. a.** 200 bicycles **b.** \$12,000 **59.** 30 and 30 **61.** $5, -5$ **63.** length, 20 units; width, 20 units

65.   **67.**   **69.** 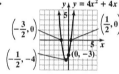 **71.**   **73.**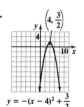

75. minimum value   **77.** maximum value   **79.** $y = x^2 + 10x + 15$ 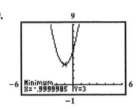   **81.** 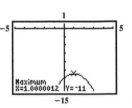   **83.** -0.84 **85.** 1.43

87. a. maximum; answers may vary   **b.** 2035   **c.** 311 million   **89.**

91.

Chapter 11 Vocabulary Check

1. discriminant   **2.** $\pm\sqrt{b}$ **3.** $\dfrac{-b}{2a}$ **4.** quadratic inequality   **5.** completing the square   **6.** $(0, k)$ **7.** $(h, 0)$ **8.** (h, k)
9. quadratic formula   **10.** quadratic

Chapter 11 Review

1. 14, 1   **3.** $-7, 7$ **5.** $\dfrac{-3 - \sqrt{5}}{2}, \dfrac{-3 + \sqrt{5}}{2}$ **7.** 4.25%   **9.** two complex but not real solutions   **11.** two real solutions   **13.** 8   **15.** $-\dfrac{5}{2}, 1$

17. $\dfrac{5 - i\sqrt{143}}{12}, \dfrac{5 + i\sqrt{143}}{12}$ or $\dfrac{5}{12} \pm \dfrac{\sqrt{143}}{12}i$ **19. a.** 20 ft   **b.** $\dfrac{15 + \sqrt{321}}{16}$ sec; 2.1 sec   **21.** 3, $\dfrac{-3 - 3i\sqrt{3}}{2}, \dfrac{-3 + 3i\sqrt{3}}{2}$ or 3, $-\dfrac{3}{2} \pm \dfrac{3\sqrt{3}}{2}i$

23. $\dfrac{2}{3}, 5$ **25.** 1, 125   **27.** $-1, 1, -i, i$ **29.** Jerome: 10.5 hr; Tim: 9.5 hr   **31.** $[-5, 5]$ **33.** $[-5, -2] \cup [2, 5]$ **35.** $(5, 6)$

37. $(-\infty, -5] \cup [-2, 6]$ **39.** $(-\infty, 0)$ **41.**   **43.**   **45.**   **47.**

49.   **51.**   **53.**   **55.** 210 and 210   **57.** $-5, 6$ **59.** $-2, 2$

61. $\dfrac{-1 - 3i\sqrt{3}}{2}, \dfrac{-1 + 3i\sqrt{3}}{2}$ or $-\dfrac{1}{2} \pm \dfrac{3\sqrt{3}}{2}i$

63. $-i\sqrt{11}, i\sqrt{11}$ **65.** $\dfrac{21 - \sqrt{41}}{50}, \dfrac{21 + \sqrt{41}}{50}$ **67.** 8,64   **69.** $[-5, 0] \cup \left(\dfrac{3}{4}, \infty\right)$ **71. a.** 95,157 thousand passengers   **b.** 2022

Chapter 11 Test

1. $\dfrac{7}{5}, -1$ **2.** $-1 - \sqrt{10}, -1 + \sqrt{10}$ **3.** $\dfrac{1 - i\sqrt{31}}{2}, \dfrac{1 + i\sqrt{31}}{2}$ or $\dfrac{1}{2} \pm \dfrac{\sqrt{31}}{2}i$ **4.** $3 - \sqrt{7}, 3 + \sqrt{7}$ **5.** $-\dfrac{1}{7}, -1$

6. $\dfrac{3 - \sqrt{29}}{2}, \dfrac{3 + \sqrt{29}}{2}$ **7.** $-2 - \sqrt{11}, -2 + \sqrt{11}$ **8.** $-1, 1, -i, i, -3$ **9.** $-1, 1, -i, i$ **10.** 6, 7   **11.** $3 - \sqrt{7}, 3 + \sqrt{7}$

12. $\dfrac{2 - i\sqrt{6}}{2}, \dfrac{2 + i\sqrt{6}}{2}$ or $1 \pm \dfrac{\sqrt{6}}{2}i$ **13.** $\left(-\infty, -\dfrac{3}{2}\right) \cup (5, \infty)$ **14.** $(-\infty, -5] \cup [-4, 4] \cup [5, \infty)$ **15.** $(-\infty, -3) \cup (2, \infty)$

16. $(-\infty, -3) \cup [2, 3)$ **17.**   **18.**   **19.**   **20.**   **21.** $(5 + \sqrt{17})$ hr ≈ 9.12 hr

22. a. 272 ft   **b.** 5.12 sec   **23.** 7.2 ft

Chapter 11 Cumulative Review

1. a. $\dfrac{1}{2}$ **b.** 19; Sec. 1.6, Ex. 6   **3. a.** $5x + 7$ **b.** $-4a - 1$ **c.** $4y - 3y^2$ **d.** $7.3x - 6$ **e.** $\dfrac{1}{2}b$; Sec. 2.1, Ex. 4   **5.** no solution; Sec. 4.1, Ex. 5
7. $(-2, 0)$; Sec. 4.2, Ex. 4   **9. a.** x^3 **b.** 256   **c.** -27 **d.** cannot be simplified   **e.** $2x^4y$; Sec. 5.1, Ex. 9   **11. a.** 5   **b.** 5; Sec. 5.7, Ex. 3
13. $-6, -\dfrac{3}{2}, \dfrac{1}{5}$; Sec. 6.6, Ex. 9   **15.** $\dfrac{1}{5x - 1}$; Sec. 7.1, Ex. 2a   **17.** $\dfrac{xy + 2x^3}{y - 1}$; Sec. 7.7, Ex. 3   **19.** $(2m^2 - 1)^2$; Sec. 6.3, Ex. 10

21. -10 and 7; Sec. 6.7, Ex. 2   **23. a.** $5x\sqrt{x}$ **b.** $3x^2y^2\sqrt[3]{2y^2}$ **c.** $3z^2\sqrt[4]{z^3}$; Sec. 10.3, Ex. 4   **25. a.** $\dfrac{2\sqrt{5}}{5}$ **b.** $\dfrac{8\sqrt{x}}{3x}$ **c.** $\dfrac{\sqrt[3]{4}}{2}$; Sec. 10.5, Ex. 1

27. $\dfrac{2}{9}$; Sec. 10.6, Ex. 5   **29.** -5; Sec. 7.5, Ex. 1   **31.** -5; Sec. 7.6, Ex. 5   **33.** $k = \dfrac{1}{6}$; $y = \dfrac{1}{6}x$; Sec. 8.4, Ex. 1   **35. a.** 3 **b.** $|x|$ **c.** $|x - 2|$

d. -5 **e.** $2x - 7$ **f.** $5|x|$ **g.** $|x + 1|$; Sec. 10.1, Ex. 5   **37. a.** $\sqrt{x}$ **b.** $\sqrt[3]{5}$ **c.** $\sqrt{rs^3}$; Sec. 10.2, Ex. 7   **39. a.** $\dfrac{1}{2} + \dfrac{3}{2}i$

b. $0 - \dfrac{7}{3}i$; Sec. 10.7, Ex. 5   **41.** $-1 + 2\sqrt{3}, -1 - 2\sqrt{3}$; Sec. 11.1, Ex. 3   **43.** 9; Sec. 11.3, Ex. 1

CHAPTER 12 EXPONENTIAL AND LOGARITHMIC FUNCTIONS

Section 12.1
Practice Exercises

1. a. $4x + 7$ **b.** $-2x - 3$ **c.** $3x^2 + 11x + 10$ **d.** $\dfrac{x + 2}{3x + 5}$, where $x \neq -\dfrac{5}{3}$ **2. a.** $50; 46$ **b.** $9x^2 - 30x + 26; 3x^2 - 2$

3. a. $x^2 + 6x + 14$ **b.** $x^2 + 8$ **4. a.** $(h \circ g)(x)$ **b.** $(g \circ f)(x)$

Vocabulary, Readiness & Video Check 12.1
1. C   **3.** F   **5.** D   **7.** You can find $(f + g)(x)$ and then find $(f + g)(2)$ or you can find $f(2)$ and $g(2)$ and then add those results.

Exercise Set 12.1

1. a. $3x - 6$ **b.** $-x - 8$ **c.** $2x^2 - 13x - 7$ **d.** $\dfrac{x - 7}{2x + 1}$, where $x \neq -\dfrac{1}{2}$ **3. a.** $x^2 + 5x + 1$ **b.** $x^2 - 5x + 1$ **c.** $5x^3 + 5x$

d. $\dfrac{x^2 + 1}{5x}$, where $x \neq 0$ **5. a.** $\sqrt[3]{x} + x + 5$ **b.** $\sqrt[3]{x} - x - 5$ **c.** $x\sqrt[3]{x} + 5\sqrt[3]{x}$ **d.** $\dfrac{\sqrt[3]{x}}{x + 5}$, where $x \neq -5$

7. a. $5x^2 - 3x$ **b.** $-5x^2 - 3x$ **c.** $-15x^3$ **d.** $-\dfrac{3}{5x}$, where $x \neq 0$ **9.** 42 **11.** -18 **13.** 0

15. $(f \circ g)(x) = 25x^2 + 1; (g \circ f)(x) = 5x^2 + 5$ **17.** $(f \circ g)(x) = 2x + 11; (g \circ f)(x) = 2x + 4$

19. $(f \circ g)(x) = -8x^3 - 2x - 2; (g \circ f)(x) = -2x^3 - 2x + 4$ **21.** $(f \circ g)(x) = |10x - 3|; (g \circ f)(x) = 10|x| - 3$

23. $(f \circ g)(x) = \sqrt{-5x + 2}; (g \circ f)(x) = -5\sqrt{x} + 2$ **25.** $H(x) = (g \circ h)(x)$ **27.** $F(x) = (h \circ f)(x)$ **29.** $G(x) = (f \circ g)(x)$

31. answers may vary; for example, $g(x) = x + 2$ and $f(x) = x^2$ **33.** answers may vary; for example, $g(x) = x + 5$ and $f(x) = \sqrt{x} + 2$

35. answers may vary; for example, $g(x) = 2x - 3$ and $f(x) = \dfrac{1}{x}$ **37.** $y = x - 2$ **39.** $y = \dfrac{x}{3}$ **41.** $y = -\dfrac{x + 7}{2}$ **43.** 6 **45.** 4

47. 4 **49.** -1 **51.** answers may vary   **53.** $P(x) = R(x) - C(x)$

Section 12.2
Practice Exercises

1. a. one-to-one   **b.** not one-to-one   **c.** not one-to-one   **d.** one-to-one   **e.** not one-to-one   **f.** not one-to-one   **2. a.** no, not one-to-one
b. yes   **c.** yes   **d.** no, not a function   **e.** no, not a function   **3.** $f^{-1} = \{(4, 3), (0, -2), (8, 2), (6, 6)\}$ **4.** $f^{-1}(x) = 6 - x$

5. 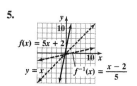   **6. a.**   **b.**   **7.**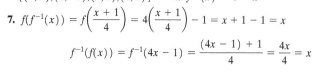

$$f(f^{-1}(x)) = f\left(\dfrac{x + 1}{4}\right) = 4\left(\dfrac{x + 1}{4}\right) - 1 = x + 1 - 1 = x$$

$$f^{-1}(f(x)) = f^{-1}(4x - 1) = \dfrac{(4x - 1) + 1}{4} = \dfrac{4x}{4} = x$$

Vocabulary, Readiness & Video Check 12.2
1. $(2, 11)$ **3.** the inverse of f **5.** vertical   **7.** $y = x$ **9.** Every function must have each x-value correspond to only one y-value.
A one-to-one function must also have each y-value correspond to only one x-value.   **11.** Yes; by the definition of an inverse function.
13. Once you know some points of the original equation or graph, you can switch the x's and y's of these points to find points that satisfy the inverse and then graph it. You can also check that the two graphs (the original and the inverse) are symmetric about the line $y = x$.

Exercise Set 12.2
1. one-to-one; $f^{-1} = \{(-1, -1), (1, 1), (2, 0), (0, 2)\}$ **3.** one-to-one; $h^{-1} = \{(10, 10)\}$ **5.** one-to-one; $f^{-1} = \{(12, 11), (3, 4), (4, 3), (6, 6)\}$
7. not one-to-one   **9.** one-to-one;

Rank in Population (Input)	1	47	16	25	36	7
State (Output)	CA	AK	IN	LA	NM	OH

11. a. 3 **b.** 1 **13. a.** 1 **b.** -1 **15.** one-to-one   **17.** not one-to-one   **19.** one-to-one   **21.** not one-to-one

23. $f^{-1}(x) = x - 4$ **25.** $f^{-1}(x) = \dfrac{x+3}{2}$ **27.** $f^{-1}(x) = 2x + 2$ **29.** $f^{-1}(x) = \sqrt[3]{x}$ **31.** $f^{-1}(x) = \dfrac{x-2}{5}$ **33.** $f^{-1}(x) = 5x + 2$

35. $f^{-1}(x) = x^3$ **37.** $f^{-1}(x) = \dfrac{5-x}{3x}$

39. $f^{-1}(x) = \sqrt[3]{x} - 2$

41. 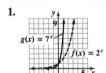   **43.** 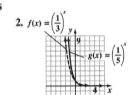   **45.** 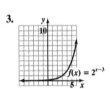   **47.** $(f \circ f^{-1})(x) = x; (f^{-1} \circ f)(x) = x$ **49.** $(f \circ f^{-1})(x) = x; (f^{-1} \circ f)(x) = x$

51. 5   **53.** 8   **55.** $\dfrac{1}{27}$ **57.** 9   **59.** $3^{1/2} \approx 1.73$ **61. a.** $(2, 9)$ **b.** $(9, 2)$

63. a. $\left(-2, \dfrac{1}{4}\right), \left(-1, \dfrac{1}{2}\right), (0, 1), (1, 2), (2, 5)$ **b.** $\left(\dfrac{1}{4}, -2\right), \left(\dfrac{1}{2}, -1\right), (1, 0), (2, 1), (5, 2)$ **c.** 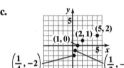   **d.**

65. answers may vary   **67.** $f^{-1}(x) = \dfrac{x-1}{3}$;   **69.** $f^{-1}(x) = x^3 - 1$;

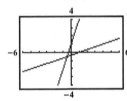   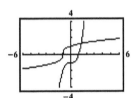

Section 12.3
Practice Exercises

1. 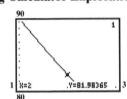   **2.** $f(x) = \left(\dfrac{1}{3}\right)^x$ **3.** 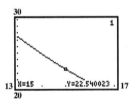   **4. a.** 2   **b.** $\dfrac{4}{3}$ **c.** -4 **5.** \$3950.43   **6. a.** 90.54%   **b.** 60.86%

Graphing Calculator Explorations 12.3

1. 81.98%;   **3.** 22.54%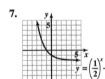

Vocabulary, Readiness & Video Check 12.3

1. exponential   **3.** yes   **5.** no; none   **7.** $(-\infty, \infty)$ **9.** In a polynomial function, the base is the variable and the exponent is the constant; in an exponential function, the base is the constant and the exponent is the variable.   **11.** $y = 30(0.996)^{101} \approx 20.0$ lb

Exercise Set 12.3

1. 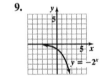   **3.**   **5.**   **7.**   **9.**   **11.**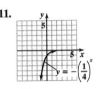

13.   **15.**   **17.** C   **19.** B   **21.** 3   **23.** $\dfrac{3}{4}$ **25.** $\dfrac{8}{5}$ **27.** $-\dfrac{2}{3}$ **29.** 4   **31.** $\dfrac{3}{2}$

33. $-\dfrac{1}{3}$ **35.** -2 **37.** 24.6 lb **39. a.** 9.7 billion lb **b.** 12.3 billion lb **41. a.** 192,927 students **b.** 463,772 students **43.** 378.0 million
45. 544,000 mosquitoes **47.** \$7621.42 **49.** \$4065.59 **51.** 4 **53.** $\varnothing$ **55.** 2, 3 **57.** 3 **59.** -1 **61.** no **63.** no **65.** C
67. D **69.** answers may vary **71.** **73.** **75.** The graphs are the same since $\left(\dfrac{1}{2}\right)^{-x} = 2^x$.

77. 24.55 lb **79.** 20.09 lb

Section 12.4
Practice Exercises
1. 136,839 **2.** 32 **3.** 47.4 g

Vocabulary, Readiness & Video Check 12.4
1. For Example 1, the growth rate is given as 5% per year. Since this is "per year," the number of time intervals is the "number of years," or 8.
3. time intervals = years/half-life; the decay rate is 50% or $\dfrac{1}{2}$ because half-life is the amount of time it takes half of a substance to decay

Exercise Set 12.4
1. 451 **3.** 144,302 **5.** 21,231 **7.** 202 **9.** 1470 **11.** 13 **13.** 712,880 **15.** 383 **17.** 333 bison **19.** 1 g **21. a.** $\dfrac{14}{7} = 2$; 10; yes
b. $\dfrac{11}{7} \approx 1.6$; 13.2; yes **23.** $\dfrac{500}{152} \approx 3.3$; 2.1; yes **25.** 4.9 g **27.** 3 **29.** -1 **31.** no; answers may vary

Section 12.5
Practice Exercises
1. a. $3^4 = 81$ **b.** $5^{-1} = \dfrac{1}{5}$ **c.** $7^{1/2} = \sqrt{7}$ **d.** $13^4 = y$ **2. a.** $\log_4 64 = 3$ **b.** $\log_6 \sqrt[3]{6} = \dfrac{1}{3}$ **c.** $\log_5 \dfrac{1}{125} = -3$ **d.** $\log_\pi z = 7$
3. a. 2 **b.** -3 **c.** $\dfrac{1}{2}$ **4. a.** -2 **b.** 2 **c.** 36 **d.** 0 **e.** 0 **5. a.** 4 **b.** -2 **c.** 5 **d.** 4
6. **7.**

Vocabulary, Readiness & Video Check 12.5
1. logarithmic **3.** yes **5.** no; none **7.** $(-\infty, \infty)$ **9.** First write the equation as an equivalent exponential equation. Then solve.

Exercise Set 12.5
1. $6^2 = 36$ **3.** $3^{-3} = \dfrac{1}{27}$ **5.** $10^3 = 1000$ **7.** $9^4 = x$ **9.** $\pi^{-2} = \dfrac{1}{\pi^2}$ **11.** $7^{1/2} = \sqrt{7}$ **13.** $0.7^3 = 0.343$ **15.** $3^{-4} = \dfrac{1}{81}$
17. $\log_2 16 = 4$ **19.** $\log_{10} 100 = 2$ **21.** $\log_\pi x = 3$ **23.** $\log_{10} \dfrac{1}{10} = -1$ **25.** $\log_4 \dfrac{1}{16} = -2$ **27.** $\log_5 \sqrt{5} = \dfrac{1}{2}$
29. 3 **31.** -2 **33.** $\dfrac{1}{2}$ **35.** -1 **37.** 0 **39.** 2 **41.** 4 **43.** -3 **45.** 2 **47.** 81 **49.** 7 **51.** -3
53. -3 **55.** 2 **57.** 2 **59.** $\dfrac{27}{64}$ **61.** 10 **63.** 4 **65.** 5 **67.** $\dfrac{1}{49}$ **69.** 3 **71.** 3 **73.** 1 **75.** -1
77. **79.** **81.** **83.** **85.** 1 **87.** $\dfrac{x - 4}{2}$ **89.** $\dfrac{2x + 3}{x^2}$ **91.** 3

93. a. $g(2) = 25$ **b.** $(25, 2)$ **c.** $f(25) = 2$ **95.** answers may vary **97.** $\dfrac{9}{5}$ **99.** 1

101. **103.** $y = \left(\dfrac{1}{3}\right)^x$ **105.** answers may vary **107.** 0.0827

Section 12.6
Practice Exercises
1. a. $\log_8 15$ **b.** $\log_2 6$ **c.** $\log_5(x^2 - 1)$ **2. a.** $\log_5 3$ **b.** $\log_6 \dfrac{x}{3}$ **c.** $\log_4 \dfrac{x^2 + 1}{x^2 + 3}$ **3. a.** $8 \log_7 x$ **b.** $\dfrac{1}{4}\log_5 7$

4. a. $\log_5 512$ **b.** $\log_8 \dfrac{x^2}{x + 3}$ **c.** $\log_7 15$ **5. a.** $\log_5 4 + \log_5 3 - \log_5 7$ **b.** $2 \log_4 a - 5 \log_4 b$ **6. a.** 1.39 **b.** 1.66 **c.** 0.28

Vocabulary, Readiness & Video Check 12.6
1. 36 **3.** $\log_b 2^7$ **5.** x **7.** No, the product property says the logarithm of a product can be written as a sum of logarithms—the expression in

Example 2 is a logarithm of a sum. **9.** Since $\dfrac{1}{x} = x^{-1}$, this gives us $\log_2 x^{-1}$. Using the power property, we get $-1 \log_2 x$ or $-\log_2 x$.

Exercise Set 12.6
1. $\log_5 14$ **3.** $\log_4 9x$ **5.** $\log_6(x^2 + x)$ **7.** $\log_{10}(10x^2 + 20)$ **9.** $\log_5 3$ **11.** $\log_3 4$ **13.** $\log_2 \dfrac{x}{y}$ **15.** $\log_2 \dfrac{x^2 + 6}{x^2 + 1}$ **17.** $2 \log_3 x$

19. $-1 \log_4 5 = -\log_4 5$ **21.** $\dfrac{1}{2}\log_5 y$ **23.** $\log_2 5x^3$ **25.** $\log_4 48$ **27.** $\log_5 x^3 z^6$ **29.** $\log_4 4$, or 1 **31.** $\log_7 \dfrac{9}{2}$ **33.** $\log_{10} \dfrac{x^3 - 2x}{x + 1}$

35. $\log_2 \dfrac{x^{7/2}}{(x + 1)^2}$ **37.** $\log_8 x^{16/3}$ **39.** $\log_3 4 + \log_3 y - \log_3 5$ **41.** $\log_4 5 - \log_4 9 - \log_4 z$ **43.** $3 \log_2 x - \log_2 y$ **45.** $\dfrac{1}{2}\log_b 7 + \dfrac{1}{2}\log_b x$

47. $4 \log_6 x + 5 \log_6 y$ **49.** $3 \log_5 x + \log_5(x + 1)$ **51.** $2 \log_6 x - \log_6(x + 3)$ **53.** 1.2 **55.** 0.2 **57.** 0.35 **59.** 1.29 **61.** -0.68

63. -0.125 **65–66.** **67.** 2 **69.** 2 **71.** b **73.** true **75.** false **77.** false **79.** because $\log_b 1 = 0$

Integrated Review
1. $x^2 + x - 5$ **2.** $-x^2 + x - 7$ **3.** $x^3 - 6x^2 + x - 6$ **4.** $\dfrac{x - 6}{x^2 + 1}$ **5.** $\sqrt{3x - 1}$ **6.** $3\sqrt{x} - 1$

7. one-to-one; $\{(6, -2), (8, 4), (-6, 2), (3, 3)\}$ **8.** not one-to-one **9.** not one-to-one **10.** one-to-one

11. not one-to-one **12.** $f^{-1}(x) = \dfrac{x}{3}$ **13.** $f^{-1}(x) = x - 4$ **14.** $f^{-1}(x) = \dfrac{x + 1}{5}$ **15.** $f^{-1}(x) = \dfrac{x - 2}{3}$

16. $y = \left(\dfrac{1}{2}\right)^x$ **17.** $y = 2^x + 1$ **18.** $y = \log_3 x$ **19.** $y = \log_{1/3} x$ **20.** 3

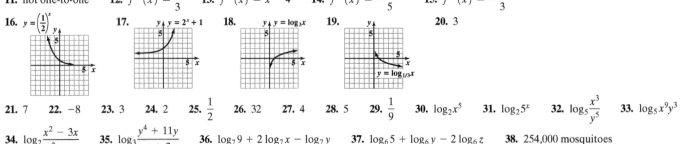

21. 7 **22.** -8 **23.** 3 **24.** 2 **25.** $\dfrac{1}{2}$ **26.** 32 **27.** 4 **28.** 5 **29.** $\dfrac{1}{9}$ **30.** $\log_2 x^5$ **31.** $\log_2 5^x$ **32.** $\log_5 \dfrac{x^3}{y^5}$ **33.** $\log_5 x^9 y^3$

34. $\log_2 \dfrac{x^2 - 3x}{x^2 + 4}$ **35.** $\log_3 \dfrac{y^4 + 11y}{y + 2}$ **36.** $\log_7 9 + 2 \log_7 x - \log_7 y$ **37.** $\log_6 5 + \log_6 y - 2 \log_6 z$ **38.** $254,000$ mosquitoes

Section 12.7
Practice Exercises
1. 1.1761 **2. a.** -2 **b.** 5 **c.** $\dfrac{1}{5}$ **d.** -3 **3.** $10^{3.4} \approx 2511.8864$ **4.** 5.6 **5.** 2.5649 **6. a.** 4 **b.** $\dfrac{1}{3}$ **7.** $\dfrac{e^8}{5} \approx 596.1916$

8. $\$3051.00$ **9.** 0.7740

Vocabulary, Readiness & Video Check 12.7
1. 10 **3.** 7 **5.** 5 **7.** $\dfrac{\log 7}{\log 2}$ or $\dfrac{\ln 7}{\ln 2}$ **9.** The understood base of a common logarithm is 10. If you're finding the common logarithm of a known

power of 10, then the common logarithm is the known power of 10. **11.** $\log_b b^x = x$

Exercise Set 12.7
1. 0.9031 **3.** 0.3636 **5.** 0.6931 **7.** -2.6367 **9.** 1.1004 **11.** 1.6094 **13.** 1.6180 **15.** 2 **17.** -3 **19.** 2 **21.** $\dfrac{1}{4}$

23. 3 **25.** -7 **27.** -4 **29.** $\dfrac{1}{2}$ **31.** $\dfrac{e^7}{2} \approx 548.3166$ **33.** $10^{1.3} \approx 19.9526$ **35.** $\dfrac{10^{1.1}}{2} \approx 6.2946$ **37.** $e^{1.4} \approx 4.0552$

39. $\dfrac{4 + e^{2.3}}{3} \approx 4.6581$ **41.** $10^{2.3} \approx 199.5262$ **43.** $e^{-2.3} \approx 0.1003$ **45.** $\dfrac{10^{-0.5} - 1}{2} \approx -0.3419$ **47.** $\dfrac{e^{0.18}}{4} \approx 0.2993$

49. 1.5850 **51.** -2.3219 **53.** 1.5850 **55.** -1.6309 **57.** 0.8617 **59.** 4.2 **61.** 5.3 **63.** $\$3656.38$ **65.** $\$2542.50$

67. $\dfrac{4}{7}$ **69.** $x = \dfrac{3y}{4}$ **71.** $-6, -1$ **73.** $(2, -3)$ **75.** answers may vary **77.** ln 50; answers may vary

79. $f(x) = e^x$

81. $f(x) = e^{-3x}$

83. 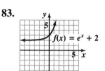 $f(x) = e^x + 2$

85. 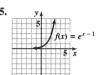 $f(x) = e^{x-1}$

87. $f(x) = 3e^x$

89. $f(x) = \ln x$

91. 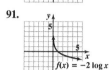 $f(x) = -2\log x$

93. 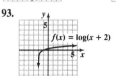 $f(x) = \log(x + 2)$

95. $f(x) = \ln x - 3$

97. answers may vary;

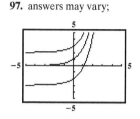

Section 12.8
Practice Exercises

1. $\dfrac{\log 9}{\log 5} \approx 1.3652$ **2.** 33   **3.** 1   **4.** $\dfrac{1}{3}$ **5.** 937 rabbits   **6.** 10 yr

Graphing Calculator Explorations 12.8

1. 3.67 years, or 3 years and 8 months   **3.** 23.16 years, or 23 years and 2 months

Vocabulary, Readiness & Video Check 12.8

1. $\ln(4x - 2) = \ln 3$ is the same as $\log_e(4x - 2) = \log_e 3$. Therefore, from the logarithm property of equality, we know that $4x - 2 = 3$.

3. $2000 = 1000\left(1 + \dfrac{0.07}{12}\right)^{12 \cdot t} \approx 9.9$ yr; As long as the interest rate and compounding are the same, it takes any amount of money the same time to double.

Exercise Set 12.8

1. $\dfrac{\log 6}{\log 3}$; 1.6309   **3.** $\dfrac{\log 3.8}{2\log 3}$; 0.6076   **5.** $\dfrac{3\log 2 + \log 5}{\log 2}$ or $3 + \dfrac{\log 5}{\log 2}$; 5.3219   **7.** $\dfrac{\log 5}{\log 9}$; 0.7325   **9.** $\dfrac{\log 3 - 7\log 4}{\log 4}$ or $\dfrac{\log 3}{\log 4} - 7$; −6.2075

11. 11   **13.** $\dfrac{1}{2}$ **15.** $\dfrac{3}{4}$ **17.** −2, 3   **19.** 2   **21.** $\dfrac{1}{8}$ **23.** $\dfrac{4\log 7 + \log 11}{3\log 7}$ or $\dfrac{1}{3}\left(4 + \dfrac{\log 11}{\log 7}\right)$; 1.7441   **25.** 4, −1   **27.** $\dfrac{\ln 5}{6}$; 0.2682

29. 9, −9   **31.** $\dfrac{1}{5}$ **33.** 100   **35.** $\dfrac{192}{127}$ **37.** $\dfrac{2}{3}$ **39.** $\dfrac{-5 + \sqrt{33}}{2}$ **41.** 103 wolves   **43.** 7582 inhabitants   **45.** 9.9 yr   **47.** 1.7 yr

49. 8.8 yr   **51.** 24.5 lb   **53.** 55.7 in.   **55.** 11.9 lb/sq in.   **57.** 3.2 mi   **59.** 12 weeks   **61.** 18 weeks   **63.** $-\dfrac{5}{3}$ **65.** $\dfrac{17}{4}$

67. $f^{-1}(x) = \dfrac{x - 2}{5}$ **69.** 15 yr   **71.** answers may vary

73. 6.93;   **75.** −3.68; 0.19   **77.** 1.74   **79.** 0.2

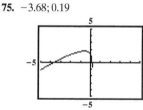   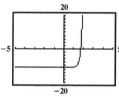   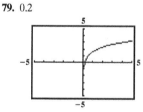

Chapter 12 Vocabulary Check

1. inverse   **2.** composition   **3.** exponential   **4.** symmetric   **5.** Natural   **6.** Common   **7.** vertical; horizontal   **8.** logarithmic
9. Half-life   **10.** exponential

Chapter 12 Review

1. $3x - 4$ **3.** $2x^2 - 9x - 5$ **5.** $x^2 + 2x - 1$ **7.** 18   **9.** −2   **11.** one-to-one; $h^{-1} = \{(14, -9), (8, 6), (12, -11), (15, 15)\}$
13. one-to-one;

Rank in Housing Starts for 2009 (Input)	4	3	1	2
U.S. Region (Output)	Northeast	Midwest	South	West

15. a. 3   **b.** 7   **17.** not one-to-one   **19.** not one-to-one   **21.** $f^{-1}(x) = x + 9$ **23.** $f^{-1}(x) = \dfrac{x - 11}{6}$ **25.** $f^{-1}(x) = \sqrt[3]{x + 5}$

27. $g^{-1}(x) = \dfrac{6x + 7}{12}$ **29.**

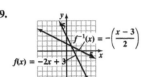

$f^{-1}(x) = -\left(\dfrac{x-3}{2}\right)$

$f(x) = -2x + 3$

31. 3 **33.** $-\dfrac{4}{3}$ **35.** $\dfrac{3}{2}$ **37.**

39.

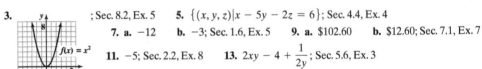

41. \$2963.11 **43.** 187,118 **45.** 8 players **47.** $\log_7 49 = 2$ **49.** $\left(\dfrac{1}{2}\right)^{-4} = 16$ **51.** $\dfrac{1}{64}$ **53.** 0 **55.** 5 **57.** 4 **59.** $\dfrac{17}{3}$ **61.** $-1, 4$

63.

65. $\log_3 32$ **67.** $\log_7 \dfrac{3}{4}$ **69.** $\log_{11} 4$ **71.** $\log_5 \dfrac{x^3}{(x+1)^2}$ **73.** $3 \log_3 x - \log_3 (x+2)$

75. $\log_2 3 + 2\log_2 x + \log_2 y - \log_2 z$ **77.** 2.02 **79.** 0.5563 **81.** 0.2231 **83.** 3 **85.** -1 **87.** $\dfrac{e^2}{2}$ **89.** $\dfrac{e^{-1}+3}{2}$

91. 1.67 mm **93.** 0.2920 **95.** \$1684.66 **97.** $\dfrac{\log 7}{2 \log 3}$; 0.8856 **99.** $\dfrac{\log 6 - \log 3}{2 \log 3}$ or $\dfrac{1}{2}\left(\dfrac{\log 6}{\log 3} - 1\right)$; 0.3155

101. $\dfrac{\log 4 + 5 \log 5}{3 \log 5}$ or $\dfrac{1}{3}\left(\dfrac{\log 4}{\log 5} + 5\right)$; 1.9538 **103.** $\dfrac{\log \frac{1}{2} + \log 5}{\log 5}$ or $-\dfrac{\log 2}{\log 5} + 1$; 0.5693 **105.** $\dfrac{25}{2}$ **107.** $\varnothing$ **109.** $2\sqrt{2}$ **111.** 22.4 yr

113. 99.0 yr **115.** 8.8 yr **117.** 0.69;

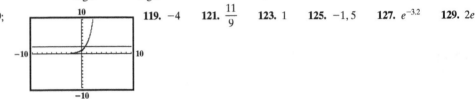

119. -4 **121.** $\dfrac{11}{9}$ **123.** 1 **125.** $-1, 5$ **127.** $e^{-3.2}$ **129.** $2e$

Chapter 12 Test

1. $2x^2 - 3x$ **2.** $3 - x$ **3.** 5 **4.** $x - 7$ **5.** $x^2 - 6x - 2$

6.

7. one-to-one **8.** not one-to-one **9.** one-to-one; $f^{-1}(x) = \dfrac{-x+6}{2}$ **10.** one-to-one; $f^{-1} = \{(0,0),(3,2),(5,-1)\}$

11. not one-to-one **12.** $\log_3 24$ **13.** $\log_5 \dfrac{x^4}{x+1}$ **14.** $\log_6 2 + \log_6 x - 3\log_6 y$ **15.** -1.53 **16.** 1.0686

17. -1 **18.** $\dfrac{1}{2}\left(\dfrac{\log 4}{\log 3} - 5\right)$; -1.8691 **19.** $\dfrac{1}{9}$ **20.** $\dfrac{1}{2}$ **21.** 22 **22.** $\dfrac{25}{3}$ **23.** $\dfrac{43}{21}$ **24.** -1.0979

25.

26.

27. \$5234.58 **28.** 6 yr **29.** 6.5%; \$230 **30.** 100,141 **31.** 64,805 prairie dogs

32. 15 yr **33.** 85% **34.** 52%

Chapter 12 Cumulative Review

1. a. $\dfrac{64}{25}$ **b.** $\dfrac{1}{20}$ **c.** $\dfrac{5}{4}$; Sec. 1.3, Ex. 4 **3.**

$f(x) = x^2$

; Sec. 8.2, Ex. 5 **5.** $\{(x, y, z) | x - 5y - 2z = 6\}$; Sec. 4.4, Ex. 4

7. a. -12 **b.** -3; Sec. 1.6, Ex. 5 **9. a.** \$102.60 **b.** \$12.60; Sec. 7.1, Ex. 7

11. -5; Sec. 2.2, Ex. 8 **13.** $2xy - 4 + \dfrac{1}{2y}$; Sec. 5.6, Ex. 3

15. $3(m+2)(m-10)$; Sec. 6.2, Ex. 9 **17.** $3x - 5$; Sec. 7.3, Ex. 3 **19. a.** 3 **b.** -3 **c.** -5 **d.** not a real number

e. $4x$; Sec. 10.1, Ex. 4 **21. a.** $\sqrt[4]{x^3}$ **b.** $\sqrt[6]{x}$ **c.** $\sqrt[6]{72}$; Sec. 10.2, Ex. 8 **23. a.** $5\sqrt{3} + 3\sqrt{10}$ **b.** $\sqrt{35} + \sqrt{5} - \sqrt{42} - \sqrt{6}$

c. $21x - 7\sqrt{5x} + 15\sqrt{x} - 5\sqrt{5}$ **d.** $49 - 8\sqrt{3}$ **e.** $2x - 25$ **f.** $x + 22 + 10\sqrt{x - 3}$; Sec. 10.4, Ex. 4 **25.** $\dfrac{\sqrt[4]{xy^3}}{3y^2}$; Sec. 10.5, Ex. 3

27. 3; Sec. 10.6, Ex. 4 **29.** $\dfrac{9 + i\sqrt{15}}{6}, \dfrac{9 - i\sqrt{15}}{6}$ or $\dfrac{3}{2} \pm \dfrac{\sqrt{15}}{6}i$; Sec. 11.1, Ex. 8 **31.** $\dfrac{-1 + \sqrt{33}}{4}, \dfrac{-1 - \sqrt{33}}{4}$; Sec. 11.3, Ex. 2

33. $[0, 4]$; Sec. 11.4, Ex. 2 **35.**

; Sec. 11.5, Ex. 5 **37.** 63; Sec. 7.6, Ex. 1 **39.** $f^{-1}(x) = x - 3$; Sec. 12.2, Ex. 4

41. a. 2 **b.** -1 **c.** $\dfrac{1}{2}$; Sec. 12.5, Ex. 3

CHAPTER 13 CONIC SECTIONS

Section 13.1
Practice Exercises

1.   **2.**   **3.**   **4.**   **5.**   **6.**

7.   **8.** $(x + 2)^2 + (y + 5)^2 = 81$

Graphing Calculator Explorations 13.1

1. 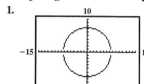 **3.** 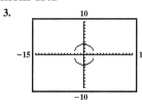 **5.** 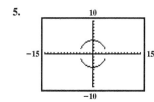 **7.**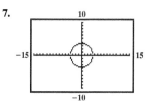

Vocabulary, Readiness & Video Check 13.1

1. conic sections **3.** circle; center **5.** radius **7.** No, their graphs don't pass the vertical line test. **9.** The formula for the standard form of a circle identifies the center and radius, so you just need to substitute these values into this formula and simplify.

Exercise Set 13.1

1. upward **3.** to the left **5.** downward **7.**   **9.**   **11.**   **13.**

15.   **17.**   **19.**   **21.**   **23.**   **25.**

27.   **29.**   **31.**   **33.**   **35.**

37.   **39.**   **41.** 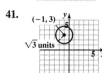 **43.** $(x - 2)^2 + (y - 3)^2 = 36$ **45.** $x^2 + y^2 = 3$
47. $(x + 5)^2 + (y - 4)^2 = 45$

49.   **51.**   **53.**   **55.** 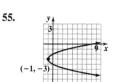 **57.**   **59.**

61. 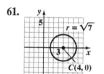 **63.** 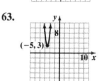 **65.** 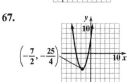 **67.** $\left(-\dfrac{7}{2}, -\dfrac{25}{4}\right)$ **69.**   **71.**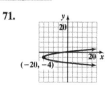

73. **75.** 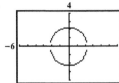 **77.** **79.** **81.** **83.**

85. $\dfrac{\sqrt{3}}{3}$ **87.** $\dfrac{2\sqrt{42}}{3}$ **89.** The vertex is $(1, -5)$. **91. a.** 16.5 m **b.** 103.67 m **c.** 3.5 m **d.** $(0, 16.5)$ **e.** $x^2 + (y - 16.5)^2 = 16.5^2$

93. a. 125 ft **b.** 14 ft **c.** 139 ft **d.** $(0, 139)$ **e.** $x^2 + (y - 139)^2 = 125^2$ **95.** answers may vary **97.** 20 m

99. 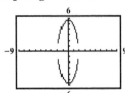 **101.**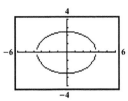

Section 13.2
Practice Exercises
1. **2.** **3.** **4.** **5.** (graph)

Graphing Calculator Explorations 13.2
1. **3.** **5.**

Vocabulary, Readiness & Video Check 13.2
1. hyperbola **3.** focus **5.** hyperbola; $(0, 0)$; x; $(a, 0)$ and $(-a, 0)$ **7.** a and b give us the location of 4 intercepts—$(a, 0), (-a, 0), (0, b),$ and $(0, -b)$ for $\dfrac{x^2}{a^2} + \dfrac{y^2}{b^2} = 1$ with center $(0, 0)$. For Example 2, the values of a and b also give us 4 points of the graph, just not intercepts. Here we move a distance of a units horizontally to the left and right of the center and b units above and below.

Exercise Set 13.2
1. ellipse **3.** hyperbola **5.** hyperbola **7.** **9.** **11.** **13.**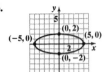

15. **17.** **19.** **21.** **23.** **25.**

27. **29.** **31.** **33.** **35.** circle 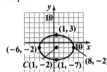 **37.** parabola

39. hyperbola **41.** ellipse **43.** parabola **45.** hyperbola **47.** ellipse

49. circle

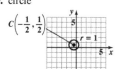

51. $-8x^5$ **53.** $-4x^2$ **55.** y-intercepts: 2 units **57.** y-intercepts: 4 units **59.** answers may vary

61. ellipses: C, E, H; circles: B, F; hyperbolas: A, D, G **63.** A: 49, 7; B: 0, 0; C: 9, 3; D: 64, 8; E: 64, 8; F: 0, 0; G: 81, 9; H: 4, 2

65. A: $\frac{7}{6}$; B: 0; C: $\frac{3}{5}$; D: $\frac{8}{5}$; E: $\frac{8}{9}$; F: 0; G: $\frac{9}{4}$; H: $\frac{1}{6}$ **67.** equal to zero **69.** answers may vary

71. $\dfrac{x^2}{1.69 \times 10^{16}} + \dfrac{y^2}{1.5625 \times 10^{16}} = 1$

73.

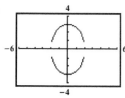

75.

77.

79.

Integrated Review

1. circle

2. parabola

3. parabola

4. ellipse

5. hyperbola

6. hyperbola

7. ellipse

8. circle

9. parabola

10. parabola

11. hyperbola

12. ellipse

13. ellipse

14. hyperbola

15. circle

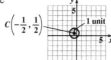

Section 13.3
Practice Exercises

1. $(-4, 3), (0, -1)$ **2.** $(4, -2)$ **3.** $\varnothing$ **4.** $\left(2, \sqrt{3}\right), \left(2, -\sqrt{3}\right), \left(-2, \sqrt{3}\right), \left(-2, -\sqrt{3}\right)$

Vocabulary, Readiness & Video Check 13.3

1. Solving for y would either introduce tedious fractions (2nd equation) or a square root (1st equation) into the calculations.

Exercise Set 13.3

1. $(3, -4), (-3, 4)$ **3.** $\left(\sqrt{2}, \sqrt{2}\right), \left(-\sqrt{2}, -\sqrt{2}\right)$ **5.** $(4, 0), (0, -2)$ **7.** $\left(-\sqrt{5}, -2\right), \left(-\sqrt{5}, 2\right), \left(\sqrt{5}, -2\right), \left(\sqrt{5}, 2\right)$ **9.** $\varnothing$

11. $(1, -2), (3, 6)$ **13.** $(2, 4), (-5, 25)$ **15.** $\varnothing$ **17.** $(1, -3)$ **19.** $(-1, -2), (-1, 2), (1, -2), (1, 2)$ **21.** $(0, -1)$

23. $(-1, 3), (1, 3)$ **25.** $\left(\sqrt{3}, 0\right), \left(-\sqrt{3}, 0\right)$ **27.** $\varnothing$ **29.** $(-6, 0), (6, 0), (0, -6)$ **31.** $\left(3, \sqrt{3}\right)$

33.

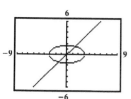

35.

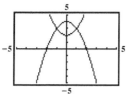

37. $(8x - 25)$ in. **39.** $(4x^2 + 6x + 2)$ m **41.** answers may vary **43.** 0, 1, 2, 3, or 4; answers may vary **45.** 9 and 7; 9 and -7; -9 and 7; -9 and -7 **47.** 15 cm by 19 cm **49.** 15 thousand compact discs; price: \$3.75

51.

53.

Section 13.4
Practice Exercises

1. **2.** **3.** **4.**

Vocabulary, Readiness & Video Check 13.4

1. For both, we graph the related equation to find the boundary and sketch it as a solid boundary for $\leq$ and $\geq$ and a dashed boundary for $<$ or $>$; also, we choose a test point not on the boundary and shade that region if the test point is a solution of the original inequality or shade the other region if not.

Exercise Set 13.4

1. **3.** **5.** **7.** **9.** 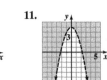 **11.**

13. **15.** **17.** **19.** **21.** **23.**

25. **27.** **29.** **31.** **33.** **35.**

37. not a function   **39.** function   **41.** 1   **43.** $3a^2 - 2$ **45.** answers may vary   **47.**

Chapter 13 Vocabulary Check

1. circle; center   **2.** nonlinear system of equations   **3.** ellipse   **4.** radius   **5.** hyperbola   **6.** conic sections   **7.** vertex   **8.** diameter

Chapter 13 Review

1. $(x + 4)^2 + (y - 4)^2 = 9$ **3.** $(x + 7)^2 + (y + 9)^2 = 11$ **5.** **7.** **9.**

11. **13.** **15.** 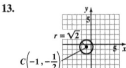 **17.** **19.**

21. **23.** **25.** **27.** **29.** **31.**

33. $(1,-2), (4, 4)$ **35.** $(-1, 1), (2, 4)$ **37.** $(0, 2), (0, -2)$ **39.** $(1, 4)$ **41.** length: 15 ft; width: 10 ft

43. **45.** 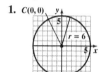 **47.** **49.** **51.** $(x + 7)^2 + (y - 8)^2 = 25$ **53.**

55. 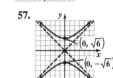 **57.** 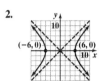 **59.** **61.** **63.** $(5, 1), (-1, 7)$ **65.**

Chapter 13 Test

1. 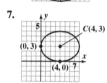 **2.** **3.** **4.** **5.** **6.**

7. **8.** **9.** $(-12, 5), (12, -5)$ **10.** $(-5, -1), (-5, 1), (5, -1), (5, 1)$ **11.** $(6, 12), (1, 2)$
12. $(1, 1), (-1, -1)$

13. **14.** 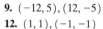 **15.** 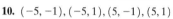 **16.** **17.** B **18.** height: 10 ft; width: 30 ft

Chapter 13 Cumulative Review

1. $\varnothing$; Sec. 9.1, Ex. 3 **3.** $\left(-\infty, \dfrac{13}{5}\right] \cup [4, \infty)$; Sec. 9.1, Ex. 7 **5.** $-2, \dfrac{4}{5}$; Sec. 9.2, Ex. 2 **7.** $24, -20$; Sec. 9.2, Ex. 3 **9.** $\dfrac{3}{4}, 5$; Sec. 9.2, Ex. 8

11. $(4, 8)$; Sec. 9.3, Ex. 2 **13.** $\dfrac{xy + 2x^3}{y - 1}$; Sec. 7.7, Ex. 3 **15.** $(-\infty, \infty)$; Sec. 9.3, Ex. 7 **17.** 16; Sec. 5.7, Ex. 4 **19. a.** 1 **b.** -4 **c.** $\dfrac{2}{5}$

d. x^2 **e.** $-3x^3$; Sec. 10.1, Ex. 3 **21. a.** $z - z^{17/3}$ **b.** $x^{2/3} - 3x^{1/3} - 10$; Sec. 10.2, Ex. 5 **23. a.** 2 **b.** $\dfrac{5}{2}\sqrt{x}$ **c.** $14xy^2 \sqrt[3]{x}$

d. $4a^2b \sqrt[4]{2a}$; Sec. 10.3, Ex. 5 **25. a.** $\dfrac{5\sqrt{5}}{12}$ **b.** $\dfrac{5\sqrt[3]{7x}}{2}$; Sec. 10.4, Ex. 3 **27.** $\dfrac{\sqrt{21xy}}{3y}$; Sec. 10.5, Ex. 2 **29.** 42; Sec. 10.6, Ex. 1
31. a. $-i$ **b.** 1 **c.** -1 **d.** 1; Sec. 10.7, Ex. 6 **33.** $-1 + \sqrt{5}, -1 - \sqrt{5}$; Sec. 11.1, Ex. 5 **35.** $2 + \sqrt{2}, 2 - \sqrt{2}$; Sec. 11.2, Ex. 3
37. $2, -2, i, -i$; Sec. 11.3, Ex. 3 **39.** $[-2, 3)$; Sec. 11.4, Ex. 4 **41.** ; Sec. 11.5, Ex. 8 **43.** $(2, -16)$; Sec. 11.6, Ex. 4
45. $\sqrt{2} \approx 1.414$; Sec. 10.3, Ex. 6

CHAPTER 14 SEQUENCES, SERIES, AND THE BINOMIAL THEOREM

Section 14.1
Practice Exercises

1. $6, 9, 14, 21, 30$ **2. a.** $-\dfrac{1}{5}$ **b.** $\dfrac{1}{20}$ **c.** $\dfrac{1}{150}$ **d.** $-\dfrac{1}{95}$ **3. a.** $a_n = 2n - 1$ **b.** $a_n = 3^n$ **c.** $a_n = \dfrac{n}{n + 1}$ **d.** $a_n = -\dfrac{1}{n + 1}$
4. $\$2022.40$

Vocabulary, Readiness & Video Check 14.1
1. general **3.** infinite **5.** -1 **7.** function; domain; a_n **9.** $a_9 = 0.10(2)^{9-1} = \$25.60$

Exercise Set 14.1

1. $5, 6, 7, 8, 9$ **3.** $-1, 1, -1, 1, -1$ **5.** $\dfrac{1}{4}, \dfrac{1}{5}, \dfrac{1}{6}, \dfrac{1}{7}, \dfrac{1}{8}$ **7.** $2, 4, 6, 8, 10$ **9.** $-1, -4, -9, -16, -25$ **11.** $2, 4, 8, 16, 32$ **13.** $7, 9, 11, 13, 15$

15. $-1, 4, -9, 16, -25$ **17.** 75 **19.** 118 **21.** $\dfrac{6}{5}$ **23.** 729 **25.** $\dfrac{4}{7}$ **27.** $\dfrac{1}{8}$ **29.** -95 **31.** $-\dfrac{1}{25}$ **33.** $a_n = 4n - 1$ **35.** $a_n = -2^n$

37. $a_n = \dfrac{1}{3^n}$ **39.** 48 ft, 80 ft, and 112 ft **41.** $a_n = 0.10(2)^{n-1}$; \$819.20 **43.** 2400 cases; 75 cases **45.** 50 sparrows in 2004: extinct in 2010

47. **49.** **51.** $\sqrt{13}$ units **53.** $\sqrt{41}$ units **55.** 1, 0.7071, 0.5774, 0.5, 0.4472 **57.** 2, 2.25, 2.3704, 2.4414, 2.4883

Section 14.2
Practice Exercises
1. 4, 9, 14, 19, 24 **2. a.** $a_n = 5 - 3n$ **b.** -31 **3.** 51 **4.** 47 **5.** $a_n = 54{,}800 + 2200n$; \$61,400 **6.** 8, -24, 72, -216 **7.** $\dfrac{1}{64}$
8. -192 **9.** $a_1 = 3$; $r = \dfrac{3}{2}$ **10.** 75 units

Vocabulary, Readiness & Video Check 14.2
1. geometric; ratio **3.** first; difference **5.** If there is a common difference between each term and its preceding term in a sequence, it's an arithmetic sequence.

Exercise Set 14.2
1. 4, 6, 8, 10, 12 **3.** 6, 4, 2, 0, -2 **5.** 1, 3, 9, 27, 81 **7.** 48, 24, 12, 6, 3 **9.** 33 **11.** -875 **13.** -60 **15.** 96 **17.** -28 **19.** 1250
21. 31 **23.** 20 **25.** $a_1 = \dfrac{2}{3}$; $r = -2$ **27.** answers may vary **29.** $a_1 = 2$; $d = 2$ **31.** $a_1 = 5$; $r = 2$ **33.** $a_1 = \dfrac{1}{2}$; $r = \dfrac{1}{5}$
35. $a_1 = x$; $r = 5$ **37.** $a_1 = p$; $d = 4$ **39.** 19 **41.** $-\dfrac{8}{9}$ **43.** $\dfrac{17}{2}$ **45.** $\dfrac{8}{81}$ **47.** -19 **49.** $a_n = 4n + 50$; 130 seats **51.** $a_n = 6(3)^{n-1}$
53. 486, 162, 54, 18, 6; $a_n = \dfrac{486}{3^{n-1}}$; 6 bounces **55.** $a_n = 3875 + 125n$; \$5375 **57.** 25 g **59.** $\dfrac{11}{18}$ **61.** 40 **63.** $\dfrac{907}{495}$
65. \$11,782.40, \$5891.20, \$2945.60, \$1472.80 **67.** 19.652, 19.618, 19.584, 19.55 **69.** answers may vary

Section 14.3
Practice Exercises
1. a. $-\dfrac{5}{4}$ **b.** 360 **2. a.** $\displaystyle\sum_{i=1}^{6} 5i$ **b.** $\displaystyle\sum_{i=1}^{4}\left(\dfrac{1}{5}\right)^i$ **3.** $\dfrac{655}{72}$ or $9\dfrac{7}{72}$ **4.** 95 plants

Vocabulary, Readiness & Video Check 14.3
1. infinite **3.** summation **5.** partial sum **7.** sigma/sum, index of summation, beginning value of i, ending value of i, and general term of the sequence

Exercise Set 14.3
1. -2 **3.** 60 **5.** 20 **7.** $\dfrac{73}{168}$ **9.** $\dfrac{11}{36}$ **11.** 60 **13.** 74 **15.** 62 **17.** $\dfrac{241}{35}$ **19.** $\displaystyle\sum_{i=1}^{5}(2i - 1)$ **21.** $\displaystyle\sum_{i=1}^{4} 4(3)^{i-1}$
23. $\displaystyle\sum_{i=1}^{6}(-3i + 15)$ **25.** $\displaystyle\sum_{i=1}^{4}\dfrac{4}{3^{i-2}}$ **27.** $\displaystyle\sum_{i=1}^{7} i^2$ **29.** -24 **31.** 0 **33.** 82 **35.** -20 **37.** -2 **39.** 1, 2, 3, ..., 10; 55 trees
41. 186 units **43.** 35 species; 82 species **45.** 30 opossums; 68 opossums **47.** 6.25 lb; 93.75 lb **49.** 16.4 in.; 134.5 in. **51.** 10 **53.** $\dfrac{10}{27}$
55. 45 **57.** 90 **59. a.** $2 + 6 + 12 + 20 + 30 + 42 + 56$ **b.** $1 + 2 + 3 + 4 + 5 + 6 + 7 + 1 + 4 + 9 + 16 + 25 + 36 + 49$
c. answers may vary **d.** true; answers may vary

Integrated Review
1. $-2, -1, 0, 1, 2$ **2.** $\dfrac{7}{2}, \dfrac{7}{3}, \dfrac{7}{4}, \dfrac{7}{5}, \dfrac{7}{6}$ **3.** 1, 3, 9, 27, 81 **4.** $-4, -1, 4, 11, 20$ **5.** 64 **6.** -14 **7.** $\dfrac{1}{40}$ **8.** $-\dfrac{1}{82}$ **9.** 7, 4, 1, -2, -5
10. $-3, -15, -75, -375, -1875$ **11.** $45, 15, 5, \dfrac{5}{3}, \dfrac{5}{9}$ **12.** $-12, -2, 8, 18, 28$ **13.** 101 **14.** $\dfrac{243}{16}$ **15.** 384 **16.** 185 **17.** -10 **18.** $\dfrac{1}{2}$
19. 50 **20.** 98 **21.** $\dfrac{31}{2}$ **22.** $\dfrac{61}{20}$ **23.** -10 **24.** 5

Section 14.4
Practice Exercises
1. 80 **2.** 1275 **3.** 105 blocks of ice **4.** $\dfrac{341}{8}$ or $42\dfrac{5}{8}$ **5.** \$987,856 **6.** $\dfrac{28}{3}$ or $9\dfrac{1}{3}$ **7.** 900 in.

Vocabulary, Readiness & Video Check 14.4
1. arithmetic **3.** geometric **5.** arithmetic **7.** Use the general term formula from Section 14.2 for the general term of an arithmetic sequence: $a_n = a_1 + (n - 1)d$. **9.** The common ratio r is 3 for this sequence so that $|r| \geq 1$, or $|3| \geq 1$; S_∞ doesn't exist if $|r| \geq 1$.

Exercise Set 14.4

1. 36   **3.** 484   **5.** 63   **7.** $\dfrac{312}{125}$ **9.** 55   **11.** 16   **13.** 24   **15.** $\dfrac{1}{9}$ **17.** -20 **19.** $\dfrac{16}{9}$ **21.** $\dfrac{4}{9}$ **23.** 185   **25.** $\dfrac{381}{64}$

27. $-\dfrac{33}{4}$ or -8.25 **29.** $-\dfrac{75}{2}$ **31.** $\dfrac{56}{9}$ **33.** $4000, 3950, 3900, 3850, 3800; 3450$ cars; $44,700$ cars   **35.** Firm A (Firm A, \$265,000; Firm B, \$254,000)

37. \$39,930; \$139,230   **39.** 20 min; 123 min   **41.** 180 ft   **43.** Player A, 45 points; Player B, 75 points   **45.** \$3050   **47.** \$10,737,418.23

49. 720   **51.** 3   **53.** $x^2 + 10x + 25$ **55.** $8x^3 - 12x^2 + 6x - 1$ **57.** $\dfrac{8}{10} + \dfrac{8}{100} + \dfrac{8}{1000} + \cdots ; \dfrac{8}{9}$ **59.** answers may vary

Section 14.5
Practice Exercises

1. $p^7 + 7p^6r + 21p^5r^2 + 35p^4r^3 + 35p^3r^4 + 21p^2r^5 + 7pr^6 + r^7$ **2. a.** $\dfrac{1}{7}$ **b.** 840   **c.** 5   **d.** 1
3. $a^9 + 9a^8b + 36a^7b^2 + 84a^6b^3 + 126a^5b^4 + 126a^4b^5 + 84a^3b^6 + 36a^2b^7 + 9ab^8 + b^9$ **4.** $a^3 + 15a^2b + 75ab^2 + 125b^3$
5. $27x^3 - 54x^2y + 36xy^2 - 8y^3$ **6.** $1,892,352x^5y^6$

Vocabulary, Readiness & Video Check 14.5

1. 1   **3.** 24   **5.** 6   **7.** Pascal's triangle gives you the coefficients of the terms of the expanded binomial; also, the power tells you how many terms the expansion has (1 more than the power on the binomial).   **9.** The theorem is in terms of $(a + b)^n$, so if your binomial is of the form $(a - b)^n$, then remember to think of it as $(a + (-b))^n$, so your second term is $-b$.

Exercise Set 14.5

1. $m^3 + 3m^2n + 3mn^2 + n^3$ **3.** $c^5 + 5c^4d + 10c^3d^2 + 10c^2d^3 + 5cd^4 + d^5$ **5.** $y^5 - 5y^4x + 10y^3x^2 - 10y^2x^3 + 5yx^4 - x^5$
7. answers may vary   **9.** 8   **11.** 42   **13.** 360   **15.** 56   **17.** $a^7 + 7a^6b + 21a^5b^2 + 35a^4b^3 + 35a^3b^4 + 21a^2b^5 + 7ab^6 + b^7$
19. $a^5 + 10a^4b + 40a^3b^2 + 80a^2b^3 + 80ab^4 + 32b^5$ **21.** $q^9 + 9q^8r + 36q^7r^2 + 84q^6r^3 + 126q^5r^4 + 126q^4r^5 + 84q^3r^6 + 36q^2r^7 + 9qr^8 + r^9$
23. $1024a^5 + 1280a^4b + 640a^3b^2 + 160a^2b^3 + 20ab^4 + b^5$ **25.** $625a^4 - 1000a^3b + 600a^2b^2 - 160ab^3 + 16b^4$ **27.** $8a^3 + 36a^2b + 54ab^2 + 27b^3$
29. $x^5 + 10x^4 + 40x^3 + 80x^2 + 80x + 32$ **31.** $5cd^4$ **33.** d^7 **35.** $-40r^2s^3$ **37.** $6x^2y^2$ **39.** $30a^9b$
41.

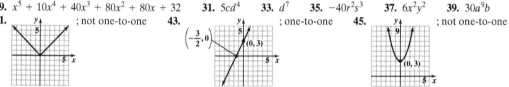

; not one-to-one   **43.** ; one-to-one   **45.** ; not one-to-one

47. $x^2\sqrt{x} + 5\sqrt{3}x^2 + 30x\sqrt{x} + 30\sqrt{3}x + 45\sqrt{x} + 9\sqrt{3}$ **49.** 126   **51.** 28   **53.** answers may vary

Chapter 14 Vocabulary Check

1. finite sequence   **2.** factorial of n **3.** infinite sequence   **4.** geometric sequence, common ratio   **5.** series   **6.** general term
7. arithmetic sequence, common difference   **8.** Pascal's triangle

Chapter 14 Review

1. $-3, -12, -27, -48, -75$ **3.** $\dfrac{1}{100}$ **5.** $a_n = \dfrac{1}{6n}$ **7.** 144 ft, 176 ft, 208 ft   **9.** $660,000; 1,320,000; 2,640,000; 5,280,000; 10,560,000; 2010:$

$10,560,000$ infested acres   **11.** $-2, -\dfrac{4}{3}, -\dfrac{8}{9}, -\dfrac{16}{27}, -\dfrac{32}{81}$ **13.** 111   **15.** -83 **17.** $a_1 = 3; d = 5$ **19.** $a_n = \dfrac{3}{10^n}$ **21.** $a_1 = \dfrac{8}{3}, r = \dfrac{3}{2}$

23. $a_1 = 7x, r = -2$ **25.** $8, 6, 4.5, 3.4, 2.5, 1.9;$ good   **27.** $a_n = 2^{n-1}; \$512; \$536,870,912$ **29.** $a_n = 150n + 750; \$1650/\text{month}$

31. $1 + 3 + 5 + 7 + 9 = 25$ **33.** $\dfrac{1}{4} - \dfrac{1}{6} + \dfrac{1}{8} = \dfrac{5}{24}$ **35.** $\sum_{i=1}^{6} 3^{i-1}$ **37.** $\sum_{i=1}^{4} \dfrac{1}{4^i}$ **39.** $a_n = 20(2)^n;$ n represents the number of 8-hour periods;

1280 yeast   **41.** Job A, \$48,300; Job B, \$46,600   **43.** -4 **45.** -10 **47.** 150   **49.** 900   **51.** -410 **53.** 936   **55.** 10

57. -25 **59.** \$30,418; \$99,868   **61.** \$58; \$553   **63.** 2696 mosquitoes   **65.** $\dfrac{5}{9}$ **67.** $x^5 + 5x^4z + 10x^3z^2 + 10x^2z^3 + 5xz^4 + z^5$
69. $16x^4 + 32x^3y + 24x^2y^2 + 8xy^3 + y^4$ **71.** $b^8 + 8b^7c + 28b^6c^2 + 56b^5c^3 + 70b^4c^4 + 56b^3c^5 + 28b^2c^6 + 8bc^7 + c^8$
73. $256m^4 - 256m^3n + 96m^2n^2 - 16mn^3 + n^4$ **75.** $35a^4b^3$ **77.** 130   **79.** 40.5

Chapter 14 Test

1. $-\dfrac{1}{5}, \dfrac{1}{6}, -\dfrac{1}{7}, \dfrac{1}{8}, -\dfrac{1}{9}$ **2.** 247   **3.** $a_n = \dfrac{2}{5}\left(\dfrac{1}{5}\right)^{n-1}$ **4.** $a_n = (-1)^n 9n$ **5.** 155   **6.** -330 **7.** $\dfrac{144}{5}$ **8.** 1   **9.** 10   **10.** -60
11. $a^6 - 6a^5b + 15a^4b^2 - 20a^3b^3 + 15a^2b^4 - 6ab^5 + b^6$ **12.** $32x^5 + 80x^4y + 80x^3y^2 + 40x^2y^3 + 10xy^4 + y^5$ **13.** 925 people; 250 people initially
14. $1 + 3 + 5 + 7 + 9 + 11 + 13 + 15; 64$ shrubs   **15.** 33.75 cm, 218.75 cm   **16.** 320 cm   **17.** 304 ft; 1600 ft   **18.** $\dfrac{14}{33}$

Chapter 14 Cumulative Review

1. a. -8 **b.** -8 **c.** 9   **d.** -9; Sec. 1.7, Ex. 4   **3.** $-2x - 1$; Sec. 2.1, Ex. 7   **5.** $y = \dfrac{1}{4}x - 3$; Sec. 3.5, Ex. 3   **7.** $-x + 5y = 23$ or

$x - 5y = -23$; Sec. 3.5, Ex. 5   **9.** $x^3 - 4x^2 - 3x + 11 + \dfrac{12}{x + 2}$; Sec. 5.7, Ex. 2   **11. a.** $5\sqrt{2}$ **b.** $2\sqrt[3]{3}$ **c.** $\sqrt{26}$ **d.** $2\sqrt[4]{2}$; Sec. 10.3, Ex. 3

13. 10%; Sec. 11.1, Ex. 9   **15.** 2, 7; Sec. 11.3, Ex. 4   **17.** $\left(-\dfrac{7}{2}, -1\right)$; Sec. 11.4, Ex. 5   **19.** $\dfrac{25}{4}$ ft; $\dfrac{5}{8}$ sec; Sec. 11.6, Ex. 5   **21. a.** 25; 7

b. $x^2 + 6x + 9$; $x^2 + 3$; Sec. 12.1, Ex. 2   **23.** $f^{-1} = \{(1, 0), (7, -2), (-6, 3), (4, 4)\}$; Sec. 12.2, Ex. 3   **25. a.** 4   **b.** $\dfrac{3}{2}$ **c.** 6; Sec. 12.3, Ex. 4

27. a. 2   **b.** -1 **c.** 3   **d.** 6; Sec. 12.5, Ex. 5   **29. a.** $\log_{11} 30$ **b.** $\log_3 6$ **c.** $\log_2(x^2 + 2x)$; Sec. 12.6, Ex. 1

31. \$2509.30; Sec. 12.7, Ex. 8   **33.** $\dfrac{\log 7}{\log 3} \approx 1.7712$; Sec. 12.8, Ex. 1   **35.** 18; Sec. 12.8, Ex. 2   **37.** 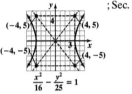 ; Sec. 13.2, Ex. 4

$\dfrac{x^2}{16} - \dfrac{y^2}{25} = 1$

39. $(2, \sqrt{2})$; Sec. 13.3, Ex. 2   **41.** 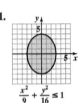 ; Sec. 13.4, Ex. 1   **43.** 0, 3, 8, 15, 24; Sec. 14.1, Ex. 1   **45.** 72; Sec. 14.2, Ex. 3

47. a. $\dfrac{7}{2}$ **b.** 56; Sec. 14.3, Ex. 1   **49.** 465; Sec. 14.4, Ex. 2

$\dfrac{x^2}{9} + \dfrac{y^2}{16} \le 1$

APPENDIX A   OPERATIONS ON DECIMALS/PERCENT, DECIMAL, AND FRACTION TABLE

1. 17.08   **3.** 12.804   **5.** 110.96   **7.** 2.4   **9.** 28.43   **11.** 227.5   **13.** 2.7   **15.** 49.2339   **17.** 80   **19.** 0.07612   **21.** 4.56   **23.** 648.46
25. 767.83   **27.** 12.062   **29.** 61.48   **31.** 7.7   **33.** 863.37   **35.** 22.579   **37.** 363.15   **39.** 7.007

APPENDIX B   REVIEW OF ALGEBRA TOPICS

B.1 Practice Exercises

1. -4 **2.** $\dfrac{5}{6}$ **3.** $-\dfrac{3}{4}$ **4.** $\dfrac{5}{4}$ **5.** $-\dfrac{1}{8}, 2$

Exercise Set B.1

1. $-3, -8$ **3.** -2 **5.** $\dfrac{1}{4}, -\dfrac{2}{3}$ **7.** 1, 9   **9.** 0   **11.** 5   **13.** $\dfrac{3}{5}, -1$ **15.** no solution   **17.** $\dfrac{1}{8}$ **19.** 0   **21.** 6, -3 **23.** all real numbers
25. $\dfrac{2}{5}, -\dfrac{1}{2}$ **27.** $\dfrac{3}{4}, -\dfrac{1}{2}$ **29.** 29   **31.** -8 **33.** $-\dfrac{1}{3}, 0$ **35.** $-\dfrac{7}{8}$ **37.** $\dfrac{31}{4}$ **39.** 1   **41.** $-7, 4$ **43.** 4, 6   **45.** $-\dfrac{1}{2}$
47. a. incorrect   **b.** correct   **c.** correct   **d.** incorrect   **49.** $K = -11$ **51.** $K = 24$ **53.** -4.86 **55.** 1.53

B.2 Practice Exercises
1. a. $3x + 6$ **b.** $6x - 1$ **2.** $3x + 18.1$ **3.** 14, 34, 70   **4.** \$450

Vocabulary & Readiness Check B.2
1. $>$ **3.** $=$ **5.** 31, 32, 33, 34   **7.** 18, 20, 22   **9.** $y, y + 1, y + 2$ **11.** $p, p + 1, p + 2, p + 3$

Exercise Set B.2
1. $4y$ **3.** $3z + 3$ **5.** $(65x + 30)$ cents   **7.** $10x + 3$ **9.** $2x + 14$ **11.** -5 **13.** 45, 225, 145   **15.** approximately 1612.41 million acres
17. 7747 earthquakes   **19.** 1275 shoppers   **21.** 23%   **23.** 417 employees   **25.** 29°, 35°, 116°   **27.** 28 m, 36 m, 38 m
29. 18 in., 18 in., 27 in., 36 in.   **31.** 75, 76, 77   **33.** Fallon's ZIP code is 89406; Fernley's ZIP code is 89408; Gardnerville Ranchos' ZIP code is 89410
35. 55 million; 97 million; 138 million   **37.** biomedical engineer: 12 thousand; skin care specialist: 15 thousand; physician assistant: 29 thousand
39. B767-300ER: 207 seats; B737-200: 119 seats; F-100: 87 seats   **41.** \$430.00   **43.** \$446,028   **45.** 1,800,000 people   **47.** 40°, 140°
49. 64°, 32°, 84°   **51.** square: 18 cm; triangle: 24 cm   **53.** 76, 78, 80   **55.** Darlington: 61,000; Daytona: 159,000   **57.** Tokyo: 36.67 million; New
York: 19.43 million; Mexico City: 19.46 million   **59.** 40.5 ft; 202.5 ft; 240 ft   **61.** incandescent: 1500 bulb hours; fluorescent: 100,000 bulb hours;
halogen: 4000 bulb hours   **63.** Milwaukee Brewers: 77 wins; Houston Astros: 76 wins; Chicago Cubs: 75 wins   **65.** Guy's Tower: 469 ft; Queen Mary
Hospital: 449 ft; Galter Pavilion: 402 ft

B.3 Practice Exercises

1.   **a.** Quadrant IV   **b.** y-axis   **c.** Quadrant II   **d.** x-axis   **e.** Quadrant III   **f.** Quadrant I

2. $y = -3x - 2$

3.

Exercise Set B.3

1. $(5, 2)$ **3.** $(3, 0)$ **5.** $(-5, -2)$ **7.** $(-1, 0)$ **9.** Quadrant I   **11.** Quadrant II   **13.** Quadrant III
15. y-axis   **17.** Quadrant III   **19.** x-axis   **21.** Quadrant IV   **23.** x-axis   **25.** Quadrant III
27.

29.

31.

33.

35. 1   **37.** -4 **39.** 1, 3   **41.** $g(-1) = -2$

B.4 Practice Exercises

1. a. $3xy(4x - 1)$ **b.** $(7x + 2)(7x - 2)$ **c.** $(5x - 3)(x + 1)$ **d.** $(x^2 + 2)(3 + x)$ **e.** $(2x + 5)^2$ **f.** cannot be factored
2. a. $(4x + y)(16x^2 - 4xy + y^2)$ **b.** $7y^2(x + 3y)(x - 3y)$ **c.** $3(x + 2 + b)(x + 2 - b)$ **d.** $x^2y(xy + 3)(x^2y^2 - 3xy + 9)$
e. $(x + 7 + 9y)(x + 7 - 9y)$

Exercise Set B.4

1. $2y^2 + 2y - 11$ **3.** $x^2 - 7x + 7$ **5.** $25x^2 - 30x + 9$ **7.** $2x^3 - 4x^2 + 5x - 5 + \dfrac{8}{x + 2}$ **9.** $(x - 4 + y)(x - 4 - y)$
11. $x(x - 1)(x^2 + x + 1)$ **13.** $2xy(7x - 1)$ **15.** $4(x + 2)(x - 2)$ **17.** $(3x - 11)(x + 1)$ **19.** $4(x + 3)(x - 1)$ **21.** $(2x + 9)^2$
23. $(2x + 5y)(4x^2 - 10xy + 25y^2)$ **25.** $8x^2(2y - 1)(4y^2 + 2y + 1)$ **27.** $(x + 5 + y)(x^2 + 10x + 25 - xy - 5y + y^2)$ **29.** $(5a - 6)^2$
31. $7x(x - 9)$ **33.** $(b - 6)(a + 7)$ **35.** $(x^2 + 1)(x + 1)(x - 1)$ **37.** $(5x - 11)(2x + 3)$ **39.** $5a^3b(b^2 - 10)$ **41.** prime
43. $10x(x - 10)(x - 11)$ **45.** $a^3b(4b - 3)(16b^2 + 12b + 9)$ **47.** $2(x - 3)(x^2 + 3x + 9)$ **49.** $(3y - 5)(y^4 + 2)$
51. $100(z + 1)(z^2 - z + 1)$ **53.** $(2b - 9)^2$ **55.** $(y - 4)(y - 5)$ **57.** $A = 9 - 4x^2 = (3 + 2x)(3 - 2x)$

B.5 Practice Exercises

1. a. $\dfrac{2n + 1}{n(n - 1)}$ **b.** $-x^2$ **2. a.** $-\dfrac{y^3}{21(y + 3)}$ **b.** $\dfrac{7x + 2}{x + 2}$ **3. a.** $\dfrac{20p + 3}{5p^4q}$ **b.** $\dfrac{5y^2 + 19y - 12}{(y + 3)(y - 3)}$ **c.** 3   **4.** 1

Exercise Set B.5

1. $\dfrac{1}{2}$ **3.** $\dfrac{1 + 2x}{8}$ **5.** $\dfrac{2(x - 4)}{(x + 2)(x - 1)}$ **7.** 4   **9.** -5 **11.** $\dfrac{2x + 5}{x(x - 3)}$ **13.** -2 **15.** $\dfrac{(a + 3)(a + 1)}{a + 2}$ **17.** $-\dfrac{1}{5}$
19. $\dfrac{4a + 1}{(3a + 1)(3a - 1)}$ **21.** $-1, \dfrac{3}{2}$ **23.** $\dfrac{3}{x + 1}$ **25.** -1 **27. a.** $\dfrac{x}{5} - \dfrac{x}{4} + \dfrac{1}{10}$ **b.** Write each rational expression term so that the denominator
is the LCD, 20.   **c.** $\dfrac{-x + 2}{20}$ **29.** b   **31.** d   **33.** d

APPENDIX C   AN INTRODUCTION TO USING A GRAPHING UTILITY

The Viewing Window and Interpreting Window Settings Exercise Set

1. yes   **3.** no   **5.** answers may vary   **7.** answers may vary   **9.** answers may vary
11. Xmin $= -12$ Ymin $= -12$ **13.** Xmin $= -9$ Ymin $= -12$ **15.** Xmin $= -10$ Ymin $= -25$ **17.** Xmin $= -10$ Ymin $= -30$
        Xmax $= 12$ Ymax $= 12$ Xmax $= 9$ Ymax $= 12$ Xmax $= 10$ Ymax $= 25$ Xmax $= 10$ Ymax $= 30$
        Xscl $= 3$ Yscl $= 3$ Xscl $= 1$ Yscl $= 2$ Xscl $= 2$ Yscl $= 5$ Xscl $= 1$ Yscl $= 3$
19. Xmin $= -20$ Ymin $= -30$
        Xmax $= 30$ Ymax $= 50$
        Xscl $= 5$ Yscl $= 10$

Graphing Equations and Square Viewing Window Exercise Set

1. Setting B   **3.** Setting B   **5.** Setting B
7.

9.

11.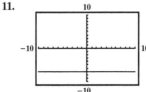

13.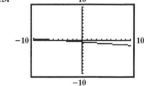

15. 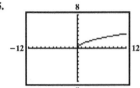 **17.** 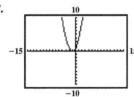 **19.** 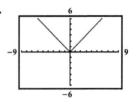 **21.**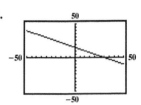

APPENDIX D SOLVING SYSTEMS OF EQUATIONS BY MATRICES

Practice Exercises
1. $(2, -1)$ **2.** { } or $\varnothing$ **3.** $(-1, 1, 2)$

Exercise Set
1. $(2, -1)$ **3.** $(-4, 2)$ **5.** { } or $\varnothing$ **7.** $\{(x, y) \mid 3x - 3y = 9\}$ **9.** $(-2, 5, -2)$ **11.** $(1, -2, 3)$ **13.** $(4, -3)$ **15.** $(2, 1, -1)$
17. $(9, 9)$ **19.** { } or $\varnothing$ **21.** { } or $\varnothing$ **23.** $(1, -4, 3)$ **25.** c

APPENDIX E SOLVING SYSTEMS OF EQUATIONS BY DETERMINANTS

1. 26 **3.** -19 **5.** 0 **7.** $(1, 2)$ **9.** $\{(x, y) \mid 3x + y = 1\}$ **11.** $(9, 9)$ **13.** 8 **15.** 0 **17.** 54 **19.** $(-2, 0, 5)$ **21.** $(6, -2, 4)$

23. 16 **25.** 15 **27.** $\dfrac{13}{6}$ **29.** 0 **31.** 56 **33.** $(-3, -2)$ **35.** { } or $\varnothing$ **37.** $(-2, 3, -1)$ **39.** $(3, 4)$ **41.** $(-2, 1)$

43. $\{(x, y, z) \mid x - 2y + z = -3\}$ **45.** $(0, 2, -1)$ **47.** 5 **49.** 0; answers may vary **51.** 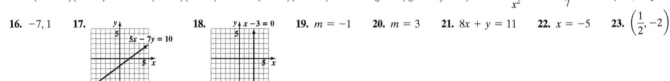 **53.** -125 **55.** 24

APPENDIX F MEAN, MEDIAN, AND MODE

1. mean: 29, median: 28, no mode **3.** mean: 8.1, median: 8.2, mode: 8.2 **5.** mean: 0.6, median: 0.6, mode: 0.2 and 0.6
7. mean: 370.9, median: 313.5, no mode **9.** 1214.8 ft **11.** 1117 ft **13.** 6.8 **15.** 6.9 **17.** 85.5 **19.** 73 **21.** 70 and 71
23. 9 **25.** 21, 21, 24

APPENDIX G REVIEW OF ANGLES, LINES, AND SPECIAL TRIANGLES

1. $71°$ **3.** $19.2°$ **5.** $78\dfrac{3}{4}°$ **7.** $30°$ **9.** $149.8°$ **11.** $100\dfrac{1}{2}°$ **13.** $m\angle 1 = m\angle 5 = m\angle 7 = 110°; m\angle 2 = m\angle 3 = m\angle 4 = m\angle 6 = 70°$

15. $90°$ **17.** $90°$ **19.** $90°$ **21.** $45°, 90°$ **23.** $73°, 90°$ **25.** $50\dfrac{1}{4}°, 90°$ **27.** $x = 6$ **29.** $x = 4.5$ **31.** 10 **33.** 12

PRACTICE FINAL EXAM

1. -48 **2.** -81 **3.** $\dfrac{1}{64}$ **4.** $-\dfrac{1}{3}$ **5.** $-3x^3 + 5x^2 + 4x + 5$ **6.** $16x^2 - 16x + 4$ **7.** $3x^3 + 22x^2 + 41x + 14$ **8.** $(y - 12)(y + 4)$

9. $3x(3x + 1)(x + 4)$ **10.** $5(6 + x)(6 - x)$ **11.** $(a + b)(3a - 7)$ **12.** $8(y - 2)(y^2 + 2y + 4)$ **13.** $\dfrac{y^{14}}{x^2}$ **14.** $\dfrac{25}{7}$ **15.** $(-\infty, -2]$

16. $-7, 1$ **17.** **18.** **19.** $m = -1$ **20.** $m = 3$ **21.** $8x + y = 11$ **22.** $x = -5$ **23.** $\left(\dfrac{1}{2}, -2\right)$

24. no solution; { } or $\varnothing$ **25.** $9x^2 - 6x + 4 - \dfrac{16}{3x + 2}$ **26. a.** 0 **b.** 0 **c.** 60 **27.** x-intercepts: $(0, 0), (4, 0)$; y-intercept: $(0, 0)$;

domain: $(-\infty, \infty)$; range: $(-\infty, 4]$ **28.** $401, 802$ **29.** $2\dfrac{1}{2}$ hr **30.** 120 cc **31.** $\{x \mid x \text{ is a real number}, x \neq -1, x \neq -3\}$ **32.** $\dfrac{19x - 6}{2x + 5}$

33. $\dfrac{2(x + 5)}{x(y + 5)}$ **34.** $\dfrac{3a - 4}{(a - 3)(a + 2)}$ **35.** $\dfrac{5y^2 - 1}{y + 2}$ **36.** $\dfrac{30}{11}$ **37.** -6 **38.** no solution **39.** 5 or 1 **40.** $6\sqrt{6}$ **41.** 5

42. $\dfrac{8a^{1/3}c^{2/3}}{b^{5/12}}$ **43.** $-x\sqrt{5x}$ **44.** -20 **45.** $1, \dfrac{2}{3}$ **46.** $\left(\dfrac{3}{2}, 5\right]$ **47.** $(-\infty, -2)\cup\left(\dfrac{4}{3}, \infty\right)$ **48.** $\dfrac{3 \pm \sqrt{29}}{2}$ or $\dfrac{3}{2} \pm \dfrac{\sqrt{29}}{2}$ **49.** 2, 3

50. $\left(-\infty, -\dfrac{3}{2}\right) \cup (5, \infty)$ **51.**   **52.** 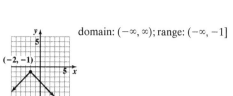 domain: $(-\infty, \infty)$; range: $(-\infty, -1]$ **53.**

54. 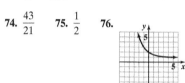 domain: $(-\infty, \infty)$; range: $(-3, \infty)$ **55.** $f(x) = -\dfrac{1}{2}x$ **56.** $f(x) = -\dfrac{1}{3}x + \dfrac{5}{3}$ **57.** $2\sqrt{26}$ units   **58.** $\left(-4, \dfrac{7}{2}\right)$ **59.** $\dfrac{3\sqrt{y}}{y}$

60. $\dfrac{8 - 6\sqrt{x} + x}{8 - 2x}$ **61.** 16   **62.** 7 ft   **63. a.** 272 ft   **b.** 5.12 sec   **64.** $0 - 2i\sqrt{2}$ **65.** $0 - 3i$ **66.** $7 + 24i$ **67.** $-\dfrac{3}{2} + \dfrac{5}{2}i$

68. $(g \circ h)(x) = x^2 - 6x - 2$ **69.** one-to-one; $f^{-1}(x) = \dfrac{-x + 6}{2}$ **70.** $\log_5 \dfrac{x^4}{x + 1}$ **71.** -1 **72.** $\dfrac{1}{2}\left(\dfrac{\log 4}{\log 3} - 5\right)$; -1.8691 **73.** 22

74. $\dfrac{43}{21}$ **75.** $\dfrac{1}{2}$ **76.**   **77.** 64,805 prairie dogs   **78.**   **79.**   **80.**

81. $(-5, -1), (-5, 1), (5, -1), (5, 1)$ **82.** $-\dfrac{1}{5}, \dfrac{1}{6}, -\dfrac{1}{7}, \dfrac{1}{8}, -\dfrac{1}{9}$ **83.** 155   **84.** 1   **85.** 10   **86.** $32x^5 + 80x^4y + 80x^3y^2 + 40x^2y^3 + 10xy^4 + y^5$

Index

A

Absolute value, 12, 559
Absolute value bars, 560
Absolute value equations
  explanation of, 559, 580
  method to solve, 559–562, 580–582
Absolute value inequalities
  explanation of, 564, 581
  methods to solve, 566–568
  solution set of, 564–566
Absolute value property, 560
Acute angles, 895
Addends, 35, 36
Addition
  applications with, 38–40
  of complex numbers, 636, 644
  of decimals, 848
  distributive property of multiplication
    over, 62–64
  of fractions, 19–21
  of functions, 713, 716
  of polynomials, 323–326, 366
  of radical expressions, 611–613, 643
  of rational expressions, 460–464, 468–471, 503
  of real numbers, 35–40, 44–45, 70–71
  words/phrases for, 30
Addition method. See Elimination method
Addition property
  associative, 61–62
  commutative, 61
  of equality, 85–90, 158
  of inequality, 146–147
Additive inverse. See also Opposites
  explanation of, 39, 65
  method to find, 39–40
  of polynomial, 324
Adjacent angles, 896
Algebraic expressions
  evaluation of, 28–29, 45–46, 406
  explanation of, 28
  methods to simplify, 78–81, 855–857
  method to write, 855–857
  review of, 157
  word phrases written as, 81, 90–91
Alternate interior angles, 896
Angles
  complementary, 47, 93, 895
  explanation of, 47
  finding measure of, 107–108, 290–291
  review of, 895–898
  supplementary, 47, 93, 895
  types of, 895, 896

Applications. See Applications index;
    Problem solving
Approximation
  decimal, 588
  of logarithms, 757
  of roots, 588
Area, 115
Arithmetic operations. See Division; Multiplication;
    Order of operations; Subtraction
Arithmetic sequences
  common difference of, 817, 818
  explanation of, 817–818, 826
  general term of, 818–820, 842
  partial sums of, 830–831, 843
Array of signs, 889
Associative property, 61–62
Asymptotes, 792
Axis of symmetry
  explanation of, 689
  of parabola, 780

B

Bar graphs, 169
Base
  explanation of, 25
  of exponential expressions, 25, 307, 309
Binomial formula, 839
Binomials. See also Polynomials
  division of polynomials by, 360
  expansion of, 837–840
  explanation of, 318, 319
  factoring, 402–406, 432
  FOIL method for, 338, 366, 382
  square of, 338–339, 366
Binomial theorem, 839–840, 843
Boundary lines, 571–572, 574–576
Boyle's law, 538–539
Brackets, 28
Break-even point, 289–290

C

Calculators. See also Graphing calculators
  checking solutions to equations
    on, 100, 478
  exponential expressions on, 32
  logarithms on, 759
  negative numbers on, 57–58
  order of operations on, 32
  scientific notation on, 350
Cartesian coordinate system. See Rectangular
    coordinate system
Celsius conversions, 117–118, 714

Center
  of circle, 783–785
  of ellipse, 789–791
  of hyperbola, 791
Change of base formula, 761
Circles
  center and radius of, 783–785
  equation of, 783–786
  explanation of, 783
  on graphing calculator, 786
  graphs of, 128, 783–785, 796, 807
  illustration of, 780
  standard form of equation of, 783, 796
Coefficients, 77, 318, 365
Combined variation, 540–541
Common denominators. *See also* Denominators
  adding and subtracting rational expressions with, 460–461
  least, 20–21
Common difference, of sequence, 817, 818, 842
Common factors, 444
Common logarithms
  evaluation of power of 10, 758–759
  explanation of, 757, 772
Common ratio, 820, 821, 833, 843
Common terms, 444
Commutative property of addition, 61
Commutative property of multiplication, 61
Complementary angles, 47, 93, 895
Completing the square
  explanation of, 652
  to solve quadratic equations, 654–656, 705
  to write quadratic function, 697
Complex conjugates, 637–638, 645
Complex fractions
  explanation of, 495
  method to simplify, 495–499, 505
Complex numbers
  addition and subtraction of, 636, 644
  division of, 637–638
  explanation of, 635, 644
  multiplication of, 636–637, 644
  powers of i and, 638–639
Complex number system, 634
Composite functions, 714–716, 770
Composite numbers, 17
Compound inequalities
  containing the word *and,* 552–554
  containing the word *or,* 555–556
  explanation of, 150, 162, 552, 580
  method to solve, 150–153, 162
Compound interest
  explanation of, 657–658, 760, 766
  on graphing calculator, 766–767
Compound interest formula, 733
Congruent triangles, 897–898
Conic sections, 780, 796. *See also* Circles; Ellipses;
    Hyperbolas; Parabolas
Conjugates
  complex, 637–638, 645

  explanation of, 619, 643
  rationalizing denominators using, 619–620, 643
Consecutive integers
  even and odd, 91, 108, 424–425, 855
  explanation of, 91
  solving problems with, 108–109
Consistent systems of linear equations
  in three variables, 273
  in two variables, 252, 254
Constant of variation, 536–537, 539–540
Continually compounded interest
    formula, 760, 772
Coordinate plane. *See* Rectangular
    coordinate system
Coplanar lines, 896
Corresponding angles, 896
Cost function, 289–290
Counting numbers. *See* Natural numbers
Cramer's rule
  explanation of, 886, 887
  to solve system of three linear equations, 890–891
  to solve system of two linear equations, 887–889
Cross products, 482–484, 504
Cube root functions, 591–592
Cube roots
  explanation of, 588, 642
  method to find, 588–589
Cubes, sum or difference of two, 405

D

Decimal approximation, 588
Decimal equivalents table, 850
Decimals
  equations containing, 98–99
  operations with, 53, 848
  rational and irrational numbers written as, 10
Degree
  of polynomials, 319–320, 365
  of term, 319
Denominators. *See also* Common denominators;
    Least common denominator (LCD)
  common, 460–461
  explanation of, 16
  least common, 20–21, 462–464
  of rational exponents, 597
  of rational expressions, 460–461, 468–471
  rationalizing the, 617–620
Dependent equations, 253, 254, 273
Dependent variables, 231
Descending powers, of polynomial, 318
Determinants
  Cramer's rule and, 886–891
  evaluation of 2×2, 886
  evaluation of 3×3, 889–890
  explanation of, 886
Difference of squares, 339–340, 402–404
Direct variation, 536–537, 546
Discount problems, 129

Discriminant, 665–666
Distance, 609
Distance formula, 115, 607, 642
Distance problems, 115–116, 139–140, 488–490, 607–608
Distributive property
    of multiplication over addition, 62–64
    to multiply polynomials, 331–332
    to multiply radicals, 614
    to remove parentheses, 79–80, 87
    use of, 79–81
Dividend, 55
Division
    applications with, 57
    of complex numbers, 637–638, 645
    of decimals, 848
    of fractions, 19, 451
    of functions, 713
    long, 354–357
    of polynomials, 353–357, 360–362, 367
    of rational expressions, 453–455, 502
    of real numbers, 54–56, 71
    symbol for, 55
    synthetic, 360–362, 367
    words/phrases for, 30
    by zero, 55
Divisor, 55
Domain
    of functions, 232–233
    of rational functions, 440–441
    of relations, 227

E
Elementary row operations, 881, 882
Elements, of matrix, 881
Elimination method
    explanation of, 265
    to solve nonlinear system of equations, 799–800
    to solve systems of linear equations in three
        variables, 274–276, 300
    to solve systems of linear equations in two variables,
        265–269, 299
Ellipses
    center of, 789–791
    equation of, 789, 790
    explanation of, 789
    focus of, 789
    on graphing calculator, 793–794
    graphs of, 789–791, 796, 807
    illustration of, 780
    standard form of equation of, 789, 796
Empty set, 99
Equality
    addition property of, 85–88, 158
    logarithm property of, 763–764, 772
    multiplication property of, 88–90, 158
    words/phrases for, 30
Equality symbol, 7, 29

Equations. *See also* Linear equations; Linear
        equations in one variable; Linear equations in
        two variables; Nonlinear systems of equations;
        Quadratic equations; Systems of linear equations;
        specific types of equations
    absolute value, 559–562, 580–581
    on calculator, 100, 199, 478, 515, 524
    of circle, 783–786
    dependent, 253, 254, 273
    of ellipse, 789, 790
    equivalent, 85–86, 158, 262
    explanation of, 29
    exponential, 763–764
    on graphing calculator, 100, 199, 478, 515, 524,
        878–879
    graphs of, 184
    of hyperbolas, 791–793
    independent, 253, 254
    of inverse of function, 722–723
    of lines, 217–222, 512–513
    logarithmic, 743–746, 764–765
    nonlinear systems of, 797–800, 808
    of parabola, 780, 784
    percent, 127–128
    in quadratic form, 672–675
    radical, 524–627, 644
    rational expressions in, 474–478, 483, 503–504, 872–873
    review of, 914–915
    slope-intercept form of, 217–219, 253, 255
    solutions of, 29–30, 85, 174–176
    of vertical and horizontal lines, 220–221
Equivalent equations, 85–86, 158, 262
Equivalent fractions, 20
Estimation. *See* Approximation
Expanding by the minors, 889, 890
Exponential decay, 738–740
Exponential equations
    logarithmic notation for, 743–744
    method to solve, 731–732, 763–764
    method to write, 743
    solving problems modeled by, 732–734
Exponential expressions
    base of, 25, 307, 309
    on calculators, 32
    evaluating of, 307–308
    evaluation of, 25–26
    explanation of, 25, 70, 307
    methods to simplify, 309–315, 344–346
Exponential functions
    applications for, 732–734
    explanation of, 729, 771
    graphs of, 729–731
Exponential growth, 738–739
Exponential notation, 25
Exponents
    explanation of, 307, 365
    negative, 344–346, 366, 498
    power of quotient rule for, 312, 598

Exponents (*continued*)
power rule for, 310–311, 598
product rule for, 308–310, 598
quotient rule for, 312–313, 344, 598
rational, 596–600, 642
summary of rules for, 346
zero, 314, 598
Expressions. *See* Exponential expressions; Rational
expressions
Exterior angles, 896

F
Factored form, 374
Factorials, 838, 843
Factoring out greatest common factor, 374, 376–378,
386, 393, 431
Factors/factoring. *See also* Polynomials
binomials, 402–406, 432
common, 444
difference of two squares, 339–340, 402–404
explanation of, 16, 374
greatest common, 374–378, 386, 393, 431
by grouping, 378–380, 397–401, 432
perfect square trinomials, 393–395
to solve quadratic equations, 412–419, 433
strategy for, 409–411, 432–433, 869–870
sum or difference of two cubes, 405
trinomials of form $ax^2 + bx + c$, 389–392, 397–401
trinomials of form $x^2 + bx + c$, 382–386, 431
Fahrenheit conversions, 117–118, 714
Fibonacci (Leonardo of Pisa), 812
Fibonacci sequence, 812, 817
Finite sequences, 813, 842
Finite series, 825
First-degree equations in one variable.
See Linear equations in one variable
First-degree equations in two variables.
See Linear equations in two variables
First-degree polynomial equations.
See Linear equations in one variable
Focus
of ellipse, 789
of hyperbola, 791
FOIL method
explanation of, 337–338, 366
use of, 339, 382
Formulas. *See also* specific formulas
explanation of, 115, 159
solved for specified variables, 119–120
solving problems with, 115–121, 159
Fraction bar, 27
Fraction equivalents table, 850
Fractions. *See also* Ratios
addition of, 19–21
complex, 495–499
division of, 19, 451
equivalent, 20
explanation of, 16, 69

fundamental principle of, 17
in lowest terms, 16
multiplication of, 18–19, 53, 451
reciprocal of, 19
simplified, 16
solving linear equations containing, 97–98, 121
subtraction of, 19–21
unit, 455–457
Function composition, 714–716
Function notation
explanation of, 231–232, 519–520, 545–546
writing equations of lines using, 512–513
Functions. *See also* specific functions
algebra of, 713–716, 770
composite, 713–716, 770
cube root, 591–592
domain of, 232–233
explanation of, 227, 241, 519
exponential, 729–734, 771
graphs of, 228, 230, 231, 520–521
identification of, 227–228
inverse, 718–725
linear, 511–515, 529, 545
logarithmic, 742–744, 771–772
nonlinear, 522–523, 530, 545–546
one-to-one, 718–722, 725, 731
piecewise-defined, 528–529, 546
polynomial, 320–321, 365
quadratic, 689–701
radical, 591–592, 642
range of, 233
rational, 440–441, 446
relations as, 227–228
square root, 591–592
vertical line test for, 228–231
Fundamental principle of fractions, 17
Fundamental principle of rational
expressions, 442

G
General term
of arithmetic sequence, 818–820, 842
of geometric sequence, 821, 843
of sequence, 814–815
Geometric progression. *See* Geometric sequences
Geometric sequences
explanation of, 820–822
general term of, 821, 843
partial sums of, 832–834, 843
sum of terms of infinite, 833–834
Geometry, 895
Geometry review
angles, 895–898
triangles, 898–900
Graphing calculators. *See also* Calculators
addition of functions on, 716
checking solutions to equations on, 100, 478
circles on, 786

compound interest on, 766–767
ellipses on, 793–794
equations on, 100, 199, 478, 515, 524, 878–879
evaluating expressions on, 406
explanation of, 876
factoring patterns on, 406
features of, 190
inverse functions on, 725
patterns on, 222–223
polynomials on, 326
quadratic equations on, 418–419, 658–659
quadratic functions on, 695
radical equations on, 629
rational expressions on, 446, 478
scientific notation on, 350
to sketch graphs of more than one equation on same
    set of axes, 210–211
systems of equations on, 255
TRACE feature on, 734–735
windows and window settings on, 876–879
Graphs
    bar, 169
    of circles, 128, 783–785, 796, 807
    of cube root functions, 591–592
    of ellipses, 789–791, 796, 807
    of exponential functions, 729–731
    of functions, 228, 230, 231
    of horizontal and vertical lines, 197–198
    of hyperbolas, 791–793, 796, 807–808
    of inequalities, 146
    of inverse functions, 723, 724
    line, 170
    of linear equations in two variables, 184–190, 866–868
    of linear functions, 511–515, 529
    of linear inequalities, 146, 571–574, 581–582
    of logarithmic functions, 747
    method to read, 169–172
    of nonlinear functions, 522–523, 530, 545–546
    of nonlinear inequalities, 802–803
    of one-to-one functions, 720–721
    of parabolas, 689–694, 697–701, 707, 780–783,
      796, 806
    of piecewise-defined functions, 528–529, 546
    plotting ordered pairs on, 171–178, 238, 864–866
    of quadratic equations, 418–419
    of quadratic functions, 689–694, 697–701, 707
    reflecting, 533–534, 546
    of relations, 228
    review of common, 529–532
    slope-intercept form and, 205, 217–218
    to solve systems of linear equations, 251–255, 298–299
    of square root function, 530–531
    of systems of linear equations, 251–255
    of systems of linear inequalities, 575–576
    of systems of nonlinear inequalities, 803–805, 808
    vertical and horizontal shifting and, 531–533
Greatest common factor (GCF)
    explanation of, 374, 431

factoring out, 374, 376–378, 386, 393
    of list of terms, 375–376
    method to find, 374–375
Grouping method
    explanation of, 378, 432
    factoring by, 378–380, 397–401, 431
Grouping symbols, 26–28. *See also* Brackets; Parentheses

H
Half-life, 740
Half-plane, 571, 574
Hooke's law, 537
Horizontal lines
    equations of, 221, 513
    explanation of, 198, 512
    graphs of, 197–198
    slope of, 206–207
Horizontal line test, 720–721, 770
Horizontal shifts, 532–533
Hyperbolas
    equation of, 791–793
    explanation of, 791
    focus of, 791
    graphs of, 791–793, 796, 807–808
    illustration of, 780
    standard form of equation of, 792, 793, 796
Hypotenuse, 425

I
Identities
    for addition and multiplication, 64–65
    explanation of, 100
    with no solution, 99–100
Identity properties, 64–65
Imaginary numbers, 634, 635
Imaginary unit (*i*)
    explanation of, 634
    powers of, 638–639
Inconsistent systems of linear equations
    in three variables, 273
    in two variables, 252–254
Independent equations, 253, 254
Independent variables, 231
Index, 589
Index of summation, 825
Inequalities. *See also specific types of inequalities*
    absolute value, 564–568, 581
    addition property of, 146–147
    applications of, 152–153
    compound, 150–153, 162, 552–556, 580
    linear, 145–153, 161–162
    multiplication property of, 147–148
    nonlinear, 682–686, 802–803, 808
    on number line, 146
    polynomial, 682–685, 706
    quadratic, 682
    rational, 685–686, 706–707
    review of, 915–916

Inequalities (*continued*)
  simple, 150
  solution set of, 145–146, 150, 552
  systems of linear, 575–576
  systems of nonlinear, 803–805
Inequality symbols, 7–8, 145, 147, 152
Infinite sequences
  explanation of, 813, 842
  sum of terms of, 833–834
Infinite series, 825
Integers. *See also* Signed numbers
  consecutive, 91, 108–109, 424–425, 855
  explanation of, 9
  negative, 9
  on number line, 9
  positive, 9
  quotient of, 10
Intercepts. *See also* x-intercepts; y-intercepts
  explanation of, 194, 239
  finding and plotting, 195–197
  identification of, 194–195
Interest
  compound, 657–658, 733, 760, 766, 772
  simple, 657
Interest formula, 115
Interest problems, 141–142
Interior angles, 896
Intersecting lines, 896
Intersection, of solution sets of inequalities, 552–554, 580
Intersection symbol, 552
Interval notation
  compound inequalities and, 552–554
  explanation of, 146
  use of, 146
Inverse functions
  explanation of, 721
  on graphing calculator, 725
  graphs of, 724–725
  one-to-one, 718–722, 725, 770
Inverse of functions
  equation for, 722–724
  method to find, 721–722, 770
Inverse variation, 538–539, 546
Investment problems, 141–142
Irrational numbers, 10, 588
Isosceles triangles, 108

J
Joint variation, 539–540, 546

K
Kelvin scale, 714

L
Least common denominator (LCD). *See also*
    Denominators
  explanation of, 20–21
  method to find, 462–464
  of rational expressions, 462–464

Least squares method, 521
Leonardo of Pisa (Fibonacci), 812
Like radicals, 611–612, 643
Like terms
  explanation of, 77, 78
  method to combine, 2–3
  polynomials with, 321–323
Linear equations. *See also* Linear equations
    in two variables; Systems of linear equations
Linear equations in one variable. *See also*
    Equations; Systems of linear equations
  containing decimals, 98–99
  containing fractions, 97–98, 121
  explanation of, 85, 851
  with no solution, 99–100
  solution of, 174
  steps to solve, 95–97, 158, 852–854
Linear equations in two variables. *See also* Equations;
    Systems of linear equations
  examples of, 185
  explanation of, 184, 239, 570
  forms of, 222
  graphs of, 184–190, 866–868
  point-slope form of, 219–220, 222, 512
  slope-intercept form of, 205, 217–219, 222, 512
  solution of, 174–175
  standard form of, 184, 222, 239, 866
Linear functions
  explanation of, 511, 545
  graphs of, 511–515, 529
Linear inequalities. *See also* Inequalities
  compound, 150–153, 162
  graphs of, 571–574, 581–582
  methods to solve, 146–153, 161–162
  in one variable, 145
  solution of, 145–146, 571
  steps to solve, 149
  systems of, 575–5776
  in two variables, 571–574
Line graphs, 170
Lines
  boundary, 571–572, 574–576
  coplanar, 896
  equations of, 217–222, 512–513
  horizontal, 197–198, 206–207, 221, 512
  intersecting, 896
  parallel, 201, 207–209, 222, 514, 896
  perpendicular, 207–209, 222, 514–515, 896
  slope of, 202–210, 240–241
  vertical, 197–198, 206–207, 220–221, 896
Logarithmic equations
  method to solve, 745–746, 764–765
  method to write, 743–744
Logarithmic functions
  characteristics of, 748
  explanation of, 746, 771–772
  graphs of, 747
Logarithmic notation, 743–744

Logarithm property of equality, 763–764, 772
Logarithms
  common, 757–759, 772
  evaluation of, 744
  explanation of, 743, 771
  natural, 757, 759–760, 772
  power property of, 752
  product property of, 750–751, 753
  properties of, 745–746, 750–754, 772
  quotient property of, 751–753
Long division, 354–357
Lowest terms, 16

M

Mark-up problems, 129
Mathematical statements
  explanation of, 7
  translating sentences into, 8–9
Mathematics class
  exam performance in, 5
  exam preparation for, 4–5, 903–905, 909
  exams for, 904
  getting help in, 4, 909, 911
  homework assignments for, 907, 908
  learning new terms for, 905
  notebooks for, 906
  organizational skills for, 906, 908
  resources available for, 910
  study skills builders for, 903–911
  textbooks and supplements for, 910, 911
  time management for, 5, 907
  tips for success in, 2–3
  use of textbook for, 3–4
Matrices
  element of, 881
  explanation of, 881
  to solve systems of three
    equations, 883–885
  to solve systems of two equations, 881–883
  square, 886
Maximum value, 701–702
Mean, 893, 894
Measurement conversions, 455–457
Measures of central tendency, 893–894
Median, 893, 894
Midpoint, 608, 609
Midpoint formula, 608, 643
Minimum value, 701
Minor, 889
Mixed numbers, 21–22, 69
Mixture problems, 131–132, 160
Mode, 893, 894
Money problems, 140–141
Monomials. *See also* Polynomials
  dividing polynomials by, 353
  division of, 353–354
  explanation of, 318, 319
  multiplication of, 330–331

Multiplication. *See also* Products
  applications with, 57
  of complex numbers, 636–637, 644
  of decimals, 848
  distributive property of, 62–64
  of fractions, 18–19, 53, 451
  of functions, 713
  of polynomials, 330–333, 339–341, 366
  of radical expressions, 614, 643
  of rational expressions, 451–453, 455, 502
  of real numbers, 51–55, 71
  symbol for, 16
  words/phrases for, 30
Multiplication property
  associative, 61–62
  commutative, 61
  of equality, 88–91, 158
  of inequality, 147–148
Multiplicative inverse, 54, 65

N

Natural logarithms
  evaluation of powers of *e*, 759–760
  explanation of, 757, 772
Natural numbers, 7
Negative exponents
  explanation of, 344–345, 366, 598
  simplifying expressions with, 345–346
Negative integers, 9
Negative numbers
  on calculators, 57–58
  explanation of, 11
Negative reciprocals, 208
Negative square root, 587, 641
Nonlinear functions, graphs of, 522–523, 530, 545–546
Nonlinear inequalities
  in one variable, 682–686, 706–707
  systems of, 803–805, 808
  in two variables, 802–803, 808
Nonlinear systems of equations
  elimination method to solve, 799–800
  explanation of, 797, 808
  substitution method to solve, 797–799
Nonnegative square root. *See* Principal square root
Notation. *See* Symbols/notation
*n*th roots, 589
Null set, 99
Number line
  explanation of, 7
  inequalities on, 146
  integers on, 9
  real numbers on, 7, 35, 36
Numbers. *See also* Complex numbers; Integers;
    Real numbers
  composite, 17
  finding unknown, 104–105
  irrational, 10, 588
  mixed, 21–22, 69

Numbers (*continued*)
  natural, 7
  negative, 11, 57–58
  opposite of, 39
  positive, 11
  prime, 16, 17
  rational, 10
  signed, 11
  whole, 7
Numerator
  explanation of, 16
  rationalizing the, 620–621
Numerical coefficients. *See* Coefficients

O

Obtuse angles, 895
One-to-one functions
  explanation of, 718–719, 770
  exponential functions as, 731
  horizontal line test to determine, 720–721
  inverse of, 721–722, 725
Opposites, 39, 324. *See also* Additive inverse
Ordered pairs
  data represented as, 173–174
  explanation of, 171, 238
  method to plot, 864–866
  as solution to equations, 174–176,
    185–190, 226, 227
  as solution to system of linear
    equations, 250
Ordered triples, 273, 300
Order of operations
  on calculators, 32
  to evaluate expressions, 26–27
  explanation of, 26, 70
Order property for real numbers, 12
Origin, 171

P

Paired data, 173–174. *See also* Ordered pairs
Parabolas. *See also* Quadratic equations; Quadratic
    functions
  equation of, 780, 784
  explanation of, 530, 780
  graphs of, 689–694, 697–701, 707, 780–783,
    796, 806
  illustration of, 780
  vertex of, 689–691, 700–701
Parallel lines
  cut by transversal, 897
  equations of, 514
  explanation of, 201, 207, 896
  slope of, 207–209, 222
Parentheses
  distributive property to remove, 79–80, 87
  explanation of, 28
  with exponential expressions, 307

Partial sums
  of arithmetic sequences, 830–831
  explanation of, 826–827, 843
  of geometric sequences, 832–834
Pascal's triangle, 837–838
Percent, 734, 858
Percent equations, 127–128
Percent equivalents table, 850
Percent problems
  increase and decrease, 130–131
  strategies to solve, 127–128, 160, 859
Perfect squares, 588
Perfect square trinomials
  completing the square for, 654, 655
  explanation of, 393, 401, 432
  factoring, 393–395
Perimeter
  of rectangles, 117–121
  of triangle, 115
Perpendicular lines
  equations of, 514–515
  explanation of, 207, 896
  slope of, 207–209, 222
Piecewise-defined functions, 528–529, 546
Plane, 895–896
Plane figures, 896
Point-slope form
  in applications, 221–222
  equations in, 219–220, 512
  explanation of, 219, 241
Polygons, 897
Polynomial equations. *See* Quadratic equations
Polynomial functions
  explanation of, 320–321, 365
  problem solving with, 321
Polynomial inequalities, 682–685, 706
Polynomials. *See also* Binomials; Factors/factoring;
    Monomials; Trinomials
  addition of, 323–326, 366
  combining like terms to simplify, 321–323
  degree of, 319–320, 365
  descending powers of, 318
  division of, 353–357, 360–362, 367
  explanation of, 318, 365
  FOIL method to multiply, 337–339, 366, 382
  on graphing calculator, 326
  grouping to factor, 378–380
  multiplication of, 330–333, 339–341, 366
  subtraction of, 325, 326, 366
  term of, 319, 365
  types of, 318–319
Positive integers, 9
Positive numbers, 11
Positive square root. *See* Principal square root
Power, 307
Power of product rule, 311
Power of quotient rule, 312

Power property of logarithms, 752
Power rules
    for exponents, 310–312, 598
    to solve radical equations, 624–625
Powers of 10, 758–760
Prime factorization, 17
Prime numbers, 16, 17
Principal square root, 522, 587, 641
Problem solving. *See also* Applications index; Word
    phrases; *specific types of problems*
    with addition, 38–40
    with consecutive integers, 108–109
    with division, 57
    with exponential equations, 732–734, 765–766
    with formulas, 115–121, 159
    general strategy for, 104–106, 126, 138, 159, 161, 857–859
    with inequalities, 152–153
    with logarithmic equations, 765–766
    with multiplication, 57
    with percent, 127–128, 130–131
    with point-slope form, 221–222
    with polynomial functions, 321
    with proportions, 484–486
    with Pythagorean theorem, 425–426, 628–629
    with quadratic equations, 421–426, 433–434, 657–658,
      666–668, 675–677
    with radical equations, 486–490, 504, 644
    with rational functions, 446
    with relationships among unknown quantities,
      106–108
    with sequences, 815, 820, 822, 831, 832, 834
    with subtraction, 46–47
    with systems of linear equations, 280–291, 301
    with variation, 536–541
Product property of logarithms, 750–751, 753
Product rule
    for exponents, 308–310, 598
    for radicals, 603, 605, 606
Products. *See also* Multiplication
    cross, 482–484, 504
    explanation of, 16
    power rule for, 311–312
Profit function, 325
Proportionality, constant of, 536
Proportions. *See also* Ratios
    explanation of, 482, 504
    method to solve, 482–484
    problem solving using, 484–486
Pure imaginary numbers, 634, 635
Pythagorean theorem
    applications of, 425–426, 900
    explanation of, 425, 628, 899
    use of, 627–629

Q

Quadrants, 171
Quadratic equations. *See also* Parabolas
    completing the square to solve, 654–656, 705

    with degree greater than two, 416–417
    discriminate and, 665–666
    explanation of, 412, 652
    factoring to solve, 413–418, 433, 652
    on graphing calculator, 418–419, 658–659
    graphs of, 418
    quadratic formula to solve, 662–668, 706
    solving problems modeled by, 421–426, 433–434,
      657–658, 666–668
    solving problems that lead to, 675–677
    square root property to solve, 652–657
    standard form of, 412, 663, 664
    steps to solve, 415, 672–675, 852–854
    x-intercepts of graph of, 418
    zero factor property to solve, 413–415
Quadratic form, equations in, 672–675
Quadratic formula
    explanation of, 662
    to solve quadratic equations, 662–668, 673, 706
Quadratic functions
    explanation of, 689
    of form $f(x) = ax^2$, 692–693
    of form $f(x) = a(x - h)^2 + k$, 692–694
    of form $f(x) = (x - h)^2$, 690–691
    of form $f(x) = x^2 + k$, 689–690
    of form $y = a + (x - h)^2 + k$, 697–700
    on graphing calculator, 695
    graphs of, 689–694, 707
Quadratic inequalities, 682
Quadrilaterals, 94, 112
Quotient property of logarithms, 751–753
Quotient rule
    for exponents, 312–313, 344, 598
    power of, 312
    for radicals, 604–606
Quotients
    power rule for, 312
    of two real numbers, 54–55

R

Radical equations
    explanation of, 624, 644
    on graphing calculator, 629
    method to solve, 624–627
Radical functions, 591–592, 642
Radical sign, 587, 596
Radicals/radical expressions. *See also* Roots; Square roots
    addition and subtraction of, 611–613, 643
    distance formula and, 607–608
    like, 611–612, 643
    method to simplify, 600, 605–607, 642–643
    midpoint formula and, 608
    multiplication of, 614
    product rule for, 603, 605, 606
    quotient rule for, 604–606
    rationalizing denominators of, 617–620
    rationalizing numerators of, 620–621
    review of, 641–644

Radicals/radical expressions (*continued*)
  solving equations that contain, 524–627
  use of formulas containing, 607–608
  use of rational exponents to simplify, 600
Radicands, 587, 605
Radius, 783–785
Range
  of functions, 233
  of relations, 227
Rate of change, 209–210
Rational equations
  problem solving with, 486–490, 504
  as proportions, 483, 484
Rational exponents
  denominator of, 597
  explanation of, 596
  $a^{-m/n}$, 597–598
  $a^{m/n}$, 596–597
  $a^{1/n}$, 596
  rules for, 598–599, 642
  to simplify expressions, 598–599
  to simplify radical expressions, 600
Rational expressions. *See also* Complex fractions;
    Fractions
  addition and subtraction of, 460–464, 468–471, 503
  common denominator of, 460–461
  complex, 495–499
  division of, 453–455, 502
  domain of, 440–441
  equations with, 474–478, 483, 503–504, 872–873
  explanation of, 440, 502, 872
  fundamental principle of, 442
  on graphing calculator, 478
  least common denominator of, 462–464
  method to simplify, 441–445, 502
  multiplication of, 451–453, 455, 502
  review of, 481
  writing equivalent forms of, 445
Rational functions
  domain of, 440–441
  explanation of, 440
  on graphing calculator, 446
  problem solving with, 446
Rational inequalities, 685–686, 706–707
Rationalizing the denominator
  explanation of, 617
  of radical expressions, 617–620, 643
  use of conjugates for, 619–620
Rationalizing the numerator, 620–621, 644
Rational numbers, 10. *See also* Fractions
Ratios. *See also* Fractions; Proportions
  common, 820, 821, 833, 843
  explanation of, 482, 504
Real numbers
  absolute value of, 12–13
  addition of, 35–40, 44–45, 70–71
  division of, 54–56, 71
  explanation of, 10, 99, 100

  multiplication of, 51–55, 71
  order property for, 12
  properties of, 61–65, 71–72
  set of, 10–11
  subtraction of, 43–47, 71
Reciprocals. *see also* Multiplicative inverse
  explanation of, 19, 54, 65, 538
  negative, 208
Rectangles
  area of, 115
  perimeter of, 117–121
  volume of, 115
Rectangular coordinate system
  explanation of, 171–172, 238–239, 865
  plotting ordered pairs on, 864–865
Reflecting graphs, 533–534, 546
Relations
  domain of, 227
  explanation of, 227, 241
  as functions, 227–228
  graphs of, 228
  range of, 227
Remainder theorem, 362
Revenue function, 289–290, 325
Right angles, 895
Right triangles
  explanation of, 899
  Pythagorean theorem and, 425–426, 627–629, 899–900
Rise, 202
Roots. *See also* Radicals/radical expressions;
    Square roots
  cube, 588–589, 642
  method to find, 587–588
  nth, 589
Rounding. *See* Approximation
Row operations, 881, 882
Run, 202

S

Scatter diagrams, 173
Scientific notation
  on calculator, 350
  conversions between standard notation and, 348–349
  explanation of, 347, 367
  performing operations with, 349
  writing numbers in, 348
Second-degree equations. *See* Quadratic equations
Sequences
  applications of, 815, 820, 822, 831, 832, 834
  arithmetic, 817–820, 826, 830–831, 842
  common difference of, 817, 818
  explanation of, 813, 842
  Fibonacci, 812, 817
  finite, 813, 842
  general term of, 814–815
  geometric, 820–822, 832–834, 842
  infinite, 813, 833–834
  terms of, 813–814

Series
  explanation of, 825, 843
  finite, 825
  infinite, 825
  partial sum, 826–827
  summation notation and, 825–826
Set notation, 99
Sets
  empty or null, 99
  explanation of, 7, 9, 11, 68–69
  of integers, 9, 10
  intersection of two, 552–554
  of real numbers, 10–11
  union of two, 555–556
Sigma (Σ), 825, 826
Signed numbers, 11. *See also* Integers
Similar triangles, 485, 486, 898, 899
Simple inequalities, 150
Simple interest formula, 115, 657
Simplification
  of complex fractions, 495–499, 505
  of exponential expressions, 309–315, 344–346
  of fractions, 16
  of polynomials, 321–323
  of radical expressions, 600, 605–607, 642
  of rational expressions, 441–445, 502
  review of, 912–914
Slope. *See also* Point-slope form
  explanation of, 202–203, 240
  of horizontal and vertical lines, 206–207
  methods to find, 203–210
  as rate of change, 209–210
  undefined, 206
Slope-intercept form
  equations in, 218–219, 253, 255, 512
  explanation of, 205, 217, 241
  to graph equations, 217–218
  shifting and, 531
Solutions
  of equations, 29–30, 85, 174–175
  of linear inequalities, 145–146, 571
Solution set
  of inequalities, 145–146, 150, 552–555, 803
  of quadratic equations, 652
Special products
  explanation of, 337, 338
  FOIL method to find, 337–339, 366
  product of sum and difference of same two terms as, 339–340
  to square binomials, 338–339
  use of, 340–341
Square root function, 530–531
Square root property
  explanation of, 652, 705
  to solve quadratic equations, 652–657
Square roots. *See also* Radicals/radical expressions
  approximation of, 588
  explanation of, 522

  method to find, 587–588
  negative, 587, 641
  principal, 522, 587, 641
Squares. *See also* Completing the square
  of binomials, 338–339, 366
  factoring difference of two, 339–340, 402–404
  perfect, 588
  sum and difference of, 339–340
Standard form
  of equation of circle, 783, 796
  of equation of ellipse, 789, 796
  of equation of hyperbola, 792, 793, 796
  of equation of parabola, 780, 796
  of linear equations, 184, 222, 239, 866
  of linear equations in two variables, 184, 222, 239, 866
  of quadratic equations, 412, 663, 664
  of quadratic inequalities, 682
  scientific notation converted to, 348–349
  of system of equations, 881
Straight angles, 895
Study guide outline, 912–916
Study skills builders, 902–911. *See also* Mathematics class
Substitution method
  explanation of, 258
  to solve nonlinear system of equations, 797–799
  to solve systems of linear equations, 258–263, 277–278, 299
  use of, 674, 706
Subtraction
  applications with, 46–47
  of complex numbers, 636, 644
  of decimals, 848
  of fractions, 19–21
  of functions, 713
  of polynomials, 325, 326, 366
  problem solving using, 46–47
  of radical expressions, 611–613, 643
  of rational expressions, 460–464, 468–471, 503
  of real numbers, 43–47, 71
  words/phrases for, 30, 31
Summation notation, 825, 826, 843
Sum of squares, 339–340
Sum or difference of two cubes, factoring, 405
Supplementary angles, 47, 93, 895
Surface area, 539–540
Symbols/notation
  absolute value, 560
  division, 55
  empty or null set, 99
  equality, 7, 29
  exponential, 25
  fraction bar, 27
  function notation, 231–232, 512–513, 519–520, 545–546
  grouping, 26–28
  inequality, 7–8, 145, 147, 152
  intersection, 552
  interval, 146
  logarithmic, 743–744

Symbols/notation (*continued*)
  multiplication, 16
  radical, 587, 596
  scientific notation, 347–350
  set, 99
  sigma (Σ), 825, 826
  summation, 825, 826, 843
  union, 555
Synthetic division
  to divide polynomials, 360–362
  explanation of, 360, 367
Systems of linear equations
  consistent, 252, 254, 273
  elimination method to solve, 265–269, 274–277, 299
  explanation of, 250
  on graphing calculator, 255
  graphing to solving, 251–255
  inconsistent, 252–254, 273
  matrices to solve, 887–891
  problem solving by using, 280–291, 301
  substitution method to solve, 258–263, 299
Systems of linear equations in two variables
  consistent, 252, 254
  Cramer's rule to solve, 887–889
  elimination method to solve, 265–269, 299
  finding solutions to without graphing, 254–255
  on graphing calculator, 255
  graphing to solve, 251–254, 298–299
  inconsistent, 252–254
  ordered pair as solution to, 250
  problem solving with, 280–290, 301
  substitution method to solve, 258–263, 299
Systems of linear equations in three variables
  consistent, 273
  Cramer's rule to solve, 890–891
  elimination method to solve, 274–277, 300
  explanation of, 273
  inconsistent, 273
  possible patterns of solutions to, 273
  solving problems modeled by, 290–291
  substitution method to solve, 277–278
Systems of linear inequalities, 575–576
Systems of nonlinear equations. *See* Nonlinear
    systems of equations

T
Table of values, 176–177
Temperature conversions, 117–118, 714
Terms
  common, 444
  degree of, 319, 365
  explanation of, 77, 318
  greatest common factor of list of, 375–376
  like, 77–79, 321–323
  of sequence, 813–815
  unlike, 77, 78

Test point, 573
Three-part inequalities. *See* Compound
    inequalities
Transformations
  explanation of, 529
  reflection, 533–534, 546
  shifting of, 531–533
Transversal, 896, 897
Triangles
  congruent, 897–898
  explanation of, 897
  finding dimensions of, 425–426
  isosceles, 108
  Pascal's, 837–838
  perimeter of, 115
  right, 425–426, 899–900
  similar, 485, 486, 898–899
  sum of angles of, 94
Trinomials. *See also* Polynomials
  explanation of, 318, 319
  factoring, 382–386, 389–392, 431–432
  of form $ax^2 + bx + c$, 389–392,
      397–401, 432
  of form $x^2 + bx + c$, 382–386
  perfect square, 393–395, 401, 432, 654, 655

U
Union, of linear inequalities, 555–556, 580
Union symbol, 555
Uniqueness of b^x, 731–732
Unit fractions, 455–457
Unlike terms, 77, 78

V
Variables
  dependent, 231
  explanation of, 28
  independent, 231
Variation
  combined, 540–541
  constant of, 536–537, 539–540
  direct, 536–537, 546
  inverse, 538–539, 546
  joint, 539–540, 546
Vertex, 689–691, 700–701
Vertex formula, 700–701
Vertical angles, 896
Vertical lines
  equations of, 220–221
  explanation of, 198
  graphs of, 197–198
  slope of, 206–207
Vertical line test, 228–231, 241,
    531, 721
Vertical shifts, 531–532
Volume, 115, 120

W

Whole numbers, 7
Word phrases. *See also* Problem solving
  for addition, 30
  for division, 30
  for equality, 30
  for multiplication, 30
  for subtraction, 30, 31
  written as algebraic expressions, 81, 90–91
Work problems, 487–488, 675–676

X

x-axis, 171, 533
x-coordinates, 171–172, 865
x-intercepts
  explanation of, 194, 239, 867
  finding and plotting, 195–197, 240
  of graph of quadratic equations, 418
  method to find, 867–868

Y

y-axis, 171
y-coordinates, 171–172, 865
y-intercepts
  explanation of, 194, 239, 867
  finding and plotting, 195–197, 240
  method to find, 867–868
  slope-intercept form and, 205

Z

Zero
  products involving, 52
  quotients involving, 55
Zero exponent, 314, 598
Zero factor property
  explanation of, 413
  to solve quadratic equations, 413–415, 433, 674

Photo Credits

Chapter 1
Page 5 Stylephotographs/Dreamstime
Page 9 Martin Fischer/Shutterstock
Page 15 Thinkstock
Page 28 Digital Vision/Thinkstock
Page 39 Dorling Kindersley, Inc.
Page 41 (top) Endless Traveller/Shutterstock
Page 41 (bottom) ALCE/Fotolia
Page 49 (top) Peter Zaharov/Shutterstock
Page 49 (bottom) Rjlerich/Dreamstime
Page 57 Lunamarina/Fotolia

Chapter 2
Page 93 Georgiy/Fotolia
Page 94 (top) Dmitryp/Dreamstime
Page 94 (bottom) Dmitryp/Dreamstime
Page 95 Wavebreakmedia, Ltd./Shutterstock
Page 106 Editorial Image, LLC/Alamy
Page 107 Kristoffer Tripplaar/Alamy
Page 108 Bpperry/Dreamstime
Page 109 Yuri Arcurs/Fotolia
Page 113 (left) Eastimages/Shutterstock
Page 113 (right) Evgeny Prokofyev/Shutterstock
Page 114 Nmaverick/Fotolia
Page 116 Diana Jo Currier/Shutterstock
Page 123 Michael Dwyer/Alamy
Page 124 Bruce MacQueen/Shutterstock
Page 125 Guy Cali/Glow Images
Page 126 (left) WaterFrame/Alamy
Page 126 (right) Gracious Tiger/Shutterstock
Page 130 Digital Vision/Thinkstock
Page 131 (top) 300dpi/Shutterstock
Page 131 (bottom) Deklofenak/Dreamstime
Page 136 (top) IlFede/Shutterstock
Page 136 (bottom) Kuzma/Shutterstock
Page 153 Deepfrog17/Dreamstime
Page 163 Amalia Ferreira-Espinoza/Shutterstock

Chapter 3
Page 168 Interlight/Shutterstock
Page 169 Stephen Coburn/Shutterstock
Page 177 Pcruciatti/Dreamstime
Page 180 (top) Franckgrondin/Dreamstime

Page 456 Christopher Parypa/Shutterstock

Page 457 Testing/Shutterstock

Page 487 Digital Vision/Thinkstock

Page 501 (**top**) SVLuma/Shutterstock

Page 501 (**bottom**) Ffooter/Shutterstock

Page 508 James Steidl/Shutterstock

Chapter 8

Page 510 Light Poet/Shutterstock

Page 520 Longimanus/Shutterstock

Page 526 Image100/Corbis Royalty Free

Page 539 Neil Roy Johnson/Shutterstock

Page 542 Johanna Goodyear/Shutterstock

Chapter 9

Page 551 Oleksiy Mark/Shutterstock

Chapter 10

Page 586 Zinaida/Shutterstock

Page 602 Jerryb8/Dreamstime

Page 611 Jorg Hackemann/Shutterstock

Page 631 Tramper2/Dreamstime

Chapter 11

Page 651 Typhoonski/Dreamstime

Page 658 Stockbyte/Thinkstock

Page 661 Andy Z./Shutterstock

Page 670 (**left**) Copyright © National Institute for Fusion Science, Japan

Page 670 (**right**) Tim Hester Photography/Shutterstock

Page 675 EDHAR/Shutterstock

Page 679 Vibrant Image Studio/Shutterstock

Page 680 Phillip Minnis/Shutterstock

Page 705 Daniel Yordanov/Shutterstock

Page 708 Keith10999/Dreamstime

Chapter 12

Page 712 Pryzmat/Dreamstime

Page 736 Blend Images/Shutterstock

Page 765 Franant/Dreamstime

Page 776 (**top**) George Doyle & Ciaran Griffin/Stockbyte/Thinkstock

Page 776 (**bottom**) George Doyle & Ciaran Griffin/Stockbyte/Thinkstock

Chapter 13

Page 779 Alex Melnick/Shutterstock

Appendix B

Page 859 Pcruciatti/Dreamstime